THE **COMPLETE GUIDE** TO

FOODS

— THAT —

HARM

FOODS

— THAT —

HEAL

HEALTH GUIDE AND COOKBOOK

Reader's digest

The Reader's Digest Association, Inc.
New York, NY • Montreal

ISBN 978-1-62145-230-0

The Complete Guide to Foods That Harm, Foods That Heal comprises two books previously published by Reader's Digest:

Foods That Harm, Foods That Heal
Copyright © 2013 The Reader's Digest Association, Inc.
ISBN 978-1-62145-001-6
Photo credits: Photos on pages x, 16, 53, 76, 86, 88, 93, 141, 172, 189, 252, 347, and 349:
   © Getty Images. All other photos: © Shutterstock.

Foods That Harm, Foods That Heal Cookbook
Copyright © 2013 The Reader's Digest Association, Inc.
ISBN 978-1-62145-058-0
Photo credits: All images copyright Shutterstock/Getty Images.

We are committed to both the quality of our products and the service we provide to our customers. We value your comments, so please feel free to contact us.
   The Reader's Digest Association, Inc.
   Adult Trade Publishing
   44 South Broadway
   White Plains, NY 10601

For more Reader's Digest products and information, visit our website:
   www.rd.com (in the United States)
   www.readersdigest.ca (in Canada)

Printed in China

1 3 5 7 9 10 8 6 4 2

NOTE TO OUR READERS

The information in this book should not be substituted for, or used to alter, medical therapy without your doctor's advice. For a specific health problem, consult your physician for guidance.

Eating eggs or egg whites that are not completely cooked poses the possibility of salmonella food poisoning. The risk is greater for pregnant women, the elderly, the very young, and persons with impaired immune systems. If you are concerned about salmonella, you can use reconstituted powdered egg whites or pasteurized eggs.

contents

FOODS THAT HARM, FOODS THAT HEAL

Part 1: Nutrition

Part 2: Foods

Part 3: Ailments

FOODS THAT HARM, FOODS THAT HEAL COOKBOOK

Part 1: Foods

Part 2: Recipes

Part 3: Ailments

FOODS
THAT
HARM
FOODS
THAT
HEAL

The Best and Worst Choices to Treat Your Ailments Naturally

Fran Berkoff, RD, and Joe Schwarcz, PhD,
Consultants

Reader's digest

The Reader's Digest Association, Inc.
New York, NY · Montreal

ABOUT THE NEW EDITION

New edition, new foods, new format, and an all new way to look at how diet affects health

Welcome to the 2013 edition of *Foods That Harm, Foods That Heal*. The first edition of this pioneering book, published in 1997, changed the way we view food and its impact on our bodies, capturing the explosion of scientific research about the links between nutrition and health and highlighting the benefits of fresh whole foods. What's changed since then?

Well, an apple may still be an apple, but our understanding of the benefits of foods and how nutrients act in our bodies continues to evolve. For a while, we've known that apples have always been a good source of fiber, which can help lower cholesterol. Now we've also identified antioxidants in apples, like procyanidins, which may protect against colon cancer, and quercetin, which helps stave off Alzheimer's disease.

Also, food itself and our food supply has continued to evolve. Many foods are now fortified or enriched with added nutrients, from omega-3s in eggs and prebiotics in breads. And foods that were once considered exotic can now be found on more and more grocery shelves. So we've updated the book with dozens of new healing foods, such as passion fruit, which can pump up your immune system, and jicama, which can help strengthen bones. We've also added more than a dozen ailments that you can prevent or treat by choosing the right foods.

Along with a wealth of new and updated entries, this totally revised edition has been entirely reformatted to make it easier for you to find the facts you need at a glance. This edition of *Foods That Harm, Foods That Heal* is divided into three sections: Nutrition, Foods, and Ailments. The first section is wholly new and presents the big picture on what you need to know to eat healthy. Turn to this part for an overview on how to get the right balance of carbs, fats, and proteins; whether or not you need a multivitamin or other dietary supplements; when you need to be concerned about pesticides and other chemicals; and how to preserve nutrients when you cook.

The second part of the book is an A-to-Z listing of more than 170 foods with explanations about how they can improve health and help remedy specific conditions. As part of this edition, the food listings contain handy additions such as typical serving sizes, buying and storing tips, and detailed descriptions of their health benefits.

In the third section of the *Foods That Harm, Foods That Heal* you'll find an alphabetical listing of more than 100 ailments. These include health issues that are as everyday as a cold and as serious as cancer. Within each entry, we show which foods can cause or exacerbate that condition, and which can help prevent or treat it. For example, those with lupus should seek out inflammation-taming foods such as broccoli, salmon, and flaxseeds but avoid foods with the compound psoralens, such as celery, parsnips, or parsley.

In addition, throughout the book are special features and sidebars. You'll learn how to eat smart and safe while traveling, figure out whether probiotics are for you, and discover the differences between energy bars. Filled with the latest and most authoritative information plus practical advice on how to put that information to use, this new edition of *Foods That Harm, Foods That Heal* offers a fresh menu for better living.

contents

PART 2
Foods

An A-Z Guide to Foods that Harm, Foods That Heal

PART 3
Ailments

A Condition-by-Condition Guide to What Foods Harm, What Foods Heal

NUTRITION

The Real Deal on All the Ways Foods Harm and Heal

"Let thy food be thy medicine and thy medicine be thy food." This advice is as true today as it was more than 2,000 years ago when Hippocrates, the famous Greek physician, coined the phrase. But exactly what foods should you be eating to keep the doctor away?

The answer is more complex than you might think. How each food affects you depends on how much of it you eat, when you eat it, and what you eat it with. In addition, how the food is grown, stored, and cooked can make a big difference, as can medications you're taking. For instance, cooking spinach helps your body to absorb the antioxidants lutein and zeaxanthin, which can prevent age-related macular degeneration. But cook it too long and it loses a lot of its immunity-boosting vitamin C. To help your body absorb the iron, calcium, and other minerals in spinach, it's best to pair spinach with other foods rich in vitamin C. But be careful to wash spinach thoroughly to reduce the likelihood of *E. coli* contamination. And if you're on a blood thinner such as heparin or warfarin, don't eat too much, as it can interfere with the medication.

Despite all of these variables, the basics of good nutrition don't have to be hard to follow. This section will first give you an overview of the substances in our foods that are actually doing all the work—the carbohydrates that give us energy, the vitamins that keep your brain and body functioning, the antioxidants that fight disease, and much more. Here we'll give you the real deal on what types of fat are good or bad for you, whether low-carb diets really work, and which vitamins and minerals you need more of.

Next we tackle the controversial subject of food safety. We cut through all the white noise about whether or not pesticides, additives, and genetically modified foods are really harmful or not, and tell you when it's really worth spending more on organic grapes or grass-fed beef.

Finally, we sum up the latest science on nutrition to give you simple guidelines on what and how much to eat for vibrant good health, along with tips on the best ways to store foods to preserve freshness and avoid contamination and the best cooking methods to retain or even boost nutrients in your favorite foods.

THE REAL DEAL ON NUTRITION

It makes intuitive sense to most of us that foods can harm you or heal you. But how? The connection is nutrition, a subject we all know something about, thanks to Mom's admonitions to eat our veggies. But thanks to an explosion of new research over the past 20 years, it's also a subject that's much misunderstood.

To comprehend how good nutrition helps keep your body healthy, it's a good idea to start with the basics: macronutrients and micronutrients. Macronutrients are carbohydrates, fat, and protein—the nutrients you need in relatively large amounts. By contrast, vitamins and minerals and other substances are deemed micronutrients, because you need them in smaller amounts. Every day, it seems, a new nutrient is touted as *the* key to good health—there are diets that revolve around lean protein, fiber, omega-3 fats, antioxidants, vitamin D, and much more. In reality, what you need is the right mix of nutrients. In this section, we'll give you a quick overview of each one and what you really need.

How Carbohydrates Harm and Heal

In recent years, carbohydrates—or "carbs"—have endured close scrutiny and extensive debate as low-carb diets such as the Atkins and South Beach diets have captured the public's attention. As a result, many people have come to believe that carbohydrates are inherently bad. But that's not the case. In fact, carbs are our body's primary source of energy.

All carbohydrates are made up of different types of sugars. Common sugars include fructose (found in fruits) and lactose (found in dairy foods). Our body breaks them down into glucose or blood sugar. Glucose is essential for the functioning of the brain, nervous system, muscles, and various organs.

Canadian and American nutritional authorities recommend that 45 to 65% of children's, teens', and adults' total calories come from carbs, though pregnant and lactating women need more. If your diet has 1,800 calories per day, then you should eat about 200 g of carbs daily. Most of these carbs should come from whole grains, fruits, and vegetables (including beans), rather than sodas, baked snacks, ice cream, and sweets. Carbohydrates are divided into two groups: simple and complex. The typical North American diet provides an overabundance of simple carbs and heavily processed starches, and too few unprocessed complex carbs.

Simple Carbohydrates

Simple carbohydrates, or sugars, are so-called because they are chemically made of just one or two sugars. They can generally form crystals that dissolve in water and are easily digested. Naturally occurring sugars are found in a variety of fruits, some vegetables, and honey. Processed sugars include table sugar, brown sugar, molasses, and high-fructose corn syrup.

It's hard to overdo it with foods that contain natural sugars; you'd have to eat a lot of fruits and vegetables to equal the amount of sugar in one piece of candy or one can of soda. Processed sugars, on the other hand, we overdo without realizing it. Most of the sugar in North Americans' diets is added during food processing at the manufacturer—even to foods we don't think of as sweet, like barbecue sauce or bread. These added sugars account for about 16% of the calories that Americans eat.

Reducing the amount of added sugar in your diet is a quick way to reduce calories without cutting out a lot of important nutrients. The American Heart Association, for instance, recommends that most women limit themselves to 100 calories a day from added sugar, men to no more than 150—about what you'd get in a plain 1.5-oz chocolate bar or 12-oz soda.

When examining food labels for added sugar, look for the words *corn sweetener*, *corn syrup*, or *corn syrup solids* as well as *high-fructose corn syrup*. Also look for other words ending in "ose" (like sucrose, lactose, maltose, glucose, and dextrose).

THE REAL DEAL — High-Fructose Corn Syrup

High-fructose corn syrup is found in many frozen foods. It gives bread an inviting color and soft texture. It is found in beer, bacon, soft drinks, and even ketchup.

Some research suggests that this liquid sweetener may upset human metabolism and encourage overeating, raising the risk for heart disease and diabetes. Other experts, though, say it functions just like regular fructose. There's no question, though, that it adds calories and that we eat too much of it—North Americans consume nearly 63 pounds of this sugar per person per year.

Certain diseases may require adjustments to carb intake:

Diabetes. Contrary to popular belief, sugar does not cause diabetes, nor do people with diabetes have to completely avoid sugar. But people with diabetes must manage the total amount and type of carbs they eat at each meal and snack. Knowing the glycemic index or glycemic load can help (see page 262).

Heart disease. People with heart disease need to emphasize high-fiber, complex carbohydrates in their diet. Soluble fiber, found in oat bran and fruit pectin, helps lower cholesterol and plays an important role in preventing atherosclerosis.

Cancer. People with cancer are often advised to increase their carbohydrate intake and decrease fat intake, especially if they have cancers of the breast, colon, uterus, prostate, or skin. But make sure those carbs come from high-fiber and antioxidant-rich whole grains, fruits, and vegetables. A few studies suggest that refined carbs that cause blood sugar to spike may also feed cancer cells.

Complex Carbohydrates

Complex carbohydrates are made of complex chains of sugars and can be classified as starches or fiber. Our digestive system can metabolize most starches but lacks the enzymes needed to break down most fiber. But both are important to good health; while starches provide glucose for energy, dietary fiber promotes colon function and may help prevent some types of cancer, heart attacks, and other diseases.

Starches and fiber are naturally found in most grains and vegetables and some fruits, which also provide essential nutrients such as B vitamins, iron, and other minerals. Unprocessed whole grains are

Old School
Fewer carbs is healthier.

New Wisdom
Choosing the healthiest carbohydrates, especially whole grains, is more important to your well-being.

the best source. At least seven major studies show that women and men who eat more whole grains have 20 to 30% less heart disease. And in a 2010 study of more than 13,000 adults, those who ate the most servings of whole grains had lower body weight.

On the other hand, choosing refined grains such as white bread, sugary cereal, white rice, or white pasta can boost your heart attack risk by up to 30%. And refined grains are associated with insulin resistance and high blood pressure. The refining process removes fiber and many essential nutrients, making refined grains too easy to digest and thus flooding the body with too much glucose.

American and Canadian guidelines, for example, urge people to make sure that whole grains account for at least half of all grain foods. Unfortunately, less than 5% are getting the minimum recommended amount.

When shopping for whole grains, don't be fooled by deceptive label claims such as "made with wheat flour" or "seven grain." Or by white flour breads topped with a sprinkling of oats or colored brown with molasses. Often, they're just the same old refined stuff. Instead, look for a fiber content of at least 3 g per serving and for the first ingredient to be a whole grain such as:

- Brown rice
- Bran
- Bulgur
- Kasha
- Oats
- Quinoa
- Rye
- Whole wheat

In addition to unprocessed grains, get plenty of legumes, beans, and raw or slightly cooked vegetables and fruits. The glycemic index and glycemic load (page 262) can be helpful tools to identify the best types of carbohydrates to eat.

How Fats Harm and Heal

Fat is a dietary evil—or so you may have heard. Not only are fats a more concentrated source of calories than carbs or protein, but studies indicate that the body more readily stores fats. So a diet rich in high-fat foods makes you gain more weight. Plus, some types of fat have been implicated in a higher risk of heart attack, diabetes, and other diseases.

But the truth is that fat, in small amounts, is essential to health. Some fats, like those found in fish and olive oil, actually lower your risk of heart disease and can even help you stick to a weight loss plan.

Fats add flavor and a smooth, pleasing texture to foods. Because they take longer to digest, fats let us feel full even after the proteins and carbohydrates have left our stomach. Fats also stimulate the intestine to release cholecystokinin, a hormone that suppresses the appetite and signals us to stop eating.

Fats supply the fatty acids that are essential for numerous chemical processes, including growth and development in children, the production of sex hormones and prostaglandins, the formation and function of cell membranes, and the transport of other molecules into and out of cells.

Finally, fats are needed for the transport and absorption of the fat-soluble vitamins A, D, E, and K. A tablespoon of vegetable oil is sufficient to transport all the fat-soluble vitamins we need in a day.

American and Canadian nutritional authorities recommend that adults restrict their total fat intake to 20 to 35% of each day's calories. If you're getting 2,000 calories per day, that works out to 44 to 78g of fat daily, most of it ideally the unsaturated kind.

As with carbohydrates, the type of fats we eat is more important than the total amount. Fats fall into two main categories: saturated and unsaturated. Most foods naturally contain both types but are higher in one. In addition, many commercially produced foods are made with trans fats, which are rarely found in nature.

Saturated Fats

Saturated fats generally come from animal sources, but there are some plant sources as well. Common sources of saturated fat include meat, poultry, butter, cheese, and coconut and palm oils.

Most saturated fats are solid at room temperature. A diet high in saturated fats can raise blood cholesterol levels, one of the leading risk factors for heart disease. Saturated fat has also been linked to other health problems, such as colorectal, prostate, and ovarian cancer. Experts recommend that no more than 10% of your daily calories come from saturated fat, especially animal fats. (Some researchers believe that the type of saturated fat in coconut oil increases good HDL cholesterol as well as bad LDL cholesterol, so it's been touted as more of a good fat in recent years.)

Unsaturated Fats

In general, unsaturated fats are healthier than saturated fats; they either lower blood cholesterol or have no effect on it, and may also help lower blood sugar and blood pressure. Most unsaturated fats are liquid at room temperature and solid or semisolid under refrigeration. Unsaturated fats fall into two main categories: monounsaturated and polyunsaturated. Polyunsaturated fats, in turn, are divided into omega-3 and omega-6 fats. Each type affects your health in different ways.

Monoun-saturated fats (sometimes called MUFAs) improve blood cholesterol levels and may benefit insulin levels, thus lowering your risk of heart disease and type 2 diabetes. Major food sources include olives, nuts, avocados, and olive, canola, and peanut oil.

Omega-3 fats help steady heart rhythm, lower artery-clogging triglycerides, cool chronic inflammation in the arteries, prevent blood clotting, and produce a modest drop in blood pressure, all of which cut your risk of a heart attack or stroke. Findings from 30 large studies conducted around the world show that people who consume just 1 or 2 servings of omega-3-rich fish per week lower their risk of a fatal heart attack by an average of 36%. And mounting evidence suggests that omega-3 fatty acids help the brain with its normal day-to-day function.

Omega-3 fats are found in fatty fish such as salmon, mackerel, herring, and sardines, as well as flaxseed, walnut, and canola oils and some newer products such as omega-3-rich eggs.

Omega-6 fats, on the other hand, increase inflammation if you consume too much. Omega-6 food sources include safflower, sunflower, and corn oil, and some nuts and seeds. While there are a variety of opinions on the optimal ratio of omega-3 to omega-6,

experts agree that we tend to eat far more omega-6 fats than we need and too few omega-3s.

Trans Fats

Trans fats are created when a vegetable oil undergoes hydrogenation, a process that lengthens foods' shelf life. Trans fats are found in:

- Partially hydrogenated vegetable oils
- Some margarines
- Crackers
- Cookies
- Commercially fried foods

Hydrogenation makes polyunsaturated vegetable oils act like saturated fats: They raise LDL cholesterol levels. Thus, nutritionists recommend that you consume as few trans fats as possible.

Fortunately, many people seem to have gotten this message in recent years. In the past few years, the trend has been for manufacturers and restaurants to cut back on trans fat in their foods. In a study from 2012, researchers compared blood samples from white adults taken in 2000 and 2009. Levels of trans fat in the samples fell by 58% during this time. Along with this change came a drop in LDL ("bad") cholesterol.

How Proteins Harm and Heal

Protein is the quintessential nutrient that every cell in the human body requires for growth or repair. The antibodies that protect us from disease, the enzymes needed for digestion and metabolism, and hormones like insulin are all proteins. Cholesterol travels through the bloodstream attached to lipoproteins (fat-carrying proteins). Connective tissue made from protein forms the matrix of bones. Keratin, still another type of protein, is used by the body to make hair and nails.

With so many essential functions linked to protein, you might assume that it should make up the bulk of your diet, but this is not the case. In an ideal balanced diet, only 10 to 12% of your daily calories should come from protein. Healthy adults only need 0.36 g per lb (0.8 g per kg) of body weight of protein every day, though if you exercise regularly, you may need more. Thus, a person weighing 154 lbs (70 kg) requires 56 g of protein per day—the amount in a 3-oz serving of chicken.

Animal Protein

Proteins are made of amino acids. The human body requires 20 different amino acids to build all the proteins it needs. Of these, 11 can be made in the body, but the other nine, referred to as essential amino acids, must come from the diet. Just as the letters in the alphabet are joined to make words, so too are amino acids arranged in an almost infinite number of different ways to form the more than 50,000 different proteins in the body. DNA (deoxyribonucleic acid), the genetic material that is found in the nucleus of each body cell, provides the blueprint for how amino acids are arranged to form individual proteins.

With the exception of oils and pure sugar, all foods contain at least some protein, but its quality varies according to the amino acids it provides. Animal protein (with the exception of gelatin) provides all nine essential amino acids in the proportions required by the body and is therefore referred to as complete, or high-quality, protein. Unfortunately, though, many animal proteins also come with relatively high amounts of saturated fat.

Plant Protein

In contrast, plant proteins (with the exception of soy) lack one or more of the essential amino acids. That doesn't mean that vegetarians can't get complete proteins, though. They simply need to make sure that they eat foods with the right combination of amino acids. For example, grains are high in the essential amino acid methionine, but they lack lysine. This essential amino acid is plentiful in dried beans and other legumes, which are deficient in methionine. By combining a grain with a legume, you can obtain the complete range of amino acids.

Interestingly, many cuisines include classic combinations that do just that. For example:

- Refried beans and corn tortillas of Mexico
- Rice and dahl of India

Low-carb, low-fat, or high-protein—which diet really works to help you lose weight?

In a study from Australia, researchers asked 118 men and women who were obese to spend a year on a low-carb or a low-fat diet. They provided the same number of calories. Both diets let to a similar amount of weight loss—about 25 to 32 pounds. Participants also lost a similar amount of body fat.

The truth is, *any* change to your eating habits that leads you to cut calories will result in weight loss. There really is no secret formula.

But some weight loss trends are safer than others, and some are easier to maintain. Low-carb diets, for instance, tend to boost red meat consumption; over a long period of time, the high levels of protein and fat in red meat adversely affect kidney function, bone health, cardiovascular function, and cancer rates. In addition, these diets are generally low in beneficial fruits and vegetables. Because fats are key to making us feel satisfied, our body naturally craves them, so low-fat diets are tough to stick to over time. Other diet fads, such as those based on liquid fasts, HCG (human chorionic gonadotropin), or other "magic" ingredients, can be downright dangerous.

To lose weight safely and keep it off, choose low-glycemic and high-fiber foods, such as fruits, vegetables, and whole grains, along with lean protein and low-fat dairy.

- Tofu, rice, and vegetable combinations in Asian cuisine
- Chickpeas and bulgur wheat in Middle Eastern dishes

If an essential amino acid is missing from the diet, the body breaks down lean tissue to get it. Most North Americans, though, eat too much protein rather than not enough.

How Vitamins and Minerals Harm and Heal

Google "vitamins" and you'll get 142 million results. That's more than what you get for "Brad Pitt," but the descriptions are just as breathless. As you navigate the maze of sites, you'll see phrases claiming that vitamin supplements can "increase energy," "stimulate brain function," and "improve sex drive."

It all helps explain why Americans shell out $7.5 billion a year on vitamins, hoping to prolong life, slow aging, and protect against a bevy of illnesses. But new research not only refutes many of these claims, it also shows that some of these vitamins may, in fact, be harmful in excess.

Vitamins got their name from their link to "vitality," and indeed they are vital for your health. But it's important to get them from the right place and in the right amounts. Similarly, while minerals such as calcium, iron, and zinc are essential to keep your body and brain functioning properly, many are highly toxic if consumed in large quantities.

Vitamins

To date, 13 vitamins essential to human health have been discovered. Vitamins are classified as fat soluble or water soluble, according to how they are absorbed and stored in the body.

The fat-soluble vitamins (vitamins A, D, E, and K) need fat in order to be absorbed into the bloodstream from the intestinal tract. Thus, people who have fat-malabsorption disorders can develop deficiency symptoms even if their diet supplies adequate amounts of a vitamin. Many people with celiac disease, for instance, which impairs the absorption of dietary fat, have low vitamin D levels. On the other hand, because the body can store fat-soluble vitamins in the liver and fatty tissue, toxic amounts may build up if a person takes high doses of these supplements.

As water-soluble vitamins, the B vitamins and vitamin C are more easily absorbed than fat-soluble vitamins. However, since the body stores water-soluble vitamins in only small amounts and excretes the rest in urine, they need to be consumed more often. (This also means that you're not likely to overdose on water-soluble vitamins.)

Minerals

Minerals, which constitute about 4 percent of our body weight, are generally classified according to the amount we require each day:

- Calcium, phosphorus, and magnesium are classified as macrominerals because you need and can store larger amounts.
- Iron, fluoride, manganese, iodine, selenium, zinc, chloride, potassium, sodium, molybdenum, chromium, and

QUICK TIP:
Skip protein powders

Purified protein and amino acid powders or pills are often promoted as high-energy, muscle-bulking supplements for athletes and bodybuilders, as well as weight loss aids for dieters. Research doesn't show that most athletes benefit from high protein intake; in fact, amino acid supplements can upset normal protein synthesis, setting the stage for nutritional imbalances. A balanced diet provides all the needed protein; any excess is just excreted.

copper are classified as trace or micro-minerals, because the requirements are much smaller and they are stored in extremely small amounts in the body.

Some of these minerals—including calcium, chloride, magnesium, phosphorus, potassium, and sodium—are also classed as electrolytes, substances that are involved in generating electrical impulses to transport nerve messages. Electrolytes also maintain the proper balances of fluids and body chemicals.

All of these minerals are vital to health, and because the body is unable to make them on its own, they must be provided by food.

How Antioxidants and Other Phytochemicals Heal

If you pay any attention to health news, you've no doubt heard about the miraculous healing powers of antioxidants, polyphenols, flavonoids, and a whole host of hard-to-pronounce chemicals. All of these substances fall under the broad category of phytochemicals—literally, chemicals in plants. While not technically nutrients, research has shown that many phytochemicals play a critical role in our health.

There are several major groups of phytochemicals:

- **Polyphenols** include the subgroup flavonoids, such as resveratrol, quercetin, hesperidin, and anthocyanidins, found in grapes, berries, broccoli, kale, and many other fruits and vegetables. Flavonoids may help prevent heart disease and cancer, lower blood pressure, and destroy some bacteria in foods. One group of flavonoids

VITAMIN DAILY RECOMMENDATIONS

VITAMIN	BEST FOOD SOURCES	ROLE IN HEALTH
FAT-SOLUBLE VITAMINS		
Vitamin A (from retinols in animal products or beta-carotene in plant foods)	**Retinols:** Liver; salmon and other cold-water fish; egg yolks; fortified milk and dairy products. **Beta-carotene:** Orange and yellow fruits and vegetables, such as carrots, squash, and cantaloupes; leafy green vegetables.	Prevents night blindness; needed for growth and cell development; maintains healthy skin, hair, and nails, as well as gums, glands, bones, and teeth; may help prevent lung cancer.
Vitamin D (calciferol)	Fortified milk; fortified soy and rice beverages; butter; egg yolks; fatty fish; fish-liver oils. Also made by the body when exposed to the sun.	Necessary for calcium absorption; helps build and maintain strong bones and teeth.
Vitamin E (tocopherols)	Eggs, vegetable oils, margarine, and mayonnaise; nuts and seeds; fortified cereals.	Protects fatty acids; maintains muscles and red blood cells; important antioxidant.
Vitamin K	Spinach, broccoli, and other green leafy vegetables; liver.	Essential for proper blood clotting.
WATER-SOLUBLE VITAMINS		
Biotin	Egg yolks; soybeans; whole grains; nuts, and yeast.	Energy metabolism.
Folate (folic acid, folacin)	Liver; yeast; spinach and other leafy green vegetables; asparagus; orange juice; fortified flour; avocados; legumes.	Needed to make DNA, RNA, and red blood cells, and to synthesize certain amino acids. Important for women to have sufficient folate before and after pregnancy to prevent birth defects.
Niacin (vitamin B3, nicotinic acid, nicotinamide)	Lean meats, poultry, and seafood; milk; eggs; legumes; fortified breads and cereals.	Needed to metabolize energy; promotes normal growth. Large doses lower cholesterol.
Pantothenic acid (vitamin B5)	Almost all foods.	Aids in energy metabolism; normalizing blood sugar levels; and synthesizing antibodies, cholesterol, hemoglobin, and some hormones.
Riboflavin (vitamin B2)	Fortified and enriched cereals and grains; lean meat and poultry; milk and other dairy products; fortified soy and rice beverages; raw mushrooms.	Essential for energy metabolism; aids adrenal function; supports normal vision and healthy skin
Thiamine (vitamin B1)	Pork; legumes; nuts and seeds; fortified cereals; and grains.	Energy metabolism; helps maintain normal digestion, appetite, and proper nerve function.
Vitamin B6 (pyridoxine, pyridoxamine, pyridoxal)	Meat, fish, and poultry; grains and cereals; bananas; green leafy vegetables, potatoes, and soybeans.	Promotes protein metabolism; metabolism of carbohydrates and release of energy; proper nerve function; synthesis of red blood cells.
Vitamin B12 (cobalamins)	All animal products.	Needed to make red blood cells, DNA, RNA, and myelin (for nerve fibers).
Vitamin C (ascorbic acid)	Citrus fruits and juices; melons and berries; peppers, broccoli, potatoes; and many other fruits and vegetables.	Strengthens blood vessel walls; promotes wound healing; and iron absorption; helps prevent atherosclerosis; supports immunity; key antioxidant.

Below are the Institute of Medicine's recommendations for daily vitamin intake.
The amounts may vary for pregnant and lactating women.

DAILY RECOMMENDED DIETARY ALLOWANCE (RDA) FOR ADULTS		SYMPTOMS OF DEFICIENCY	SYMPTOMS OF EXCESS
MALES 19+	FEMALES 19+		
900 mcg	700 mcg	Night blindness; stunted growth in children; dry skin and eyes; increased susceptibility to infection.	Headaches and blurred vision; fatigue; bone and joint pain; appetite loss and diarrhea; dry, cracked skin, rashes, and itchiness; hair loss. Can cause birth defects if taken in high doses before and during early pregnancy.
15 mcg (20 mcg after age 70)	15 mcg (20 mcg after age 70)	Weak bones, leading to rickets in children and osteomalacia in adults.	Headaches, loss of appetite, diarrhea, and possible calcium deposits in heart, blood vessels, and kidneys.
15 mg	15 mg	Unknown in humans.	Excessive bleeding, especially when taken with aspirin and other anti-clotting drugs.
120 mcg*	90 mcg*	Excessive bleeding; easy bruising.	May interfere with anti clotting drugs; possible jaundice.
30 mcg*	30 mcg*	Scaly skin; hair loss; depression; elevated blood cholesterol levels.	Apparently none.
400 mcg	400 mcg	Abnormal red blood cells and impaired cell division; anemia; weight loss and intestinal upsets; deficiency may cause birth defects.	May inhibit absorption of phenytoin, causing seizures in those with epilepsy taking this drug; large doses may inhibit zinc absorption.
16 mg	14 mg	Diarrhea and mouth sores; pellagra (in extreme cases).	Hot flashes; liver damage; elevated blood sugar and uric acid.
5 mg*	5 mg*	Unknown in humans.	Very high doses may cause diarrhea and edema.
1.3 mg	1.1 mg	Vision problems and light sensitivity; mouth and nose sores; swallowing problems.	Generally none, but may interfere with cancer chemotherapy.
1.2 mg	1.1 mg (1.5 mg after age 50)	Depression and mood swings; loss of appetite and nausea; muscle cramps. In extreme cases, muscle wasting and beriberi.	Deficiency of other B vitamins.
1.3 mg (1.7 mg after age 50)	1.3 mg (1.5 mg after age 50)	Depression and confusion; itchy, scaling skin; smooth, red tongue; weight loss.	Sensory nerve deterioration.
2.4 mcg	2.4 mcg	Pernicious anemia; nerve problems and weakness; smooth or sore tongue.	Apparently none.
90 mg	75 mg	Loose teeth; bleeding gums; bruises; loss of appetite; dry skin; poor healing. In extreme cases, scurvy and internal hemorrhages.	Diarrhea; kidney stones; urinary-tract irritation; iron buildup; bone loss.

MINERAL DAILY RECOMMENDATIONS

MINERAL	BEST FOOD SOURCES	ROLE IN HEALTH
MACROMINERALS		
Calcium	Milk and milk products; fortified soy and rice beverages; canned sardines and salmon (including bones); dark green vegetables; tofu.	Builds strong bones and teeth; vital to muscle and nerve function, blood clotting, and metabolism; helps regulate blood pressure.
Magnesium	Leafy green vegetables; legumes and whole grain cereals and breads; meats, poultry, fish, and eggs; nuts.	Stimulates bone growth; necessary for muscle and nerve function and metabolism; supports immunity.
Phosphorus	Meat, poultry, fish, egg yolks; legumes; dairy products.	Helps maintains strong bones and teeth; component of some enzymes; essential for proper metabolism.
MICROMINERALS		
Chromium	Brewer's yeast, whole grain products; liver; cheese; chicken; mushrooms; molasses; shellfish; legumes; nuts; prunes.	Works with insulin to metabolize glucose.
Copper	Liver, meat, shellfish; legumes; nuts and seeds; prunes; whole grains.	Promotes iron absorption; essential to red blood cells, connective tissue, nerve fibers, and skin pigment. Component of several enzymes.
Fluoride	Fluoridated water; tea.	Helps maintain strong bones and teeth.
Iodine	Iodized salt, seafood, foods grown in iodine-rich soil.	Necessary to make thyroid hormones.
Iron	Liver, meat, seafood; eggs; legumes; fortified cereals; dried fruits; whole grains; leafy greens; nuts and seeds.	Needed to produce hemoglobin, which transports oxygen throughout the body.
Manganese	Tea; nuts and seeds; legumes; bran; leafy greens; whole grains; egg yolks.	Component of many enzymes needed for metabolism; necessary for bone and tendon formation.
Molybdenum	Liver and other organ meats; dark green leafy vegetables; whole grain products, legumes, nuts.	Component of enzymes needed for metabolism; instrumental in iron storage.
Selenium	Brazil nuts and other nuts; fish, seafood; whole grain products; onions, garlic, mushrooms; brown rice; organ meats.	Antioxidant that works to protect cell membranes from oxidative damage.
Zinc	Oysters, meat, poultry; yogurt, milk, eggs; wheat germ; nuts; legumes.	Instrumental in metabolic action of enzymes; essential for growth and reproduction; supports immune function.
Chloride	Table salt; seafood; milk, eggs, meat.	With sodium, maintains fluid balance and normal cell functions.
Potassium	Avocados, bananas, citrus and dried fruits; legumes and many vegetables; whole grain products; dairy products.	Along with sodium, helps to maintain fluid balance; promotes proper metabolism and muscle function.
Sodium	Table salt; dairy products; seafood; seasonings; most processed foods.	With potassium, regulates the body's fluid balance; promotes proper muscle and nerve function.

Below are the Institute of Medicine's recommendations for daily mineral intake. The amounts may vary for pregnant and lactating women.

DAILY RECOMMENDED DIETARY ALLOWANCE (RDA) FOR ADULTS		DAILY TOLERABLE UPPER INTAKE LEVELS (UL) FOR ADULTS OVER 19
MALES 19+	FEMALES 19+	
1,000 mg* 19–50 years; 1,200 mg* 51+	1,000 mg* 19–50 years; 1,200 mg* 51+	2,500 mg
400 mg 19–30 years; 420 mg 31+	310 mg 19–30 years; 320 mg 31+	350 mg**
700 mg	700 mg	4,000 mg
35 mcg* 19–50 years; 30 mcg* 51+	25 mcg* 19–50 years; 20 mcg* 51+	Not established
900 mcg	900 mcg	10,000 mcg
4 mg*	3 mg*	10 mg
150 mcg	150 mcg	1,100 mcg
8 mg	18 mg 19–50 years; 8 mg 51+	45 mg
2.3 mg*	1.8 mg*	11 mg
45 mcg	45 mcg	2,000 mcg
55 mcg	55 mcg	400 mcg
11 mg	8 mg	40 mg
2,300 mg* 19-50 years ; 2,000 mg* 50-70 years; 1,800 mg* 71+	2,300 mg* 19-50 years ; 2,000 mg* 50-70 years; 1,800 mg* 71+	3,600 mg
4,700 mg	4,700 mg	Not established
1,500 mg* 19-50 years; 1,300 mg* 50-70 years; 1,200mg* 71+	1,500 mg* 19-50 years; 1,300 mg* 50-70 years; 1,200mg* 71+	2,300 mg

*These values represent daily Adequate Intake (AI).

These tables presents daily Recommended Dietary Allowances (RDAs), except where there is an asterisk. The RDAs are set to meet the known needs of practically all healthy people. The term *Adequate Intake* is used rather than *RDA* when scientific evidence is insufficient to estimate an average requirement.

**The UL for magnesium represents intake from a pharmacological agent only and does not include intake from food and water.

Source: Institute of Medicine, Food and Nutrition Board. National Academy Press, Washington, D. C.

found in soy, called isoflavones, may mimic the actions of estrogen (and are therefore also sometimes called phytoestrogens) and play a role in easing menopausal symptoms and protecting against hormone-dependent cancers such as some types of breast cancer.

- **Carotenoids**, such as beta-carotene, lycopene, lutein, and zeaxanthin—found in carrots, tomatoes, and watermelon—may also reduce the risk of some cancers and have powerful antioxidant effects.
- **Allyl sulfides**, found in garlic and onions, help strengthen the immune system.

While phytochemicals play a wide variety of roles in the body, most research has focused on their potential as antioxidants, which are molecules that stabilize free radicals. Free radicals, unstable molecules that can damage healthy cells, are created every time a cell in our body uses oxygen to derive energy from digested food. Free radicals contain an unpaired electron, and electrons prefer to pair up. So these free radicals search for a molecule from which they can steal an electron. The molecular victim then goes in search of another electron and sets off a chain reaction that results in the creation of more free radicals. A molecule that has lost electrons in this manner is said to have been "oxidized."

Excessive free radicals can damage DNA and other genetic material. The body's immune system seeks out and destroys these mutated cells, in much the same way as it eliminates invading bacteria and other foreign organisms. This mechanism declines with age, however, and the body becomes more vulnerable to free-radical damage. Over time, this damage can become irreversible, leading to cancer. And it's oxidized cholesterol that blocks arteries, leading to a heart attack or stroke.

Thus, by neutralizing free radicals, antioxidants help prevent cardiovascular disease and cancer. Researchers have identified hundreds of substances that act as antioxidants in our foods, including vitamins C and E, selenium, and carotenoids such as beta-carotene and lycopene.

THE REAL DEAL   **Vitamin D**

Vitamin D may be best known for its role in protecting your bones. But experts are looking into whether this vitamin might ward off a variety of other problems, too. In a 2012 article from the journal *Pharmacotherapy*, experts cited some evidence to suggest that vitamin D may help:

- Prevent falls, especially in older people
- Prevent and treat muscle pain in people taking cholesterol-lowering statin drugs
- Reduce the risk of multiple sclerosis
- Ward off depression
- Prevent and control asthma
- Prevent different types of cancer, including colorectal cancer

Despite this impressive list, vitamin D is not a cure-all. The effectiveness of vitamin D for preventing many health problems still needs a lot more research. But if you're older, obese, vegetarian, have dark skin or little exposure to sunlight, or suffer from Crohn's disease, cystic fibrosis, or celiac disease, you're at high risk of having low vitamin D and should ask your doctor to measure your level and recommend supplements if needed.

For most people who aren't at risk of vitamin D deficiency, getting about 15 minutes of sun exposure daily is an easy way to keep up your level of this vitamin. (If you live in a northern climate, this may only be true in spring and summer. Ask your doctor if you need a supplement during winter, when the angle of the sun prevents it from converting on our skin.)

ANTIOXIDANT GUIDE

ANTIOXIDANT	FUNCTION	FOOD SOURCE
Vitamin C	May lower your risk of cardiovascular disease (by strengthening blood vessel walls and preventing atherosclerosis) and certain kinds of cancer. May also help protect against cataracts and gout; promotes wound healing and iron absorption; supports immunity.	Citrus fruits and juices; melons and berries; peppers, broccoli, potatoes; and many other fruits and vegetables.
Vitamin E	May prevent heart attacks and strokes and lower the risk of death from bladder cancer.	Eggs, vegetable oils, margarine, and mayonnaise; nuts and seeds; fortified cereals.

CAROTENOIDS

Beta-carotene	Helps prevent night blindness and age-related macular degeneration. May protect against certain types of cancer, especially lung cancer; maintains healthy skin, hair, nails as well as gums, glands, bones and teeth.	Orange, yellow, and dark green fruits and vegetables, including carrots, sweet potatoes, squash, broccoli, kale, spinach; apricots, peaches, cantaloupe.
Lutein, zeaxanthin	Protects against cataracts and age-related macular degeneration.	Collard greens, kale, spinach, turnip greens, green peas, broccoli.
Lycopene	May protect against cancer, including prostate, stomach, and lung cancer.	Tomatoes, pink grapefruit, watermelon, pink guavas.

FLAVONOIDS

Anthocyanidins	May protect against cancer and heart disease; may slow signs of aging.	Blueberries, cherries, cranberries, blackberries, black currants, plums, red grapes.
Hesperidin	May reduce risk of heart disease and cancer.	Citrus fruits and juices.
Isoflavones	May lower the risk of heart disease, breast cancer, and osteoporosis.	Soy, legumes, peanuts.
Quercetin	May help lower the risk of cancer and heart disease. May help lower high blood pressure and high cholesterol.	Onions; apples; citrus fruits; tea; red wine.
Selenium	May lower the risk of colorectal cancer, lung cancer, and prostate cancer. May help prevent coronary artery disease.	Brazil nuts and other nuts; fish, seafood; whole grain products; onions, garlic; mushrooms; brown rice; organ meats.
Coenzyme Q10	May help protect against heart disease.	Organ meats; salmon, tuna; whole grains.

Prebiotics & Probiotics:
Beneficial Bacteria

You are born with none, but your digestive system is quickly colonized and by the time you are two weeks old, you will have a large population of bacteria that will stay with you for your entire life. These beneficial bacteria keep your intestinal tract healthy; if they become depleted, such as when you take a course of antibiotics, potentially harmful bacteria can multiply, causing digestive and other health issues. Among the most commonly studied probiotics are *Lactobacillus acidophilus, L. rhamnosus GG,* and bifidobacteria.

In order to make sure you have enough helpful bacteria, you may want to eat them. These organisms are called probiotics, and you can find them in some yogurts. Probiotics are also available as a dietary supplement in pill or powder form. Like many items sold in health-food stores, commercial probiotics vary considerably in their effectiveness. When buying probiotic foods or supplements, consider the following:

The health effects are species- and strain-specific and cannot be generalized to other bacteria. For example, *L. rhamnosus GG* has been shown to be helpful for childhood diarrhea but not for Crohn's disease, while other products have been shown to be helpful in Crohn's disease. Find out which probiotics have been studied for the condition you want treated.

Look for a product with billions of bacteria in it. You need this many to effectively colonize your intestine. The bacteria should be available at time of consumption, not at time of preparation, so look on the label for the viable count at time of use. Also, look for the specific strains of bacteria in the product. If they are not listed on the label, they may not be there.

Look for live cultures of acidophilus or bifidobacteria, or both. Products that are pasteurized or have been sitting in the refrigerator for a long time will have very few active bacteria.

Store probiotic supplements in a cool, dry place, such as the refrigerator.

Scientists have also started to explore the foods we eat that help probiotics flourish in the human gut—these are known as prebiotics. Prebiotic properties are found in onions, garlic, leek, chicory, Jerusalem artichokes, legumes, and whole grains.

THE BOTTOM LINE

- Probiotics are bacteria that help maintain the health of your digestive tract.
- Probiotics can be found in fermented foods such as yogurt.
- When shopping for probiotic foods or supplements, look for live cultures and remember that health effects are species- and strain-specific.
- Prebiotics are foods that feed probiotics.

Dietary Supplements:
Do You Need Them?

Millions of North Americans take dietary supplements. In 2009, Americans spent more than $26 billion—yes, billion with a "b"—on supplements.

Even though supplements have become astoundingly popular, researchers have a tough time proving their benefits. The effects of supplements depend on the level of nutrients already being absorbed from the diet, as well as factors that influence nutrient absorption and metabolism.

And just because these supplements are sold over the counter doesn't mean they're safe or that you can't get too much of a good thing. "Taking more than a DRI [dietary reference intake] of vitamins is associated with problems, such as osteoporosis, which is caused by too much vitamin A," says Michael Roizen, MD, Cleveland Clinic's chief wellness officer, and coauthor of the *You: The Owner's Manual* series. And because drugs and nutrients share the same route of absorption and metabolism in our bodies, supplements may interact with medications. Research does support supplements for some people:

- Pregnant women and women of childbearing years require extra folic acid to help prevent birth defects.
- Older adults, especially postmenopausal women, may want to take calcium and vitamin D. While a recent U.S. Preventive Services Task Force report indicated that there wasn't sufficient evidence that the typical doses of calcium supplements prevents osteoporotic fractures, some studies show that vitamin D plays an important role in the absorption of calcium and in boosting bone health.
- People over 50 may benefit from vitamin B12 supplements.
- Young women with anemia may benefit from iron supplements.
- People on very restricted diets or with many allergies may want to take a multivitamin.
- Those at risk for age-related macular degeneration—an eye problem—may benefit from antioxidant and zinc supplements.

If you fall into any of these categories, ask your doctor about appropriate doses. In general, though, it's best to get your vitamins and minerals from food rather than pills. Supplements appear to be less effective than eating foods rich in the same nutrients; there is a good deal of evidence that antioxidant supplements in particular are usually not helpful, and may in fact be harmful. Plus, foods contain other important nutrients, such as fiber, essential fatty acids, and antioxidant phytochemicals.

THE BOTTOM LINE

- It's best to get your nutrients from food, rather than supplements.
- Most healthy adults don't need supplements, as long as they eat a balanced diet.
- If you think you might need a supplement, talk to your doctor first to make sure it doesn't interact with any medications you are taking.

THE REAL DEAL ON FOOD SAFETY

Every year, millions of people across North America are sickened by food-borne illnesses (commonly called food poisoning). These lead to thousands of hospitalizations and even deaths.

But the germs responsible for these illnesses aren't the only concerns lurking in our food. These days, many are worried about pesticides, pollutants, and additives in our food, as well as genetic manipulation in the plants and animals that wind up on our plates. Even the chemicals used in food containers have given cause for concern.

However, a watchful eye goes a long way in protecting yourself from these possible threats. You can reduce your—and your family's—exposure to foods that may be a worry. And you can run your kitchen so germs will have less chance to intrude into your food. Here's what you should know before serving your next meal.

Do Pesticides and Other Chemicals Harm?

The remarkable productivity of modern agriculture depends to a large degree on a wide array of complex chemicals. These include fertilizers and pesticides applied to crops, antibiotics and hormones given to livestock, and additives included in animal feed. In North America, these chemical solutions provide an abundance of food at a very low cost.

Inevitably, though, most crops retain traces of pesticides, and animal products may contain somewhat larger amounts. Because high doses of certain pesticides have been linked to health problems in animals, it is not surprising that North Americans are concerned that residues of them in foods we eat could cause birth defects, neurological diseases, and even cancer. Environmental pollutants in the air, water, and soil—heavy metals such as mercury and toxic compounds such as PCBs (polychlorinated biphenyls) and dioxins—may also make their way into the food supply.

Just because traces of a substance are there, however, doesn't mean they're harmful. The risk to your health depends not only on the toxicity of a substance, but on the extent and type of exposure you receive. In both the U.S. and Canada, pesticides are among the most strictly regulated chemical products, and food surveys find that North Americans have very low overall exposure to pesticide residues. And remember that for contaminants we can't avoid, our bodies are remarkably well equipped with preventive mechanisms to detoxify them. But the cumulative effects of the many different pesticides in our food supply may combine to do more damage than we can know from studying them individually.

And some populations, such as infants, who take in more food per body weight than adults, may be more susceptible. One group of pesticides called organophosphates is of particular concern because they irreversibly block an enzyme critical to nerve function. According to researchers at the University of California at Berkeley, children exposed to the highest levels of organophosphates during pregnancy had IQ scores that were an average of seven points lower than the scores of kids with the lowest pesticide exposures. So while you don't need to spend thousands

THE REAL DEAL Mercury

Mercury enters the atmosphere primarily from coal-burning electric utilities, then becomes more toxic when bacteria in lakes and oceans convert it into methylmercury, which fish and shellfish absorb into their tissues. The bigger a predatory fish—like swordfish—the more methylmercury it's likely to harbor.

Methylmercury is particularly toxic to pregnant women, nursing mothers, and young children. Even low-level exposure can affect the developing brain and have neurological and behavioral effects. In adults, dietary methylmercury may increase the risk of heart disease.

Seafood is nutritious—a low-saturated-fat source of high-quality protein rich in heart-healthy omega-3 fatty acids—so public health experts are eager to determine the level of mercury in seafood that can be safely consumed.

Based on the current FDA standard, women of childbearing age (especially if they are already pregnant or nursing) and young children should avoid shark, swordfish, king mackerel, and tilefish, and limit themselves to 12 oz (340 g) of any other fish or seafood per week. Choose seafood sources that are lowest in mercury such as catfish, flounder, salmon, shrimp, haddock, pollock (used in frozen fish products), sardines, crab, and scallops. When choosing canned tuna, select "light" over "white" varieties.

Organic Foods:
Are They Worth the Cost?

Only a few decades ago, organic foods were found solely in health food stores or at farmers' markets. Today, the organic industry's annual growth is consistently outpacing the growth of total food sales and gaining its share of the market. More than $28 billion worth of organic products are now sold in North America each year.

Consumers are clearly willing to spend more money for organic foods, which have improved in quality and variety in recent years. But what are shoppers getting for the money?

THE MEANING OF "ORGANIC"

Organic food is produced by farmers who protect the environment for future generations by rotating crops (which promotes biological diversity), conserving and renewing the soil, and protecting sources of water. These crops are grown, handled, and processed without synthetic fertilizers, pesticides, or herbicides; artificial in-

gredients; or preservatives. By law, organic food is not irradiated, and if the product is labeled "100% organic," it also doesn't contain genetically engineered ingredients. Organic meat, poultry, eggs, and dairy products come from animals that are given no antibiotics or growth hormones.

Organic food crops can, however, be grown with pesticides—just not synthetic ones. And not all organic pesticides are harmless. Pyrethrins, for example, are natural insecticides isolated from flowers and can cause allergic reactions. Naturally occurring copper compounds can also be used in organic agriculture, even though they are potentially toxic.

ARE ORGANIC FOODS MORE NUTRITIOUS?

In 2012, the *Annals of Internal Medicine* published an analysis of 240 research studies that compared the health effects of conventionally grown and organic crops. There were few differences. Other research, however, indicates that organic foods appear to have consistently higher levels of antioxidants, so the debate is sure to continue. But remember, the "certified organic" label is not a nutrition claim, and just because a food is organic does not automatically mean it's healthy. Organic meat is just as high in saturated fat as the conventionally raised kind, and organic sugar adds just as many calories as regular table sugar.

ARE ORGANIC FOODS SAFER?

While organic foods can still be contaminated with synthetic agricultural chemicals that persist in the soil or are introduced during warehousing, in one study of 94,000 food samples from more than 20 major food crops, sponsored by the nonprofit Consumers Union, organically grown foods had about one-third the residues of conventionally grown foods. But it's unclear whether these residues are harmful to consumers.

There may be a greater benefit in shielding children from pesticide residues since their bodies are smaller and they eat a less-varied diet. Organic foods tend to be processed less, so they may be less likely to be contaminated, but they are not immune to foodborne pathogens.

ORGANIC BUYING GUIDE

Because organic food is typically more expensive, it makes sense to shop selectively. Although there is no evidence that fruits and vegetables with higher residues (as identified by nonprofit research groups such as Consumers Union and the Environmental Working Group) pose a hazard, selecting the organic versions of these foods is a logical place to start:

- Apples
- Strawberries
- Spinach
- Imported grapes
- Potatoes
- Lettuce
- Celery
- Peaches
- Imported nectarines
- Sweet bell peppers
- Domestic blueberries
- Kale and collard greens

Save money with nonorganic low-residue foods, including:

- Onions
- Pineapples
- Asparagus
- Mangoes
- Cabbage
- Sweet potatoes
- Mushrooms
- Avocados
- Sweet peas
- Eggplants
- Cantaloupes
- Kiwis
- Watermelons
- Grapefruits

Finally, consider organic meat. While most people worry about produce, animals actually accumulate residues from the foods they eat, which is stored in their fat. So you may want to buy organic hamburger, steak, pork chops, and lamb to avoid a more concentrated exposure.

THE BOTTOM LINE

- Organic foods are grown or processed without synthetic pesticides, fertilizer, or herbicides. Organic foods also do not contain artificial ingredients or preservatives.
- Pesticide levels in organic foods are about one-third of conventionally grown foods.
- Children may benefit the most from eating organic foods.
- Food labeled "100% organic" can't be irradiated or contain genetically engineered ingredients.
- Organic food confers the same level of nutrition as conventionally grown foods.

to go all-organic, it can't hurt to take a few precautions to lower your exposure to pesticides and other chemicals, such as:

Eat a wide variety of foods. Doing so helps keep you from overeating any one type of food that may have high levels of pollutants or pesticides.

Eat plenty of fresh fruits and vegetables. They're rich in fiber and antioxidants that may help protect the body from carcinogens. In addition, broccoli, cauliflower, cabbage, watercress, and brussels sprouts contain compounds that release isothiocyanates, which in turn stimulate the liver to produce enzymes that can detoxify carcinogens before they can cause harm. Phenolic compounds (in apples and other fruits) and bioflavonoids (high in citrus fruits) protect in similar ways.

Trim the animal fat. Whether a contaminant is harmful or not depends on how long it lingers. A substance that resists chemical or biological breakdown accumulates as it is ingested by one species after another, steadily building up as the food chain progresses from small species to the large and dominant. The highest levels of pollutants, therefore, are ingested by large animals, such as cattle. Many of these persistent pollutants are stored in an animal's fat, which is why choosing lower-fat foods and trimming fat from meat can help to reduce the amount of pollutants you consume.

Consider buying organically grown foods. Organic foods are grown or processed without the use of any synthetic chemicals such as pesticides, herbicides, preservatives, growth hormones, and antibiotics (although some may be treated by natural pesticides, which can also be toxic).

THE REAL DEAL Functional Foods

Not all additives are put into foods simply to improve their color, boost their flavor, or make life easier for the food manufacturer. Some ingredients are added to foods for your health! In general, health experts recommend that you get nutrients from foods in which they occur naturally. But functional or enriched foods, which have nutrients added during production, are still a better source than supplements. Nutrients commonly added to foods include:

- **Folate.** Also known as folic acid, this B vitamin is added to many grain foods such as bread and cereal. It's important for women of childbearing age to get plenty of this nutrient early in pregnancy to reduce the risk of neural tube defects (like spina bifida) in their children.
- **Omega-3 fatty acids.** These have earned a positive reputation in recent years for their link to heart health. They're found naturally in salmon and some other fish, but food makers are engineering the omega-3s into many types of foods, including eggs and peanut butter.
- **Vitamin D and calcium.** Vitamin D isn't found naturally in many foods that people like to eat (unless you *like* cod liver oil). But it's added to milk and some breakfast cereals. It plays a role in bone health and has many other jobs throughout your body. Calcium is also well-known for protecting your bones. But if you don't like milk, another common breakfast drink—orange juice—is widely available with added calcium (and vitamin D).

Just keep in mind that the phrase "now with omega-3!"—or other trendy nutrients—on the label doesn't necessarily mean that a food is healthy. Nor does it mean you can eat an unlimited amount. Make sure not to overload on any food just to get a particular nutrient if it's going to add up to more calories or fat than you really want or need.

Do Additives Harm or Heal?

For centuries, people have enhanced their foods with various flavorings, preservatives, and dyes. But some ingredients on today's food labels—with their complicated, chemistry set–like names—can seem downright alarming.

The truth is, these ingredients are in foods for a purpose. Few foods reach today's supermarkets free of additives—substances that do not occur naturally in a food but are added for various reasons. These include preservatives to prevent spoilage; emulsifiers to prevent water and fat from separating; thickeners; vitamins and minerals (either to replace nutrients lost in processing or to increase nutritional value); sweeteners (both natural and artificial), salt; flavorings to improve taste; and dyes to make everything from candies to soft drinks more visually appealing.

In all, North American food processors can choose from thousands of additives. Although many people question the safety of these additives, their use is governed by stringent regulations. Authorities require extensive studies before an additive is allowed on the market. The appropriate use of additives allows us to enjoy history's safest and most abundant assortment of foods.

In short, the majority of food additives are safe to eat. However, they are generally not nutritious. The most common additives are sugar, corn syrup, sodium, and trans fats, which can contribute to obesity, high blood pressure, heart disease, and many other health problems. So focus on whole, natural foods like fresh fruits and vegetables, whole grains, beans, and nuts. And when buying packaged foods, look for those with shorter ingredient and additive lists.

In addition, while additives in general are safe, some are best left on the shelves. The Center (CSPI) for Science in the Public Interest, a nonprofit organization, urges *everyone* to avoid these:

Acesulfame-potassium. The organization questions the research that supported the safety of this artificial sweetener.

Artificial colorings. According to the CSPI, blue no. 2, green no. 3, red no. 3, and yellow no. 6 have been linked to cancer in lab animals. Yellow no. 5 triggers allergic-like reactions in some people.

BHA (butylated hydroxyanisole). This chemical, which prevents rancidity in foods, has been linked to cancer in rodents.

Caramel coloring. Found in colas, this common coloring can be contaminated with chemicals that some experts call carcinogenic.

Potassium bromate. Found in some bread, bromate is linked to cancer in animals.

Propyl gallate. Some studies suggest that this preservative might cause cancer in animals.

Saccharin. This artificial sweetener has shed some of its decades-long reputation as a carcinogen. But it still makes the CSPI's avoid list due to lingering cancer concerns.

Sodium nitrate and sodium nitrite. Used to preserve and color meats like bacon, ham, and smoked fish, these additives can encourage the creation of cancer-causing chemicals.

Some other additives pose problems for people with certain medical conditions:

- Anyone with high blood pressure or any condition that mandates a low-salt diet should check the labels on processed foods for forms of sodium.
- People trying to reduce sugar intake should look for lactose and other ingredients ending in "ose"; these are forms of sugar.

> *Old School*
> The MSG in Chinese food can trigger headaches and other reactions.
>
> *New Wisdom*
> People are most likely reacting to histamine, tyramine, and phenylethylamine.

Food additives play a vital role in today's food supply. Consumer concerns over food additives often stem from misinformation. All additives must receive federal government approval.

COMMON FOOD ADDITIVES

TYPE OF ADDITIVE	FOUND IN	FUNCTION
PRESERVATIVES		
Benzoic acid	Acidic foods.	Protects food from spoiling.
Sodium nitrite and sodium nitrate*	Processed meats, such as sausages, hot dogs, bacon, ham, lunch meats; smoked fish.	Protects food from spoiling; preserves color; adds flavor.
Sulfites	Dried fruits; processed potato products; wine.	Preserves color; prevents bacterial growth.
Ascorbic acid (vitamin C)	Fruit products (juices, jams, canned fruits); cured meats; cereals.	Preserves color and flavor; adds to vitamin content.
BHA or BHT*	Fatty foods that can turn rancid, such as baked products, cereals, potato chips, fats and oil.	Protects food from spoiling.
Tocopherols (vitamin E)	Vegetables; cereals.	Prevents fats and oils from becoming rancid.
COLORINGS		
Blue No. 1, blue No. 2, caramel, carmine/cochineal, citrus red No. 2, green No. 3, red No. 3, red No. 40, titanium dioxide, yellow No. 5, yellow No. 6*	Many processed foods, including soft drinks, candy, gelatin, cake frosting, gum. Also used in bologna and other processed meats.	Makes food look more appetizing by meeting people's food color expectations—for example, turning cherry Jell-O red.
FLAVOR ENHANCERS		
Disodium guanylate	Soups, sauces, other processed foods.	Enhances existing flavors.
Hydrolyzed vegetable protein	Soups, sauces, other processed foods.	Enhances existing flavors.
Monosodium glutamate (MSG)	Chinese food; soup mixes; stock cubes; canned, processed, frozen meats.	Heightens taste perception so that foods seem to taste better.
EMULSIFIERS, STABILIZERS, AND THICKENERS		
Carrageenan Cellulose Glycerol Guar gum Gum arabic Lecithin Pectins	Sauces, ice cream, low-fat and artificial cream cheese, cottage cheese, condiments, jams, jellies, chocolate, puddings, cake frosting, pie filling, margarine, other processed foods.	Improves texture and consistency of processed foods by increasing smoothness, creaminess, and volume. Hold in moisture and prevent separation of oil and water.

*The Center for Science in the Public Interest (CSPI) recommends avoiding these additives.

- Those with hemochromatosis should avoid iron-enriched breads, cereals, and other products.
- Sulfites used to preserve the color of dried fruits, frozen french fries, and sauerkraut can trigger an asthma attack in susceptible people.
- Some people may experience headaches after eating foods preserved with nitrites, and in rare cases children with attention deficit disorder may respond adversely to certain food colorants.

Do Genetically Modified Foods Harm or Heal?

For centuries, food growers have tampered with plant and animal genetics by crossbreeding in order to bring out desirable traits while suppressing less-welcome ones. The refinement of such techniques has enabled farmers to produce increasingly abundant crops.

In recent years, food biotechnology has added a new dimension, thanks to genetic modification. Scientists can add desirable hereditary traits to almost any plant. Possibilities include producing more nutritious foods—for example, corn with increased high-quality protein, or a version of the seed used in making canola oil that produces more unsaturated fatty acids.

Agricultural scientists are also trying to make plants more productive or more able to withstand adverse growing conditions, such as drought, and resist insects. This has tremendous potential for overcoming world food shortages.

The production of genetically modified (GM) foods and genetically modified organisms (GMOs) is regulated in the U.S. and Canada. Soybeans, corn, and canola are widely produced GM crops that furnish a

A chemical called BPA has given people a reason to pay more attention to the packaging and storage containers for their foods and drinks.

BPA—short for bisphenol A—is a chemical used in making polycarbonate plastics, which are used for some water bottles. It can also find its way into canned food when it's used to coat the inside of the cans.

According to the National Institutes of Health (NIH), in 2003 and 2004, urine testing of thousands of people age six and older found BPA in most of the samples. Although many people are understandably concerned about the thought of having food-packaging chemicals in their system, the health risk may not be significant.

The U.S. Food and Drug Administration's stance on BPA, as of 2012, is that: "The scientific evidence at this time does not suggest that the very low levels of human exposure to BPA through the diet are unsafe."

But if you want to limit your—and your kids'—exposure to this stuff, the NIH recommends:

- Look for the recycling code on plastic containers. Those marked with a 3 or 7 may be made with this chemical.
- Use fewer canned foods.
- Avoid microwaving polycarbonate plastic food containers.
- Choose BPA-free baby bottles.

number of ingredients used in highly processed foods.

Despite the benefits of genetic modification, some people are concerned that this type of manipulation may create adverse consequences. For example, insects might become resistant to the pesticides produced by crops that have been genetically modified to make them, or the herbicide resistance of a GM crop might be transferred to a weed.

Factory Farming

From a distance, the farms that satisfy much of North Americans' craving for meat may look like the bucolic scene that the word *farm* evokes. But when you get up close, you'll see that they look more like factories tasked with feeding thousands of hungry mouths—in fact, they're nicknamed "factory farms." Another name is CAFO, or "concentrated animal feeding operation." In Canada, these may be called "confined feeding operations" or "intensive livestock operations."

Efficiency and proximity are the norm at these facilities, which have been criticized as being cruel to animals and environmentally unfriendly. In addition, there is concern that the antibiotics used to keep the animals healthy in close quarters and the hormones used to help them grow quickly may be passed on to people, with unknown effects on human health.

In response, small farms that offer an alternative have been proliferating. These farms offer grass-fed beef, free-range chickens, and other organic livestock (which have been raised without antibiotics or hormones). Although it's impossible to quantify the health benefits of these types of meat, it certainly can't hurt. Plus, it's better for the animals and for the environment. And some folks believe that they just plain taste better.

60 to 70% of processed foods contain at least one genetically engineered ingredient.

Genetic modification looks like it's going to remain a factor in our food supply in the future, so savvy eaters will want to stay well-educated about the benefits and possible concerns related to these foods as research continues. In the meantime, if you're concerned, buy foods labeled organic, which must be free from GMOs.

How Foodborne Pathogens Harm

E. coli in spinach. Listeria in cantaloupe. Salmonella in pistachios. Outbreaks of foodborne illnesses grab media headlines because they can potentially affect anyone or any food. According to the U.S. Centers for Disease Control and Prevention, about 3,000 people die each year from food poisoning (see page 31). A wide variety of bacteria, viruses, parasites, and toxins can cause different diseases, and food can be contaminated at any point from harvesting to transporting to processing to displaying for sale. While farms, food manufacturers, and restaurants are all subject to inspection by government agencies, it's impossible to completely avoid contamination. But proper food storage and preparation can reduce your risk. See page 32 for more details.

Also, irradiation (exposing foods to x-rays and other forms of ionizing radiation) kills many molds, bacteria, and insects. Irradiation can provide an extra measure of safety for those with AIDS and others with lowered immunity. Irradiated foods are not radioactive, but if you prefer to avoid them, look for the irradiation treatment symbol.

Fast Food: Is It Possible to Eat Healthy on the Run?

The North American landscape is heavily dotted with fast-food and take-out restaurants—even in hospitals and schools. Some critics blame our affection for supersized portions of fast food, which is typically high in fat and calories, for the fact that more than 50 percent of adult North Americans are overweight. Though most fast-food establishments offer some lower-calorie, more healthful fare, the overwhelming majority of the foods we eat at fast-food chains—burgers, fries, hot dogs, fried chicken, and pizza—are loaded with fat, salt, and calories. Even some of the healthier sounding options, such as salads or smoothies, can contain more calories and fat than traditional choices if they contain a creamy dressing, cheese, breaded meat, or lots of sugar.

Your best bet is to avoid fast food restaurants as much as possible but if you must eat on the run, these suggestions can help you find the healthiest choices:

Hamburgers. Choose a basic hamburger, no cheese, no mayonnaise, no bacon. Order it dressed with mustard, pickle, fresh onion, tomato, and lettuce. Basic hamburgers are in the 250- to 350-calorie range, with about 10 to 20 g of fat, while deluxe, all-dressed cheeseburgers weigh in at about 500 calories (or more), with 26 g of fat (or more).

French fries. Of course we often want fries with that, but eating them comes with a nutritional price. Just one medium serving of French fries delivers between 360 and 450 calories and a hefty 17 to 22 g of fat. A large order of fries from several chains provides almost 600 calories with 27 g of fat. If you must have fries, get the smallest size. And if possible, order wide, large-cut fries. They are usually slightly lower in fat and salt than the skinny ones because in an entire order of fries, there is less surface area for the oil to cling to.

Tacos. A regular beef taco with lettuce in a hard taco shell has about 180 calories, with 10 g of fat. Stick to one taco, with only the regular toppings.

Pizza. There's no question that pizza ranks at the top of many people's list of favorite fast foods. Unfortunately, it is also a major source of fat. One 14-in (35 cm) commercial pizza could have about 22 to 36 g of fat or more. When eating pizza, stick to one slice. And load your pizza with vegetable toppings. They have the least calories and fat and the most nutrients. Lean meats like chicken and ham are better choices than fatty sausages and pepperoni. While you're at it, ask for more sauce and less cheese.

THE BOTTOM LINE

- Supposedly healthy fast-food options such as salads may be loaded with calories because of dressings and toppings.
- Additions such as mayonnaise and cheese dramatically increase the amount of fat and calories in fast-food sandwiches.
- Stick to the smallest size of fries.
- Limit yourself to one taco or slice of pizza; there's plenty of calories in each.

THE REAL DEAL ON EATING TO HEAL

If your head is spinning from all of these facts and figures, take a deep breath and relax. While there is new nutrition research being published every day, the majority of it only serves to prove that Mom was right: Eat your fruits and veggies (and whole grains, too), stay away from junk food, and don't eat too much. For most of us, following those simple rules will go a long way toward ensuring that you get enough calories and the right balance of nutrients to keep your body working properly while avoiding ingredients like sugar, sodium, and trans fats that harm your body.

If you read through several of the entries in Part 3 of this book, which outlines what's best to eat for different health conditions, you'll notice a theme. Most of them call for a diet rich in fruits and vegetables, whole grains, lean protein (with an emphasis on plant proteins and seafood), and some dairy. That's because these are the foods highest in the vitamins, minerals, antioxidants, and other phytochemicals that are proving to be instrumental in healing and preventing disease. So while there are definitely some nutrients that have a specific effect on certain ailments, and there are specific foods rich in those nutrients—which we've chosen to highlight in each entry—overall, your best bet for health lies in a varied diet of whole foods, minimally processed and simply prepared.

How Much to Eat for Health

Both the new U.S. Dietary Guidelines (depicted as a plate divided into four sections for fruits, vegetables, grains, and protein, with dairy on the side) and Canada's Food Guide (laid out in a rainbow scheme) call for this breakdown of macronutrients:

- **Carbohydrates** (45 to 65%), primarily from whole grain sources
- **Fat** (20 to 35%), primarily monounsaturated and polyunsaturated omega-3s
- **Protein** (10 to 12%), primarily from lean sources

The Institute of Medicine, a nonprofit organization, has established nutrition recommendations that have been adopted by both the U.S. and Canadian governments. These guidelines list a "recommended dietary allowance" (RDA), the average amount in the daily diet that will meet the nutrient needs of almost every healthy person of a particular age and gender. If experts don't have enough data available to establish an RDA, they will list an "adequate intake" (AI), an amount likely to meet the needs of most people of that age and gender. Because too much of any one nutrient is also a problem, the "tolerable upper intake level" (UL) is also noted; this is the highest level that a person can get on an ongoing day-to-day basis that is likely to pose no risk of harmful side effects in most people. You'll find charts on pages 10 and 12 with their recommendations for vitamin and mineral intake. Guidelines have not been established for antioxidants and other phytochemicals.

The RDAs are used to calculate the "recommended daily value" (RDV) or "percent daily value" (% DV) printed on food labels in the U.S. and Canada. These are usually based on a 2,000-calorie diet.

While each person's calorie needs are different, depending on height and activity level, 2,000 calories is widely accepted as a reasonable goal for most men of average height (women should probably aim a little bit lower).

In order to get all of these nutrients without going overboard on calories, the key is to choose nutrient-dense foods (those with a high proportion of nutrients to calories) and keep your portions reasonable. Remember, even when we list a particular food as being healing for a condition, that doesn't mean you should eat as much as you can of that food. Just like any medicine, the right "dose" is important. In our supersized world, the portions that we serve ourselves at home or see on our plates in restaurants are often much larger—sometimes as much as four or five times larger—than the recommended serving sizes that are best for our health and fitness. Here are some handy comparisons to envision:

- **Sliced cheese and meat:** About 2 to 3 oz is the equivalent of a stack of three CDs.
- **Beans and hot cereal:** About ½ cup equals two golf balls.
- **Meat, chicken, and salmon:** 3 to 4 oz equals a deck of cards.
- **Rice, pasta, and cereal:** About 1 cup equals a baseball.
- **Rolls, potatoes, and starches:** About ⅔ cup equals a tennis ball.
- **Cheese:** One ounce equals four dice.
- **Medium baked potato:** Roughly equal to a personal-size bar of soap.
- **Peanut butter:** Two tablespoons is the size of a ping-pong ball.

> **QUICK TIP: Downsize portions**
>
> To fool your eye into thinking you're getting more food, use a salad plate instead of a dinner plate for your entrée and a small cereal bowl instead of a giant pasta bowl for your pasta.

- **Salad dressing:** Two tablespoons equals a shot glass.
- **Juice:** Six ounces equals the size of a small yogurt container.

How to Eat for Health

During the past few decades, we've made amazing strides in understanding the impact of food on our lives. Now, more than ever, we have come to realize that foods can both harm and heal us.

Any healthy diet plan needs to center on foods you can keep eating for a lifetime—and it helps if those foods will also help protect you from disease. Here are some tips for eating healthier naturally and permanently.

Eat breakfast, and don't skip meals. Eat more often to avoid a completely empty stomach, which can make you overeat at your next meal. Instead of skipping meals, plan to eat four to six small meals or snacks, spaced 3 to 5 hours apart.

QUICK TIP:
Keep eggs in the carton

Eggs are porous and will absorb refrigerator odors. Store them in their carton, not in the refrigerator door compartment.

Pick carbs carefully. Despite what the popular media might have you believe, you don't need to avoid all carbohydrates. But you should shy away from simple carbohydrates, such as sugar, white bread, white pasta, and white rice. These foods are quickly turned into glucose by the body, and the influx of glucose causes a rapid rise in the hormone insulin, whose job is to escort glucose out of the bloodstream and into cells. A surge of insulin is followed by a glucose "crash," which leaves you hungry in no time. Instead of simple or refined carbs, focus your attention on complex carbohydrates, found in whole grain foods as well as vegetables and fruits. These are more likely to be low-glycemic, which helps prevent or manage diabetes (see page 262).

Choose bulky foods. Foods that contain plenty of fiber, water, or air are "bulky" or "high-volume" and will help you stay fuller longer. These include high-fiber fruits and vegetables as well as beans. Instead of eating a handful of raisins, choose water-dense grapes. If you're making chili, add more beans to bulk it up without adding a lot of calories. Other low-cal, high-volume foods to favor are broth-based soups. Studies show that people who start a meal with soup eat less at that meal and later in the day. Just be sure to avoid cream soups, which are high in calories.

Cut the fat (in some cases). Sometimes, cutting fat from your diet makes sense, because fat is the most concentrated source of calories. Replace some of the red meat you eat with fish or poultry. Remove the skin from poultry before you cook it, and banish the frying pan in favor of steaming, grilling, baking, or microwaving. Choose lean cuts of meat and trim off visible fat. And stay away from sausages, bacon, and cold cuts.

But don't strive for a fat-free life. Don't attempt to cut all the fat out of your diet. Research has shown that people are better able to maintain their weight loss when their diets allow at least some foods that contain healthy fats—for example, nuts, avacados, and olive oil.

Drink plenty of fluids—especially water. Drink water and lots of it. Seltzer and mineral water are good choices. Fluids quench your thirst and reduce your appetite as well. Fruit juice is healthy, but adds calories without fiber. Coffee or tea is fine. Allow yourself to have an occasional glass of wine or beer if you wish, but be aware that they add more than 100 calories per glass.

Eat more calcium-rich foods. Some researchers suggest that calcium may stimulate fat loss by suppressing hormones that cause fat to be stored rather than burned. Adding calcium-rich foods such as milk, yogurt, or other dairy products to a low-calorie diet may make it easier for your body to mobilize fat stores and burn fat.

Avoid depriving yourself. Let yourself have small portions of your favorite high-calorie foods once in a while so you don't get frustrated and end up bingeing. And keep in mind that fasting can be bad for your health. Also, weight loss gained by fasting is rarely sustained once you resume eating.

How to Store Foods for Health

The techniques used to clean, store, and prepare food not only affect its taste, texture, and nutritional value, but are also instrumental in preventing spoilage and foodborne illness. By using the proper methods to prepare and store foods, you can keep them wholesome and nutritious; preserve their appetizing appearance, taste, and texture; and use them economically, helping keep your food expenses low.

Protecting yourself starts when you buy your food. Refrigerate or freeze all perishables within 2 hours of purchase. If the weather is hot, reduce that time to 1 hour and use a cooler for high-risk foods, which include meat, fish, shellfish, poultry, eggs, dairy products, mayonnaise mixtures, and moist foods such as poultry stuffing.

How to Prepare Foods for Health

Even if you selected the freshest foods and stored them properly, it's possible to spread food poisoning because of how you prepare them. Before you begin and anytime you've handled raw meat, poultry, or fish, you should wash your hands in warm water with soap for at least 20 seconds. Remove rings and make sure your fingernails are clean.

1 to 3 days after eating contaminated food is when symptoms typically occur.

Use hot, soapy water to thoroughly wash food preparation surfaces, such as chopping boards and countertops.

Wash plates and utensils used for raw meat or poultry before using them for cooked meat or other food. Also, wash your dishcloth or sponge with hot water and soap after every use. Never allow cooked food to touch an unwashed surface where traces of raw food remain. This will avoid the possibility of cross-contamination and the spread of bacteria. In addition:

- Wash poultry and fish under running water and pat it dry with paper towels before preparation.
- Wash all fruits and vegetables— including melons and citrus fruits— with a produce brush and water before eating, peeling, slicing, or cooking.
- Don't use soap or produce washes. Clean running water is best.
- Do not soak vegetables at any stage during preparation because some of vitamins are soluble in water.

Follow these guidelines to store food to preserve nutrients, avoid contamination, and make them last longer.

FOOD STORAGE GUIDE

FOOD	STORAGE TIPS
STAPLES	• Heat and humidity greatly increase the risk of food spoilage, so store nonrefrigerated and nonfrozen foods away from moisture in a 50°F to 70°F (10° to 21°C) temperature range. • Keep grains and flours in plastic, metal, or glass containers with tight-fitting lids so that insects can't get to them. • Whole grain flours and nuts can quickly turn rancid at room temperature, so store them in the refrigerator or freezer. • Store tightly sealed oils in a dark cupboard or the refrigerator. Exposure to light and warm temperatures robs oils of vitamins A and E. The cloudiness that forms in some refrigerated oils clears at room temperature.
FRUITS AND VEGETABLES	• Raw fruits and vegetables often slowly lose their vitamins when kept at room temperature, but tropical fruits deteriorate rapidly if stored in the cold. • Most produce is best stored at about 50°F (10°C); if refrigerated, put it in the crisper section; the restricted space slows down moisture loss. • Avoid storing fruits and vegetables for long periods in sealed plastic bags; they cut off the air supply, causing the produce to rot. Paper and cellophane are better storage materials because they are permeable. • Leave the stems on berries until you're ready to use them, and refrigerate peas and beans in their pods. Cut the green tops off root vegetables, such as carrots, beets, parsnips, and turnips, or they will continue to draw nourishment from the roots. • Frozen vegetables should be cooked straight from the freezer; thawing encourages the destructive activity of residual enzymes and microorganisms. Do not refreeze foods that have been thawed.
MEAT AND SEAFOOD	• Store meats and fish in the coldest part of the refrigerator. Wrap meat for freezing in freezer paper. Avoid using gas-permeable plastic wrap; it allows moisture to evaporate and causes freezer burn. • Shellfish cannot be kept more than a few hours at refrigerator temperature, but they last 2 or 3 days on ice or at a temperature below 32°F (0°C). • Never defrost meat, poultry, or fish at room temperature. Defrost on the bottom shelf of the refrigerator. If using the microwave to defrost, cook immediately.
DAIRY	• Fresh milk and cream should be tightly sealed to prevent tainting by odors from other foods. Milk retains its nutritional value better in cartons, because exposure to light destroys some of the vitamin A and riboflavin.
HERBS AND SPICES	• Exposure to air, light, moisture, and heat increase how fast herbs and spices lose flavor and color so store them in tightly covered containers in a dark place away from sunlight, such as inside a cupboard or drawer. • To store fresh herbs, wash them and stand them upright in a glass containing 1 or 2 in (2.5 or 5 cm) of cold water. Cover with a plastic bag and refrigerate.

- For root vegetables such as onions, peel away the outer skin. But if you plan on cooking vegetables, such as potatoes, with their skin on, then wash them like any other fruit or vegetable.
- Bruised or lightly damaged produce is safe to eat if you cut off all damaged flesh, where bacteria can grow.
- Do not, however, eat rotten or moldy fruits and vegetables. They're home to potentially harmful bacteria and should be composted or thrown away.

QUICK TIP: Leave the skins

You retain more of the nutrients if you leave skins on, especially for vegetables such as carrots and potatoes, when cooking. Vitamins and minerals are often concentrated in and near the skin. However, it's important to clean vegetables very thoroughly when the skins are left on.

How to Cook for Health

Upon your kitchen counter sits a cornucopia of nutritious food: Lean cuts of meat, fresh vegetables (perhaps plucked from your own garden), juicy fruits, and rich, nutty whole grains.

But the benefits of all this wholesomeness can still dwindle before it gets to your plate. Some methods of cooking can slather foods with saturated fat or blast important nutrients right out of them. Eating a diet rich in foods that heal requires learning to cook in the healthiest ways possible. Forget frying, and give some of these methods a try for your next meal:

Boiling or steaming: Both of these methods cook vegetables, meats, and fish quickly without adding any extra fat. Skip the salt and don't overcook them. You can use herbs and spices to add flavor instead. Cook vegetables whole or in large pieces in a minimum amount of water to prevent water-soluble vitamins from leaching into the water and being poured down the drain.

Stir-frying: Because cooking is so quick, the flavors, colors, and nutrients of meat, poultry, and vegetables are retained, and the method uses little oil. Use an oil that can withstand a high cooking temperature, such as corn, or canola oil. Chop all ingredients ahead of time into similar-size pieces, and marinate meat and poultry first to help tenderize and add flavor without too much salt.

Baking and roasting: Meats, poultry, fish, and vegetables can all be baked and roasted with minimal added fat, though you may want to baste them with some liquid to prevent drying out. You can also make low-sugar low-fat versions of your favorite cakes, cookies, and pies, by replacing some of the butter or oil with applesauce or other pureed fruits; reducing sugar and adding cinnamon or other spices for extra flavor; and substituting high-calorie ingredients such as cream cheese with lower-calorie ingredients such as nonfat ricotta cheese.

Microwaving: Although foodies may frown upon it and some people are still nervous about radiation, the microwave is a great alternative to the oven if you're in a hurry. Be sure to use microwave-safe dishes and keep food covered.

Grilling: Particularly popular during the summer, grilling gives flavor to quick-cooking meat, vegetables, and fruit without adding oil. Pre-grill preparation requires little more than a light brushing with oil to prevent food from sticking to the grill, followed by a dusting of herbs.

THE REAL DEAL — Grilling and Cancer

Cancer-causing substances can form when fat from meat drips onto hot coals and is then deposited onto food through smoke. To minimize risks, take the following steps:

- **Defrost first.** Allow plenty of time for frozen meat to thaw before grilling. Trying to cook frozen meat tends to burn the surface.
- **Trim the fat.** Choose lean cuts, and trim all visible fat from meat. Keep meat portions small so they don't have to spend as long on the grill.
- **Grill for a finishing touch.** Partly bake the food, then finish it off with a few minutes on the grill to achieve a crusty exterior and succulent interior.
- **Wrap it up.** Cover the grill with punctured aluminum foil before you cook. The foil protects the food from the smoke and fire.
- **Rely on indirect heat.** Don't place the heat source directly under the meat. For example, place coals slightly to the side so the fat doesn't drip on them.
- **Avoid flare-ups.** Burning juice or fat can produce harmful smoke. If smoke from dripping fat is too heavy, move the food to another section of the grill or reduce the heat.
- **Slice off charred parts.** Cook meat until it is done without charring it. Remove any charred pieces—don't eat them.

Dietary Restrictions:
Should You Go Vegetarian, Vegan, Dairy-Free, or Gluten-Free?

As the old saying goes, there's no such thing as a free lunch. But many people do choose to make their lunches—and breakfasts and dinners—free of certain foods or ingredients. Some people choose to avoid certain foods for ethical, moral, or general health reasons, such as vegetarians and vegans. Others steer clear of ingredients that aggravate a medical condition such as celiac disease, gluten sensitivity, or lactose intolerance. If you eliminate whole categories of foods from your life, you may need to be extra-vigilant about ensuring that you get all the nutrients you need.

VEGETARIAN AND VEGAN

Technically, a vegetarian is defined as a person who does not eat meat, fish, or fowl or products that contain them. However, in reality, the eating patterns of vegetarians can vary considerably. Vegans consume no meat, poultry, fish, dairy, or eggs, and may also exclude honey. Lacto-ovo-vegetarians include milk and products made from milk, as well as eggs, but avoid meat, fish, and poultry in their diets. Lacto-vegetarians consume milk and products made from milk. And some self-described vegetarians may even include occasional fish, chicken, and meat.

Plant-based diets have been associated with lower rates of obesity, heart disease, high blood pressure, type 2 diabetes, and cancer. Along with the health benefits, though, are some concerns. Vegetarians, especially vegans, need to make up for the lack of animal sources of several important nutrients. Here are dietary considerations for vegans:

Protein. Vegans can meet their protein needs by combining complementary plant protein sources to make complete proteins.

Calories. Because plant-based diets are high in fiber and lower in calorie-dense foods, care needs to be taken to make sure there is adequate energy in the diet, especially for children. Foods with higher caloric density, such as nuts and dried fruits, should be included often in meals and snacks.

Vitamin B12. Because plant foods don't contain B12, vegans need to include a reliable source in their diet daily, such as nutritionally enriched yeast, or a B12 supplement.

Vitamin D. Your two best sources of vitamin D are sun exposure and foods fortified with vitamin D, such as cow's milk and fortified soy and rice beverages. If you don't get enough sun exposure and fortified foods, then vitamin D supplements are recommended.

VEGAN KIDS

Children have high nutrient requirements, but they have small stomachs, so careful planning is needed to make sure a vegan diet can support a growing child's needs. The daily diet should include three meals plus plenty of appealing snacks like trail mix, muffins, and whole grain cookies; sources of fat, such as nuts, seeds, and avocados; and plenty of protein-rich foods like tofu, nut butters, and soy cheese.

Minerals. Iron, calcium, zinc, and some other minerals are not as readily available from plant sources, so vegans need to develop strategies to make sure they're getting adequate amounts—such as eating iron-enriched cereals, including sources of vitamin C at meals to help absorption of iron from plant foods, and eating dark green vegetables, tofu, legumes, almonds, and sesame seeds to ensure adequate calcium intake.

DAIRY-FREE

Your body requires an enzyme—lactase—to break down a sugar in dairy foods called lactose. Some people don't make enough lactase in their digestive system to handle a lot of dairy. A cup of milk or bowl of ice cream may cause belly pain and bloating, gas, and diarrhea. Here's how to approach dairy differently without running short of important nutrients, especially calcium and vitamin D.

Seek specialty brands. Buy brands of milk that are low in lactose or even lactose free.

Add supplements. Take a lactase supplement before you consume milk or other dairy foods.

Experiment. You may be able to comfortably handle small amounts of dairy food at a time, especially if you have them with other foods. And some types of foods—like hard cheese and yogurt—may be easier to digest than others.

Boost calcium intake. Eat other foods containing calcium, such as salmon and sardines with the bones, dark green leafy vegetables, and fortified soymilk. You can get vitamin D by exposing your skin to sunlight for brief periods or by taking a supplement.

GLUTEN-FREE

Gluten is a protein found in wheat, barley, and rye (and sometimes oats) and ingredients made from these grains. For those who react to it, here are a few suggestions:

Consult with a doc and dietician. If you suspect you have a gluten sensitivity, talk to your doctor about getting diagnosed. Work with a dietitian to create a well-rounded diet.

Read labels more carefully. "Gluten-free" on a label means just that—it contains no gluten. But these words on a label indicate gluten: wheat, barley, rye, oats (some contain gluten from processing, so look for gluten-free oats), and malt (unless it's from a gluten-free source).

Add more grains. Grains are an important part of a healthy diet. Be sure to eat enough grains that are gluten free. Options include brown rice, wild rice, whole corn, amaranth, buckwheat, quinoa, and millet.

> **THE BOTTOM LINE**
> - If you are vegetarian or vegan, make sure you get enough protein, vitamin B12, vitamin D, and minerals such as iron, calcium, and zinc.
> - If you are dairy free, look for other sources of calcium and vitamin D, such as dark green leafy vegetables and soy.
> - If you are gluten free, look for gluten-free grains such as brown rice, whole corn, buckwheat, and quinoa.

2

FOODS

An A-to-Z Guide to Foods That Harm, Foods That Heal

Some folks view food as energy. For others, it's all about the taste. Then, there are some who see what's on their plate like a sort of medicine cabinet. Food is all of these things—and much more.

On the following pages, you'll find your favorite foods with detailed descriptions about how they can boost specific aspects of your health. For example, that humble cup of coffee can protect against Parkinson's and liver disease. You'll also read about many foods that you may not normally include in your diet but might want to consider adding to your menu.

So think of this section as sort of a periodic table of foods. Each entry includes a brief description and a list of the ailments or the parts of your body that the food may affect. These lists are not meant to be comprehensive—some foods, like berries, are bursting with antioxidants that can aid you in dodging heart disease, stroke, diabetes, and many other chronic conditions. They also help ward off cancer, prevent birth defects, keep skin looking young, and have many more benefits than we had room to fit in these pages.

Within each entry, the ailments that foods may heal or harm are listed roughly in order of how much they may boost or hurt health. This treatment allows you to weight the possible benefits of a food versus its potential risks. One such example: Ginger is loaded with cancer-fighting phytochemicals and is well-known as a treatment for motion sickness and nausea. It has the potential, though, to inhibit blood clotting and even lead to miscarriage—but these are risks only for certain people.

In addition to the healthful and potentially harmful effects of specific foods, you'll see typical serving sizes (as a general idea, no need to measure everything out!); learn how to buy food at its ripest, most nutrient-rich time; find out how to store foods to maintain freshness; and get ideas on quick and easy ways to incorporate them into your diet.

Watch for specific food-drug interaction warnings throughout this section. For example, drinking cranberry juice while on warfarin or other blood-thinning medications may cause bleeding and bruises.

So, whet your appetite and find out which foods to feast on for better health!

ACORN SQUASH

See Squash, page 196

AGAVE SYRUP

See Sugar and Other Sweeteners, page 197

ALCOHOL

Typical serving size: One 12-oz wine cooler; one 5-oz glass of wine; one 12-oz beer; or one 1 ½-oz cocktail, 80 proof

HOW IT HARMS
Heart disease
Blood sugar swings
Fetal alcohol syndrome
Drug interactions
Liver damage
Addiction
Gout
Kidney disease
Liver disease
Stroke
Dementia

WHAT IT HEALS
Heart attack risk
Age-related dementia
Bone density
Stress
Appetite and digestion
Mood

ALCOHOL FACTS
- On average, it takes the liver 3 to 5 hours to completely metabolize 1 oz of alcohol.
- Almost any sweet or starchy food—potatoes, grains, honey, grapes and other fruits, even dandelions—can be turned into alcohol.

While people drink alcohol mainly for its mood-altering effects, the results of recent studies suggest that there are benefits to moderate drinking. However, overindulgence undoes those benefits. The adverse effects of alcohol can be devastating and include addiction, liver damage, and wild swings in blood sugar.

Health Benefits

Reduces heart attack risk. Moderate consumption, defined as an average of 8 servings of alcohol a week, can cut heart attack risk by raising HDL cholesterol and reducing the risk of blood clot formation. For heart health, experts suggest that men drink no more than two drinks a day; women, no more than one.

May stave off dementia. Moderate drinkers are 23% less likely to develop dementia, Alzheimer's disease, and other forms of cognitive impairment.

Boosts bone density. Moderate drinking was linked to much higher bone densities in older women at the spine and in the hip.

Lowers stress. The relaxing effect alcohol has on your body can also cause you to feel less stressed.

Aids appetite and digestion. Moderate alcohol consumption can increase appetite. Also, drinking alcohol while eating slows digestion and can help you feel fuller longer.

Boosts mood. One of the main reasons people drink alcoholic beverages is to improve their mood. Ever hear of "Happy Hour"?

Health Risks

Addiction. It's estimated that in the United States there are over 17 million people addicted to alcohol. And according to a paper published by the World Health Organization in 2011, alcoholism has been directly linked to more than 2.5 million deaths each year worldwide.

Cancer risk. Over time, moderate to high alcohol intake increases cancer risk. Women at risk for breast cancer who consume alcohol daily have a higher risk of breast cancer than those who do not. The risk increases with the amount of alcohol consumed.

Heart problems. Alcohol's heart benefits stop after that second drink. A third does more harm than good, actually raising triglyceride levels without reducing LDL cholesterol.

Blood sugar roller coaster. Most studies don't show increased risks for a single glass of an alcoholic beverage. But skip mixed cocktails, because they tend to be loaded with sugar. And drinking on an empty stomach can spike blood sugar.

Fetal alcohol syndrome. Overindulging while pregnant can cause physical and behavioral abnormalities in the fetus, such as attention deficits and hyperactivity.

Adverse medication interactions. Alcohol mixed with certain medications can cause a host of symptoms, including drowsiness, fainting, nausea, vomiting, and headaches.

Liver damage. Even one weekend of heavy drinking causes a buildup of fatty cells in the liver. Continued use of alcohol can lead to permanent liver damage and problems with glucose metabolism, and eventually scarring or cirrhosis.

Mood swings, aggression, and hangovers. We've all seen people, after a few drinks, who change from being sweet to aggressive, or from feeling happy to sad. And many of us know about the headaches and nausea that hangovers can cause. One recent study found that people who tend to express anger do so more frequently and openly after drinking alcohol.

Several other ailments. Drinking too much alcohol may greatly boost your risk of developing gout, high blood pressure,

95% of alcohol is absorbed directly into the bloodstream within an hour.

cardiac arrhythmias, kidney disease, liver disease, stroke, dementia, and psychological disturbances. Excess alcohol also raises your risk for cancer, including cancer of the mouth, throat, breast, liver, pancreas, and esophagus.

Eating Tips

- Mull fruity red wine with honey, lemon juice, and a pinch of cloves.
- Splash some vodka into tomato pasta sauce to boost the flavor.
- Macerate melon balls in a light syrup of sugar, rum, lime juice, and grated peel.

Old School
You'll sleep better after a nightcap.

New Wisdom
Drinking alcohol before bed may disrupt sleep and increase wakefulness in healthy adults.

WHAT'S IN THE GLASS?

The amount of calories varies from beverage to beverage. Low-calorie beers can weigh in at about 55 calories per 12-oz serving, but heavier beers such as stouts can top 330 calories per glass. Wine falls within a similar calorie-count range.

Some wines provide small amounts of iron and potassium, and beer contains niacin, vitamin B6, chromium, and phosphorus. To benefit from the nutrients in these beverages, though, you would have to consume much more than the recommended limit of two drinks per day for a man or one for a woman.

MIXED DRINKS
- Alcohol volume: 8% to 38%
- Serving size: 2 oz to 7 ½ oz
- Calories: 165 to 550

WINE
- Alcohol volume: 6% to 9%
- Serving size: 3 oz to 12 oz
- Calories: 65 to 220

BEER*
- Alcohol volume: 2% to 12%
- Serving size: 12 oz
- Calories: 55 to 330

Storing Tips

- Most beer has a shelf life of about 3 to 6 months. Wine should be stored between 45°F and 65°F (7.2°C and 18.3°C) and can be stored for years in these conditions. Most liquors can be stored for months or years. However, after opening the taste may degrade. All alcohol should be stored out of sunlight and not be subjected to temperature changes.

WARNING! FOOD-DRUG INTERACTION

Common medications that interact with alcohol include allergy medications containing loratadine, medications to manage high cholesterol such as lovastatin, and even over-the-counter pain medications containing ibuprofen.

ALMONDS

See Nuts and Seeds, page 138

APPLES

Typical serving size: 1 medium apple (5 oz or 142 g)

HOW THEY HARM
Pesticide residues
Bacterial infection
Allergies

WHAT THEY HEAL
Alzheimer's disease
Colon cancer
High blood pressure
Weight gain
Blood sugar swings

Heart disease
High cholesterol
Teeth and gums

Apples are pretty much the perfect snack. They're easy to carry, flavorful, filling, and low in calories. The average apple contains only 80 calories, and dried apples provide about 70 calories per ounce (30 g). In addition to vitamin C, a medium-size apple also contains 3 to 5 g of fiber. Apples can be eaten fresh or cooked in myriad ways—baked into pies, crisps, and tarts; added to poultry stuffing; and made into jelly, apple butter, and sauce.

Health Benefits

Staves off Alzheimer's disease. Apples contain quercetin, a powerful antioxidant that protects brain cells from degeneration in rats and might do the same in humans. Be sure to eat the skin, because it's especially rich in disease-fighting compounds.

Protects against colon cancer. When the natural fiber in apples ferments in the colon, it produces chemicals that help fight the formation of cancer cells, according to recent research from Germany. Other studies have shown that one type of antioxidant found in apples, called procyanidins, triggered a series of cell signals that resulted in cancer cell death.

Prevents high blood pressure. Adults who eat apples are 37% less likely to have hypertension, according to a recent food database analysis.

Helps keep you slim. They're packed with fiber and water, so your stomach will want less. Plus, studies out of Washington State and Brazil have shown that people who eat at least three apples or pears a day lose weight.

Evens out your blood sugar. Want to keep your blood sugar on an even keel? Heed the old saying about eating apples to

APPLE FACTS
- Dried apples are less likely to promote cavities than other dried fruits.
- Ever wonder why apples don't sink during bobbing contests? One-quarter of an apple's volume is air!

keep the doctor away. Apples are loaded with soluble fiber, which slows the digestion of food and thus the entry of glucose into the bloodstream. One group of researchers discovered that women who ate at least one apple a day were 28% less likely to develop diabetes than those who ate none.

Helps fend off heart disease. A fresh apple is an ideal snack. Apples are rich in flavonoids, antioxidants that help prevent heart disease—if you eat the skin.

Fights high cholesterol. Apples are low in calories and high in the soluble fiber pectin, which helps lower artery-damaging LDL blood cholesterol levels.

Boosts dental hygiene. Apples have long been called nature's toothbrush; while they don't actually cleanse the teeth, biting and chewing an apple stimulates the gums, and the sweetness of the apple prompts an increased flow of saliva, which reduces tooth decay by lowering the levels of bacteria in the mouth.

Health Risks

Pesticides. Apple trees thrive in most temperate climates, but because they are vulnerable to worms, scale, and other insects, they are usually sprayed with pesticides several times. Apples should always be washed carefully before eating; some experts even suggest peeling them, especially if they have been waxed. The wax itself is not a problem but it may prevent pesticide residues from being rinsed off.

Bacterial and other infections. *Escherichia coli (E. coli)* and cryptosporidium have caused serious illness in people who consumed unpasteurized apple juice or apple cider. While the risk of becoming ill from these products is low, children, the elderly, and people with weakened immune systems are most susceptible and should take precautions by drinking pasteurized juice or cider. Most juices you buy

QUICK TIP:
Doc-approved baby food

Because applesauce is pleasant tasting and easily digested, doctors recommend it as an early baby food.

in grocery stores are pasteurized (check the labels), but use caution when you buy drinks at roadside stands, country fairs, or visits to local orchards.

Allergies. Sulfur dioxide is often added to dried apples to preserve moistness and color; it can provoke allergic reactions in susceptible people.

Eating Tips

- Sauté sliced apples and red onion to serve with pork tenderloin.
- Stir slivered Granny Smith apple into a red cabbage coleslaw.
- Simmer a chopped apple in a pot of chili for a touch of fruity sweetness.

Buying Tips

- Choose smaller apples. Larger apples ripen faster and may already be on their way out.
- Buy apples that are firm with no soft spots.
- Avoid apples that are discolored for their variety.

Storing Tips

- Store apples in plastic bags in the refrigerator to slow ripening.
- Apples will become overripe and mealy if they're not refrigerated.
- Refrigerated apples will last up to 6 weeks.
- Check apples often, and remove any apples that begin to decay or else the others will do the same.

APRICOTS

Typical serving size: 3 medium apricots (4 oz or 114 g), or ¼ cup, dried (1.2 oz or 35 g)

HOW THEY HARM
- Allergies
- Cavities
- Cyanide poisoning

WHAT THEY HEAL
- Cancer
- High cholesterol
- High blood pressure
- Nerves and muscles
- Eyes

APRICOT FACT

- Although eating fresh apricots is a way to get the most vitamin C (which is depleted by exposure to heat and air when apricots are dried), other substances, like beta-carotene and pectin, are actually made *more* available to the body when apricots are cooked.

Rich in antioxidants and other nutrients, apricots are tasty, easy to digest, low in calories (about 50 calories in three fresh apricots and 85 in 10 dried halves), virtually fat free, and highly nutritious. One-half cup (83 g) of sliced apricots contains just 40 calories.

Health Benefits

Prevents cancer. Apricots' deep color indicates the presence of carotenoids, specifically the antioxidant beta-carotene, which are linked with cancer prevention.

Lowers LDL cholesterol. Apricots contain the soluble fiber pectin, which helps lower LDL cholesterol.

Eases high blood pressure. Apricots are a particularly good source of potassium. They also have lots of fiber, iron, and beta-carotene. The drying process actually increases the concentration of these nutrients, all of which are good for your circulatory system.

Helps nerves and muscles. Regardless of form, apricots are high in iron and potassium, a mineral essential for proper nerve and muscle function that also helps maintain normal blood pressure and balance of body fluids.

Staves off eye diseases. The beta-carotene in apricots may help prevent cataracts and age-related macular degeneration. Some studies suggest that consuming high levels of vitamin A may reduce the risk of developing cataracts by up to 40%.

Health Risks

Allergic reactions. Sulfite preservatives in some dried apricots can trigger an allergic reaction or asthma attack in people susceptible to these disorders. Also, a natural salicylate in apricots may trigger an allergic reaction in aspirin-sensitive people.

Cavities. Dried apricots leave a sticky residue on teeth that can lead to cavities.

Cyanide poisoning. Doctors warn that apricot pits in any form should not be ingested. They contain relatively large amounts of amygdalin, a type of carbohydrate that reacts with digestive enzymes to produce hydrogen cyanide. It's unlikely, though, that anyone would be being able to crack and eat very many apricot seeds.

Eating Tips
- Dollop whipped goat cheese into pitted halves and sprinkle with fresh basil for an elegant appetizer.
- Mix chopped apricots, sweet onion, and mustard for a turkey sandwich condiment.
- Stir nutritious chopped dried apricots into a batch of oatmeal cookies.

Buying Tips
- Look for plump apricots with as much golden orange color as possible.
- Stay clear of fruit that is pale yellow, greenish yellow, very firm, shriveled, or bruised.
- Slightly soft apricots have the best flavor, but they must be eaten immediately.

- Steer clear of apricots that have been treated with sulfites. They will be brown, not orange.

Storing Tips

- Apricots will ripen at room temperature.
- To help them ripen, place them in a paper bag with an apple.
- When they yield to gentle pressure, they are ready to eat.
- Refrigerate ripe apricots, unwashed, in a paper or plastic bag up to 2 days.

ARTICHOKES

Typical serving size: 1 medium artichoke, cooked (4 oz to 114 g)

HOW THEY HARM
Allergies

WHAT THEY HEAL
Skin cancer
Indigestion

The artichokes grown in the United States that make their way to your plate are cultivated in California. In fact, Castroville, California, claims to be the Artichoke Capital of the World. Artichokes, a relative to the thistle, are actually a flower bud, and blossoms can be up to 7 in (18 cm) in diameter.

Health Benefits

Prevents skin cancer. Artichokes are a great source of silymarin, an antioxidant that may help prevent skin cancer.

Helps indigestion. Artichoke leaf extract may aid indigestion by increasing the flow of bile, which is needed to digest fats. Choose an extract that is standardized for caffeoylquinic acids and follow the package directions.

Health Risk

Potential allergic reactions. Eating artichokes may provoke allergic reaction in people sensitive to ragweed.

Eating Tips

- Bake thawed frozen hearts drizzled with olive oil and ground almonds.
- Steam trimmed globes in a quarter-inch of water in a covered microwaveable dish for 5 minutes.
- Stuff hollowed globe artichokes with a turkey meat loaf mixture.

Buying Tips

- High-quality artichokes are usually compact and heavy for their size.
- When squeezed, a fresh artichoke will make a squeak.
- The thickness of each stalk should correspond to the size of the artichoke.
- Thin stalks signal dehydration, so look for stalks that are firm without "give."

Storing Tips

- Artichokes remain fairly constant in appearance for weeks, but flavor is adversely affected from the moment they are cut.
- For maximum taste and tenderness, cook as soon as possible.
- Refrigerate unwashed, in a plastic bag, for up to 1 week.

QUICK TIP:
How to eat an artichoke

To eat, pull off leaves, dip the leaves in lemon juice, and eat the fleshy ends attached to the plant. Lift out the cone and cut out the core, which is the fuzzy portion at the center. The heart is a true delicacy and will break easily with a fork.

- The ancient Greeks and Romans believed asparagus possessed medicinal properties, from alleviating toothaches to preventing bee stings. Such things are mythical, but asparagus does contain a good supply of vitamins and minerals.
- Asparagus can be found in green and white varieties. Green asparagus is the most common in the U.S., while the white is more popular in Europe.

ASPARAGUS

Typical serving size: ½ cup, cooked (90 g)

HOW IT HARMS

Gout

WHAT IT HEALS

Helps fight cancer

Slows aging

Fights cognitive decline

Aids in glucose transport

Reduces edema

Eases stress

Asparagus is low in calories—six spears have just 20 calories. It also contains vitamins C and K and folate.

Health Benefits

Slows aging. The antioxidants in asparagus may help put a brake on the aging process.

Fights cognitive decline. The folate in asparagus works with vitamin B12 to help prevent cognitive impairment.

Reduces edema (swelling). Asparagus contains the natural diuretic asparagine, which helps your body get rid of excess fluid and salt. This is especially helpful for people with edema caused by high blood pressure or other heart-related diseases.

Relieves stress. Asparagus is high in folate—this B vitamin helps combat stress.

Health Risk

Gout. Asparagus contains purines, substances that promote the overproduction of uric acid that precipitates painful attacks of gout. If you have gout, keep your asparagus consumption to a minimum.

Eating Tips

- Dress steamed asparagus with a blend of olive oil and orange juice.
- Refrigerate cooked, cooled asparagus pieces for snacks or salad add-ins.
- Wrap slices of smoked turkey around steamed spears for a fast appetizer.

Buying Tips

- Choose firm, yet tender, stalks.
- For the green variety, choose stalks with deep green or purplish tips that are closed and compact.
- Avoid excessively sandy spears.
- Stalks with a narrow diameter are more tender than thick ones.

Storing Tips

- Store stalks, with bottoms wrapped in a damp paper towel, in the crisper section of the refrigerator. If you don't have a crisper, put them in plastic bags and place them in the coldest part of the refrigerator.
- Eat asparagus within a day or two, because the flavor lessens with each passing day.

50% of people will have smelly urine after eating asparagus.

AVOCADOS

Typical serving size: ½ cup, cubed (75 g)

HOW THEY HARM
Weight gain

Allergies

WHAT THEY HEAL
High cholesterol

Heart disease

Cancer

Blood sugar swings

Insulin resistance

Hair

Avocados contain vitamin B6, vitamin E, potassium, magnesium, and folate. They're also cholesterol and sodium free. This fruit contains 60% more potassium per ounce than bananas and is an excellent source of monounsaturated fat. Although it's healthy fat, be sure to enjoy avacados in moderation. One half-cup serving contains 120 calories—100 of them from fat.

Health Benefits

Lowers cholesterol. Avocados are rich in plant sterols, compounds shown to lower cholesterol.

Reduces risk of heart disease. Studies have shown that substituting saturated fat with unsaturated fat, like the kind in avocados, can reduce heart disease risk better than merely lowering total fat intake. Just remember that even healthy fats are high in calories, so watch your portions.

Lowers cancer risk. Healthy monounsaturated fats (like those in avocados and its oil) will help your body better absorb anticancer antioxidants such as lycopene and beta-carotene.

Keeps blood sugar steady. Add some avocado to a sandwich, and the fat will slow digestion of the bread, thus making it easier on your blood sugar. The soluble fiber in this tasty fruit also stabilizes blood sugar and lowers cholesterol.

Reverses insulin resistance. The good fat in avocados (as well as olive oil and nuts) can help fight insulin resistance, helping your body steady its blood sugar levels.

Maintains hair health. Avocado moisturizes hair shafts and loads them with protein, making them stronger. Thoroughly mix a ripe, peeled avocado with a teaspoon of wheat germ oil and a teaspoon of jojoba oil. Apply it to freshly washed hair and spread it all the way to the ends. Cover your scalp with a shampoo cap or a plastic bag, wait 15 to 30 minutes, then rinse thoroughly.

Health Risk

Allergic reaction. People who are sensitive to latex may have an allergic reaction to avacados.

Eating Tips

- Puree ripe avocado with canned coconut milk for a chilled soup.
- Combine chunks with shrimp, pink grapefruit wedges, sliced scallion, and cilantro.
- Mash and spread on bread instead of mayonnaise for a creamy, healthier taste.

Buying Tips

- Look for firm avocados if you're planning on using them later in the week; otherwise, select fruit that yields to gentle pressure for immediate use.
- Color alone will not tell you if the avocado is ripe. Ripe fruit will be slightly firm but will yield to gentle pressure.
- To speed the ripening process, place the avocado in a paper bag and store at room

temperature until ready to eat (usually 2 to 5 days). Placing an apple together with the avocado speeds up the process even more.

Storing Tips

- Avocados start to ripen only after being cut from the tree.
- Mature fruit can be left on the tree for 6 months without spoiling. Once picked, it will ripen in a few days.
- To retain a fresh green color, avocados should either be eaten immediately or should be sprinkled with lemon or lime juice or white vinegar.

BACON

See Pork, page 172

BANANAS

Typical serving size: 1 banana (4 oz to 114 g)

HOW THEY HARM
   Allergies

WHAT THEY HEAL
   Stress, anxiety, and depression
   High blood pressure
   Blood sugar swings
   Muscles
   Teething pain
   Sleeplessness

The banana is food genius. It comes in its own sealed, portable container and is one of the healthiest foods on the planet. One banana has about 100 calories, is loaded with potassium (400 mg) and fiber (3 g) while containing no fat. The very popular yellow banana of Cavendish is the banana we see in grocery stores. Plantains, finger bananas, and red bananas are also popular.

Health Benefits

Reduces stress, anxiety, and depression. Bananas contain tryptophan and 30% of your day's vitamin B6, which helps the brain produce mellowing serotonin. Tryptophan and B6 will help you get through the day with less stress. Tryptophan also helps to relieve depression and anxiety.

   Controls high blood pressure. The potassium in bananas helps to keep your blood pressure levels down.

   Keeps blood sugar levels steady. The vitamin B6 in bananas helps even out blood sugar levels, helping you to avoid blood-glucose highs and lows.

   Boosts your workouts. The natural sugars in bananas give you long-lasting energy, while the potassium helps keep you alert and prevent muscle fatigue.

   Eases teething pain. Offer your baby a frozen banana (peeled, of course). The banana thaws quickly as your baby chews on it, and the cool fruit soothes the gums.

   Combats sleeplessness. Tryptophan, the same amino acid that eases stress, can also help induce sleepiness. Have one before bed for better shut-eye.

Health Risks

Allergic reaction. If you are latex-sensitive, bananas may also trigger an allergic reaction.

Eating Tips

- Puree frozen ripe slices in a food processor or blender for instant ice cream.
- Mash and stir into whole wheat pancake batter.
- Fry slightly underripe quarters in oil and cumin as a side dish for pork chops.

Buying Tips

- Avoid bananas with brown spots that seem very soft.
- Choose fruit that is firm and free of bruises. Most have a soft texture when ripe. Best eating quality has been reached when the solid yellow skin color is speckled with brown.
- Bananas with green tips or with practically no yellow color have not developed their full flavor.
- Bananas are overripe when they have a strong odor.

Storing Tips

- To further ripen bananas, leave at room temperature for a couple of days.
- Once ripe, you can store them in the refrigerator for 3 to 5 days. The peel may turn brown in the refrigerator, but the fruit will not change.

BARLEY

See also Grains, page 104

Typical serving size: ½ cup, cooked (79 g)

HOW IT HARMS
Allergies

WHAT IT HEALS
Heart disease
Weight gain
Blood sugar swings
Anemia
Muscles and nerves

Barley is a good source of low-fat, easily digested complex carbohydrate and is most often used in soups and casseroles, where its starch acts as a thickener. Barley also works well in salads. Barley is used to make bread, and it remains a key component in brewing beer.

BARLEY FACTS
- When barley is refined, it loses much of its vitamins and minerals.
- Idaho is a major producer of barley.

Health Benefits

Cuts risk of heart disease. The big bonus of barley is its fiber. It contains the same kind of cholesterol-lowering fiber found in oats, which has been shown to lower cholesterol and cut the risk of heart disease. Its soluble fiber is found throughout the grain, so even refined products like barley flour are beneficial. The niacin (B3) in unrefined barley can also protect against cardiovascular disease and help lower cholesterol.

Helps maintain healthy weight. Because the insoluble fiber slows the rate at which food leaves the stomach, barley helps you feel full on fewer calories.

Helps manage blood sugar. The soluble fiber in barley helps stabilize blood sugar, making it a good choice for people with diabetes.

Protects against cellular damage. Barley is high in selenium, an antioxidant that protects cells from damage, and iron, which is necessary for the production of red blood cells, for good muscle and brain function and preventing anemia.

Maintains brain and nervous system health. The thiamin (B1) in unrefined barley helps promote healthy brain activity. B vitamins are also vital for proper nerve function and can help boost metabolism.

Health Risks

Allergies. Those with celiac disease and those sensitive to gluten should avoid barley and products containing barley.

Eating Tips

- Substitute barley for rice in pilaf.
- Mix cooked barley into bean salads.
- For a healthy side dish, blend fresh, canned, or frozen corn to cooked barley along with olive oil; wine vinegar; chopped fresh basil; salt; pepper; and chopped tomatoes, bell peppers, and onions.

Buying Tips

- Pearl barley is often used in soups and casseroles as a thickener.
- Scotch or pot barley is less processed and contains more fiber than pearl barley.
- Barley meal is produced by grinding barley grains into a meal or flour, which can be used in breads or stirred into soups and casseroles as a thickener.
- Whole barley is the most nutritious. You can often find whole, hull-less barley in the natural foods section.

Storing Tips

- To keep your barley fresh, place it in an airtight container.
- Can be stored in the refrigerator or freezer for up to 6 months.

QUICK TIP: Use barley flour

Barley flour is higher in fiber than all-purpose flour, so it's a healthier choice. Because of its lower gluten content, though, you can't substitute it for all the flour when baking. In leavened breads, replace one-quarter of the flour with barley flour; in quick breads and cookes, replace up to half.

BEANS AND LEGUMES

See also Lentils, page 126; Peanuts and Peanut Butter, page 158; Peas and Pea Pods, page 160; Soy, page 192

Typical serving size: ½ cup fresh, dried or canned (2.6 oz or 75 g)

HOW THEY HARM
  Nutrient absorption
  Gout
  Favism
  Allergies
  Drug interaction
  Flatulence

WHAT THEY HEAL
  Heart disease
  High cholesterol
  Cancer
  Diabetes
  Weight gain

The 13,000 varieties of legumes that are grown worldwide all produce seed-bearing pods and have nodules on their roots. Otherwise, the members of this plant family differ greatly: Some are low-growing plants (bush beans, lentils, and soybeans) or vines (many peas and beans); others are trees (carob) or shrubs (mesquite). Although peanuts are often classified as nuts, they are actually legumes.

All beans are a subset of legumes (also called pulses). Beans come in two main varieties: pod or shelled. Pod beans, such as green beans, French beans, pole, and snap beans, are served fresh or canned in their pod. Shelled beans such as chickpeas, lentils, and kidney, black, navy, and pinto beans are usually sold dried or canned.

Beans and legumes are nutritional powerhouses, high in protein, fiber, B vitamins, iron, potassium, and other minerals, while low in fat.

Health Benefits

Prevents heart disease. Legumes contain a range of important disease-fighting phytochemicals, including isoflavones, which are protective against heart disease. Additionally, beans and legumes provide large amounts of fiber, including the soluble type that is important in controlling blood cholesterol levels. Studies have shown that people who eat more legumes have a lower risk of heart disease.

Lowers cholesterol. Studies find that about 10 g of soluble fiber a day—the amount of ½ cup to 1½ cups of navy beans—reduces LDL cholesterol by about 10%. Legumes and beans contain saponins, which help lower cholesterol, and phytosterols, which have anticancer and cholesterol-lowering properties.

Fights cancer. Beans contain a wide range of plant chemicals, including isoflavones and phytosterols, which are associated with reduced cancer risk.

Helps manage diabetes. Legumes and beans are also good for diabetes because their balance of complex carbohydrates and protein provides a slow, steady source of glucose instead of the sudden surge that can occur after eating simple carbohydrates.

Aids weight loss. If you are trying to lose weight, a serving of legumes will help you to feel full more quickly. The rich fiber content fills your stomach and causes a slower rise in blood sugar, staving off hunger for longer and giving you a steady supply of energy.

Health Risks

Absorption of vitamins. Soybeans, for example, contain substances that interfere with the absorption of beta-carotene and vitamins B12 and D. Heating and cooking inactivates most of these substances, but to compensate for vitamin loss, balance legume consumption with ample fresh fruits and yellow or dark green vegetables (for beta-carotene), lean meat or other animal products (for vitamin B12), and cooked greens, wheat germ, fortified cereals, seeds, nuts, and poultry (for vitamin E).

Gout. People with gout are often advised to forgo dried peas and beans, lentils, and other legumes because of their high purine content. In susceptible people, purines increase levels of uric acid and can precipitate a gout attack.

Old School
Legumes must be eaten at the same time as grains to get a "complete" protein.

New Wisdom
Have a mix of amino acids throughout the day and this won't be necessary.

22% lower risk of obesity is associated with eating beans.

Favism. Some people of Mediterranean or Asian descent carry a gene that makes them susceptible to favism, a severe type of anemia contracted from eating fava beans. Anyone with a family history of this disease should avoid these beans.

Allergies. Some legumes, especially peanuts, trigger an allergic reaction or migraine headaches in susceptible people. In such cases, the offending foods should be eliminated from the diet.

Gas. Dried beans, lentils, and peas are notorious for causing intestinal gas and flatulence. While not really a health risk, this can certainly be uncomfortable or embarassing! The method of preparation can help reduce gas production. Change the water several times during the soaking and cooking process. Always rinse canned beans and chickpeas; combining cooked legumes with an acidic food may reduce gas production. Some herbs, especially lemon balm, fennel, and caraway, can help to prevent flatulence.

Eating Tips

- Add cooked lentils to a spinach salad with warm bacon dressing.
- Add steamed green beans to penne pasta with pesto sauce.
- Roast chickpeas, lightly oiled and dusted with Cajun seasoning, in a preheated 375°F oven.
- Combine cooked black beans with quinoa for a protein-packed vegetarian meal.

Buying Tips

- When buying fresh beans, such as fava, look for unblemished pods that are plump and smooth. If you can see the fresh bean shapes within the pod, they're overgrown and likely tougher. Avoid fresh beans with mushy tips or with white mold.
- When buying dried beans, look for beans that are not cracked or chipped. This indicates age.
- When buying canned beans, look for beans that have no added salt and check the sell-by date.

BEAN COUNTING

When planning meals with beans, here's how to judge the amount of beans you'll need:

15-oz can of beans	= 1½ cups cooked beans, drained
1 lb dry beans	= 6 cup cooked beans, drained
1 lb dry beans	= 2 cup dry beans
1 cup dry beans	= 3 cup cooked beans, drained

Storing Tips

- Wash fresh beans before storing to retain moisture. Leave the ends of fresh beans on until you're ready to cook. Fresh beans can be stored in a refrigerator for up to 5 days.
- Store dried beans in the bag in a cool, dry place. If dried beans are hermetically sealed, they can be stored for up to 10 years.
- Before you soak dried beans, be sure to pick through them and discard any that are discolored or shriveled. Also pick out any foreign matter. Rinse well.
- After cooking dried beans, use them as quickly as possible, as they spoil easily.

BEAN SPROUTS

Typical serving size: 1 cup (104 g)

HOW THEY HARM
Bacterial infection
Lupus

WHAT THEY HEAL
Cancer

QUICK TIP:
Bacteria avoidance

If you are a healthy adult, you can minimize your risk of consuming harmful bacteria by buying crisp sprouts with the buds attached. You can also reduce risk of illness by cooking sprouts before eating them.

A sprout is a vegetable seed that just begins growing. Sprouts grow from the seeds of vegetables, grains, and various beans. Wiry, yet delicate tasting, bean sprouts weigh in at a scant 31 calories per cup and pack a lot of nutrition in a small package. Mung bean sprouts, for example, have 23% of the recommended daily value of vitamin C along with other nutrients, such as iron, protein, fiber, and calcium.

Health Benefit

Can help prevent cancer. Bean sprouts are are a rich source of sulforaphane, one of the most potent anticancer compounds isolated from a natural source. Sprouts can contain 50 times more sulforaphane than mature beans.

Health Risks

Harmful bacteria. Because sprouts have been associated with outbreaks of salmonella and *E. coli* infection, people at high risk from exposure to these bacteria, such as children, the elderly, and people with weak immune systems, should avoid eating sprouts. It's okay to eat most sprouts raw, as long as they're free of bacterial contamination. An important exception: sprouted soybeans, which contain a poten-

tially harmful toxin that is destroyed by cooking.

Lupus flare-ups. People with lupus should avoid alfalfa sprouts; alfalfa in any form can prompt a flare-up of symptoms.

Eating Tips

- Garnish chicken or beef noodle soup with sprouts.
- Sprinkle a layer of sprouts on a whole grain tuna salad wrap.
- Add sprouts to a veggie omelet.
- Sprinkle on gazpacho.

Buying Tips

- Look for sprouts with firm, white roots that are slightly moist.
- Avoid musty-smelling, slimy, or dark sprouts.

Storing Tips

- Keep sprouts refrigerated and use them promptly.
- Wash the sprouts thoroughly with water to remove any dirt.
- Most sprouts can be kept in a plastic bag in the crisper of the refrigerator for up to 3 days.
- Rinsing daily under cold water may extend their life.
- Sprouts can be frozen for up to a year if you're going to cook them in the future.

SPROUT FACT
- Sprout varieties include: Mung bean, broccoli, green leaf, alfalfa, radish, sunflower, pumpkin, wheat, and lentil, among others.

BEEF AND VEAL

Typical serving size: 3 oz (85 g)

HOW THEY HARM
Heart disease
Cancer
Bacterial infection
Hormones

WHAT THEY HEAL
Anemia
Weight gain
Bones, muscles, cartilage, skin,
  and blood

- Lean beef has less than 10 g of fat, 4.5 g or less of saturated fat, and less than 95 mg of cholesterol per 100 g. Extra lean beef has less than half that amount of fat and saturated fat.
- A live steer weighs about 1,000 lb and yields about 450 lb of edible meat.

Beef and veal aren't the heart attack–causing culprits they have been made out to be. Many cuts are 20% leaner than they were 14 years ago—great news if you want to indulge in a steak or beef stew every now and again. Beef and veal are excellent sources of high quality protein, as well as vitamin B12, selenium, vitamin B6, and zinc. It's also a good source of iron, phosphorus, and potassium, and contains some vitamin D.

Health Benefits

Helps prevent anemia. Beef and veal are good sources of iron, which your body uses to carry oxygen in the blood. Many teenage girls and women in their child bearing years have iron-deficiency anemia.

Aids weight loss. The protein in beef and veal can keep hunger at bay by reducing the impact of blood sugar after meals.

Strengthens immunity. A 3-oz serving of lean, cooked beef provides more than 25% of your required selenium, a trace mineral essential in a healthy immune system.

Serves as healthy building blocks. The protein in beef and veal function as building blocks for bones, muscles, cartilage, skin, and blood. They are also building blocks for enzymes, hormones, and vitamins.

Health Risks

Heart disease. Beef fat contains saturated fat, which can increase blood cholesterol levels and the risk of cardiovascular disease. Choose leaner cuts and smaller portions.

Cancer risk. A high-meat diet may raise the risk of colon cancer and other cancers.

Harmful bacteria. Raw beef may contain *Staphylococcus aureus, Listeria monocytogenes, E. coli,* and salmonella. Raw veal may contain *E. coli* and salmonella. You can avoid consuming these bacteria by handling the meat properly and cooking it thoroughly. Be careful, too, of cross-contaminating raw food (and its juices) with cooked. This may be a problem especially with ground beef.

Pink slime. It's estimated that 70% of the ground beef in the U.S. contains pink

QUICK TIPS: Trim the fat

Trim all visible fat from your meat. Reduce fat further by broiling, grilling, or roasting on a rack (so fat can drip away).

Another approach is to cook stews and soups in advance, chill them so that the congealed fat can be removed easily, and then reheat the dishes before serving.

A quick way to remove the fat is to drop an ice cube into the cooled liquid. The fat will harden around the ice cube and can be easily removed.

Instead of making gravy or sauce, serve your meat "au jus," after skimming off all the fat.

slime—which are lean bits of meat derived from muscle and connective tissue (the beef industry calls it "lean finely textured beef"). These beef trimmings are often treated with ammonia to kill the *E. coli*, salmonella, and other bacteria they may contain because the trimmings are cut from the outside of the meat, where bacteria are most likely to live.

Hormone-fed cattle. Some researchers are concerned that hormone-fed cattle can pass on complications such as increased risk for some types of cancer. And for those who want to avoid hormones in beef, choose meats grown organically.

Eating Tips

- Use ¾ cup (177 mL) of pineapple juice, two peeled cloves of garlic, and other herbs to make an inexpensive and lower-fat marinade for sirloin, round, or kabobs.
- Grind lower-priced veal stew meat in the food processor to add to pasta sauce.
- Add slivers of beef to nutritious barley soup.

Buying Tips

- When buying raw meat, select it just before checking out at the register. If available, put the packages of raw meat in disposable plastic bags, to contain any leaks that could cross-contaminate other foods in your cart.
- The use-by date means that the peak quality begins to lessen, but the product may still be used afterward.

Storing Tips

- Keep beef and veal in original packaging until you use it.
- If possible, freeze meat in its original packaging to minimize the possibility of any contamination. Or, after separating a larger quantity of meat, tightly wrap in plastic wrap or freezer paper.

- If freezing longer than 2 months, overwrap these packages with airtight heavy-duty foil, plastic wrap, or freezer paper, or place the package inside a plastic bag.

MAKE THE RIGHT CUT

Here's your guide to beef and veal cuts.

BEEF

Looking for a good cut of beef? The following cuts of beef are listed in order of leanness, and all contain less than 10 g of total fat, 4.5 g of saturated fat or less, and fewer than 95 mg of cholesterol per serving.

- Eye round roast
- Top round steak
- Mock tender steak
- Top sirloin steak
- Shank crosscuts
- Bottom round roast
- T-bone steak
- Round tip roast
- 95% lean ground beef

- Arm pot roast
- Top loin steak, such as strip or New York steak
- Flat half of a brisket
- Tenderloin steak
- Flank steak
- Shoulder steak
- Tri-tip roast
- Rib eye steak

VEAL

When you examine a package of veal, the label can help you identify the cut of meat in the package. The following cuts are listed in order of leanness:

- Leg (round)
- Sirloin
- Loin
- Shoulder (chuck, arm or blade roast
- Rib (chop)
- Shank
- Breast

BEER

See Alcohol, page 38

BEETS

Typical serving size: 1 cup (85 g)

HOW THEY HARM
Kidney stones
Gout
Discolored urine and stools

WHAT THEY HEAL
Cancer
Heart disease
Dementia
High blood pressure
Constipation
Eyes and nerves

Beets are a highly versatile vegetable. They can be cooked and served as a side dish, pickled and eaten as a salad or condiment, or used as the main ingredient in borscht, a popular Eastern European soup. Beet greens, the most nutritious part of the vegetable, can be cooked and served like spinach or Swiss chard. What's even better: Beets contain lots of important nutrients, including vitamins A, B6, C, E, and K as well as protein, folate, dietary fiber, calcium, iron, and potassium, among others.

Health Benefits

Fights cancer. Beets contain betacyanin, a type of plant pigment, which some preliminary research indicates might be helpful in defending cells against harmful carcinogens. Studies have shown that beets contain high levels of antioxidant and anti-inflammatory agents that may help to reduce the risk of some cancers. High levels of unique beet fiber may be linked to a lower colon-cancer risk.

Lowers risk of heart disease. Beets are a wonderful source of folate and betaine, nutrients that together help to lower blood levels of homocysteine, which causes inflammation that can damage your arteries and boost your risk of heart disease.

Reduces dementia risk. Beets produce nitric acid in your body, which helps to increase blood flow throughout your body—including to your brain. MRIs done on older adults showed that after eating a high-nitrate diet (including beet juice), these adults had more blood flow to the white matter of their frontal lobes.

Lowers blood pressure. Several studies have found that drinking beet juice can lower blood pressure.

Combats constipation. Beets are high in fiber, which is well known for helping to keep your digestive system running smoothly.

Boosts eye and nerve-tissue health. Beets contain a wide variety of phytochemicals that may help improve the health of your eyes and nerve tissues. And beet greens are a good source of lutein, an antioxidant that helps protect the eyes from age-related macular degeneration and cataracts.

Health Risks

Kidney stones and gout. If you are prone to kidney stones or gout, avoid beet greens, because they are high in oxalates, which can form

BEET FACTS

• Beets have one of the highest sugar content of any vegetable, yet are low in calories.

• Drain the juice from a can of beets to use as a natural food coloring.

small crystals and contribute to the development of kidney stones.

Discolored urine and stool. This isn't really a health risk, but it may seem like one if it happens to you. Actually, it's a harmless condition that can scare you if you mistake the red color for blood.

Eating Tips

- Mix chopped cooked beets with plain Greek yogurt, dill, and scallions.
- Stir-fry chopped beet tops with roasted garlic and a dash of sesame oil.
- Wrap beets in foil and grill over indirect heat until tender.

Buying Tips

- The most flavorful beets are small, with greens still attached.
- Beets are available year-round, but the best time to buy them is June through October, which is when they are most tender.
- Choose beets with unblemished skin and sturdy, unwilted greens.
- Beets are available canned and precooked so you can more readily include this incredibly healthy vegetable in your menu planning.

Storing Tips

- Trim each beet, but leave about 1 in (2.5 cm) of the stem.
- Chill them for up to 2 weeks.
- The greens (which are rich in nutrients) wilt quickly, so use them within a day or two.

BERRIES

See also Cranberries, page 88

Typical serving size: ½ cup (weight varies based on type of berry)

HOW THEY HARM
  Allergies
  Kidney and bladder stones
  Pesticide residue
  Intestinal irritation
  Drug interaction
  Dark stools

WHAT THEY HEAL
  Cancer
  Diabetes
  Brain function
  High cholesterol
  High blood pressure
  Birth defects
  Macular degeneration
  Constipation
  Aging skin

Whether it's blackberries, blueberries, raspberries, or strawberries, these sweet, juicy fruits are powerhouses of healthy nutrients. In addition to being low in calories and high in vitamin C and potassium, berries are high in fiber, making them an excellent snack. Cranberries, boysenberries, loganberries, and olallieberries are tart and primarily used in jams and pies.

BERRIES FACTS

- Blueberries tend to change color during cooking. Acids, like lemon juice and vinegar, make them turn red. In an alkaline environment, such as a batter with too much baking soda, they may turn greenish-blue.
- North America is the world's leading blueberry producer, accounting for nearly 90% of world production.
- People in many cultures have found strawberries useful for certain conditions. The Chinese claim that a handful of them is a cure for a hangover. Strawberries are also said to whiten teeth and are used to get rid of garlic breath.

Health Benefits

Fights cancer. The antioxidants in berries neutralize free radicals, unstable compounds that can damage cells and lead to diseases including cancer. Berries also contain anthocyanins, plant pigments that have been shown to prevent cancer and heart disease, as well as ellagic acid, another cancer-fighting substance.

Lowers diabetes risk. In one study, obese volunteers lowered their diabetes risk by drinking a smoothie loaded with blueberries twice a day. The blueberries increased insulin sensitivity, which helps keep blood sugar levels healthy. And another study, in mice, suggested the fruit can help prevent hardening of the arteries.

Boosts brain function. Studies show that berries are loaded with valuable antioxidants that can slow down brain aging and enhance your memory. Blueberries appear to be especially healthy. They're rich in anthocyanins, flavonoids that seem to offer brain benefits.

Helps cholesterol and blood pressure. Adults who ate about a cup of berries a day lowered their blood pressure and raised their HDL (good) cholesterol after 8 weeks, according to a study from Finland. Berries are also rich in pectin, a form of soluble fiber that can lower total cholesterol levels.

Reduces risk of macular degeneration. Blueberries are one of the richest fruit forms of antioxidants. One study found that people who ate the greatest amount of fruit were the least likely to develop age-related macular degeneration, the leading cause of blindness in older people.

Prevents birth defects. Strawberries and raspberries are also a good source of folate, a nutrient needed by expectant mothers to stave off birth defects. One cup provides about 30 mcg, or roughly 7% of the RDA.

Relieves constipation. There are 7 g of fiber in a cup of raw raspberries. The seeds in raspberries provide insoluble fiber that helps prevent constipation.

Repairs aging skin. The anthocyanins in berries may even prevent some of the effects of aging, such as skin damage from ultraviolet light. Studies have also shown that ellagic acid may also repair skin damaged by the sun.

Health Risks

Allergies. If you're allergic to aspirin, you may want to avoid blackberries, raspberries, and strawberries. These berries are natural sources of salicylates, substances related to the active compound in aspirin. In addition, blueberries can cause allergic reactions in some people. Common symptoms are itchy hives and swollen lips.

Kidney and bladder stones. Strawberries and raspberries contain oxalic acid, which can aggravate kidney and bladder stones in susceptible people. It can also reduce the body's ability to absorb iron and calcium.

Pesticide residue. Strawberries may contain relatively high levels of pesticide residues, so consider buying organic varieties.

Bowel irritation. The seeds in strawberries provide insoluble fiber, which helps prevent constipation. But they can be irritating to people with such intestinal disorders as inflammatory bowel disease or diverticulosis.

Dark stools. Though not really a health risk, blueberries can make stools dark and tarry, which could be mistaken for intestinal bleeding.

Eating Tips

- Snack on bagged frozen berries for a mini-burst of berry sorbet.
- Simmer mixed berries with honey and cinnamon, then add a splash of lime juice for

an antioxidant-rich dessert sauce.

- Sprinkle strawberries or blueberries on a peanut butter sandwich in place of high-sugar jelly.
- Add quartered strawberries to a shrimp salad.
- Mix finely chopped berries with ricotta and honey as a spread.

Buying Tips

- Choose berries that are firm, plump, and deep in color, while avoiding those that are soft, mushy, or moldy.
- Stay away from containers of berries with juice stains, which may be a sign that the berries are crushed and possibly moldy; soft, watery fruit, which means the berries are overripe; and dehydrated, wrinkled fruit, which means the berries have been stored too long.

Storing Tips

- After you purchase berries, check the fruit and toss out any moldy or deformed berries.
- Eat overripe berries within 24 hours.
- Keep other berries in the original container or arrange unwashed berries in a shallow pan lined with paper towels and wash topped with another paper towel to absorb any additional moisture. Cover the pan with plastic wrap.
- Wash just prior to use and eat within a week after purchase.
- If you can't eat them that soon, store in a freezer for up to 1 year without losing flavor.
- Raspberries spoil faster than most berries because of their delicate structure and hollow core. Blueberries last a little longer than other berries because they have a protective light powdery coating on the skins.

QUICK TIP: Wait to wash

Berries should be washed well but gently, using the light pressure of the sink sprayer if possible, just before eating or recipe preparation.

BLACKBERRIES

See Berries, page 55

BLUEBERRIES

See Berries, page 55

BRAN

See also Grains, page 104

Typical serving size: 1 tsp (6 g) to 1 cup (94 g)

HOW IT HARMS
Irritable bowel syndrome
Mineral absorption

WHAT IT HEALS
Cancer
Heart attack risk
Weight gain
Diverticulitis
Diabetes
Constipation
Hemorrhoids

Bran, one of the richest sources of dietary fiber, is the indigestible outer husk of wheat, rice, oats, and other cereal grains. At one time, most bran was discarded or used for animal feed when grains were milled. Different types of bran contain

BRAN FACT
- The phytic acid in raw bran inhibits absorption of important minerals. So it's best to eat bran in cereals and breads; the heat and enzymes in yeast destroy most of the phytic acid.

B

different types of fiber—soluble and insoluble. Both are important for health, digestion, and preventing diseases.

Health Benefits

Lowers cancer risk. Bran's high fiber content may reduce the risk of colon and other obesity-related cancers.

QUICK TIP: A little at a time

Severe bowel obstruction can occur if you eat large amounts of bran, especially if you don't drink enough water. If you're new to the bran game, gradually increase intake until your body gets used to it.

Reduces heart attack risk. Many societies whose diets are high in fiber have lower risk of heart attacks. The fiber in bran reduces blood cholesterol levels, a risk factor for heart disease.

Helps fight weight gain. All types of bran, as well as other high-fiber foods, play an important role in weight control by promoting a feeling of fullness without overeating.

Prevents diverticulitis. Including wheat bran in a high-fiber diet can help prevent diverticulitis, an intestinal disorder in which small pockets bulging from the colon wall become impacted and inflamed.

Lowers diabetes risk. Oat bran is high in soluble fiber, which is sticky and combines with water to form a thick gel. It appears to improve glucose metabolism in people with diabetes, which may reduce their need for insulin and other diabetes medications.

Helps prevent constipation and hemorrhoids. The fiber in bran helps prevent constipation and may also help people suffering from hemorrhoids.

Health Risks

Intestinal discomfort. Consuming too much bran can cause bloating, gas, and intestinal discomfort. It may also aggravate irritable bowel syndrome.

Mineral absorption. The phytic acid in raw bran inhibits the body's absorption of calcium, iron, zinc, magnesium, and other important minerals.

Eating Tips

- Stir a couple spoonfuls of oat bran into a stew to add more fiber, making the stew more filling.
- Use wheat bran instead of bread crumbs to top casseroles.
- Add a few spoonfuls to pancake or waffle batter.

Buying Tips

- You can find wheat and oat bran in the cereal or baking section of grocery and natural food stores.
- Bran can go rancid, so buy products in well-sealed containers.
- Buy from a store that has a high product turnover.
- Makes sure the bran doesn't contain any clumps, which can indicate moisture.

Storing Tips

- Store bran in a tightly sealed container because it can go rancid.
- Store it in a dark, dry, cool place and it will stay good for up to 3 months; store in a fridge, 6 months; in the freezer, about a year.

BREAD

See also Grains, page 104

Typical serving size: 1 slice (about 25 g)

HOW IT HARMS
Celiac disease
Allergies
Diabetes (white bread)
Fat storage (white bread)
High blood pressure (high-sodium bread)

WHAT IT HEALS
Diabetes (whole grain bread)
Weight control (whole grain bread)
Anemia (fortified or enriched bread)

Bread has been called the "staff of life," implying that it alone is all that is required for total nutrition. While bread does provide starch, protein, and some vitamins and minerals, it is far from being nutritionally complete. Many of the nutrients in the grain are destroyed by milling and processing, but some (typically folate, iron, thiamine, riboflavin, and niacin) are added later.

Health Benefits

Helps diabetes symptoms. Whole grain breads are a good source of fiber, which we digest more slowly, making us feel fuller longer and preventing blood sugar spikes.

Helps lose weight. Make sure you choose a bread that's high in fiber, vitamins, and minerals, and with a low glycemic load (lots of fiber is usually a good indicator). Select a bread with the words "100% whole wheat" or "whole grain" before the name of the grain.

Prevents anemia. Some fortified breads provide good amounts of iron, which can help keep anemia at bay.

Health Risks

Celiac disease. Celiac disease damages the lining of the small intestine and causes diarrhea, constipation, and abdominal pain. The intestinal damage is because of a reaction to eating gluten, which is found in most breads, wheat, barley, rye, triticale, and possibly oats.

Allergies. People with food allergies may react to specific ingredients; for example, people allergic to molds may react to sourdough or very yeasty breads. If you have a food allergy, be sure to check labels for any offending ingredients.

Diabetes. White breads, made from refined flour, break down very quickly to glucose, causing blood sugar to spike.

Fat storage. Low-fiber foods (including white breads) cause blood sugar surges that keep insulin levels rising. Elevated insulin levels can lead to greater fat storage in our bodies.

Blood pressure. Some fortified or enriched breads may be high in salt, which could adversely affect blood pressure. Be sure to read labels carefully for any salt or sodium-related ingredients, and choose low-sodium breads.

Eating Tips

- Grind chunks of stale bread in the food processor to make crumbs for other cooking needs, instead of buying the boxed crumbs.
- Make a salad with whole grain bread cubes, tomatoes, onions, cucumbers, olive oil, and wine vinegar.
- Drizzle catfish fillets with butter, sprinkle with panko—a bread crumb made from light wheat bread—and bake.

Old School
Bread is fattening and should be avoided whenever possible.

New Wisdom
A slice of bread contains just 65 to 80 calories. Adding butter, margarine, or fatty spreads boosts calories.

QUICK TIP:
Look for sourdough bread

Sourdough bread has a relatively mild effect on blood sugar compared to other white breads.

Buying Tips

- Choose breads with a low glycemic load (page 262). This rating is particularly important if you're trying to control blood sugar and lose weight. Breads made with whole grains and higher in fiber usually have a lower glycemic load. Look for at least 3 g of fiber per serving.
- Go for heft. High-fiber breads should feel slightly heavier than low-fiber breads.

Storing Tips

- Store bread at room temperature or freeze.
- Sliced and wrapped bread should always be kept in its wrapper. You'll see the "best before" date on the plastic tie or wrapper.
- If you live in a humid area where mold is a problem, freeze the bread and defrost slices as you need them.
- You can keep wrapped bread in the freezer for up to 3 months.
- Eat crusty bread and rolls the day you buy them, because they become stale quickly.

BROCCOLI

Typical serving size: ½ cup, cooked (36 g)

HOW IT HARMS
Bloating and flatulence

WHAT IT HEALS
Bladder cancer
Colorectal cancer
Breast cancer
Lung cancer
Heart disease
Bone health
Colds
Skin
Weight gain

One of the most nutritious and studied vegetables, broccoli has an abundance of vitamins, minerals, and other powerful disease-fighting substances that give it the ability to protect against many common cancers among other diseases. Nobody is sure why, but broccoli seems to be even more protective than other cruciferous vegetables (members of the cabbage family).

Broccoli contains sulforaphane, which may help to stop the spread of cancer. In some laboratory tests, it has been shown to reduce the spread of tumors, and reduce the number of carcinogens and free radicals in the body.

Health Benefits

Prevents bladder cancer. One study found that men who ate 5 servings or more per week of cruciferous veggies were half as likely to develop bladder cancer, one of the most common cancers, over a 10-year period as men who rarely ate them. Broccoli and cabbage were singled out as the most protective foods.

Reduces risk of colorectal cancer. This vegetable is packed with folate, fiber, and anti-oxidants that may reduce the risk of colorectal cancer.

Increases breast cancer survival. Eating broccoli and other cruciferous vegetables may improve your odds for breast cancer survival, a new study suggests. Of women in China diagnosed with breast cancer, those who consumed the most cruciferous vegetables were 62% less likely to die of breast cancer and 35% less likely to have a recurrence of the disease, compared with those who consumed the least.

Helps fight lung and heart disease. The sulforaphane in broccoli may help your body fight off the infections that cause inflammation in the lungs and arteries.

Keeps bones strong. The vitamin K in broccoli helps boost bone health.

Helps fight colds. Broccoli contains high levels of vitamin C—the vitamin that can help stave off colds.

Gives skin a healthy glow. Broccoli's vitamin C helps create collagen, which plays a role in healthy skin.

Helps with weight loss. Most Americans consume too little vitamin C, and one study showed that adults deficient in vitamin C may be more resistant to losing fat. Conversely, people who had adequate vitamin C levels burned 30% more fat during a bout of exercise than those low in C.

Health Risks

Bloating and gas. Although filled with fiber and vitamins, broccoli can also cause gas and bloating.

QUICK TIP:
Nutritious cooking techniques

The best ways to cook broccoli are to steam it, roast it, cook it in the microwave, or stir-fry it with a little broth or water. These methods are better than boiling. Some of the vitamin and mineral content are lost from the vegetable and end up in the cooking water when it is boiled. Cooked broccoli should be bright green in color, and tender enough so that it can be pierced with a sharp knife and still remain crisp.

Eating Tips

- Toss steamed florets with Italian tomato sauce and toasted walnuts.
- Peel stems and cut into thick sticks for dipping into roasted garlic hummus.
- Scatter steamed florets atop a frozen pizza.

Buying Tips

- Choose bunches that are dark green. Good color indicates high nutrient value.
- Florets that are dark green, purplish, or bluish green contain more beta-carotene and vitamin C than paler or yellowing ones.
- Choose bunches with stalks that are very firm. Stalks that bend or seem rubbery are of poor quality.
- Avoid broccoli with open, flowering, discolored, or water-soaked bud clusters and tough, woody stems.

Storing Tips

- Store fresh broccoli unwashed in an open plastic bag and place in the crisper drawer of the refrigerator.
- Broccoli is best if used within a day or two after purchasing.

BROCCOLI FACT

- Frozen broccoli may contain 35% more beta-carotene by weight than fresh broccoli.

BRUSSELS SPROUTS

- Brussels sprouts were named after the capital of Belgium, where it is thought that they were first cultivated.
- Brussels sprouts are not actually sprouts. Nor are they baby cabbages.
- French settlers in Louisiana introduced the sprouts to America.
- Most brussels sprouts are grown in California. They are available all year round, but their peak growing season is autumn through early spring.

Typical serving size: ½ cup, cooked (78 g)

HOW THEY HARM
Bloating and flatulence

WHAT THEY HEAL
Cancer
Heart disease
High blood pressure
Birth defects
Digestion
Cataracts
Weight gain

Brussels sprouts look like miniature heads of cabbage. They are similar to cabbage in taste, but they are slightly milder in flavor and denser in texture. Brussels sprouts and cabbage are members of the cruciferous vegetable family. These vegetables are an excellent source of vitamin C.

Health Benefits

Fights cancer. Brussels sprouts contain antioxidants that detoxify cancer-causing free radicals. Studies link higher consumption of cruciferous vegetables with a lower incidence of several types of cancer.

Combats heart disease. Just ½ cup (78 g) of brussels sprouts provides 80% of the vitamin C you need each day and a good amount of vitamin A, both of which help fight heart disease.

Lowers blood pressure. The potassium in brussels sprouts helps to lower blood pressure.

Reduce risk of birth defects. The folate in brussels sprouts may help prevent birth defects, specifically neural tube defects.

Aids digestive health. Fiber is well known for helping to maintain a healthy digestive tract and brussels sprouts are a good source of this nutrient.

Staves off cataracts. Vitamins A and C in brussel sprouts help ward off cataracts, which can cause blurry vision.

Helps with weight loss. The fiber in brussel sprouts helps you feel fuller longer so you eat less.

Health Risk

Gas. Brussels sprouts contain a fair amount of fiber, which can cause gas and bloating.

Eating Tips

- Sauté thinly sliced sprouts with minced garlic over high heat to caramelize.
- Roast lightly oiled sprouts with chopped walnuts.
- Toss quartered sprouts into a stir-fry.

Buying Tips

- Choose firm, compact sprouts that are bright green in color, with unblemished leaves.
- Fresh brussels sprouts should be displayed in stores chilled. If they are kept at room temperature, their leaves will turn yellow quickly. Yellow or wilted leaves are signs of age or mishandling.
- Old sprouts also have a strong, cabbage-like odor.
- It is best to choose sprouts individually from bulk displays rather than pint or quart tubs.
- Select sprouts that are similar in size, so they will cook more evenly.
- Avoid sprouts that are puffy or soft.

Storing Tips

- Do not wash or trim sprouts before storing them, but you may remove the yellow or wilted outer leaves.
- If you have purchased sprouts that have been packaged in a cellophane-covered container, take off the wrapping, examine the sprouts, remove any that are in bad condition, return them to the container, re-cover with cellophane, and refrigerate.
- Place loose sprouts in perforated plastic bag.
- Fresh sprouts will keep for 3 to 5 days.

BUCKWHEAT

See Grains, page 104

BULGUR

See Grains, page 104

BUTTER AND MARGARINE

Typical serving size: 1 pat (5 g)

HOW THEY HARM
High cholesterol
Obesity

WHAT THEY HEAL
High cholesterol
Bones and teeth
Skin

Used sparingly, both butter and margarine can be incorporated into a healthful diet. Butter is made from animal fat, and contains cholesterol and saturated fat, which can contribute to the risk of heart disease. Margarine, made from vegetable oils, was created as a more healthful alternative. But some margarines contain trans fats, which have also been shown to have adverse effects on cholesterol levels and heart health. So look for trans fat–free margarines, and use them sparingly.

Old School
Opting for margarine instead of butter is a much healthier decision, saving lots of calories.

New Wisdom
Butter and margarine have about the same calories.

Health Benefits

Helps lower cholesterol. Just 2 Tbsp (30 mL) of margarine with plant sterols added are needed per day to reduce blood cholesterol.

Strengthens bones and teeth. Vitamin D, added to many margarines, helps strengthen bones and teeth.

Keeps skin young. Essential fatty acids found in most margarines protect against dermatitis. They may also lower the risk of heart disease and stroke.

Health Risks

Obesity. Butter and margarine are high in calories, all of which come from fats, which increases the risk of obesity, heart disease, cancer, and many other diseases.

High cholesterol. The fat in butter is mostly saturated, which is presumed to raise blood cholesterol levels more than other types of fat. Similarly, some studies suggest that trans-fatty acids in some margarine raise LDL cholesterol and lower HDL cholesterol, increasing risk of heart disease.

Eating Tips

- Keep butter and margarine well chilled and you'll be able to spread less on the bread.
- Mix soft-tub margarine with mashed roasted garlic and chopped basil for a savory topping.

Buying Tips

- When buying margarine, look for brands that are trans fat–free with as little saturated fat as possible. Opt for light tubs or sticks made from blended oils like canola, olive, or soybean.
- If you're concerned about high cholesterol, look for products with added plant sterols.
- If you want to cook with it, check for the warning "not recommended for frying or baking."

Storing Tips

- Butter and margarine can turn rancid, so store away from light, heat, and air.
- Don't store butter at room temperature. For easier spreading, leave butter outside of the refrigerator for about 15 minutes.
- Keep butter in vapor proof containers, because it can quickly absorb odors from other foods.
- Butter will stay fresh for about 2 weeks when stored in a refrigerator.
- To freeze butter, place in a vapor proof freezer package. This will prevent freezer burn and other odors from seeping into the butter.
- Frozen butter will keep for up to 9 months.

BUTTERNUT SQUASH

See Squash, page 196

CABBAGE

Typical serving size: ½ cup, cooked (75 g), or 1 cup raw (89 g)

HOW IT HARMS

Bloating and flatulence
High in calories
Sulfites

WHAT IT HEALS

Colon cancer
Breast cancer
Cancers of the uterus and ovaries
Diabetes
Obesity

Cabbages are members of the cruciferous family of vegetables, a family associated with numerous health benefits. Very low in calories (a cup of chopped raw green cabbage contains a meager 20 calories), the lowly cabbage is a rich source of vitamin C (with 33 mg per cup). Red cabbage contains almost twice as

QUICK TIP: Lose the fat, keep the flavor

A teaspoon of butter imparts as much flavor as a tablespoon, with one-third the fat. Reduce the amount of butter or margarine you need to use by boosting its flavor with herbs, spices, or low-fat ingredients. For example, top baked potatoes with chives and blended fat-free cottage cheese. When making cakes, to cut the amount of butter or margarine by one-third to one-half, add about ½ cup (118 mL) of applesauce for moisture. Top whole grain breads with fruit preserves.

much vitamin C as the green cabbage, while the green variety contains twice as much folate as the red; both red and green cabbages contribute potassium and fiber. Savoy cabbage is a good source of beta-carotene.

Health Benefits

Helps prevent colon cancer. People who eat large amounts of cabbage have low rates of colon cancer. Cabbage contains bioflavonoids and other plant chemicals that inhibit tumor growth and protect cells against damage from free radicals.

Protects against breast cancer. Cabbage contains sulphoraphane, which has potent anticancer properties. One study found that women who ate the most cabbage and its cruciferous cousins, like broccoli and brussels sprouts, had a 45 percent lower breast cancer risk than women who ate the least. Other chemicals in cabbage also speed up the body's metabolism of estrogen, a hormone that, in high amounts, is associated with breast cancer.

Helps prevent cancers of the female reproductive system. The chemicals that hasten estrogen metabolism may also protect against cancers of the uterus and ovaries. Of particular interest is indole-3-carbinol, a component that in animal studies reduced the risk of cancer.

Helps protect against and manage diabetes. Red cabbage is rich in natural pigments called anthocyanins, which new research suggests may help boost insulin production and lower blood sugar levels. High in fiber and low in calories, cabbage is low-glycemic, especially when prepared with vinegar, which also helps manage diabetes.

May help you lose weight. You can fill up on cabbage without adding many calories.

Health Risks

Bloating and flatulence. Cabbage contains bacteria that live naturally in the intestinal tract and cause gas and bloating. Avoid it if you have a gastrointestinal condition such as Crohn's disease or ulcerative colitis and if it triggers inflammation.

Some cabbage dishes can be high in calories or salt. Be wary of store-prepared coleslaw, which can be soaked in mayonnaise and thus outweigh any nutritional benefits. Rinse sauerkraut before heating to get rid of excess sodium. When preparing coleslaw yourself, reduce calories by using low-fat yogurt, vinegar, and oil.

Certain preparations contain sulfites. Sulfites are often used to preserve cabbage color; asthma sufferers or anyone allergic to sulfites should check package labels.

Old School
Cabbage juice is a miracle cure for ulcers.

New Wisdom
There's no proof that cabbage juice cures ulcers, but there's no harm in it.

Eating Tips

- Sauté shredded cabbage and onion, then stir in broth and dill to make soup.
- Toss shredded red cabbage, carrot, and onion in Thai peanut sauce for a salad.
- Top tacos with slivered Napa cabbage instead of lettuce.

Buying Tip

- Look for tight, heavy heads of cabbage that do not have any wilted leaves.

QUICK TIP: Cook it fast

To minimize the odor that accompanies cooked cabbage, cook the cabbage quickly in an uncovered pan with as little water as possible. Overcooking also destroys cabbage's stores of vitamin C.

C

- Fresh, uncut heads of cabbage can be stored in the refrigerator for up to 2 weeks when covered loosely with a plastic bag.
- Do not wash cabbage before storing; the excess water will encourage spoiling.

CAKES, COOKIES, AND PASTRIES

Typical serving size: Varies depending on size, weight, and product, such as 3 Oreo cookies (2 oz or 57 g), a small muffin (2 oz or 57 g), or a small slice of cake (2.7 oz or 57 g)

HOW THEY HARM
    High blood sugar
    High cholesterol
    Tooth decay

WHAT THEY HEAL
    Low energy

Although high on most people's list of favorite foods, cakes, cookies, pies, and other pastries are low in nutrition. Many are high in fats, sugar and other sweeteners, and calories—but relatively low in vitamins, minerals, protein, and starches.

Basic components of most cakes, cookies, and pastries include refined flour, sugar, fat, eggs, and milk or cream. Although these ingredients are not "bad" in and of themselves, excess consumption can lead to health problems, such as weight gain and diabetes. Additionally, most packaged crackers and baked goods are loaded with trans fats, man-made fats that contribute to heart disease (page 5). Limit added sugars to about 6 tsp (30 mL)—or 100 calories worth of sweets—per day, which is equal to about 13 animal crackers. If you want to enjoy the occasional baked treat without guilt, stick with moderate portions. You may want to bake your own healthier versions, or look for gluten-free, sugar-free, or vegan versions, which have fewer calories and trans fats.

Health Benefit

Provides a source of quick energy. Cookies, cakes, and pastries are generally high in sugar, which breaks down into glucose, the body's main source of energy. Consuming these in small amounts can boost energy levels in the short term.

Health Risks

High blood sugar. Because baked goods often contain high amounts of sugar and refined flour, they spike up blood sugar levels. Consumed in large quantities over time, blood sugar imbalance can contribute to insulin resistance, which in turn can cause diabetes, obesity, high blood pressure, and heart disease.

Cholesterol. Solid and highly saturated fats, such as vegetable shortening, lard, butter, and palm and coconut oils, are generally more suitable for baking than liquid vegetable oils and reduced-fat margarines.

QUICK TIP: Beat a craving for sweets with nuts and water

Drink two glasses of water and eat an ounce of nuts (6 walnuts, 12 almonds or 20 peanuts). Within 20 minutes, this can extinguish your craving for sweets and dampen your appetite by changing your body chemistry.

Thus, the fats found in most baked goods are the types that are most likely to raise the blood levels of the detrimental low-density lipoprotein (LDL) cholesterol.

Tooth decay. Sugary and starchy foods may cause cavities.

Eating Tips

- Toast a slice of angel food cake and drizzle with microwave-warmed cashew butter and toasted coconut.
- Crumble almond cookies over sliced fresh peaches.
- Use day-old croissants in a bread pudding.

Buying Tips

- Check ingredient labels for products and do not buy if it contains sources of trans-fatty acids, such as margarine or vegetable shortening.
- Opt for low-fat and low-calorie options such as angel food cake, or inquire about such options before ordering at restaurants.
- Watch out for "healthier" alternatives. Some commercially baked goods, such as carrot or zucchini cake, are promoted as healthy, but may contain negligible amounts of the fruit or vegetable, are still high in fat and sugar, or are topped with large amounts of frosting. Check labels or ask about ingredients.

Storing Tips

- Store cookies, cakes, and pastries in an air-tight container.
- Most will last up to about a week.

TIPS FOR HEALTHIER BAKING

You don't have to banish sweet stuff from your kitchen. Instead use these tips to stir up healthier versions of your favorite recipes:

- Use applesauce, strained prunes, mashed bananas, and other pureed fruits as substitutes for at least some of the fat in cookie and cake recipes. The fruit adds the moisture and texture, as well as sweetness and extra flavor.
- Reduce or even eliminate sugar in fruit pies; use extra cinnamon and other spices to perk up flavor.
- Cut the fat content in pies by using one crust; reduce it even further with a low-fat graham cracker crust or make a deep-dish crustless pie or cobbler.
- Discard half the egg yolks and increase the number of whites when baking a cake or cookies; this increases the protein and at the same time cuts down on fat and cholesterol.
- Substitute condensed skim milk for cream in frostings and pie fillings. Similarly, try strained yogurt cheese instead of high-fat cream cheese for toppings and fillings. Fruit and fruit sauces are other options for low-calorie toppings.

CANDIES

Typical serving size: Varies per candy bar or item

HOW THEY HARM
Weight gain
Blood sugar swings
Tooth decay
Blood pressure in susceptible people
Allergies

WHAT THEY HEAL
Hypoglycemia

Candies offer little nutritional value, but as an occasional part of a balanced diet, most healthy people can enjoy them.

CANDY FACTS

- The word *candy* is derived from the Arabic pronunciation of *khandakah*, the Sanskrit word for "sugar."
- Candies were rare treats until the widespread cultivation of sugarcane and the development of large-scale refining processes in the 17th and 18th centuries.

Our preference for sweet tastes is evident at a very early age and is considered to be part of human evolution. Edible berries and fruits contain natural sugars and sweetness as opposed to the bitter taste of many poisonous plants.

Health Benefit

Is a quick fix for those who have hypoglycemia. Five or six pieces of hard candy (less for children) are recommended for those experiencing severe drops in blood glucose.

Health Risks

Weight gain. All candies are packed with simple sugars—sucrose, corn syrup, fructose—that add extra calories that add up quickly.

Blood sugar imbalance. Unfortunately, the rapid rise in blood sugar from eating candies can causes insulin levels to spike, which encourages the liver to convert sugar into fat. And when your blood sugar crashes after a high, you're likely to feel hungry and tired.

Tooth decay. Sweets and sugary foods form an acid bath that is corrosive to tooth enamel and create an environment where destructive, caries-causing bacteria flourish. Candies that linger in the mouth are more damaging than those quickly swallowed. Brush your teeth regularly.

Blood pressure. Natural licorice is known to raise blood pressure in certain people. If you know you're hypertensive, you may be better off avoiding licorice. However, most "licorice" candies in North America are artificially flavored and do not originate from the licorice root, so they don't affect on blood pressure.

> **QUICK TIP: Chew sugarless gum for dental health**
>
> Sugarless gum may help stimulate saliva flow and flush food particles out of the mouth. It may contain artificial sweeteners or "sugar alcohols," such as xylitol.

Allergies. Most hard candies contain artificial flavors and colorings. Although there is no scientific evidence that the rigorously tested food dyes allowed in candy cause allergies or adverse reactions, some people may be hypersensitive to these ingredients. If you are allergic to dyes, check the labels before consuming.

Eating Tips

- Satisfy a sweet tooth by melting 1 oz (28 g) of dark chocolate as a dip for dried fruit.
- Chewy chunks of candied ginger make a zesty replacement for jelly beans.
- Choose a single-serving candy with nuts to avoid spiking your blood sugar.

Buying Tip

- Check expiration dates before purchasing. Some candies can get hard or dry out.

Storing Tip

- Store candies in a cool, dark place away from sunlight.

CANTALOUPE

See Melons, page 131

CARROTS

Typical serving size: ½ cup (2.25 oz or 64 g) fresh carrots

HOW THEY HARM
Skin yellowing

WHAT THEY HEAL
High cholesterol
Diabetes
Cancer

Macular degeneration

Cataracts

Night blindness

Native to Afghanistan, carrots are our most abundant source of beta-carotene, a compound that can function as an antioxidant and can also be converted by the body into vitamin A. The more vivid the color of the carrot, the higher the levels of this important carotenoid. One cup of cooked carrots has 70 calories, 4 g of fiber, and about 18 mg of beta-carotene. This provides more than 100% of the Recommended Dietary Allowance of vitamin A—a nutrient essential for healthy hair, skin, eyes, and bones.

Carrots are usually orange, but also come in purple, red, white, and yellow colors. "Baby carrots" aren't actually baby carrots—they're regular-size carrots that have been cut and shaped by machines to achieve a uniform appearance.

Health Benefits

Reduces the risk of cardiovascular disease. A U.S. government study found that volunteers who ate about one cup of carrots a day had an average 11% reduction in their blood cholesterol levels after only 3 weeks. The cholesterol-lowering effect is likely because of the high soluble-fiber content of carrots, mostly in the form of pectin.

Reduces the risk of diabetes. Beta-carotene is linked to a lower risk of diabetes. One study found that people with the highest blood levels of beta-carotene had 32% lower insulin levels (suggesting better blood sugar control) than those with the lowest levels.

Helps prevent cancer. Carrots also contain other carotenoids, including alpha-carotene as well as bioflavonoids, which have been linked to reducing the risk of

QUICK TIP: Consume carrots with a small amount of fat

To properly absorb beta-carotene, the body needs a small amount of fat, because carotenoids are fat soluble. Adding a pat of butter or a tsp of olive oil to cooked carrots will help body will fully utilize this nutrient.

cancer, especially lung cancer. However, studies have shown that beta-carotene supplements may be particularly harmful to smokers.

Helps prevent certain vision problems. Carrots will help protect against two sight-robbing conditions, macular degeneration and cataracts. It also prevents and treats night blindness, an inability of the eyes to adjust to dim lighting or darkness.

Health Risk

Yellowish tinge in the skin. Excessive consumption of carrots may cause a yellowish tint in the skin. This harmless condition called carotenemia will disappear with reduced intake. If the yellow skin color persists, or if the white portions of the eyes are also discolored, consult your doctor to rule out jaundice, a liver disorder.

Eating Tips

- Serve shredded carrots, tossed with lemon and garlic sauce, on cucumber slices.
- Cook with potatoes, then coarsely mash.
- Add ½ cup shredded carrots to tomato ragú.

Old School
Raw carrots are more nutritious than cooked carrots.

New Wisdom
Cooking increases carrots' nutritional value; it breaks down the tough cellular walls that encase the beta-carotene.

Buying Tips

- Buy carrots with bright green tops; this indicates freshness.
- If the carrots are on display without their green tops, look for firm carrots with smooth, even color without cracks.

Storing Tips

- Store carrots with the green tops trimmed; during storage, the greens rob the carrots of nutrients and moisture.
- Carrots keep in the crisper drawer of the refrigerator for several weeks in perforated plastic bags.

CAULIFLOWER

Typical serving size: ½ cup, cooked (62 g), or ½ cup raw (50 g)

HOW IT HARMS
Bloating and flatulence

WHAT IT HEALS
Cancer
Weight gain

Cauliflower is a cruciferous vegetable in the same family as broccoli, brussels sprouts, cabbage, and kale. It is rich in vitamin C, folate, and various other phy-

80% of folate is lost in cooking so eat cauliflower raw.

tochemicals linked with good health. A cup of raw cauliflower florets has more than 50% of the Recommended Dietary Allowance (RDA) of vitamin C, 15% of the RDA for folate, and reasonable amounts of potassium and vitamin B6. It also has bio-

QUICK TIP:
Cook cauliflower fast

To retain flavor and reduce nutrient loss, cook cauliflower rapidly by boiling in a minimum amount of water or steaming. Too much cooking turns cauliflower mushy and releases sulfurous compounds, resulting in an unpleasant odor and bitter taste.

flavonoids, indoles, and other chemicals that protect against cancer.

Health Benefits

May prevent cancer. The high amounts of vitamin C in cauliflower help protect against inflammation that can lead to cancer. The vegetable is also rich in folate, which may help prevent damage to DNA that can lead to cancer.

Helps lose weight. Because cauliflower is high in fiber and low in calories (25 calories per cup of florets), it's an ideal snack food for weight watchers.

Health Risks

Bloating and flatulence. Cauliflower and other vegetables in the Brassica family can cause discomfort, especially those who suffer from gastric disorders such as ulcerative colitis. Avoid cauliflower if it triggers symptoms.

Eating Tips

- Save the brine from store-bought pickles and pack it with florets into a jar; refrigerate for several days.
- Season steamed florets with olive oil, roasted red pepper slivers, and olives.
- Roast oiled florets with slivered garlic until well browned.

Buying Tips

- Look for a head with firm, compact florets and a snowy white color. Leaves should be crisp and green.
- Avoid cauliflower with brown spots or loose sections.

Storing Tip

- Refrigerate cauliflower in a plastic bag for up to 5 days in the refrigerator crisper.

CELERIAC

Typical serving size: ½ cup, cooked (78 g)

WHAT IT HEALS
Heart disease
Weight gain

A winter root vegetable also called celery root, knob celery, and German celery, fresh celeriac resembles a large, round, knobby turnip. But when the tough outer skin is peeled away, the flesh is white, and has a flavor and odor similar to celery. A half-cup serving of cooked celeriac contains 25 calories, 1.5 g of fiber, 5 mg of vitamin C, and some B6 and phosphorus.

Celeriac has a mild flavor and lends itself to a variety of dishes. For example, it is often grated raw into salads; boiled and pureed to add body and flavor to soups and stews; chopped into poultry stuffing; or sliced, dipped in an egg batter, and sautéed to serve as a meat substitute. It is also served as an accompaniment to haddock, salmon, and spicy pork.

Health Benefits

Helps weight loss. Because celeriac is low in calories and contains no fat, it serves as a great stand-in for dishes requiring potatoes or other starches, such as mashed potatoes or french fries. Celeriac has a moderate amount of fiber per serving, which may help you feel fuller longer so you avoid packing on additional pounds.

Reduces risk of heart disease. The vitamin C in celeriac fights free radicals and inflammation, while the vitamin B6 it contains helps reduce the risk of heart disease.

Eating Tips

- Mash cooked celeriac and potatoes seasoned with prepared horseradish.
- Roast chunks of celeriac, carrot, and onion with rosemary chicken.
- Add shredded celeriac to vegetable soup.

Buying Tip

- Choose small- to medium-size celeriacs that are firm and do not have any soft spots.

Storing Tips

- Store in an unsealed plastic bag in the refrigerator for up to a week.
- If celeriac turns soft, do not eat it.

QUICK TIP:
Prevent discoloration

When preparing celeriac, place the peeled vegetable in some water with a squeeze of lemon juice immediately after cutting. This prevents it from changing color.

CELERY

Typical serving size: ½ cup, raw (60 g)

WHAT IT HEALS
Weight gain
High blood pressure
Inflammation
Cancer

Dieters tend to eat lots of celery because it is low in calories. Two stalks of celery contain less than 10 calories (celery is about 95% water by weight), yet their fiber content makes them very filling; the serving also delivers small amounts of vitamin C and some folate. Although it is not very high in nutrients, it adds a unique flavor to a variety of foods—from soups to salads and poultry stuffing.

Health Benefits

Helps reduce weight. The fiber in celery helps induce feelings of satiety, leading you to eat less.

Aids with high blood pressure. Celery is a good source of potassium, a mineral that aids muscle function and offsets some of sodium's damaging effects on blood pressure.

May help treat certain inflammatory conditions. Herbalists have advocated fresh celery and celery seed tea to treat gout and other forms of inflammatory arthritis, as well as high blood pressure and edema. Studies indicate that phthalides in celery may reduce the body's levels of certain hormones that constrict blood vessels and raise blood pressure. Phytochemicals found in celery help reduce production of certain prostaglandins, body chemicals that can cause inflammation.

May help reduce the risk of certain cancers. Phytochemicals in celery help destroy benzopyrene, a carcinogen that occurs in foods cooked at a high temperature.

Eating Tips

- Add celery leaves to tossed salads.
- Cut ribs into pieces and fill with reduced-fat refried beans and a drizzle of salsa.
- Sauté chunks of celery, carrot, and onion with sage.

Buying Tips

- Look for stalks that are light green, crisp, and firm without any bruises.
- Leaves should be a uniform color.

Storing Tip

- Refrigerate celery in a loosely sealed plastic wrap for about a week.

QUICK TIP: Use the leaves

Celery leaves are the most nutritious part of the plant, containing more calcium, iron, potassium, beta carotene, and vitamin C than the stalks. Save the leaves for soups, salads, and other dishes enhanced by the flavor of celery.

Old School
Chewing celery consumes more calories than it provides.

New Wisdom
It's an urban myth that celery has "negative" calories but, with less than 10 calories per serving, it's great to munch on to lose weight.

CEREALS

See also Grains, page 104

Typical serving size: 1 cup (8 oz or 226 g), but varies by type and product

HOW THEY HARM
High in salt, sugar, or fat

High in calories

Nutrient absorption

Bloating and flatulence

WHAT THEY HEAL
Heart disease

Cancer

Constipation

Weight gain

Cereals are one of the most popular members of the complex carbohydrate, or starch, food group. More than 90% of all commercial cereals are enriched or fortified with various vitamins and minerals, especially iron, niacin, thiamine, vitamin B6, and folic acid. Regulations about adding nutrients to cereals differ in the U.S. and Canada.

Wheat, corn, rice, and oats are the most familiar grains used to make cereals. Most flaked cereals are varying combinations of flour, water, sugar, and salt that are mixed into a dough, rolled thin, and then toasted. Served hot or cold, cereals can be a healthful, low-calorie breakfast. But be sure to read the label and minimize added sugar, sodium, preservatives, and other additives.

Health Benefits

Helps prevent heart disease. Oat cereals are high in soluble fiber that helps lower blood cholesterol levels, thereby reducing the risk of heart disease.

May help prevent cancer. Some cereals, especially those made from whole grains or with added bran, are high in insoluble fiber. These help prevent constipation and may also reduce the risk of some cancers, including colon cancer.

Helps reduce constipation. The high fiber content of cereals aids regular bowel movements. Look for a cereal with "whole grain" listed as the first ingredient, that contains at least 4 g of fiber per serving.

Aids weight loss. Eating low-calorie, fiber-rich cereals as part of a healthy breakfast can help you lose weight. Fibers fill you up, and research has shown that people who eat breakfast have more success in losing weight than those who skip it.

Health Risks

May be high in salt, sugar, or fat. Many commercial cereals, especially those for children, are high in sugar, and some are also high in salt. Granola-type cereals are often high in fat from added oils. Check the nutrition labels before purchasing. It also helps to add skim or low-fat milk instead of whole milk to minimize the amount of saturated fat.

Can be high in calories. Pay attention to serving sizes; some cereals are low in calories only when consumed in small amounts.

Possibly hinders absorption of nutrients. Products made with bran may prevent absorption of nutrients, such as calcium.

May cause flatulence and bloating. Although bran cereals are a convenient way to add fiber to your diet, they can cause

13 g is the most amount of sugar per serving that a cereal should contain.

bloating, abdominal discomfort, and gas if added suddenly and in large amounts. Add them gradually to your diet.

Eating Tips

- Top salads with mini shredded wheat.
- Stir a few tablespoons of bran fiber cereal into muffin batter.
- Add rolled oats to bread stuffing.

Buying Tips

- Check nutrition labels carefully before buying. Look for cereals that have at least 4 g of fiber and no more than 13 g of sugar per serving.
- Buy plain cereal, then add your own fresh fruit, raisins, seeds, and nuts.

Storing Tip

- Keep cereal in an airtight container in a cool, dark place for 1 to 2 weeks.

CHEESE

See also Milk and Dairy Products, page 133

Typical serving size: Varies; 1 oz (30 g) of hard or semihard cheese, or ½ cup (2.1 oz or 60 g) of cottage cheese

HOW IT HARMS
High in saturated fat and sodium
Migraines
Allergies
Bacterial infection

WHAT IT HEALS
Diabetes
Metabolic syndrome
Bones
Muscles
Tooth decay

One of our most versatile and popular foods, cheese is used for everything from snacks to main courses and desserts. It's an ancient food that can be made from the milk of almost any animal—cows, goats, yaks, camels, and buffaloes.

Most cheeses are made by adding a mixture of enzymes, known as rennet, to milk to curdle it. The liquid that remains after the curds have formed is known as whey. When it is drained away, we are left with cottage or farmer's cheese. Or the curds may be mixed with other ingredients, injected with special molds or bacteria, soaked in wine or beer, pressed or molded, or smoked or aged to make any of hundreds of different cheeses.

Health Benefits

May help prevent diabetes. Cheese is an excellent source of calcium, and studies show that getting plenty of calcium from food may help prevent insulin resistance, a harbinger of diabetes.

May prevent metabolic syndrome. According to a study, women who get plenty of calcium from dairy products also have a significantly lower risk of developing metabolic syndrome, which is linked to both diabetes and heart disease.

Supports bone and muscle health. Consumed moderately, cheese provides good amounts of calcium and protein necessary for bone and muscle strength, making it an ideal food for vegetarians, growing children and adolescents, and people with osteoporosis, a weakening of the bones. People who cannot digest milk because of lactose intolerance can often eat hard cheese. The bacteria and enzymes used to make cheese break down some of the lactose (milk sugar). A typical 1-oz (30-g) serving of cheese contains about 200 mg of calcium (along with 115 calories and 9 g of fat).

Fights cavities. The fat naturally contained in cheese coats your teeth and acts as a natural barrier against bacteria. Also, all cheese contains casein, which provides a natural tooth protection. Finally, the calcium and phosphorus found in cheese help remineralize tooth enamel.

Health Risks

Saturated fat and sodium. Doctors often advise patients with heart disease, elevated blood cholesterol, high blood pressure, or weight problems to reduce the amount of cheese they consume. Because most cheese is high in saturated fat, it increases the risk of atherosclerosis, the clogging of arteries with fatty deposits. Try lower-fat cheeses which still provide protein and calcium with less fat. Large amounts of sodium, also found in most cheeses, can be a hazard for people with high blood pressure.

Migraines and allergies. Aged cheese can trigger a migraine headache in some susceptible people. The likely culprit is tyramine, a naturally occurring chemical in cheddar, blue cheese, camembert, and certain other ripe cheeses. People who are allergic to penicillin may react to blue cheese and other soft cheeses that are made with penicillin molds. Also, those who are allergic to cow's milk may react to cheese, especially cottage and other fresh cheeses. Cheeses made from goat or sheep's milk are less likely to be allergenic.

Harmful bacteria. Pasteurized milk must be used to make commercial cheese in both the U.S. and Canada. Occasionally, health food stores and specialty shops sell imported or homemade unpasteurized cheese. Such cheeses can harbor dangerous salmonella and other bacteria.

Eating Tips

- Mix parmesan with toasted bread crumbs as a low-fat topping for pasta.
- Breakfast on part-skim ricotta topped with kiwi, raspberries, and agave nectar.
- Sprinkle shredded sharp cheddar on apple slices and broil briefly to melt.

Buying Tips

- Check the expiration date and the packaging.
- Avoid any cheese with missing or incomplete labels, or those without factory seals.
- Look for the words "pasteurized milk" in the ingredient list to avoid potentially harmful bacteria.
- For most cheeses, look for uniformity in color and texture.
- Take advantage of the broad range of low-fat cheeses on the market. Production methods have improved to allow for smoother texture and better taste.

Storing Tips

- The best way to store cheese varies depending on the type, but all should be kept in the vegetable drawer, where the temperature is cold and stable. In general, the harder the cheese, the longer it lasts.
- Wrap hard cheese such as parmesan or gouda in waxed paper, then in plastic wrap.
- Wrap blue cheeses and semihard cheeses in plastic wrap.
- Keep fresh cheeses in water, such as mozzarella or feta, in their packaging and change the water every couple of days.

CHEESE FACTS
- It takes about 10 lbs (4.5 kg) of milk to create a single lb (454 g) of firm cheese, such as cheddar, muenster, or swiss.
- Cream cheese, brie, and other soft cheeses are comparable to hard cheeses in calories and fat, but have less calcium.
- Cottage cheese has the fewest calories of all cheeses—about 90 in a half-cup serving. However, it has only half the calcium of milk.

- The most popular sweet cherries in North America are Bing and other dark-colored varieties, and Lamberts, which are a bright crimson. Queen Annes are yellow with tinges of red, large, and very sweet.
- Commercial maraschino cherries are made by bleaching the fruit (usually the yellow Queen Anne variety) in a sulfur dioxide brine, then toughening it with lime or calcium salt. The cherries are then dyed bright red, sweetened, flavored, and packed in jars.

CHERRIES

Typical serving size: ½ cup, fresh (2.5 oz or 70 g), or ¼ cup, dried (1.2 oz or 35 g)

HOW THEY HARM
Allergies

WHAT THEY HEAL
Inflammation
Cancer
Cholesterol
Gout
Arthritis

A member of the plant family that includes plums, apricots, peaches, and nectarines, cherries are generally lower in vitamins and minerals than their larger cousins. Still, recent research suggests that the small fruit can impart important health benefits. Both sweet and sour cherries are a source of beta-carotene, vitamin C, and potassium, but sour cherries are much higher in beta-carotene.

The flavor and low calorie content of the cherry varieties make them an ideal snack or dessert during the short time they are in season. Sour cherries, which are more nutritious than the sweet types, are used mostly for making jams and other preserves, or they are baked into pies and other pastries.

Health Benefits

Fights inflammation. Both sweet and sour cherries are rich in beta-carotene, a heart-healthy compound, and vitamin C, an antioxidant that fights free radical activity. One study showed that adults who ate 1½ cups of tart cherries had increased levels of antioxidants in their bodies, specifically anthocyanins, which help prevent heart disease and other inflammatory conditions.

May prevent cancer. Sour cherries are an abundant source of quercetin, a flavonoid with anticarcinogenic and antioxidant activities.

Evens blood cholesterol levels. Cherries are a good source of pectin, a soluble fiber that helps control blood cholesterol.

Treats gout. Alternative health practitioners often advocate sour cherries to treat gout. Research suggests that a substance in cherries called cyanidin has anti-inflammatory properties, an attribute that might help reduce the swelling and pain of gout.

Eases arthritis pain. Limited research also shows that sour cherries have the potential to alleviate the symptoms of arthritis.

Health Risks

Allergic reactions. People who are allergic to apricots and other members of the plum family may also suffer a reaction to cherries. The most likely symptoms are hives and a tingling or itching sensation in or around the mouth.

Eating Tips

- Add quartered sweet cherries to pancakes.
- Scatter sweet cherries over skinless chicken thighs before roasting.
- Make a sauce with cherries and pomegranate juice thickened with arrowroot.

Buying Tips

- Look for plump, firm fruit with green stems.
- Imported cherries are not as flavorful as the local fruit that is picked and marketed at the height of its ripeness.

Storing Tips

- Keep cherries unwashed, with the stems attached, in an open bag or container in the refrigerator.
- Cherries spoil quickly, so eat them as soon as possible.

CHIA

See Nuts and Seeds, page 138

CHICKEN

See Poultry, page 174

CHICKPEAS

See Beans and Legumes, page 48

CHILES

Typical serving size: ½ cup (75 g); may vary depending on type of pepper

HOW THEY HARM
   Hemorrhoids
   Gastric discomfort

WHAT THEY HEAL
   Cancer
   Blood clots
   Nasal congestion
   Weight gain

A popular ingredient in Southwestern cooking, chiles, or hot peppers, add spice and interest to many foods. Some of the milder varieties are consumed as low-calorie snacks.

The heat in chiles comes from capsaicinoids, substances that have no odor or flavor themselves but act directly on the mouth's pain receptors. This results in teary eyes, runny nose ("salsa sniffles"), and sweating experienced by people who indulge in the hotter varieties. Capsaicin and other capsaicinoids are concentrated mainly in the white ribs and seeds, which can be removed to produce a milder flavor.

Chiles are more nutritious than sweet peppers, and the red varieties generally have a higher nutritional content than the green ones.

Health Benefits

Prevents cancer. Chiles are very good sources of antioxidants, especially beta-carotene and vitamin C. Just one raw, red hot pepper (1 ½ oz/45 g) contains about 75 mg of vitamin C, almost 100% of the Recommended Dietary Allowance (RDA). Chiles also contain bioflavonoids, plant pigments that some researchers believe may help prevent cancer.

Reduces chance of blood clots. Research indicates that capsaicin may act as an anticoagulant, perhaps helping to prevent blood clots that can lead to a heart attack or stroke.

Fights against colds and allergies. Chiles can act as a decongestant. For those with a cold or allergies, eating chiles or foods prepared with chiles can provide temporary relief from nasal and sinus congestion.

May aid in weight loss. Some studies show that very spicy foods can temporarily increase your metabolism. Specialist grocers often stock many different kinds

CHILES FACTS

- The hottest pepper on record is the Trinidad moruga Scorpion, which is rated as high as 2 million Scoville units. By contrast, the serrano comes in at about 5,000 to 15,000 Scoville units. Pure capsaicin rates 16 million units.
- Incorporated into creams, capsaicinoids alleviate the burning pain of shingles and can help with the pain of arthritis. They may also reduce the mouth pain associated with chemotherapy.

of peppers. Buy one type a week and add some to various meals. Spice up your scrambled eggs with minced jalapeño, and add a little fire to beef stew with half a Scotch bonnet pepper.

Health Risks

Old School
Drink water to quell the fire from a hot pepper.

New Wisdom
Drink 2% milk or eat regular yogurt. The fat will help neutralize the fat-soluble capsaicinoids in hot peppers.

Hemorrhoids. Consuming chiles may cause rectal irritation.

Gastric discomfort. Although there is no evidence that chiles cause ulcers or digestive problems, they may lead to stomach discomfort, especially if you suffer from acid reflux.

Eating Tips

- Season melon chunks with minced chiles and sugar for a sweet-hot-cool combo.
- Grill jalapeño halves stuffed with ground beef, shredded cheddar, and cilantro.
- Add a drop of chile sauce to noodle soup for surprising zip.

Buying Tips

- To buy good-quality chile peppers that are fresh, look for smooth skin with deep color and no bruises or spots.
- Dried chile peppers can be purchased in packages.

Storing Tips

- Store fresh chile peppers in a bag in the refrigerator for up to 2 weeks.
- Store dried chile peppers in an airtight container in a cool, dry place away from sunlight for up to 4 months.

CHIPS AND CRACKERS

See Convenience and Processed Foods, page 85

CHOCOLATE

Typical serving size: Varies; in general, 1 oz (28 g)

HOW IT HARMS
- High in sugar and fat
- Migraines

WHAT IT HEALS
- High blood pressure
- Heart disease
- Mood disorders

Chocolate is made from beans found in the pods of the cocoa tree, an evergreen that originated in the river valleys of South America. Native Central and South Americans valued cocoa so highly that they used cocoa beans as currency.

Cocoa powder is low in calories and fat, but most chocolates contain refined sugar and milk. Cocoa does contain antioxidants but they can be destroyed in processing. Choosing dark chocolate is best—look for bars with at least 60% cocoa.

CHOCOLATE FACTS

- The returning crew of Columbus's fourth voyage in 1502 brought the first cocoa beans from the New World to Europe.
- The chocolate bar, first marketed around 1910, captured the public's imagination when it was issued to the U.S. armed forces as a "fighting food" during World War II.

Although chocolate's aphrodisiac qualities have been debunked, it is an endless temptation and a culinary source of pleasure in its myriad forms.

Health Benefits

Helps lower high blood pressure. Researchers at the University Hospital of Cologne, Germany, gave 44 people with borderline or mild hypertension 30 calories a day of dark or white chocolate. After about 4 months, the number of dark chocolate eaters diagnosed with hypertension dropped from 86% to 68%. Researchers attribute this to the antioxidant effects of dark chocolate.

May help lift mood. Dark chocolate stimulates the production of endorphins, chemicals in the brain that bring on feelings of pleasure. It also boosts levels of the brain chemical serotonin, which acts as an antidepressant.

Health Risks

High sugar and fat. Many commercial chocolates contain milk fat that is highly saturated and high amounts of sugar. It's better to opt for dark over milk chocolate.

Migraines. Chocolate is rich in PEA, which can trigger headaches in some people.

Canker sores. Chocolate can cause or exacerbate canker sores.

Eating Tips

- Stir a spoonful of cocoa powder into a pot of chili.
- Sprinkle cocoa nibs on frozen yogurt.
- Shave dark chocolate curls over orange wedges.

Buying Tips

- For the most nutritional benefit, choose dark over milk or white chocolate.

- If you can see the chocolate before purchasing, look for a smooth, shiny surface.
- Avoid chocolate that has whitish or gray coating, or blooming, which may indicate faulty production, warm storage conditions, or age.

Storing Tips

- Keep chocolate tightly sealed in a cool, dry place for up to 2 weeks.
- Do not place chocolate in the refrigerator; this causes blooming, or separation of cocoa butter from the chocolate.

Old School
Chocolate is a good source of caffeine.

New Wisdom
Commercial chocolate products contain no more than about 0.1% caffeine, less than a cup of decaffeinated coffee.

CLAMS

See Shellfish, page 187

COCONUTS

Typical serving size: 1 cup coconut meat, raw (80 g)

HOW THEY HARM
High cholesterol

WHAT THEY HEAL
Heart disease
Cravings
Digestion
Weight gain

The coconut, the seed of a palm tree that grows mostly in tropical coastal areas, yields numerous food and nonfood products. The oil is used in vegetable shortening, nondairy creamers, some spreads, and many commercial baked goods; it is also an ingredient in shampoos, moisturizing lotions, soaps, and various cosmetics. Creamy coconut meat is eaten raw or used to flavor ice cream, confectionery products, and baked goods. Canned coconut milk, made from the grated meat and water, is used in curries. Coconut water, the liquid found inside young coconuts before they mature, has become a popular alternative to sports drinks; unlike other coconut products, it's low in calories, contains no fat, and is rich in potassium.

Health Benefits

Helps reduce risk of heart disease. Coconut water contains potassium, an essential mineral that ensures proper function of all cells, tissues, and organs, and helps decrease health risks associated with high blood pressure. In populations where coconut oil is commonly eaten, heart disease is not common.

Satisfies cravings. A half cup of coconut meat has about 3.5 g of fiber, which can help you feel fuller longer.

Aids digestion. The fatty acids in coconut milk and coconuts are easily processed by the body.

Promotes weight loss. In a 2009 study, coconut oil was shown to decrease waist circumference and improve the ratio of "bad" LDL to "good" HDL cholesterol. Coconut oil definitely isn't a low-fat food (1 Tbsp contains 117 calories and 13.6 g of fat), but its "medium chain" fatty acids are touted for—remarkably—weight loss.

Researchers believe coconut oil may create diet-induced thermogenesis, increasing your body heat and burning calories.

Health Risk

Saturated fat. More than 90% of the fatty acids in coconuts are classified as saturated; remarkably, coconut oil is more highly saturated than the fat in butter or red meat. This high level of saturation results in an oil that resists turning rancid, making coconut oil ideal for commercial baking. However, it is a notable nutritional drawback, as saturated fats tend to raise blood cholesterol levels. In light of this, people who have elevated cholesterol levels or any other cardiovascular risk factors are typically advised to avoid products made with coconut oil.

Eating Tips

- Sprinkle toasted unsweetened coconut over pureed squash soup.
- Shave raw coconut over fruit salads.
- Add shredded fresh coconut to spring roll filling.

Buying Tips

- Choose a coconut with a firm shell.
- Check it carefully to make sure there are no dark or soft spots.

Storing Tips

- Store whole coconuts at room temperature for up to 1 month.
- Once opened, wrap the coconut tightly in plastic wrap and store in the refrigerator for up to 5 days.

COFFEE

Typical serving size: 1 small cup (6 oz or 180 mL)

HOW IT HARMS
High blood pressure
Cardiac arrhythmia
Infertility
Bone loss
Caffeine withdrawal
Sleep problems
Irritability and jittery feeling

WHAT IT HEALS
Diabetes
Memory and mental function
Colon cancer
Parkinson's disease
Liver disease
Skin cancer

A major source of caffeine, coffee is the substance millions of North Americans use to stay alert. In and of itself, coffee is a low-calorie drink: a 6-oz (180-mL) cup of sugar-free black coffee has only 4 calories. However, some specialty coffee drinks have more fat and calories than a rich dessert. A cup of whole milk mocha topped with whipped cream is on par with a hot fudge sundae.

Like many other foods and drinks, coffee is best consumed in moderation. Cut back on coffee and other caffeinated drinks such as black tea if your caffeine consumption is more than 450 mg per day, or about four cups of coffee.

Health Benefits

May decrease risk of diabetes. Coffee contains polyphenol antioxidants that may help even out blood sugar levels. A study from the Harvard School of Pub-lic Health found that among more than 88,000 women, drinking just one cup of coffee a day (caffeinated or decaffeinated) was associated with a 13% lower risk of developing type 2 diabetes compared with non–coffee drinkers; drinking two to three cups a day was associated with a 32% lower risk.

Improves memory and mental function. A study on aging revealed that coffee helped older people think more quickly, improve their memory, and have better reasoning. Another study reported that women over 80 with a history of coffee consumption had better performance results on tests of mental function. Lifetime coffee consumption has even been linked to a lower risk of Alzheimer's disease.

May help protect against colon cancer. Researchers at the National Cancer Institute found that those who drink four or more cups of coffee a day—regular or decaf—have a 15% lower risk of colon cancer versus those who do not drink coffee.

Protects against Parkinson's and liver disease. The antioxidant protection from coffee has been shown to help prevent a number of illnesses, including diseases of the liver and Parkinson's disease.

May protect against skin cancer. Studies from Brigham and Women's Hospital and Harvard Medical School show that coffee intake may help reduce the risk of basal cell carcinoma.

Old School
Decaffeinated coffee contains no caffeine.

New Wisdom
Decaffeinated coffee has up to 5 mg of caffeine in a 5-oz (150-mL) cup.

Health Risks

Although healthy in moderation, drinking more than 450 mg a day of caffeine can pose a number of health problems, such as:

Heart problems. Caffeine prompts a temporary rise in blood pressure; it can

CAFFEINE: The Buzz on Our Most Popular Stimulant

By far our most popular (and least harmful) addictive drug, caffeine is the stimulant in coffee, tea, chocolate, and soft drinks. It is also added to some painkillers, cold medications, weight loss supplements, and drugs used to promote mental alertness.

Within a few minutes after caffeine is ingested, it is absorbed from the small intestine into the bloodstream and carried to all the body's organs. It speeds the heart rate, stimulates the central nervous system, increases the flow of urine and the production of digestive acids, and relaxes smooth muscles, such as those that control the blood vessels and the airways.

HOW IT HARMS

May cause insomnia. Ingestion of caffeine late in the day can result in a sleepless night, and excessive intake can lead to caffeinism, a syndrome marked by insomnia, feelings of anxiety and irritability, a rapid heartbeat, tremors, and excessive urination. These symptoms abate with the gradual withdrawal of caffeine.

Irritates the stomach. Caffeine, especially in coffee, increases the production of stomach acid; ulcer patients or people with GERD should limit caffeine consumption.

Reduces calcium absorption. Caffeine reduces calcium absorption, which can increase the risk of osteoporosis, especially in older women.

Can cause withdrawal symptoms. Sudden withdrawal can often cause headaches, irritability, and other symptoms that vary in severity from one person to another.

Aggravates heart conditions. People with some types of heart-valve disease are very often advised to forgo caffeine altogether because it can provoke heart palpitations or other cardiac arrhythmias. Caffeine can also prompt a modest, temporary rise in blood pressure and speed up the heart rate.

HOW IT HEALS

Provides a boost of energy. For many people a cup of coffee helps them "get going" in the morning, and coffee or tea breaks during the day give them a boost when energy lags.

May reduce cancer risk. More than three cups a day lowers women's risk of developing the most common skin cancer by 20%. Caffeine also cuts men's risk of dying from prostate cancer.

Wards off depression. Consuming at least two cups daily reduces women's chances of becoming depressed by up to 20%.

Enhances athletic performance. The stimulant in caffeine enhances mental performance by increasing alertness and the ability to concentrate. Studies confirm that 250 mg of caffeine (about two cups of strong coffee) increases endurance, presumably because caffeine increases your ability to burn fat for fuel.

May help control diabetes. A study of 14,000 people in Finland found that women who drank three to four cups of coffee a day cut their risk of developing diabetes by 29%. For men, it was 27%. Researchers aren't sure why, but they suspect that the anti-oxidants in coffee help deliver insulin.

Knocks down migraines. Although caffeine may trigger migraines in some people, when a migraine strikes, a few cups of coffee do help relieve the pain. Caffeine is so effective at helping to shrink swollen blood vessels in the brain, it's one of the key ingredients in over-the-counter migraine medicines.

WHO SHOULD LIMIT CONSUMPTION

The following people should limit coffee consumption to one or two cups a day. Tea and other caffeinated beverages may be okay.

- Ulcer sufferers
- Heart patients
- Seniors with hypertension
- Women, especially those who are pregnant, nursing, or have osteoporosis
- Migraine sufferers

THE BOTTOM LINE

- Caffeine is a double-edged sword. It has both benefits and drawbacks. For example, it can trigger or help alleviate migraine headaches.
- For most people, caffeine is safe, but if you have ulcers, heart disease, hypertension, or osteoporosis, or are pregnant or breastfeeding, you will want to limit consumption.

AVERAGE CAFFEINE CONTENT

ITEM	MG	ITEM	MG	ITEM	MG
COFFEE (5 OZ/148 ML)		**SOFT DRINKS (12 OZ/355 ML)**		**CHOCOLATE**	
Decaffeinated	1–5	Coca-Cola (Cherry, Classic, or diet)	46	Baking chocolate (2 oz/60 g)	70
Espresso (2 oz/60 mL)	90–100	Diet Pepsi	36	Cold chocolate milk (8 oz/237 mL)	2–7
Drip method	100–180	Dr. Pepper (regular and diet)	40		
Instant	65–120			Hot cocoa (6 oz/180 mL)	5
TEA (5 OZ/148 ML)		Pepsi-Cola	38	Sweet or dark chocolate (2 oz/60 g)	40
Brewed, 1 min	9–33	RC Cola (regular and diet)	48		
Brewed, 5 min	20–50	Sunkist Orange	40		
Decaffeinated	1–5				
Iced tea (from mix)	22–36				

also provoke cardiac arrhythmias in susceptible people.

Infertility. A number of studies have found that consuming more than 300 mg a day of caffeine is associated with a delay in conception.

Bone loss. Coffee increases calcium excretion in the urine. To compensate for this loss, heavy coffee drinkers should consume extra calcium-rich foods.

Caffeine withdrawal. Heavy coffee drinkers who stop imbibing coffee abruptly may suffer headaches, irritability, and other withdrawal symptoms for a few days. Cut back gradually.

Increase in urine. Caffeine is a diuretic, which increases the rate of urination. This is a concern for men with prostate problems.

Sleep problems. Depending on the amount of coffee you drink, caffeine may make falling asleep difficult or may disturb sleep.

Irritability. Drinking large amounts of coffee may cause jittery nerves.

Eating Tips

- Freeze leftover brewed coffee in ice cube trays for iced coffee anytime.
- Replace water in chocolate cake recipes with coffee to boost the flavor.
- Add ½ cup brewed coffee to beef stew to intensify the taste.

Buying Tips

- Coffee will maintain flavor and aroma for 7 to 10 days after roasting. So if you're buying whole roasted beans, look for ones that have been roasted most recently.
- Avoid oily coffee beans; oiliness indicates age.

Storing Tips

- Keep coffee beans and ground coffee in airtight containers in a cool, dry place away from light, air, and moisture.

- Do not store coffee in the refrigerator or the freezer if you are using the coffee daily. The fluctuations in temperature cause changes to flavor.
- You can freeze whole beans for up to a month if you're not taking them out during the period.

COLD CUTS

See Smoked and Cured Meats, page 189

COLLARD GREENS

See Kale and Other Cooking Greens, page 120

CONDIMENTS

See also Mayonnaise, page 130; Mustard, page 136; Pickles, page 164; Sauces and Salad Dressings, page 184

Typical serving size: Usually 1 Tbsp

HOW THEY HARM
  Cancer
  High blood pressure
  Weight gain

WHAT THEY HEAL
  Variety

While condiments certainly add zest to food, they generally contribute little nutrition and sometimes add a lot of sugar, fat, or sodium. Popular condiments include mayonnaise, made from egg and oil;

mustard, made from the mustard seed; ketchup, usually based on tomatoes; salsas, mixtures of finely chopped vegetables or fruits, frequently tomato-based; chutneys, which can be sweet or spicy and made from a variety of ingredients, including mango, lemon, coriander, mint, or date; hummus, most commonly made from chickpeas but sometimes from other types of beans; and dips and spreads ranging from creamy ranch to trench onion to spinach-artichoke. Salsas, chutneys, mustards, and hummus tend to be the lowest in fat and calories, although commercially prepared versions may still contain excess sugar or fat, so read labels carefully or make your own.

Health Benefits

Adds variety with minimal calories. Condiments add flavor and flair to a meal and since they are usually used in small amounts, they usually don't add alot of extra calories.

Health Risks

Cancer risk. A diet that is high in salt, such as in many types of condiments, has been linked to an increased risk of stomach and esophageal cancers. This is thought to stem from their high levels of nitrates, which are converted to cancer-causing nitrosamines during digestion.

Blood pressure. The high salt content in most condiments may be harmful to people with high blood pressure or on a low-salt diet, as it may raise blood pressure.

Weight gain. Some dips, such as ranch and french onion, can be very dense in saturated fat, calories, and sodium. Use just a tablespoon or two, or substitute a lower-fat alternative.

Eating Tips

- Stir some salsa into potato salad.
- Mix ½ cup plain yogurt with 1 mashed ripe avocado, 1 diced tomato, and chili powder to taste. Serve as a dip with tortilla chips or a sauce for enchiladas or hamburgers.
- Blend pureed beets into hummus for a festive-colored dip.

Buying Tips

- When purchasing, examine the lid and container to confirm that the seal has not been broken.
- Bacteria rarely grow in these mixtures, but molds and yeasts may flourish on imperfectly sealed surfaces.

Storing Tips

- Store condiments in a cool, dry place and use within a year. After opening, refrigerate unused portions.

CONVENIENCE AND PROCESSED FOODS

Typical serving size: Varies; consult packaging for servings

HOW THEY HARM
Heart disease
High blood pressure
Weight gain
Diabetes

HOW THEY HEAL
Convenient healthy foods

Almost everyone consumes some convenience foods, which are foods that require little or no preparation—from ready-to-eat breakfast cereals and canned, dried, or frozen fruits and vegetables to prepack-

QUICK TIP:
Avoid double dipping

Double-dipping chips can be more serious than a *Seinfeld* gag. One study found an average of 1,000 bacteria were transferred by one person dipping in the same bowl three to six times. To avoid double dipping, serve small, one-dip chips and pick thick dips that are less likely to run back into the bowl.

aged heat-and-serve meals. Nutritionally, some of these products are much less healthy than home-cooked versions. For example, instant soups are loaded with artificial flavorings, emulsifiers, fillers, and preservatives. Also, most convenience foods usually contain more sugar, salt, and fat than homemade.

Some, however, such as frozen vegetables and fruit canned in natural juices, are minimally processed and can be healthy choices that help busy cooks put meals together quickly.

Health Benefits

Makes healthy foods convenient. Processing often strips vitamins and minerals from foods, but there are exceptions. Vegetables and many fruits harvested and quick-frozen at their peak often have more vitamins than those picked before maturity, shipped long distances, and then placed on shelves. Most enriched cereals and breads provide more nutrients than

those made just with the original grains. In addition, since processing helps foods last longer, it makes preparing healthy meals quicker and easier.

Health Risks

Heart disease risk. Many convenience foods, such as muffins and crackers, contain trans fats. Research shows that trans fats are twice as dangerous for your heart as saturated fat and cause an estimated 30,000 to 100,000 premature heart disease deaths each year. Limit or avoid foods containing vegetable shortening or other hydrogenated fats. Also, many convenience foods contain refined grains, such as white bread, rolls, sugary low-fiber cereal, and quick-microwave white rice. Choosing refined grains over whole grains can boost your heart attack risk by up to 30%. Opt for products that are labeled "whole grain."

Blood pressure. Three-quarters of the sodium in our diets isn't from the salt-shaker. It's hidden in processed foods, such as canned vegetables and soups. Excess salt increases blood volume and restricts arteries, which increases blood pressure. Scan the nutrition panel carefully, and keep the daily sodium intake to 1,500 mg, about the amount in ¾ tsp of salt.

Weight gain and diabetes. Research suggests that the high-fructose corn syrup in many processed foods encourages overeating and may upset the human metabolism, raising the risk for diabetes. It is found in many frozen foods, breads, spaghetti sauce, and ketchup. Read the ingredient lists carefully and avoid anything with the words "corn sweetener," "corn syrup," or "corn syrup solids" as well as "high-fructose corn syrup." Many processed foods also contain fat, which contributes to weight gain.

QUICK TIP:
Add a fresh side salad

When preparing a meal consisting of processed food, like frozen lasagna, add a fresh green side salad to provide a wide assortment of valuable nutrients.

Eating Tips

- Stir frozen baby peas into a grain pilaf a few minutes before serving.
- Try plain tomato puree seasoned with garlic and oregano as a sugar-free pasta or pizza sauce.
- Stir some cooked cannellini beans into tuna salad in vinaigrette.

Buying Tips

- Marketing claims such as "lite" and "reduced sodium" can be tricky to decipher, so it's best to read the nutritional panels on the packaging to find out the exact amounts of sugar, salt, and fat per serving.
- Check ingredient lists carefully for harmful components such as high-fructose corn syrup and any hydrogenated fats, and avoid products containing these ingredients.

Storing Tips

- Store according to package directions.
- Check "Use by" dates to consume before expiration date.

CORN

Typical serving size: 1 medium ear; ½ cup (82 g) of kernels

HOW IT HARMS
Pellagra

WHAT IT HEALS
Heart disease
Cancer
Macular degeneration

Corn is the most abundant grain crop; worldwide, it is exceeded only by wheat as a cereal grain. Sweet corn, which is harvested while still immature, is the type consumed as a vegetable. Indigenous to the Western Hemisphere, different varieties are used to make cereal, cornmeal, and tortillas. It can be cooked on the cob or with the soft kernels removed and served fresh, frozen, or canned for future use. And popcorn makes a light, low-calorie snack, so long as it isn't drowned in butter, salt, or other toppings. One medium ear of corn contains 77 calories, and one cup of kernels provides 13% of the Recommended Dietary Allowance (RDA) for folate. It is also a source or potassium, thiamine, and fiber.

Corn is high in starch and protein, but it lacks two essential amino acids—lysine and tryptophan; as a result, it is not a suitable protein substitute by itself. However, this problem is easily remedied by consuming black beans or other legumes along with corn.

Health Benefits

Reduces risk of heart disease and cancer. In addition to its antioxidant benefits, cooked sweet corn contains a phenolic compound called ferulic acid, which may inhibit cancer-causing substances.

CORN FACTS

- The average ear of corn has 800 kernels, arranged in 16 rows. There is one piece of silk for each kernel.
- Mexicans and South Americans don't develop pellagra, even though their diets are made up mostly of corn. Combining the corn with an alkaline substance releases the niacin in niacytin; thus, mixing cornmeal with lime water to make tortillas prevents pellagra.

Corn   **87**

Supports eye health. Corn is a good source of lutein, a powerful antioxidant that may help lower the risk of age-related macular degeneration, a common cause of blindness in older adults.

QUICK TIP:
Tap into antioxidants

Cooking sweet corn unleashes beneficial nutrients that can substantially reduce your risk of heart disease and cancer, according to a study in the *Journal of Agricultural and Food Chemistry*. The researchers found that the longer the corn was cooked, the higher the level of antioxidants.

Health Risk

An unbalanced diet rich in corn may lead to pellagra. Most of the niacin in corn is in the form of niacytin, which is not broken down in the human digestive tract. Although rare in North America, cases of pellagra, a deficiency of niacin or tryptophan, are common in countries where corn is a staple. Symptoms of the ailment include mental confusion or delusions, inflamed mucous membranes, skin flaking, and diarrhea. A high-protein diet and B vitamin supplements are used to treat the condition.

Eating Tips

- Mix corn kernels and chopped bell pepper with ground pork for a robust burger.
- Sprinkle corn on the cob with lemon-pepper seasoning.
- Add some cooked kernels to a smoothie.

Buying Tips

- Choose ears with moist, green husks, shiny silks, and tight rows of kernels. To check the condition of the kernels, don't strip the husk—it dries out the corn and leaves it susceptible to fungus (and annoys the grocer or farmer); instead, feel around the silk end to make sure the kernels are plump and healthy all the way to the tip.
- Look for ears that have some heft for their size. Good weight can mean the center hasn't been eaten away by bugs or fungus.
- Opt for frozen corn rather than canned, which can have a lot of excess sodium. If you must choose canned, look for "no salt added" brands.

Storing Tips

- Store corn with husks attached, and use as quickly as possible—within 1 to 2 days.

CRANBERRIES

See also Berries, page 55

Typical serving size: ½ cup, cooked or canned (1.7 oz or 48 g), or ¼ cup, dried (1.2 oz or 35 g)

HOW THEY HARM
    Blood sugar spikes
    Drug interaction

WHAT THEY HEAL
    Urinary tract infections
    Heart disease
    Cancer

Cranberries are a native North American plant. Although they still grow wild in boggy areas, most are cultivated in Massachusetts, Wisconsin, British Columbia, Oregon, Washington, and New Jersey.

Once served mostly as a condiment at Thanksgiving and Christmas, cranberries are now consumed throughout the year as juice, a dried snack fruit, and an ingredient in muffins and other baked goods.

Health Benefits

May prevent and treat urinary tract infections. Studies show that cranberries contain a natural antibiotic substance that makes the bladder walls inhospitable to the organisms responsible for urinary tract infections. This prevents the bacteria from forming colonies; instead, they are washed out of the body in the urine.

May help prevent heart disease. Cranberries are rich sources of anthocyanins, flavonols, and proanthocyanidins, plant chemicals that prevent LDL cholesterol from oxidizing, a process that makes it more likely to stick to artery walls. These chemicals also keep red blood cells from getting too sticky. An added bonus: They initiate a complex chemical reaction that helps blood vessels relax. Plus they decrease LDL cholesterol levels. Additionally, University of Scranton researchers reported that three glasses of cranberry juice a day can raise HDL levels up to 10%.

May help prevent cancer. Not only do cranberries contain fiber and vitamin C, both of which help prevent cancer, but they also have bioflavonoids, plant pigments that help counter the damage of free radicals. Studies have singled out anthocyanin as the bioflavonoid that has an anticancer effect.

Health Risks

Blood sugar. Most commercial cranberry juice contains large amounts of sugar or other sweeteners. To avoid spikes in blood sugar that can contribute to onset of diabetes, use a juicer to make your own cranberry juice or buy pure 100% cranberry juice. To reduce the amount of sugar needed, dilute 1 cup of concentrated juice with 2 to 3 cups of apple juice and then sweeten to taste.

Eating Tips

- Simmer cranberries, orange marmalade, and grated ginger to make chutney.
- Coat ½ cup fresh cranberries with flour and fold into pound cake batter.
- Toss dried cranberries into a spinach salad.

WARNING! FOOD-DRUG INTERACTION
Do not drink cranberry juice if you are on the medication warfarin. The interaction between the juice and the drug may lead to bleeding.

Buying Tips

- When buying fresh cranberries, look for firm, bright red fruit.
- Berries that are at their peak will bounce when dropped; those that don't are likely to be soft and past their prime.
- When buying dried cranberries, look for unsweetened ones, which have fewer calories and more fiber per serving.

Storing Tips

- Because cranberries are high in acidity, they will last a long time. Store them in their original plastic packaging or tightly wrapped in the refrigerator.
- Refrigerated cranberries can be kept up to 1 month; frozen cranberries, a year.

CUCUMBERS

Typical serving size: ½ cup (51 g)

WHAT THEY HEAL
Weight gain

Cucumbers belong to the same plant family as melons, pumpkins, and winter squash, but they are not as nutritious. One cup of sliced cucumber provides only about 6 mg of vitamin C and smaller amounts of folate and potassium. The skin

CUCUMBER FACTS
- Cucumbers originated in India.
- The largest cucumber in the world weighed in at 59 lb, or 26.7 kg.
- On a hot sunny day, the interior flesh of cucumbers is around 20 degrees cooler than the outside temperature.

contains some beta-carotene, but cucumbers are often peeled, especially if they've been sprayed with wax to retard spoilage.

In North America, cucumbers are used mostly as a salad ingredient or as pickles. Commercially, they are used mainly to make pickles and relishes; cucumber juice and extracts are found in cosmetic products.

Health Benefit

Helps you lose weight. Because cucumbers are approximately 95% water, they are very low in calories; a cup of slices contains fewer than 15 calories. Folk healers often recommend cucumbers as a natural diuretic, but any increased urination is probably because of their water content rather than an inherent substance.

Eating Tips

- Stir-fry sliced English cucumber and scallions, season with rice vinegar and chile paste.
- Toss chunks of pickling cucumbers with red onion, lemon juice, and sugar.
- Create a crostini spread of chopped shrimp, cucumber, avocado, and dill.

Buying Tips

- Look for firm cucumbers that have bright-colored skin. Avoid ones with soft spots.
- Cucumbers are available year-round, but summertime is when they look and taste the best.

Storing Tips

- Store cucumbers unpeeled and unwashed in a plastic bag in the refrigerator. Once they have been peeled or cut, consume within 1 to 2 days.

DATES FACTS

- Dates most likely originated from the area near the Persian Gulf.
- In ancient times, a bowl of dates was offered on the table at each meal as a sign of hospitality from the host to his guest. A date would often accompany a cup of unsweetened coffee or tea; the date would provide the sweetness for the drink.
- Dates contain only 30% moisture, making them the fruit with the lowest moisture content.

DATES

Typical serving size: 5 to 6 dates (about 1.4 oz or 40 g)

HOW THEY HARM
Weight gain
Tooth decay
Drug interaction

WHAT THEY HEAL
Cancer
Bone loss
Heart disease
High blood pressure

Prized for their sweet fruits, date palms are among the oldest cultivated trees; they have been grown in North Africa for at least 8,000 years. These desert trees are extraordinarily fruitful, producing up to 200 dates in a cluster.

Fresh dates are classified according to their moisture content, falling into three categories: soft, semisoft, and dry. Most varieties in North America are semisoft, which are marketed fresh, as well as dried after part of their moisture has been evaporated.

Health Benefits

Reduces risk of heart disease and bone loss. Dates contain high amounts of potassium, an important mineral. A serving of 12 dates provide 650 mg, more than a comparable amount of other high-potassium foods, such as bananas and oranges. Studies have shown that potassium can not only help prevent bone loss in women, it can also reduce the risk of cardiovascular disease, as well as supporting muscle function.

Helps prevent cancer. According to the U.S. Department of Agriculture (USDA), dates are higher in total polyphenols than any of the most commonly consumed fruits or vegetables. The reason? They grow in deserts, and the harsh environment causes polyphenols to provide protection from oxidative stress to the palm's fruit. The polyphenols, along with vitamin B6 and fiber, may help prevent certain types of cancer.

Lowers blood pressure. A serving of 12 dates provides 15% or more of the Recommended Dietary Allowance of iron and niacin. It also contains calcium, manganese, magnesium and zinc; these minerals all work together with potassium to help lower blood pressure.

Health Risks

Weight gain. With 60 to 70% of their weight coming from sugar, dates are one of the sweetest of all fruits. One-half cup (about 12 medium dates) contains about 275 calories—many more than most fruits.

Consume with nuts or other sources of protein to avoid spikes in blood sugar levels.

Tooth decay. Both dried and fresh dates are very sticky, and because of their high sugar content, they can lead to dental decay if bits are allowed to adhere to the teeth.

Eating Tips

- Mix chopped dates into lemon yogurt.
- Simmer a compote of dates and orange wedges in orange juice, then sprinkle on walnuts.
- Serve fresh dates with an herbed cream cheese dip.

Buying Tips

- Choose dates that are shiny, uniformly colored, and not broken.

Storing Tips

- Store dates at room temperature in an airtight container for several months.
- Refrigerated dates last up to 1 year.

DUCK

See Poultry, page 174

EDAMAME

See Soy, page 192

EGGPLANT FACTS

- Eggplants are technically berries, not vegetables.
- Research from a 1993 study published in The *New England Journal of Medicine* showed that eggplant has the highest level of nicotine of any vegetable. However, a person would have to eat between 20 to 40 lb of it to get the same amount available in a cigarette.

EGGPLANTS

Typical serving size: ½ cup, cooked (51 g)

HOW THEY HARM
Added calories

WHAT THEY HEAL
Weight gain

Eggplants are members of the nightshade family, which also includes tomatoes, potatoes, and peppers. Eggplants provide very little nutrition, but are among our most versatile vegetables and a component of many popular ethnic dishes, including Indian curries, Greek moussakas, Middle Eastern baba ghanoush, and French ratatouille. Eggplants are filling, yet low in calories—a cup has 40 calories, and it provides a fair amount of fiber.

Health Benefits

Helps with weight loss. Prepared with little fat, eggplants can be a part of a healthy diet and can help you lose weight. It also contains fiber, which helps you feel full.

Health Risk

Added calories. Eggplants' spongy texture soaks up fat. Deep-fried eggplants soak up four times as much fat as french-fried potatoes. For best results, prepare it in

**QUICK TIP:
Swap eggplant for meat**

Eggplants' texture and versatility make them a good meat substitute. Use it in place of meat in stews, casseroles, and sandwiches.

QUICK TIP: Get rid of the bitterness with salt

To eliminate the bitter flavor in some eggplants, sprinkle cubed or sliced eggplant with salt. Let it stand for half an hour, then drain it and blot it dry. The salt draws out the excess moisture and reduces bitterness.

a way that requires minimal fat, such as broiling, baking, roasting, or stewing. If sautéing, use a nonstick pan and little oil.

Eating Tips

- Grill sliced Japanese or Italian eggplant drizzled with olive oil and rosemary.
- Bake halved baby eggplant stuffed with seasoned ground lamb.
- Coat sticks in seasoned panko, lightly oil, and bake for eggplant fries.

Buying Tips

- Look for firm eggplants with thin skins; these have the mildest flavor.
- Larger eggplants are likely to be seedy, tough, and bitter.
- Choose eggplants that are heavy for their size, without cracks or discolored spots.
- Skin ranges in color from deep purple to light violet and white.

Storing Tips

- Keep eggplants in the crisper drawer in the refrigerator.
- They are best when used within 5 to 7 days.

EGGS

Typical serving size: 1 egg

HOW THEY HARM
- Allergies
- Bacterial infection

WHAT THEY HEAL
- Heart disease
- Cancer
- Cataracts and macular degeneration
- Nails and hair
- Memory

When you think about eggs and health, the first thing that comes to mind is their high cholesterol content. But it turns out that eggs have gotten a bad rap; they don't actually contribute to high blood cholesterol. In fact, eggs are an inexpensive source of many nutrients and come packaged in one of nature's best designs. They're portable, versatile, and delicious.

A large egg contains about 75 calories, 5 g of fat, 1.5 g of saturated fat and 190 mg of cholesterol. Studies show that for most healthy people, it is saturated fat (found in fatty meat, chicken skin, full-fat dairy products, and coconut and hydrogenated vegetable oils) and trans fats (found in processed and snack foods) that have the greatest effect on blood cholesterol levels. In general, the cholesterol we get from our food (and that includes eggs) is not an important factor in raising blood cholesterol.

There are, however, some people who are especially sensitive to cholesterol in foods. So if you have high cholesterol already, it's generally suggested that you eat no more than three egg yolks a week. Only the yolks contain cholesterol. People with diabetes should also limit consumption.

QUICK TIP: Take the freshness test

To check if an egg is fresh, place it in a bowl of cold water. Fresh eggs sink; stale eggs will float because air will have entered and increased the size of the air cell.

Another way to tell a fresh egg from an old one is by breaking the shell and tipping the contents onto a plate: A fresh egg has a high, rounded yolk and the white is thick and gel-like. In an older egg, the yolk will be flatter and the white will be thin and spread widely.

Health Benefits

Strengthens nails and hair. The zinc and iron in eggs can help your hair shine and your nails resist chipping.

Prevents macular degeneration. The carotenoids lutein and zeaxanthin in eggs are linked to a reduced risk of age-related macular degeneration, which is a leading cause of loss of vision in older adults.

Boosts brain health. Lecithin—a natural emulsifier found in eggs—is rich in choline, which helps to move cholesterol through the bloodstream, as well as aiding fat metabolism and repairing some types of neurological damage. Choline is thought to be important for early brain development and may improve memory later in life.

Reduces risk of heart disease, cancer. Egg yolks are one of the few foods that contain vitamin D, which helps reduce the risks of some cancers and heart disease, can boost the immune system, and fight diabetes. Vitamin A, meanwhile, supports eye health while the B vitamins (especially vitamin B12) are essential for proper nerve function and vitamin E maintains muscles and red blood cells. Eggs are also a complete protein; they contain all nine of the essential amino acids that cannot be made by the body.

Health Risks

Allergy trigger. Eggs are among the foods most likely to trigger allergic reactions. If you are allergic to eggs, be on the lookout for obvious sources, such as sauces and mayonnaise, pancakes and bakery items as well as ice cream. Check food labels, which must declare the presence of all ingredients derived from eggs. Avoid flu shots and other vaccines incubated in eggs.

Salmonella risk. One egg in 7,000 may be found to harbor salmonella bacteria. Although the risk of food poisoning is relatively low these days, it is best to avoid eating raw or partly cooked eggs. People at special risk include the frail elderly, young children, pregnant women, and anyone with lowered immunity due to illness. If you are at risk, avoid Caesar salads, fresh mayonnaise, egg-based sauces and dressings, mousses, and ice cream. To be certain that eggs have been cooked for long enough, boil them for at least 4 minutes, poach them for 5 minutes. or fry them for 3 minutes. Both the yolk and the white should be firm. Omelets and scrambled eggs should be cooked until firm and not runny.

Old School
Avoid eggs because of cholesterol content.

New Wisdom
Keep cholesterol in check by monitoring saturated fats.

Eating Tips

- Poach eggs in the microwave for 1 minute on medium heat.
- Scramble with a little bit of cream cheese and fresh herbs.

- Top a piece of sourdough toast with grilled tomatoes, mushrooms, greens, and a poached egg.

Buying Tips

- Open the carton and make sure no eggs are cracked or stuck to the bottom.
- Brown eggs and white are equally nutritious; they simply come from different breeds of chickens.
- Free-range eggs may have slightly higher levels of carotenoids but otherwise are the same.
- Look for omega-3 enhanced eggs, which are laid by hens fed a diet high in omega-3 fats. Their yolks contain omega-3s, the polyunsaturated fats that are associated with lower risk of heart disease and stroke. These eggs are low in saturated fat and are a better source of vitamin E than regular eggs.

Storing Tips

- Keep eggs in the main part of the refrigerator, which is cooler than the shelves on the inside of the door.
- Store the pointed end of the egg down, so that the yolk remains centered in the shell away from the air pocket at the larger end.
- Refrigerated eggs can be kept safely for up to 3 weeks.
- Eggs age more in one day at room temperature than in one week in the refrigerator.

FENNEL

Typical serving size: 1 cup (88 g)

HOW IT HARMS
- Skin irritation

WHAT IT HEALS
- High blood pressure
- Weight gain
- High cholesterol
- High blood sugar
- Cancer

Fennel is sometimes called "sweet anise" and has a delicate licorice flavor. A member of the parsley plant family, fennel contains fiber and is low in calories—a 1-cup serving has only 25 calories. Fennel is also a good source of potassium and contains some vitamin C, iron, calcium, and folate; the leaves contain beta-carotene and vitamin C.

All parts of the plant are edible, and it can be prepared in many ways: raw in salads, or braised or sautéed as a side dish. Stuffed bulbs are a flavorful vegetarian entrée, and the chopped leaves make a colorful, nutritious garnish for other vegetable dishes.

Health Benefits

Helps with weight loss. Because fennel is filling and low in calories, it is an ideal food for people trying to lose weight.

Regulates blood pressure. Fennel is a good source of potassium, an electrolyte that is responsible for balancing the body's sodium levels and helps regulate blood pressure.

Lowers blood sugar and cholesterol levels. Fiber plays an important role in reducing high blood cholesterol and blood glucose levels, which in turn reduces the risk of heart disease and diabetes. It also helps a person feel full and provides bowel regularity.

May prevent cancer. Studies show that the fiber in fennel may help reduce certain types of cancer, such as colon cancer.

Health Risk

Skin irritation. Some people may have an allergic reaction to the oils in fennel seeds.

Eating Tips

- Roast slices drizzled with olive oil and lemon juice.
- Shave some raw fennel bulbs into a red cabbage slaw.
- Top raw wedges cut from bulbs with pimiento cheese spread.

Buying Tips

- Look for firm bulbs and stalks and leaves that are bright green.
- Choose ones that do not have any blemishes.

Storing Tips

- Store fennel unwashed in a sealed plastic bag in the refrigerator crisper.
- Properly stored fennel lasts up to 5 days.

FENNEL FACTS

- Physicians through the ages have prescribed fennel and fennel seeds for a variety of ailments: to stimulate milk production in nursing mothers; prevent bad breath; and treat kidney stones, gout, and liver and lung disorders.
- Aromatic fennel seeds are one of our oldest spices. They also can be used to make a refreshing tea that is said to alleviate bloating, flatulence, and other intestinal problems.

QUICK TIP:
Use all the parts

The bulb is what's most commonly used in recipes, but fennel stalks can be added to flavor soups and stocks. And the leaves can be used as garnish.

Fennel   95

FIG FACTS

- Introduced to North America in about 1600, figs were planted throughout California by Spanish missionaries in the 1700s but were not cultivated commercially until the 20th century.
- Technically, figs are not fruit, but flower receptacles; the true fruits are the seeds that develop, along with the inconspicuous flowers, inside the fleshy bulb.

FIGS

Typical serving size: 2 small figs (2.8 oz or 80 g), or ¼ cup, dried (1.2 oz or 35 g)

HOW THEY HARM
   Diarrhea
   Tooth decay
   Canker sores

WHAT THEY HEAL
   Heart disease
   High cholesterol
   Cancer
   Diabetes
   Bone loss
   Constipation

Figs are a delicious summer fruit that can be perfectly paired with cheeses and tossed in salads. They are also very high in fiber, potassium, manganese, and a rare fruit source of calcium.

When fresh figs are not available, canned or dried figs provide taste as well as nutritional benefits. Although high in calories, dried figs are a highly nutritious snack food, contributing about 10% or more of the RDA for calcium, as well as 4 g of fiber, 300 mg of potassium, and reasonable amounts of vitamin B6. Consuming figs with a citrus fruit or another source of vitamin C will increase the absorption of their iron.

Health Benefits

May lower the risk of heart disease. Both fresh and dried figs are good sources of pectin, a soluble fiber that helps lower blood cholesterol and may reduce the risk of heart disease. Figs are also rich in potassium, which aids in normal electrical activity of the heart.

May help prevent diabetes. The fiber content in figs may help prevent type 2 diabetes, and lower insulin and blood sugar levels.

Helps reduce the risk of cancer. Some research suggests that high-fiber foods such as figs may help reduce the risk of certain cancers, such as colon, breast, and prostate.

Supports bone health. The calcium content of figs may help prevent bone loss associated with age.

Relieves constipation. Figs may also have a laxative effect, so they are especially beneficial to people who suffer from chronic constipation.

Health Risks

Diarrhea. Because of figs' laxative effect, overindulging in them may provoke diarrhea for some people.

Cavities. Especially in dried form (or put into fig bars), the high sugar content may cause the fruit to stick to teeth and contribute to tooth decay.

Canker sores. Steer clear of figs if you're prone to these painful sores.

Eating Tips

- Halve fresh fruit and top with whipped cream cheese and pistachios.
- Add chopped dried figs to trail mix.
- Glaze pork roast with no-sugar-added fig spread.

Buying Tips

- Figs do not ripen after picking, so choose the ripest ones possible.
- Look for unblemished figs with deep purple skin—they should be soft but not mushy. Avoid ones with signs of mold.
- For the sweetest figs, connoisseurs say to look for a drip of moisture at the hole on the bottom of the fruit. You can also take a whiff and pass on those with a scent of fermentation.

Storing Tips

- Store figs in the refrigerator and eat them within 2 days—they are prone to spoilage.

FISH THAT HARM, FISH THAT HEAL

Buying fish can be a little confusing. Some fish are higher in omega-3 fatty acids than others. And other fish may contain higher levels of mercury and other toxins. To sort out your next catch, follow these fishy guidelines:

Choose These Fish
The best sources of omega-3 fats are oily coldwater fish such as salmon, mackerel, trout, sardines, herring, and anchovies. You'll also find omega-3s in halibut, bluefish, ocean perch, bass, red snapper, and smelts.

Limit These Fish
Large bottom-feeders such as tuna, shark, king mackerel, tilefish, and swordfish are high in mercury.

FISH

Typical serving size: About the size of a deck of cards (3 oz or 85 g)

HOW IT HARMS
Pollutants
Parasites
Bacteria and viruses
Drug interaction

WHAT IT HEALS
Heart disease
Stroke
Inflammation
Decline in memory
Macular degeneration

Although a forkful of fish is a gold mine of concentrated nutrients, North Americans consume an average of only 15 lb (6.8 kg) a year, compared to the annual per capita intake of beef and chicken of close to 100 lb (45 kg).

Unlike red meat, which typically contains large amounts of saturated fat, fish and shellfish are rich in protein with fewer calories and less fat per serving. The fats in fish are particularly high in good-for-you poly-unsaturated fats, which remain liquid even when chilled. (If fish had a lot of saturated fat, it would congeal into a solid mass and prevent them from moving in their cold-water habitat.) And although some shellfish do contain cholesterol, they are low in saturated fats and are no more likely to increase blood cholesterol than skinless poultry.

Additionally, all fish are rich in nutrients, especially protein, niacin, vitamin B12, zinc, magnesium, and more. Oily fish are particularly rich in vitamins A and D. In addition, the bones in canned salmon and sardines are an excellent source of calcium.

Health Benefits

Decreases risk of heart disease. Eating fish three times a week has been associated with a significant decrease in the rate of heart disease, and the American Heart Association and the Canada Food Guide recommends eating a variety of fish at least twice a week. The omega-3 fatty acids in fish oils decrease the stickiness of blood platelets, making it less likely to form clots. They also reduce inflammation of the artery walls and lower triglyceride levels.

Reduces the risk of stroke. A study of more than 43,000 men, published in 2003, showed that men who ate about 3 to 5 oz (85 to 142 g) of fish one to three times a month were 43% less likely to have an ischemic stroke, the most common type of stroke, which is caused by blood clots.

Diminishes effects of other inflammatory diseases. The human body uses omega-3 fatty acids to manufacture prostaglandins (type of hormone), some of which can reduce inflammation and boost the immune system. The anti-inflammatory effects of omega-3 fats are being studied as a possible treatment for Crohn's disease and ulcerative colitis.

Helps prevent decline in memory. Some studies also suggest that people who eat fish regularly (especially varieties rich in omega-3s) are less likely to suffer from a decline in age-related thinking skills such as memory.

Protects against macular degeneration. A study from Australia involving more than 3,500 older adults found that eating fish just one to three times per month appeared to protect participants against age-related macular degeneration, the leading cause of blindness in older adults.

> **WARNING!**
> **FOOD-DRUG INTERACTION**
>
> Fish oil supplements may be advisable for some people, but check with your doctor first. Supplements may thin the blood, which could be a problem for people on warfarin, heparins or other blood-thinning medications. Look for a product with a combination of DHA and EPA (two omega-3 fatty acids). Avoid fish liver oil capsules, which are a concentrated source of vitamins A and D. These vitamins can be toxic when taken in large amounts for long periods.

Health Risks

Pollutants. Large bottom-feeders such as tuna, shark, king mackerel, and swordfish may accumulate heavy-metal contaminants—especially mercury—that are toxic to the human nervous system and can be dangerous for unborn babies. Because of this potential hazard, pregnant women should avoid these fish. In addition, check with your local health department to see if fish caught locally are safe for consuming.

Parasites. Some raw fish preparations, particularly sushi, can harbor parasites. Dutch "green" herring and Scandinavian gravlax (pickled salmon) are also raw, but the pickling process used in herring and properly made gravlax eliminates worms and eggs. To avoid risk of parasites, buy fish that has been commercially frozen beforehand, or inquire about it before ordering at restaurants.

Bacteria and viruses. Shellfish from waters polluted by human waste bring a threat of viral hepatitis as well as bacterial infections that can cause severe gastrointestinal upset. In addition, coastal waters are times affected by a species of algae (*Karenia brevis*), which causes "red tide." Shellfish from red tide areas should not be eaten because they concentrate a toxin produced by the algae.

Eating Tips

- Roll drained canned sardines in a flatbread wrap with veggies.
- Fold chunks of cooked salmon into a red-skinned potato salad in vinaigrette.
- Braise cod with green olives and onions.

Buying Tips

- Shop at a busy fish counter; lots of customers mean lots of turnover and fresher fish. Or look for markets that keep fish covered (both top and bottom) with ice.

- When buying whole, fresh fish, look for eyes that are bright, bulging, and clear. Avoid ones with gray or cloudy eyes. The inside of the gills should be bright red, not grayish or even pink. The skin should be bright and glossy with tight scales and firm flesh.
- When buying fish fillets, look for moist, resilient skin. Avoid ones with any discoloration or gaps in the flesh.
- Smell is also a good indicator of freshness; choose fish or fish fillets that have a fresh, briny odor, and skip those that have a distinctively fishy odor.
- Buy light canned tuna that is packed in water; oil-packed tuna is higher in calories, while albacore canned tuna tends to be higher in mercury.

Storing Tips

- Wrap fresh fish in plastic wrap and store it in the coldest part of the refrigerator. Use in 1 to 2 days.
- To freeze, wrap the fish tightly in plastic wrap and label it with the date of purchase, and the type of fish.
- For best results, use frozen fatty fish, such as salmon, catfish, or flounder, within 3 months; use frozen lean fish, such as red snapper and rock cod, within 6 months of the purchase date.

QUICK TIP: No-stick fish

Grilling is one of the healthiest ways to prepare fish, but it's a little trickier than flipping a steak. To keep fish from sticking to the grill, wrap each piece in a lettuce or cabbage leaf. Secure with a poultry trussing pin or a toothpick that has been well soaked in water. Brush the leaf with oil and place on an oiled grill. Discard the leaf before serving.

FLAX

See also Nuts and Seeds, page 138

Typical serving size: 1 to 2 Tbsp, ground (7 to 14 g)

HOW IT HARMS
Fetus and nursing infants
Bleeding problems

WHAT IT HEALS
Heart disease
High cholesterol
Symptoms of menopause
Cancer
Constipation

Flaxseed, traditionally known as linseed, is a tiny seed packed with a variety of components that can play an important role in your diet. It is inexpensive and has a pleasant nutty flavor. There is no recommended daily amount, but many studies use 1 to 2 Tbsp of ground flaxseed daily. Flax is available in different forms. Flaxseed oil provides the omega-3 fatty acids that flaxseed does, but not the fiber. Flaxmeal is ground flaxseed that can be incorporated in baking recipes and smoothies.

Health Benefits

Helps prevent heart disease. Flax is a rich source of alpha-linolenic acid (ALA), an omega-3 fatty acid, which aids circulation by reducing the stickiness of blood platelets. Flax also contains soluble fiber, which helps lower cholesterol levels and consequently lowers heart disease risk. Studies at the University of Toronto showed that 25 to 50 g of flax per day helped lower blood cholesterol significantly.

Relieves mild menopausal symptoms. Flax contains lignans, which convert in the body to compounds similar to estrogen. Thus, eating flaxseed may improve mild menopausal symptoms caused by reduced estrogen levels, but you have to take enough: Taking 40 g of flaxseed daily helps reduce hot flashes and night sweats in women with mild symptoms, but a lower dose of 25 g per day may not have an effect.

May help protect against certain types of cancer. A 2007 study showed that flaxseed reduced growth of breast cancer cells in mice. More human studies are still needed to find out if the effects hold true for humans.

May help relieve constipation. Flax is a great source of soluble and insoluble fiber, which promotes regular bowel movements.

50% of flaxseed oil is made of alpha-linolenic acid, a heart-healthy omega-3 fatty acid.

Health Risks

Fetus and nursing infants. Because flax acts like the hormone estrogen, it can pose a risk for fetuses and nursing infants, although more research is needed. To be safe, do not consume while pregnant or nursing.

Blood clotting. It may increase the risk of bleeding in people with bleeding disorders. Avoid flax if you have a bleeding disorder.

Eating Tips

- Stir flaxmeal into a smoothie.
- Add a splash of flaxseed oil in salad dressings.
- Sprinkle flaxmeal onto a yogurt fruit parfait.

WARNING!
FOOD-DRUG INTERACTION
Because the lignans in flax are phytoestrogens, it may affect drugs such as tamoxifen that are being used to treat hormone-sensitive conditions; while some research suggests that it helps these conditions, more studies are needed. Talk to your doctor before eating flax while on tamoxifen, or if you have hormone-sensitive ailments such as breast or uterine cancer, endometriosis, or fibroids.

Buying Tips

- Buy whole flax if you have a blender or food processor in which you can grind it yourself, because the lignans in flaxseed are much better absorbed by the body if the seeds are eaten ground or crushed. Or you can buy it already ground.
- In the grocery, you can find flaxseeds and flaxmeal on the same aisle as flour. Often, flaxseed oil is found in the pharmacy section.

Storing Tips

- Flaxseed oil should be kept in the fridge and has limited shelf life; check best-before date.
- Once ground, store what you don't use in an airtight, opaque container in the fridge or freezer.

FLOUR

See Grains, page 104

GARLIC

See also Herbs and Spices, page 110

Typical serving size: 3 cloves (9 g)

HOW IT HARMS
  Bleeding problems
  Skin irritation
  Toxic drug interaction

WHAT IT HEALS
  High blood pressure
  Atherosclerosis
  Heart disease
  Diabetes
  Colon and rectal cancers
  Infections
  Tick bites

Herbalists and folk healers have used garlic to treat myriad diseases for thousands of years. Ancient Egyptian healers prescribed it to build physical strength, the Greeks used it as a laxative, and the Chinese traditionally used it to lower blood pressure. In the Middle Ages, eating liberal quantities of garlic was credited with providing immunity from the plague.

Louis Pasteur, the great 19th-century French chemist, was the first to demonstrate garlic's antiseptic properties, information that was put to use during World Wars I and II by the British, German, and Russian armies. Since then, numerous studies have confirmed that garlic can be effective against bacteria, fungi, viruses, and parasites. Today, many proponents of herbal medicine prescribe garlic to help prevent colds, flu, and other infectious diseases.

Health Benefits

Much of the scientific research surrounding garlic focuses on its sulfur compounds. One of the most active of these compounds, allicin, is formed when garlic is cooked, cut, or chewed.

Can lower high blood pressure. Research shows that garlic can reduce blood pressure in people with high blood pressure by as much as 7 to 8%. In addition, garlic seems to reduce atherosclerosis, the hardening of arteries, a condition brought on by age.

Reduces risk of heart disease. Although research is mixed on whether garlic lowers cholesterol, it still may benefit the heart. Ajoene, created when allicin breaks down, may reduce the risk of heart attacks by preventing the formation of blood clots.

50% reduced risk of cancer is associated with eating a clove of garlic a day, according to a National Cancer Institute study of men in Shanghai.

May help reverse diabetes. A recent animal study found that high doses of raw garlic significantly reduced blood sugar levels, in effect helping to reverse diabetes. Since supplements show no blood sugar benefits, enjoy garlic the old-fashioned way.

Can fight certain types of cancers. Garlic may help reduce the risk of colon, stomach, and rectal cancers. Garlic contains sulfur compounds that may stimulate the immune system's natural defenses against cancer and may have the potential to reduce tumor growth. Studies suggest that garlic can reduce the incidence of stomach cancer by as much as a factor of 12. However, garlic supplements do not offer the same benefit.

Wards off infections. Garlic contains compounds that act as powerful natural antibacterial, antiviral, and antifungal agents. It has been shown to inhibit the fungi that cause athlete's foot, vaginal yeast infections, and many cases of ear infection. It may be as effective against certain fungi as antifungal medications.

May prevent tick bites. Research shows that people who eat high amounts of garlic over a 5-month period have fewer tick bites than those who do not eat garlic.

Health Risks

Bleeding problems. Garlic, especially raw garlic, might increase bleeding because it thins the blood in a manner similar to aspirin. Stop consuming garlic 2 weeks before any scheduled surgeries or dental work.

Stomach irritation. Garlic can irritate the gastrointestinal tract. Limit amounts if you suffer from stomach or digestion problems.

Toxic risk. While many people like to store chopped garlic in oil, these preparations are potentially dangerous if the garlic has not been thoroughly cleaned. Minute amounts of adhering soil can harbor spores of the *Clostridium botulinum* bacterium that can germinate and cause botulism, a deadly form of food poisoning. This can occur without any evidence of spoilage. Buy only commercial preparations that contain preservatives such as salt or acids.

WARNING!
FOOD-DRUG INTERACTION
Garlic may interfere with the effectiveness of saquinavir, a drug used to treat HIV infection.

Eating Tips

- Drop peeled cloves into any simmering vegetable that will be pureed for soup.
- Stir minced garlic into tuna or egg salad.
- In season, use fresh garlic and garlic slivers in any recipe calling for scallions.

Buying Tips

- Look for bulbs that are dry and have lots of papery sheath covering them.
- Buy bulbs that look and feel plump and firm.

Storing Tips

- Keep garlic in a cool, dry place with plenty of circulation and away from sunlight.
- Do not place in the refrigerator; it changes the texture and flavor.

GINGER

See also Herbs and Spices, page 110

Typical serving size: Varies

HOW IT HARMS
    Bleeding problems
    Miscarriage
    Inflamed membranes

WHAT IT HEALS
    Motion sickness and nausea
    Pain
    Cancer
    Flatulence

Ginger is an herb and a rhizome, an underground root. Fresh ginger can be found at any supermarket, but dried and powdered forms are readily available, as are ginger juices and teas. In addition to being used for medicinal purposes, it's widely employed as an important cooking spice, especially in Asian countries such as India and China.

The key active components of the ginger are thought to be volatile oils and phenol compounds, such as gingerols and shogaols.

Health Benefits

Helps relieve nausea and motion sickness. Various forms of ginger—nonalcoholic ginger ale or beer, pills, and candied gingerroot—have been used to counter the nausea and vomiting of motion sickness. One study found that ginger was as effective as the prescription medication scopolamine in preventing motion sickness, without causing the drowsiness that sometimes comes with the drug.

Relieves pain. Because ginger blocks the pro-inflammatory hormones, it may also be useful in helping people who suffer from the pain of migraines; studies suggest that taking ginger at the first sign of a migraine can help reduce symptoms. Furthermore, ginger may help those afflicted by arthritis. Studies have shown that people with osteoarthritis or rheumatoid arthritis experienced less pain and swelling when they took powdered ginger daily.

May help prevent certain types of cancer. A number of studies point to cancer-fighting properties of ginger. In one from the University of Michigan, ginger was found to cause ovarian cancer cells to die; in another, gingerroot supplements reduced inflammation in the colon, which suggested that ginger may have potential as a preventive measure. Tumors induced

QUICK TIP: Relieve a cold with ginger tea

Here's a comforting way to relieve the chills and congestion of a cold: Make ginger tea by simmering one or two slices of fresh gingerroot in water for 10 minutes; add a pinch of cinnamon for extra flavor.

in laboratory animals grow much more slowly if the animals are pretreated with beta-ionone, a compound found in ginger.

Can reduce flatulence. Ginger, like peppermint and chamomile, can be used to treat gas, along with its associated bloating and pain. Adding a slice or two of peeled raw ginger to bean dishes is said to reduce the flatulence these foods often cause.

Health Risks

Blood clotting. Do not eat ginger if you have bleeding disorders as it may inhibit clotting.

Low blood sugar. Ginger may lower blood sugar levels, so monitor your sugar carefully or talk to your doctor about changing medication.

Pregnancy. Some studies raise concerns of miscarriage and other problems with intake of ginger during pregnancy, such as risk of malformation. However, other studies state ginger is safe to use for morning sickness if taken for short periods (no longer than 4 days). Discuss benefits and drawbacks with your doctor.

Mouth and mucous membranes. In botanical medicine, ginger is considered a warming herb, one that causes the inside of the body to generate more heat, which can inflame the mouth and mucous membranes. Avoid it if you find consuming it uncomfortable.

Eating Tips

- Add a slice to tea as it brews.
- Sprinkle chopped candied ginger over morning oatmeal.
- Stir a heaping spoonful of grated ginger into mashed sweet potatoes.

Buying Tip

- When buying fresh ginger, look for plump roots without blemishes.

Storing Tips

- Store unpeeled ginger in a sealed plastic bag with all the air pressed out in the refrigerator.
- Make sure there is no moisture on the ginger before storing.
- Sealed in this manner, the ginger should last 2 weeks.
- Ginger can also be frozen for 1 to 2 months.

WARNING!
FOOD-DRUG INTERACTION
Consuming ginger while on medications that slow bleeding, such as warfarin, may cause bleeding and bruises. If you are on these medications, do not eat ginger.

GRAINS

See also Barley, page 47; Bran, page 57; Oats, page 140; Rice, page 181; Wheat and Wheat Germ, page 208

Typical serving size: Varies per grain

HOW THEY HARM
Heart disease (refined grains)
Diabetes (refined grains)
Celiac disease

WHAT IT HEALS
Diabetes (whole grains)
Heart disease (whole grains)
Cancer (whole grains)
Digestive health (whole grains)
Diverticular disease (whole grains)
Anemia (whole grain and enriched flours)
Healthy weight

Since prehistoric times, grain products have been one of the basic foodstuffs of agrarian societies. Almost every culture has a staple grain around which its cuisine is centered. North Americans still tend to make the greatest use of native wheat, which is ground into flour and made into bread and other baked goods. To a lesser extent, North Americans also consume corn, rice, oats, barley, millet, and other grains.

Whole grains are rich in complex carbohydrates, fiber, and many vitamins and minerals, such as the B vitamins, vitamin E, magnesium, iron, zinc, and an assortment of phytochemicals. They are also very low in fat, and when eaten in combination with beans, peas, and other legumes, grains are a good source of complete protein.

Refined grain has had the fibrous outer coating and the germ (which spoil more quickly than the rest of the plant) removed. Unfortunately, those are the very parts with all the phytonutrients. What's left is the starchy interior, which is essentially devoid of nutrients.

Grains are used to create a variety of flours that are ingredients in breads, pasta, pastries, and other baked goods. Flours can also be used as thickening agents or as additives. Look instead for unrefined whole grain flours. Whole grains include barley, brown rice, buckwheat, millet, oats, quinoa, spelt, and whole wheat. In addition, if you have a gluten sensitivity, you can find flours made from all sorts of grains, nuts, and other foods, including potato, almonds, rice, chickpeas, and buckwheat.

Health Benefits

Decrease the risk of diabetes and cardiovascular disease. The Iowa Women's Health Study followed almost 35,000 women age 55 to 69 and found that the more whole grains eaten, the lower the risk of dying from heart disease. Another study found that adults with the highest intake of whole grains were 35 percent less likely to develop type 2 diabetes than those with the lowest intake.

Reduce the risk of cancer. Although the data is mixed, a large, 5-year study among nearly 500,000 men and women showed that eating whole grains, but not dietary fiber, offers modest protection against colorectal cancer.

Support digestive health. Whole grains are rich in fiber, which keeps the stool soft and bulky. The fiber also helps prevent diverticular disease.

May aid in weight loss. The fiber from whole grain flours may help you feel fuller faster, which aids in weight loss. The B vitamins in whole grain flours also play a key role in metabolism. But because flours can be relatively high in calories, be sure to keep your portions in check.

Support normal iron levels. Whole-grain flours are also rich in folate and iron, which helps the body form red blood cells, making these flours helpful in warding off the effects of anemia.

In addition flour helps deliver concentrated dose of calories. Flour is a more concentrated source of calories than its source material because the moisture has been removed. For example, 1 lb (453 g) of potato flour contains 1,600 calories, compared with 350 in a pound of raw potatoes; a cup of cornmeal has about 400 calories, while a cup of cooked corn only has 100. In effect, eating breads and other foods made with flours are a good way to increase calorie intake for those who need to gain weight.

17% higher risk of diabetes is associated with eating five or more servings of white rice per week than eating white rice less than once a month.

Health Risks

Heart disease, diabetes, and other diseases. Refined grain products, including flours, breads, and breakfast cereals, are fortified with iron, thiamine, riboflavin, folate, and niacin. But despite these additions, they still have fewer vitamins, minerals, and dietary fiber than whole grain products. In the Iowa Women's Health Study, women in the highest quintile of refined-grain intake had a 16% greater risk of total mortality than did women in the lowest quintile.

Empty calories. Many nutrients are lost in flour milling and processing. When making white flour from wheat, the bran and germ from wheat are removed, reducing the fiber and the amounts of the 22 vitamins and minerals found in the whole grain. For best nutritional value, choose whole-grain flours or those that are enriched.

Malabsorption. Those suffering from celiac disease or gluten intolerance may not be able to absorb nutrients in certain grains. People who have celiac disease cannot consume grains such as wheat, bulgur, and rye. Gluten, the protein in these grains, produces changes in the lining of the small intestine, which results in malabsorption of nutrients.

Eating Tips

- Use cooked, cooled red quinoa in place of pasta in a salad.
- Create a risotto-style dish with barley and mushrooms.
- Add cooked wheat berries to minestrone soup.
- Use distinctive rye flour to make home-made pretzels or crackers.

Buying Tips

- When shopping for whole grain breads and cereals, read labels carefully. Look for the words "whole wheat flour" as the first in-gredient. A product simply labeled "wheat flour" is actually white flour.

Storing Tips

- Keep whole grains in airtight containers or bags with the air pressed out.
- Store in a cool, dry place, or in the refrig-erator for 2 to 3 months or the freezer for 6 to 8 months.

GRANOLA

Typical serving size: 1 cup (about 4.3 oz or 122 g)

HOW IT HARMS
Weight gain
High in calories, sugar, and fat

WHAT IT HEALS
High cholesterol
Heart disease
Free radical damage

This mixture of oats, nuts, dried fruit and honey became synonymous with the counterculture of the 1960s and '70s, but Dr. John Harvey Kellogg came up with the name *granola* in the late 1800s for his cold cereal made of flour, cornmeal, and oat-

meal. Packaged granola cereals and other products have gone mainstream since the sixties, but have also become less nutri-tious. Read ingredient lists carefully or make a healthful version at home.

Health Benefits

Reduces cholesterol. Most types of granola contain oats, a whole grain and a good source of soluble fiber. Oats have been shown to help lower cholesterol and cut the risk of heart disease. Nuts, another key component of granola, also contain fiber.

Promotes heart health. Look for gra-nola with walnuts, a great source of the omega-3 fatty acids that help promote heart health. Nuts contain monounsatu-rated fats, which can help reduce choles-terol and prevent heart disease.

Protects with antioxidants. Choose a granola with dried fruits such as blueber-ries and cranberries, which are packed with antioxidants that protect cells from damage caused by free radicals. Nuts, too, offer the powerful antioxidant vitamin E, which also contributes to heart health.

Health Risks

Unwanted calories. Many processed granola cereals and bars are loaded with sugar and are high in fat and calories. Check the labels for amount of calories and fats per serving size. Some types of processed granola cereals can contain as much as 18 g of sugar per serving, while some granola bars are the nutritional equivalent of candy bars.

Eating Tips

- Add a little granola topping for an appeal-ing crunch to yogurt or ice cream.
- Combine old-fashioned oats with nuts, seeds, a little brown sugar or honey, vanilla extract, and a bit of vegetable oil and toast

in the oven until crisp for healthy, home-made granola.

- Roll bananas in granola, then freeze them for a healthy snack.

Buying Tips

- Buy cereals that are high in fiber and lower in fat, sugar and calories. Look for those with 3 g or less of fat, 5 g or less of sugar, and less than 150 calories per ¼ cup serving.
- Look for oats, nuts, and dried fruits high on the ingredient list.
- Look for granola bars with 5 g of fiber and no more than 150 calories per bar.

Storing Tips

- Store in airtight containers on the pantry shelf for up to 2 months or freeze for long-term storage.

GRAPEFRUITS

Typical serving size: ½ a grapefruit, or ¾ cup (6 oz or 177 mL) juice

HOW THEY HARM
Allergies
Canker sores
Drug interaction

WHAT THEY HEAL
High cholesterol
Cancer
Weight gain
Inflammation

It's easy to understand why flavorful and nutritious grapefruits are no longer just a breakfast food. Half a grapefruit provides more than 45 percent of the adult Recommended Dietary Allowance (RDA) of vitamin C; it also has 175 mg potassium and 2 g fiber. The pink and red varieties are high in beta-carotene, which the body then converts to vitamin A. A cup of unsweetened grapefruit juice has 95 mg of vitamin C, more than 100 percent of the RDA, and most of the other nutrients found in the fresh fruit.

Health Benefits

Protects against high cholesterol. Grapefruits are especially high in pectin, a soluble fiber that helps lower blood cholesterol.

Reduces the risk of cancer. Grapefruit contains other substances that may prevent disease. Pink and red grapefruits, for example, are high in lycopene, an antioxidant that appears to lower the risk of prostate cancer. A 6-year Harvard study involving 48,000 doctors and other health professionals has linked 10 servings of lycopene-rich foods a week with a 50% reduction in prostate cancer. Other protective plant chemicals found in grapefruits include phenolic acid, which inhibits the formation of cancer-causing nitrosamines; limonoids, terpenes, and monoterpenes, which induce the production of enzymes that help prevent cancer; and bioflavonoids, which inhibit the action of hormones that promote tumor growth.

Helps weight loss. Grapefruits are a good food to include in a sensible weight-loss

> **WARNING! FOOD-DRUG INTERACTION**
> Grapefruit juice should not be consumed if you are taking certain medications. Compounds in the juice enhance the effects of the drug, possibly resulting in adverse effects. Drugs to watch out for include those for blood pressure, such as felodipine, anxiety, depression, and elevated lipids, among others. As a precaution, it is best to avoid taking any drug with grapefruit juice until you have asked your doctor or pharmacist if it is safe to do so.

diet. A serving contains less than 100 calories, and its high-fiber content satisfies hunger.

Eases pain associated with inflammatory disorders. Some people with rheumatoid arthritis, lupus, and other inflammatory disorders find that eating grapefruit daily seems to alleviate their symptoms. This may occur because plant chemicals block prostaglandins, some of which can cause inflammation.

> **Old School**
> Grapefruit will help you burn fat.
>
> **New Wisdom**
> No food can help you burn fat, but grapefruit can be a part of a healthy weight loss plan.

Health Risks

Allergic reaction. Those people who are allergic to other citrus fruits are likely to react to grapefruits. The sensitivity may be to the fruit itself or to an oil in the peel.

Canker sores. If you're prone to these painful mouth sores, steer clear of grapefruits and other citrus fruits.

Eating Tips

- Serve honey-coated red grapefruit sections with grilled salmon.
- Make a layered salad of thinly sliced grapefruit, red onion, and avocado.
- Cut into wedges and eat out-of-hand like an orange.

Buying Tips

- Look for grapefruit that are firm and heavy for their size.
- The skin should be bright and colorful, without bruises or wrinkles.

Storing Tips

- Grapefruit can be stored at room temperature for several days. To keep them longer, store them in the crisper drawer in the refrigerator.

GRAPES AND RAISINS

Typical serving size: ½ cup or about 15 grapes (1.6 oz or 46 g) ¼ cup raisins (1.2 oz or 35 g)

HOW THEY HARM
Asthma attacks in sulfur-sensitive people
Allergies in people with aspirin allergies

WHAT THEY HEAL
Heart disease
Cancer
Muscle cramps
Anemia

Low in calories, grapes are favored for their sweet, juicy flavor. One of the oldest and most abundant of the world's fruit crops, grapes are cultivated on six of the seven continents. Most of the 60 million metric tons grown worldwide annually are fermented to produce wine. Grapes are also made into jams and spreads, used in cooking, and eaten raw as a snack food.

The dried grapes, or raisins, provide the same antioxidant benefit as the juicy version. However, because of the dehydration, raisins have more calories. A serving of about 30 raisins is 78 calories.

Health Benefits

Wards off heart disease. Anthocyanins found in red and purple grapes have numerous health benefits including lowering heart disease. Grapes contain quercetin, a plant pigment that is thought to regulate the levels of blood cholesterol and also reduce the action of clot-forming platelets.

Some researchers theorize that it is quercetin that lowers the risk of heart attack among moderate wine drinkers.

May reduce the risk of cancer. The skin of red grapes contains resveratrol, a potent phytochemical that is linked to a reduction in cancer, as well as heart disease and stroke. Grapes also contain ellagic acid, thought to protect the lungs against environmental toxins. A cup of European table grapes provides about 20% of the RDA for vitamin C, about four times that found in the American varieties.

Prevents cramps and anemia. Most types provide fair amounts of potassium and iron, which help ward off muscle cramps and anemia.

Health Risks

Asthma attacks. Commercially grown grapes are usually sprayed with pesticides and are treated with sulfur dioxide to preserve their color and extend shelf life: They should always be washed before being eaten. People with asthma should either avoid grapes or look for those that have not been treated with sulfur to prevent an attack.

Allergic reaction. Grapes naturally contain salicylates, compounds similar to the major ingredient in aspirin. Salicylates have an anticlotting effect. People who are allergic to aspirin may react to grapes and grape products.

Eating Tips

- Stir halved white grapes into gazpacho.
- Top french toast with sliced red grapes and a drizzle of maple syrup.
- Toss some slices into a pasta salad.

Buying Tips

- Look for plump grapes without blemishes.
- Avoid grapes that are wrinkled, brownish, or white where the stem meets the fruit.

- Buy single-serving boxes of raisins to make sure you stick to small portions of this otherwise good-for-you food.

Storing Tips

- Store grapes unwashed in a ventilated plastic bag in the refrigerator for 1 week.
- Do not store at room temperature, which causes fermentation.

QUICK TIP: Go for color

To reap the full benefit of grapes, buy red or purple varieties: They seem to contain the highest concentration of healthful compounds.

GREEN BEANS

See Beans and Legumes, page 48; Peas and Pea Pods, page 160

GUAVAS

Typical serving size: 1 medium guava (3.17 oz or 90g)

HOW THEY HARM
Allergies

WHAT THEY HEAL
Cancer
Heart disease
Constipation
Weight gain

A small tropical fruit that originated in southern Mexico and Central America, the guava fruit can be round, ovoid, or pear-shaped. The thin skins vary in color from pale yellow to yellow green.

- European grapes encompass most of the varieties used for table food and wine.
- American grapes have skins that slip off easily and are used mostly to make jams, jellies, and juice.
- The European type is the more nutritious of the two, but neither ranks high on the nutritional scale when compared to other fruits.

Most varieties have meaty deep-pink flesh, although some are yellow, red, or white. Ripe guavas have a fragrant, musky aroma and a sweet flavor, with hints of pineapple or banana. You may also find canned guava, guava jelly, dried guava, and other guava products; most of these are processed with a lot of sugar, so stick to the fresh fruit.

Health Benefits

Offers cancer protection. By weight, guavas have almost twice as much vitamin C as an orange: One medium guava provides 165 mg, compared to only 75 mg in a fresh orange. Vitamin C, an important antioxidant, helps protect cells from free radical damage: People who consume high amounts of vitamin C through foods generally have lower rates of many types of cancer, such as lung, breast, and colon.

Reduces risk of heart disease. One guava contains 256 mg of potassium and 5 g of fiber, much of it in the form of pectin, a soluble fiber that lowers high blood cholesterol.

Relieves constipation. The fiber in guava also promotes good digestive function.

Aids weight loss. One whole guava has about 45 calories, making it a low-calorie treat any time of day. The fiber also helps you feel full. About half of the guava fruit is filled with small, hard seeds. Although in some varieties, such as Sweet White Indonesian, the seeds are fully edible, most people discard them. If the seeds are eaten, they contribute extra fiber and lesser amounts of the same nutrients found in the flesh.

Health Risks

Allergic reactions. Dried guavas are often treated with sulfites, which may provoke asthma attacks or allergic reactions in those who are sulfur sensitive.

Eating Tips

- Stir-fry sliced guava and red onion with chicken breast.
- Add peeled guava chunks to a fruit salad.
- Serve wedges with manchego cheese and wheat crackers.

Buying Tips

- Look for fresh guavas during the late fall and early winter.
- When selecting guavas, choose fruits that are firm but not hard.
- A guava is ripe when the skin yields slightly when pressed.

Storing Tip

- If the guava is not ripe enough, place it in a brown paper bag with a banana or an apple to hasten ripening.

HERBS AND SPICES

See also Garlic, page 101; Ginger, page 102

Typical serving size: Varies according to recipe

HOW THEY HARM
Allergies
Pesticides

WHAT THEY HEAL
Digestion
Bloating and flatulence
Inflammation
High blood pressure
Colds and flus
Cancer
Nausea and motion sickness
Fainting
Stomach cramps

For thousands of years, herbs and spices have been used as flavorings, medicines, perfumes, dyes, and even weapons of war. Today, they are prized for the variety they lend to the diet.

Both fresh and dried herbs provide a wide variety of active phytochemicals that promote health and protect against chronic diseases. Herbs are the leaf of the plant while spices, which are usually dried and powdered, are the fruits, flowerbuds, roots, or bark of plants. Rich in minerals and antioxidants, herbs and spices help prevent or treat a variety of ailments.

Health Benefits

Aids in digestion. Many spices, including allspice, coriander, ginger, nutmeg, and turmeric, have long been recognized as tonics for the tummy. Allspice, which gets its name from its aromatic blend of cinnamon, nutmeg, and clove notes, is believed to aid digestion. Cinnamon, an ancient spice obtained from the dried bark of two Asian evergreens, is a carminative, a chemical that relieves bloating and gas. Coriander seed is thought to be helpful in relieving stomach cramps and may have the ability to kill bacteria and fungus. Large amounts of freshly chopped coriander greens (also known as cilantro) are a good source of vitamin C. Ginger is a common motion sickness remedy, and sipping flat ginger ale may help to ease nausea. Nutmeg has antibacterial properties that may destroy the foodborne bacteria *E. coli*. Turmeric, beloved by Indian cooks, is used by Ayurvedic practitioners to treat digestive disorders. Fresh leaves or seeds of coriander may be chewed to ease indigestion.

Eases inflammation. Ginger is an anti-inflammatory that may help reduce arthritis symptoms. Turmeric is a natural antibiotic used to treat inflammation.

Lowers blood pressure. Chives, tiny onion relatives, contain sulfur compounds that may lower blood pressure if eaten in large amounts.

Fights colds. Basil, a mainstay in many dishes, is used in larger quantities as a tonic and cold remedy. Thyme can be brewed as tea as a gargle for a sore throat, or as syrup for a cough or congestion. When oregano is brewed as tea, it is said to aid digestion and alleviate congestion.

Protects against cancer. Caraway seeds, a popular flavoring for breads, cakes, cheese, and red cabbage, contain a chemical called limonene that may reduce cancer risk. Cumin, a hot spice that seasons chili, curries, and hummus, is being investigated for potential antioxidant and anticancer effects. Substances in ginger—gingerol, shogaol, and zingiberene—have antioxidant capabilities that may help prevent cancer as well as heart disease. Mustard seeds contain allyl isothiocyanates, which studies suggest inhibit the growth of cancer cells.

> **QUICK TIP: Grow your own**
>
> As long as you have a windowsill or even a sunny table or countertop, you can grow an herb garden. Fill a large pot with several different herbs, or plant them individually in smaller pots. Make sure that the pots allow for drainage and that the nearest window gets at least 6 hours of sunlight.

25% of all prescription medicines containcompounds from herbs and other plants.

Helps prevent fainting. Black pepper, which accounts for 25% of the world's spice trade, may help prevent fainting attacks. Sort of like sniffing salts, the odor

H

of black pepper provides a zing that helps some folks snap out of a swoon.

Health Risks

Allergic reactions. Some people may be allergic to individual spices. Curry, paprika, and fennel are among the common ones that cause reactions.

Pesticides. Recent routine USDA testing found more than 30 unapproved pesticides on cilantro. Cilantro was the first fresh herb to be tested in the 20-year-old program, so it's possible that other herbs are harboring potentially dangerous pesticides.

Eating Tips

- Stir-fry cauliflower with mustard seeds.
- Sprinkle nutmeg on sautéed mushrooms.
- Flavor baked butternut squash with cumin.
- Stir some turmeric into macaroni and cheese before baking.
- To make a simple pesto, blend fresh basil, garlic, pine nuts, and olive oil until smooth, then simmer on high heat for 3 minutes. Strain the mixture, then drizzle it over grilled chicken or vegetables.

Buying Tips

- Whenever possible, purchase whole spices to grind at home in a spice grinder or mortar and pestle. The taste will be fresher and more pungent.
- Buy fresh organic herbs to avoid pesticide exposure.
- Fresh herbs should be brightly, consistently colored with no brown spots.
- Fresh herbs should smell robust, not moldy.
- Grab a handful of fresh herbs—they should stand on their own, not be limp.
- Spices are sold bottled in supermarkets and, less expensively, in bulk food stores and ethnic markets.

Storing Tips

- The flavor of spices is lodged in their essential oils, which lose their pungency when exposed to light, heat, and air. Store spices in airtight containers in a dark, dry cupboard.
- Replace spices and dried herbs annually.
- Store fresh herbs in a refrigerator to make them last a few days longer.
- Bunched herbs, such as basil, can be stood in a glass of water and stored in the refrigerator to last longer.

HONEY

See also Sugar and Other Sweeteners, page 197

Typical serving size: 1 to 2 Tbsp or 15 to 30 mL

HOW IT HARMS
High in calories
Risk for babies
Allergies

WHAT IT HEALS
Low blood sugar
Coughs
High cholesterol

Despite all the claims that honey is a wonder food, its nutritional value is very limited: Honeys are mostly sugars—fructose and glucose, with some sucrose. Some types provide minute amounts of B complex and C vitamins. Honey (especially dark varieties) does contain some antioxidants, but fruits and vegetables are much better sources. Some new studies are looking into the antimicrobial and wound-healing properties of honey. The flavor of honey varies based on the type of flowers from which the bees collected their pollen.

Health Benefits

Raises blood glucose levels. The high sugar content of honey can boost low blood sugar levels for those with hypoglycemia. When hypoglycemia strikes, eat one tablespoon of honey and wait 15 minutes before eating anything else.

Helps quiet coughing. In one study, children age 2 and older with upper respiratory tract infections were given up to 2 tsp (10 mL) of honey at bedtime. The honey seemed to reduce nighttime coughing and improve sleep. Honey appeared to be as effective as the cough suppressant dextromethorphan in typical over-the-counter doses. However, note that it may be dangerous for a child under 1 year of age.

Helps lower "bad" cholesterol. A study from Dubai in the United Arab Emirates found total and low-density lipoprotein (LDL) cholesterol levels dropped while "good" high-density lipoprotein (HDL) levels rose in healthy people after they drank a solution containing honey, but not after they drank solutions containing glucose.

Health Risks

Weight gain. Volume for volume, honey is higher in calories than sugar: A tablespoon of honey contains 64 calories, compared to 46 in a tablespoon of sugar. This is partly because a tablespoon of honey weighs more than the same volume of sugar. Limit intake if on a weight loss plan.

Risk for babies. Spores of *Clostridium botulinum* have been found in about 10% of honeys sampled by the Centers for Disease Control and Prevention in the United States. Although not dangerous to adults and older children, infants should not be fed honey because *C. botulinum* can cause serious illness in the first year of life.

Allergic reactions. Honeybees collect and store pollen from one flower to another. For people who are allergic to certain types of plants, the honey containing the pollen from the plants may trigger life-threatening allergic reactions.

Eating Tips

- Whisk with lemon juice and cinnamon as a fresh fruit dip.
- Brush honey over apple slices, then dip into chopped peanuts.
- Microwave a mug of milk with a spoonful of honey and a dash of nutmeg.

Buying Tips

- Most commercial honeys are blends from different plant sources.
- Honey ranges from pale off-white to dark brown; in general, the deeper the color, the stronger the flavor.

Storing Tips

- Store honey in a cool, dry place. It will keep up to a year.
- Heat the bottle of honey in a pot of shallow water if it crystallizes.

QUICK TIP:
Substitute honey for sugar

Honey can be substituted for sugar at the ratio of one part honey for every 1¼ parts sugar: The liquid in the recipe may need to be decreased, however, to compensate for the water that is present in honey.

HONEYDEW

See Melons, page 131

HUMMUS

See Condiments, page 84

ICE CREAM

See also Milk and Dairy Products, page 133

Typical serving size: About 4 to 5 oz or 113 to 142 g

HOW IT HARMS
High in fat and sugar

WHAT IT HEALS
Bone loss
Lack of calories and protein during illness

The creamy frozen treat may not be a particularly nutritional food, but it is a popular and delicious staple of summer. The deliciousness is attributed to fat, which gives ice cream its smooth texture.

In general, it's best to treat ice cream as a "sometimes" food and opt for other frozen treats, such as sherbets, fruit ices, or frozen yogurt. However, manufacturers of fat-free and low-fat ices and frozen yogurts often compensate for the lack of fat by increasing the sugar—by up to twice the amount—and beating in less air. These products may contain less unhealthy saturated fat than ice cream, but may not necessarily be a better choice in terms of calories or sugar.

Health Benefits

Supports bone health. Ice cream has substantial amounts of calcium, an essential nutrient for strong bones and teeth.

QUICK TIP: Choose cones wisely

A sugar cone contains 60 calories, while a chocolate-dipped waffle cone has more than 200.

Delivers calories and protein. For those who are recovering from surgery or are ill, ice cream is an efficient way to provide calories and protein.

Health Risks

High in fat and sugar. Although ice cream has useful nutrients, it contains a large helping of saturated fats, which can lead to heart disease, certain cancers, obesity and other conditions. Limit servings, or opt for alternatives, such as fruit sorbets or low-fat frozen yogurt.

Eating Tips

- Melt vanilla ice cream to use as "instant" cream sauce.
- Make portioned sandwiches with chocolate graham cracker quarters and chocolate chip ice cream.
- Create a lower-calorie float with strawberry ice cream in a glass of lemon sparkling water.

Buying Tips

- Look for containers that do not have ice chips or an icy coating on them. This indicates that the ice cream has melted at some point and refrozen, which will diminish the taste and texture of ice cream.
- Slow-churned or double-churned types of light or reduced-fat ice cream contain up to half the fat and two-thirds the calories of the original. Low-fat ice cream can have no more than 3 fat grams per serving.
- The least expensive ice creams contain the minimum 10% fat and maximum air, while premium commercial brands have double the fat and half the air.

Storing Tips

- Store in the freezer and consume within 2 to 4 months of purchase date.

JAMS, JELLIES, AND OTHER SPREADS

Typical serving size: About 1 to 2 Tbsp or 15 to 30 mL

HOW THEY HARM
High in sugar

WHAT THEY HEAL
Low energy
Hypoglycemia

Jams were developed in ancient times as a means of preserving fruits that would otherwise quickly spoil. When preserved, fruits resist spoilage because they lack the water that microorganisms need in order to grow. Surface molds can be prevented by sealing homemade preserves with an airtight layer of paraffin.

Fruits boiled in sugar will gel via the interaction of fruit acids and pectin, a soluble fiber that is drawn out of the fruit cell walls by cooking. Apples, grapes, and most berries contain enough natural pectin; other fruits, such as apricots and peaches, need to have it added. Low-calorie, reduced-sugar jams are gelled with a special pectin that sets at lower acidity and with less sugar. These products are often sweetened with concentrated fruit juice and thickened with starches, which provides the flavor and texture of the jellied fruit without the calories of the full-sugar version.

The supermarket shelves are stocked with many other types of spreads, ranging from soft processed cheese products to chocolate-flavored nut butters and whipped marshmallow. It's best to consume these products in moderation.

Health Benefits

Provides a quick boost of energy. Jams and jellies and other spreads that are high in simple sugars can provide a quick source of energy because the sugars are digested by the body quickly. They may be useful to people prone to hypoglycemia.

Health Risks

High in sugar. There's no comparison between jams and fresh fruits, because most of the vitamin C and other nutrients in fruits are destroyed by intense cooking. While fruit preserves contain substantial amounts of pectin—a soluble fiber that helps control blood cholesterol levels—this benefit is offset by their high sugar content.

Little nutritional value. Most of the cheese-based products provide small amounts of vitamin A and calcium but are high in sodium, fat, and cholesterol. Chocolate and marshmallow spreads offer little more than calories and sugar.

Eating Tips

- Brush grilled chicken with jalapeño pepper jelly.
- Dab some all-fruit cherry spread on a plain sugar cookie.
- Swirl all-fruit apricot spread into plain Greek yogurt.

- Dip sliced Asian pear into sunflower seed spread.

Buying Tips

- When buying jams and jellies, look for sugar-free options or all-fruit versions.
- When buying nut butters, look for no added oils, salt, sugar, or preservatives or any other additives.
- Fructose and corn syrup are often added to spreads and jellies; avoid those.

Storing Tips

- Once opened, store jams, jellies, and dairy-based spreads in the refrigerator for about a month.
- Low- or no-sugar versions will keep in a refrigerator for about 3 weeks.

JICAMA

Typical serving size: ½ cup (57 g)

HOW IT HARMS
    Allergies

WHAT IT HEALS
    Heart disease
    Stroke
    Weight gain
    High blood sugar
    Constipation
    Skin health
    Cataracts
    Osteoporosis

Grown in Mexico and Central America, the jicama (pronounced HICK-uh-muh) is a root tuber, similar to a potato. In fact, it's often called a Mexican potato or a "yam bean," though it looks more like a turnip. It's crunchy and mildly sweet, and is often eaten raw with dip, in a salad, or stir-fried. A common Mexican street food, jicama is served sliced with a squeeze of lime and a sprinkle of chili powder. Jicama is becoming more common in supermarkets, and you can spot it year-round, though its peak season is from late fall through spring.

Health Benefits

Helps reduce heart disease risk. Jicamas are loaded with fiber, which can help lower cholesterol, cut the risk of heart disease, and help control blood sugar levels. The potassium in jicama helps lower blood pressure, which can help prevent strokes and heart disease.

Manages weight. The fiber in jicamas helps you feel full longer, helps maintain regular bowel function, and may lower the risk of some cancers.

Boosts skin health. A cup of jicama contains 40% of your daily requirement of vitamin C, a powerful antioxidant, which can help prevent cataracts, improve skin health, and help prevent chronic diseases.

Strengthens bones. Potassium also helps improve calcium absorption, which can help guard against osteoporosis.

Health Risk

Allergic reaction. Jicama is a legume that can cause an allergic reaction in some people.

Eating Tips

- Serve it with hummus or your favorite dip as an addition to relish trays.
- Cubed jicama adds a pleasing crunch to tropical fruit salads.
- Toss sliced jicama into a stir-fry instead of water chestnuts.

Buying Tips

- When it comes to jicama, bigger isn't necessarily better. While they can grow very large, choose 1- to 2-lb (0.4 to 0.9 g) jicamas, as larger ones may prove less sweet.
- Look for jicamas with firm, smooth, slightly shiny skin.
- Be sure to peel jicama and remove the fibrous white area just beneath the skin.

Storing Tips

- Store uncut jicamas for 2 to 3 weeks in a plastic bag in the refrigerator.
- Once cut, wrap in plastic and stash in the fridge for up to a week.

JUICES

Typical serving size: ½ cup (4 oz or 118 mL)

HOW THEY HARM
Weight gain
High blood pressure
Delayed development (in infants)

WHAT THEY HEAL
Lack of nutrients
High cholesterol
Hypoglycemia

Most guidelines call for 5 to 10 servings of fruits and vegetables each day—more than what most North Americans now consume. One of the easiest ways to get more servings of fruits and vegetables is by drinking juice. About 4 oz (118 mL) of juice is equal to one serving of fruit or vegetable.

Health Benefits

Delivers necessary nutrients quickly. Fruit and vegetable juices provide fluids—keeping your body hydrated—as well as most of the nutrients in the fruits and vegetables they were made from.

Helps reduce high cholesterol. Drink two glasses of orange juice every morning, but make sure it's a brand spiked with the same kind of cholesterol-lowering plant sterols found in margarine spreads like Benecol. Researchers found that those who drank sterol-fortified juice lowered bad cholesterol levels by 7%.

Levels blood glucose. For those who suffer from bouts of hypoglycemia, a small glass of fruit juices may be a good way to stabilize blood glucose levels.

Health Risks

Weight gain. Despite the nutrition in every glass, the calories from the natural fruit sugar and added sugar can add up quickly and lead to weight gain.

Blood pressure. Although vegetable juices tend to have less sugar than fruit juices, canned or bottled vegetable juice often has a higher salt content, which can affect blood pressure. Check labels carefully, and select a low-sodium or no-salt-added juice.

Health of infants. Fruit juice should not be given to infants under 6 months, according to a report from the American Academy of Pediatrics. Drinking lots of juice can lead to diarrhea, poor weight gain or delayed development (because it doesn't have the nutrients that breast milk or formula have), and tooth decay. Older children should be encouraged to eat whole fruits, which have more fiber, instead of juices.

Eating Tips

- Freeze leftover juice from canned fruit in ice cube trays to pop into smoothies.
- Deglaze a pork chop skillet with apple juice.
- Stir some orange juice into chili close to the end of the cooking.

TRAVEL:
Eating Healthy on the Road

While travel is good for the soul, it may be difficult to resist fast food or find fresh food at the airport or rest stops. Follow these tips to maintain your healthy eating habits on the go:

AT THE AIRPORT

Once you get through airport security, there is no going back, which means you are essentially trapped in a fast food prison. But luckily, there are healthy choices at many airports. Here's what you can do:

Go high end. Recently, airports have added higher-end restaurants, which tend to offer more salads and sandwiches light on the dressing and sauce. Or check out the pizza places—but stick to a thin-crust vegetarian slice. Many pizza joints also offer some simple salads or soups that are healthier options. Check the websites of airport restaurants so you know what food choices are available.

Skip beer. Don't be lured into grabbing a pint at the airport bar while you wait. Not only does alcohol add calories, but it's also dehydrating.

Be a kid again. At chain restaurants, you can trim calories and feel lighter for your travels by ordering from the children's menus.

ON THE PLANE

Planning ahead is key to avoiding jet lag and being hungry.

Preview airline menus. Some airlines have picked up on the healthy trend and are offering better alternatives, from snack boxes with pita chips to meals of turkey sandwiches. You can find meal options on airlines websites. Some airlines also provide special diet meals if you can request them when you book your flight.

Carry on more than luggage. If nothing is appealing or healthy, then plan on bringing some healthier options. Some good portable choices include yogurt cups with fruit and granola, wedge salads, and chicken wraps.

Chug lots of water. Stay hydrated with bottled water. Avoid alcohol and anything caffeinated during your flight. Both can dehydrate your body, mess up your internal clock, and exaggerate jet lag symptoms.

ON ROAD TRIPS

If you are driving to your destination, you may have no choice but to hit a fast-food restaurant at a rest stop. To sort out your best options, see the Fast Food feature on page 27. Of course, the smartest thing you could do is pack your own food in the car. Here are some great healthy portable options for your road trip:

Chew tropical dried fruit. The sweetness and chewiness satisfy you.

Pack some soy nuts and wasabi peas. Dried soy nuts are an excellent alternative to other high-calorie nuts, without giving up that satisfying crunch. Craving something sweet, salty *and* spicy? Reach for a package of wasabi peas for surprising flavor on the go.

Pack a couple of frozen bottles of water. It will keep any food chilled for a couple of hours, then provide a cold, calorie-free drink.

Shop smart at the mini-mart. If provisions run low, look for fresh fruit, low-fat yogurt, whole grain cereal, or string cheese at a gas station mini-mart.

IN FOREIGN COUNTRIES

Trying new foods should be part of any trip, especially if you're exploring new parts of the world. Here's how to taste a little adventure but not upset your stomach:

Opt for hot. The Centers for Disease Control and Prevention estimates there are 50,000 cases of traveler's diarrhea each day. When food is cooked—ideally right in front of you—you will know if it's hot enough to kill some of the illness-causing bacteria. Choose foods that are freshly cooked and served at very hot temperatures— just don't burn your tongue.

Sip from bottles. Avoid nonpotable water, which hasn't been purified to drinking water standards. Also avoid ice cubes made from this water. Instead, go for beverages in bottles.

Overcome language barriers. You don't need a dictionary-size vocabulary to order healthier food in foreign countries. But you should learn a few key words of the language so that if you're pressed, you can order for yourself. For example, if you can express the words chicken and grilled, you should be served something you can eat. And if you have to, eyeball what other people in a restaurant are eating, and point.

THE BOTTOM LINE

- Airlines and airports have stepped up some of their offerings, so seek out healthier meal options like salads, soups, and sandwiches. Stay hydrated by drinking lots of water and avoiding alcohol and caffeine.
- Pack healthy snacks like dried fruit, soy nuts, and wasabi peas when you travel.
- When abroad, stick to cooked food and bottled beverages to avoid traveler's diarrhea.

Buying Tips

- When you buy juices, choose unsweetened varieties that do not have added sugars.
- Avoid juices labeled "fruit drink" or "fruit punch." These drinks are not generally nutritionally equivalent to fruit juice. They tend to be higher in sugar (usually corn syrup) and other additives with less actual fruit juice.
- Look for juices that are fortified with sterols.

Storing Tips

- Store fruit and vegetable juices in the refrigerator, and consume them as quickly as possible.
- Juices can also be stored in the freezer and thawed before drinking.

QUICK TIP: Don't throw out tough leaves

If the leaves of cooking greens are tough and fibrous, remove the stem, roll the leaves up like a cigar and sliver them for quick cooking.

the types of kale that form leafy red, yellow, and purple heads are used more often for decorative purposes (both in the garden and on the table) than as a food, all varieties are edible and highly nutritious.

Kale and other dark leafy greens, such as collard greens, mustard greens, and Swiss chard, are excellent sources of vitamin C and beta-carotene, which the human body converts to vitamin A: In fact, a 1-cup serving of cooked kale contains almost a day's supply of vitamin A and well over 50 percent of the daily requirement of vitamin C. Other nutrients found in a cup of kale include 20 mcg (micrograms) of folate, 100 mg of calcium, 1 mg of iron, and 310 mg of potassium. It also provides more than 1 g of fiber and has only 50 calories.

Health Benefits

Prevents heart disease. Kale and other cooking greens are rich in vitamin C that may help lower the levels of "bad" LDL cholesterol, which in turn can reduce the risk of heart disease. The high amounts of potassium can help lower high blood pressure, which also aids in heart health.

Fights cancer. Bioflavonoids, carotenoids, and other cancer-fighting compounds are abundant in cooking greens. They also contain indoles, compounds that can lessen the cancer-causing potential of estrogen and induce production of enzymes that protect against disease.

Promotes bone health. Most dark leafy greens are rich in calcium and magne-

KALE AND OTHER COOKING GREENS

Typical serving size: ½ cup, cooked (65 g)

HOW THEY HARM
Bloating and flatulence

WHAT THEY HEAL
Heart disease
Cancer
Eye conditions
Bone healthy

A member of the cabbage family, kale looks like collards but with curly leaves. It is a hardy autumn vegetable that grows best in a cool climate, and exposure to frost actually improves its flavor. Although sium, which are important minerals for strong bones.

Prevents macular degeneration. Kale and other dark green leafy vegetables contain lutein, which helps protect your vision against macular degeneration and cataracts.

Aids in weight loss. Kale is low in calories but is very filling, making it an ideal, highly nutritious food for anyone who is weight conscious.

Health Risks

Causes bloating and flatulence. Like other vegetables in the cabbage family, kale and similar cooking greens may cause gas.

Eating Tips

- Add some raw slivered curly kale to salads.
- Braise chopped mustard greens with plenty of chopped garlic.
- Layer chopped cooked chard in lasagna.

Buying Tips

- Look for leaves that have crisp edges and a deep color.
- Avoid wilted, yellow leaves.

Storing Tips

- Place in the refrigerator rinsed and slightly damp in a paper towel and in a plastic bag.
- Use within 3 to 5 days.

KETCHUP

See Condiments, page 84

KIWIS

Typical serving size: 1 large kiwi (3.2 oz or 90 g)

WHAT THEY HEAL
High blood pressure
High cholesterol
Cancer
Macular degeneration
Weight gain

On the outside, a kiwi looks like a fuzzy brown egg; on the inside its bright green flesh is sprinkled with a ring of small, black seeds. It has a distinctive, somewhat tart flavor with overtones of berries.

Kiwis were once considered an exotic fruit, but they have become increasingly plentiful. Kiwis are harvested while green and can be kept in cold storage for 6 to 10 months, making them available for most of the year. Ripe kiwis are eaten raw; even the skin is edible if it is de-fuzzed.

Health Benefits

Reduces high blood pressure and cholesterol. Kiwis provide potassium, which helps lower blood pressure, and pectin, a soluble fiber that helps control blood cholesterol levels.

Protects against cancer. A large kiwi provides about 80 mg of vitamin C and contains vitamin E, both strong antioxidants. The fruit is also endowed with other phytochemicals, which help fight free radical damage that can eventually lead to cancer.

Prevents macular degeneration. Kiwis contain both lutein and zeaxanthin, antioxidants associated with eye health.

Encourages weight loss. A large kiwi has about 55 calories and is packed with filling fiber.

Eating Tips

- Stir chunks of kiwi into a ceviche.
- Top a toasted whole wheat bagel with cream cheese and kiwi slices.
- Toss chunks with red leaf lettuce in poppy seed dressing.

Buying Tips

- Look for firm, unblemished fruit in any size.
- The flesh of ripe kiwis should give in to slight pressure.

QUICK TIP:
Tenderize meat with kiwis

Kiwi contains an enzyme (actinidin) that is a natural meat tenderizer. The fruit can be used as a marinade to tenderize tough meats. Rubbing the meat with a cut kiwi and waiting 30 to 60 minutes before cooking will tenderize the meat without imparting any flavor from the fruit.

Storing Tips

- Store kiwi at room temperature. They will last about 7 days.
- For longer storage, keep them in the refrigerator; they will last up to 4 weeks.

Health Benefits

Protects against certain types of cancer. Kohlrabi is high in bioflavonoids, plant pigments that work with vitamin C and other antioxidants to prevent the cell damage that promotes cancer. Kohlrabi is also high in indoles, chemicals that reduce the effects of estrogen, and thus may reduce the risk of breast cancer. Isothiocyanates, another group of compounds in kohlrabi, promote the action of enzymes that may protect against colon cancer.

    Supports heart health. The vitamin C in kohlrabi may help prevent the oxidative damage that leads to cardiovascular disease and the potassium is a crucial mineral for heart function.

Health Risks

May cause gas. People who get gas after eating other cruciferous vegetables may have the same response to kohlrabi.

Eating Tips

- Roast oiled peeled chunks of the bulb until browned.
- Mash cooked chunks with a dab of butter.
- Make latkes from grated kohlrabi instead of potatoes.
- Chop leaves and use them in salads.

KOHLRABI

Typical serving size: 1 cup, raw (135 g)

HOW IT HARMS
Bloating and flatulence

WHAT IT HEALS
Cancer

Heart disease

Similar to both cabbages and turnips, kohlrabi comes from the same cruciferous plant family. It is a good source of vitamin C: A 1-to 2-cup serving of raw kohlrabi provides almost 100% of the RDA for adult women. It has about 450 mg of potassium, some fiber, and only 40 calories. The green leaves are edible and contain iron.

Buying Tip

- Look for small to medium-size kohlrabi that have a diameter of less than 3 in; the larger kohlrabis can be tough and woody.

Storing Tip

- Remove leaf stems and store in the refrigerator in a sealed plastic bag. It can be kept this way for several weeks.

LAMB

Typical serving size: 3 oz or 85 g

HOW IT HARMS
Weight gain

WHAT IT HEALS
Muscles
Anemia
Immunity

Lamb is a high-quality, nutritious meat, rich in easily absorbed minerals and B vitamins, particularly B12. Lamb comes from sheep less than 1 year of age. Mutton comes from sheep older than 1 year, and it has a more robust taste. Lamb comes in a variety of cuts including legs, shoulder, roast, chops, ground, foreshank, and spareribs.

Among red meats, lamb stands out for its high nutritional value. In addition to protein, lamb contains B vitamins, as well as iron, phosphorus, calcium, and potassium. The meat is tender, because it is the relatively little-used muscle of young animals. Furthermore, because it is easily digestible and almost never associated with food allergies, it is a good protein food for people of all ages.

Lamb is the primary meat in parts of Europe, North Africa, the Middle East, and India, but it has never enjoyed the same popularity in North America.

Health Benefits

Helps build muscles. Lamb is a rich source of muscle-building protein. A 3-oz (85-g) portion of roasted lean lamb contains about 22 g of protein.

Avoid iron deficiency. The iron in lamb is easily absorbed by the body, so it helps prevent anemia. Iron is also necessary for energy.

Boosts immunity. Lamb is a good source of zinc, which is important for a healthy immune system.

Health Risks

Weight gain. Some cuts of lamb are high in fat. However, it is not marbled like beef with lines of fat. Instead, lamb is marbled with flecks of fat throughout. Much of its fat is on the outside of the meat, which can be trimmed before cooking.

Eating Tips

- Use thin slices of lamb in a stir-fry with bell peppers and onion.
- Make meatballs with ground lamb, minced garlic, parsley, and ground almonds.
- Serve lamb stew on a bed of braised kale.

Buying Tip

- Look for meat that is firm with red coloring and some white marbling (white flecks of fat within the meat muscle).

Storing Tips

- Keep lamb refrigerated at 40°F (4°C) or below.
- Use ground lamb or stew meat within 1 to 2 days; lamb chops, roasts, and steaks within 3 to 5 days.
- To freeze, wrap tightly in plastic wrap. Ground lamb can be frozen for 3 to 4 months; roasts, steaks, and chops between 6 to 9 months.

LEEKS

Typical serving size: 1 leek (3.14 oz or 89 g)

HOW THEY HARM
Flatulence

WHAT THEY HEAL
Cancer
High cholesterol
High blood pressure

Leeks are closely related to onions—as the similarity in flavor shows—and are distant cousins of asparagus. All three are members of the lily family. Although the entire leek is edible, most people prefer to eat the white, fleshy base and tender inner leaves, and to discard the bitter dark green leaf tops. The flavor is sweeter and milder than that of an onion.

Health Benefits

Prevents certain types of cancer. Kaempferol is an anticancer substance found in leeks. It may help to block the development of cancer-causing compounds. For example, one Chinese study found that men

QUICK TIP:
Don't toss the green part

The green tops of leeks, which are usually discarded, can be saved and added to soups and stocks.

who ate at least 1 Tbsp of chopped onions and other related vegetables (garlic, scallions, chives, and leeks) a day had about half the risk of developing prostate cancer compared to men who ate less than ¼ Tbsp of these veggies daily.

May lower cholesterol. Like onions, leeks contain sulfur compounds that may help to lower cholesterol and high blood pressure. One leek also contains 30% of your RDA of vitamins A and C, both linked to heart health.

Health Risk

Flatulence. In addition to bad breath, leeks can cause gassiness in some people.

Eating Tips

- Braise whole leeks in chicken broth.
- Sauté sliced leeks with sliced red potatoes.
- Stir-fry 2-in pieces of leek and asparagus with garlic and fresh mint.

Buying Tips

- Look for firm, crisp stalks with as much white and light green regions as possible.
- Avoid leeks with yellow or withered tops.

Storing Tip

- Refrigerate unwashed leeks in plastic bag for up to 2 weeks.

LEGUMES

See Beans and Legumes, page 48

LEMONS AND LIMES

Typical serving size: Varies depending on recipe

HOW THEY HARM

- Skin irritation
- Fungicides and pesticides
- Sun sensitivity
- Canker sores
- Tooth enamel damage

WHAT THEY HEAL

- High cholesterol
- Cancer
- Heart disease
- Kidney stones
- Varicose vein pain
- Dry mouth

Ideal for flavoring everything from fish to vegetables to tea, lemons are one of the most widely used of all citrus fruits. Sweetened, diluted, and chilled, fresh lemonade is an old-fashioned summer thirst quencher. It's also an excellent source of vitamin C: One cup of lemon juice has about 55 mg of vitamin C, or more than 70% of the Recommended Dietary Allowance (RDA) for adult women.

Limes are also very high in this essential nutrient. In the mid-1700s, James Lind, a Scottish naval surgeon, discovered that drinking the juice of limes and lemons prevented scurvy, the scourge of sailors on long voyages. Soon British ships carried ample stores of the fruits, earning their sailors the nickname "limey." It was later learned that vitamin C deficiency causes scurvy.

In addition to vitamin C, lemons and limes contain other antioxidant bioflavonoids and add flavor to other foods without adding calories.

Health Benefits

Prevents high cholesterol. Four tablespoons (59 mL) of lemon or lime juice will give you almost half the vitamin C you need for the day. Antioxidants like vitamin C make cholesterol less likely to stick to your artery walls. Lemons and limes are also packed with a natural disease-preventing compound called limonene that may help lower cholesterol.

Helps prevent cancer. Vitamin C and bioflavonoids, found in lemons and limes, are powerful antioxidants, which help protect against caner. Limonene, found mainly in the zest of lemons and limes, may also help reduce cancer risk.

Supports heart health. The same bioflavonoids and antioxidants that may help prevent cancer, such as vitamin C, also protect the heart.

Dissolves kidney stones. The citric acid in lemon and lime juice also helps stave off kidney stones by reducing the excretion of calcium in the urine.

Reduces varicose vein pain. Lemon rind is rich in a compound called rutin, which strengthens the walls of veins and capillaries, potentially reducing the pain and severity of varicose veins.

Treats dry mouth. Licking a lemon or a lime or sipping unsweetened diluted lemon juice can stimulate saliva flow in people who have a dry mouth. This remedy should be used in moderation, however, since the high acidity can damage tooth enamel.

> ### QUICK TIP:
> **Tenderize fish and poultry**
>
> Limes tenderize and heighten the flavors of other foods, especially fish and poultry. Lime juice can also be used as a salt substitute for meat and fish dishes.

Health Risks

Skin irritation. The limonene in lemon peels can irritate the skin in susceptible persons.

Fungicides. Because lemons are often sprayed with fungicides to retard mold growth and pesticides to kill insects, it's important to wash them thoroughly before grating the peel.

Sun sensitivity. Lime peels contain psoralens, chemicals that make the skin sensitive to the sun; thus, care should be taken to minimize skin contact with lime peels. Cut away the peels before squeezing the fruit so that the citrus oil containing the psoralens doesn't get into the juice.

Canker sores. Citrus fruits like lemons and limes make canker sores even more painful.

Eating Tips

- Lay some paper-thin peeled lemon slices on a salmon and lettuce wrap.
- Squeeze lemon juice on bean soup to brighten the flavor.
- Squeeze limes over chunks of ripe mango and eat as a healthy snack.
- Sprinkle grated lemon peel and olive oil over halved plum tomatoes before baking.

Buying Tips

- Select lemons and limes that have not been waxed: The wax may seal in the fungicide used to prevent mold.
- Look for lemons and limes that are heavy for their size, with bright skin.
- Pass on lemons with any bruises, wrinkles, or discoloration.
- Small brown areas on the skin of limes should not affect flavor, but avoid ones with large blemishes or soft spots.

Storing Tips

- Like other citrus fruits, lemons will keep at room temperature for several days.
- Store limes and lemons in a plastic bag in the crisper drawer of your refrigerator, where they can last for about 2 weeks.
- Whole lemons should not be frozen, but once peeled and squeezed, the peels and juices can be frozen separately.

LENTILS

See also Beans and Legumes, page 48

Typical serving size: ½ cup (3.5 oz or 99 g)

HOW THEY HARM
Bloating and flatulence

WHAT THEY HEAL
High cholesterol
Blood sugar spikes
Weight gain
Constipation
Anemia
Heart disease
Reproductive health
Cancer

Sometimes called pulses, lentils date back to the Stone Age and were among the first crops humans cultivated. They come in a variety of colors—red, green, brown, and black—but all varieties are high in protein and low in calories and fat. They're also inexpensive, quick cooking, and packed with protein, fiber, iron, and B vitamins.

Health Benefits

Lowers cholesterol. Lentils are loaded with fiber—16 g in each cup of the cooked legumes—and it's the soluble fiber found in lentils that is the key to their cholesterol-lowering abilities.

Evens out blood sugar. The fiber in lentils protects against spikes in blood sugar, which aids in diabetes management.

Aids in weight loss. Lentils are a source of low-glycemic carbohydrates, which help sustain energy, keep you full, and keep you regular.

Can help prevent anemia. Lentils are a good source of iron, necessary for energy and preventing anemia.

Boosts heart health. The niacin (B3) in lentils protects against cardiovascular disease and helps lower cholesterol, while folate (B9) helps regulate hormones and supports reproductive health. The potassium and magnesium in lentils help regulate blood pressure.

Protect against cancer. The B vitamins in lentils act as anti-cancer agents.

Health Risks

Bloating and flatulence. Like other legumes, lentils have hard-to-digest sugars called oligosaccharides that can cause gas and bloating. While lentils do not require soaking, minimize digestive problems by soaking and draining lentils before cooking thoroughly.

Eating Tips

- Add nutrition and fiber to pilafs by substituting lentils for some of the rice.
- Simmer a pound of lentils in 2 qt of chicken or vegetable stock, a can of diced tomatoes, and chopped carrots and onions for a simple-to-make stew.
- Toss cooked lentils with a little red wine vinegar, extra-virgin olive oil, chopped scallions, parsley, salt, and freshly ground black pepper for a flavorful and nutritious salad.

Buying Tips

- The common khaki-colored lentils are widely available in supermarkets; the more delicate green and red lentils may be harder to find. Red lentils cook faster than the khaki ones.
- Choose bagged lentils and sort through them before cooking, discarding any that are shriveled.

Storing Tips

- Store lentils in a cool, dry place for up to 6 months.
- Don't mix new lentils with older ones, because older lentils will take longer to cook.

LETTUCE AND OTHER SALAD GREENS

Typical serving size: Varies per salad green

HOW THEY HARM
Food poisoning

WHAT THEY HEAL
Cancer
Heart disease
Weight gain

A green salad is often part of a healthy dinner, and although many vegetables may be used in it, lettuce is by far the most popular ingredient. Lettuce is the second most popular vegetable sold in supermarkets, topped only by potatoes.

Some types of lettuce and other salad greens contain high amounts of beta-carotene, folate, vitamin C, calcium, iron, and potassium, but the amounts vary considerably from one variety to another. In general, those with dark green or other deeply colored leaves have more beta-carotene and vitamin C than the paler varieties. Romaine lettuce, for example, has five times as much vitamin C and more beta-carotene and folate than iceberg lettuce.

Greens such as chicory, escarole, and mâché are all more nutritious than lettuce. Many people also find them more flavorful, and they are becoming more readily available. Arugula, a member of the same plant family as broccoli, cabbage, and other cruciferous vegetables, has a tangy, peppery flavor when grown during the cool spring and fall months, and a stronger, mustard-like taste if harvested during the summer. This is one of the most nutritious of all salad greens: A 2-cup serving has more calcium than most other salad greens and is a source of vitamin C, · beta-carotene, iron, and folate—all for only 12 calories. Watercress, another cruciferous vegetable, is also a nutritional winner: 1 cup contains a mere 5 calories, yet it provides 15 mg of vitamin C and 45 mg of calcium.

Health Benefits

Prevents cancer. Deeply colored lettuces and greens are high in bioflavonoids, plant pigments known to work with vitamin C and other antioxidants to prevent cancer-causing cell damage.

Supports heart health. Vitamin C and beta-carotene in salad greens are antioxidants that can prevent oxidative damage to the heart.

Aids in weight loss. Weight watchers are especially partial to salads—they are low in calories yet filling, since they are high in fiber. Unfortunately, a large green salad that contains only 50 calories can quickly become more fattening than a steak if it's drowned in a creamy high-fat dressing. Instead of dressing, use an herb vinegar mixed with a little olive oil, a sprinkling of herbs and lemon juice, or low-fat yogurt or buttermilk combined with garlic, chopped parsley, and lemon juice.

Health Risks

Food poisoning. Note that all lettuce needs to be washed, even if labeled organic. One of the biggest outbreaks of *E. coli* was associated with a batch of organic mixed greens from California. Packaged salad mixes should also be rinsed and the best-before date respected. Bacteria can multiply dangerously after this date.

Eating Tips

- Stuff and roll large lettuce leaves with a spring roll filling, such as snow peas and slices of peppers, leeks, and celery.
- Grill radicchio slices and drizzle with balsamic vinegar.
- Combine red leaf romaine and red onion for a ruddy Caesar salad.

Buying Tip

- Look for fresh, green leaves without wilting or blemishes.

Storing Tips

- For maximum and long-lasting freshness, first remove any brown or wilted leaves from the lettuce head. Then separate the remaining leaves and rinse them under running wa-

---

QUICK TIP: Toss greens with a little bit of oil

Make your salad with a variety of beta carotene-rich salad greens, like watercress, chicory, and escarole, and a little flavored vinegar, lemon juice, and oil. Oil enhances the absorption of beta-carotene, which plays an important role in preventing cancer and vision loss.

ter, then spin them dry. Layer them between sheets of paper towel. Stored in this manner, lettuce will last up to a week.

- If using within 3 days, you can store lettuce and other salad greens in a plastic bag in the refrigerator.

LIMES

See Lemons and Limes, page 125

LIVER

See Organ Meats, page 150

LOBSTER

See Shellfish, page 187

MANGOES

Typical serving size: 1 medium mango (7.3 oz or 207 g)

WHAT THEY HEAL
 Cancer
 High blood pressure
 High cholesterol
 Excess weight

Mangoes used to be regarded as an exotic fruit in North America: However, as more of the fruit is grown in Florida, California, and Hawaii, or imported from Mexico and Central America, mangoes are becoming increasing popular. The soft, juicy flesh of a ripe mango makes it difficult to peel and messy to eat, but it's worth the effort. Mangoes are considered a comfort food in many parts of the world. They also contain an enzyme with digestive properties similar to papain found in papayas—which also makes them a very good tenderizing agent.

Health Benefits

Prevents cancer. Like other orange and deep yellow fruits, mangoes are exceptionally high in beta-carotene, which the body converts to vitamin A. One medium-size (8-oz/227-g) mango has 135 calories and 57 mg vitamin C, which is more than 50% of the RDA. This powerful antioxidant helps protect against cancer.

May help lower blood pressure and cholesterol. One medium-size mango also provides 4 g of fiber and a healthy amount of potassium, which helps manage blood pressure. Mangoes are high in pectin, too, a soluble fiber that is important in controlling blood cholesterol.

Aids weight loss. The high fiber content in mangoes may help induce feelings of fullness.

Eating Tips

- Make a mango quesadilla with a flour tortilla and shredded monterey jack cheese.
- Stir mango chunks into rice pudding.
- Serve mango slices with an Indian chicken curry.

Buying Tips

- Look for a mango with flesh that yields slightly when gently pressed.
- Large dark spots may mean that the flesh is bruised. If the skin is completely green, the fruit may not ripen; a fruit past its prime will have shriveled skin.

Storing Tips

- Store mangoes at room temperature and out of the sun until ripened. The ideal storage temperature for mangoes is 55°F (13°C).

- Mangoes have a shelf life of 1 to 2 weeks.
- Mangoes will not ripen in the refrigerator, but you can store them there once ripe.
- Store cut mangoes in a plastic bag for no more than 3 days.
- If you place an unripe mango in a paper bag in a cool location, it will ripen in 2 or 3 days. A flowery fragrance indicates that the mango is ripe and flavorful. Eat ripe mangoes as soon as possible.

MARGARINE

See Butter and Margarine, page 63

MAYONNAISE

See also Condiments, page 84

Typical serving size: 1 Tbsp or 15 mL

HOW IT HARMS
   High in fat and calories
   Allergies
   Celiac disease
   Salmonella risk

WHAT IT HEALS
   Free radical damage

The rich flavor and creamy texture of mayonnaise accounts for its wide popularity as a sandwich spread, salad dressing, and general condiment. There are several ways to make mayonnaise, but all involve the same basic ingredients—vegetable oil, eggs, and vinegar, lemon juice, or another acidic liquid—whipped together to form a semisolid spread. Mustard, salt, pepper, sugar, and other seasonings may be added.

Mayonnaise-type salad dressings contain less fat and fewer calories than regular mayonnaise, but have a more acidic flavor. That can be tempered by adding a small amount of yogurt, whipped fat-free cottage cheese, or fat-free sour cream.

Low-fat, cholesterol-free, and nonfat mayonnaise substitutes are available. The low-fat versions substitute air, water, starches, and other fillers for some of the oil; fat-free varieties may be made with tofu, yogurt, and other such ingredients.

Health Benefits

Offers antioxidant protection. Most types of mayonnaise are good sources of vitamin E, yielding about 10% of the adult RDA in 1 Tbsp. The vitamin is an antioxidant, which helps protect cells against damage caused by free radicals. Mayonnaise made with sunflower, cottonseed, and safflower oils are highest in this antioxidant.

Health Risks

Can be high in fat and calories. A tablespoon of mayonnaise provides about 100 calories, about the same amount found in a tablespoon of butter or margarine. The eggs in mayonnaise do contribute protein and some minerals, but the amounts are negligible. And the yolks add dietary cholesterol, the intake of which should be limited by anyone with high blood cholesterol, atherosclerosis, or heart disease.

Can trigger allergic reactions. Anyone allergic to eggs should avoid mayonnaise. The vinegar may also trigger an allergic reaction in people sensitive to molds.

May contain fillers with gluten. Some commercial types of mayonnaise and salad dressing have fillers made of gluten, which should be avoided by anyone with celiac disease or gluten intolerance. Check labels for ingredients.

Poses risk of salmonella. The raw egg yolks in mayonnaise may harbor salmonella bacteria. However, commercial may-

If you're concerned about the type of oil used, you can make your own mayonnaise at home. Most recipes call for olive oil, which is largely monounsaturated fat, although polyunsaturated oils, such as corn or safflower, can be substituted for a lighter flavor. The raw eggs used in homemade mayonnaise are a potential source of salmonella; this risk can be avoided by using a pasteurized egg substitute. Note that fresh mayonnaise should be used within 2 or 3 days. Even then, it can become a source of food poisoning if allowed to stand at room temperature for more than an hour.

onnaise is generally safer, because its high vinegar content and antioxidant preservatives discourage the growth of disease-causing organisms. The elderly, young children, and anyone who is immuno-compromised should avoid mayonnaise made with raw eggs, such as homemade versions or those from restaurants.

Eating Tips

- Combine mayonnaise and horseradish for a higher-impact, lower-fat condiment.
- Lightly coat fish fillets with mayonnaise, coat in panko crumbs, and bake.
- Make a turkey sandwich sing with mayonnaise and sriracha sauce.

Buying Tip

- If you're watching your weight or heart health, buy low-fat mayonnaise or ones made with canola oil.

Storing Tips

- Once opened, store mayonnaise in the refrigerator.
- Consume by the use-by date.

MELONS

Typical serving size: ½ cup (3 oz or 85 g)

HOW THEY HARM
Bacterial infection

WHAT THEY HEAL
Cancer
Heart disease
High blood cholesterol
Excess weight

There are many varieties of melons: cantaloupe, casaba, crenshaw, honeydew, Persian, watermelon—and the list goes on. Although mostly water, melons are very nutritious, providing vitamin A (in the form of beta-carotene), vitamin C, potassium, and other minerals.

Although some melons have been recently linked to dangerous bacterial outbreaks, these cases are rare. You can minimize the bacteria by thoroughly washing the rind before cutting and storing the fruit properly.

Health Benefits

Helps ward off cancer. Cantaloupes and other yellow varieties are high in beta-carotene, which the body converts to vitamin A: One-quarter of a cantaloupe provides about 55 mg of vitamin C and 320 mg of potassium. Many melon varieties are high in bioflavonoids, carotenoids, and other plant pigments that help protect against cancer. Watermelon is a very good source of lycopene, an antioxidant linked with a lower risk of prostate cancer.

Prevents heart disease. Melons contain ample amounts of bioflavonoids and carotenoids—studies show that diets rich in these antioxidant compounds are associated with reduced risk of heart disease. Melons are also rich in potassium, which helps the heart by supporting heart function and easing the high blood pressure placed on the heart from excess sodium.

Lowers high blood cholesterol. Although melon flesh is free of strings and other sources of insoluble fiber, it does contain pectin, a type of soluble fiber that helps keep blood cholesterol levels in check.

Facilitates weight loss efforts. Because melons are mostly water, they are generally very low in calories. A ½-cup serving of any of the varieties, diced, contains only 30 to 35 calories.

Health Risks

Bacteria exposure. Although incidences are rare, some melons may harbor bacteria such as *E. coli*, salmonella, and listeria, which are bacteria commonly found in soil. An outbreak of listeria killed 84 people across the United States in the fall of 2011 and was traced back to cantaloupe. According to the Centers for Disease Control and Prevention (CDC), the bacteria can be minimized by washing hands thoroughly with soap and water for at least 20 seconds before and after handling a whole melon, scrubbing the surface of the melon with a clean vegetable brush, and drying the melon before cutting. Small children, the elderly, pregnant women, and people with chronic diseases can sidestep the concerns by avoiding melons such as cantaloupe, honeydew, and watermelon, because some pathogens, such as *E. coli*, may more readily grow on their surfaces.

Eating Tips

- Puree honeydew chunks with white grape juice for a chilled summer soup.
- Layer thinly sliced cantaloupe with lox on a bagel.
- Make a salad with watermelon chunks, spinach, and feta crumbles.

Buying Tips

- Avoid melons that are lopsided or have a flat side.
- They should not have cracks, soft spots, or dark bruises.
- Melons do not continue to ripen post-picking. In order to select a vine-ripened melon with peak flavor, check the stem area for a smooth, slightly sunken scar; this indicates that the melon was ripe and easily pulled from its vine.
- Avoid ones with stems on the scar; those were picked while still green and not fully ripe.
- Check for a scent; a ripe melon will have a deep, intense fragrance.
- A ripe watermelon should rattle when you shake it because the seeds loosen as the fruit matures: Thumping the melon should produce a slightly hollow sound.
- To best preserve nutritional content, buy melons whole (some stores offer halves or quarters). Certain nutrients, especially vitamin C, are diminished by exposure to the air.

Storing Tips

- Store whole melons unwashed in the refrigerator crisper and consume them within 5 days.
- The riper they are, the shorter they will keep.

- Before eating, scrub the skin with a clean vegetable brush under running water. Blot it dry before cutting. Proper washing ensures that melons such as cantaloupe do not harbor harmful bacteria.
- To minimize the chances of bacterial growth, keep cut melons refrigerated at or less than 40°F (32°F to 34°F is best) for no more than 7 days. Toss cut melons that have been left at room temperature for more than 4 hours.

MILK AND DAIRY PRODUCTS

See also Butter and Margarine, page 63; Cheese, page 74; Ice Cream, page 114; Yogurt, page 210

Typical serving size: 1 cup of milk (8 fl oz or 236 mL)

HOW THEY HARM
High cholesterol
Lactose intolerance
Allergies
Acne

WHAT THEY HEAL
Bone loss
Insulin resistance

Milk is a good source of dietary calcium, a mineral needed to build healthy bones and teeth and to maintain many of the basic functions of the human body. The milk sold in North American markets is also fortified with fat-soluble vitamin D, and homogenized for a smooth texture. Two to four servings a day of milk and other dairy foods are recommended.

THE RAW MILK ISSUE

The controversy surrounding raw milk continues to stir up debate. Enthusiasts claim that raw milk is fresher and tastier and that it cures certain ailments. However, unpasteurized milk may contain disease-causing organisms from the cow, from its human handlers, or from the milking and processing equipment. In the pasteurization process, milk is heated hot enough and long enough to kill most microorganisms without compromising the taste or the nutritional content of the milk. The sale of unpasteurized milk is illegal in North America, and health regulatory bodies urge pregnant women and people with weakened immune systems to avoid raw-milk cheese.

Widely available types of milk include regular whole milk (not less than 3.25% fat), low-fat and skim milk (with fat from 2% to less than 0.5%), and cultured buttermilk (less than 1% fat). Another type of milk known as UHT (ultra-high temperature) is processed at high temperatures so that it can be stored without refrigeration for long periods. To make evaporated milk, 50 percent of the water is evaporated. Then, for condensed milk, sugar is added—up to 40 to 45%. Dry, or powdered milk, has had all the moisture removed. Flavored milk, such as strawberry and chocolate, has about 4 tsp or about 64 calories of added sugar per 8-oz carton.

Cream, which is made from skimming off the butterfat from the top of milk, is dense with calories—a mere tablespoon has 25 calories. Other common dairy products include cheese, ice cream, and yogurt.

Milk and dairy products in North America are almost always made from cow's milk, but other types of milk have been gaining popularity. For example, goat's milk can be used exactly like cow's milk. It's usually a little thicker and creamier in texture and can have a musky odor. It can be easier to digest and is a rich source of vitamin A and riboflavin. However, those with lactose allergies may still be affected by goat's milk, too.

60% of adults in the United States cannot digest lactose, the sugar in milk.

Health Benefits

Helps support bone health. One cup of milk contains about 300 mg of calcium. A diet rich in calcium can help prevent osteoporosis.

Prevents insulin resistance. Two Harvard studies found that people who made dairy foods part of their daily diets were 21% less likely to develop insulin resistance and 9% less likely to develop type 2 diabetes.

Health Risks

High blood cholesterol. One cup of whole milk contains 5 g of saturated fat, which is 25% of the Recommended Daily Intake (RDI) for saturated fat. A steady habit of drinking whole milk, in turn, can lead to high blood cholesterol.

Lactose intolerance. Many North Americans have some degree of intolerance to milk because they lack the enzyme that is needed to digest milk sugar, called lactose (page 305). The alternative is lactose-reduced milk or even small amounts of regular milk. The body also digests the lactose in yogurt and cheese more easily than in milk.

Allergies. Cow's milk can cause reactions in children and should be kept out of the diet during the first year of life.

Acne. Research suggests that consuming milk may increase the levels of pimple-producing hormones known as androgens in the body, which can lead to more outbreaks in both adults and teenagers.

Eating Tips

- Mix evaporated skim milk into soup, which will give it extra body without extra calories.
- Make your own homemade whipped cream and avoid preservatives by beating a cup of cream with a whisk.
- Stir some fat-free dry milk powder into baked goods to boost the calcium.

Buying Tips

- When buying milk and dairy products, pay attention to the date on the carton, which indicates the last day on which the milk can be sold.
- Look for milk dated several days in the future.

Storing Tips

- Milk is a low-acid food and is prone to spoiling: Even pasteurized milk contains bacteria and will quickly spoil unless refrigerated.
- Before the expiration date, extend the shelf life of milk by 4 to 5 days by zapping it in the microwave for 60 to 90 seconds.
- Place milk toward the back of the refrigerator, where it is colder than on the door.
- A temperature just above freezing is ideal, but milk should not be frozen.
- Milk is very sensitive to light, which rapidly breaks down the riboflavin and causes unpleasant changes in taste. Cardboard

containers preserve their content better than clear plastic or glass bottles: Milk stored in bottles should be kept in the dark.

MUSHROOMS AND TRUFFLES

Typical serving size: ½ cup, cooked (2.8 oz or 78 g); or ½ cup, raw (1.4 oz or 35 g)

HOW THEY HARM
May be poisonous

WHAT THEY HEAL
Heart disease
High blood pressure
High cholesterol
Prostate and breast cancer
Immunity
Weight gain

Mushrooms and truffles are fungi, primitive plants that draw their nutrients from the partially decomposed tissues of more complex vegetation, such as trees. Their cell walls are made of chitin, a cholesterol-lowering dietary fiber.

The common white mushroom was first cultivated by the French more than 300 years ago in abandoned gypsum quarries near Paris, but only recently has it become possible to cultivate a number of other species on a commercial scale. Thanks to this development, a wide range of mushrooms is now offered by many supermarkets.

Truffles grow underground among the roots of certain oak, hazel, and linden trees. As a result of overharvesting and deforestation, truffles are now so rare and expensive that only minute shavings are used to flavor dishes. Attempts to grow them on a commercial scale have been unsuccessful so far.

Health Benefits

Supports heart health. Mushrooms are one of the best plant-based sources of niacin: Studies have shown that niacin can help reduce the risk of heart disease and atherosclerosis. Three ounces (85 g) of portobello mushrooms provide almost 20% of the daily niacin requirement. The same-size serving of white mushrooms provides 17%, while shiitakes yield 6%.

Lowers cholesterol and blood pressure. All mushrooms contain good amounts of potassium, which can have a positive effect in lowering blood pressure, and a substance called eritadenine, which helps lower cholesterol by promoting cholesterol excretion. In addition, tree-ear mushrooms, used in many Chinese dishes, inhibit blood clotting and are thought to lower cholesterol.

Protects against cancers of the breast and prostate. Portobello and white mushrooms are good sources of selenium. Selenium may help prevent prostate cancer—it is known to work with vitamin E to clean up the free radicals that damage cells. The Baltimore Longitudinal Study of Aging found that men with the lowest levels of selenium in their blood were four to five times more likely to have prostate cancer than men with high selenium levels. Additionally, mushrooms are rich in disease-fighting phytochemicals, and eating them regularly has been linked to a lower risk of breast cancer in Chinese and Korean women, according to studies.

Supports the immune system. Japanese studies have shown that certain mushrooms may favorably influence the immune system, with potential benefits in fighting cancer, infections, and such autoimmune diseases as rheumatoid arthritis

QUICK TIP:
Keep color with lemon juice

When preparing mushrooms, retain their color by squeezing a little lemon juice.

and lupus. This effect may be related to the high content of glutamic acid, an amino acid that seems to be instrumental in fighting infections, among other immune functions. Shiitake mushrooms contain lentinan, a phytochemical that may help boost immune activity,

Helps cut calories. Extremely low in calories (a half cup contains only 10), mushrooms are virtually fat-free and a valuable source of dietary fiber.

Health Risks

Can be poisonous. Many common species of wild mushrooms produce toxins that are quickly lethal whether eaten raw or cooked. Because there is no feature that distinguishes dangerous mushrooms, and poisonous varieties often closely resemble edible ones, never gather or eat wild mushrooms unless a mushroom expert has identified them as safe. Additionally, some wild mushrooms, although safe to eat on their own, can be deadly when consumed with alcohol.

Eating Tips

- Make soup with sautéed mushrooms, broth, diced tomatoes, garlic, and rosemary.

- Stuff baked mushroom caps with chunks of chicken sausage.
- Spoon jarred truffle paste over scrambled eggs and chives.

Buying Tips

- When buying mushrooms, look for firm buttons with no bruises. All mushrooms are handpicked but bruise easily. Handle them carefully.
- Look for size: Flavor develops as the mushrooms grow, so the largest of any variety have the most flavor.

Storing Tips

- Place mushrooms in paper bags and store in the vegetable crisper of the refrigerator. Do not store mushrooms in cling wrap or plastic.
- Five days should be the maximum storage time in the refrigerator.
- Rinse mushrooms only just before using them, but do not peel them or remove the stalks—the skin is where the nutrients are. Simply slice, quarter, or chop with the skins on.

MUSTARD

See also Condiments, page 84

Typical serving size: 1 tsp or 5 mL

HOW IT HARMS
Diarrhea or vomiting
Allergies
Skin irritation

WHAT IT HEALS
Cancer
Heart disease
Inflammation
Bone strength

When you think of mustard, the first thing that probably comes to mind is the condiment. So you may be surprised to learn that mustard is good for more than just a sandwich spread, dip, or salad dressing ingredient.

In addition to the condiment, you can find mustard in the form of seeds or a powder made from ground mustard seeds. The seeds that are used to make traditional mustard come from a cruciferous plant, and the mustard greens from that plant can also be eaten for additional health benefits.

You probably won't be eating enough mustard to gain all the health benefits, but in combination with other foods rich in the same nutrients, it can help several conditions.

Health Benefits

Protects against cancer and heart disease. Mustard is a source of selenium, a mineral with antioxidant properties that may help protect against certain cancers, prevent cardiovascular disease, defend your cells against damaging free radicals, and give your immune system a boost.

Decreases inflammation. Mustard is a source of magnesium, which can help reduce inflammation, lower blood pressure, balance blood sugar, and relax muscles.

Eases PMS symptoms. The manganese in mustard can help strengthen bones. Mustard contains manganese and phosphorus, which contributes to strong bones and teeth and helps the body process carbohydrates and fats in protein synthesis.

Health Risks

Digestive problems. Ingesting too many mustard seeds (or more than a teaspoon of mustard powder) could result in diarrhea or vomiting.

Allergies. In rare cases, mustard may be a food allergen: It may also irritate the skin when used topically, despite being revered for its typically skin-soothing properties.

Eating Tips

- Add mustard to salad dressings, sauces, and marinades.
- Stir in some spicy mustard with grilled brussels sprout halves to add some spice to the vegetable.
- For a little kick to your next stew or roast, add a couple teaspoons of mustard.

Buying Tips

- Yellow mustard is milder than Dijon mustard, which is pungent and a bit spicy.
- Stone ground is usually more coarse, leaving larger chunks of mustard seed, creating a more spicy flavor and a pronounced texture. Nutritionally, most mustards are the same. However, Dijon-style mustards often have a bit more sodium than regular yellow mustard.

QUICK TIP:
Make Your Own Mustard

Create this condiment by adding 2 to 3 Tbsp (30 to 45 mL) of liquid (vinegar, wine, water, and/or flat beer) to about ¼ cup (59 mL) dry mustard (seeds and powder), and dress it up with turmeric (for a bright yellow tint), garlic, sugar or honey, salt, tarragon, or other herbs.

MORE MUSTARD USES

If you have an aching back, arthritis pain, or sore muscles, add 6 to 8 oz of mild yellow mustard to a bath, or rub the mustard directly on the painful area (do a spot test first to make sure the mustard doesn't irritate your skin). You can use mustard as a decongestant; simply rub prepared mustard on your chest and put a hot wet washcloth over it. Mustard can also help soothe and stimulate skin, so consider using it for your next facial mask.

Storing Tips

- Refrigerate prepared mustard after opening.
- Mustard seeds and powder can be stored in a dry, dark place.
- Seeds are typically good for a year; mustard powder keeps well for about 6 months.

MUSTARD GREENS

See Kale and Other Cooking Greens, page 120

NECTARINES

See Peaches and Nectarines, page 156

NUTS AND SEEDS

See also Flax, page 99; Peanuts and Peanut Butter, page 158

Typical serving size: 1 oz or 28 g

HOW THEY HARM
- High in fat and calories
- Allergies
- Dehydration

WHAT THEY HEAL
- Diabetes
- Heart disease
- High cholesterol
- Cancer
- Low energy
- Constipation
- Anemia
- Weight gain

The embryos of various trees, bushes, and other plants, nuts and seeds are packed with all the nutrients needed to grow an entire new plant and have been valued for their nutritional content since prehistoric times. Nut- and seed-bearing plants have been cultivated since 10,000 BC.

Nuts have been shown to lower cholesterol and help control weight. Eating more nuts is also associated with a lower risk of stroke. Their healthy qualities may be attributed to their fatty acid profile along with their protein, fiber, and magnesium content. Nuts and seeds are one of the best food sources of vitamin E, an important antioxidant that enhances the immune system, protects cell membranes, and helps make red blood cells. Nuts and seeds also contain folate and other minerals such as iron, calcium, selenium, manganese, zinc, and potassium, flavonoids as well as plant sterols.

Seeds, such as chia, are also increasingly incorporated in our diets. These tiny seeds have been dubbed a "superfood" that delivers big results. The chia plant is native to Central and South America, but is also grown in Western Australia, now the world's largest producer of the seeds. Unlike flaxseeds, chia seeds do not need to be ground. Chia seeds are gluten free and a good source of heart-healthy omega-3 fats.

Health Benefits

Prevents diabetes. Nuts and seeds are good for blood sugar. Harvard researchers discovered that women who regularly ate nuts (about a handful five times a week) were 20% less likely to develop type 2 diabetes than those who didn't eat them as often.

Wards off heart disease. Several large studies have found that a regular intake of nuts protects against heart disease. The Nurses' Health Study found that women who ate more than 5 oz (142 g) of nuts per week had a 35% lower risk of heart attack and death from heart disease compared with those who never ate nuts or ate them less than once a month. Part of the reason may come from the high potassium content, which helps lower blood pressure by balancing sodium levels: A half-cup serving of almonds, peanuts, pine nuts, pistachios, or sunflower seeds provides more than 500 mg of potassium, more than is in a whole banana.

Lowers cholesterol. One recent study found that when people with high levels of "bad" LDL cholesterol ate about 1.5 oz (42 g) of sesame seeds a day for 4 weeks as part of an already heart-healthy diet, their LDL levels dropped by almost 10% more than when they followed the same diet without sesame seeds. Not surprisingly, their LDL levels went back up after they stopped eating the sesame seeds. Nuts also contain plant sterols that can lower cholesterol. One study showed that almonds significantly lowered LDL cholesterol in those who already had elevated cholesterol levels, and another study found that a diet that includes unsaturated fats from almonds and walnuts may have 10% more cholesterol-lowering power than a traditional cholesterol-lowering diet. Walnuts are also rich in heart-healthy omega-3 fatty acids; in one study men and women with high cholesterol levels who added walnuts to a healthy Mediterranean diet saw a drop in their LDL cholesterol.

May help prevent cancer. Nuts are rich in cancer-fighting antioxidants. A 1-oz (28-g) serving of almonds provides almost 50% of the Recommended Dietary Allowance (RDA) of vitamin E, and a similar serving of hazelnuts provides about 30%. Walnuts in particular are especially rich in ellagic acid, an antioxidant that may inhibit the growth of cancer cells. Brazil nuts are high in selenium, another antioxidant. One-quarter ounce (7 g) provides more than twice the RDA for this mineral. Plant sterols may also contribute to anticancer effects.

Boosts energy. Nuts are a "slow-burning" food containing a mix of fat and protein, and thus provide sustained energy.

Helps alleviate constipation. Most nuts and seeds are a good source of dietary fiber. A cup of almonds, for example, provides about 15 g.

Fights anemia. By weight, both pumpkin and sesame seeds have more iron to combat anemia than liver does.

Aids in weight loss. Researchers at Purdue University tested various snack foods, including unsalted peanuts, other nuts, and rice cakes. They found that following a peanut or peanut butter snack, hunger was reduced for 2½ hours, while other snacks caused hunger to return within a half hour. Interestingly, the peanut snackers adjusted their calorie intake spontaneously and did not add extra calories to their daily diet. Furthermore, there was a positive change in the fatty-acid profile of the diet reflecting the good-quality fats (monounsaturated) found in the peanuts.

Supports a vegetarian diet. Most nuts provide good amounts of protein. With the exception of peanuts, however, they lack lysine, an essential amino acid necessary to make a complete protein. This amino acid can easily be obtained by combining nuts with legumes.

Health Risks

High in fat and calories. The bad news is that nuts are high in calories and fat, but the good news is that with the exception of coconuts and palm nuts, their

Old School
Nuts are junk food.

New Wisdom
Nuts are excellent sources of protein and other nutrients as long as you keep servings to a handful.

fat is mostly mono- or polyunsaturated. These are considered heart-friendly fats, especially when they replace saturated fats. Still, nuts should be consumed in moderation. Macadamia nuts have more

30% to 50% lower risk of heart disease is associated with eating nuts several times a week.

than 1,000 calories per cup; Brazil nuts are a close second. Other nuts and seeds contain about 700 to 850 calories per cup.

Allergies. Some nuts, especially peanuts (although technically these are not nuts but legumes), provoke allergic reactions in many people. Symptoms range from a tingling sensation in the mouth to hives and, in extreme cases, to anaphylaxis, a life-threatening emergency. But because the different varieties are not closely related, a person who is allergic to walnuts, for example, may be able to eat another type of nut or seed.

Dehydration. Chia seeds can absorb a significant amount of liquid—you just don't want them to do that during digestion. To avoid the problem and actually help maintain hydration, soak chia seeds in water before eating.

Eating Tips

- Sprinkle toasted sesame seeds on oatmeal.
- Dissolved in water, chia seeds create a gel that can be added as a thickener to soups and stews.
- Drizzle melted bittersweet chocolate over hazelnuts, and let stand to set.
- Toast nuts at 350°F for about 5 to 10 minutes before blending into a recipe; it helps bring out the flavor.
- Garnish chili with toasted pumpkin seeds.

- Create an easy holiday candy by combining 1½ lb (680 g) of melted white, dark, or milk chocolate confectionery coating and one can of mixed nuts. Drop by teaspoonfuls onto waxed paper to harden.

Buying Tips

- Look for plump nuts that are uniform in color and size.
- Both roasted and raw nuts are healthy, but if you buy them roasted, look for unsalted ones.

Storing Tips

- Oils in nuts and seeds quickly turn rancid. Store nuts and seeds in airtight containers or in sealed plastic bags with the air pressed out in the refrigerator for up to 6 months.

OATS

See also Grains, page 104

Typical serving size: ½ cup, cooked with water (4.2 oz or 117g)

HOW THEY HARM
Blood sugar spikes

WHAT THEY HEAL
Heart disease
High cholesterol
High blood pressure
Diabetes
Constipation
Weight gain

Oatmeal and other whole grain products such as oat bran and oat flakes are tasty, convenient, versatile, and economical sources of nutrients and phytochemicals. Commonly used as a breakfast cereal and in baking, oats can be added to many dishes, including meat loaf, burgers, and fish cakes, and can be used to thicken soups and sauces or as a topping for fruit crisps. They have beneficial effects on cholesterol, blood pressure, blood sugar, satiety, and gastrointestinal health.

On a weight-for-weight basis, oats contain a higher concentration of protein, fat, calcium, iron, manganese, thiamin, folacin, and vitamin E than other unfortified whole grains. Oats also contain polyphenols and saponins, powerful antioxidants with disease-fighting properties.

Health Benefits

Reduces risk of heart disease. In 1997, the U.S. Food and Drug Administration granted the first food-specific health claim for use on oatmeal labels, stating, "Soluble fiber from oatmeal, as part of a diet low in saturated fat and cholesterol, may reduce the risk of heart disease."

Manages cholesterol levels. Oat bran is high in beta-glucan, a soluble fiber that can help lower blood cholesterol levels, thus possibly reducing the risk of heart attacks. Eating 3 g of beat-glucan a day (which is about the amount in one cup of cooked oat bran) can reduce blood cholesterol by about 5% and lower heart attack risk by about 10%. Some studies have shown that oats not only lower LDL cholesterol but may also boost levels of the protective HDL cholesterol. Oats contain a unique blend of antioxidants, including the avenanthramides that prevent LDL cholesterol (the "bad" cholesterol) from being converted to the oxidized form that damages arteries.

Lowers blood pressure. A study in Minnesota looked at a group of people who were taking medication for high blood pressure. Half of them were asked to consume about 5 g of soluble fiber per day in

QUICK TIP: Use oats instead of bread crumbs

Add rolled oats instead of bread crumbs in meat loaf, or use it to coat chicken or fish patties before cooking.

the form of 1 ½ cups of oatmeal and an oat-based snack, while the other half ate cereals and snacks with little soluble fiber. The people who were consuming the oats showed a significant reduction in blood pressure. And Yale researchers have found that eating a large bowl of oatmeal may improve the harmful reduction in blood flow that may happen after eating a high-fat meal.

Prevents diabetes. Oats also have been shown to reduce both blood sugar and insulin levels, an important asset in controlling diabetes. Human studies confirm that oat-soluble fiber reduces after-meal blood sugar and insulin in both healthy people, and those with diabetes.

Helps bowel regularity. As mentioned, oats also contain some insoluble fiber, which prevents constipation.

Aids weight loss. Oats have a high satiety value, meaning they take a long time to digest and therefore keep you feeling full longer. It is thought that both the protein and fiber in oats contribute to this effect. In one study comparing oatmeal to a sugared flaked cereal for breakfast, researchers found that subjects who ate oatmeal at breakfast consumed one-third fewer calories for lunch, thus helping with weight management.

Health Risk

Blood sugar spike. Unlike steel-cut or whole oat products, instant oatmeal ranks high on the glycemic load and can cause blood sugar to spike. Instant oatmeal can also contain higher levels of sodium, compared to the steel-cut version.

Eating Tips

- Make a savory pilaf with steel-cut oats.
- Fry skillet cakes from cold leftover cooked oatmeal.
- Replace one-quarter of the flour with rolled oats in banana bread.

Buying Tips

- Avoid preflavored or instant oatmeal. Instead, buy plain oatmeal and sweeten and flavor it yourself during or after cooking.

Storing Tips

- Store oats in an airtight container and place in a cool, dry place.
- For best results, use within the recommended storage time, which is usually within a year. If it smells rancid, toss.
- Alternatively, oats can be frozen in a plastic bag with the air squeezed out for up to 3 months.

OILS

Typical serving size: 1 Tbsp or 15 mL

HOW THEY HARM
High in saturated fat
Bacterial infection

WHAT THEY HEAL
High cholesterol
Hormone production
Nutrient absorption

Oils, which are made from a variety of vegetables and seeds, are pure fat and have 9 calories per gram, or 240 to 250 per oz. Before refrigeration, preserving foods with oil was critical to survival. Today, even with a limitless supply of healthy foods, oils are an important diet component. They provide a concentrated source of energy and fatty acids that are essential to build and maintain cell walls. They also add an appetizing flavor, aroma, and texture to foods, and because they take longer to digest than the other main food groups, they satisfy hunger.

Health Benefits

Can be heart healthy. Oils contain varying amounts of saturated, monounsaturated, and polyunsaturated fatty acids. Polyunsaturated and monounsaturated fats tend to lower LDL cholesterol, especially when they replace saturated fats in the diet. This is the reason people who are concerned about cholesterol are encouraged to avoid most saturated fats and replace them with mono- and polyunsaturates. The best all-purpose dietary oils are canola, corn, olive, peanut, safflower, soybean, and sunflower oils, which contain predominantly mono- or polyunsaturated fats with very low levels of saturated fats. Vegetable oils contain no cholesterol.

Promotes hormone production. Fats such as oils are also necessary to make growth and sex hormones and prostaglandins, the hormonelike substances that regulate many body processes.

Improves nutrient absorption. Fats such as oils can help the body absorb and use fat-soluble vitamins A, D, E, and K.

Health Risks

High in saturated fats. Saturated fats tend to raise levels of artery-clogging LDL (low-density lipoprotein) cholesterol. The saturated fatty acids mostly responsible for raising cholesterol are lauric, myristic, and palmitic acids. Coconut, cottonseed, palm, and palm kernel oils all contain high levels of these damaging fatty acids. Palm, palm kernel, and coconut oils, like animal fats, are solid at room temperature and are highly saturated.

Dangerous bacteria. If you like to make flavored oils by adding herbs, garlic, or other ingredients, keep them refrigerated and throw them out after 2 days. Oil can support the growth of the bacterium that causes botulism, which is potentially fatal. Commercially prepared flavored oils usually contain additives that prevent bacteria from growing.

Eating Tips

- Drizzle extra-virgin olive oil over steamed greens.
- Flavor a radicchio and pear salad with walnut oil.
- Make chocolate fondue creamier by blending in a tablespoon of canola oil.

Buying Tip

- Buy single-source oils, such as pure canola or pure olive, rather than blended oils. Blended oil often has an overwhelming proportion of the cheapest and probably least healthful oil mentioned, with only a negligible amount of the more expensive, better-quality oil.

Storing Tips

- Store oils in a cool, dark place.
- Oil will retain its flavor for about 6 months.

33% of calories in an average American's diet today comes from fats and oils.

OKRA

Typical serving size: ½ cup cooked sliced (2.8 oz or 80 g)

WHAT IT HEALS

High cholesterol

Constipation

Weight gain

A relative of the hibiscus, okra was brought to the Americas from Africa in the 1600s. The dark green pods are the main ingredient in spicy Creole stews or gumbos. In fact, okra is nicknamed "gumbo" in many parts of the world.

This starchy vegetable is low in calories—a ½-cup serving contains just 18 calories. It is also a source of the antioxidant vitamins A and C, folate, and potassium, an electrolyte that maintains proper fluid balance, helps to transmit nerve impulses, and is needed for proper muscle function and metabolism. It also contains thiamin and magnesium.

Okra's gummy consistency may be off-putting to some people. To minimize the gumminess, try steaming or blanching the pods until just tender. Don't slice the okra before cooking—less juice will be released if the inner capsule remains intact. Prepare okra along with an acidic vegetable, such as tomatoes, to reduce its gelatinous consistency. Some people prefer eating okra raw with dips, as part of a fresh vegetable tray, or in a salad.

OKRA FACTS

- In a 2011 *Consumer Reports* survey, okra was one of the vegetables least likely to be regularly consumed.
- Okra can be used to produce top-of-the-line paper, the kind used to make fine documents and currency.

O

Health Benefits

Lowers cholesterol. Okra contains high amounts of pectin, which helps decrease blood cholesterol levels by interfering with bile absorption in the intestines and forcing the liver to use circulating cholesterol to make more bile.

Regulates bowels. The large amount of soluble fibers helps prevent constipation by absorbing water and adding bulk to the stool.

Aids in weight loss. Okra is a low-calorie food. The high fiber content may help induce feelings of fullness.

QUICK TIP:
Thicken soups with okra

Okra is high in starch, pectin, and soluble fibers, which help thicken soups and stews when it is cooked. As okra cooks, its fats are released and naturally thicken the soups and stews.

Eating Tips

- Stir-fry sliced baby okra with plum tomato and onion.
- Grill oiled okra sprinkled with Cajun seasoning.
- Pack baby okra in a jar of leftover pickle juice and refrigerate for several days.

Buying Tips

- Look for firm pods that are bright green.
- Avoid any okra with discoloration or blemishes.

Storing Tips

- Store unwashed okra in the vegetable crisper loosely wrapped in perforated plastic bags for up to 3 days.
- Avoid moisture, as dampness will cause slime and mold growth.

OLIVES AND OLIVE OIL

See also Oils, page 142

Typical serving size: 3 to 4 olives; 1 tsp to 1 Tbsp (5 to 15 mL) of olive oil

HOW THEY HARM
Blood pressure

WHAT THEY HEAL
High blood cholesterol
Breast cancer
Inflammation
Immunity
Weight gain

The all-purpose crop of the Mediterranean area, olives are indispensable in this region in the preparation of traditional dishes, such as braised duck and lamb stew. In contrast, North Americans tend to use them as a relish or garnish for salads and pizzas. A medium-size olive contains approximately 5 calories if green and 9 calories if ripe. High in monounsaturated fats, which may raise levels of the beneficial high-density lipoprotein (HDL) cholesterol, and very low in saturates, olives and their oil are thought to contribute to the low rate of heart disease in the Mediterranean countries.

Olive oil is an essential part of a heart-healthy Mediterranean diet. Made from pressed olives, it has a wide variety of uses, including salad dressings, cooking oil, and canning fish as well as cosmetics and high-quality soap. It contains 120 calories per tablespoon. Extra virgin and virgin olive oil are cold pressed and unrefined and contain the highest amount of nutrients.

Health Benefits

Decreases "bad" cholesterol levels. The high monounsaturated fat content in olives and olive oil helps keep a diet heart healthy. One study found that adults who consumed about 2 Tbsp (30 mL) of virgin olive oil daily for just 1 week had lower LDL and higher levels of antioxidants in their blood. Numerous other studies conducted over the past 40 years attest to the oil's heart benefits, including studies finding that olive oil not only lowers LDL but also raises HDL. Olive oil also contains phytochemicals and vitamin E, which help to clear cholesterol from arteries. However, note that these benefits occur only when used in place of saturated fats such as butter and margarine, not in addition to them.

Safeguards against cancer. The antioxidant phytochemicals hydroxytyrosol and oleuropein in olives and olive oil may work together, according to laboratory studies, to help protect against breast cancer. Lignans that are present in extra-virgin olive oil may protect against cancer by suppressing early cancer changes in cells.

Cools inflammation. Olive oil helps decrease inflammation, which contributes to arthritis, heart disease, and many other health problems. It is also linked to boosting immunity and helps your body use plant chemicals from other foods. For instance, lycopene, the fat-soluble antioxidant in tomatoes, is best absorbed when eaten with some fat.

Helps with weight loss. Studies suggest that olives and olive oil may slow stomach contractions, helping you feel full longer.

Health Risk

Blood pressure. Olives that are pickled in brine or dry cured are high in sodium, which may raise blood pressure in some.

30% of calories in a traditional Greek diet comes from monounsaturated fats, mostly from olive oil.

Eating Tips

- Mix chopped green olives into a turkey burger mixture.
- Drizzle extra-virgin olive oil over cannellini beans.
- Dab olive tapenade on a multigrain cracker spread with goat cheese.

Buying Tips

- Because the heat and chemicals used in processing olive oil can diminish nutrient content, it is best to choose oils that are minimally processed, such as extra-virgin or cold-pressed oil.
- Raw black olives are more pungent than raw green olives, which are picked sooner. However, in most canned versions, the difference in taste is more difficult to determine.
- Low-sodium versions of canned olives are available. You can save about 70 mg of sodium per serving by opting for the

low-sodium version. Rinse the olives once or twice in water before using to save even more.

- Look for the date of extraction or use-by date on the label before purchasing.

Storing Tips

- To preserve flavor, store olive oil in an airtight container in the refrigerator or other dark, cool place. Refrigerated olive oil will solidify; it will need to reach room temperature before it can be poured.
- Stored properly, olive oil will last for years. If the oil turns cloudy, its nutritional properties may have changed; toss and buy a new bottle.
- Keep olives in the refrigerator, where they can be stored for up to 2 months.

ONIONS

Typical serving size: ½ cup, raw (45 g)

HOW THEY HARM
Bloating and flatulence

WHAT THEY HEAL
Lung and other cancers
Heart attacks
High cholesterol
High blood sugar
Bacterial infections

Onions are members of the allium plant family, which also includes garlic, leeks, and shallots. Onions are divided into two categories: spring onions, which have a mild flavor and whose green tops and bulbs are eaten; and globe onions, which have a more pungent flavor and dry outer skins that are discarded. Shallots possess features of both onions and garlic, but are milder. Red onions have a mild, somewhat sweet flavor, which makes them a favorite

for salads and sandwiches. Stronger white and yellow varieties are ideal for cooking, because they become milder and sweeter upon heating and they also impart a pleasant flavor to other foods.

Although onions in general are not high in vitamins and minerals, the green tops of spring onions are a good source of vitamin C and beta-carotene. A cup of boiled onions provides about 225 mg of potassium. They are rich in phytochemicals like flavonoids which protect against disease.

Health Benefits

Protects against lung cancer. A study published in the *Journal of the National Cancer Institute* reported on the significant correlation between the high intake of dietary flavonoids and a reduced risk of lung cancer. Foods with the flavonoids that offer the best protection include onions as well as apples and white grapefruit.

Fends off other types of cancer. Sulfur compounds and flavonoids in onions may block the cancer-causing potential of some carcinogens. One Chinese study found that men who ate at least 1 Tbsp day of chopped onions and other related vegetables (garlic, scallions, chives, and leeks) had about half the risk of developing prostate cancer compared to men who ate less than ¼ Tbsp (4 mL) of these vegetables daily.

Prevents heart attacks. Folk healers have long recommended onions as a heart tonic: Researchers have now documented that adenosine, an aspirin-like substance in onions, hinders dangerous clot formation that causes heart attacks.

May boost "good" cholesterol levels. Studies indicate that onions may protect against the artery-clogging damage of cholesterol by raising the levels of the protective high-density lipoproteins (HDLs).

Stabilizes blood sugar levels. In one Egyptian study of diabetic rats, onion juice reduced blood sugar levels by an amazing 70%. One of few published studies in humans, from India, dates back some 30 years, but it found that people with diabetes who ate 2 oz (57 g) of onions a day experienced a significant drop in blood sugar levels. Researchers credit these effects to the sulfur compounds in onions as well as their flavonoids. Furthermore, onions are one of the richest food sources of chromium, a trace mineral that improves the body's ability to respond to insulin.

May stop skin infections. Onions contain substances that have a mild antibacterial effect, which may validate the old folk remedy of rubbing a raw onion on a cut to prevent infection. However, more research is necessary.

Health Risks

Bloating and gas. Onions contain fructose, a common sugar that causes gas. Although it may cause discomfort, gas and bloating is usually not harmful.

Eating Tips

- Make a sliced red onion, goat cheese, lettuce, and pumpernickel sandwich.
- Sprinkle raw minced sweet onion on bean dishes.
- Splash caramelized pearl onions with sherry vinegar as a condiment for roasts.

QUICK TIP: Eat them raw

Cooking onions at a high heat significantly reduces the benefits of diallyl sulfide, their cancer-protective phytochemical. Fresh raw onion offers the most health benefits, and mincing (or even chewing) the onion helps to release its phytochemical power.

20% lower risk of heart disease was observed in people who ate the most onions along with other foods rich in flavonoids.

Buying Tips

- Globe onions should be firm, with crackly, dry skin. Reject any that feel soft, have black spots, which indicate mold, or have green sprouts showing at the top—these are well past their prime. They should have a mild odor. A strong, oniony smell indicates decay.
- Scallions, or green onions, should have crisp, dark green tops and firm white bottoms. In general, the ones with more slender bottoms will have a sweeter taste.

Storing Tips

- Globe onions should be stored in a cool, dry place away from direct light, which can give them a bitter taste. Do not store them near potatoes, which give off moisture and a gas that causes onions to spoil more quickly.
- Store scallions in the refrigerator. They can be kept for several days, but use them as quickly as possible before they begin to soften.

ORANGES AND TANGERINES

Typical serving size: 1 medium orange (131 g), 1 medium tangerine tangerine (109 g) or ½ cup juice (4 fl oz or 125 mL)

HOW THEY HARM
Allergies
Tooth enamel erosion
Drug interactions
Canker sores

WHAT THEY HEAL
Cancer, including thyroid cancer
High blood pressure
High cholesterol
Stomach upset
Inflammation
Weight gain

Oranges and tangerines are usually associated with vitamin C, and for good reason: One medium-size orange provides about 70 mg, more than 90% of the Recommended Dietary Allowance (RDA) for women. Oranges contain smaller amounts of other vitamins and minerals, such as thiamine and folate. The fruit is also a good source of potassium.

WARNING! FOOD-DRUG INTERACTION
Orange juice, as well as grapefruit and apple juice, may block the effects of certain drugs, such as the anticancer drug etoposide; beta-blockers to treat high blood pressure; cyclosporine; and some antibiotics. Speak to your doctor about any concerns.

A half-cup of freshly squeezed juice provides roughly the same amount of nutrients found in the fresh fruit, but much of the pulp and membranes are strained out of most commercial brands so you lose out on most of the fiber and flavonoids.

Tangerines are low in calories (about 35 calories in a medium fruit) and are richer in vitamin A (in the form of beta-carotene) than any other citrus fruit. A medium-size tangerine contains high levels of vitamin A as well as 130 mg of potassium.

Tangerines, along with clementines and satsumas, are actually types of mandarin oranges. These sweet citrus fruits with loose-fitting skins originated in China, but they are now grown in many parts of the world. As they moved into other tropical and subtropical areas, the original mandarin oranges were crossed with other citrus fruits to produce a variety of hybrids, including clementines, tangelos and tangors.

Health Benefits

Limits growth of tumors. Oranges are powerful cancer fighters. Vitamin C is an antioxidant that protects against cell damage by the free radicals produced when oxygen is used by the human body. Additionally, oranges contain rutin, hesperidin, and other bioflavonoids, plant pigments that may help to prevent or retard tumor growth. Beta-cryptoxanthin, a carotenoid in oranges and tangerines, may help prevent colon cancer. Furthermore, nobiletin, a flavonoid found in the flesh of oranges, may have anti-inflammatory actions and tangeretin, the flavonoid found in tangerines, has been linked in experimental studies to a reduced growth of tumor cells.

May decrease risk of thyroid cancer. Results of a study in the Republic of Korea suggest that high consumption of raw vegetables, persimmons, and tangerines may decrease thyroid cancer risk and help prevent early-stage thyroid cancer.

Decreases blood pressure. According to a French study, orange juice can help lower blood pressure: Researchers believe it is due to the effects of hesperidin, a flavonoid that comprises 90% of total flavonoids in orange juice. Oranges also have good amounts of potassium, which help control blood pressure by lessening the effects of sodium. To that end, the American Heart Association recommends oranges and orange juice as foods that are potassium-rich.

Lowers cholesterol. Oranges contain a fair amount of pectin in the membranes between the segments of the fresh fruit. Pectin is a soluble dietary fiber that helps control blood cholesterol levels.

Relieves digestive distress. The Chinese use tangerines to help settle digestive upsets and alleviate nausea, while in France, the fruit is given to children to relieve indigestion and hiccups.

Fights inflammation. A medium-size tangerine fulfills about 30% of the adult Recommended Dietary Allowance (RDA) for vitamin C. This antioxidant helps to prevent harmful free radicals that are produced by the body's digestive process and by exposure to tobacco smoke, radiation, and other environmental toxins.

QUICK TIP: Eat the pith
Eat the orange with the pith, the spongy white layer between the zest and the pulp. Although bitter, the pith stores a good amount of the fruit's fiber and antioxidant plant chemicals.

Helps with weight loss. Oranges are low in calories—one orange contains approximately 60. When you eat the whole fruit instead of drinking the juice, you also benefit from the fiber content, which may help you reach satiety faster than other low-fiber foods.

Health Risks

Allergic reactions. Orange peels may be treated with sulfites, which can trigger serious allergic reactions in susceptible people. Also, orange peels contain limonene, an oil that is a common allergen. Many people who are allergic to commercial orange juice, which becomes infused with limonene during processing, find they can tolerate peeled oranges.

Tooth enamel erosion. According to a study from the University of Rochester, orange juice reduced tooth enamel hardness by 84% in those who drank it every day for 5 days. Researchers attribute it to the high acidity of orange juice.

Canker sores. Oranges and tangerines, like other citrus fruits, can make these painful mouth sores even worse.

Eating Tips

- Replace pineapple with peeled orange slices in an upside-down cake recipe.
- Sauté tangerine sections, and drizzle with brown sugar and cinnamon.
- Combine blood oranges, red onion, and spinach leaves in salad.

- Marinate chicken wings in orange juice and a splash of hot sauce.
- Add tangerine sections to whole cranberry sauce.

Buying Tips

- All varieties should be firm, heavy for their size, and have bright orange skin.
- Oranges may be ripe even if they have green spots.
- Avoid fruit with bruised, wrinkled skin or discoloration; this indicates age or improper storing condition.
- Avoid canned oranges, which lose most of their vitamin C and some minerals during processing, and are usually packed in high-sugar syrups.
- While most tangerine varieties are available from November to March, tangerines are especially popular at Christmas.

Storing Tips

- Oranges can be stored at room temperature or inside the crisper drawer for up to 2 weeks.
- Store tangerines in the refrigerator for up to 2 weeks.
- Avoid freezing the whole fruit, but fresh-squeezed juice and grated peel or zest may be refrigerated or frozen separately.

ORGAN MEATS

Typical serving size: 3 to 4 oz or about 85 g to 113 g

HOW THEY HARM

Toxins

Gout

High cholesterol

Vitamin A toxicity

Creutzfeldt-Jakob disease risk

WHAT THEY HEAL

Anemia

Vitamin B12 deficiency

Protein deficiency

Despite high nutritional value, organ meats, or offal, have never achieved in North America the popularity that they enjoy in Europe. Pâtés and popular luncheon meats, such as liverwurst, are often made from organ meats and perhaps other variety cuts, such as the feet.

Organ meats vary in nutrition, but most offer high amounts of vitamin B12 and potassium—tripe and heart contain both. Many organ meats are low in fat but most are high in cholesterol, for example, beef brain and pork brain contain more than 2,000 mg per 4-oz (113-g) serving. Liver, probably the most popular organ meat in North America, provides more than 10 times the Recommended Dietary Allowance (RDA) of vitamin A, 50 times the RDA of vitamin B12, and 50% or more of the RDAs for folate, niacin, iron, and zinc. One drawback, however, is that liver is high in cholesterol.

Health Benefits

Helps with anemia and vitamin B12 deficiency. Brains, heart, kidneys, and tongue all provide large amounts of iron and vitamin B12, which is necessary for keeping the body's nerve and blood cells healthy. It also prevents a type of anemia called megaloblastic anemia, characterized by weakness and fatigue.

Provides high-quality protein. Not all organ meats are high in fat or cholesterol. The heart, liver, and kidneys are leaner than other types, and also contain such useful minerals as iron.

Health Risks

Dangerous toxins. Because one of the liver's main functions is to metabolize and detoxify various chemical compounds, it may harbor residues of antibiotics and other drugs fed to meat animals as well as environmental toxins. For this reason, some doctors advise against eating liver on a regular basis.

Gout attacks. Organ meats are high in purines, which break down into uric acid in the body. An excess of uric acid causes painful inflammation that characterizes the trademark symptoms of gout, such as joint pain and toe tenderness. Therefore, organ meats are best avoided by those with gout and those who have a genetic predisposition to the disease.

Cholesterol. For most people, eating organ meats regularly will not affect their cholesterol levels. However, for people with heart disease or who are on cholesterol-lowering diets, the American Heart Association recommends consuming organ meats only occasionally.

Vitamin A toxicity. Liver is one of the richest dietary sources of vitamin A. When a person consumes more vitamin A than is needed, the excess is stored in the body; over time, vitamin A buildup can result in liver damage, fatigue, and other problems. Normally, it's difficult—if not impossible—to consume toxic amounts of vitamin A from an ordinary diet. But because liver is so high in this nutrient, an individual who regularly consumes it several times a week may develop toxicity.

Creutzfeldt-Jakob disease. Organ meats from animals infected by mad cow disease (bovine spongiform encephalitis) can contain prions, abnormal protein cells related to the disease. Although a link has yet to be proved, there are concerns that eating infected organ meats could lead to a similarly fatal new human variant of the brain disease, Creutzfeldt-Jakob disease.

Eating Tips

- Replace half the beef with chunks of beef kidney in a stew.
- Simmer a smoked pig's foot with sauerkraut.
- Braise beef tongue in place of traditional beef pot roast.

Buying Tips

- It's best to purchase organ meats from a local butcher you trust. The butcher can cut or trim the organs to your liking.
- At the supermarket, look for the Safe Food Handling label on packages of organ meat. This label means the meat has undergone safe processing and includes handling and cooking tips.
- Make sure that the organ meat is tightly wrapped and cold to the touch.

Storing Tips

- Store organ meats in the coldest part of the refrigerator or in the refrigerator's meat drawer or bin.
- Use organ meats within 2 days.

OYSTERS

See Shellfish, page 187

P

PAPAYAS

Typical serving size: 1 medium-size papaya (10.8 oz or 304 g)

HOW THEY HARM
Allergies

WHAT THEY HEAL
Heart disease
Colon cancer
Inflammation
Arthritis
Macular degeneration

Native to Central America, papayas are now grown in tropical climates around the world. Like most yellow-orange fruits, papayas are high in vitamin C and beta-carotene, the plant form of vitamin A. One medium-size papaya supplies more than twice the adult Recommended Dietary Allowance (RDA) of vitamin C, almost 30% of the RDA of folate, and 800 mg of potassium.

Health Benefits

Helps fight heart disease. In addition to Vitamin C and beta-carotene, papayas are a good source of vitamins E and A; these antioxidants help limit the oxidization of cholesterol in the bloodstream, which is associated with a lower risk for heart attack and stroke.

Protects against colon cancer. Papaya's fiber is able to bind to cancer-causing toxins in the colon and keep them away from the healthy colon cells. In addition, papayas are high in folate and beta-carotene, which are also associated with a reduced risk of colon cancer.

Reduces the effects of inflammation. Papaya contains several protein-digesting enzymes that may help lower inflammation and improve healing from burns. Some research has found that these enzymes may also help reduce the severity of inflammation-related symptoms for people living with asthma, osteoarthritis, and rheumatoid arthritis.

Keeps arthritis at bay. A study of more than 20,000 people found that those who consumed the lowest amounts of vitamin C–rich foods were more than three times likely to develop arthritis than those who consumed higher amounts. One papaya provides more than twice the daily dose.

Protects against macular degeneration. Eating 3 or more servings of fruit per day, such as papayas, may lower your risk of age-related macular degeneration, the primary cause of vision loss in older adults, by 36%, compared to persons who consume less than 1.5 servings of fruit daily.

Health Risk

Allergic reaction. Papayas are one of several fruits that have been associated with allergic reaction in people who are sensitive to latex. If you are latex-sensitive, choose organic papayas as these have not been treated with ethylene gas, which may increase the amount of enzymes that trigger the allergic reaction.

Eating Tips

• Green papaya is the unripe fruit. In Southeast Asian cuisines, it is often used raw in salads or cooked in curries or stews.

• Papaya seeds are thrown away, but they can be dried and used like peppercorns; sprinkle them over baked catfish.

• Toss chunks with lime juice and coconut.

• Serve shrimp salad on a bed of sliced papaya.

Buying Tips

- Choose fruits with reddish-orange skin that are slightly soft to the touch.
- Yellow patches indicate the fruit needs more time to ripen.

Storing Tips

- Store at room temperature and use within a day of purchase unless further ripening is required.
- To speed ripening, place in a paper bag with a banana.
- Uncut ripe fruit can be stored in a paper or plastic bag for up to 3 days.

PARSNIPS

Typical serving size: 1 cup, cooked (156 g)

HOW THEY HARM
   Allergies

WHAT THEY HEAL
   High cholesterol
   Weight gain
   Constipation
   Cancer
   Birth defects

Introduced to North America in the 1600s, parsnips look sort of like long, pale carrots and are a low-calorie food that's both nutritious and starchy. They have a sweet, nutty flavor that pairs well with other vegetables in soups or stews. Alternately, they can be served as a side dish or instead of potatoes. Because parsnips are too fibrous to be eaten raw, they are served cooked. A 1-cup (156-g) serving has only 111 calories and as much fiber as 3 slices of whole wheat bread; it also provides 573 mg of potassium, 20 mg of vitamin C, and 90 mcg (micrograms) of folate.

Health Benefits

Lowers cholesterol. Parsnips are an excellent source of both soluble and insoluble dietary fiber. A 1-cup (156-g) serving provides about 6 g of fiber, about one-quarter of the total amount that is recommended per day. Adequate fiber in the diet helps reduce cholesterol levels, obesity, and constipation conditions.

QUICK TIP: Keep the skin

The most nutritious part of a parsnip is just below the surface of the skin so for maximum nutrient value, don't peel them before cooking.

Fights cancer and birth defects. While they look a bit like carrots, they actually contain much more heart-friendly potassium and folate than the popular orange root vegetable. Folate is a B vitamin your body needs to create healthy cells; having insufficient levels has been linked to some forms of cancer and birth defects. And while parsnips may have only half the protein and vitamin C of potatoes, they provide more fiber, making them a healthy substitute in a number of dishes.

Health Risks

Allergic reactions. People with a known history of allergies to birch pollen as well as to foods like walnuts, figs, carrots, and parsley may develop a sensitivity to parsnips. Symptoms are usually limited to slight swelling and itching of the lips and mouth, but sensitive people might be better off avoiding parsnips.

Eating Tips

- Season oiled parsnip sticks with salt, rosemary, and black pepper, and bake at 450°F, for about 20 minutes to make fries.
- Roast chunks of parsnips and sweet potatoes with a pork roast.
- Add some cooked cubed parsnips to potato salad.

Buying Tips

- This winter root vegetable tastes best after the first frost because exposure to cold begins to convert its starch into sugar.
- Select ones about the size of a medium carrot; avoid parsnips that are covered with roots or are soft and shrunken.

Storing Tips

- If the tops are still attached, cut them off before storing so they don't draw moisture from the roots.
- Parsnips can be kept for about 3 weeks in the refrigerator.

PASSION FRUIT

Typical serving size: 3 medium passion fruit (1.6 oz or 45 g)

HOW IT HARMS

Bloating and flatulence

WHAT IT HEALS

Vision

Bones

Cell functions

Immunity

Collagen production

Constipation

Weight gain

Passion fruit is a delicious tropical fruit that has either dark purple or yellow, dimpled skin. The tough shell is inedible; when it wrinkles, then you know the fruit is ripe. The seeds can be eaten or the juicy pulp inside can be strained.

> **QUICK TIP:**
> **Easily remove seeds**
>
> If you'd like to remove passion fruit seeds, simply strain the pulp and juice through a cheesecloth or another nonaluminum sieve.

Health Benefits

Boosts vision and bone health. The vitamin A in passion fruit contributes to healthy vision and bone health. It stimulates white blood cell production and activity, and regulates other cell functions. It boosts your immune system and may also reduce your risk of cancer.

Pumps up the immune system. Filled with the powerful antioxidant vitamin C, passion fruit defends against harmful free radicals, also helps fortify your immune system, and fights off infection. It stimulates collagen production, which supports healthy bones, teeth, gums, and blood vessels.

Aids digestion. Passion fruit is a great source of dietary fiber if you eat the seeds. This helps improve digestion and prevent constipation and it makes you feel fuller faster, which can help with weight control.

Health Risks

Digestive discomfort. While passion fruit is delicious, eating too many of them in one sitting could boost your dietary fiber too quickly and cause gas, bloating, cramps, or diarrhea.

Eating Tips

- Spoon out the pulp and eat it plain, put it on ice cream, or add it to yogurt.
- Strain passion fruit pulp, cook it over medium heat in a saucepan for 5 minutes, then drizzle it over strawberry shortcake.

- Look for passion fruit that is heavy and firm.
- If the skin is green, it may not be ripe yet. As the fruit ripens, the skin will turn red, purple, or yellow.
- Don't let ugly skin scare you off. Even if the skin looks dimpled or wrinkled, as long as the fruit doesn't feel too soft, it should be in good shape.

Storing Tip

- When the passion fruit is ripe, it can be stored in the refrigerator for about a week.

PASTA

Typical serving size: ½ cup (2.5 oz or 70 g)

HOW IT HARMS
Weight gain (white pasta)
Diabetes (white pasta)

WHAT IT HEALS
Mood
Diabetes (whole grain pasta)
Heart disease (whole grain pasta)
Colon cancer

First introduced to North America by Thomas Jefferson, pasta has become a staple in many homes. Made from a variety of grains, pastas are a good source of iron (about 2 mg in a 1-cup serving); many are also enriched with thiamine, niacin, and other B vitamins. Although the protein in white pasta (about 5 to 7 grams in a 1-cup serving) lacks some essential amino acids, these can easily be obtained from a sprinkling of Parmesan cheese as a low-calorie (25 calories per tablespoon) topping.

Nutrition profiles differ slightly with each type of pasta. For instance, egg noodles provide complete protein while varieties flavored with spinach or tomato offer a few more antioxidants and high protein pastas are enriched with soy flour and milk solids. These variations, however, are not significant.

210 calories are in a typical serving of pasta, which should be about the size of a baseball.

The big difference is between pastas made with refined flours and those made with whole grains. Whole grain pastas, such as those made from quinoa, buckwheat, or whole wheat, offer two to three times the fiber of white pastas, which helps with a variety of health conditions.

Health Benefits

Improves your mood. Carbohydrate-rich pastas can help increase levels of serotonin in the brain, which make you feel good.

Stabilizes blood sugar. Whole grain pasta, which contains about three times the fiber of white pasta, won't cause dramatic blood sugar swings, so it's a great alternative for people with diabetes who must build their menus around complex carbohydrate choices.

Improves heart health. The fact that whole grain pasta is fiber rich also means it's good for a healthy heart. Fiber helps lower cholesterol levels and can aid weight loss, two critical factors to long-term heart health.

Reduces cancer risk. Whole grain pastas can reduce the risk of colon cancer. A Swedish study found that for those who consumed more than 4.5 servings of whole grains daily had 35% lower risk of colon cancer than those who ate less than 1.5 servings of whole grains a day.

Health Risks

Weight gain or diabetes. White pasta is made from refined flour. Because refined flour is digested quickly, a large plate of pasta can send your blood sugar levels soaring, only to crash several hours afterward and trigger renewed hunger. Such blood-sugar swings are linked with weight gain and may also lead to diabetes.

**QUICK TIP:
Stop sticky pasta**

When cooking pasta, adding a small amount of oil (1 tsp) to the water may help prevent spillovers and keep pasta from sticking. Salt is often added to pasta water, but it doesn't prevent stickiness; it's for flavor. And to reduce the boiling time, add the salt after the water is boiling.

Eating Tips

- Simmer leftover sauced pasta in broth for an instant soup.
- Brown cheese tortellini in a buttered skillet, then sprinkle bread crumbs lightly over the pasta to add texture.
- Serve a stir-fry on whole wheat penne in place of rice.

Buying Tips

- Fresh pasta is best for delicate sauces; dried pasta is better for more robust sauces.
- Fresh pasta is made with eggs, so it may be higher in cholesterol content than dried pasta.
- If you're watching your cholesterol, skip egg noodles. However, eggless "egg" noodles are available, too.

- You'll get about three times the fiber per serving if you choose whole wheat over white pasta. Experiment to find one you like.
- White pasta is enriched with iron and B vitamins, but pasta that's 100% whole grain is not.
- New high-fiber, high-protein varieties are even friendlier to your blood sugar. Some are made from grains such as oats, spelt, and barley in addition to durum wheat, which means they're higher in soluble fiber.

Storing Tips

- Because it's highly perishable, fresh pasta must be refrigerated in an airtight container. It should be used within a few days of purchase or frozen.
- Keep frozen pasta up to a month.
- Dried pasta can be kept in a cool, dry place indefinitely.

PEACHES AND NECTARINES

Typical serving size: 1 medium peach (3.5 oz or 98 g) or 1 medium nectarine (5 oz or 142 g)

HOW THEY HARM
Allergies
Cyanide poisoning

WHAT THEY HEAL
High cholesterol
Cancer
Chronic diseases
Weight gain
Constipation
Nerves
Muscles

Nutritious and versatile, peaches and nectarines can be enjoyed fresh, added to fruit salads, or cooked with meat and poultry dishes. They can also be baked, grilled, broiled, or poached to create pies, cobblers, and other desserts. The color makes a slight difference: White peaches and nectarines are sweeter than the orange and yellow varieties.

Nectarines, which are often described as peaches without the fuzz, are especially high in beta-carotene, an antioxidant that the body converts to vitamin A. They provide some potassium and vitamin E as well as C and E.

Health Benefits

Lowers cholesterol. Peaches and nectarines contain fiber, especially pectin, a soluble fiber that is instrumental in lowering high cholesterol.

Protects against cancer. The flesh of peaches and nectarines are rich in antioxidants—especially carotenoids—that help to protect against cancer and other chronic diseases.

Encourages regular bowel movements. The skins of nectarines contribute insoluble fiber, which helps prevent or treat constipation.

Aids in weight loss. For those watching their weight, peaches are a healthy way to add sweets to the diet. Canned and frozen peaches are higher in calories than fresh; a cup of sweetened frozen peaches contains 235 calories, compared to 190 in those canned in heavy syrup and 110 in juice-packed brands, whereas a fresh peach has only about 40 calories. Because peaches are a good source of dietary fiber, you're more likely to feel fuller longer.

Boosts nerve and muscle health. Two small peaches or nectarines have slightly more of the essential mineral potassium than a medium banana.

Health Risks

Allergic reactions. Dried peaches often contain sulfites, a preservative that produces an allergic reaction in susceptible people. Peaches may produce an allergic reaction in people with allergies to related fruits such as apricots, plums, and cherries as well as almonds. They also contain salicylates, which may provoke a reaction in aspirin-sensitive people.

Pits may cause cyanide poisoning. Nectarine and peach pits contain amygdalin, a compound that releases cyanide in the stomach. Although accidentally swallowing an occasional pit is not harmful, consuming several of them at a time can cause cyanide poisoning.

Eating Tips

- Top french toast with sliced peaches.
- Grill peach or nectarine halves to accompany pork chops or barbecued chicken.
- Spread sliced nectarines with vanilla pudding, sprinkle with brown sugar, and broil until bubbly.

Buying Tips

- Look for peaches or nectarines that are yellow or creamy with a rosy blush on their cheeks.
- Avoid peaches or nectarines with green undertones; they were picked too early.
- Select peaches with unwrinkled skin and no bruises.
- Avoid fruit that is rock hard. Purchase fruit that is moderately firm.
- Sniff the stem end of the peach or nectarine. You should be able to smell the peachy fragrance.
- Watch out for peaches or nectarines with tan circles. It's an early sign of decay.
- In North America, the season for peaches runs from April through mid-October, peaking in July and August. Peaches do not increase in sweetness after picking.

P

Storing Tips

- Choose relatively soft peaches if they are to be eaten right away.
- If you buy firm peaches or nectarines, placing them in a paper bag at room temperature will hasten the ripening process, usually within 2 or 3 days.
- Unless they are going to be eaten within the day, store ripe peaches or nectarines in the refrigerator; they will keep for 3 to 5 days.

QUICK TIP:
Prevent browning

Cutting or peeling a nectarine releases an enzyme that causes a darkening of the flesh that does not affect flavor or nutritional value. The discoloring can be slowed by immediately dipping the fruit in an acidic solution (for example, a tsp of vinegar diluted in a cup of water) or tossing sliced nectarines with a little lemon or lime juice.

PEANUTS AND PEANUT BUTTER

See also Beans and Legumes, page 48

Typical serving size: 1 oz or 28 g of peanuts; 1 to 2 Tbsp or 15 to 30 mL of peanut butter

HOW THEY HARM
High in trans fats
Allergies

WHAT THEY HEAL
Diabetes
High blood pressure
Low energy

Despite its name, the peanut is not actually a nut. It is a pulse and belongs to the legume family along with lentils and beans. The majority of the peanuts grown in North America are ground into peanut butter. The high fat content of peanuts makes them easy to grind into a paste, but the oil quickly turns rancid when exposed to oxygen and light. Many commercial peanut butters are made with preservatives, stabilizers, and added salt and sugar; you can avoid these ingredients by buying fresh-ground peanut butter made solely from nuts. Use this type of peanut butter within 2 weeks. The oil that rises to the top of the jar can be poured off to reduce the fat content.

Health Benefits

Protects against diabetes. The Nurses' Health Study found that women who ate peanut butter at least five times a week were as much as 30% less likely to develop diabetes.

Wards off heart disease. Peanuts are rich in plant compounds called sterols, one of the top proven cholesterol busters. Eating peanuts several times a week keeps high blood pressure under control. Both are risk factors for heart disease.

Provides a ready source of energy. In moderation, peanuts and peanut butter make satisfying healthy for children, who need extra dietary fat for proper growth and development. About 15 peanuts or one tablespoon (15 mL) contains about 95 calories, with 4 g of protein, 6 g of healthy fats, and significant amounts of potassium, magnesium, folate, and vitamin E.

Health Risks

Unhealthy fats. Peanut butters often contain hydrogenated vegetable oils. This means they are full of trans-fatty acids, which are bad for the heart. Check the ingredient list and labels for hydrogenated ingredients.

Allergic reactions. In some people, peanut products may trigger serious allergic reactions. Symptoms can range from a tingling sensation in the mouth to hives and, in extreme cases, to anaphylaxis, a life-threatening emergency.

Eating Tips

- Roll small balls of peanut butter in oats for a fun snack.
- Whisk peanut butter, lime juice, and soy sauce to marinate flank steak.
- Coat chicken tenders in chopped peanuts.
- Toss roasted peanuts into a pork stir-fry.

Buying Tips

- Read the ingredient labels carefully before buying peanut butter. Avoid ones with added sugar, salt, or trans fats.
- Opt for unsalted peanuts and you'll save more than 200 mg of sodium per 1-oz serving.

Storing Tips

- Refrigerate or freeze shelled nuts. Their oil turns rancid within 2 weeks.
- Never eat peanuts that are moldy or have an "off" taste; molds that grow on peanuts create aflatoxins, substances that cause liver cancer.
- It's best to store peanut butter in a glass container in the refrigerator for up to year, where the darkness prevents the loss of B vitamins and the cold retards oil separation.

2 hours is how much longer your appetite can be satisfied after eating peanut butter instead of a high-carb snack.

PEARS

Typical serving size: 1 medium pear (5.9 oz or 166 g)

HOW THEY HARM
- Allergies
- Tooth decay (dried pears)

WHAT THEY HEAL
- High cholesterol
- Constipation
- High blood pressure
- Diabetes

Called the "butter fruit" by many Europeans because of its smooth texture, a pear makes an ideal snack, dessert, or even a sweet or spicy side dish. Pears are a delicious treat when served fresh, but they can also be baked, poached, or sautéed. One medium pear has about 100 calories and provides about 6 g of fiber. Canned pears lose most of their vitamin C due to the combined effect of peeling and heating. They are also higher in calories, especially if they are packed in heavy syrup. There are about a dozen common varieties of pears—such as Bartlett, Anjou, and Bosc—and they have similar nutritional values.

Health Benefits

Lowers cholesterol levels. Pears are loaded with several types of fiber, including pectin, a soluble fiber that helps control blood cholesterol levels.

Relieves constipation. Cellulose in pears, an insoluble fiber, is also known as a bulk-forming fiber and has a mild laxative effect, helping to promote normal bowel function.

Helps lower blood pressure. Loaded with potassium, pears can help keep blood pressure under control.

May lower diabetes risk. Pears are a good source of antioxidants, and that may be especially important for people concerned about type 2 diabetes. According to a 2012 Harvard study, eating anthocyanin-rich foods such as pears more than five times a week was associated with a lower risk of developing type 2 diabetes. Pears also have a low glycemic index and load, which is helpful for people with diabetes

Health Risks

Allergic reactions. While fresh pears rarely cause allergic reactions, dried pears often contain sulfites, which can provoke asthma attacks or allergic reactions in susceptible people.

Tooth decay. Dried pears provide a more concentrated form of calories and nutrients than fresh pears; their high sugar content and sticky texture may promote tooth decay.

Eating Tips

- Add pear chunks to a spinach salad with blue cheese crumbles.
- Cook pears into a chunky sauce seasoned with nutmeg.
- Poach pears in pomegranate juice.

Buying Tips

- Once ripened, pears are highly perishable, so the fruit you buy at the market is likely to be slightly underripe.
- Pears are ripe when the skin is less shiny, the flesh at the stem yields slightly to the touch, and the fruit has a slight fragrance.

- Choose pears with smooth skin, and avoid any that are dark or bruised.

Storing Tips

- Allow pears to ripen at room temperature for a few days (speed up the process by leaving them in a brown paper bag).
- Once ripe, you can refrigerate them for a few days until ready to eat.

PEAS AND PEA PODS

See also Beans and Legumes, page 48

Typical serving size: ½ cup, shelled (1.7 oz or 49g)

HOW THEY HARM
Gout

WHAT THEY HEAL
Cancer
Constipation
High cholesterol
Macular degeneration

Throughout history, the pea has been a plant of significance. It is mentioned in the Bible, and dried peas have even been found in Egyptian tombs. In the mid-1800s, pea plants provided data for Gregor Johann Mendel, the founder of modern genetics. Peas are classified as legumes, and as such, they form a complete protein when combined with grains. Fresh green peas are more convenient than dried legumes, because they do not require a long cooking time and can even be eaten raw.

Green peas are lower in calories and fat than other high-protein foods: A half-cup serving contains about 60 calories and 4 g of protein. Snow peas are often used in

Chinese stir-fried dishes and are available fresh or frozen. They are eaten in their flat pod, because they are harvested while still immature; consequently, they contain less protein than green peas. However, they are higher in vitamin C (a half cup supplies about 40 mg, or 50% of the RDA for women) and have slightly more iron. Eaten in their fibrous pods, a serving of snow peas has about 35 calories per cup.

Health Benefits

Reduces risk of stomach cancer. A study in Mexico City published in the *International Journal of Cancer* showed that daily consumption of green peas along with other legumes lowers risk of stomach cancer, especially when daily coumestrol (a phytochemical that acts similarly to estrogen in the body) intake from these legumes is about 2 mg or higher. Because one cup of green peas contains at least 10 mg of coumestrol, it's not difficult to obtain this protective health benefit.

Relieves constipation. If eaten whole, green pea pods are high in insoluble fiber, a bulk-forming type of fiber that helps alleviate constipation.

Lowers LDL cholesterol. In addition to being high in protein, fresh green peas are a good source of pectin and other soluble fibers, which help control blood cholesterol levels. There is no truth to the notion that eating three dried peas a day lowers blood cholesterol.

Preserves eyesight. Peas contain lutein, a plant chemical linked to lowered risk of macular degeneration, the leading cause of blindness in older adults.

Health Risks

Gout. Green peas are high in purines, which can precipitate a flare-up of gout symptoms in people with this disorder.

Eating Tips

- Stir frozen baby peas into stews just before serving.
- Stuff pea pods with herbed cream cheese and top with grated carrot.
- Add frozen peas to cheese tortellini and broth for soup.

> **QUICK TIP:**
> **Preserve the nutrients**
>
> To minimize the loss of vitamins, peas should be cooked in as little water as possible until just tender. Cooking some of the pods with the peas or with soup stock adds flavor and nutrition.

Buying Tips

- Only about 5% of the peas grown are sold fresh; the rest are either frozen or canned.
- Frozen peas are better than canned, which have fewer nutrients, added salt and sugar, and less color and flavor.
- If buying fresh, the younger the green peas are, the sweeter and more tender they are; very young peas can be eaten in their pods. Younger peas have less-developed seeds.

Storing Tips

- Once picked, fresh peas should be eaten or refrigerated, because their sugar quickly converts to starch.
- Unwashed, unshelled peas stored in the refrigerator in a bag or unsealed container will keep for several days.

PECANS

See Nuts and Seeds, page 138

PEPPER, GROUND

See Herbs and Spices, page 110

PEPPERS

Typical serving size: ½ cup (46 g)

HOW THEY HARM
Digestion
Joint function
Pesticides
Canker sores

WHAT THEY HEAL
Cancer
Heart disease
Immunity
Macular degeneration

Sweet peppers are related to chiles, or hot peppers. Both are native to the Western Hemisphere and were named by Spanish explorers who confused them with the unrelated peppercorn. The four-lobed bell peppers are the most common of the sweet varieties in North America. Depending on the degree of ripeness, bell peppers range in color from green to yellow to red. Other varieties of peppers include banana peppers, which derive their name from their yellow color and elongated shape; cubanelles, which are tapered, about 4 in (10 cm) long, and range from green to red in color; and orange-red pimientos, which are heart shaped.

One medium pepper contains only 32 calories, and volume for volume they're a better source of vitamin C than citrus fruits. However, the vitamin content does vary according to color. One medium green pepper provides more than 100% of the adult Recommended Dietary Allowance (RDA) for vitamin C, whereas red peppers provide 50% more of this antioxidant. In contrast, a green pepper has about a tenth of the amount of beta-carotene compared to red peppers. Peppers supply smaller amounts of vitamin B6 and folate as well.

Health Benefits

Fights cancer. Deeply colored peppers are high in bioflavonoids, plant pigments that help prevent cancer; phenolic acids, which inhibit the formation of cancer-causing nitrosamines; and plant sterols, precursors of vitamin D that are believed to protect against cancer.

Supports heart health. Both the beta-carotene and vitamin C in peppers help to prevent atherosclerosis, which can lead to heart disease.

Strengthens immunity. Antioxidants like vitamin C in peppers help protect against infection, and also contribute to healthy bones, teeth, hair, and skin.

Aids eyesight. Peppers also supply lutein and zeaxanthin, antioxidants linked to a reduced risk of macular degeneration, the leading cause of blindness in older adults.

Health Risks

Joint and digestive health. A member of the nightshade family, bell peppers contain alkaloids that can impact digestive function and may also compromise joint function in sensitive individuals.

Pesticides. Bell peppers consistently rank among the top 15 foods to avoid if you want to limit your exposure to pesticides, according to the Environmental Working Group. Fortunately, bell peppers are easy to grow in most gardens, and organic options are usually available in any season.

May cause canker sores. If you're prone to these painful mouth sores, steer clear of green peppers.

Eating Tips

- Stuff poblanos for grilling with rice pilaf, corn, tomatoes, and queso fresco.
- Puree roasted red peppers, almonds, olive oil, and sherry vinegar for a dip.
- Top a veggie pizza with strips of banana peppers.

Buying Tips

- Although peppers are available throughout the year, they are most abundant and tasty during the summer and early fall months.
- Look for peppers that feel heavy for their size and select those that have smooth, unwrinkled skin without any soft or dark spots.
- Peppers, which ripen only on the vine, grow sweeter as they ripen. Red ones are sweeter than yellow ones, which are sweeter than green ones.

Storing Tips

- Refrigerate for up to a week.

PERSIMMONS

Typical serving size: 1 medium persimmon (6 oz or 168 g)

HOW THEY HARM
 Bloating and flatulence

WHAT THEY HEAL
 Cancer
 Immunity
 Blood pressure
 Digestion
 Weight gain

The persimmon is an exotic fruit with yellow-orange skin, which is at its sweetest when very ripe. There are two major varieties of persimmon in North America. One is the sweet, tomato-shaped Fuyu; the other is the juicier, crispier, acorn-shaped Hachiya. Fuyus, or nonastringent persimmons, are eaten when hard, as you would an apple. They're crisp, sweet, and crunchy, and you can eat both the skin and the flesh.

The Hachiya persimmon has an almost jelly like-texture, with flesh that tastes like honey and vanilla. However, unripe they are bitter. The trick is to let the persimmon ripen way beyond what you would normally expect. It must be soft, squishy, and almost bursting out of its skin with ripeness. When ready to eat or to use in cooking, cut off the top, scoop out the pulp, and discard the seeds.

Health Benefits

May reduce cancer risk. Persimmons are high in vitamin A, which regulates cell functions, boosts your immune system, and may reduce your risk of cancer.

Boosts immune system. A powerful antioxidant, the vitamin C in persimmons helps fight off harmful free radicals, boosts your immune system, and protects against infection.

Lowers blood pressure. Persimmons are a good source of potassium, which can improve blood pressure by offsetting some of the harmful effects of sodium. Potassium may also lower your risk of recurring kidney stones and osteoporosis.

50% of your Daily Recommended amount of Vitamin A is in a single, medium-size persimmon.

Aids in digestion and weight loss. Like other fruits, persimmons are a good source of dietary fiber. The fiber in them can help improve digestion, prevent constipation, and make you feel fuller faster, which can help you lose weight or maintain a healthy weight.

Health Risks

Digestive trouble. A perfectly ripe persimmon can be delectable, but as with any fruit, eating too many of them in one sitting could prove to be too much of a good thing and you could end up with gas, bloating, cramps, or diarrhea.

Eating Tips

- Add a cup of persimmon pulp to bread recipes for an additional zing.
- Chop up some persimmons and add to salsa.
- Freeze ripe fruit, then scoop out the insides and eat like sherbet.

Buying Tips

- Hachiya persimmons should be very soft when ripe, while Fuyu are crisper.
- Seek out unblemished, deeply colored reddish-orange fruit with glossy skin.

Storing Tips

- Enjoy soft, ripe fruit immediately, because overripe persimmons can become mushy or mealy.
- Allow any firmer, unripe persimmons to ripen before eating,
- To ripen firm fruit, place it in a paper bag at room temperature for 1 to 3 days. Put an apple in the bag with the persimmon to speed up the ripening process.
- Ripe persimmons can be stored in the refrigerator inside a plastic bag for up to 3 days.
- Store puréed persimmon flesh in the freezer for up to 6 months.

PICKLES

See also Condiments, page 84

Typical serving size: Varies

HOW IT HARMS
Blood pressure
Weight gain
Cancer risk
Potential gluten source

WHAT IT HEALS
Scurvy

Before the advent of the modern freezer, pickling was an essential means to keep sufficient food stores over the winter. Today, however, popular pickled foods are consumed mostly for their taste. In pickling, food is preserved by saturating it with acid, which prevents most microorganisms from growing. Two basic methods are used: soaking in acid, usually a vinegar-based solution; and brining, a fermentation process that takes place through the action of acid-producing bacteria.

Bacteria rarely grow in these mixtures, but molds and yeasts may flourish on imperfectly sealed surfaces. Fermented pickles, such as dill pickles, are vegetables that are immersed in a brine that is strong enough to inhibit the growth of unwanted bacteria but mild enough to nourish several species that produce lactic acid. This and other compounds contribute to the characteristic flavor.

Health Benefits

Prevents scurvy. Long before vitamin C and other essential nutrients were identified, sauerkraut—pickled cabbage—was used to prevent scurvy during extended sea voyages. While scurvy is hardly a modern health problem, sauerkraut is still an excellent source of vitamin C and provides almost 2 mg of iron, and useful amounts of the B vitamins, calcium, potassium, and fiber.

Jazzes up your diet. While most pickled foods have limited nutritional value, they contain little to no fat and can certainly add flavor and flair to a meal without a lot of extra calories, especially with the enormous variety now available.

Health Risks

Can be a potential cancer risk. A diet that is high in pickled or salt-cured foods and condiments has been linked to an increased risk of stomach and esophageal cancers. This is thought to stem from their high levels of nitrates, which are converted to cancer-causing nitrosamines during digestion.

May raise blood pressure. The high salt content in most condiments may be harmful to people with high blood pressure or on a low-salt diet.

Eating Tips

- Stir thin slices of pickled jalapeños into egg salad.
- Layer thinly sliced gherkins on a grilled cheese sandwich.
- Chop up pickles and add to tuna, chicken, and egg salads.

Buying Tips

- Pickles and other condiments are sold in bottles and cans. When purchasing, examine the lid and container to confirm that the seal has not been broken.
- Some pickle canners offer lower sodium options.

Storing Tips

- Store canned pickles and condiments in a cool, dry place and use within a year.
- After opening, refrigerate unused portions.

PINEAPPLES

Typical serving size: 1 cup (4 oz or 115 g)

HOW THEY HARM
   Allergic reactions
   Canker sores

WHAT THEY HEAL
   Cancer
   Blood clots
   Metabolism

Native to South America, pineapples are now grown in tropical areas worldwide. They are available in frozen and dried forms, but the majority of the crop is reserved for canned varieties, juices, or fresh fruit. The sweet and tangy flavor makes fresh pineapple a delicious choice: It can be added to fruit salads, and grilled or baked with seafood, ham, poultry, or other meats.

Health Benefits

Curbs cancer risk. Pineapple is a good source of ferulic acid, a plant chemical that helps prevent the formation of cancer-causing substances.

Helps prevent heart attack and stroke. Bromelain, an enzyme in pineapples, is an anti-inflammatory. Preliminary research suggests that it may reduce the risk of blood clots, thereby lowering the risk for heart attack and stroke. This is surprising because, being a protein, bromelain is mostly broken down in the digestive tract before it can be absorbed into the bloodstream.

Aids metabolism. Pineapple is an excellent source of the trace mineral manganese, which the body needs for a number of important enzymes to work properly. Manganese plays a role in the metabolism of fats, cholesterol, and protein as well as in building bones and healing wounds.

Health Risks

Allergic reactions. Despite its potential to help control swelling, a chemical in pineapples, bromelain, can also cause skin irritation or allergic dermatitis in susceptible people if they come in contact with pineapples.

Canker sores. If you're prone to these painful mouth sores, steer clear of pineapples.

Eating Tips

- Drizzle grilled pineapple slices with caramel sauce.
- Stir pineapple chunks into chicken salad.
- Thread fresh pineapple chunks on shrimp and bell pepper kebabs.

QUICK TIP: Use pineapple as a meat tenderizer

Fresh pineapple contains bromelain, an enzyme that dissolves proteins. Consequently, fresh pineapple is a natural meat and poultry tenderizer when it is added to stews or marinades.

Buying Tips

- After picking, a pineapple will not ripen further.
- When buying a pineapple, look for one that exudes a fragrant odor and has light yellow or white flesh.
- If you are buying the fruit whole, make sure that it seems dense and heavy for its size and that the leaves are green.
- When buying canned pineapple, opt for 100 percent fruit juice, as opposed to heavy syrup. Pineapple in heavy syrup has almost three times the calories and sugar content of pineapple in 100 percent juice.
- Although pineapples are available year-round, their peak season takes place during June and July.

Storing Tips

- Fresh pineapples will keep for a few days on the counter at room temperature.
- Refrigerate cut portions in an airtight container for up to 3 days.
- Brown patches indicate spoilage.

PLUMS AND PRUNES

Typical serving size: 2 fresh plums (4.6 oz or 132 g); ½ cup prunes (1.2 oz or 35 g)

HOW THEY HARM
- Allergies
- Cyanide poisoning
- Tooth decay

WHAT THEY HEAL
- Cancer
- Obesity
- Constipation
- Bone loss

Whether they are eaten whole, added to fruit salads, baked goods, compotes, puddings, or meat dishes, plums are a nutritious low-calorie food. One medium-size fresh plum contains only 36 calories It also supplies several nutrients, including dietary fiber, vitamin C, and potassium. Canned plums contain comparable amounts of riboflavin and potassium but are significantly lower in vitamin C (one canned plum provides only 1 mg).

Although all prunes are plums, not all plums are prunes. Prunes, also called dried plums, are the dried fruit from a few particular species of plum trees whose fruit has firm flesh and is naturally high in sugar and acidity. Prunes are rich in fiber: five prunes contain 3 g of fiber as well as good amounts of iron and potassium. Unlike other types of juice, prune juice retains most of the fruits' nutrients because it is made by pulverizing the dried prunes and then dissolving them in hot water.

Health Benefits

Reduces cancer risk. Plums contain anthocyanins, the reddish-blue pigments that lend them their intense color. These antioxidant pigments may help protect against cancer by mopping up free radicals, unstable molecules that damage cells.

Curbs appetite. Plums are low in calories and contain fiber, making them an ideal snack to curb hunger pangs when dieting. In one recent study at San Diego State University, participants snacking on plums were less hungry than the control group, which snacked on low-fat cookies instead. Follow-up blood tests also confirmed that the group eating plums experienced less of a rise in blood sugar and lower amounts of a hunger-regulating hormone called ghrelin.

Eases constipation. Prunes are popular as a remedy for preventing or treating constipation. This effect can be attributed to prunes' high dietary fiber content; they also contain isatin, a natural laxative. In fact, prunes may be even more effective than psyllium (the type of fiber in popular laxative formulas) in fighting constipation, according to results from a 2011 study at the University of Iowa, which makes them an attractive food-based alternative to over-the-counter products.

Helps slow bone loss. In a 2011 study at the University of Florida, researchers followed 236 postmenopausal women and gave them daily calcium supplements along with prunes or dried apples. They tested the subjects after 3, 6, and 12 months and found that the group that had been snacking on prunes had significantly less bone loss than the other women. Researchers believe the high levels of potassium and vitamin K in prunes may contribute to the bone-boosting benefits.

Health Risks

Allergic reactions. Plums may produce an allergic reaction in individuals with confirmed allergies to apricots, almonds, peaches, and cherries, which come from the same family. Similarly, people who are allergic to aspirin may also encounter problems after they have eaten plums.

Cyanide poisoning. Like peaches and apricots, the pits of plums contain amygdalin, a compound that breaks down into hydrogen cyanide in the stomach, and can cause cyanide poisoning if consumed in large amounts.

Tooth decay. Prunes are high in calories and sugar (a half cup of the stewed fruit or five large pitted prunes contain approximately 115 calories), and they leave a sticky residue on the teeth that can cause cavities.

Eating Tips

- Bake sliced plums with agave nectar and cinnamon.
- Replace half the chocolate chips with chopped prunes in cookies.
- Dab halved plums with ricotta cheese whipped with orange peel.
- Bake a salmon fillet covered with plum slices in teriyaki sauce.

Buying Tips

- Overripe plums tend to be soft, with a bruised or discolored skin, and they are sometimes leaky.
- Color which varies from one variety to another, may not be a good indicator of ripeness. Instead, look for brightly colored fruit that yields slightly to the touch.
- Look for prunes that are bluish-black and blemish free.

- Choose plums that are slightly soft and somewhat flexible as these are signs of tenderness.

Storing Tips

- Firm plums can be stored for a day or two at room temperature to soften them.
- Store prunes in an airtight container in a cool, dark place for up to 6 months.

POMEGRANATES

Typical serving size: ½ cup seeds (3 oz or 87 g)

HOW THEY HARM
Drug interaction

WHAT THEY HEAL
Prostate cancer
High cholesterol
Hypertension
Erectile dysfunction

The word *pomegranate* is old French for "seeded apple," a fitting name for this apple-size fruit filled with jewel-like clusters of red seeds. Pomegranates have a leathery, deep red to purplish rind. The interior is bursting with hundreds of tiny, edible seeds packed into compartments called arils and separated by bitter, cream-colored membranes. The fruit can be eaten by deeply scoring it vertically and then breaking it apart. The clusters of juice sacs are then lifted out and eaten. Pomegranates are a good source of potassium. One fruit contains about 400 mg, more than in most oranges. They also contain vitamin C and fiber. Pomegranates and their juice are rich in anthocyanins and ellagic acid, both of which have antioxidant properties.

WARNING!
FOOD-DRUG INTERACTION

Pomegranates can affect how the liver processes medications. Eating a pomegranate or drinking pomegranate juice can increase the side effects of medications, too. Such medications include fluoxetine, codeine, and ondansetron. Also, some heart medications, such as ACE inhibitors, can be affected by pomegranates. Eating pomegrantes while taking blood pressure medication could cause your blood pressure to go too low.

Health Benefits

Helps treat prostate cancer. Researchers at UCLA measured patients' prostate-specific antigen (PSA) blood levels, which help indicate the presence of cancer. They found that drinking 8 oz (237 mL) of pomegranate juice daily significantly slowed rising PSA levels in patients previously treated for the disease.

Lowers cholesterol levels. Research has shown that pomegranate juice has two to three times the antioxidant capacity of equal amounts of red wine or green tea, and anthocyanins make an important contribution to the pomegranate's antioxidant power. A recent study suggests that drinking as little as one-quarter cup of pomegranate juice daily may improve cardiovascular health by significantly reducing oxidation of LDL cholesterol.

Lowers blood pressure. Because of the rich antioxidant levels pomegranate juice provides, researchers have also found it can play a role in reducing hypertension.

Improves erectile dysfunction. A study published in the *International Journal of Impotence Research* found that drinking about 8 oz of 100% pomegranate juice

each day can help with erectile dysfunction and impotence. At the end of the study, 47% of the participants reported that their erections improved with the use of pomegranate juice.

Health Risks

Drug interactions. While the benefits of pomegranate juice are clear, there have been a few reports of the juice causing complications for people taking some heart medications. If you're under the care of a physician for heart disease, it's a good idea to talk with your doctor before drinking regular amounts of pomegranate juice.

Eating Tips

- Add pomegranate seeds to mixed green salads.
- Make a virgin sangria with pomegranate juice.
- Stir pomegranate seeds into guacamole.

Buying Tips

- Choose those that are heavy for their size and have a bright, fresh color and blemish-free skin.
- If purchasing a juice, look for products labeled "100% pure pomegranate juice" for the most nutritional value.

Storing Tips

- Refrigerate fresh pomegranates for up to 2 months or store in a cool, dark place for up to a month.

QUICK TIP: Add anti-sun seeds

Tossing some pomegranate seeds onto your summer salads may be good for your skin. Scientists have discovered that nutrients in pomegranates can reduce the ability of UVB radiation to cause cancer-promoting damage in skin cells, including alteration of NF-kappa, a pre-cancerous biomarker.

Pomegranates   **169**

SUPERFOODS:
Do They Live Up to the Hype?

With all the crazy cleanses and deprivation diets out there, it's often hard to separate food fact from fad, especially when there's a whole trend of calling the latest food to pop on the media radar a "superfood."

In recent years, we've seen foods such as açai, goji berries, and matcha dubbed the latest and greatest things you can put in your mouth. No single food can be the ultimate cure-all, but some foods certainly have more nutrition and healing ability than others. And it's a good idea to incorporate these foods into your diet. Scientists estimate that about 30 to 40% of all cancers, for example, could be avoided with proper diet, and we know that eating right can reduce your risk of heart disease, type 2 diabetes, and stroke. So, make the following miracle munchies—chosen for their nutrition content, ability to help prevent or treat major ailments, and ease of availability—a regular part of your diet:

FISH

Certain fish, such as salmon and mackerel are loaded with omega-3 fatty acids, which have been shown to lower your risk of heart disease, decrease inflammation in the body, and even improve brain function.

TOMATOES

These juicy red vegetables are packed with lycopene, a carotenoid known to lower your risk for developing heart disease and many kinds of cancer. Studies found that cooking tomatoes actually makes the lycopene much more potent.

BROCCOLI

Remember all those times your mother told you to eat your broccoli? Well, she might have been on to something. Cruciferous vegetables have been shown to protect against bladder cancer.

BLUEBERRIES

These natural sweet treats are loaded with antioxidants and vitamin C, which help fight disease, as well as anthocyanins, shown to boost brainpower.

GARLIC

This antioxidant-rich food is not only flavorful, but can reduce your risk of developing colon tumors.

DARK CHOCOLATE

Not like you need an excuse to indulge in chocolate, but a few ounces a day of the concentrated, 75% cocoa stuff, can actually lower your bad cholesterol, prevent your arteries from clogging, and reduce stress.

GREEN LEAFY VEGETABLES

Dark leafy greens like spinach, Swiss chard, and kale are like the ultimate superfoods. They are packed with iron, beta-carotene, vitamins C and E, folate, and calcium, all essential for a strong, healthy body. They also contain lutein, which can protect against macular degeneration and cataracts.

SOY

Tofu and other soy products aren't just for vegetarians. Consuming soy can reduce your risk of developing colorectal cancer, lower cholesterol, and boost your bone strength. It can even help with hot flashes in menopausal women.

NUTS

Certain nuts like almonds and walnuts are like snacking powerhouses when it comes to your health. Almonds can keep your heart healthy, reduce stress, and rid your body of free radicals. Walnuts contain omega-3 fatty acids, making them a body-boosting alternative for those who can't eat fish.

POMEGRANATE

Pomegranate juice can reduce cancer-causing inflammation in the body and stave off the progression of coronary heart disease.

FLAXSEEDS

These small brown seeds are packed with fiber and loaded with lignans, which have been shown to slow down tumor growth in women with breast cancer. They also contain magnesium to help control blood sugar and omega-3 fatty acids to lower triglycerides and reduce inflammation.

BEANS

Whether you're meat free or not, beans are a healthy protein alternative, full of B vitamins to protect your heart and relieve stress; iron, calcium; and a hearty amount of fiber to help clean out your system.

THE BOTTOM LINE

- Lots of foods are touted as "superfoods," but no one food is a magic solution to convey of the all of the nutrients your body needs.
- A "superfood" doesn't do you much good if it's hard to find. There are plenty of easy-to-find, amazingly nutritious foods available.

P

PORK

See also Smoked and Cured Meats, page 189

Typical serving size: 4 oz. or 113 g

HOW IT HARMS
High cholesterol

Parasites

WHAT IT HEALS
Bones

Muscles

Heart, muscle, and nervous system function

Anemia

Immunity

Thrifty cooks used to boast that when it came to pigs, they could use everything but the squeal. A pig yields chops and other cuts of fresh meat; cured or processed products, such as ham and bacon; and skin for gelatin.

Most cuts of fresh pork are leaner than they used to be because of selective breeding techniques. Lean roast pork is nutritionally close to skinless poultry in its fat and calorie content.

Many pork products, however, like ham, sausage, and bacon, do contain excessive amounts of fat. Two slices of pork bacon contain 6 g of fat and 73 calories. Bacon also contains nitrates, which can lead to the formation of carcinogens.

Health Benefits

Helps build bones and muscles. Pork provides a complete protein to help your body build and maintain strong bones and muscles.

Helps convert food to energy. Pork is a major source of thiamin, a B vitamin that is instrumental in the conversion of carbohydrates into energy for the body and brain. It's also crucial for heart, muscle, and nervous system function.

Can prevent anemia. About half the iron in pork is heme iron, the most readily absorbed and digested type of dietary iron.

Boosts immune system. Commonly known for its ability to strengthen the immune system, the zinc in pork helps build protein and DNA, heals wounds, and is necessary for keeping your senses of smell and taste intact.

Health Risks

Cardiovascular disease. The saturated fat in fatty cuts of pork, such as rib roasts, blade chops, and pork products like ham, bacon, and sausage, can lead to a host of health problems, including high cholesterol. For a healthy diet, be sure to choose lean cuts of pork.

Parasites. If you eat raw or undercooked pork, you could get a tapeworm infection. Cook pork at 140°F (60°C) or higher to avoid tapeworm infection.

Eating Tips

- Shred pork and serve in tacos instead of ground beef or chicken.

- Cube cooked pork and toss in a salad.
- Wrap bacon around a dried apricot that's been moistened with orange juice.

Buying Tips

- Fresh pork should be smooth and pink, not gray or damp looking.
- Seek out lean cuts of pork, like pork tenderloin, which is low in saturated fat.
- Always check the date stamp on packages of vacuum-sealed bacon, ham, and sausage to make sure it's fresh. The date reflects the last date of sale.
- If pork has to be part of your breakfast meal from time to time, opt for bacon instead of sausage. A slice of bacon, cooked thoroughly, has fewer calories than a typical sausage. Your best bet is a slice of lean back bacon with the rind and fat cut off, rather than fat-streaked bacon.

Storing Tips

- Fresh pork should keep for up to 3 days in the refrigerator, though keep in mind that smaller cuts may spoil quicker.
- Cooked pork can be stored in the refrigerator for up to 5 days.
- Cooked bacon and ham can be frozen and then reheated in a microwave.
- Store sliced, cooked meat, such as ham, away from other uncooked meats in the refrigerator.

POTATOES

Typical serving size: 1 medium potato (6 oz or 173 g)

HOW THEY HARM
Toxic risk
Digestion
Joint function
Weight gain
Diabetes

WHAT THEY HEAL
Cancer
Hypertension

Although they are often associated with Ireland, potatoes are native to the Andes Mountains and were first cultivated by Peruvian Indians at least 4,000 years ago. Spanish explorers introduced potatoes to Europe in the 1500s, where they became a staple food source for the poor. Potatoes are now cultivated worldwide; in fact, they are the world's largest and most economically important vegetable crop.

For most North Americans, potatoes are a major component of the diet—usually in processed forms that are high in fat and salt. However, on their own, potatoes are surprisingly nutritious and low in calories. A medium-size baked or boiled potato has between 120 and 150 calories, a small amount of protein, and almost no fat. The same potato turned into potato chips has 450 to 500 calories and up to 35 g of fat; 4 oz (113 g) of french fries contain about 300 calories and 15 to 20 g of fat. When eaten with the skin, they are high in complex carbohydrates and fiber and also provide vitamins B6, and C, and magnesium.

Health Benefits

Fights cancer. Potato skins are rich in chlorogenic acid, a phytochemical that has anticancer properties. Korean scientists found that potato peel can contain up to 20 times more chlorogenic acid than the pulp.

Lowers blood pressure. It's well known that potatoes are low in sodium and rich in potassium, which means they're an ideal food for fighting hypertension. However, there may be some other factors at play. A recent British study discovered compounds in potatoes called kukoamines, which may also play a role in lowering blood pressure levels. While

- In October 1994, the potato became the first vegetable to be grown in space.
- French fries were introduced to the United States when Thomas Jefferson served them in the White House.
- Don't eat potato eyes, because they contain higher levels of solanine, a chemical that can cause gastrointestinal and neurological disorders.

it's not yet known how much of this phytonutrient is needed in the diet to make a difference, this discovery has revealed that potatoes offer much more nutritional potential than had been previously assumed.

Health Risks

Toxic risk. Green and sprouted potatoes may contain solanine, a potentially toxic alkaloid substance if consumed in great quantities. Fortunately, most varieties grown in North America contain only trace amounts.

Digestion and joint function. Potatoes are a member of the nightshade family, a group of vegetables that contain alkaloids, which can impact digestive function and may compromise joint function in sensitive individuals.

Weight gain. Potatoes are relatively low in calories and are only fattening when they are fried or served with butter.

Diabetes. Potatoes may pose some issues for people with diabetes or people trying to lose weight by following a diet that prevents blood sugar swings, because potatoes score relatively high on the glycemic index (GI) and glycemic load (GL) (page 262). However, the type of potato and the way it's prepared can change its score. For example, mashed potatoes are higher on the GL than boiled potatoes.

> **QUICK TIP: Save the skins**
>
> When preparing potatoes, it is best not to remove the skin because the fiber is in the skin and many of the nutrients are near the surface. Instead, scrub them under water with a vegetable brush. Baking, steaming, or microwaving preserves the maximum amount of nutrients.

Eating Tips

- Simmer sliced red-skinned potatoes and leeks in broth for quick soup.
- Fry cubed potatoes and cauliflower with curry powder and cilantro.
- Fry patties of cold leftover mashed potatoes mixed with scallions.

Buying Tips

- Choose potatoes that are firm and blemish free.
- New potatoes may be missing some of their feathery skin, but other types should not have any bald spots.
- Avoid potatoes that are wrinkled, sprouted or cracked, or that have a green tinge to them.

Storing Tips

- Store potatoes in a dark, cool place, but not in the refrigerator, for up to 2 weeks.
- Temperatures below 45°F (7°C) convert the starch to sugar, giving the potato an unpleasant taste.
- Don't store potatoes and onions together; the acids in onions aid the decomposition of potatoes, and vice versa.

POULTRY

See also Smoked and Cured Meats, page 189

Typical serving size: 3 oz or 85 g, cooked

HOW IT HARMS
Bacterial contamination

WHAT IT HEALS
Bone loss
Heart disease

Poultry—including chicken, turkey, Rock Cornish game hen, duck, goose, guinea fowl, squab, pheasant, and quail—is an excellent source of high-quality protein, with all the essential amino acids, as well as calcium, iron, phosphorus, potassium, and zinc. And while all poultry has a similar range of nutrients, the main difference (apart from flavor) is in the fat content. A 3-oz (85-g) portion of roasted, skinless light turkey is the lowest in calories and fat, with 135 calories, 3 g of fat, and 25 g of protein, compared to 170 calories, 9 g of fat, and 20 g of protein in a comparable portion of skinless roasted duck. A 3-oz (85-g) serving of roasted chicken breast without skin has 26 g of protein, 142 calories, and 3 g of fat compared to the same serving with skin at 195 calories and 8 g of fat.

Health Benefits

Protects against bone loss. Because chicken is packed with protein, it may strengthen bones. Researchers think that protein levels may be a factor in slowing down bone loss.

Fights heart disease. Not only is chicken a lower-fat alternative to red meat, but it is also an excellent source of vitamin B6. This vital nutrient plays a an important role in the body's ability to manage homocysteine, a type of molecule that can build up in the blood stream and damage blood vessel walls. Just 4 oz (113 g) of chicken supplies about one-third of a person's daily needs for vitamin B6.

Health Risk

Bacterial growth. Because most poultry is sold with its skin intact, it is susceptible to spoilage from bacteria that remain on the skin and in the cavity after processing. Kept at 40°F (4°C), the average refrigerator temperature, the chicken will develop slimy skin in about 6 days, indicating a 10,000-fold increase in bacteria. You should wash your hands often during preparation, and scrub knives and cutting boards in hot, soapy water. Of particular concern is a bacteria called campylobacter, which can cause cramps, diarrhea, and fever. Organic chickens are less likely to harbor this bacteria.

165°F (74°C) is the temperature ground chicken or turkey should be cooked at to ensure safety.

Eating Tips

- Roast a small turkey breast for additive-free sandwich cold cuts.
- Replace beef in chili with ground boneless skinless chicken thighs.
- Make a salad with leftover roast chicken, cooked broccoli, and chopped tomatoes.

Buying Tips

- When buying poultry, you can be confident that a bird is young and tender if its legs and wings spring back after being pulled out.
- Store-bought rotisserie chicken should be golden brown, free of extra grease, and hot when purchased. Look for time stamps on the chicken to see when it was prepared. Purchasing one within 2 to 4 hours since preparation is best.
- Canned chicken has a sodium content that's higher than fresh chicken.
- Skin color does not affect the taste, but don't buy poultry with rough, dry, or bruised skin, which may be a sign that the texture and flavor of the meat are inferior.

Old School
To minimize fat and calories, always remove the skin before cooking chicken.

New Wisdom
Cooking poultry with the skin intact helps preserve its natural juices. Cook with the skin and remove before serving.

Storing Tips

- Store poultry in the coldest part of the refrigerator for up to 3 days and make sure it is securely wrapped so that its juices don't contaminate other foods.
- Cooked poultry will keep in the refrigerator for up to 3 days.
- Frozen raw poultry should be used within 2 months for maximum flavor; if cooked, used frozen chicken within a month.

PRUNES

See Plums and Prunes, page 167

PUMPKINS

Typical serving size: 1 cup, cooked (8.6 oz or 244 g)

HOW THEY HARM
Choking hazard (seeds)

WHAT THEY HEAL
Cancer
High blood pressure
Crohn's disease

To most North Americans, pumpkins (a type of winter squash) are a symbol of Halloween and Thanksgiving. In fact,

QUICK TIP:
Bake some seeds

Pumpkin seeds are easy to prepare. Scoop out the seeds, wash them and let dry, then bake them on an oiled baking sheet at 250°F (121°C) for an hour. Commercial varieties, sometimes sold as "pepitas," are often salted.

they have more uses than just as traditional jack-o'-lanterns and pie filling—the strong-flavored flesh of pumpkins can be cooked and enjoyed in many ways. One cup (244 g) of cooked canned pumpkin contains 83 calories, 7 g of fiber (almost as much as you'd get from 4 slices of whole wheat bread), and 3.4 mg of iron, which is almost 20 percent of the Recommended Dietary Allowance (RDA) for women. Because pumpkins absorb water, they lose some nutrients and have fewer calories when they are boiled. Sugar pumpkins, which are smaller and sweeter than the large deep-orange pumpkins, are the best choice for cooking.

Although the seeds are often thrown away, they are a rich source of protein. One ounce (28 g) of pumpkin seeds provides 7 grams of protein—almost as much as an equal serving of peanuts—as well as 3 mg of iron (20 to 30 percent of the adult RDA). They are high in unsaturated fats, a source of vitamin E, and rich in B vitamins. When the coverings are consumed too, the seeds are high in fiber.

Health Benefits

Helps protect against cancer. Like all orange-pigmented vegetables, pumpkins are rich in beta-carotene, the plant form of vitamin A: Two cups of canned or baked pumpkin provides more beta-carotene than a carrot. Studies have shown that this antioxidant may help prevent some forms of cancer. Pumpkin seeds, too, appear to have anticancer properties and have been incorporated into some supplement formulas that may help fight prostate cancer.

Lowers blood pressure. Pumpkins are a rich source of potassium, which is an important nutrient for good blood pressure control. One cup of pumpkin has more than 500 mg, although regular canned pumpkin will provide about the same amount of sodium, so it's best to cook it yourself and control the added salt—or look for a no-salt-added brand, if sodium is a problem for you.

Helps those with Crohn's disease. Although no one diet seems to work for people living with the inflammatory bowel problems associated with Crohn's disease, pumpkins and pumpkin seeds are among a handful of foods that seems to be well tolerated by most.

Health Risk

Choking hazard. While the risk may be small, it's quite real. The American Academy of Pediatrics advises not giving pumpkin seeds to children under the age of 5.

Eating Tips

- Make a stew with canned pumpkin, white beans, bell peppers, and chili powder.
- Sprinkle pumpkin seeds on muffins before baking.
- Add canned pumpkin to pancake batter with powdered ginger.

Buying Tips

- Choose pumpkins that are free from blemishes and heavy for their size.

Storing Tips

- Because pumpkins have hard shells, they are ideal for storing.
- Pumpkins last about a month in a cool, dry place.

QUINOA

Typical serving size: ½ cup, cooked (3.3 oz or 93 g)

HOW IT HARMS
Kidney stones

WHAT IT HEALS
Celiac disease
Cancer
Heart disease
Diabetes
Obesity

Although it is often classified as a grain, quinoa is actually a member of the same plant family as spinach. While the green leafy quinoa (pronounced KEEN-wah) tops are edible, it's the seeds that are served most frequently. For more than 5,000 years, quinoa has been the staple food of peoples of the Andes, where it is one of the few crops that grows well in the dry mountainous climate and poor soil.

The tiny quinoa seeds are packed with important nutrients: A ½-cup serving provides about 2 mg of iron, more than any unfortified grain product. It also contributes large amounts of several other essential minerals, including 45 mg of magnesium, 87.5 mg of phosphorus, 157.5 mg of potassium, and 0.75 mg of zinc, as well as numerous B vitamins, especially B6, folate, niacin, and thiamine.

Most of the calories in a cup of cooked quinoa come from complex carbohydrates. However, it also provides protein, which is of a higher quality than similar products because it provides lysine, an amino acid missing in corn, wheat, and other grains.

QUINOA FACTS
- Since nutrient-rich quinoa is drought resistant and grows well on poor soils without irrigation or fertilizer, it's been designated a "super crop" by the United Nations for its potential to feed the hungry poor of the world.
- NASA has shown interest in quinoa, recommending it be considered as an ideal food on long space flights.
- Inca warriors relied on balls of quinoa mixed with fat to supply them with necessary calories on the battlefield.

Health Benefits

Provides nutrient boost to gluten-free diets. While the only "cure" for celiac disease is the complete removal of gluten from the diet, gluten-free grains like quinoa can help ward off certain nutritional deficiencies that may accompany going gluten free. According to some recent research out of Columbia University, incorporating quinoa into a healthy gluten-free diet can result in measurable improvement in protein, iron, calcium, and fiber levels.

Protects against cancer and heart disease. Quinoa is a good source of saponins, phytochemicals that help to prevent cancer and heart disease.

Helps regulate blood sugar and high blood pressure. Researchers in Brazil found that quinoa has important potential for helping people with diabetes regulate their blood sugar and high blood pressure better. Out of 10 different grains and cereals studied, quinoa provided the most quercetin and antioxidant levels overall. Its low glycemic index and load are also helpful for blood sugar control.

Fights obesity. While quinoa's high fiber content makes it an obvious choice for helping control the appetite, some exciting new lab findings in Paris seem to indicate that quinoa may eventually play a more specific role in fighting obesity. Researchers there observed that mice fed a high-fat diet didn't continue to gain weight after their meals were supplemented with quinoa extract. They also noted that the mice showed less insulin resistance and that several inflammation markers in their blood were reduced as well.

Health Risks

Kidney stones. Quinoa is related to spinach, chard, and beets, so it also contains oxalates (sometimes in substantial amounts), which can lead to the development of some types of kidney stones in people who are prone to them. The oxalate content of quinoa ranges widely, but even the lower end of the oxalate range puts quinoa on the caution or avoidance list for an oxalate-restricted diet.

Eating Tips

- Add some cooked quinoa to a corn relish.
- Use quinoa flour in place of half of the all-purpose flour in muffin recipes.
- Cook quinoa with raisins and cinnamon for breakfast.

Buying Tips

- With its popularity on the rise, quinoa can be found in most health food stores and supermarkets alongside the rice.
- There are more than 120 varieties of this tiny, bead-shipped grain but the most frequently sold are white, red, and black in color.

Storing Tips

- Store quinoa in an airtight package in a cool, dark place for up to 6 months.
- Freeze indefinitely for longer storage.

RADISHES

Typical serving size: 5 medium radishes (0.8 oz or 23 g)

HOW THEY HARM
  Bloating and flatulence
  Allergies

WHAT THEY HEAL
  Obesity
  Cancer

A member of the cruciferous family, the radish is closely related to cabbage, kale, turnips, and cauliflower. While not especially high in most essential nutrients, radishes are tasty as well as low in calories, making them ideal for snacking and as a spicy addition to salads, soups, and vegetable side dishes. Summer radishes have a more intense peppery flavor than those cultivated during spring or fall. Although the bright red globe variety is the best-known in North America, other types include black radishes, daikons, and white icicles.

Health Benefits

Provides some nutrients but few calories. A fair source of vitamin C, radishes also contain small amounts of iron, potassium, and folate. Five medium-size raw radishes provide 5 mg of vitamin C and yield only 5 calories, making them an ideal snack for those trying to lose weight.

May lower cancer risk. Like other cruciferous vegetables, radishes supply sulfurous compounds that may protect against cancer. One study of about 1,500 people in Poland found a particularly strong decrease in the risk of stomach cancer among those who consumed the most radishes and onions.

Health Risks

Gas. Radishes can cause bloating and gas in some people, especially those sensitive to other types of cruciferous vegetables like broccoli and cauliflower.

Allergies. Radishes contain salicylates—compounds similar to the active ingredient in aspirin: Many people sensitive to aspirin may suffer an allergic reaction to radishes.

Eating Tips

- Dip radishes into peanut sauce for a spicy snack.
- Add some grated radish to coleslaw.
- Toss slivered radishes with sautéed asparagus pieces.

Buying Tips

- The peak season for radishes spans from April to July, but most varieties are available year-round.
- When selecting red globe radishes, avoid the larger ones if possible, as they may be pithy.
- A bright color indicates freshness.
- If there are leaves on the stems, make sure they are green and crisp.
- Regardless of which variety of radish you are buying, the vegetables should feel solid and have an unblemished surface.

Storing Tips

- Unless the radishes are going to be served the same day, you should remove any leaves and tops. They will stay fresh longer without the tops.
- If they are not already packaged, store radishes in plastic bags.
- They will keep for about 2 weeks.

QUICK TIP: Skip the singe

To avoid the "hot" flavor found in some varieties of radish, simply peel the skin.

RAISINS

See Grapes and Raisins, page 108

RASPBERRIES

See Berries, page 88

RHUBARB

Typical serving size: 1 cup (122 g)

HOW IT HARMS
Poisonous (leaves)
Mineral absorption
Kidney stones
Gallstones

WHAT IT HEALS
Cancer
High blood pressure

Rhubarb is botanically a vegetable, although everyone calls it a fruit. It is available in frozen and canned forms, but most people prefer to cook the fresh stalks. One cup of fresh diced rhubarb yields a mere 26 calories, provides 10 mg of vitamin C, 350 mg of potassium, and 2 g of fiber. A popular springtime pie filling often combined with strawberries, rhubarb can also be made into preserves or stewed to make a sauce to complement poultry, meats, pork, and desserts.

QUICK TIP:
Create a sugar-free compote

For each cup of chopped rhubarb in a nonaluminum saucepan, mix in ¼ cup golden raisins and ¼ cup pineapple juice. Simmer for about 10 minutes, or until softened. Serve warm or cold.

Health Benefits

May prevent cancer. Researchers in Great Britain discovered that baking rhubarb for 20 minutes releases high levels of anticancerous polyphenols. Scientists are now hoping to use the results to study the effect that rhubarb's antioxidants may play in treating leukemia.

Keeps cells healthy. The antioxidant vitamin C in rhubarb helps to prevent harmful free radicals that are produced by the body's digestive process and by exposure to tobacco smoke, radiation, and other environmental toxins.

Helps control blood pressure. The potassium in rhubarb lessens the effects of sodium in raising blood pressure.

Health Risks

Poisonous. If eaten, rhubarb leaves (not the stalks) cause oxalic acid poisoning. Symptoms can include difficulty breathing, vomiting, and diarrhea. It would take a great deal of leaves for the poisoning to be fatal. The rhubarb stalks are perfectly safe to eat.

Mineral absorption. Even though one 1 cup (244 g) of fresh diced rhubarb contains more than 100 mg of calcium, it is not considered a good source of this mineral. That's because rhubarb also contains oxalic acid, which blocks the absorption of calcium needed for healthy bones and teeth.

Kidney stones or gallstones. Large amounts of rhubarb should be avoided by those who have a tendency to develop oxalate-containing kidney stones or gallstones.

Eating Tips

- Cook equal parts of chopped rhubarb and dates for a spread.
- Replace berries with finely chopped rhubarb in muffins.
- Add some rhubarb to a pork and vegetable ragout.

Buying Tips

- Choose firm, blemish-free red stalks with red flesh.

Storing Tips

- Cut off the leaves (if attached) and discard.
- Wash the knife with hot soapy water to make sure no poisonous residue from the leaves remains.
- Wash the stalks in cold water, then pat dry.
- Store in a plastic bag in the refrigerator crisper. Use within 1 week.
- Do not use if the stalks become mushy or discolored.
- Freeze rhubarb for future use by washing the stalks and cutting them into ½-in pieces. Pack the pieces into a sealed plastic container and freeze for up to 1 year.

RICE

Typical serving size: ½ cup, cooked (2.8 oz or 79 g)

HOW IT HARMS
Blood sugar (white rice)

WHAT IT HEALS
Colon cancer (brown rice)
Diarrhea
Diabetes (brown and wild rice)
Celiac disease

For thousands of years, rice has been the staple food for more than half of the world's population. Like barley and oats, rice grows in a protective husk that has to be removed if the grain is to be used as food. Many nutrients are lost with the bran and germ that are removed in milling to make white rice. Brown rice—intact kernels that retain their bran layers—is somewhat more nutritious than white rice.

Rice is a true staple in menu planning. Risottos, made with fat-free broth and vegetables, and pilafs, based on fat-free broth, chopped nuts, and dried fruits, are economical, nutritious, low-fat entrées. Rice is an ingredient of hot and cold breakfast cereals, an excellent base for salads, and a natural companion to vegetables, fish, meats, and cheese. Rice bran adds bulk to baked goods.

Health Benefits

Helps prevent colon cancer. Consumption of brown rice at least once a week reduced the risk of colorectal polyps by 40%, according to the results of a California study of 2,800 subjects who had undergone a colonoscopy.

Soothes troubled bowels. Rice has a binding effect in diarrhea and, as such, is part of the BRAT (banana, rice, applesauce, and toast) diet. It helps restore normal bowel function and provides needed energy for someone recovering from diarrhea.

Helps control diabetes. While white rice can increase the chance of developing type 2 diabetes, some studies show that brown rice and wild rice—which retain fiber, vitamins, and minerals—help regulate glucose metabolism in people with diabetes by providing a slow, steady supply of glucose.

Doesn't trigger allergies. Along with lamb and a few other foods, rice rarely, if ever, provokes an allergic reaction. This quality makes rice ideal as the basis of the strict elimination diet that is sometimes used to identify food allergens. It's also why it is often recommended as a first food for babies.

Is safe for those with celiac disease. Rice does not contain gluten—a type of protein found in wheat, barley, rye, and other cereal grains—so it is safe and digestible for individuals with celiac disease and gluten intolerance.

Prevents protein deficiency in vegetarians. The protein content of rice, ranging from 2 to 2.5 mg per half cup, is less than that of other cereals, but when eaten with dried beans, rice makes a complete protein.

QUICK TIP:
Stir up some rice pudding

Rice pudding made with low-fat milk and flavored with cinnamon is a soothing, easy-to-digest dish for and those who are convalescing or need easy-to-swallow food.

Health Risk

Blood sugar spikes. Because white rice is a refined carbohydrate, it is digested quickly, elevates blood sugar levels, and provides energy, but with less nutritional value and fiber content than brown rice.

Eating Tips

- Toss cooked cooled wild rice with lime juice and toasted coconut for salad.
- Bake thin patties of leftover risotto, drizzled with olive oil, until crisp.
- Make southwestern fried rice with leftover brown rice and taco seasoning.

Buying Tips

- When buying in a bulk section, make sure that the bins are covered and the rice is dry.
- Rice is classified by size and shape (long, medium, and short grain). Long-grain rice remains dry and separate when cooked; short-grain rice, which is wetter and stickier, is more often used in Asian and Caribbean cooking.
- All varieties can be brown or white. Opt for the healthier brown rice.

Storing Tips

- Store white rice in an airtight container in a cool, dry cupboard for up to 1 year.
- Store brown rice in an airtight container in the refrigerator or freezer for up to 6 months. Otherwise, the nutritious oil in the bran can go rancid.
- Cooked rice is highly prone to spoilage. Store cooled, cooked rice in an airtight container in the coldest part of the refrigerator for no more than 5 days or in the freezer for up to 6 months.

RYE

See Grains, page 104

SALSA

See Sauces and Salad Dressings, page 184

SALT AND SODIUM

Typical serving size: 1 dash (0.01 oz or 0.3 g)

HOW THEY HARM
Hypertension
Fluid retention
Kidney stones
Osteoarthritis

WHAT THEY HEAL
Nerve function

While the terms are often used interchangeably, salt and sodium are not the same. Sodium is an element that joins with chlorine to form sodium chloride, or table salt. Sodium occurs naturally in most foods, and salt is the most common source of sodium in the diet. Sodium works to maintain the body's acid-alkaline balance and helps maintain the body's fluid balance. It also helps control nerve function and muscle movement.

On the other hand, "salt" actually refers to a class of substances composed of ions held together by virtue of their opposite charges. Calcium carbonate (chalk) is a salt, as is sodium bicarbonate (baking soda). Sodium chloride is the most abundant salt occurring naturally in food.

The amount of sodium the body needs daily is far less than what is usually consumed. Circumstances and climate will dictate the amount needed, but in general, you need 1,300 to 1,500 mg a day to meet your body's needs. A typical North American diet can have 4,000 to 7,000 mg per day. One tsp of salt supplies more than 2,000 mg of sodium.

Some people are more salt-sensitive than others, and they will get the biggest payoff from cutting back on salt. African Americans and people with diabetes tend to be more sensitive to salt, as are older people.

The increase in blood volume that occurs during pregnancy temporarily increases the body's need for salt, but the amount required is normally supplied in a varied, balanced diet. Pregnant women should prepare meals with only a little salt and not add salt to food at the table.

Health Benefits

Promotes proper nerve function. Sodium plays an essential role in the way cells maintain their integrity and how nerve impulses are transmitted throughout the body. These functions also include muscle contraction and heart rhythm.

5 WAYS TO CUT SALT

1. Use fresh herbs and spices that don't contain sodium: garlic powder or fresh garlic, onion flakes (instead of onion salt), dry mustard, coriander, lemon, mint, cumin, chili, curry, rosemary, thyme, basil, bay leaves, ginger, hot peppers, black pepper, chives, and parsley.
2. Make your own salad dressing and flavored vinegars instead of salt for extra taste.
3. Eat more fresh or frozen fruits and vegetables rather than canned. If you use canned vegetables, buy low-sodium or no-salt-added versions. Use fresh potatoes rather than instant, and fresh cucumbers instead of pickles. Add spices and herbs instead of salt to the water in which you cook vegetables.
4. Eat fresh or frozen fish instead of canned or dried varieties, and choose sliced roast beef or chicken over bologna, salami, or other processed meat.
5. Reeducate your taste buds. Taste food before adding salt. Cook from scratch instead of from packages. Adapt your favorite recipes by using half the salt called for.

Health Risks

Hypertension. People with high blood pressure, or hypertension, are typically advised to cut back on salt, because sodium affects the kidneys' ability to rid the body of wastes and fluid. When the body's sodium level is low, the kidneys retrieve the chemical from the urine and return it to the circulating blood. Some individuals, however, have a genetic tendency to conserve sodium, which may predispose them to high blood pressure. As the kidneys retain more salt than necessary, they excrete less urine so that fluid is available to maintain the sodium at the correct concentration. As a result, the heart is forced to pump harder to keep this extra fluid in circulation, and the blood pressure increases to maintain the blood flow. Restricting salt intake may correct this form of high blood pressure.

Kidney stones and osteoarthritis. Those who have high-salt diets may be at an increased risk of kidney stones and osteoarthritis. As the salt leaves the body, it also takes some calcium with it, which can lead to those conditions, according to a 2012 study from the University of Alberta. Sodium and calcium may be regulated by the same functions within the body, so when the sodium is expelled, calcium is, too.

QUICK TIP:
Check your water softener

The use of a home water softener may add a substantial amount of sodium to your drinking water. You may prefer to drink bottled water instead.

Eating Tips

- Kosher salt has larger grains so it tastes saltier and you can use it more sparingly so you get less sodium.
- Add salt after water boils. Putting salt in before raises the boiling point, and the water takes longer to boil.

Buying Tips

- The major sources of sodium in the diet are processed and preserved foods.
- Cereals, cold cuts, canned soups, canned vegetables, prepackaged meals, and commercial baked goods are usually high in sodium.
- Sodium is also found in MSG (monosodium glutamate), garlic salt or other seasoned salts, sea salt, meat tenderizers, commercially prepared sauces and condiments (ketchup, soy sauce, chili sauce, and steak sauce) soups, cured or smoked foods, olives, and pickles.
- Sea salt is nutritionally similar to table salt, and there are no documented health advantages to sea salt.

Storing Tips

- Keep salt in a cool, dry, sealed container away from sunlight.
- The shelf life of iodized salt is about 5 years.
- Seasoned salt has a shelf life of about a year.
- Drop a few grains of rice into salt shakers to prevent salt from clumping.

SAUCES AND SALAD DRESSINGS

Typical serving size: Varies depending on type

HOW THEY HARM
Weight gain (high-fat, and high-sugar sauces
Blood pressure (high-sodium sauces)

WHAT THEY HEAL
Weight gain (low-fat sauces
Blood sugar swings (low-sugar sauces)

Sauces are the signature of different types of cuisine. For example, smoky, mesquite-flavored barbecue sauce is slathered over Southwest-style cooking. The buttery, creamy hollandaise sauce covers fine French entrées. Pasta sauces, such as marinara, are as Italian as spaghetti. Salsa is a must-have side to Mexican fare, and gravies are always found around the holidays.

Salad dressings come in a colorfully wide variety. However, the creamier, heavier ones can turn an otherwise healthy salad into a diet-buster. For example, just 2 Tbsp (30 mL) of ranch dressing can add 148 calories and 15 g of fat. Vinaigrette dressings are a healthier option, with only about 60 calories in 2 Tbsp and 5 g of fat.

For just about any sauce or salad dressing, homemade is often the better option. Store-bought versions contain high levels of sodium—often topping 30% of the RDA. Indeed, the word *sauce* comes from the root meaning "salty." Early sauces were heavily salted and spiced to preserve food and mask the flavors of any tainted meats.

Health Benefits

Helps maintain healthy weight. Salsa, with its primarily tomato base, supplies fiber that can make you feel fuller longer. Preliminary studies indicate that vinegar can also help satiety so you eat less.

Stabilizes blood sugar. Sauces based on fresh vegetables and olive oil are good sources of vitamins, fiber, complex carbohydrates, and unsaturated fat, which all help manage blood sugar. In addition, several studies have suggested that vinegar may reduce blood sugar levels, so vinegar-based salad dressings are a good choice.

Health Risks

Weight gain. Sauces made from butter, flour, cream, and egg yolks (such as hollandaise and beurre blanc) and creamy salad dressings (such as ranch) are very high in fat, saturated fat, and cholesterol.

Blood pressure. Asian-style sauces, such as peanut sauce and soy sauce, and some store-bought salsas are high in salt and can spike blood pressure. These should be avoided by people on low-sodium diets.

High in sugar. Some sauces, like Worcestershire and barbecue sauce, are hidden sources of processed sugar.

QUICK TIP:
Go beyond a chip dip

Dollop freshly made tomato, fruit, or vegetable salsa on grilled seafood, poultry, or pork. Or use as a dressing for a rice-and-vegetable salad.

Eating Tips

- Remove sautéed chicken cutlets from the skillet, and deglaze with lemon juice and rosemary for a pan sauce.
- Make your own healthy vinaigrette by whisking three parts olive oil into one part white, balsamic, or red wine vinegar. Add a pinch of no-salt seasoning (try a Cajun, Italian, or Southwest blend).
- Poach halibut steaks in marinara sauce.
- Make a lower-fat turkey gravy by thickening with a flour-water mixture instead of roux.

Buying Tips

- Avoid bottled sauces and dressings made with cream, butter, egg yolk, and cheese, which are very high in fat and cholesterol. They should be used only sparingly, and people with high cholesterol levels should avoid them altogether.

- Choose refrigerated or bottled sauces and dressings made with fine-chopped vegetables or fruits, herbs, olive oil, and vinegar or lemon juice, with low or no salt added.

Storing Tip

- Refrigerate according to the package directions.

SAUSAGES

See Smoked and Cured Meats, page 189

SEAWEED

Typical serving size: Varies depending on recipe

HOW IT HARMS
High in sodium

WHAT IT HEALS
Thyroid function
Muscles
Immunity
Metabolism

Seaweed is a versatile and tasty vegetable that can be used in a broad spectrum of ways. There are more than 2,500 varieties of seaweed, which include everything from the algae that forms on ponds to kelp and other marine plants. Seaweed is usually classified according to its color—brown, red, green, and blue-green.

In Japan, seaweed is also used to enhance flavors in a variety of dishes, due to its high natural MSG content. Kombu, a type of kelp (a brown plant that is one of the most common seaweeds), is used to flavor soup stocks. Wakame, another type of kelp, is used in Japan in soups and stir-fries. Nori, the algae used to make sushi rolls, is known as laver by the Irish and Welsh.

Health Benefits

Boosts thyroid health. Most seaweeds are a rich source of iodine, which the thyroid gland needs to produce the hormones that regulate body metabolism.

Helps build muscles. A ½-cup (113-g) serving of raw nori has a mere 40 calories yet provides about 6 g of protein, with no fat or cholesterol.

Boosts the immune system. Beta-carotene, a precursor of vitamin A, boosts the body's resistance to disease while aiding vision, bone growth, and cell function. A ½-cup serving of raw nori provides 5,200 IU of vitamin A as beta-carotene.

Prevents folate deficiency. A ½-cup serving of kelp contains almost 200 mcg (micrograms) of folate (50% of the adult Recommended Dietary Allowance) which the body uses as folic acid to build DNA and red blood cells. Because folate is not stored in the body in large amounts, you must eat it regularly to maintain levels of it in the blood.

Health Risk

High in sodium. A ½-cup portion of raw wakame contains approximately 900 mg of sodium; an equivalent amount of dried spirulina yields more than 1,100 mg. (A recommended daily sodium intake for a

QUICK TIP:
Swap seafood for seaweed

Protein-rich sea vegetables make a terrific replacement for fish and shellfish for vegetarians.

healthy person should not exceed 2,300 mg.) The same amounts of kelp and nori are lower in sodium, containing 250 mg and 60 mg, respectively. Anyone on a low-salt diet should avoid foods containing seaweed.

Eating Tips

- Stir crumbled nori into tuna salad.
- Add arame or dulse seaweed to miso soup.
- Stir-fry soaked dried hijiki seaweed with kale, garlic, ginger, and sesame oil.

Buying Tips

- Sold in Asian groceries, natural food stores, and specialty grocers, nori are dried, and sometimes toasted sheets of seaweed used to season salads, soups, and noodles.
- Nori can be soaked to use as wrappers for rice cakes and sushi.
- Fresh or bagged salted seaweeds are available in Asian markets.
- Arame has a particularly high calcium content and can be bought already shredded in a dark-green tangle. A small amount makes an exciting addition to mushroom or seafood risottos as well as Asian rice dishes. It needs a 5-minute soak and then 30 minutes of cooking.
- Kombu seaweed can be cooked with dried beans. It speeds up their cooking time and contributes flavor.
- Dulse seaweed, available fresh and dried, is good in soups and in vegetable or grain dishes. You can eat it deep-fried or, after a brief soak to soften it, shred it into salads or their dressings.

Storing Tip

- Dried seaweed can be stored, well-wrapped in a cool cupboard for up to a year.

25% of dishes in Japan are made with some type of seaweed.

SHELLFISH

Typical serving size: 2 to 3 oz (56 g to 85 g), shelled

HOW IT HARMS
   Allergies

WHAT IT HEALS
   Cancer
   Weight gain
   Heart health
   Anemia
   Thyroid function

Shellfish **is the catchall term** applied to mollusks and crustaceans—water-dwelling creatures that wear their skeletons on the outside. Mollusks, such as oysters and mussels, lead a sedentary life inside rigid shells, which they affix with threadlike excretions to rocks or pilings. Scallops are found in two groups—the larger sea scallop or the much smaller bay scallop. Octopus and squid, which are free swimming and have no shells, are also mollusks. Another exception is snails, which are mollusks that live on dry land or in the water and move about, carrying their shells.

The soft bodies of crustaceans, such as lobster, shrimp, and crab, are covered by hinged plates of chitin, like suits of armor, that allow mobility but shield them from predators. Soft-shell crabs are taken in the molting season, when they have discarded their old shells but before the new shells have hardened.

Health Benefits

May lower cancer risk. The mineral selenium in shellfish is an important antioxidant linked to lower cancer risk.

Helps maintain a healthy weight and healthy heart. In contrast to protein from warm-blooded animals, shellfish protein is very low in actual fat. Shellfish are very low in saturated fat, the lipid most likely to raise blood cholesterol levels, and contain heart-healthy omega-3 fatty acids.

Can prevent anemia. Shellfish also contain iron and vitamin B12, deficiencies of which can cause anemia.

Boosts thyroid health. Shellfish is naturally rich in iodine, which is needed for production of hormones by the thyroid gland and for normal cell metabolism. Lack of enough iodine can lead to hypothyroidism.

Health Risks

Allergic reactions. Many people are allergic to shellfish, and an allergic reaction to one type often means that the others should be avoided, too. A severe reaction, with widespread hives, swelling, and difficulty breathing, indicates possible anaphylaxis, a life-threatening emergency. People allergic to shellfish may react to the iodine used in many of the dyes administered for contrast x-rays. Tell your doctor if you have ever experienced an allergic reaction to shellfish.

Environmental contamination. If grown in polluted waters, shellfish may be contaminated with bacteria and carry a particular risk for hepatitis. Don't gather shellfish at the seashore or near wharf pilings or built-up areas. Shallow-water shellfish, such as clams and mussels, are the most susceptible to pollution. Sea scallops and other deep-water varieties are less likely to be exposed to waste.

Old School
Avoid squid and shrimp, which contain fairly high levels of cholesterol.

New Wisdom
The dietary cholesterol in shellfish appears to have relatively little effect on blood levels of cholesterol.

Eating Tips

- Dollop baked clams with green chili salsa.
- Serve seared scallops on curly endive with mustard dressing.
- Make a soup with mussels and chickpeas, flavored with two garlic cloves, two tsp of cumin, half a tsp of chili powder and a cinnamon stick.

Buying Tips

- Buy from markets and food stores that keep live shellfish well covered with ice or, in the case of lobsters, in tanks with circulating water aerated with oxygen.
- Fresh shellfish, whether in the shell or shucked, should smell briny, without any hint of iodine or fishiness.
- Shrimp and crabmeat are exceptions to the live-shellfish rule. Most shrimp are trimmed and frozen in bulk at sea, then thawed for sale. Shrimp processed in this way should be labeled "previously frozen."
- Most crabmeat is cooked in the shell, or extracted and pasteurized, then frozen. Shellfish that is frozen or canned is usually ready to eat as purchased.
- Because crabmeat is separated from the shell by being passed through rubber rollers, however, it should be picked over to remove shell fragments.

Storing Tips

- Store fresh shellfish in a shallow pan on a bed of ice in the coldest part of the refrigerator.
- Cook and eat within 24 hours of purchase.
- Purchased frozen shellfish can be kept frozen for up to 6 months.

SHRIMP

See Shellfish, page 187

SMOKED AND CURED MEATS

Typical serving size: Varies depending on type

HOW THEY HARM
Cancer
Cardiovascular disease
High blood pressure
Migraines
Listeriosis
Toxoplasmosis
Drug interaction

HOW THEY HEAL
Muscle growth

Before the development of refrigeration, people the world over used similar methods for preserving meat: salting, smoking, and air drying. Although curing is no longer essential in industrialized countries, our taste for salty, smoky flavors persists.

Smoking preserves meat and fish both by slow cooking at a low temperature and by treatment with chemicals in the smoke. The method is now used primarily for flavor—for example, the distinctive hickory or oak aroma that is associated with smoked bacon, and the mesquite and other aromatic wood chips that are used to enhance the taste of grilled foods.

Air curing, or preserving by dehydration, has been used for thousands of years. Prosciutto is an air-cured meat. Drying gener-ally concentrates some nutrients, especially minerals, but the vitamin content of dried meat is much less than that of fresh.

Salt-cured meats, such as country ham or bacon, are preserved either in a brine solution or a dry salt bed. The salt draws water from the meat and from bacteria and molds through the process of osmosis. While the meat remains wholesome, the microorganisms shrivel and die.

50% by weight is the legal U.S. limit for the amount of fat in fresh pork sausages.

Link sausages are typically made from pork or beef with cereal fillers, herbs and spices, and preservatives. Because sausages go through several stages of handling, they are more susceptible to contamination than fresh meat and should be cooked very thoroughly before consumption.

The term *cold cuts* technically refers to any cooked meats that are sliced and served cold, but it is frequently also used to refer to cured and smoked meats.

All cold cuts and cured and smoked meats are high in sodium, frequently more than 30% of RDA. Many, especially cold cuts and sausages, also contain fillers such as corn syrup or cereal (and therefore should be avoided by people with celiac disease or gluten intolerance). Some, especially those made from pork or beef, are also high in saturated fats; turkey or chicken versions usually have lower levels of fat.

Health Benefits

Can boost muscle growth. Several cold cut options are loaded with protein, which is essential to building and repairing muscles. Opt for cuts that are low-sodium and for lean, low-fat meats, such as turkey breast.

Health Risks

Cancer. The reddish-pink color of cured meats, including the cold cuts at the deli counter, is due to the presence of nitrites, chemicals that enhance the effect of salt by inhibiting bacterial growth and slowing fat oxidation. Nitrites can cause tumors in laboratory animals that consume it in very high doses. But the meat industry and the government insist that nitrites should be retained because they are extremely effective against *Clostridium botulinum,* the microorganism that causes botulin poisoning, or botulism.

> **WARNING!**
> **FOOD-DRUG INTERACTION**
> The amino acid tyrosine, which is found at high concentrations in cured meats, can cause migraines, an abrupt rise in blood pressure, and even fatal collapse in persons taking monoamine oxidase (MAO) inhibitors to treat depression.

High blood pressure and cardiovascular disease. Because of their high sodium content, cold cuts and other cured meats can increase blood pressure, a leading risk for heart problems.

Migraines. Tyramine, a metabolic product of the amino acid tyrosine, is found at high concentrations in cured meats. It can trigger migraine attacks in susceptible people.

Listeriosis and toxoplasmosis. Listeria, a bacteria found in deli meats, infects an estimated 2,500 people per year with listeriosis, which causes flulike symptoms. The bacterium is killed by the pasteurization process and cooking; but some deli foods are contaminated after processing. While the infection is rarely serious for healthy adults, pregnant women should limit the amount of cold cuts they eat because it poses a serious risk to the baby. Uncooked air-cured or salt-cured meats may be infected with the toxoplasmosis parasite, which can have similar risks for fetuses.

Eating Tips

- Add slivers of corned beef to sautéed cabbage.
- Simmer smoked pork hock with barley vegetable soup.
- Stir some diced salami into artichoke salad.

Buying Tips

- Lower-sodium options are available for most varieties of cold cuts. But "lower" doesn't mean much—some brands still top 460 g of sodium per serving in their lower-sodium versions.
- Buy lean cuts of white meat as a healthier option to most cold cuts.
- Select cured meat products just before checking out at the supermarket register.
- Look for cured meat products with a use-by date. Be aware that dating is a voluntary program and not required by the federal government. It is the last date recommended for the use of the product while at peak quality. The date has been determined by the manufacturer of the product.

- All cured meats, smoked meats, and sausages—except dry sausage and some canned hams—are perishable and must be kept refrigerated.
- Fresh sausages can be refrigerated, unopened, for up to 2 days before cooking.
- Hot dogs, unopened, can be refrigerated for up to 2 weeks.
- Bacon, unopened, can be refrigerated for up to 1 week.
- Deli-sliced luncheon meats and fully cooked ham can be refrigerated for up to 5 days.
- Commercially packaged luncheon meats can be refrigerated for up to 2 weeks.
- Sausages and bacon can be frozen for up to 6 months.

SOFT DRINKS

Typical serving size: 1 can (12 fl oz or 355 mL)

HOW THEY HARM
Obesity
Tooth decay
Bone loss
High blood pressure

WHAT THEY HEAL
Nausea
Low energy

Carbonated waters were originally invented to cash in on an 18th-century fad for naturally sparkling mineral water. The taste for carbonated drinks (originally hangover cures) has never faltered. The average North American consumes about 48 gal (182 L) a year.

Soft drinks are broadly defined as nonalcoholic beverages, and carbonated soft drinks are classified as soda pop or, in some areas, simply sodas or pop. They consist mostly of carbonated water mixed with sugar or an artificial sweetener, plus coloring agents and various patented natural or artificial flavorings. Many of them also contain caffeine.

1 soda a day leads to a 60% greater chance for a child to grow up to be obese.

Apart from a quick energy boost from the caffeine or sugar, most soft drinks and soda pop offer little or no nutritional value. An 8-oz (237-mL) cola contains about 100 calories; a diet soft drink, because it is artificially sweetened, is less than 10 calories, although it may have caffeine.

Health Benefits

Calms the tummy. Sipping ginger ale or cola can help to quell nausea and provide energy for people unable to take solid food.

Acts as a pick-me-up. Carbonated drinks are refreshing and may provide a quick, but temporary energy boost from their sugar or caffeine.

Health Risks

Weight gain. A U.S. study published in *The Lancet* suggests that a soft drink can lead to obesity. Researchers found that for every can or glass of sugar-sweetened beverage a child drank during that time, the child's body mass index inched up and the chances of becoming obese increased 60%. One possible explanation for this link might be that while people tend to eat less at a meal if they have consumed excess calories at a previous one, they don't tend to do that if those extra calories come from beverages.

Cavities. Sodas and fruit-flavored drinks are bad for the teeth. Their sugar encourages the growth of cavity-causing bacteria, and many contain acids that can erode tooth enamel.

> **Old School**
> Any carbonated drink is bad for you.
>
> **New Wisdom**
> Sodium-free seltzer with a wedge of lemon or lime quenches the thirst without hurting your health.

Bone growth. Colas contain large amounts of phosphates, which may impair calcium absorption. A greater concern is that soft drinks cause a decrease in calcium intake by displacing milk from the diet. Children and adolescents who drink soft drinks instead of milk are missing the calcium critical to the growth of their bones.

Blood pressure. In adults, excessive caffeine from soft drinks may raise blood pressure and cause irregular heartbeat. People who react to caffeine should choose one of the decaffeinated soft drinks. Also consider that when a 60-lb (27-kg) child drinks a 12-oz (355-mL) cola containing 50 mg of caffeine, he's getting the equivalent of a couple cups of coffee in a 175-lb (80-kg) man. A child who is restless or sleepless may be experiencing the effects of too much soda pop.

Eating Tips

- Simmer sliced carrots in ginger ale and a dab of butter.
- Simmer cooked great northern beans in root beer and chili powder.
- Marinate pork chops in cherry cola.

Buying Tip

- Choose the smallest serving size of a drink you really like for an ocassional treat.

Storing Tips

- Soft drinks can be stored indefinitely, but it's best not to. If it's not on the shelf, you can't drink it.

SOY

See also Beans and Legumes, page 48

Typical serving size: 2 oz or 57 g

HOW IT HARMS
Cancer risk
Thyroid function

WHAT IT HEALS
Heart health
Breast and prostate cancers
Osteoporosis
Menopause

Soybeans are one of the most nutritious and versatile plant foods available. This legume dates back nearly 3,000 years in Chinese culture and is used to make many different food products. For example, tofu comes in firm, soft, or silken textures. It's made from pureed soybeans and processed into a "cake." It can be stir-fried, grilled, added to soups, lasagna, and cheesecake, or blended into dips or smoothies. Green soybeans (also called edamame) are bought shelled or still in the pod fresh or frozen, and can be served as a snack or a vegetable dish.

Soy is often used to provide protein in vegetarians' diets. Soy powder made from isolated soy protein can be added to shakes or smoothies for a protein-powered breakfast.

Health Benefits

Boosts heart health. A large body of evidence indicates that replacing some animal products with soy protein can reduce the risk of heart disease. This is because soy lowers levels of the artery-clogging LDL cholesterol without reducing levels of the beneficial HDL cholesterol. The evidence is so convincing that the U.S. Food and Drug Administration gave food manufacturers permission to put labels on products that are high in soy protein indicating that these foods may help lower the risk of heart disease.

Can prevent cancer. Throughout Asia, where soy has long been a dietary staple, the rates of breast and prostate cancer are much lower than in Western countries. Epidemiological studies of Asians show that it is soy intake early in life that is protective. Some researchers attribute the low incidence of these cancers to isoflavones found in soy, which reduce the effects of estrogen on breast and prostate tissue.

Combats osteoporosis. Recent research has indicated that soy isoflavones may delay bone loss and might even build bone density. Not all research is consistent in this finding, however, with some studies showing no effect of soy on bone loss.

Relieves menopausal symptoms. For some women, diets rich in soy foods can reduce menopausal symptoms, particularly the frequency and severity of hot flashes. The extent of improvement, however, varies from woman to woman.

Grows muscles. Soybean protein contains all of the essential amino acids, making it the only plant protein that equals animal products in providing a complete source of protein. This makes it a terrific choice for those looking for alternatives to meat products.

Health Risks

Iron absorption. Although many soy products are high in iron, it is not well absorbed. Improve absorption by adding foods high in vitamin C—such as orange juice, tomatoes, peppers, strawberries, or melons—to your meal.

Cancer risk. Some researchers have cautioned that there may be some health risks for those who consume large amounts of soy foods or who take soy supplements. Some recent findings have suggested that high isoflavone levels might actually increase the risk of certain cancers, particularly breast cancer. The concerns center on isolated isoflavones in supplement form, not in whole soy foods. However, until further research helps clarify the role of isoflavones in human health, it is wise to avoid isoflavone supplements. People who are being treated, or who have been treated, for breast or prostate cancer should speak to their physician or exercise caution before adding more soy to their diet.

Thyroid function. Some studies have linked soy consumption to suppressed thyroid function. The risk is linked only to taking soy supplements or eating huge amounts of soy foods, but more research is needed to clarify this relationship.

> **QUICK TIP: Stir it up**
>
> Triangles of tofu stir-fried with thin slices of meat and vegetables is a delicious way to include soy in your diet.

Eating Tips

- Add a few teaspoons of miso paste, made from fermented soybeans (find it in the refrigerated section of natural food stores) to soup bases, dips, and marinades for a salty, nutty flavor, or use in place of butter on potatoes or pasta.
- Make mocha pudding with soymilk.
- Stir chopped soy nuts into cookies.

Buying Tips

- Edamame, green soy beans, are available in the pod in the produce section of some supermarkets or shelled in the frozen food and produce sections.
- Purchase refrigerated tofu in packs with sell-by dates. Baked flavored tofu may contain added salt or sugar.
- Purchase soy flour and soy protein powder in packages with use-by dates.

Storing Tips

- Refrigerate edamame pods for up to 5 days before cooking, shelling, and eating.
- Refrigerate tofu in the package. Cook after opening.
- Store soy flour in an airtight container in a cool cupboard for up to 1 year.
- Store full-fat soy flour in an airtight container in the freezer for up to 1 year.

SPICES

See Herbs and Spices, page 110

SPINACH

Typical serving size: ½ cup, cooked (90 g), or 1 cup, raw (30 g)

HOW IT HARMS
Mineral absorption
Kidney and bladder stones
Drug interaction

WHAT IT HEALS
Macular degeneration
Cancer
Congenital neurological birth
   defects
Anemia
Bone health

QUICK TIP: Ditch the dirt

Before serving spinach, be careful to remove all the sand and dirt. One effective method is to submerge the spinach in a bowl of cold water and let the sand fall to the bottom, then remove and rinse the leaves. Dry them if making a salad. If you are cooking the spinach, the water left on the leaves may be just about the right amount with which to steam it.

Spinach is a popular dark green leafy vegetable that can be served either raw or cooked.

Contrary to popular belief, spinach is not an especially good source of iron. The myth about its high iron content arose from an analysis in which a decimal point was erroneously displaced. But the vegetable's dark green leaves do contain many other valuable nutrients. For example, a mere half cup of cooked spinach provides a full day's supply of vitamin A, and 419 mg of potassium, as well as vitamin C, riboflavin, and vitamin B6.

To avoid losing its vitamin content, don't overcook spinach. Instead, steam or stir-fry it. These cooking methods also preserve texture and flavor. Although some of these nutrients are lost in cooking, a ½-cup (179 g) serving of the cooked vegetable actually provides more nutrition than 1 cup (28 g) served raw because it takes a full 2 cups of leaves to cook down into a ½-cup serving. In addition, heating makes the protein in spinach easier to break down. The value of raw spinach can be enhanced by serving it with citrus slices for added vitamin C.

Health Benefits

Promotes vision health. Spinach is rich in carotenoids, plant pigments that are responsible for its dark green color. Among these carotenoids are lutein and zeaxanthin, which help prevent macular degeneration, the leading cause of blindness in older adults. Cooking spinach helps to convert lutein into more bioavailable forms. To enhance the carotenoid absorption, eat spinach with some heart-healthy fat.

Can help prevent cancer. The antioxidants and bioflavonoids in spinach help block cancer-causing substances and processes.

May help prevent birth defects. A half cup of cooked spinach provides 105 mcg (micrograms) of folate, more than 25% of the Recommended Dietary Allowance (RDA). Folate is especially important for women who are pregnant or who may be planning a pregnancy, because it helps prevent congenital neurological defects. Folate deficiency can also cause a severe type of anemia.

Boosts bones. Phylloquinone is the most common form of vitamin K found in dark greens such as spinach. Vitamin K is needed for proper blood clotting and may play a role in preserving bone health. Some research suggests that it may increase bone density and reduce fracture rates. Both the Nurses' Health Study and the Framingham Heart Study found that people who consume the most vitamin K have a lower risk of hip fractures than those who consume less.

100% of the vitamin A you need every day is in ½ cup cooked spinach.

Health Risks

Mineral absorption. The nutritional benefits of spinach are somewhat offset by its high concentration of oxalic acid which inhibits the absorption of the iron, calcium, and other minerals found in spinach. To increase mineral absorption eat spinach with other foods that are rich in vitamin C. Oxalic acid can also pose a problem for people susceptible to kidney and bladder stones that form from oxalates.

WARNING!
FOOD-DRUG INTERACTION

Spinach may interfere with blood-thinning drugs. If your physician has prescribed blood-thinning medication, such as heparin or warfarin (Coumadin), it is wise to moderate your intake of vitamin K–rich foods, such as spinach. Excess vitamin K can counteract the effects of these drugs.

Eating Tips

- Mix chopped cooked spinach and roasted red pepper into hummus.
- Top crostini with sautéed baby spinach, garlic, and lemon juice.
- Use baby spinach on sandwiches instead of lettuce.

Buying Tips

- Fresh spinach is available in supermarkets year-round, sometimes with the roots attached, sometimes prewashed and bagged.
- Select leaves that are dark green and fresh looking instead of wilted or yellowing.
- If buying frozen spinach, choose brands with no added sauce.

Old School
When it comes to spinach, raw is always better.

New Wisdom
Cooking spinach makes some of its nutrients a bit easier to absorb.

SQUASH

Typical serving size: ½ cup, cooked (3.2 oz or 90 g)

WHAT IT HEALS
Vision
Bone growth
Reproductive health
Cell functions
Immunity
Constipation
High cholesterol
Weight gain

Members of the same family as melons and cucumbers, squash are gourds—fleshy fruits protected by a rind. Squash is divided into two categories. The summer squashes include the chayote, patty pan, yellow crooknecks and straightnecks, and zucchini varieties. Summer squash can be eaten raw. If it is cooked, stir-frying or steaming minimizes nutrient loss and keeps the vegetable from becoming too mushy. The mild flavor complements stews, soups, and mixed vegetables, but squash can make some dishes watery. To avoid this problem, lightly salt the squash slices or pieces and place them on absorbent paper towels; rinse the pieces before adding them to the recipe.

Winter squashes are harvested when fully mature with hard shells and large seeds. They are larger, darker in coloring, and richer in nutrients than summer squash. Varieties include acorn, banana, butternut, delicata, dumpling, hubbard, spaghetti, and turban varieties. The flowers, fruits, and seeds are all edible.

Health Benefits

Supports healthy vision, bones, and cells. Winter squashes such as acorn and butternut are rich in beta-carotene, which the body converts to vitamin A. The darker the flesh, the more nutritious. Half a cup (90 g) of acorn squash contains enough beta-carotene to fulfill almost 100% of the RDA for vitamin A, and that may protect your cells against the effects of free radicals. Vitamin A also plays a role in healthy vision, bone growth, reproduction, cell functions, and the immune system.

Prevents constipation. Winter squash seeds, dried or baked for snacks, are high in insoluble fiber, which helps prevent constipation. They are rich in iron, potassium, zinc, and other minerals, and provide some protein, beta-carotene, and B vitamins.

Lowers cholesterol. The flesh of winter squash contains soluble fiber, which helps to reduces low-density lipoprotein (LDL), the "bad" cholesterol, by carrying it out of the body before it can be absorbed into the bloodstream.

Aids in maintaining healthy weight. Summer squashes are a wonderful food to help curb appetite. They help fill you up without filling you out. Because zucchini and other summer squashes have a high water content, they are extremely low in calories (20 per cup, raw). Despite the low calories, a 1-cup serving of raw summer squash provides about 15% of the Recommended Dietary Allowance (RDA) of vitamin C, 25 mcg (micrograms) of folate, and small amounts of beta-carotene. Intensely colored squashes have more beta-carotene than paler ones.

Eating Tips

- Grill yellow summer squash halves stuffed with chicken salad.
- Toss cooked spaghetti squash with pesto.
- Add butternut squash cubes to beef stew in place of carrots.

Buying Tips

- Select firm squash with unblemished skin or rind.
- For winter squash, press hard—there should be no give. Don't choose winter squash with shiny green stems; instead, buy those with duller, brown stems.
- Buy butternut squash with long necks and smaller bottoms. The neck contains more flesh and is easier to cut than the bottom.
- Summer squash should have shiny skin, but some light bruising and scratching is okay. Avoid summer squash with pitted skin or a spongy texture.

Storing Tips

- Refrigerate summer squashes for up to 1 week.
- If any soft or discolored spots develop on the squash, cut them away and discard before eating.
- Winter squash can be stored for several months in a cool, dark place. Do not refrigerate because temperatures below 40°F (4°C) speed deterioration.

STRAWBERRIES

See Berries, page 88

SUGAR AND OTHER SWEETENERS

Typical serving size: 1 teaspoon (0.15 oz or 4.2 g) of granulated sugar

HOW THEY HARM
Obesity
Cavities

WHAT THEY HEAL
Low energy

Refined sugar is a relatively new food in the human diet, widely available only since the 1500s. It didn't take long for this sweetener to become a major commodity. Sugars have been described as a "standard currency" for living organisms because all plants and animals store energy chemically as sugar.

White table sugar is made from sugarcane or sugar beets; some liquid sweeteners, such as molasses, are by-products of sugar refining. Manufacturers favor liquid sweeteners such as high-fructose corn syrup because their sweetness and thickness can be regulated.

Other popular natural sources of sugar are honey and maple syrup. Agave syrup, extracted from the spiky succulent native to the southern U.S., Mexico, and South America, has recently been hailed as a more healthful alternative to sugar because of its low glycemic index; however, some agave products actually cause blood sugar swings.

Health Benefits

Boosts energy. All forms of sugar provide about the same energy value: 4 calories per gram. In everyday terms, a cup of white sugar contains 770 calories, compared to 820 in a cup of densely packed brown sugar. A tablespoon of white sugar has 50 calories, and an individual serving packet, 25. Although sugar itself is not especially high in calories, many sweet foods, such as chocolates and pastries, are also high in fat, which contains 9 calories per g.

Health Risks

Obesity. Any unburned amount of sugar in your system will turn to fat, and consistently high amounts may lead to insulin resistance. Keep your intake to under 40 g (about 10 tsp) of sugar a day. That's about one can of Coke.

Cavities. All types of sugar—white table sugar, brown sugar, honey, molasses—encourage the growth of the oral bacteria that are responsible for causing cavities. And when starchy foods are broken down by the enzymes in saliva, they, too, form cavity-causing sugars. More dangerous than the amount of sugar is the length of time the sugar remains in contact with the teeth. Thus, much of the damage can be prevented by brushing soon after eating a sweet.

Eating Tips

- Add a sprinkle of sugar to a pot of boiling corn on the cob to increase the flavor and juiciness.
- Grill peaches or pineapples, and sprinkle brown sugar over them.
- Mix 2 cups sugar, 2 cups vinegar, 4 large sliced cucumbers and ½ cup of chopped dill for a refreshing salad.

Buying Tips

- Neither brown sugar nor honey is more nutritious than white sugar, but brown sugar can be substituted for white sugar in any recipe. Brown sugar is made by coating white sugar crystals with molasses.
- Sugar alcohols, such as sorbitol, xylitol, maltitol, and lactitol, are used as sweeteners in chewing gums, candies, ice cream, and many baked goods. They provide fewer calories per gram than sucrose, do not promote tooth decay, and do not cause sudden jumps in blood glucose but can produce a laxative effect in some people.

Storing Tips

- Keep white sugar in a cool, dry place in an airtight container.
- Store brown sugar in a cool, moist area in a sealed container.
- Use within the first 6 months of purchase for maximum flavor.

SWEET POTATOES AND YAMS

Typical serving size: 1 medium sweet potato, cooked (4 oz or 114 g)

WHAT THEY HEAL
- **High blood pressure**
- **Eyes and skin**
- **Immunity**
- **Heart disease**
- **Diabetes**
- **Prostate and breast cancer**
- **High blood sugar**
- **High cholesterol**
- **Insulin resistance**

Sweet potatoes are a Native American plant that was the main source of nourishment for early homesteaders and for soldiers during the Revolutionary War. These tuberous roots are among the most nutritious vegetables and are excellent sources of the antioxidants beta-carotine and vitamin C.

There are two varieties of sweet potatoes: the pale yellow with a dry flesh and the dark orange with a moist flesh. The dark-orange variety is plumper in shape and somewhat sweeter and moister than the yellow variety. Because most of the nutrients in sweet potatoes are next to the skin, cook them whole whenever possible. Yams and sweet potatoes are very similar and often confused for one another, but they aren't the same. However, they are interchangeable in most recipes.

While sweet potatoes and yams are very healthy if simply cooked, many recipes—such as candied yams or sweet potato fries—pile on butter, sugar, and oil. So avoid these add-ons to get the most nutrition from these sweet tubers.

Health Benefits

Lowers blood pressure. Eating sweet potatoes and yams is a smart move if you have high blood pressure. That's because they're rich in potassium, a mineral known for bringing pressure down. You'll get more potassium from a sweet potato than you will from a banana.

Keeps skin and eyes healthy. The high levels of beta-carotene in sweet potatoes protect eye health and keep your skin looking great.

Guards against infections. Rich in beta-carotene, sweet potatoes and yams may help your body stave off infections.

Fights heart disease. Beta-carotene and vitamin C may also help combat heart disease.

Avoid diabetes complications. The vitamin C in sweet potatoes protect against complications of diabetes, such as nerve and eye damage.

Boosts cancer survival. A recent study found that among almost 2,000 men studied, those whose diets were richest in beta-carotene and vitamin C—two nutrients plentiful in sweet potatoes—were more likely to survive prostate cancer than those whose diets contained little of the two nutrients.

Reduces breast cancer risk. The famous Nurses' Health Study at Harvard Medical School found that women who ate lots of foods rich in beta-carotene, such as sweet potatoes, reduced their risk of breast cancer by as much as 25%.

Helps blood sugar and cholesterol. Sweet potatoes are packed with disease-fighting soluble fiber to help lower blood sugar and cholesterol.

May reduce insulin resistance. Sweet potatoes are extraordinarily rich in carotenoids, orange and yellow pigments that play a role in helping the body respond to insulin. These tubers are also rich in the natural plant compound chlorogenic acid, which may help reduce insulin resistance.

Eating Tips

- Bake thick sticks coated with oil and five-spice powder.

SWEET POTATO AND YAM FACTS

- Sweet potatoes contain an enzyme that converts most of its starches into sugars as the potato matures. This sweetness continues to increase during storage and when you cook them.
- Canned sweet potatoes are often labeled yams.
- Yams derive their name from the Senegalese word *fiam*, meaning "to eat."

Old School
Sweet potatoes and yams are different names for the same vegetable.

New Wisdom
Yams and sweet potatoes are unrelated.

- Add to hash browns.
- Make a meal of baked sweet potato topped with cooked spinach, ham, and shredded Swiss.

Buying Tips

- Choose firm, dark, smooth sweet potatoes or yams without wrinkles, bruises, sprouts, or decay.
- Even if you cut them away, decayed spots may have already caused the whole vegetable to take on an unpleasant flavor.

Storing Tips

- To keep sweet potatoes and yams fresh, store them in a dry, cool (55°F to 60°F or 13°C to 15.5°C) place such as a cellar, pantry, or garage. They will keep here for a month or longer.
- Don't store them in the refrigerator, because they may develop a hard core and a bad taste.
- If you keep them at normal room temperature, you should use them within a week of purchase.
- Don't wash them until you're ready to cook them. The moisture from washing will make them spoil faster.

TANGERINES

See Oranges and Tangerines, page 158

TEA

Typical serving size: 6 fluid oz or 177 mL

HOW IT HARMS

Iron absorption

Increased urination

Insomnia

Migraines

WHAT IT HEALS

Weight gain

Stroke

Diabetes

Heart disease

Cancer

Asthma

Dental health

Diarrhea

Tea, a shrub in the camellia family, is the world's most popular nonalcoholic beverage. Most tea is grown in India, Sri Lanka, China, Japan, Taiwan, and Indonesia. Like coffees, the best-quality teas are grown in the shade at high altitudes, and the finest leaves are plucked from the youngest shoots and unopened leaf buds, which also contain the highest levels of phenols, enzymes, and caffeine. Researchers are discovering evidence that tea may offer not only soothing warmth and mild stimulation, but also health benefits. Tea contains hundreds of compounds, including various flavonoids, a class of chemical with powerful antioxidant properties. A subclass of flavonoids, the catechins, is responsible for the flavor as well as many health benefits. The extent to which these compounds are present in the beverage depends on how the leaves are processed.

White tea is made from the green buds and young leaves that are steamed and dried. It is the least processed type of tea.

Green tea is made by steaming the leaves to halt any enzyme activity. Black tea is made by crushing, fermenting (exposing the leaves to the air), and drying the leaves. Oolong tea is only partially fermented. The highest concentration of catechins is found in green tea and white tea, although black tea is also a good source. Brand-name teas are mixtures of as many as 20 different varieties of leaves, blended to ensure a consistent flavor.

Herbal teas are not true tea. They are infusions, or tisanes, of various pleasant-tasting plants such as chamomile, fennel, lavender, and peppermint. Because most of them do not contain caffeine, they offer an alternative for people who prefer to avoid this stimulant.

Health Benefits

Promotes weight loss. The results from a number of randomized, controlled intervention trials have shown that consumption of green tea catechins (270 mg to 1200 mg a day) may reduce body weight and fat, possibly by increasing energy expenditure and promoting the oxidation of fat.

Helps prevent stroke. One study found that the risk of stroke was reduced by about 70% in men who drank five or more cups of black tea a day: Other studies showed that the risk of having a heart attack was reduced by more than 40% for men and women who consumed one or more cups of tea per day. Flavonoids in tea may protect against stroke in two ways. They reduce the ability of blood platelets to form clots, the cause of most strokes. They also block some of the damage caused to arteries by free radicals, unstable molecules that are released when the body consumes oxygen.

Fights diabetes. Research suggests that people who drink green tea are less likely to develop type 2 diabetes and have a lower risk of death from cardiovascular disease. The biological mechanisms are still unknown but a popular hypothesis is that the epigallocatechin gallate (EGCG) in green tea decreases blood pressure, lowers blood sugar, and increases blood flow.

Fosters heart health. The antioxidants in tea may explain the fact that people who drink a lot of tea are much less likely to die from heart disease. Antioxidants prevent the oxidation of cholesterol, making it less likely to stick to artery walls.

Inhibits cancer. A number of studies have shown that tea may offer protection against a variety of cancers. EGCG is thought to be responsible for tea's anticancer properties. EGCG protects the DNA in cells from cancer-causing changes. It may also inhibit an enzyme that cancer cells need in order to replicate.

Fights infections. Researchers report in the Proceedings of the National Academy of Sciences that they have found a chemical in tea that boosts the body's defense against disease fivefold. They say they isolated from ordinary black tea a substance called L-theanine, also found in green and oolong tea. L-theanine is broken down in the liver to ethylamine, a molecule that primes the response of an immune blood cell called the gamma-delta T cell. Gamma-delta T cells in the blood are the first line of defense against many types of bacterial, viral, and parasitic infections.

Alleviates asthma symptoms. Naturally occurring theophyllines in tea dilate the airways in the lungs and have been found to help some people with asthma and other respiratory disorders to breathe more freely. In fact, theophyllines have been developed as drugs to treat asthma and other constrictive lung disorders.

Supports dental health. Tannins, which are found in wine as well as tea, are chemi-

TEA FACT
- Commercial iced teas, flavored with fruit syrups and sweetened with sugar, contain about as many calories as soft drinks.

cals that bind surface proteins in the mouth, producing a tightening sensation together with giving the impression of a full-bodied liquid. They also bind and incapacitate plaque-forming bacteria in the mouth. The fluoride in tea—particularly green tea—also protects against tooth decay.

Quells diarrhea. Tea's binding action makes it useful against diarrhea.

Health Risks

Iron absorption. The tannins in tea can cut iron absorption by more than 80% when tea is sipped with an iron-rich meal. Tea-drinking vegetarians are especially susceptible. Individuals with a tendency to anemia can drink citrus juice at mealtimes to promote iron absorption; squeezing a wedge of lemon or adding milk to tea also binds the tannins and partly blocks their effect on iron. Tea drinking between meals does not affect iron absorption.

Excessive urination. Tea has a diuretic effect, which increases the kidneys' output of urine. Excessive urination can upset the body's fluid and chemical balance by washing potassium from the body.

Insomnia. Tea leaves contain twice as much caffeine, weight for weight, as coffee beans do. But when measured by volume, tea has only half as much caffeine as coffee because tea is drunk weaker and coffee is more completely extracted from the grounds. A cup of black or green tea contains 35 to 45 mg of caffeine. Theobromine, which is also found in tea, has effects similar to those of caffeine but milder.

Migraines. Tea may trigger a migraine headache in hypersensitive people; for others, it may alleviate headaches when taken with aspirin or similar painkillers.

Eating Tips

- Use cooled brewed black tea in place of wine in poultry braises.
- Poach prunes and dried apricots in red rooibos tea.
- Freeze double-strength green tea in cubes, then crush in the food processor to make granita.

Buying Tips

- For best flavor and healing properties, purchase whole tea leaves.
- Look for unbleached natural fiber tea bags.

Storing Tips

- Store tea leaves in a metal container in a cool spot for up to a year.
- Tea bags retain flavor for about a year.

TOFU

See Soy, page 192

TOMATOES

Typical serving size: 1 medium tomato (4.3 oz or 123 g)

HOW THEY HARM
   Indigestion and heartburn
   Allergies
   Headaches
   Canker sores

WHAT THEY HEAL
   Cancer
   Heart diseases

Tomatoes are actually a type of berry, and were called "love apples" in the 16th century. Varieties include baby plum, beefsteak, cherry, plum, vine, and yellow cherry.

Equally delicious raw or cooked, tomatoes are low in calories and rich in vitamins and other healthful substances. One medium-size ripe tomato contains only 26 calories, together with about 23 mg of vitamin C and 20 mcg of folate.

Tomatoes, like potatoes, sweet peppers, and eggplants, belong to the nightshade family. Brought to Europe from Central America by the Spanish during the 16th century, tomatoes were grown as decorative plants in northern Europe, where it was feared that the poisons in the leaves might be present in the fruit as well. Colonists emigrating from that area imported this misconception to the New World. Meanwhile, the Spanish and Italians discovered that tomatoes were indeed edible, and as they immigrated to North America, they brought their taste for tomatoes with them. Today, the tomato is one of the world's leading vegetable crops, although botanically the tomato is a fruit.

Health Benefits

Helps prevent cancer. A well-known Harvard study showed that men who regularly ate tomato-based foods had lower rates of prostate cancer. Researchers theorize that lycopene—a powerful antioxidant—is the natural cancer-fighting agent in tomatoes. The best way to get lycopene is in tomato sauce, tomato paste, tomato juice, and even ketchup. Lycopene is most concentrated in tomato paste. Tomatoes also contain a compound called chlorogenic acid, which may help guard against cancer by blocking the effects of certain environmental toxins—for instance, nitrosamines, cancer-causing compounds in tobacco smoke and cured meat.

Prevents heart disease. The jellylike substance surrounding tomato seeds is high in salicylates, which have an anti-clotting effect on the blood. This may be

50% more lycopene is contained in a Crimson type of tomato vs. a regular tomato.

partially responsible for tomatoes' protection against heart disease. Researchers also are finding that lycopene plays a role in heart health, lowering LDL cholesterol, increasing activity of the antioxidant enzyme superoxide dismutase (SOD), and reducing in DNA damage in white blood cells.

Health Risks

Digestive distress. An unidentified substance in tomatoes and tomato-based products can cause acid reflux, leading to indigestion and heartburn. People who often have digestive upsets should try eliminating tomatoes for 2 or 3 weeks to see if there is any improvement.

Allergies. Tomatoes are a relatively common cause of allergies.

Headaches. Solanines are toxic substances present in minute quantities in all members of the nightshade family: They may trigger headaches in susceptible people.

Canker sores. Tomatoes can make these mouth sores even more painful.

Eating Tips

- Add sliced tomatoes to a breakfast egg sandwich.
- Bake sliced tomatoes, breadcrumbs, parmesan and garlic into a ready-made pie crust.
- Stuff tomatoes with tuna salad.

TOMATO FACT
- Lycopene, the powerful antioxidant in tomatoes, is fat-soluble. So adding a little olive oil or other healthy fat to tomato dishes increases absorption.

Buying Tips

- Choose fresh tomatoes that are a deep red color for highest lycopene content.
- Vine-ripened tomatoes have more lycopene than those that are picked early and allowed to ripen off the vine. So it makes sense to grow your own tomatoes or buy from a local farmers' market.
- Choose canned or jarred tomatoes with reduced or no sodium added.

Storing Tips

- Ripe tomatoes should be stored at room temperature. At 40°F (4°C) or below, the flesh becomes mealy.
- Store unopened canned, jarred, or tetra-pack tomatoes in a cool cupboard for up to 1 year.

TURNIPS

Typical serving size: ½ cup, cooked (2.75 oz or 78 g)

HOW THEY HARM
Bloating and flatulence
Thyroid function

WHAT THEY HEAL
Cancer
High cholesterol
Vision
Bones
Reproduction
Immune system

Turnips (including the yellow rutabagas) are economical, healthful, and easy to prepare and cultivate (even in soil of poor quality), and full of vitamin C and some essential amino acids. One cup of boiled turnips yields only 35 calories while providing 18 mg of vitamin C, 35

QUICK TIP: Go beyond boiling

Most people serve boiled turnips, but they can also be baked, braised, or steamed. The roots and green tops make a tasty addition to salads, stews, and soups.

mg of calcium, and 210 mg of potassium. They also contain lysine, an amino acid that may help to prevent and manage cold sores.

The turnip tops, or greens, which many cooks discard, are even more nutritious than the roots themselves. One cup of boiled greens provides 40 mg of vitamin C, about 200 mg of calcium, and nearly 300 mg of potassium. In addition, unlike the roots, the greens are an excellent source of beta-carotene, an important antioxidant nutrient that the body converts to vitamin A. The same cup of boiled greens yields nearly 7,500 IU of vitamin A and 5 g of fiber.

Health Benefits

Protects against some cancers. As a member of the cruciferous family, which includes cabbage, broccoli, and radishes, turnips contain sulfurous compounds that may protect against certain forms of cancer.

Lowers cholesterol. Both the tops and roots of turnips are a useful source of fiber, including soluble dietary fibers that help soak up LDL ("bad") cholesterol.

Promotes total body health. One cup of cooked turnip greens contains generous amounts of beta-carotene which the body converts to vitamin A. This antioxidant plays a role in healthy vision, bone growth, reproduction, cell functions, and a healthy immune system.

Health Risks

May cause flatulence. Like other cruciferous vegetables, turnips can cause bloating and gas.

   Thyroid function. Turnips contain two goitrogenic substances, progoitrin and gluconasturtin, which can interfere with the thyroid gland's ability to make its hormones. These compounds do not pose a risk for healthy people who eat moderate amounts of turnips, but anyone with hypothyroidism should cook this vegetable since cooking appears to deactivate goitrogens.

Eating Tips

- Puree cooked turnip roots and serve with steamed turnip greens.
- Roast chunks with sweet potatoes and onions.
- Add baby white turnips to a crudité platter.
- Small turnips of about 2 in in diameter may only need to be well scrubbed, not peeled, before cooking.

Buying Tips

- Turnips should be firm and feel heavy for their size, with smooth skin that has no mushy or sunken brown spots.
- Turnips with the tops attached should be brightly colored and fresh, with no signs of wilting or yellowing.
- Don't buy turnips larger than 3 in (7.6 cm) in diameter. They'll likely have a more woody taste.

Storing Tip

- Refrigerate turnips in a plastic bag in the crisper for up to 2 weeks.

VINEGAR

Typical serving size: Varies according to recipe

HOW IT HARMS
Allergies

WHAT IT HEALS
Weight loss

For centuries, vinegar was a by-product of wine- and beer-making. The name even comes from the French word *vinaigre*, which means "sour wine." Apple cider and wine remain the most popular basic ingredients, but almost any product that produces alcoholic fermentation can be used to make vinegar. In fact, vinegar can be produced from any high-sugar or high-starch food that can be fermented, as evidenced by the dozens of varieties available today.

   Although many people have accorded various healing powers to vinegar over the years—rapid weight loss to relief from allergies—It does, however, provide a low-sodium, low-calorie flavoring. All vinegars are 4 to 14% acetic acid. Vinegar can be transformed into a flavored or gourmet vinegar simply by adding various herbs, spices, or fruits—for example, dill, tarragon, lemon balm, mint, or garlic. These and many other varieties are widely available, or you can make your own by adding fresh herbs or fruit to distilled, cider, or wine vinegars.

Health Benefits

Aids in weight loss. Vinegar is virtually devoid of calories, so it's an ideal alternative to fatty salad dressings. To reduce its acid bite, the vinegar can be mixed with orange juice or fruit syrup and a little oil.

Health Risks

Allergies reaction. People who are allergic to molds may react to vinegar as well as to foods preserved with it. Symptoms include a tingling or itching sensation around the mouth and possibly hives.

Eating Tips

- Add a spoonful of apple cider vinegar to a smoothie.
- Sprinkle red wine vinegar on grilled vegetables.
- Make a spritzer with rice wine vinegar, sparkling water, and mint.

Buying Tips

- Consider the intended use before purchasing any vinegar. Inexpensive white vinegar will work best if you're making pickles. A mellow sherry vinegar would be ideal blended with olive oil as a vinaigrette for mixed green salad. Choose Japanese rice wine for making sushi.
- Seek out a shop that offers samples of different vinegars before buying.
- Some shops now sell bulk vinegars, which allows you to buy small amounts of a variety of types.

Storing Tips

- Stored in a cool dark cabinet, unopened vinegar will keep indefinitely.
- After opening, it can be kept for up to 6 months.

QUICK TIP: Beat exhaustion

Apple cider vinegar contains potassium and enzymes that may relieve that tired feeling. Next time you're feeling beat, add 1 or 2 Tbsp of apple cider vinegar to a glass of chilled vegetable drink or water.

WATER AND ENHANCED WATER

Typical serving size: 8 fl oz or ¼ L

HOW THEY HARM
Gastrointestinal illnesses
Weight gain (enhanced water)
High blood sugar

WHAT THEY HEAL
Dehydration
Digestion
Blood supply
Joints
Tooth decay
Cramps

Two parts hydrogen and one part oxygen, water is the most abundant substance in the human body, accounting for up to 60% of our body weight. If you are properly hydrated, your urine will be pale, not dark or bright yellow. For the average adult, this may translate to 6 to 8 glasses of water a day. Most of this comes from drinks—plain water, enhanced waters (fortified with vitamins, caffeine, electrolytes, and other additives), coffee, tea, juices, and soft drinks—but surprisingly, there's a substantial amount in foods as well. Fruits and vegetables, for example, are 70 to 95% water, compared to 75% of an egg; 40 to 60% of meat, poultry, and fish; and 35% of bread.

Our daily needs vary a lot. We need more water in hot weather, during exercise, or when we have a fever, cold, or other illness. Women need more during pregnancy, and nursing mothers need to increase their fluid intake to produce breastmilk, which is 87% water.

Thirst decreases with age, so older people should drink water often even if they don't feel thirsty. As well, thirst may lag behind the body's need for water during intense exercise or when it's extremely hot and humid. By the time you feel thirsty, you may already be dehydrated. If you drink more fluid than you need, the kidneys excrete the excess by increasing the volume of urine. If you drink more water than the kidneys can handle, excess is absorbed by your cells.

Enhanced water is water with added vitamins or minerals, including electrolytes, that help your body retain fluids. Recently, many companies have rolled out versions of enhanced water that contain calories in addition to nutrients. Check the label to be sure the water is, well, close enough to water.

Health Benefits

Provides vital bodily functions. Water is essential to life. Even though water has no calories or other nutrients, we can go for only a few days without it. In contrast, a healthy person can survive for 6 to 8 weeks without food. A loss of only 5 to 10% of body water results in serious dehydration, while a 15 to 20% loss is usually fatal. Water is vital to virtually every body function, including digestion, absorption, and transport of nutrients; elimination of body waste; and regulation of body temperature, as well as many other chemical processes. It provides a protective cushion for body cells and, in the form of amniotic fluid, protects a developing fetus. Water is needed to build all body tissues and is the base of all blood and fluid secretions such as tears, saliva, and gastric juices, as well as the fluids that lubricate our organs and joints. It also keeps our skin soft and smooth.

Prevents cramps. Enhanced waters containing electrolytes, sodium chloride, and potassium work with water to replenish your system, prevent dehydration, and keep cramps at bay.

Health Risks

Gastrointestinal illnesses. North Americans generally enjoy some of the world's safest and most reliable water supplies. However, especially in recent years, there have been significant episodes of serious waterborne illnesses. In addition, a growing number of public health officials are warning that surface water supplies are becoming increasingly polluted by industrial waters, fertilizer runoff, pesticides, and chemical and nuclear wastes. Some of the most common or serious contaminants that may be affecting water safety are: arsenic, chlorine, lead, turbidity, and parasites, which may cause more than just an upset stomach. When traveling to places that may have unsanitary water, bring water purification tablets or a water purification pump, or simply stick to bottled water or other beverages.

Weight gain. Be sure to read the nutrition label and avoid enhanced waters that contain sugars. The sugar will not only raise your blood sugar levels but also contribute empty

QUICK TIP:
Filter for purer H_2O

You can also choose to use a water filter system, or switch to bottled water, but there is no guarantee that these options will totally eliminate contaminants from your drinking water. Different filter systems will remove different contaminants as well as varying levels of these contaminants. You can research the type of filter that's best for your needs through the NSF International in Ann Arbor, Michigan (www.nsf.org), an independent, nonprofit agency that works closely with the federal government in both the United States and Canada in setting standards in many areas, including water filters.

calories. Unfortunately, sugar can end up offsetting the benefits of additional vitamins and minerals in enhanced water.

Drinking Tips

- For better-tasting coffee or tea, use bottled or filtered water.
- Carry water in a stainless steel container or lined container, and clean between uses.
- To make water more flavorful, add a slice of cucumber, lemon, or lime.
- Swirl a couple of fresh mint sprigs into your water for a fresh, minty taste.
- Throw in a few pieces of frozen fruit, such as pineapple, strawberries, or blueberries. Your water gets cool and flavored.

Buying Tips

- Check with your local water department for a report on the cleanliness of the water coming out of your tap.
- If purchasing bottled water, check the expiration or use-by date.
- Athletes may want to purchase bottled water that contains electrolytes to prevent dehydration and keep cramps at bay.

Storing Tips

- Store unopened bottled water products in a dry place out of direct sunlight for up to 1 year. If you suspect any of your stored bottled water has become contaminated (smells funny, showing algae growth, etc.), discard it.
- Opened containers of bottled water should be refrigerated in case potentially harmful bacteria have been introduced.

WATERCRESS

See Lettuce and Other Salad Greens, page 208

WATERMELON

See Melons, page 131

WHEAT AND WHEAT GERM

See also Grains, page 104

Typical serving size: Varies based on recipes; wheat germ, about 1 oz or 28 g

HOW THEY HARM
High blood sugar
Allergies

WHAT THEY HEAL
High cholesterol
Gastrointestinal distress
Obesity
Cardiovascular disease
High blood pressure
Inflammation
Anemia

Wheat nourishes more people worldwide than any other cereal crop. It is most nutritious when left unrefined. If you want to enjoy the full health benefits gained from this great grain, choose 100% whole wheat products.

Wheat germ is the nutritional heart of the wheat kernel. Two tablespoons of toasted wheat germ contain 55 calories, with more than 15% of the Recommended Dietary Allowance (RDA) of vitamin E, thiamine, zinc, and phosphorus, as well as 10% of the RDA for folate and magnesium, and useful amounts of other B vitamins, iron, copper, potassium, and manganese. It also contains 4 g of protein and almost 2 g of fiber.

Health Benefits

Lowers cholesterol. The soluble fiber in whole wheat helps lower cholesterol.

Keeps your digestive system on track. The insoluble fiber in whole wheat regulates waste and helps prevent constipation.

Helps with a healthy weight. Whole wheat is packed with fiber, which fills you up and helps you lose or maintain your weight.

Promotes heart health. The vitamin E in wheat germ is a powerful antioxidant that is linked to heart health as well as a strong immune system. The fat in wheat germ (1.5 g in 2 Tbsp) is predominantly polyunsaturated fat, which can help lower LDL cholesterol levels when it replaces saturated fat in the diet. Wheat germ is also a source of plant sterols that help lower cholesterol levels.

Manages blood pressure. Wheat is a good source of magnesium, which can act as an anti-inflammatory, lower blood pressure, balance blood sugar, and relax muscles.

Prevents anemia. Wheat has high levels of iron, which is used to make the proteins hemoglobin and myoglobin that help carry and store oxygen in the body. Iron also helps prevent anemia.

Health Risks

Blood sugar. Refined wheat can raise blood sugar and cause insulin resistance over time, which is associated with obesity, hypertension, high triglycerides, type 2 diabetes, and other chronic health conditions.

Allergies. Many people are confused about the difference between a wheat allergy and gluten intolerance, or the more severe celiac disease. They are separate conditions. With a wheat allergy, the allergic reaction is to proteins contained in the wheat, and it is only associated with wheat products. Gluten intolerance and celiac disease apply to wheat and all other foods that contain gluten. Symptoms for all three conditions can range from mild to severe; the best course of action is to avoid any wheat products if you have one of these ailments.

Eating Tips

- Mix wheat germ into pizza dough.
- Sprinkle a couple tablespoons of wheat germ over breakfast cereal.
- Mix crunched-up wheat bran flakes to veggie burgers to provide more texture and add fiber.

Buying Tips

- Always check the nutrition label and choose "100% whole wheat" products; avoid refined wheat products.
- Experiment with the many varieties of this whole grain, including bulgur, cracked wheat, farina (Cream of Wheat), rolled wheat flakes, wheat berries, wheat germ, and wheat bran.

Storing Tips

- Store wheat flour in a cool, dry place, or in the refrigerator.
- Once wheat germ has been opened, keep the wheat germ jar tightly sealed and refrigerated to prevent it from going rancid.
- Defatted wheat germ contains much less vitamin E and does not need refrigeration. It can be kept in the cupboard.

> **QUICK TIP:**
> **Swap for "white" whole wheat**
>
> If someone in your family turns a nose up at whole wheat products, try baking with and seeking out wheat products made with "white" whole wheat flour. It's just as nutritious, but it's whiter in color.

WINE

See Alcohol, page 38

WRAPS AND TORTILLAS

See Bread, page 59

YAMS

See Sweet Potatoes and Yams, page 198

YOGURT

See also Milk and Dairy Products, page 133

Typical serving size: 1 cup (8 oz or 237 mL)

HOW IT HARMS
Phenylketonuria

WHAT IT HEALS
Digestion
Bone health
High blood pressure

To make yogurt, pure cultures of bacteria are added to pasteurized milk. Fermentation is allowed to proceed until the desired acidity is reached, then it is stopped by cooling the yogurt to refrigerator temperature. A mixed culture of *Lactobacillus bulgaricus* and *Streptococcus thermophilus* consumes the milk sugar, or lactose, for energy and excretes lactic acid, which curdles the milk.

Dried milk solids, gelatin, or other ingredients may be added for body.

The finished product reflects the fat, mineral, and vitamin content of the raw material, whether it be whole or skim milk. Following fermentation, yogurt has only one-third to two-thirds the amount of lactose found in milk, and therefore is more easily digested by people with intolerance to milk.

Frozen yogurt is a lower-fat alternative to ice cream, often cutting the amount of fat per serving by half or more. But frozen yogurt can sometimes be higher in sugar content. Some varieties may have 17 g or more of sugar per half-cup serving.

Greek yogurt can have double the protein of regular yogurt. Its thick creaminess makes it a good swap for sour cream. Greek yogurt is made by straining out the liquid whey, which creates a thicker texture than regular yogurt. Also, more milk is used in the production of Greek yogurt than standard yogurt.

Another recently popular yogurt product is kefir, which is a cultured milk product made by adding grains to partially skimmed cows milk and allowing it to ferment for 24 hours. During this time, the bacteria and yeast ferment the milk, lower the pH, and change its texture and composition. The final product contains live bacteria and yeast that have health benefits, such as aiding digestion.

Health Benefits

Aids digestion. Yogurt is a healthful food and a useful source of minerals and vitamins. What's more, yogurts that contain live or "active" bacteria cultures may help suppress the growth of harmful microorganisms in the body.

Boosts bone health. As an excellent source of calcium and phosphorus, yogurt can help strengthen bones.

Helps lower blood pressure. The calcium in low-fat yogurt can help keep blood pressure levels under control.

Provides a low-calorie, high-nutrient snack option. An excellent quick snack and a versatile dessert, yogurt can be served chilled or frozen, plain or flavored. Low-fat frozen yogurt contains only 110 calories in a ½-cup (118 mL) serving and gives almost the same pleasure as ice cream, with fewer calories and without the harmful saturated fats.

Health Risks

Phenylketonuria. Fat-free yogurt sweetened with aspartame is the least calorie laden, but this sweetener is not recommended for children and is unsafe for people with phenylketonuria.

Eating Tips

- Marinate chicken in plain yogurt before grilling.
- Use Greek yogurt instead of mayonnaise in dip recipes.
- Combine plain yogurt and shredded cheddar as a base for broccoli casserole.

Buying Tips

- Purchase low-fat versions of yogurt to save on calories, fat, and sugar.
- Avoid the fruit-added yogurt. Often those fruit-on-the-bottom varieties are nothing more than desserts, with as much sugar as a couple of cookies. If you want fruit in your yogurt, slice your own fresh fruit and blend it into plain yogurt.

Storing Tips

- Refrigerate yogurt as soon as possible after purchasing.
- Eat yogurt within a week of the use-by date.
- Don't freeze yogurt, because it ruins the taste and texture.

YUCCA

Typical serving size: ½ cup, raw (3.6 oz or 103 g)

HOW IT HARMS
Bloating and flatulence

WHAT IT HEALS
Immunity
Collagen production
Digestion
Celiac disease
Gluten intolerance

Yucca is a dietary staple in many parts of the world, including Africa, Asia, the Caribbean, and Latin America. Yucca is considered a "tuber." It's a tropical root vegetable that has thick, barklike, brown skin and a white, starchy interior (like a potato but firmer because it contains more starch). Yucca root is also known as "manioc" or "cassava."

Health Benefits

Boosts immune sysem. A ½ cup (99 g) serving of yucca yields 35% of the daily recommended vitamin C, an antioxidant that helps fight harmful free radicals, strengthens your immune system, and guards against infection.

Increases collagen production. The vitamin C in yucca also stimulates collagen production, thereby contributing to healthy bones, teeth, gums, and blood vessels.

Helps with weight loss. The fiber in yucca helps your body digest food and prevent constipation. It also adds bulk to your diet, so it makes you feel fuller faster, which can be useful if you're trying to lose weight or maintain a healthy weight.

Provides alternative to gluten. Yucca is also gluten-free, so it is a good starch for people with celiac disease or gluten intolerance.

Health Risks

Bloating and gas. Yucca contains a lot of fiber, so eating too much of it in one meal could cause digestive discomfort, such as gas, bloating, cramps, or diarrhea.

Eating Tips

- Substitute yucca for potatoes in soups and stews for an extra boost of vitamin C.
- Use yucca flour as a thickener, or add it to noodles and baked goods.

Buying Tips

- Look for firm yucca with unblemished skin.
- This tuber is available year-round.

Storing Tips

- Treat yucca the way you would a potato: Store it somewhere that is dry, cool, and dark. It should stay good for up to a week.
- You can also peel yucca, place it in water, and refrigerate it for up to 3 days or after peeling, wrap it and freeze it for up to about 3 months.

ZUCCHINI

See also Squash, page 196

Typical serving size: 1 cup, raw (4.4 oz or 124 g)

WHAT IT HEALS
High cholesterol
Weight control

Elongated, dark green zucchini are sometimes mistaken for cucumbers. And there is a golden variety of zucchini, as well as some that have dark green stripes. Although both zucchini and cucumbers are members of the gourd family, zucchini are closer cousins to pumpkins than to cucumbers. Zucchini are by far the most popular summer squash in North America. Picked and eaten while still immature, zucchini have a soft shell and tender light-colored flesh that has a delicate, crisp, fresh flavor.

One cup (124 g) of raw sliced zucchini has 20 calories and provides 28 mcg (micrograms) of folate, about 7% of the adult RDA, as well as 12 mg of vitamin C and 250 mg of potassium.

Health Benefits

Lowers cholesterol. The flesh of zucchini contains soluble fiber which helps to reduces LDL, the "bad" cholesterol, by carrying it out of your body before it can be absorbed into your bloodstream.

Helps with weight loss. Zucchini can sate your appetite because of its fiber and high water content.

Eating Tips

- Add shredded zucchini to marinara sauce.
- Bake hollowed zucchini halves filled with Italian chicken sausage.
- Toss zucchini chunks with rice vinegar and sesame oil.

Buying Tips

- Zucchini taste best when eaten small— ideally 6 to 9 in (15 to 23 cm) long.
- Look for specimens that feel firm and heavy when you pick them up.

Storing Tip

- Although they can be refrigerated for a few days, zucchini tend to spoil quickly.

Snacking: The Best Way to Beat Your Cravings

It's 3 p.m., and your energy is dipping, just like your eyelids. You're thinking about raiding the vending machine, and your resolve is weakening. The good news: Snacking is good for you because going too long without eating sets you up for a huge blood sugar dip that could negatively affect your food choices for the rest of the day. The bad news: Most of the snacks in the vending machine are rotten choices. Follow these tips for healthy snacking:

Time your snacks strategically. Eating a low-calorie snack during a long stretch between meals can take the edge off hunger and prevent overeating at the next meal. If snacks are well timed, they may help to boost flagging energy, especially in children. Some people intentionally blunt their appetites with a low-calorie snack before an event where calorie-laden foods are served.

Decrease serving sizes for snacking. The same foods that make up a small meal can work well, so a sandwich, a bowl of hearty vegetable soup, cheese and crackers, yogurt with fruit, or a low-fat muffin all make the nutritional grade.

Fulfill nutrient needs with snacks. Snacks can also provide several of the recommended daily servings of starchy foods or the 5 to 10 servings of fruits and vegetables. Half a bagel with an apple, or a pita pocket filled with chopped raw vegetables, makes a filling, nutritious snack. Other quick, low-fat foods include bags of fresh raw vegetables and dips such as hummus or low-fat yogurt blended with herbs.

Shop with snacking in mind. Add several healthy snacking foods to your weekly shopping list. When you have the right foods on hand, it's easy to prepare snacks to take on trips, to school, or to work. Stay away from prepackaged high-fat items, such as potato and tortilla chips.

Avoid snack traps. Everybody knows that a raw carrot is healthier than a frosted doughnut, but some snack foods that sound nutritious are not much better than a doughnut. Read labels carefully to find hidden sugar and fats. Some common traps include granola bars; they are often loaded with sugar and fat. Fruit drinks may contain very little fruit juice but have large amounts of added sugar, such as high-fructose corn syrup. Coffee drinks similarly can have large amounts of high-fat cream or sugar. Microwave popcorn is often high in fat, as are trail mixes and other packaged combinations of nuts and seeds.

THE BOTTOM LINE

- Snacking throughout the day can keep hunger (and overeating) at bay but keep portions small.
- Healthy-sounding foods, such as granola bars, may be loaded with calories, fats and sugars.
- Be prepared with healthy snacks, such as fresh fruit or veggies with hummus.

3

AILMENTS

A Condition-by-Condition Guide to What Foods Harm, What Foods Heal

When we're sick, our first thought is to turn to doctors, prescriptions, and pharmacies. But more and more, people are rediscovering the healing power of foods. While very few diseases can actually be cured by food, what we eat plays a major role in our well-being. Eating the right foods provides the nutrients our body needs to ease symptoms, combat disease, and heal itself.

Maybe you or someone you know has been affected by one of the more than 100 conditions in this section. If so, look up the ailment in the alphabetical listing and you'll find foods that may harm or heal, tips for ensuring you're eating the best nutrients in the right combinations at the optimal time, and suggestions for other helpful actions. These entries contain research that reflects the latest thinking about how foods can tame inflammation, stop asthma attacks, and even guard against heart disease and stroke. You'll see some of the most common ailments, such as the simple but pesky cold (page 252) and rarer conditions, such as lupus (page 306).

Each entry begins with a quick list, so you can see at a glance which foods may cause additional symptoms or worsen an ailment and which foods may improve or prevent it. These aren't comprehensive lists, but just highlight the best and worst foods to eat if you suffer from that condition. And because ailments often affect different people in different ways, we also highlight foods that you may consider limiting. For example, those affected by stress (page 340) may want to limit fatty foods, spicy foods, and caffeinated beverages.

At the heart of each entry is what we call the Nutrition Connection, an in-depth explanation of the preventive and healing power of foods. Here, we share how specific nutrients in foods work to counteract conditions. To ease the inflammation of shingles (page 338), eat fresh fruits and vegetables that have plenty of vitamin C. Bananas are high in potassium, which helps ensure normal blood pressure (page 235). And read about hay fever (page 280) to learn which plant foods can actually trigger symptoms.

ACNE

FOODS THAT HARM
Dairy products
High-glycemic foods, such as
    potatoes, soft drinks, white flour,
    and refined sugars

FOODS THAT HEAL
Broccoli
Cabbage
Oranges
Berries
Kiwi
Melons
Peppers
Spinach and other dark
    leafy greens
Fish
Poultry
Whole grains
Lentils
Avocados
Potatoes
Bananas
Oysters
Flaxseed

FOODS TO LIMIT
Kelp supplements
Iodized salt
High doses of vitamin
    B6 and B12 supplements

WHO'S AFFECTED?
- Teenagers
- Adults, especially women: 50% of women ages 20 to 29
- Post-menopausal women

Old School
Chocolate does not cause acne.

New Wisdom
It's not chocolate itself, but the dairy and sugar in the chocolate that likely cause acne.

Almost everyone experiences an occasional flare-up of acne. It's most prevalent during adolescence, afflicting 85% of teenagers to some degree. A growing number of adults also experience acne especially women in their twenties and again after menopause.

Hormones, including testosterone and insulin, are thought to be responsible for most cases of acne. But the connection between foods and pimples isn't just old wives' tales—recent research indicates there may be a link after all.

Specifically, dairy may cause a rise in testosterone, while refined sugars cause a spike in insulin.

In rare instances, sensitivity to a food may exacerbate existing acne. For instance, kelp, a type of seaweed, can cause severe cystic acne, and iodized salt can provoke an acne flare-up. If you think you're sensitive to certain foods, try eliminating them from your diet for several weeks to see if your acne improves.

Heredity is suspected in some cases of severe acne. A number of medications can also cause acne; major offenders include steroids and other hormonal agents, iodine preparations, lithium, and anticonvulsants. Stress often triggers a flare-up of acne, most likely by altering hormone levels and stimulating food cravings.

Nutrition Connection

Clear, glowing skin reflects overall good health. A healthy, balanced diet that follows these guidelines can help prevent acne and boost overall skin quality.

Limit dairy products and high-glycemic foods. Cut down on your consumption of milk if you suspect that it's causing acne flare-ups. Cut down on sugary soft drinks and foods made with white flour, or avoid them altogether.

Eat vitamin A- and C-rich foods. They help build and maintain healthy skin. Sebum, fat, and epithelial cells in the oily secretion of the sebaceous gland contribute to acne. Beta-carotene, which is converted by the body into vitamin A, may reduce the production of those cells. Vitamin C is a powerful antioxidant and may help stimulate the growth of new skin cells. The best dietary sources of beta-carotene are brightly colored fruits and dark green vegetables. Citrus fruits, berries, kiwi, melons, peppers, broccoli, and cabbage are especially rich in vitamin C.

Eat foods rich in vitamin B6. It's found in meat, fish, poultry, whole grains, beans, lentils, avocados, nuts, potatoes, bananas, and leafy greens. Vitamin B6 may reduce acne by helping to regulate hormones implicated in the development of acne lesions.

Eat foods rich in zinc. Some studies link this mineral to skin health and claim it may help to improve acne. Zinc promotes healthy hormone levels and advances healing. Seafood—especially oysters—red meat, poultry, and whole grains are rich in zinc.

Eat foods rich in omega-3s. Omega-3 fatty acids can help ward off the inflammation of acne. Fish and flaxseed are rich in these healthy fats.

Do not attempt to self-treat acne with supplements. In most cases, it's best to obtain nutrients through food, and taking high doses of vitamins and minerals might worsen the condition. Some studies show that high doses of vitamins B6 and B12 can aggravate acne, and high doses of vitamin A can cause dry, flaking skin and hair loss. Excessive intake of vitamin A has also been linked with the risk of osteoporosis.

Beyond the Diet

Good nutrition is the first line of defense, but these other measures can help.

Exercise. Regular exercise improves circulation and helps the skin look its best.

Avoid smoking. Nicotine causes narrowing of the blood vessels, which hinders blood flow to the skin.

Try over-the-counter medications. Most persistent mild to moderate acne can be controlled with proper skin care, good nutrition, and nonprescription drugs, such as 2.5 to 10% strength benzoyl peroxide gel, lotion, or ointment.

See a dermatologist. A dermatologist may prescribe tretinoin, a topical medication derived from vitamin A. Isotretinoin (Accutane), a potent oral drug, is reserved for severe cystic acne. For severe cases of hormonal acne, a dermatologist may prescribe spironolactone, an anti-androgen.

ADHD

FOODS THAT HARM

Some children with ADHD may be sensitive to foods containing salicylates, including:

   Processed foods

   Foods containing dyes, pariticularly red or orange dyes

   Dried fruits

FOODS THAT HEAL

Salicylate-free foods, such as:

   Bananas

   Pears

   Lentils

   Whole grain breads and cereals

   Fish

   Lean meat and poultry

   Milk and cheese

   Eggs

FOODS TO LIMIT

Sugary foods, such as cookies and soft drinks

WHO'S AFFECTED?
- Children, ages 4 to 17
- Adults can also be affected, and parents of children with ADHD are two to eight times more likely to have ADHD themselves

As of 2007, some 5.4 million children ages 4 to 17 were diagnosed with ADHD—that's nearly one in 10 children. And a growing number of adults are also being diagnosed.

An ADHD diagnosis means someone has six or more symptoms of inattentiveness, hyperactivity or impulsivity. Symptoms must have lasted at least 6 months in at least two different settings, such as home and school. Symptoms might include: making careless mistakes; being easily distracted and forgetful; talking excessively; interrupting others; and fidgeting.

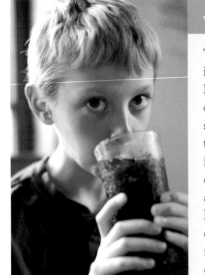

WHAT ABOUT CAFFEINE?

The jury is still out as to whether caffeine improves or worsens ADHD symptoms. Because it's a stimulant, it makes sense to think caffeine might help ADHD symptoms, just as stimulant drugs can. Researchers support this theory and say that caffeine can lessen impulsiveness and hyperactivity. But if children drink caffeine late enough in the day so that it affects their sleep, it could worsen symptoms. At least one study suggests that women who drink caffeinated soft drinks during pregnancy are more likely to have children who, at 18 months old, have ADHD symptoms (interestingly, coffee didn't have the same effects).

especially fish. Here's how:

Nix simple carbs. Candy and fruit drinks, soft drinks, and foods sweetened with corn syrup, honey, and sugar can raise blood sugar levels and may contribute to attention problems.

Eat complex carbs. Especially later in the day, offering kids a complex carb–rich snack can promote relaxation and sleep. Good choices include whole-grain breads and cereals.

Focus on protein. Choose foods like beans, eggs, low-fat cheese, fish, and lean meat for breakfast and for after-school snacks. Protein foods may improve concentration.

Avoid foods that contain salicylates. Some children with ADHD may be sensitive to salicylates, chemicals that occur naturally in many fruits and vegetables (especially dried fruits) as well as in processed foods, foods containing dyes, and many medications and household products. If you think certain foods affect your child's behavior, eliminate them over time to see if symptoms approve.

Nutrition Connection

In a 2012 paper in *Pediatrics*, researchers at Children's Memorial Hospital in Chicago studied the diet factor in ADHD. They concluded that some children with ADHD do respond to strict elimination diets such as the Feingold diet, which removes many foods with salicylates from the diet. But these diets are time-consuming and disruptive to the entire family—and they're hard to implement, especially as kids get older. For most kids, simply avoiding junk food and processed foods is enough to ease ADHD symptoms; instead, focus on a diet rich in whole grains, plenty of fruits and vegetables, and lean proteins,

Beyond the Diet

Your doctor will likely suggest behavioral strategies to help your child manage his or her attention problems. Beyond following that advice, try these tactics.

Stick to a medication schedule. If your doctor prescribes medication for your child, makes sure it is taken as directed and at the same time every day.

Limit TV and electronic games at night. These can overstimulate children before bed and make it harder for them to get the 7 to 8 hours of sleep they need.

Play, preferably outdoors. Encourage your kids to be active for at least 20 to 30 minutes most days of the week.

Do some deep breathing. Teach your kids to stop what they're doing and take slow deep breaths for a few minutes, whenever they feel angry or stressed.

AGE-RELATED MACULAR DEGENERATION

See Eye Problems, page 269

AIDS AND HIV INFECTION

FOODS THAT HARM
Shellfish, hamburgers, sushi, homemade mayonnaise, and other undercooked food

FOODS THAT HEAL
Fish
Lean meats
Poultry without skin
Legumes
Cooked fruits and vegetables
Quionoa
Barley
Buckwheat
Olive oil
Walnuts
Flaxseed

FOODS TO LIMIT
Sugary foods, such as cookies and soft drinks
Raw fruits and vegetables
Red meat, butter, and other foods with saturated fats

AIDS is a wasting disease, and death is often triggered by weight loss rather than other HIV complications. It's imperative for a patient to eat as many nutrient-dense foods as possible. Unfortunately, maintaining good nutrition is complicated by the manner in which AIDS affects the digestive system. The disease reduces absorption of nutrients, especially folate, riboflavin, thiamine, and vitamins B6 and B12; it often causes intractable diarrhea, which causes further nutritional loss; and it increases the risk of intestinal infections. Many of those with AIDS also suffer appetite loss and bouts of nausea, either from the disease or from medications. Some AIDS specialists advise artificial feeding if nutrients are not being absorbed properly.

Nutrition Connection

Asymptomatic HIV-infected individuals should follow the same dietary practices recommended for healthy people. Eat high-quality foods. A diet comprised of fruits, vegetables, whole grains, legumes, and lean protein sources can contribute to your health and well-being. Sugary foods, such as cookies and soft drinks, provide empty calories that don't convey needed nutrition and should be limited. The following guidelines will help you get the most out of your diet:

Aim for 5 to 6 servings of vegetables and fruits per day. A colorful array will ensure a range of vitamins and nutrients. Be sure to wash them thoroughly. Many doctors advise following the same precautions as when traveling abroad: Eat only

WHO'S AFFECTED?
- About 1.5 million in North America
- Men who have sex with other men, intravenous drug users, and hemophiliacs are most affected
- The majority of those diagnosed with AIDS are between 24 and 49 years old

cooked vegetables, and eat fruits that are peeled, stewed, or canned. Some counsel that salads and raw fruits and vegetables are safe but may be difficult to digest.

Make sure at least 50% of carbohydrates should come from whole grain sources. These include quinoa, barley, and buckwheat.

Keep protein in check. Extremely high amounts of protein can strain the kidneys.

Consume heart-healthy foods. People with HIV may suffer from medication-related high cholesterol and triglyceride levels. Avoid saturated fats, which increases the risk of cardiovascular disease, and instead opt for polyunsaturated and monounsaturated fats, which help protect against heart disease. Sources include fatty fish such as salmon, olive oil, walnuts and flaxseed oil.

Practice food safety. Because HIV attacks the immune system, it makes a person more vulnerable to infections, including food poisoning from salmonella, shigella, campylobacter, and other bacteria. See pages 18 to 26 for food safety practices.

Seek help after rapid weight loss. Someone experiencing dramatic weight loss may require artificial feeding (hyperalimentation). This is generally administered through a gastric feeding tube inserted into the stomach or an intravenous line that pumps predigested nutrients into the bloodstream.

Adjust your diet when you suffer from frequent bouts of diarrhea. Avoid raw fruits and vegetables and high-fiber foods such as whole grain breads and cereals. Also avoid gassy foods such as onions, beans, cabbage, spicy foods, and carbonated beverages. Stay away from rich, fatty foods, such as fatty meats, butter, and whole milk. It's also a good idea to avoid caffeine, alcohol, and chocolate.

Drink fluids after nausea. When you suffer from nausea or diarrhea—common side effects of many HIV medications—drink plenty of fluids to replace what you've lost, such as water, broth, or flat ginger ale, or eat popsicles. When you are ready to eat, start with bland foods such as toast or crackers.

Beyond the Diet

For people with HIV or AIDS, there are more than 20 drugs available. Often taken in combinations tailored to each person's specific needs, these drug cocktails have proven effective in warding off the symptoms of AIDS and extending people's lives. In addition, those with HIV or AIDS need to take extra precautions with health matters:

Watch upper RDAs for supplements. Nutritionists often recommend that HIV-positive people take a multiple vitamin and mineral pill to prevent nutritional deficiencies. However, supplements with more than 100% of the RDA should only be used if prescribed by a doctor.

Avoid self-medicating with herbs. There is no evidence supporting the efficacy of herbs, and some herbal preparations contain substances that can cause serious side effects or interact with medications.

Go easy with mouth infections. When mouth or throat infections, such as thrush or ulcers, make eating uncomfortable, try the following. Eat soft, moist foods that

---

QUICK TIP: Avoid harmful dietary approaches

Some advocate taking high doses of zinc and selenium to bolster the immune system. There is no proof that these nutrients protect against infections; in fact, studies show that taking 200 mg to 300 mg of zinc a day for 6 weeks actually lowers immunity. Excessive selenium can also cause vomiting and diarrhea.

---

are easy to swallow, like mashed potatoes and gravy. Use a straw for liquids. Keep food at room temperature. Avoid foods and juices with high acid content.

ALCOHOLISM

FOODS THAT HARM
Alcohol in any form

FOODS THAT HEAL
Legumes
Whole grain or fortified and
   enriched grain products
Lean meat and poultry
Nuts
Mushrooms
Broccoli
Cabbage
Dairy products
Spinach
Kale

Alcoholism is defined as chronic drinking that interferes with one's personal, familial, or professional life. While an occasional drink is not likely to be harmful, it's important to recognize that alcohol is easily abused.

Various factors can foster alcoholism. Genetic predisposition, learned behavior, and childhood experiences, including abuse, are all thought to foster alcoholism. Progression of the disease varies from one person to another. For some, it develops as soon as they begin to drink. For most people, it progresses slowly from periodic social drinking to more frequent indulgence until the person is addicted.

Chronic overuse of alcohol takes a heavy psychological and physical toll. Alcoholics often do not appear to be intoxicated, but their ability to work and go

HOW LIKELY ARE YOU TO BECOME AN ALCOHOLIC?

Your gender and the amount you drink influences the likelihood of becoming an alcoholic. If you're a man who has 15 more drinks a week, you're a woman who has 12 or more or you have five or more drinks at one sitting at least once a week, you're at risk for becoming alcohol dependent.

about daily activities becomes increasingly impaired. On average, alcoholism shortens life expectancy; it raises the risk of other life-threatening diseases, including cancer of the pancreas, liver, and esophagus. Women who drink heavily while pregnant may have a baby with fetal alcohol syndrome or birth defects.

Nutrition Connection

Alcoholism can lead to malnutrition, not only because chronic drinkers tend to have poor diets, but also because alcohol alters the digestion and metabolism of most nutrients. There is no one diet for all recovering alcoholics, so these guidelines focus on overall well-being:

Eat a healthy, balanced diet. Take small steps to include colorful fruits and vegetables, whole grains such as oats, brown rice, and whole wheat bread, and lean protein such as fish and skinless chicken breast.

Ask doctors about supplementation. Supplements can be prescribed to treat certain nutritional deficiencies. Common deficiencies among alcoholics include thiamine, which is marked by muscle cramps, nausea, appetite loss, nerve disorders, and depression. Deficiencies of folate, riboflavin, vitamin B6, and selenium are also

WHO'S AFFECTED?
- About 17.6 million Americans and 4 to 5 million Canadians
- Children of alcoholics are two to seven times more likely to become alcohol dependent
- Lifetime alcohol dependence is greater among whites and males

common. Also, legumes, whole grain or fortified and enriched grain products, lean meat and poultry, nuts, mushrooms, and cruciferous vegetables like broccoli and cabbage are good sources of these vitamins and minerals.

Add calcium. Many alcoholics are at risk of bone fractures and osteoporosis because they suffer from deficient levels of vitamin D, which helps the body absorb calcium. Dairy and dark leafy greens such as spinach and kale are good sources of calcium.

Beyond the Diet

Recovering from alcohol dependency is difficult, but these measures help take the edge off:

Exercise regularly. It helps decrease stress and releases endorphins, which helps boost your mood and outlook on life.

Cope with stress in healthier ways. Dependence on alcohol may start as an emotional crutch for handling stress. Meditation, yoga, or other breathing or relaxation techniques are encouraged.

Lean on support networks. Having friends and family who will listen and support you contributes to the recovery process.

ALLERGIES, FOOD

FOODS THAT HARM

Almost any food can provoke an allergic reaction. Eight foods that account for 90% of allergic reactions:

Milk and milk products

Eggs (especially egg whites)

Soy and soy products

Wheat and wheat products

Peanuts

Tree nuts

Fish

Shellfish

Food allergies may not be as prevalent as some might think. It is estimated that almost one-third of people say that they, or a family member, have a food allergy. But, in fact, only 2 to 8% of children, and 1 to 2% of adults in the U.S. have clinically proven allergic reactions to food.

True food allergies involve the body's immune system, whereas food intolerance originates in the gastrointestinal system and is associated with an inability to digest or absorb certain substances. Doctors do not completely understand why so many people have allergies, although heredity appears to be a major factor. If both parents have allergies, their children will almost always have them as well, although the symptoms and allergens may be quite

QUICK TIP: Look for switches

Eggs may be listed on labels as an emulsifier. And some cooks swap vegetable oil for a tropical oil such as coconut oil, which may be a concern for those allergic to coconut.

different. Food allergies in infants and children, however, tend to lessen as they grow, and the problem may disappear by adulthood. There is no doubt that breast-feeding and the delayed introduction of solid foods reduces a child's chances of developing food allergies.

Beyond the Diet

There are many symptoms of food allergies, including nausea, vomiting, diarrhea, constipation, indigestion, headaches, skin rashes or hives, itching, shortness of breath (including asthma attacks), and, in severe cases, widespread swelling of the skin and mucous membranes. Some people can tolerate small amounts of an offending food; others are so hypersensitive that they react to even a minute trace. Here is what you need to know to reduce the effect of food allergies:

Pinpoint allergens. Some allergens are easily identified because symptoms will develop immediately after eating the offending food. The most allergenic foods in infancy are eggs, milk, peanuts, wheat, and soy (about 85% of children lose their sensitivity within the first 3 to 5 years of life). In older children and adults tree nuts, peanuts, and seafood are the most likely to cause severe reactions. Many people have mild allergies to various fruits and vegetables. Cooking can often reduce the allergenic potential of foods, as proteins responsible for allergies are degraded by heat.

Keep a diary. If allergens are not readily identified, keep a carefully documented diary of the time and content of all meals and the appearance and timing of subsequent symptoms. After a week or two, a pattern may emerge. If so, eliminate the suspected food from the diet

Old School
A peanut allergy is a lifelong sentence.

New Wisdom
A blood test can measure peanut-specific antibodies and identify if someone has outgrown their allergy.

WHERE COMMON ALLERGENS LURK

COMMON ALLERGENS	MAJOR SOURCES	HIDDEN SOURCES
Milk and milk products	Dairy products, such as milk, cheeses, yogurt, cream, ice cream, cream soups, and certain baked goods and desserts	Deli meats cut on same slicer as cheese, some canned tuna, nondairy products, and prepared meats
Eggs (especially egg whites)	Cakes, mousses, ice cream, sherbets, and other desserts; mayonnaise, salad dressings, French toast, waffles, and pancakes	Toppings on specialty desserts, some egg substitutes, processed cooked pasta, some soups
Soy and soy products	Soy, soybeans, tofu, textured vegetable protein, hydrolyzed protein, miso, soy sauce, tamari, tempeh, natural and artificial flavors, vegetable broth, and vegetable starch	Major ingredient in processed foods
Wheat and wheat products	Cereals, bread or bread products, dry soup mixes, cakes, pasta, gravies, dumplings, products containing flour, beer and ale	Some hot dogs, ice cream, imitation crab, and imitation meats
Peanuts	Peanuts and peanut oil, peanut butter, peanut flour, baked goods and candy with nuts, natural flavoring	Many candies, and African, Chinese, Mexican, Thai, and Vietnamese foods
Tree nuts	Candy and baked goods with pecans, walnuts, almonds, cashews, hazelnuts, and pistachios; oils from nuts	Natural and artificial flavors, barbecue sauce, some cereals, crackers, and ice cream
Fish	Fresh, canned, smoked, or pickled fish, fish-liver oils, caviar, foods containing fish, such as bisques, broths, and stews	Caesar salad dressings and imitation crab
Shellfish	Crustaceans, such as shrimp, crab, lobster, and crayfish; mollusks (clams, oysters, and scallops); and seafood dishes	Caesar salad dressings and imitation crab

for at least a week, and then try it again. If symptoms develop, chances are you have identified the offending food.

Go for testing. In more complicated cases, allergy tests may be required. The most common is a skin test, but your doctor may also try RAST (radioallergosorbent test) blood study or a medically supervised elimination diet and challenge tests.

Look for hidden triggers. Once allergens have been identified, eliminating those foods from the diet should solve the problem. But this can be more complicated than it sounds. Some of the most common food allergens are hidden ingredients in many processed foods. Also, many foods are chemically related; thus, a person allergic to lemons may also be allergic to oranges and other citrus fruits. In some cases, the real culprit may be a contaminant or an accidental additive in food. For example, some people who are allergic to orange juice may actually be able to tolerate the peeled fruit, since it is limonene (the oil in citrus peels) that produces the allergic reaction.

WHAT IS ANAPHYLACTIC SHOCK?

Severe allergic reactions to foods can result in anaphylactic shock, a life-threatening collapse of the respiratory and circulatory system. If you have had, or believe you may be susceptible to an anaphylactic reaction, you should wear medical identification, and carry emergency medical information in your wallet. Your doctor may also recommend that you carry an epinephrine self-injector (EpiPen).

ALLERGIES, SEASONAL

See Hay Fever, page 280

ALZHEIMER'S DISEASE

FOODS THAT HARM
Alcohol

FOODS THAT HEAL
Olive oil
Tomatoes
Green beans
Zucchini
Cauliflower
Brussels sprouts
Eggplant
Peppers
Salmon
Mackerel

FOODS TO LIMIT
Red meat, butter, and other foods with saturated fats
Sugary foods, such as cookies and soft drinks

Alzheimer's disease is the leading cause of dementia in people over the age of 65, affecting almost 6 million North Americans, and is the sixth-leading cause of death in the U.S. The disease is characterized by abnormal deposits of a protein called beta-amyloid (plaque) in the brain as well as by twisted fibers caused by changes in a protein called 'tau' (tangles). Before arriving at a diagnosis, tests are needed to rule out a stroke, brain tumor, and other possible causes of dementia. Blood tests can uncover genetic markers for the disease.

The cause of Alzheimer's disease remains unknown, but researchers theorize that chromosomal and genetic factors are responsible for some cases.

In addition, hormonal factors are being studied. Women are afflicted more often than men; studies suggest that estrogen replacement may be protective if taken before the age of 65, but more research is needed. Thyroid disorders are also linked to the disease.

Nutrition Connection

Researchers are finding many links between diet and dementia, and there is evidence that some foods and nutrients are powerful allies in the battle against Alzheimer's. Below are ways to boost your diet to help protect against Alzheimer's.

Go Mediterranean. According to a 2010 Columbia University study published in the journal *Archives of Neurology*, people who consumed a Mediterranean-type diet were 38% less likely to develop Alzheimer's disease over the next four years. The diet includes olive oil, fish, tomatoes, eggplant, zucchini, peppers, and green beans, and less amounts of foods with saturated fat, such as red meat and butter.

Eat fatty fish at least three times a week. The brain is rich in DHA (docosahexaenoic acid), an omega-3 fatty acid that is plentiful in fatty fish such as salmon, mackerel, halibut, herring, and sardines. Insufficient levels of this fat have been associated with age-related dementia, including Alzheimer's disease.

Cut down on saturated fats and sugar. Many studies suggest that people who develop type 2 diabetes—made more likely if you eat a fatty or sugary diet—have a high risk of developing Alzheimer's.

Get your B vitamins. Studies have shown that people with Alzheimer's have high homocysteine levels, and there is evidence that high concentrations of homocysteine in healthy adults may lead to Alzheimer's.

Folate, found in legumes and cruciferous vegetables, such as cauliflower and brussels sprouts, works with vitamins B6 and B12 to help regulate homocysteine levels.

Add antioxidants. Antioxidants, found in a wide variety of fruits and vegetables, mop up free radicals and have been touted as possible preventives of Alzheimer's because the body's ability to neutralize free radicals declines with age. Recent research published in the *Journal of Alzheimer's Disease* suggests that lowering iron levels and increasing antioxidant levels can help protect the brain from the changes associated with Alzheimer's disease.

Monitor nutrition carefully. Those with the disease may forget to eat or eat only their favorite foods. So their diet needs to be monitored to make sure it's nutritionally balanced. A multivitamin may also be advisable; high-dose supplements should not be administered unless specifically recommended by a physician.

50% to 80% of dementia cases are due to Alzheimer's disease, making it the most common cause of dementia.

Avoid alcohol. Even in small amounts, alcohol destroys brain cells, a loss that a healthy person can tolerate but one that can accelerate the progression of Alzheimer's disease. Alcohol also interacts with medications prescribed for Alzheimer's patients.

Beyond the Diet

Think of your brain as a muscle: The more you use it, the healthier it will be. So, in addition to eating better, try these other tips to help ward off the effects of Alzheimer's:

Get moving. In a study of middle-age and elderly adults with mild memory problems, those who started walking several times each week scored significantly higher on memory tests after just 6 months.

Learn something new. Research has found that people who had spent more years in school or had worked in mentally demanding jobs stayed sharper, even when they were affected by Alzheimer's disease. Keep your brain agile with puzzles, games, and museum visits.

Make time for friends. A Harvard study found that socially connected people kept more of their memory intact as they aged—up to twice as much, according to one measure.

ANEMIA

WHO'S AFFECTED?

- Older adults and the elderly
- People with intestinal disorders that affect nutrient absorption
- Surgery patients
- Women of childbearing age
- Women with heavy menstrual periods
- Endurance athletes
- Alcoholics
- Those on very restricted vegetarian diets

FOODS THAT HARM

Iron supplements, unless prescribed by a physician

FOODS THAT HEAL

Organ meats
Beef
Poultry
Fish
Egg yolks
Soy
Green leafy vegetables
Iron-enriched breads and cereals
Citrus fruits
Broccoli
Red peppers

FOODS TO LIMIT

Spinach
Rhubarb
Swiss chard
Chocolate
Bran
Nuts
Tea

Anemia is the umbrella term for a variety of disorders characterized by the inability of red blood cells to carry sufficient oxygen. This may be due to an abnormality of a low level of hemoglobin, the iron- and protein-based red pigment in blood that carries oxygen from the lungs to all body cells. Symptoms of anemia, therefore, reflect oxygen starvation. In mild anemia, this may include general weakness, pallor, fatigue, and brittle nails. Severe cases are marked by shortness of breath, fainting, and cardiac arrhythmias.

In North America, the most common type of anemia is due to iron deficiency, which is usually caused by blood loss of some type. Other types of anemia exist. Hemolytic anemia occurs when red blood cells are destroyed more rapidly than normal. Pernicious, or megaloblastic, anemia is caused by a deficiency of vitamin B12, which is necessary to make red blood cells. Relatively rare types of anemia include thalassemia, an inherited disorder, and aplastic anemia, which may be caused by infection, exposure to toxic chemicals or radiation, or a genetic disorder.

Nutrition Connection

The human body recycles iron to make new red blood cells. Because the body absorbs only a small percentage of dietary iron, the Recommended Dietary Allowance (RDA) calls for consuming more iron than the amount lost: 8 mg per day for men and postmenopausal women, 18 mg for women under 50, and 27 mg for pregnant women. Here are some general dietary recommendations to boost iron levels.

Consume as much iron from foods as possible. The best sources of iron are animal products—meat, fish, poultry, and egg yolks. The body absorbs much more of the heme iron found in these foods than the nonheme iron from plant sources, such as green leafy vegetables, dried fruits, soy and other legumes, and iron-enriched breads and cereals.

Boost iron absorption by eating vitamin C–rich foods, especially if you're vegetarian. Plant sources of iron are poorly absorbed by the body. Adding a vitamin C–rich food, such as citrus fruits, broccoli, or red pepper, to a plant-based meal can enhance absorption of nonheme iron.

If you're over 50, get your B12. Up to one-third of older adults produce inadequate amounts of stomach acid and can no longer properly absorb B12 from food. People over 50 may have to meet their needs by consuming foods rich in B12, such as meats and egg yolks, or by taking a supplement containing B12.

Avoid drinking tea during meals. Tea contains natural compounds called tannins, which bind with iron and make it unavailable for absorption. Drink tea between meals to enjoy its health benefits.

Watch for foods that prevent absorption of iron. Oxalates found in spinach, rhubarb, Swiss chard, and chocolate as well as phytates in nuts and bran cereal can prevent the body from using iron.

Avoid iron supplements, unless directed by a physician. Unless you have had a blood test that confirms iron deficiency, excess iron can be dangerous.

Beyond the Diet

In addition to dietary measures, you can add iron to your diet by cooking with iron pots. Ironware may discolor food, but taste is unaffected.

ANOREXIA NERVOSA

FOODS THAT HEAL

- Eggs
- Milk and other dairy foods
- Meat, fish, and poultry
- Whole grains
- Calorie-enriched liquid supplements
- Multivitamin supplements, if approved by a doctor

FOODS TO LIMIT

- Low-calorie diet foods and soft drinks
- Foods that have diuretic or laxative effect

WHO'S AFFECTED?

- Between 2 and 6% of North Americans
- 1 in 200 women in the U.S.
- Adolescents—the average age of onset is 19, and 95% of those who have eating disorders are between the ages of 12 and 25.8
- About 10% of anorexia sufferers are men

The self-starvation that is a hallmark of anorexia nervosa is caused by a complex psychiatric disorder that afflicts mostly adolescent or young adult females. The cause of anorexia is unknown. Researchers believe that a combination of hormonal, social, and psychological factors are responsible. The disease often begins in adolescence, a time of tremendous hormonal and psychological change. The behavior is marked by obsessive or strict dieting and exercise, preoccupation with food, and self-induced vomiting or use of laxatives.

As the disease progresses, menstruation ceases and nutritional deficiencies develop. Physical indications of anorexia include fatigue, nervousness or hyperactivity, dry skin, hair loss, and intolerance to cold. More serious consequences include cardiac arrhythmias, loss of bone mass, kidney failure, and in about 5 to 10% of cases, death in the first 10 years of contracting the disease.

Anorexia often requires intensive long-term treatment, preferably by a team experienced with eating disorders: a doctor to treat starvation-induced medical problems, a psychiatrist, and a dietitian. Family members can also benefit from counseling.

Nutrition Connection

The biggest hurdle for someone with anorexia is to overcome an abnormal fear of food and a distorted self-image of being fat. To that end, these are the steps to achieving a stable weight:

Think small, then gradually increase food intake. In the beginning, small portions of nutritious and easily digestible foods are best. Portion sizes and the variety of foods are increased gradually to achieve a steady weight gain.

Replace lost nutrition. A doctor or a dietitian can help formulate a balanced, varied diet that provides adequate protein for rebuilding lost lean tissue, complex carbohydrates for energy, and a moderate amount of fat for extra calories. Good foods include eggs, milk and other dairy products, meat, fish, poultry, and whole grains. Extra calcium and multivitamins may also be given.

Monitor food intake closely. Relapses are common and close monitoring may be necessary to ensure that the person with anorexia is really eating. But avoid making food a constant source of attention and conflict.

Beyond the Diet

Seek support. Talk therapy, such as cognitive behavioral therapy, group therapy, or family therapy can help. Support groups can also aid in treatment.

Consider medication. Doctors may prescribe antidepressants, antipsychotics, and mood stabilizers as part of a treatment program.

QUICK TIP: Have a lemon drop before a meal

Sour foods increase saliva flow, which helps stimulate appetite.

ANXIETY

See Mood Disorders, page 315

ARTHRITIS

FOODS THAT HARM
Red meat, butter, egg yolks, and other foods with saturated fats
Processed foods that contain trans fats
Refined carbohydrates, such as sugar and white flour

FOODS THAT HEAL
Salmon
Sardines
Trout
Anchovies
Citrus fruits
Kiwi
Pumpkin
Peppers

Sweet potatoes
Cabbage
Collard greens
Rhubarb
Spinach
Chia seeds
Walnuts
Pineapple
Beans
Soy products

Inflammation in one or more joints is known as arthritis. There are two main types—osteoarthritis and rheumatoid arthritis. Medications for the two types of arthritis are different but diet and lifestyle treatments are similar. Osteoarthritis causes your joints to gradually lose their cartilage—the smooth, gel-like, shock-absorbing material that prevents adjacent bones from touching. Most commonly affected are the fingers, knees, hips, neck, and spine. (Carpal tunnel syndrome, a common condition of median nerve connecting the wrist and fingers to the forearm, may be caused by osteoarthritis, as well as by repetitive motions such as typing.)

As cartilage loss continues, the friction of bone rubbing against bone can cause pain and joint instability. It's a degenerative disease, meaning that symptoms will continue to get worse over time. Osteoarthritis may be the result of decades of joint wear and tear, though genetic factors, excess weight, and impairments in the body's ability to repair cartilage may also play a role. Some cases are linked to a specific cause, such as a previous injury to a joint; the overuse of a joint occupationally or athletically; or a congenital defect in joint structure.

Rheumatoid arthritis (RA) develops when an overactive immune system attacks connective tissue in the joints and other organs, causing inflammation and pain. The cause is believed to be the result of both genetic and environmental factors. Symptoms vary, but can range from stiffness, inflammation, tenderness and warmth around the joints to severe pain, decreased range of motion, deformed joints, fever, fatigue and weight loss. Rheumatoid arthritis may be diagnosed through blood tests or x-rays. There is no cure for RA, but medications, therapies and surgery can help with pain management, minimize joint damage, and slow the progression of the disease.

Nutrition Connection

There are certain nutrients that may help reduce inflammation in the joints and pain. Here's your guide to easing osteoarthritis with diet:

Pump up antioxidants. Eating more foods that are rich in antioxidant powerhouses like vitamins C, E, and beta-carotene can benefit people with arthritis by helping to manufacture collagen, reduce inflammation, and slow the progression of this debilitating disease. The

QUICK TIP: Eat a fish a day

The human body uses omega-3 fatty acids to manufacture prostaglandins, chemicals that play a role in many processes, including inflammation and other functions of the immune system. Several studies have found that a diet that includes fish oil equivalent to the amount in an 8 oz (227 g) daily serving of fish may help relieve the painful symptoms of arthritis.

best food sources of these vitamins include citrus fruits, berries, kiwi, melons, pumpkin, broccoli, peppers, potatoes, sweet potatoes, and cabbage.

Add vitamin D and calcium. Additionally, vitamin D and calcium may reduce your risk of arthritis and fortify weight-bearing joints that have deteriorated as a result of the disease. To get more vitamin D and calcium, incorporate salmon, mackerel, herring, sardines, dairy, egg yolks, collard greens, rhubarb, and spinach into your diet.

Look for omega-3s. Research suggests that omega-3 fatty acids can help reduce inflammation and minimize pain and swelling. Enjoy fish like sardines, anchovies, and trout, as well as flaxseed, chia seed, and walnuts. Fresh or powdered ginger adds a pleasant bite to many foods.

Incorporate more bromelain in your diet. The bromelain enzyme in pineapple may also help cut down on swelling, so go for fresh, frozen, or canned pineapple without added sugar.

Find phytoestrogens. Phytoestrogens may lower the risk of osteoarthritis and stave off the negative influence of estrogen on osteoarthritis-affected joints. The two major classes of phytoestrogens are isoflavones and lignans. Food sources include beans and soy.

Steer clear of saturated fats, omega-6 fats, trans fats, and refined carbs. Saturated and omega-6 fats found in red meat and egg yolks, as well as trans fats found in processed foods, may exacerbate inflammation. Together with refined carbs such as sugar and white flour, they also lead to excess weight, which puts more pressure on your joints.

Beyond the Diet

Both osteoarthritis and rheumatoid arthritis can be treated with medications (including nonsteroidal anti-inflammatory drugs or, for rheumatoid arthritis, steroids, disease-modifying anti-rheumatic drugs, and tumor necrosis factor-alpha inhibitors) or surgery, if severe.

Engage in regular, gentle exercise. Easy-on-the-body exercises such as tai chi, yoga, and swimming can help manage symptoms of arthritis.

Drop some pounds. Even a little extra weight, strains the knees and hips. Following a healthy diet, losing weight and increasing exercise often improves symptoms.

Apply ice or heat. Ice is one of nature's painkillers and helps reduce inflammation. Use ice for acute, occasional pain and apply heat for more chronic aches.

Seek physical therapy. Working with a physical therapist can help you learn how to maintain flexibility in your joints.

Look into alternative interventions. Some people with arthritis find pain relief from acupuncture, tai chi, yoga and nutritional supplements like glucosamine sulfate.

Walk barefoot. Going shoeless reduces the load on knee joints, minimizing pain and disability from osteoarthritis by 12% compared to walking with shoes. That's the finding from a study conducted by researchers at Rush University Medical Center in Chicago.

QUICK TIP: Distract yourself from pain

When arthritis pain flares, avoid dwelling on it by keeping yourself occupied. Any engaging activity such as reading, working a puzzle, watching TV, visiting friends, working on a craft, or going to an artistic performance can help. If you're stuck with nothing to do, try mind games such as counting backward from 100, listing the 50 states, or remembering the names of all your primary school teachers.

ASTHMA

FOODS THAT HARM
- Dried fruit
- Beer
- Wine
- White grape juice
- Instant soup mix
- Instant mashed potatoes
- Cheese
- Soy sauce
- Mushrooms

FOODS THAT HEAL
- Salmon
- Mackerel
- Sardines
- Berries
- Green leafy vegetables

Asthma is a chronic lung condition in which airways narrow, causing wheezing, chest tightness, and labored breathing. Asthma is attributed to a combination of factors, including exposure to cigarette smoke, urban pollution, dust mites, cockroaches, pets, and pollen.

Although asthma is a chronic disease, the changes that occur during an attack are temporary, and the lungs generally function normally at other times. When asthma starts during childhood, the frequency and severity of attacks tend to lessen as the youngster grows and may disappear by adulthood. Some adults, however, suffer a recurrence, often as an aftermath of a viral infection.

Nutrition Connection

In many asthma sufferers, food allergies can cause asthma attacks; in these cases, identifying the culprits may require considerable detective work. See the Food Allergies entry on page 222 for more information. These general guidelines will help lessen chances of attacks or complications:

Avoid sulfites. Many foods have these preservatives added to them. Sulfites are common in dried fruits, dehydrated or instant soup mixes, instant potatoes, wine, beer, and white grape juice. Anyone sensitive to sulfites should carefully check food labels for any ingredient ending in "-sulfite" as well as sulfur dioxide. In addition to causing an asthma attack, sulfites sometimes lead to anaphylaxis in people who are hypersensitive to them.

Avoid salicylates. These compounds—which are in the same family as the active ingredient in aspirin and are also found naturally in many fruits, especially dried fruits and processed foods—can trigger attacks.

Know your trigger foods. People who are allergic to mildew or molds may react to molds in foods such as cheese, mushrooms, and hot dogs, or to fermented foods, including soy sauce, beer, wine, and vinegar. Scan ingredient labels carefully and notify restaurant personnel when eating out.

Eat more fatty fish. Omega-3 fatty acids, found in salmon, mackerel, sardines, and other cold-water fish, have an anti-inflammatory effect and may counter bronchial inflammation.

WHO'S AFFECTED?
- More than 27 million people in North America
- 300 million people worldwide
- 9.4% of people who have asthma in the United States are children

Aim for 7 to 10 servings of fruits and vegetables. Evidence continues to grow on the protective effects of fruits and vegetables on lung function. An array of different colors ensures you get a variety of vitamins, minerals, and antioxidants important for healthy lungs. Vitamin C, in particular, found in berries, green leafy vegetables, and many others, helps promote a healthy immune system and may be helpful in reducing wheezing in children with asthma.

Talk to your doctor. A healthful balanced diet is sometimes difficult if allergies require eliminating entire food groups (for example, milk and other dairy products). A doctor can recommend substitutes or supplements to maintain good nutrition, and counteract asthma drugs' side effects. For example, long-term steroid use causes bone loss, but vitamin D and calcium supplements can prevent the problem.

Beyond the Diet

Some asthma attacks are quickly reversed by a bronchodilator medication that opens the constricted airways. Other episodes are more prolonged, and may require an injection of epinephrine and a corticosteroid drug to stop the attack. Your best bet is to prevent attacks with the following tips:

Reduce exposure to triggers. Limit exposure to tobacco smoke or fumes,

---

QUICK TIP: Lessen an attack with coffee

Drink one or two cups of coffee or tea to sidestep a mild asthma attack. Caffeinated coffee and tea contain theophylline, a bronchial muscle relaxant used to treat asthma in people who are not sensitive to salicylates. (To diagnose an allergy to salicylates, doctors will often administer an exposure test.) Anyone taking a theophylline drug, however, should not drink large amounts of caffeinated beverages, as this can result in an overdose.

---

cold air, exercise, or an allergen. Seasonal asthma is usually due to various pollens, molds, and other environmental factors.

Monitor your weight. Some studies have found a correlation between weight gain and adult-onset asthma. In addition, when obese people with asthma lose weight, there can be an improvement in asthma symptoms.

ATHERO-SCLEROSIS

FOODS THAT HARM
  Processed foods that contain
    trans fats

FOODS THAT HEAL
  Olive oil
  Almonds
  Avocados
  Oats
  Lentils
  Tofu
  Salmon
  Sardines
  Apples
  Pears
  Citrus Fruit

FOODS TO LIMIT
  Red meat, butter, and other foods
    with saturated fats
  High-cholesterol foods, such as
    eggs, shrimp, and organ meats

As we become older, our arteries lose some of their elasticity and stiffen. This can lead to a progressive condition referred to as arteriosclerosis, or hardening (sclerosis) of the arteries. Atherosclerosis is the most common type of arteriosclerosis, and is caused by a build up of fatty plaque in the arteries.

Blood clots tend to form at the site of atherosclerosis fatty deposits, leading to a high risk for heart attack or stroke. Cholesterol is the major component of atherosclerotic plaque, and numerous studies correlate high levels of blood cholesterol and triglycerides with atherosclerosis.

By the time European and North American men have reached their late forties, most have some degree of atherosclerosis. In women the process is delayed, presumably due to the protective effects of estrogen during the reproductive years. After menopause, women are just as likely as men to develop severely clogged arteries.

Precisely what causes atherosclerosis is unknown. However, most experts agree that a genetic susceptibility and a combination of lifestyle factors accelerate the process; these include a diet high in fats and cholesterol, cigarette use, excessive stress, and lack of exercise. Poorly controlled diabetes and high blood pressure can also contribute.

Nutrition Connection

Researchers agree that diet plays a critical role in both the development and treatment of atherosclerosis. Here are the recommendations to delay or prevent the condition:

Limit fat intake. Total fat intake should be no more than 20 to 35% of calories, with saturated fats (found mostly in animal products) comprising no more than 10% of calories. Some strategies include downsizing meat portions; substituting olive oil for butter or margarine; eating low-fat dairy products; and increasing the amount of vegetables. In addition, experts suggest reducing intake of trans-fatty acids and hydrogenated fats. These trans fats are the result of hydrogenation and are known to raise your LDL cholesterol.

Trans fats come in packaged foods, such as cookies and crackers, and snack foods, such as chips.

Be careful with cholesterol. Although consumption of high-cholesterol foods is not thought to be as detrimental as a high-fat diet, a high intake of dietary cholesterol can raise the levels of blood lipids in some people. Experts recommend limiting dietary cholesterol to 200 to 300 mg a day—about the amount in 1½ egg yolks.

Choose heart-healthy fats. The omega-3 fatty acids in salmon, sardines, and other cold-water fish lower blood levels of triglycerides; they also reduce the tendency to form blood clots. Monosaturated fats in olive oil, almonds, and avocados can help lower LDL cholesterol when they replace saturated fats.

Eat fiber. Oat bran, oatmeal, lentils and other legumes, barley, guar gum, psyllium, and pectin-containing fruits such as pears, apples, and citrus fruits all contain soluble fiber that lowers blood cholesterol, probably by interfering with the intestinal absorption of bile acids, which forces the liver to use circulating cholesterol to make more bile.

Incorporate as many antioxidant-rich foods as possible. Colorful fruits and vegetables contain beta-carotene and vitamins C and E, which studies indicate prevent LDL cholesterol from collecting in atherosclerotic plaque. Soy protein also helps raise HDL (the "good" cholesterol) levels and provide antioxidant protection.

WHO'S AFFECTED?

- Most European and North American men in their late forties
- Post-menopausal women
- Those who smoke
- People who have high cholesterol
- People with hypertension

QUICK TIP: Eat more soy

Soy is a powerhouse of health. Just 25 g of soy protein—about 1½ cup of edamame—per day has been shown to help lower LDL levels by up to 15% in people with elevated levels.

Beyond the Diet

Medications including nitrates, beta-blockers, statins, calcium-channel blockers, are often prescribed. In addition, lifestyle changes can even help reverse the condition. Here are some suggestions:

Exercise. Studies have shown that mild to moderate exercise may protect against the development of atherosclerosis.

Quit smoking. In addition to causing a host of other ailments, smoking damages the structure and function of your blood vessels.

Learn healthy ways to cope with stress. Stress leads to higher blood pressure, which combined with atherosclerosis can increase risk of heart disease. Taking a walk or learning relaxation exercises are much better than smoking, drinking, or eating.

Get regular checkups. A doctor can help monitor your blood pressure and blood sugar levels.

BLEEDING PROBLEMS

FOODS THAT HARM
   Alcohol

FOODS THAT HEAL
   Green peas
   Spinach
   Broccoli
   Liver
   Lean meat
   Legumes
   Citrus fruits

FOODS TO LIMIT
   Omega-3 fatty acid supplements

Most bleeding disorders such as hemophilia stem from some type of thrombocytopenia, the medical term for a reduced number of platelets, the blood cells instrumental in clotting. Symptoms vary, but they typically include easy bruising, frequent nosebleeds, and excessive bleeding from even minor cuts. Bleeding gums unrelated to dental problems are common. Affected women may experience very heavy menstrual periods. Bleeding disorders due to nutritional deficiencies are uncommon in North America, but they do occur.

Nutrition Connection

No studies have examined the link between nutrition and hemophilia, but here are some general suggestions.

Eat foods rich in vitamin K. This vitamin is necessary for the blood to clot normally and is made by bacteria in the human intestinal tract. Sources include green peas, broccoli, spinach, brussels sprouts, and liver. However, foods high in vitamin K should be limited by people taking anticoagulant medication.

Consider vitamin K supplements. Supplements may help more than increasing intake of foods with vitamin K, but speak to your doctor first. Again, supplements should not be taken by those taking anticoagulants.

WARNING!
FOOD-DRUG INTERACTION
While adding more foods high in vitamin K is recommended for most people with bleeding problems, those taking an anticoagulant medication such as coumadin should limit their intake of such foods. The vitamin can counteract the desired effect of the drug.

Limit intake of omega-3 fatty acids. They can suppress platelet function. People taking high doses of fish oil supplements have an increased risk of developing bleeding problems; the risk is compounded if they are also taking aspirin.

Eat more foods with vitamin C. Vitamin C deficiency can cause bleeding gums. This deficiency may occur in alcoholics or people who eat few fruits and vegetables.

Monitor your iron levels. Chronic blood loss can lead to anemia, a blood disorder that is characterized by inadequate levels of red blood cells. Lean meat, liver, legumes plus extra iron, folate and vitamin B12.

Reduce or eliminate alcohol consumption. Alcohol can act as a blood thinner, making wounds take longer to heal and leading to more serious bleeding conditions.

Beyond the Diet

Treatment of bleeding disorders varies according to the underlying cause, but it's also helpful to take the following steps for good health:

Check all medications. Prolonged antibiotic therapy may destroy the bacteria that make vitamin K, resulting in bleeding. Overuse suppresses normal platelet function.

Exercise regularly. Exercising can build muscle and help joints function. But avoid contact sports.

BLOOD PRESSURE, HIGH

FOODS THAT HARM
Salty and processed foods, such as pickles

FOODS THAT HEAL
Green leafy vegetables
Low-fat dairy products
Legumes
Fruits, especially bananas
Nuts and seeds
Whole wheat pasta
Carrots
Sweet potatoes

FOODS TO LIMIT
Fatty foods, especially foods high in saturated fats
Alcohol
Caffeinated drinks

WHO'S AFFECTED?
- About 970 million people worldwide have hypertension, including one in three adults in the U.S. (an additional 30% of American adults have prehypertension)
- About 45% of African Americans have high blood pressure

More than 80 million North Americans have high blood pressure, also called hypertension. In its early stages, high blood pressure is symptomless, so many people don't realize they have a potentially life-threatening disease. If the condition goes unchecked, high blood pressure damages the heart and blood vessels and can lead to a stroke, heart attack, and other serious consequences. In about 5 to 10% of cases, there's an underlying cause for high blood pressure—a narrowed kidney artery, pregnancy, an adrenal gland disorder, or a drug side effect. Most often there is no identifiable cause; this is referred to as primary, or essential, hypertension.

No one fully understands precisely what leads to hypertension, although a combination of factors seems to be involved. Heredity, diabetes, obesity, and certain other disorders increase risk. Other contributors include smoking, excessive alcohol, and a sedentary lifestyle. Blood pressure also tends to rise with age so all adults over age 40 should have their blood pressure checked annually.

Nutrition Connection

Diet plays a role in both prevention and treatment of high blood pressure. Following the DASH (Dietary Approaches to Stop Hypertension) diet, which is endorsed by numerous health organizations including the American Heart Association and the Mayo Clinic, will help lower blood pressure. Here is a synopsis of the DASH diet and accompanying strategies.

Have 6 to 8 servings of grains daily. Focus on whole grains such as whole wheat pasta because they have more nutrients and fiber.

Eat 4 to 5 servings each of fruits and vegetables daily. Foods such as carrots, green leafy vegetables, sweet potatoes, and others contain beneficial nutrients that lower hypertension: fiber, vitamins, and minerals such as potassium and magnesium.

Consume 2 to 3 servings of low-fat or fat-free dairy foods. Research has shown that a diet that includes calcium-rich foods such as low-fat dairy products helps lower blood pressure. Be careful to watch sodium intake when eating low-fat or nonfat cheeses.

Limit meats, poultry, and fish to 6 oz (170 g) or less daily. It's best to cut back on meat consumption, but when eating it, opt for the leanest cuts of meat.

Eat 4 to 5 servings of nuts, seeds, or legumes per week. These foods offer an array of good minerals, but it's important to watch serving portions as they can be high in calories.

Limit fats to 2 to 3 servings daily. Avoid saturated fats and trans fats, which contribute to high blood pressure. A high-fat diet also leads to weight gain. Limit fat intake to 30% or less of total calories, with 10% or less coming from saturated animal fats. This means cutting back on butter and margarine; switching to low-fat milk and other low-fat dairy products; choosing lean cuts of meat; and shifting to low-fat cooking methods, such as broiling instead of frying.

Limit sweets to 5 servings per week. There is wiggle room for those who love sweets as long as you watch serving portions.

Limit your salt intake. A key component of what makes DASH effective is reducing sodium intake. Keep it at 1,500 mg to 2,300 mg. Beyond putting down the salt shaker, avoid most processed foods, which are usually loaded with sodium.

Pump up potassium. Some nutrients may protect against high blood pressure. Potassium, an electrolyte that helps maintain the body's balance of salt and fluids, helps ensure normal blood pressure. Potassium can be found in fruits and vegetables, such as bananas, dairy products, and legumes.

Get your calcium. Recent studies indicate that people with low levels of calcium are at greater risk of high blood pressure. A diet that low-fat dairy products, fortified soy beverages, canned salmon (with bones), and green leafy vegetables will raise levels of calcium and help decrease hypertension. However, the jury is still out on whether calcium supplements help or hinder the condition.

Reduce alcohol and caffeine consumption. Although a glass of wine or other alcoholic drink daily seems to reduce the chance of a heart attack, consuming more than this will negate any benefit and may increase the risk of hypertension. Too much caffeine can also raise blood pressure. Older adults with hypertension may be more sensitive to the effects of caffeine and should limit their intake.

Beyond the Diet

While a proper diet is instrumental in maintaining normal blood pressure, it should be combined with other lifestyle changes, such as:

Exercise. Aerobic exercise lowers blood pressure by conditioning the heart to work more efficiently. In addition, even a modest weight loss will cause a drop in blood pressure.

Quit smoking. Nicotine raises blood pressure. Quitting can drop blood pressure by 10 points or more.

Reduce stress. Stress prompts a surge in adrenal hormones and a temporary rise in blood pressure; some researchers believe that constant stress may play a role in developing hypertension. Meditation, yoga, biofeedback training, self-hypnosis, and other relaxation techniques may help lower blood pressure.

Use medications with caution. Over-the-counter cold, allergy, and diet pills can raise blood pressure. In some women, birth control pills or estrogen replacement therapy can cause high blood pressure.

Try drug therapy. If these lifestyle changes do not decrease hypertension to normal levels in 6 months, drug therapy is often instituted.

Treat underlying conditions. Diabetes and elevated blood cholesterol, both of which compound the risk of developing heart problems, may associated with high blood pressure.

BRONCHITIS

See Respiratory Disorders, page 332

BULIMIA

FOODS THAT HARM
  Trigger foods that are associated
    with binges

FOODS THAT HEAL
  Bananas
  Berries
  Apples
  Pears
  Whole grain cereals and breads
  Lean meat

WHO'S AFFECTED?
- 0.6% of the U.S. adult population over the course of a lifetime
- Adolescents and young adult women
- About 80% of bulimia patients are female

Medically, bulimia is defined as recurrent episodes of binge eating—the rapid intake of unusually large amounts of food—an average of twice a week for at least 3 months. Although *bulimia* literally means "the hunger of an ox," the majority of those with bulimia do not have excessive appetites. Instead, their tendency to overeat compulsively seems to arise from psychological problems, possibly due to abnormal brain chemistry or a hormonal imbalance.

Despite their overeating, most of them are of normal weight. They compensate for overeating by strict dieting and excessive exercise, or by purging through self-induced vomiting or abuse of laxatives or enemas.

Repeated purging can have serious consequences, including nutritional deficiencies and an imbalance of sodium and potassium, leading to fatigue, fainting, and palpitations. Acids in vomit can damage tooth enamel and the lining of the esophagus. Laxative abuse can irritate the large intestine, cause rectal bleeding, or disrupt normal bowel function, leading to chronic constipation when the laxatives are discontinued. One of the most severe consequences, however, may be an increased occurrence of depression and suicide.

Nutrition Connection

Like all eating disorders, bulimia can be difficult to treat and usually requires a team approach involving nutrition education, medication, and psychotherapy. Along with addressing psychological issues, some nutritional issues can be addressed with these guidelines, under the guidance of a dietitian or a physician.

Treat nutritional deficiencies. This is especially important if the body's potassium reserves have been depleted by vomiting or laxative abuse. High-potassium foods, such as fruits (both fresh and dried), especially bananas, and vegetables usually restore the mineral; if not, a supplement may be needed.

Emphasize foods high in protein and starches. This diet should include these foods while excluding favorite binge foods until the bulimia is under control; then those foods can be reintroduced in small quantities. At this stage of treatment, the person with bulimia learns how to give himself or herself permission to eat desirable foods in reasonable quantities, in order to reduce the feelings of deprivation and intense hunger that often lead to loss of control in eating.

Add high-fiber foods. Those with bulimia who abuse laxatives may need a high-fiber diet to overcome constipation. Whole grain cereals and breads, fresh fruits and vegetables, such as berries, apples, and pears, and adequate fluids can help restore normal bowel function.

Beyond the Diet

A complete medical checkup is the only way to be absolutely certain of a diagnosis of bulimia. Once certain, a doctor can offer guidance on the following:

Journal. Nutritional education typically begins with asking the person with bulimia to keep a diary to help pinpoint circumstances that contribute to binging. A nutrition counselor may also give the person an eating plan that minimizes the number of decisions that must be made about what and when to eat.

Treat depression. Because chronic clinical depression often accompanies bulimia, treatment usually includes giving antidepressant drugs like fluoxetine (Prozac), which also suppresses appetite, and sertraline (Zoloft).

Look at alternative therapies. Meditation, guided imagery, and progressive relaxation routines can help those with bulimia become less obsessive about weight and their eating habits.

Practice patience. Don't expect instant success; treatment often takes 3 years or longer, and even then, relapses are common.

BURNS

FOODS THAT HARM
Caffeinated drinks
Alcohol

FOODS THAT HEAL
Lean meat
Poultry
Fish
Shellfish
Eggs
Legumes
Whole grains
Citrus fruit
Melons
Water

Second- and third-degree burns that cause blistering and tissue damage are very serious; they have a high risk of becoming infected by germs that enter the body through the damaged skin. Burn victims also require extra fluids, sodium, and potassium to replace those substances that seep out through damaged skin. If this is not done, there is a danger of dehydration.

Nutrition Connection

To promote healing and tissue repair, it is essential for victims of extensive burns to have a well-balanced diet that provides extra calories, protein, vitamins, and minerals. Here's how:

Seek foods for tissue repair. A diet that provides extra calories, protein, and zinc is needed for tissue repair. Zinc is found in seafood, meat, and poultry and in lesser amounts in eggs, milk, beans, nuts, and whole grains. Zinc is essential for wound healing and also bolsters the body's immune defenses to fight infection.

Boost skin health. Fruits and vegetables that contain vitamin C, such as citrus fruits and melons may help maintain healthy skin and ward off infection. Often liquid supplements are necessary to maintain a high-calorie intake during the day.

Stay hydrated. Noncaffeinated and nonalcoholic beverages help replace lost fluids. Most people need at least 4 to 6 glasses of water a day to stay properly hydrated. Avoid caffeinated beverages and alcohol. Caffeinated beverages have a diuretic effect that accelerates fluid loss. Alcohol dehydrates the body and lowers immunity.

Beyond the Diet

Depending on the severity of the burn, the needs of the person will vary. Victims hospitalized with extensive burns are usually given intravenous fluids and antibiotics. If they are unable to eat, they will also be fed intravenously.

CANCER

FOODS THAT HARM
Foods that may contain pesticide residues and environmental pollutants

FOODS THAT HEAL
Lean meat
Fish
Shellfish
Apples
Berries
Citrus fruit
Tomatoes
Onions and garlic
Green tea
Wheat bran and wheat germ
Brown rice
Brazil nuts

C

FOODS TO LIMIT

Fatty foods, especially foods
high in saturated fat

Alcohol

Foods that have been salt-
cured, smoked, fermented, or
charbroiled

Research has dramatically changed our thinking about the role of diet in both the prevention and treatment of cancer. Studies have shown that certain dietary elements may help promote the development and spread of malignancies, while others slow or block tumor growth. Researchers estimate that at least 30% of all cancers in Western countries may be related to diet, especially one high in fat and processed foods; many of these cancers may be prevented with dietary changes.

A qualified dietitian should be part of any cancer treatment team, because both the disease and its treatment demand good nutrition as an aid to recovery.

TOP CANCER-FIGHTING FOODS

Dietary guidelines must take into account the stage and type of malignancy. In most cases of early or localized cancer, people are generally advised to follow a diet that is low in fat, high in whole grain products and other starches, and high in fruits and vegetables. Fats, especially from animal sources, are discouraged because they are believed to support tumor growth. In contrast, fruits and vegetables contain an assortment of natural plant chemicals that are thought to retard the growth and spread of cancers. Protein is essential because it helps the body repair tissue that has been damaged during treatment of the disease and helps wound healing. Apples, berries, broccoli and other cruciferous vegetables, and citrus fruits contain flavonoids, which act as antioxidants. Flavonoids are also thought to prevent DNA damage to cells.

While no foods can cure cancer, research has identified several which seem best able to fight cancer:

- Lean meat, low-fat dairy products, eggs, fish and shellfish, tofu and other soy products provide much-needed protein and zinc. Because many people with cancer find that red meat takes on an unpleasant metallic taste, other sources of protein are best.
- Tomatoes and tomato products contain lycopene, which has been found to have protective effects against prostate cancer.
- Onions and garlic contain sulfur compounds that may stimulate the immune system's natural defenses against cancer, and they may have the potential to reduce tumor growth. Studies suggest that garlic can reduce the incidence of stomach cancer by a factor of 12.
- Green tea contains EGCG, a catechin that may help fight cancer in three ways: it may reduce the formation of carcinogens in the body, increase the body's natural defenses, and suppress cancer promotion. Some scientists believe that EGCG may be one of the most powerful anticancer compounds ever discovered.
- Brazil nuts, seafood, some meats and fish, bread, wheat bran, wheat germ, oats, and brown rice are the best sources of selenium, a trace mineral that is another powerful cancer-fighter.

Weight loss is common among those with cancer. Most experience a loss of appetite as a result of the cancer itself; depression and pain may lessen any desire to eat.

Cancer treatments, especially radiation and chemotherapy, curb appetite and produce nausea and other side effects. Surgery, too, can affect appetite and requires a highly nutritious diet for healing and recuperation.

Nutrition Connection

Anyone can use the following recommendations to protect themselves against cancer. For those under treatment for cancer, nutritional needs may vary; the box at left identifies top cancer-fighting foods but consult a doctor or dietitian to personalize your diet for your needs.

Eat more fruits and vegetables. Studies associate a diet containing ample amounts of fruits and vegetables with a reduced risk of the most deadly cancers. Foods such as apples, berries, and broccoli contain bioflavonoids and other plant chemicals, dietary fiber, folate, and antioxidants beta-carotene and vitamin C.

Reduce fat intake. Numerous studies link a high-fat diet and obesity with an increased risk of cancers of the colon, uterus, prostate, skin (including melanoma, the most deadly form of skin cancer), and breast. Experts stress that no more than 30% of total calories should come from fats, and many advocate a 20% limit on fat calories. A few simple dietary changes can help lower fat intake: Choose lean cuts of meat and trim away all visible fat; eat vegetarian dishes several times a week; adopt low-fat cooking methods such as baking and steaming; and limit use of added fats such as butter, and oils.

Eat more fiber. Increased intake of fiber may protect against certain types of cancer, such as colorectal cancer. A high-fiber, low-calorie diet also protects against obesity and the increased risk of cancers linked to excessive body fat.

Limit processed foods. People who eat large amounts of smoked, pickled, cured, fried, charcoal-broiled, and processed meats have a higher incidence of stomach and esophageal tumors. Smoked foods contain polyaromatic hydrocarbons that are known carcinogens. The salt in pickled foods can injure the stomach wall and facilitate tumor formation. Nitrites, commonly found in bacon, hot dogs, and processed meats, can form nitrosamines, or established carcinogens. However, consuming these foods along with good sources of vitamins C and E reduces the formation of nitrosamines.

Consult with a doctor before using supplements. Although it seems wise to take supplements to prevent cancer, studies have established that high doses of them can actually increase damage caused by free radicals. High doses of vitamin A can also lead to toxicity. For those who are undergoing cancer treatment, it's advisable to consult a physician or a dietician; different diagnoses and conditions require different levels of supplementation, if at all.

Approach alternative therapies with caution. There is no scientific evidence to support the efficacy of consuming Japanese maitake, Chinese herbs, blue-green algae, or shark cartilage extracts to prevent or treat cancer.

Beyond the Diet

Along with a healthy diet, breaking high-risk habits and living a healthy lifestyle can help shore up your defenses against cancer.

Stop smoking. More than any other lifestyle factor, smoking increases the risk of cancer. In addition to lung cancer, smoking is strongly associated with cancers of the esophagus, mouth, larynx, pancreas, and bladder, and an increased risk of breast cancer.

Limit your alcohol intake. Heavy alcohol use is linked to increased risk of cancers of the mouth, larynx, esophagus, and liver. Excessive alcohol consumption hinders the body's ability to use beta-carotene, which appears to protect against these cancers. Alcohol can also deplete reserves of folate, thiamine, and other B vitamins, as well as selenium, all crucial nutrients in protecting the body.

Exercise. People who engage in moderate to vigorous physical activity have a lower risk of developing certain cancers, such as those of the breast, colon, and endometrium. Physical activity also helps maintain a healthy body weight and prevents obesity, which has been linked to a number of cancers.

EATING WHEN YOU HAVE CANCER

In many instances, loss of appetite, nausea, and other eating problems can be dealt with by changing daily habits and routines. The following tips have worked for many people:

- Plan your major meal for the time of day when you are least likely to experience nausea and vomiting. For many, this is in the early morning. Otherwise, eat small, frequent meals and snacks throughout the day.
- Let someone else prepare the food; cooking odors often provoke nausea. Food that is served cold or at room temperature gives off less odor than hot food.
- If mouth sores are a problem, eat bland, pureed foods—for example, custards, rice and other puddings made with milk, and eggs, porridge, and blended soups. Avoid salty, spicy, or acidic foods. Sucking on zinc lozenges may speed the healing of mouth sores.
- Get dressed to eat with others in a pleasant social atmosphere and make meals visually attractive.
- To overcome nausea, try chewing on ice chips or sucking on a ginger candy or sour lemon drop before eating. Sipping flat ginger ale or cola may also help.
- Rest for half an hour after eating, preferably in a sitting or upright position; reclining may trigger reflux, nausea, and vomiting.
- Pay extra attention to dental hygiene. If mouth sores hinder tooth brushing, make a

baking soda paste and use your finger and a soft cloth to gently cleanse the teeth. Then rinse the mouth with a weak solution of hydrogen peroxide and baking soda. Diluted commercial mouthwashes freshen the breath, but avoid full-strength products that can further irritate sores.

- If a dry mouth makes swallowing difficult, liquefy foods in a blender or moisten them with low-fat milk, sauces, or gravies.
- If diarrhea is a problem (as is often the case during chemotherapy), avoid fatty foods, raw fruits, whole grain products, and other foods that can make it worse. Instead, eat bland, binding foods, such as rice, bananas, cooked apples, and dry toast.
- A few slices of a colorful fruit give visual appeal to a bowl of oatmeal; a colorful napkin and bud vase perk up a tray of food.

CANKER SORES

See Dental Problems, page 256

CARDIO-VASCULAR DISEASE

FOODS THAT HARM
Salty foods, such as pickles

FOODS THAT HEAL
Citrus fruits
Green leafy vegetables
Salmon
Trout
Tofu
Oats
Apples
Pears
Olive oil
Whole grain breads and cereals
Flaxseed
Nuts

FOODS TO LIMIT
Red meat, butter, and other foods
   with saturated fats
Processed foods that contain trans
   fats
High-cholesterol foods, such as
   eggs, shrimp, and organ meats

Heart and blood vessel disease remain the leading causes of death in North America despite dramatic reductions in their incidence since the 1960s. More than 1.6 million heart attacks occur each year, resulting in about 500,000 deaths.

You have no control over some risk factors, such as heredity, advancing age, and gender. And some people have a higher risk because of an inherited disorder called familial hypercholesterolemia, which causes high blood cholesterol.

Far more often, cardiovascular disease is caused by lifestyle choices. Inactivity and cigarette smoking along with a poor diet are the major lifestyle factors that figure in cardiovascular disease risk. These controllable risk factors lead to high blood cholesterol, which promotes the buildup of fatty deposits in the coronary arteries and leads to angina and heart attacks. Other conditions that affect heart disease risk include obesity, which increases the risk of heart attack and contributes to other cardiovascular risk factors; high blood pressure, which can lead to a stroke and heart attack; diabetes, a disease that affects the heart, blood vessels, and other vital organs; and excessive alcohol use, which harms the heart and blood vessels.

Many studies have confirmed that diet is a major force in both the cause and prevention of heart disease.

Old School
Being obese automatically means you're at risk for heart disease.

New Wisdom
Recent research has found a subset of obese people who aren't at greater risk of cardiac events.

Nutrition Connection

If the wrong diet can promote heart disease, the right one can reduce the risk, even for those who have uncontrollable high-risk factors. A heart-healthy diet is the same commonsense one that protects against cancer, diabetes, and obesity. Here are the guidelines:

Eat lots of fruits and vegetables. Numerous studies correlate a diet rich in fresh fruits and vegetables with a 25% or better reduction in heart attacks and strokes.

WHO'S AFFECTED?
- Cardiovascular disease accounts for 40% of deaths of those 65 years and older in the U.S.
- More than 1.3 million Canadians have heart disease

Seek sources of omega-3 fatty acids. Salmon, sardines, herring, trout, and other fatty cold-water fish are high in omega-3 fatty acids, which reduce the tendency of blood to clot. Consume 2 or 3 servings of fish a week to get this benefit. Omega-3 fats are also found in plant sources including canola, soybean, and flaxseed oil; ground flaxseed; and nuts.

25% of all deaths in the United States in 2008 were caused by heart disease.

Include soluble fiber. Pectin, oat bran, and other types of soluble fiber help lower cholesterol and improve glucose metabolism in people predisposed to develop diabetes. Oats, oat bran, psyllium, flax, lentils, legumes, apples, pears, and other fruits are high in soluble fiber. A combination of legumes and whole grains is a prudent low-fat meat alternative.

Eat whole grain foods. Several studies have found that diets high in whole grain foods such as whole wheat bread and whole grain cereals reduce the risk of coronary heart disease. These foods contain a variety of important vitamins and minerals, as well as phytochemicals with antioxidant properties.

Choose healthy fats and limit intake. The omega-6 polyunsaturated fats—found in safflower, sunflower, corn, cottonseed, and soybean oils—reduce cholesterol levels when they replace saturated fats in the diet. Monounsaturated fats, found in olive and canola oils, tend to lower total and LDL cholesterol levels when they replace saturated fats in the diet. Soft margarines containing plant sterols also help lower cholesterol when consumed as part of a heart-healthy diet. For most people, a diet with less than 20 to 30% of its calories coming from these fats is recommended to help lower cholesterol.

Eat soy. Research has shown that adding soy protein to a low-fat diet lowers the risk for heart disease. Soy contains plant compounds called isoflavones that appear to benefit the heart, which help lower cholesterol levels. Soy protein can be found in tofu and soy beverages.

Talk to your doctor about supplements. Research on whether supplements help prevent heart disease has been inconclusive. Seek most nutrients from foods, and consult a professional before taking any new supplements, particularly vitamin A, fish oil, and iron supplements.

Eat a small handful of nuts daily. Nuts and seeds are rich sources of fiber, vitamin E, essential fatty acids, and minerals—all linked to heart health.

Try going vegetarian. Research has shown that a healthy low-fat vegetarian diet rich in fruits, vegetables, soy and whole grains such as oats and barley may be as effective as "statin" drugs in lowering cholesterol.

Limit alcohol intake. A glass of red wine or beer may be "heart healthy," but excessive amounts of alcohol over time may lead to increased blood pressure, obesity, or other health problems.

Beyond the Diet

For those who are not predisposed to cardiovascular disease, these measures can dramatically decrease the risk:

Don't smoke. Smoking, or being exposed to secondhand cigarette smoke, harms blood cells, the structure and function of blood vessels, and the structure of the heart.

Exercise regularly. Experts recommend getting at least 30 minutes of moderate physical activity most days of the week. This also helps maintain a healthy body weight.

Get regular checkups. A yearly visit to the doctor's office is all it takes to get your blood pressure and cholesterol levels checked. A diabetes screening can also help, especially if you have a family history of diabetes or are overweight.

CARPAL TUNNEL SYNDROME

See Arthritis, page 228

CATARACTS

See Eye Problems, page 269

CELIAC DISEASE

FOODS THAT HARM
Foods made with wheat, rye or barley, oats, bulgur, spelt, or triticale
Foods using wheat products as a thickening agent or coating, such as meat loaf and certain soups and sauces
Beverages containing gluten, such as beer
Many commercial salad dressings except pure mayonnaise

FOODS THAT HEAL
Low-fat milk
Eggs
Fish
Meat and poultry
Fresh fruits and vegetables
Legumes
Potatoes
Rice

WHO'S AFFECTED?
- About 2.5 million North Americans
- Those who have other genetic disorders including Down's syndrome and Turner's syndrome
- Those who have chronic or autoimmune diseases, such as type 1 diabetes and rheumatoid arthritis

Celiac disease, also known as celiac sprue or nontropical sprue, is a disorder that affects about one out of every 133 people in the United States and Canada. The problem is caused by gliadin, one of the proteins collectively known as gluten, found in these grains. This protein interferes with the absorption of many nutrients and damages to the lining of the gut.

Children with the disease are usually plagued with symptoms such as stomach upsets, diarrhea, abdominal cramps, bloating, mouth sores, and an increased susceptibility to infection. Their stool is pale and foul-smelling, and it floats to the top of the toilet bowl, indicating a high fat content. The child's growth may be

QUICK TIP: Read labels on nonfood items

Scan the ingredient lists on packages of supplements, medications, and body lotions for wheat, wheat proteins, and wheat products.

stunted; some children develop anemia and skin problems, especially dermatitis. Diagnosis is confirmed through an intestinal biopsy or through blood tests.

People who develop celiac disease later in life may have had a mild or symptomless form of the disease in childhood. In unusual cases, adults with no prior history of gluten sensitivity develop the condition after surgery on the digestive tract.

Once the disease has been identified, patients are advised to permanently eliminate any foods that contain gluten from their diet. Luckily, gluten-free diets have become more popular in the past decade.

Nutrition Connection

These recommendations can help make living with celiac disease a little easier:

Be a gluten sleuth. Many everyday foods contain gluten: breads, cakes, rolls, muffins, baking mixes, pasta, sausages bound with bread crumbs, foods coated with batter, sauces and gravies, soups thickened with wheat flour, and most breakfast cereals, as well as some candies, ice creams, and puddings. Many baby foods are thickened with gluten, although most commercial first-stage foods are gluten-free.

Don't deprive yourself. The market has responded to a demand for gluten-free items, so people with Celiac disease can enjoy pastas and breads, such as rice pasta and baked goods made with corn, rice, potato, or soy flours.

Prepare most foods at home. In general, it's best to cook at home to ensure a healthy diet without risking exposure to gluten.

Always read labels on packaged foods. Avoid ingredients such as flour-based binders and fillers and modified starch. Be suspicious of any label that specifies "other flours" because they are likely to include at least some wheat derivatives. Beer is made from barley and should be avoided, along with malted drinks.

Beyond the Diet

Note that gluten can appear in products besides foods and may affect your health. For example, medications and vitamins may use gluten as a binding agent. At church, check with your pastor about gluten-free communion wafers.

CHOLESTEROL, HIGH

FOODS THAT HARM
- Heavily marbled red meat
- Pizza
- Hard margarines
- Store-bought baked goods
- Fast and junk foods
- Full-fat dairy products
- Fried foods

FOODS THAT HEAL
- Sterol-fortified orange juice
- Oats and oat bran
- Kidney beans
- Apples
- Pears
- Fish
- Extra-virgin olive oil

FOODS TO LIMIT
- Salt and salty foods

Cholesterol is the fatty, waxy compound that the body uses to produce hormones, vitamin D, and fat-digesting bile acids. A little goes a long way; what's left over ends up in the arteries. There, it can form deposits called plaque on artery walls, which narrows and hardens arteries and reduces blood flow. Blockage to coronary arteries can cause chest pain and heart attack; carotid artery blockage may cause stroke, and when leg arteries are blocked, it may hurt to walk.

The proteins that carry cholesterol throughout your bloodstream are known as lipoprotein, and come in three types:

1. Low-density lipoprotein (LDL). The "bad" cholesterol, LDL builds up on artery walls and narrows them.
2. Very-low-density lipoprotein (VLDL). This contains triglycerides, a blood fat. VLDL enlarges LDL cholesterol and increases its potential to narrow blood vessels.
3. High-density lipoprotein (HDL). A "good" form of cholesterol, HDL collects excess cholesterol and moves it to your liver.

Nutrition Connection

Diet plays a key role in raising or lowering cholesterol levels. In particular, eating high amounts of saturated fats—found in fatty cuts of meat, high-fat cheeses, whole milk and cream, butter, ice cream, and palm and coconut oils—can raise cholesterol levels. And then there are the lab-produced trans fats. These insidious fats, which can spike LDL levels, form through a chemical process (hydrogenation) that increases the shelf life of oils. Some margarines, store-bought baked goods, french fries, and other fast foods can contain trans fats. Here's how to eat smarter to avoid high cholesterol:

Choose lean meats. Avoid cuts of meat that are richly marbled with fat; trim all visible fat before cooking. Also, remove poultry skin before (or at least after) cooking.

Seek out plant sterols. These substances help block the absorption of cholesterol. They are added to many food products, including spreads, orange juice, and yogurt drinks. Aim to consume 2 g a day (the amount in two 8-oz (227 g) servings of sterol-fortified orange juice. Doing so can lower LDL levels by a healthy 10%.

Skim the dairy. Select 1% or fat-free milk instead of whole or 2% milk. Most cheeses now have low-fat versions.

Get friendly with fiber. Soluble fiber reduces LDL and reduces absorption of cholesterol into the bloodstream. Good sources include oats, kidney beans, apples, pears, and prunes. Eating 5 to 10 g of soluble fiber a day can lower total and LDL cholesterol.

Cook with EVOO. Extra virgin olive is a "good fat" because it contains antioxidants that help lower your LDL and preserve healthy HDL levels.

Add omega-3s. These healthy fatty acids come from fish, some plants, and nuts and can reduce triglyceride levels (another anti-healthy heart blood fat). A low-dose omega-3 supplement containing 400 mg EPA plus DHA reduced heart attacks in a 2012 study.

Moderate your drinking. One (for women) or two (for men) drinks a day can raise HDL levels. But more is definitely not better: Heavy drinkers up their risks for high blood pressure, heart failure, and stroke.

Beyond the Diet

You can't control the genetic factors that lead to high cholesterol. However, there's good news: You can control many lifestyle

WHO'S AFFECTED?

- 35 million adult Americans
- People with a family history of high cholesterol
- Overweight people
- Sedentary people
- Women over the age of 50
- Men over the age of 60
- People with diabetes
- Smokers
- Heavy drinkers

factors that contribute to high numbers and raise the risk for heart disease.

Shed a few. Pounds, that is. While your goal should be to get to your healthiest weight, your cholesterol will drop as soon as you lose that first 5 or 10 pounds.

Get physical. Even 10-minute intervals of exercise a few times a day can lower cholesterol and raise your HDL levels.

Toss the butts. Quitting smoking can raise your HDL levels and lower your blood pressure. Within just one year, quitters can halve their heart attack risk.

CHRONIC FATIGUE SYNDROME

FOODS THAT HARM
Alcohol

FOODS THAT HEAL
Complex carbohydrates, such
  as whole grain cereals
Green leafy vegetables
Fish
Nuts
Oysters
Eggs
Melons
Kiwis
Sunflower seeds
Salty foods (only for those with
  low blood pressure)

FOODS TO LIMIT
Caffeinated drinks

A mysterious illness once known as "the yuppie flu," chronic fatigue syndrome (CFS) often has flulike symptoms and no proven cure. It is marked by persistent, debilitating fatigue, as well as other baffling symptoms that include headaches, muscle aches and weakness, tender lymph nodes, sore throat, joint pain, sleep that doesn't lead to feeling refreshed, difficulty concentrating, post exercise exhaustion that lasts for 24 hours, and short-term memory problems. There may also be a chronic or recurring low-grade fever.

There is no laboratory test for CFS, so a doctor must systematically rule out all other medical causes that produce similar symptoms.

In many cases, CFS develops in the aftermath of a viral illness, such as mononucleosis or the flu. Other possible contributing factors include prolonged stress, hormonal imbalance, low blood pressure (hypotension), allergies, immune system disorders, and psychological problems. Most CFS patients eventually recover, but it may take a year or more.

Nutrition Connection

Although there is no known cure for CFS, certain nutrients in foods may help. Doctors stress the importance of a well-balanced diet. Here's how:

Eliminate food allergies. Seek the guidance of a registered dietitian who can help you meet your nutritional needs while eliminating potential food allergies.

Start with ample starches. Fruits and vegetables help to provide the carbohydrates the body needs for energy. They also supply the vitamins needed to resist infection.

Eat to strengthen your immune system. Foods rich in zinc—such as seafood (especially oysters), meat, poultry, eggs, milk, beans, nuts, and whole grains—as well as foods rich in vitamin C—such as citrus fruits, berries, melons, kiwis, broccoli, and cauliflower—may help keep the immune system working properly. A robust immune system can help ward off certain viruses, such as flu and colds that may possibly precede the onset of CFS.

Consume more essential fatty acids. Some of the symptoms of CFS include swollen glands and inflammation of the joints, which may be relieved temporarily by foods rich in essential fatty acids. These include fish, nuts, seeds, flaxseed and flaxseed oil, canola oil, wheat germ, and leafy green vegetables.

Get more magnesium. Magnesium is associated with the contraction and relaxation of muscles. Ingesting foods with the mineral may help alleviate muscle tenderness in people with CFS. Good sources include sunflower seeds, legumes, whole grains, and green leafy vegetables.

Avoid alcohol. Alcohol lowers immunity.

Limit caffeine. Caffeinated drinks should be used in moderation to minimize sleep problems.

Get enough salt. If low blood pressure is part of your diagnosis, you may benefit from a higher salt intake.

Beyond the Diet

The rate of recovery varies greatly per individual, but some lifestyle changes and these general guidelines may help a person with CFS cope with the condition:

Keep a detailed diary. Track progress, and note symptoms, foods, and activities that affect your body.

Avoid napping during the day. Napping may exacerbate sleep problems. Instead, get 7 to 9 hours of sleep each night.

Seek counseling. Cognitive-behavioral therapy has been shown to help CFS patients gain a better sense of control.

Reduce stress. Avoid overexertion or psychological stress, which may worsen symptoms.

20% or fewer of those with chronic fatigue syndrome have been diagnosed.

Ask your doctor about exercise. Studies have shown that 75% of CFS patients who were able to exercise reported less fatigue and better daily functioning and fitness after a year.

Talk to your doctor about medication. Although no medication cures CFS, some help treat symptoms. Aspirin and other painkillers may alleviate headaches, joint pain, and muscle soreness, and antidepressant drugs help some patients.

CIRCULATORY DISORDERS

FOODS THAT HEAL
Citrus fruits
Onions
Garlic
Salmon
Sardines

FOODS TO LIMIT
Fried foods
Salty foods

WHO'S AFFECTED?
- People who have atherosclerosis
- People with diabetes
- People living in cold places and women (for Raynaud's disease)

The most common circulatory, or vascular, disorders are high blood pressure and atherosclerosis; others include various clotting abnormalities and diseases marked by reduced blood flow. Some common disorders include aneurysms, intermittent claudication, phlebitis, and Raynaud's disease.

Aneurysms are balloon-like bulges that form in weakened segments of the arteries, especially the aorta, the body's largest artery, which stems directly from the heart. Many aneurysms are due to a congenital weakness, while others are caused by atherosclerosis and high blood pressure.

Intermittent claudication symptoms include severe leg pain and cramps induced by walking. A lack of oxygen due to inadequate blood flow causes the pain. Intermittent claudication is common in those who have diabetes or atherosclerosis.

Phlebitis refers to any inflammation of a vein; the large, superficial veins in the lower legs are the most commonly afflicted. Although painful, superficial phlebitis is not as dangerous as when veins located deeper in the legs become inflamed, setting the stage for thrombophlebitis. In this condition, clots form at the site of inflammation and pieces may break away and travel to the heart and lungs.

Raynaud's disease is characterized by periods of numbness, tingling, and pain in the fingers and toes due to constriction or spasms in the small arteries that carry blood to the extremities. Typically,

20% of people with Raynaud's disease seek treatment.

Raynaud's disease is set off by exposure to the cold; in some people, stress may trigger attacks. For unknown reasons, women are nine times more likely to suffer from Raynaud's. Smoking is blamed in many cases. Some victims may also have lupus, rheumatoid arthritis, or other inflammatory autoimmune disorders.

Nutrition Connection

There are no specific dietary treatments for circulatory disorders. However, these measures may help people manage their conditions and improve their general well-being.

Adopt a low-fat, low-salt diet. Following a low-fat, low-salt diet can help prevent circulatory disorders caused by atherosclerosis and high blood pressure, especially in aneurysms.

Eat fresh fruits and vegetables. Consuming ample amounts will provide the vitamin C needed to strengthen and maintain blood vessels.

Include more onions and garlic. These vegetables are especially helpful in improving blood flow. After chopping garlic, let it rest for 10 minutes prior to cooking it. This will allow the allicin and its potent derivatives to be activated and unleash the full nutritional power of garlic.

Add more fish. A diet that includes several servings a week of fatty fish or other sources of omega-3 fatty acids, as well as foods high in vitamin E, helps reduce inflammation and clot formation. Gamma linolenic acid, a substance in evening primrose and borage oils, has a similar effect, but check with your doctor first, as these may interact with prescribed drugs.

Beyond the Diet

Combined with a balanced diet, taking the following steps can support your overall health and prevent aggravating circulatory problems further:

Exercise. An exercise program coupled with a very low-fat diet, such as the regimen championed by cardiologist Dr. Dean Ornish, can help those with circulation problems.

Avoid smoke. Don't smoke, and try your best to avoid secondhand smoke.

Try warm compresses. For those with Raynaud's disease, applying warm compresses to hands and feet, or avoiding exposure to cold temperatures can prevent or minimize attacks.

Medicate as needed. Phlebitis can be treated with aspirin and other anti-inflammatory drugs. Clot-dissolving drugs may be administered for thrombophlebitis; other measures may be required to prevent clots from reaching vital organs.

Talk to your doctor. People with severe blockages may require surgery to remove them.

CIRRHOSIS

FOODS THAT HARM
   Salty foods, such as pickles
   Alcohol

FOODS THAT HEAL
   Berries
   Papayas
   Bell peppers
   Fortified and enriched cereals
      and breads
   Soy
   Peas
   Legumes
   Fish
   Water

FOODS TO LIMIT
   Fatty foods

In cirrhosis, a chronic progressive disease, normal liver cells are replaced by scar tissue. Prolonged, heavy alcohol use is the most common cause, but cirrhosis may also result from hepatitis, inflammation or blockage of the bile ducts, inherited conditions, or a reaction to a drug or environmental toxin. About 27,000 deaths per year are caused by cirrhosis in the United States.

Symptoms of cirrhosis include weight loss, nausea, vomiting, impotence, jaundice, and swelling of the legs. People with cirrhosis often have distinctive abdominal swelling, known as ascites. The liver damage is irreversible, but the progress of cirrhosis can be arrested and the complications treated with diet and other measures.

Nutrition Connection

Don't drink alcohol. Avoiding alcohol is essential to prevent further liver damage.

Avoid sodium. High amounts can cause your body to retain water, which can worsen swelling.

Eat a healthy diet. Nutritional deficiencies are common so cover all the bases of balanced diet. Fruits and vegetables can supply essential vitamins and nutrients, especially vitamin C, which helps strengthen the immune system. Seek whole grains and healthy sources of carbohydrates, such as fortified and enriched whole wheat cereals or breads, for energy.

Eat small meals or snacks. To combat appetite loss, small, frequent meals may be better than three large ones.

Eat lean sources of protein. The recommended daily intake of protein for those with cirrhosis is 0.54 g per lb (1.2 g per kg) of body weight. This is more than the amount that is recommended for healthy people. Some evidence supports the use of vegetable protein foods such as soy, peas, and legumes, especially for people who develop mental confusion, a condition called hepatic encephalopathy.

Have healthy fats. Moderate amounts of mono-and polyunsaturated fats (oily fish, olive oil, safflower oil) provide needed calories without overburdening the liver.

WHO'S AFFECTED?
- Alcoholics and heavy drinkers
- Those with chronic hepatitis C
- More men than women

Drink lots of water. People with cirrhosis should drink about four to six glasses of water and other clear liquids a day, especially if they're dealing with ascites.

Look into supplements. Because malnutrition is common in those with cirrhosis, a doctor may be able to help fill in your nutritional gaps with supplements.

Beyond the Diet

Treatment of the underlying causes of cirrhosis may be essential to stopping liver damage. These points offer a basic guide:

Address addiction. A treatment program for alcohol addiction may be necessary for those with cirrhosis.

Get on medication. Those who have hepatitis B or C need medications, such as antiviral therapy that's a combination of interferon and ribavirin to prevent further damage to the liver.

Exercise. Obesity is becoming a common cause of cirrhosis, either as the sole cause or in combination with alcohol abuse, hepatitis C, or both.

COLDS AND FLU

FOODS THAT HEAL

Citrus fruits

Berries

Brussels sprouts

Chicken soup and other broths

Yogurt

Wheat germ and wheat bread

Colds are characterized by symptoms such as runny nose, cough, and sore throat. In the winter months, flu (short for influenza) inflicts a similar misery on people, but includes fever and joint and muscle

pain. The complications of flu—especially pneumonia—can be serious, and thousands of North Americans die from flu or its complications each year.

Colds and flu are highly contagious respiratory infections that are caused by viruses. New flu vaccines are produced yearly to protect against the prevailing strains of the virus. Doctors recommend annual flu shots for everyone over the age of 65, and people of any age who have a circulatory, respiratory, kidney, metabolic, or immune disorders. People are more vulnerable to colds and flu when their immune systems are depressed. Preventive steps include avoiding alcohol, getting plenty of rest, and reducing stress levels. Wash your hands frequently and cover your mouth when you cough or sneeze.

Nutrition Connection

While there's no cure for colds or flu, eating properly may help to prevent them, shorten their duration, or make symptoms less severe. It's a myth that you should starve either a cold or a flu. Eating provides essential nutrients that can help your body recuperate. Here's how:

Get your vitamin C. There's no evidence that big doses work to prevent colds, but some studies show that it can shorten them or lessen the symptoms. Vitamin C is also known to have a slight antihistaminic effect, so drinking more citrus juice or taking a supplement may help reduce nasal symptoms.

Drink lots of fluids. One of the worst effects of high fever is dehydration. During a cold or flu, drink a minimum of 8 to 10 glasses of fluids a day in order to replenish lost fluids, keep mucous membranes moist, and loosen phlegm. Drink water, tea, and broth. Abstain from alcohol, which dilates small blood vessels makes the sinuses feel stuffed up, and reduces the body's ability to fight infection.

Have chicken soup. It's soothing, easy to digest, and contains cystine, a compound that helps thin the mucus, relieving congestion. Scientists believe that a 12-oz (355-mL) dose of the soup may reduce inflammation of the lungs. It is thought that chicken soup slows down the activity of white blood cells that can cause the inflammation.

Eat spicy foods. Hot peppers, or chiles, contain capsaicin, a substance that can help break up nasal and sinus congestion. Garlic, turmeric, and other hot spices have a similar effect.

Eat foods rich in zinc. Zinc is important for a healthy immune system. Sources include seafood (especially oysters), red meat and poultry, yogurt and other dairy products, wheat germ, wheat bran, and whole grains. Studies have shown that supplementation in the form of zinc lozenges may help shorten the duration of a cold, but getting more than 40 mg per day over a long period of time can weaken your immune system.

Beyond the Diet

These guidelines can help you recover fast:

Get plenty of rest. Adequate rest will help your immune system get back on track.

Try over-the-counter medications. Aspirin, ibuprofen, and decongestants can help ease accompanying fever, pain, or stuffy nose.

Seek professional care. Most colds and bouts of flu go away by themselves, but see a doctor if you have a cough that produces green, yellow, or bloody phlegm; a severe pain in the face, jaw, or ear; trouble swallowing or breathing; or a fever over 100°F (37.8°C) that lasts more than 48 hours.

Old School
Feed a cold, starve a fever— or vice versa.

New Wisdom
Eat when you're hungry. Fasting weakens you at a time when you need strength.

COLD SORES

See Herpes, page 283

CONSTIPATION

FOODS THAT HEAL
Bran cereals
Beans
Legumes
Berries
Water

Many people wrongly assume that they are constipated because they don't have a daily bowel movement. In fact, it's perfectly normal for bowels to move as often as three times a day or as infrequently as once in 3 or 4 days. Regularity is different for everyone.

There are two types of constipation: atonic and spastic. Atonic constipation, the more common type, occurs when the

WHO'S AFFECTED?
- People who do not eat enough fiber
- People with diseases such as diabetes, thyroid disease, or Parkinson's disease
- People on medications such as pain relievers, antidepressants, or diuretics
- People with serious medical conditions such as colorectal cancer or autoimmune diseases

colon muscles are weak; it develops when the diet lacks adequate fluids and fiber. Spastic constipation (sometimes called irritable bowel syndrome, page 300) is characterized by irregular bowel movements and may be caused by stress, nervous disorders, excessive smoking, irritating foods, and obstructions of the colon. In addition, chronic constipation can cause hemorrhoids.

QUICK TIP:
Drink hot liquids

Hot liquids help stimulate the bowels. Drink a cup of herbal tea or a glass of hot water with lemon, or coffee in the morning.

Nutrition Connection

The foods you eat can cause or relieve constipation. These general strategies can help:

Increase intake of dietary fiber. The insoluble type of fiber that absorbs water but otherwise passes through the bowel intact is instrumental in preventing constipation. Doctors recommend a fiber intake of 25 to 38 g daily. Note that any increase in high-fiber food consumption should be gradual and accompanied by more fluids. A high-fiber foods include wheat bran, bran cereals, whole grain products, legumes, fruits and vegetables.

Drink plenty of water. Adults should drink at least eight glasses of nonalcoholic fluids every day. When a low-fiber diet coincides with a low-fluid intake, the stool becomes dry and hard, and increasingly difficult to move through the intestines.

Avoid alcohol. Alcohol causes dehydration and prevents the body from properly absorbing nutrients.

Beyond the Diet

Here are a few steps to better bowel health:

Don't delay trips to the bathroom. Poor bowel movement habits, such as putting off going to the toilet despite an urge to go, can cause constipation.

Exercise. Regular physical activity helps stimulate bowel movements; inactivity can cause constipation.

Use laxatives sparingly. Excessive laxative use reduces normal colon function. If a laxative is needed, one made of psyllium or another high-fiber stool softener is best.

Talk to your doctor about medications. One side effect of medication, especially codeine and other narcotic painkillers, reduce peristalsis, the rhythmic muscle movements that push digested food through the bowels.

CROHN'S DISEASE

See Inflammatory Bowel Disease, page 293

CYSTIC FIBROSIS

FOODS THAT HEAL
- Meat
- Poultry
- Eggs
- Milk and yogurt
- Pasta
- Cookies
- Cakes
- Salty foods
- Juices

Cystic fibrosis affects the glands that produce mucus, sweat, enzymes, and other secretions. The most serious consequences of the disease occur in the lungs, pancreas, and intestines, all of which become clogged with thick mucus. As the lungs become congested, the person is especially vulnerable to pneumonia and other infections. If the ducts that normally carry pancreatic enzymes to the small intestine become clogged, digestive problems can result, such as difficulty in breaking down fats and proteins. In addition, abnormal amounts of salt are lost in sweat and saliva, which can lead to serious imbalances in body chemistry.

There is no cure for cystic fibrosis, although scientists are testing gene therapy as a means of correcting the underlying genetic defect. In the meantime, a combination of an enriched diet, vitamin supplements, replacement enzymes, antibiotics and other medications, and regular postural drainage to clear mucus from the lungs serves as the most effective treatment and has greatly improved the outlook for people with cystic fibrosis.

Nutrition Connection

Because diet is critical in managing cystic fibrosis, the treatment team usually includes a clinical dietitian, particularly for children who need to consume many more calories than normally recommended to grow properly. There is no special diet, but the following are general guidelines:

Eat larger portions and lots of snacks. Children are encouraged to eat high-calorie foods and large amounts at meals. Frequent snacks also help. Babies with the disease may be given a formula that contains predigested fats.

Eat more protein. For older children, high-protein foods, such as meat, poultry, fish, and eggs, are emphasized. You can enrich whole milk by adding a cup of dried milk per quart or liter.

Eat more fats. Diets with as much fat as the child can tolerate are recommended. Fats provide more calories per unit than other nutrients, so they are a critical source of energy. The body also needs fat in order to absorb vitamins A, D, E, and K.

1,300 to 1,500 mg

of calcium is the recommended amount someone 9 years old or older with cystic fibrosis should consume to help avoid osteoporosis.

Balance sugary foods. About 35% of adults ages 20 to 29 and 43 of those over 30, with cystic fibrosis have cystic fibrosis–related diabetes. Unless they have diabetes, they may enjoy sugary foods; these simple carbohydrates are more easily absorbed than starches. However, sweets should be taken with protein to provide balance and supply amino acids needed for growth, immune function, and repair and maintenance of body tissue.

Consume more sodium. Because cystic fibrosis causes sweat and salivary glands to excrete abnormal amounts of sodium and chloride in perspiration and saliva, salt is an essential part of the diet. It's crucial to watch sodium levels during hot weather or exercise.

Drink fluids. Because constipation and intestinal obstruction are common in cystic fibrosis, it's important to consume adequate water and other fluids. Juices and nectars can provide a higher-calorie intake than water. A doctor may prescribe a laxative to prevent constipation.

Coordinate a medication regime. Combinations of inhaled medication and antibiotics can be used to make it easier to breathe and help fight against infections.

Talk to your doctor about supplements. Prescription enzymes that improve absorption of fats and protein have made a big difference for those living with cystic fibrosis. If digestive problems develop despite taking enzymes, supplements of predigested fats may be prescribed to help loosen and clear thick mucus from the airways.

Monitor for diabetes. Some people with cystic fibrosis may also develop diabetes if the pancreas becomes so clogged that it can no longer make adequate insulin.

QUICK TIP:
Mix a perfect meal

An omelet made with herbs and cheese provides an almost perfect mix of nutrients, protein, and calories for those with cystic fibrosis.

Beyond the Diet

The seemingly insurmountable challenges to those dealing with cystic fibrosis may be eased with the following recommendations:

Learn coughing triggers. A common treatment for cystic fibrosis teaches a person how to trigger strong coughs that help loosen and clear thick mucus from the airways.

Seek support. Counseling and therapy can help deal with the tremendous emotional stresses of the disease, including better communication between family members and health care providers, as well as preparing a patient for adult care.

DENTAL PROBLEMS

FOODS THAT HARM
- Starchy snacks and sugary foods, such as sweetened cereals and cookies
- Acidic drinks sipped over prolonged periods of time, such as wine or unsweetened fruit juice

FOODS THAT HEAL
- Low-fat dairy products
- Aged cheeses
- Fortified soy beverages
- Eggs
- Legumes
- Carrots
- Sweet potatoes
- Broccoli
- Oranges
- Dark leafy green vegetables, especially spinach
- Apples
- Celery
- Yogurt
- Rice

FOODS TO LIMIT
- Dried fruit and other sticky foods
- Salty foods

In addition to brushing and flossing, a healthful diet, with natural or added fluoride, protects teeth from decay and keeps the gums healthy. Tooth decay (cavities and dental caries) and gum disease are caused by colonies of bacteria that coat the teeth with a sticky film called plaque. If plaque is not brushed away, these bacteria break down the sugars and starches in foods to produce acids that wear away the tooth enamel. The plaque also hardens into tartar, which can lead to gum inflammation, or gingivitis.

A well-balanced diet provides the minerals, vitamins, and other nutrients essential for healthy teeth and gums. Fluoride, found in foods, water, and treated water supplies, has been determined safe and effective in preventing cavities, reducing rates by 40 to 60%.

Another common dental problem is canker sores, which appear as painful, white or yellowish raised spots. Sores are scattered through the mouth or in large clusters. Often, canker sores heal after two weeks, but larger ulcers may last months and be accompanied by fatigue, fever, and swollen lymph nodes. The cause of canker sores is unknown, but doctors believe they're related to stress or trauma.

Nutrition Connection

Eating the right foods plays a big part in having healthy teeth and gums. Follow these guidelines:

Eat foods rich in calcium. Calcium supports healthy teeth and gums. Low-fat dairy products, fortified soy and rice beverages, canned salmon or sardines (with bones), almonds, and dark green leafy vegetables are excellent sources of calcium.

Eat foods rich in vitamin D. Vitamin D helps your body absorb calcium. Find it in milk, fortified soy and rice beverages, and fatty fish such as salmon.

Eat nutrient-dense foods. Nutrients such as phosphorus, magnesium, vitamin C, and beta-carotene are also essential to dental health. Phosphorus, found in meat, fish, dairy products and eggs, and magnesium, found in whole grains, spinach, and legumes, are necessary for the formation of tooth enamel. Vitamin A helps build strong bones and teeth. Good sources of beta-carotene, which the body turns into vitamin A, include orange-colored fruits and vegetables and dark green leafy vegetables. Vitamin C, found in cruciferous vegetables and citrus fruits, prevents bleeding gums.

End your meals with the right foods. When consumed at the end of a meal, aged cheeses help prevent cavities. In addition to providing essential nutrients, hard fibrous fruits and vegetables, such as apples, carrots and celery also stimulate Fresh fruit such as apples stimulate saliva flow, which decreases mouth acidity and washes away

WHO'S AFFECTED?

- Those with chronic diseases, such as diabetes and HIV/AIDS
- Those with eating disorders
- Those with poor dental hygiene

QUICK TIP:
Look for gum with xylitol

Within 5 minutes after finishing a meal, chew gum for at least 5 minutes. Gum sweetened with xylitol helps to counter harmful bacteria in your mouth, which promote cavities.

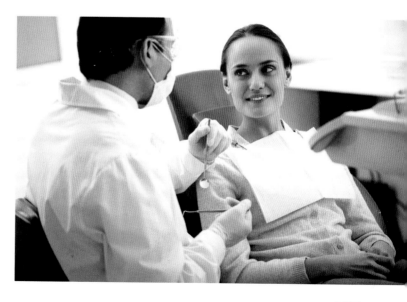

D

food particles. They also reduce buildup of cavity-causing bacteria. Avoid sticky items such as dried fruit.

Avoid starchy and sugary foods. Sugary foods may seem obviously linked to cavities, but starchy foods, such as sweetened cereals or cakes, also make teeth prone to decay. The starches mix with amylase, an enzyme in saliva, to create an acid bath that erodes enamel.

Try a diet of bland, soft food. If painful canker sores interfere with eating, try sipping liquid or pureed foods through a straw. Foods that cause the least pain include yogurt, custard, rice, and poached chicken. Avoid salty and acidic food.

Check to see if your water supply is fluoridated. Not all municipalities fluoridate their water supply, so contact your municipal office. Cavities can be prevented by giving children fluoride in the first few years of life. Fluoride is supplied through fluoridated water, beverages made with fluoridated water, tea, and some fish, as well as many brands of toothpaste and some mouthwash. Fluoride supplements are available for children who don't have access to fluoridated drinking water, but note that excess fluoride consumption can cause mottling of the teeth.

Beyond the Diet

Because a chronically dry mouth also contributes to decay, it's helpful to incorporate the following strategies to stimulate saliva and take good care of your teeth and gums:

Chew gum. Sugarless gum stimulates the flow of saliva, which decreases acid and flushes out food particles.

Rinse and brush after eating. Rinsing your mouth and brushing your teeth after eating are important strategies to prevent cavities.

Always brush your teeth before going to bed. Saliva flow slows during sleep; going to bed without brushing the teeth is especially harmful.

Check your medications. Certain drugs cut down saliva flow, such as clonidine, which is used to treat high blood pressure and ADHD in kids, and heart medications atropine and propranolol.

Take care of your gums. Left untreated, gum diseases such as gingivitis can lead to periodontitis, an advanced infection that can cause teeth to loosen and fall out. People on medications such as chemotherapy drugs or steroids are particularly at risk for gum disease, as well as those who have diabetes, heart disease, and HIV/AIDS. Furthermore, gum disease has also been linked to endocarditis, a condition where bacteria enters the bloodstream.

See a dentist every 6 months. Regular checkups keep teeth and gums healthy.

KEEP YOUR KIDS' TEETH HEALTHY

Children are particularly vulnerable to tooth decay because their teeth are still forming enamel and haven't finished hardening. Parents should:

- Provide a good diet throughout childhood
- Brush children's teeth until they're mature enough to do a thorough job by themselves (usually by 6 or 7 years old)
- Supervise twice-daily brushing and flossing thereafter
- Never put babies or toddlers to bed accompanied by a bottle of milk (which contains the natural sugar lactose), juice, or other sweet drink
- Never dip pacifiers in honey or syrup
- Eat sensibly during pregnancy to make sure that the child's teeth get off to a good start; particularly important is calcium, which helps the baby to form strong teeth and bones, and vitamin D, which the body needs to absorb calcium

DEPRESSION

FOODS THAT HARM

Aged cheeses and other foods and drinks that contain tyramine, if you are taking MAO inhibitors

FOODS THAT HEAL

Turkey

Almonds and other nuts

Pumpkin seeds and other seeds

Watercress and other green leafy vegetables

Lentils and other beans

Whole grains

Bananas

Potatoes

Corn

Asparagus

Peas

FOODS TO LIMIT

Sugary foods, such as cookies and soft drinks

Depression is a serious disorder, possibly caused by stress, hormones, certain medical conditions or medications. It can strike out of the blue and—for more fortunate sufferers—can disappear just as mysteriously.

One classic sign of depression is a dramatic change in eating patterns. Some people lose all desire to eat; others develop voracious appetites, especially for carbohydrates. People with depression typically have little energy. Other signs of depression include an unshakable feeling of sadness, inability to experience pleasure, insomnia, excessive sleepiness, inability to concentrate, and indecisiveness. Feelings of worthlessness or guilt may be accompanied by recurrent thoughts of death. Anyone who has some or all of these symptoms nearly every day for more than two weeks may be suffering from major depression.

People over the age of 65 are four times more likely to suffer from depression than younger people; however, elderly sufferers do not always exhibit the classic signs. Instead, they may show signs of dementia, complain of aches and pains, or appear agitated, anxious, or irritable.

Nutrition Connection

People with depression often eat irregularly. However, eating the right foods can help stabilize mood. Here are some nutritional guidelines:

Turn to tryptophan. Found in turkey, almonds, pumpkin seeds, and watercress, this amino acid is needed to make the mood-critical neurotransmitter serotonin. Research indicates that tryptophan can help induce sleep and may play a role in treating certain types of depression. Tryptophan supplements are banned in the US and Canada due to deaths in the 1980s.

Eat beans. Meals that are especially rich in carbohydrates have been associated with relaxation. These foods allow tryptophan to be converted into serotonin. Beans not only supply complex carbs, they also pack in plenty of protein without a lot of fat.

Limit sugar consumption. When sugar-sensitive people eat large quantities of sweets, they may experience an energetic "high" followed by a "low" with weakness and "jitters" when the sugar is metabolized.

Get a lot more B vitamins. Vitamins B6 and B12 and folate may help certain forms of depression. Vitamin B6 has been shown to provide some relief to women suffering from PMS-related depression. B6 sources are meat, fish, poultry, whole grains, bananas, and potatoes. Other research has found that many depressed people are deficient in folate and B12. Folate is found in green leafy vegetables, orange juice, lentils, corn, asparagus, peas, nuts, and seeds. B12 is found in all animal foods and fortified soy and rice beverages.

Add omega-3 fatty acids. Seek sources such as salmon, trout, mackerel, and flaxseed. Studies have shown that rates of depression are lower in countries where lots of fish is consumed and higher in countries where little fish is eaten. Fish oil supplements may help, but consult your doctor before taking them.

Balance side effects of medication. Tricyclic antidepressants, which can cause weight gain, include imipramine (Tofranil), amitriptyline (Elavil), and nortriptyline (Pamelor). If you are overweight to begin with, or gain weight while taking any of these drugs, ask your doctor to suggest an alternative.

Beyond the Diet

Depression can be life threatening. These recommendations can help treat it as quickly as possible:

Adopt healthy sleep habits. The onset of depression is predicted by insomnia; it usually accompanies it and is usually the last symptom to disappear. Set a regular sleep schedule of 7 to 9 hours per night.

WARNING! FOOD-DRUG INTERACTION

If you are taking an antidepressant drug in the class called monoamine oxidase (MAO) inhibitors, such as phenelzine (Nardil) and tranylcypromine (Parnate), your blood pressure could rise dangerously when you eat foods rich in the amino acid tyramine. Tyramines are found in protein-rich foods that have been aged, dried, fermented, pickled or bacterially treated, such as aged cheeses, pickled, or smoked fish, tofu or soy, bananas, gravies and sauces containing meat extracts, and champagne. Alcohol should be avoided. Coffee, tea, colas, chocolate, yeast, yeast extracts (such as marmite and sourdough bread), fava beans, and ginseng contain small amounts of tyramine but are generally safe enough if taken only occasionally and in small amounts.

Consult a physician. Doctors can help address persistent thoughts or feelings associated with depression. It may be a result of an illness, such as sleep apnea, or side effects of medications, including beta-blockers digoxin, corticosteroids, antihistamines, and oral contraceptives.

Think beyond antidepressants. Along with antidepressants, doctors usually suggest cognitive behavioral therapy and interpersonal psychotherapy.

DIABETES

FOODS THAT HARM
Red meat, butter, and other foods with saturated fats
Processed foods that contain trans fats

FOODS THAT HEAL
Whole grain breads, cereals, and pasta
Oats
Barley
Peas
Low-fat dairy products
Avocado
Apples
Pears
Oranges
Chicken breast
Mushroom
Blackstrap molasses

FOODS TO LIMIT
High glycemic foods, such as potatoes, soft drinks, white flour, and refined sugars

Diabetes mellitus is a serious metabolic disease that affects the body's ability to derive energy from blood sugar, or glucose.

It results when the body cannot produce or properly use insulin, a hormone needed for glucose metabolism. Because all human body tissues need a steady supply of glucose, diabetes can affect every organ. In particular, it can lead to heart disease, kidney failure, blindness, and nerve problems.

About 10% of diagnosed diabetes cases are type 1, also called juvenile-onset diabetes because the disease often develops in children. In this autoimmune disease, body does not produce adequate insulin. People with type 1 diabetes must take insulin daily. They must also strictly control their diet and phywsical activity to maintain near-normal blood glucose levels.

More than 90% of those with diabetes have type 2 diabetes, or non-insulin-dependent diabetes mellitus. Also called adult-onset diabetes, this form typically occurs in older adults who are usually overweight but is increasingly being diagnosed in children and adolescents. Although these people often have adequate or even high levels of insulin, their bodies cannot use the hormone properly. An appropriate diet can prevent or delay consequences of type 2 diabetes.

The effects of hormonal changes and weight gain during pregnancy increase demands on the pancreas and can lead to gestational diabetes with potential complications for both mother and baby.

Before people develop diabetes, they are frequently diagnosed with prediabetes, defined by having higher than normal blood sugar levels; insulin resistance, in which the body does not use insulin properly; or metabolic syndrome, a cluster of risk factors that include excess belly fat, high blood pressure, and high blood sugar levels and that together increase your risk of diabetes, heart disease, and stroke.

Nutrition Connection

Diet is the cornerstone of diabetes management for all types of diabetes, though there are slightly different considerations. Those with diabetes should consult a registered dietitian, especially if cholesterol, blood pressure, or other health issues are a concern. Here are general guidelines:

Eat balanced meals and snacks. To maintain healthy blood glucose levels, meals and snacks should be balanced to provide a mixture of carbohydrates, fats, and proteins.

Seek high quality carbohydrates. Carbohydrates, the basic currency of glucose, should account for 45 to 60% of daily calories spread evenly through the day. Low glycemic load carbohydrates such as whole grains provide vitamins, minerals, and fiber. Limit sugars and sweeteners, which provide mostly calories.

Seek fiber-rich foods. Because the fiber content of carbohydrates slows down the release of glucose, high-fiber starches, such as barley, oats, beans, peas, and lentils, are recommended to help suppress any sharp increases in blood sugar levels after meals.

Follow a low-fat diet. High-fat diets contribute to obesity, heart disease, and kidney disease. Saturated fats from animal foods and hydrogenated fats in packaged foods should also be limited. On the other hand, monounsaturated and polyunsaturated fats—such as those found in vegetable oils, nuts, fish, and avocados—are good for the heart, slow the digestion process, and may also reduce insulin resistance.

Limit foods that have a high glycemic index (GI), or load (GL). GI and GL is a measurement of how readily foods are

Old School
Those with diabetes have to give up sweets entirely.

New Wisdom
In moderation, an occasional sweet treat is fine.

GLYCEMIC INDEX AND GLYCEMIC LOAD:
The Power Behind Each Bite

Like gas for a car, food is your fuel. Just as some gas is higher octane, some foods provide better fuel. To gauge how efficiently food works its way through your digestive system to affect your blood sugar, researchers at the University of Toronto developed the glycemic index (GI). The faster a food is digested and absorbed into your bloodstream, the higher its GI. High-GI foods cause a rapid increase in blood sugar, which is dangerous, especially for people with diabetes.

But GI was based on a standard measurement (50 g of carbohydrates) for all foods. In real life, people don't tend to eat the same amounts of sugar as they do pasta or carrots.

So scientists used a little math wizardry to translate the glycemic index into more practical terms. What emerged is the glycemic load (GL). This tool considers the type of carbohydrate in the food and the amount of carbohydrate in a standard serving. By this new criterion, sugar and starchy foods and some fruits have high GL values whereas most vegetables and fruits have low GL values, meaning they are less likely to make your blood sugar spike.

Today, there are more than 750 published GL values of various foods. However, you should take all GL lists as a general guide only. As it turns out, one person's glycemic response can differ from another's. It may vary even in the same person from day to day. Also, the state of food can change its GL.

For example, small differences in a banana's ripeness can double its GL. Plus, when foods are eaten together (adding butter or sour cream to a baked potato, for instance, or having the potato with a serving of meat) the GL of the combined foods becomes much different from the GL of the potato by itself. The reason is that fat and protein slow down digestion, making the GL of the whole dish different than the GL of just a single food.

USE THE GI AND GL TO SELECT FOODS

Studies have found that people who eat diets with a high GL have a higher rate of obesity, diabetes, heart disease, and cancer. One study found that men who typically

THE BOTTOM LINE

- Remember, GI and GL only evaluate food based on how it affects your blood sugar, and shouldn't be used as the only ways to gauge your diet's impact on health. Other principles of a healthy diet—variety, balance, and moderation—still apply.
- While a low-glycemic diet will include many foods recommended in a healthy diet—fruits and vegetables, whole grains, and legumes—some high-glycemic foods, such as potatoes, contain many essential nutrients and are good sources of energy, too.

ate foods with a high GL had a 40% higher chance of developing diabetes. In the Nurses' Health Study, women who ate diets with a high GL had a 37% greater chance of getting type 2 diabetes over the 6-year span of the study. Yet another study found that swapping just one baked potato per week for a serving of brown rice could reduce a person's odds of developing type 2 diabetes by up to 30%.

Many large health organizations, including both the Canadian and American Diabetes Associations, support the use of the GL and GI as a complement to carbohydrate counting for managing diabetes. Both are useful—GI helps you choose better carbs while GL helps with portion sizes.

GLYCEMIC INDEX VS. GLYCEMIC LOAD

Below are a few common foods and their GI and GL values. Note the differences and how the GL becomes a better way to look at the effect that foods have on blood sugar.

FOOD	GI	SIZE	GL
Grains and Cereals			
Bagel, white	72	2 ½ oz (70 g)	25
Barley, pearled	25	5 oz (150 g)	11
Bread, white	71	1 oz (30 g)	10
Bread, whole grain, pumpernickel	46	1 oz (30 g)	5
Bread, whole wheat	67	1 oz (30 g)	8
Cereal, All-Bran	50	1 oz (30 g)	9
Cereal, cornflakes	80	1 oz (30 g)	21
Cereal, muesli	66	1 oz (30 g)	16
Fruits			
Apple	39	4 oz (120 g)	6
Apple juice, unsweetened	41	8 ½ oz (250 ml)	12
Banana	46	4 oz (120 g)	12
Grapefruit	25	4 oz (120 g)	3
Grapes	43	4 oz (120 g)	7
Orange	40	4 oz (120 g)	4
Peach	42	4 oz (120 g)	5
Watermelon	72	4 oz (120 g)	4
Vegetables			
Baked potato	60	5 oz (150 g)	18
Baked potato, mashed	74	5 oz (150 g)	15
Carrots	92	3 oz (80 g)	5
Kidney beans	29	5.2 oz (150 g)	7
Lentils	29	5.2 oz (150 g)	5
Peas	51	3 oz (80 g)	4
Soybeans	15	5.2 oz (150 g)	1
Sweet potato	48	5 oz (150 g)	16

converted to blood glucose. (For more information about GL, see page 262.) Limit intake of high-glycemic foods, such as potatoes, rice cakes, cornflakes, soft drinks, pretzels, and crackers. Conversely, research has found that eating foods with a low glycemic index or load can improve blood sugar control in those with diabetes. Incorporate more low-glycemic foods, which include peas, beans, lentils, apples, pears, and oranges, barley, bran cereals, whole grain pasta, milk and yogurt.

Add supplements wisely. A deficiency of the trace mineral chromium, found in foods such as wheat bran, whole grains, chicken breast, mushrooms, and black-strap molasses, has been associated with reduced glucose tolerance. Research using chromium supplements has shown that they may provide a beneficial effect on blood glucose control for those with diabetes. If you choose to take a chromium supplement, take no more than 200 mcg per day, or speak to your doctor.

Limit alcohol. Alcohol can cause swings in blood sugar levels. If you use insulin or take oral diabetes medication, speak to your doctor about the use of alcohol. If you do drink, consume alcohol with food.

Beyond the Diet

In conjunction with dietary changes, a healthier lifestyle can help control diabetes or reverse prediabetes symptoms. Consider the following:

Exercise every day. Exercise can keep blood sugar levels stable. For many, diet and exercise alone can provide effective treatment. Exercise lowers your risk of prediabetes and type 2 diabetes.

Commit to losing weight. Researchers found that those who lost modest amounts of weight cut their diabetes risk by 58%, even more for people over the age 60.

Take care of your teeth. Those with diabetes may be prone to gum disease. Talk to your doctor about medications.

Talk to your doctor about immunizations. Diabetes can affect immune system, so flu shots and pneumonia shots, among others, may be recommended.

Get regular blood tests. Early treatment can prevent critical damage to organs. Adults over the age of 50 should have their blood sugar levels tested every two years, or more often if they are overweight or have a family history of diabetes.

Get a blood test if you are pregnant. Pregnant women should get a blood test between the 24th and 28th weeks of pregnancy. If gestational diabetes is diagnosed, the mother will need to modify her diet and monitor weight gain. Although this type of diabetes usually disappears almost immediately after childbirth, women who have had it are at high risk for type 2 diabetes in later years.

DIARRHEA

FOODS THAT HEAL
Water
Herbal teas
Ginger ale
Broth
Bananas
Rice
Applesauce
Toast
Salted crackers
Chicken soup

FOODS TO LIMIT
Dairy products
Apple juice
Prunes
Sugarless chewing gum

Diarrhea—the frequent passage of loose, watery stool—is not a disease but a symptom of an underlying problem. It is most commonly brought on by food poisoning, especially among travelers. Transient looseness can be caused by overconsumption of laxative foods (such as prunes), heavy use of sugarless chewing gum sweetened with sugar alcohol (such as sorbitol), and some medications. Emotional stress that causes irritable bowel syndrome may disrupt the normal bowel pattern with alternating diarrhea and constipation; similar symptoms occur in colitis and Crohn's disease, both inflammatory bowel disorders. In many instances, diarrhea develops without any identifiable cause, but unless the problem persists or recurs often, this is not a cause for concern.

Acute infectious diarrhea is one of the world's most common ailments. An estimated five billion cases occur every year, and in North America, diarrhea is runner-up only to the common cold as a cause for absences from work. Although diarrhea causes fatalities due to dehydration, it is seldom a threat in affluent, well-nourished societies, except to vulnerable groups: babies, the elderly, and invalids.

Nutrition Connection

Most cases of diarrhea are minor and short-lived and can be managed at home with simple dietary measures, such as:

Stop solid food and rehydrate. Start by eliminating all solid foods and sipping warm or tepid drinks to prevent any further dehydration. Drinking half a cup of fluid every 15 minutes or so is usually enough. Suitable drinks include water, mineral water, herbal teas, and ginger ale. Clear broths also help replace the salts and other minerals lost in a bout of diarrhea. You can make your own rehydration fluid by mixing ½ tsp (1 mL) of baking soda, a pinch of salt, and ¼ teaspoon (1 mL) corn syrup or honey in an 8-oz (250-mL) glass of water. Commercial sports drinks may help, but avoid ones with more than 10% sugar, which can worsen diarrhea.

Slowly introduce low-fiber foods. When you feel like eating (but preferably not within the first 24 hours), start with low-fiber foods such as crackers, toast, rice, bananas, cooked carrots, boiled potatoes, and chicken. Often doctors will recommend bananas, rice, applesauce, and toast (called the BRAT diet), especially for children. Apples and other fruits high in pectin (a soluble fiber) help counteract diarrhea; that's why unsweetened applesauce is a traditional home remedy. Cooked carrots are also high in pectin. Other suitable foods include salted crackers and chicken soup, which help to replenish depleted sodium and potassium reserves.

Avoid milk products until the symptoms disappear. Some of the organisms that cause diarrhea can temporarily impair the ability to digest milk.

Avoid apple juice. While apples or applesauce can help ease diarrhea, apple juice, can have the opposite effect. The leftover carbohydrates in apple juice that aren't absorbed in the small intestine are fermented by bacteria in the colon, potentially leading to diarrhea. In fact, drinking too much fruit juice of any kind is often the cause of diarrhea in toddlers.

Beyond the Diet

Address diarrhea as soon as possible using the following suggestions:

Try over-the-counter (OTC) remedies. OTC antidiarrheal drugs may give some relief when diarrhea has no obvious cause or is due to a minor illness such as flu. Never use a nonprescription antidiarrhea product for more than 2 days without consulting your doctor.

- Those with irritable bowel syndrome (IBS) or inflammatory bowel disease (IBD), such as Crohn's disease
- People who are suffering from viruses, bacteria, or parasites
- People on medications, such as antibiotics, cancer drugs, and antacids containing magnesium
- Sufferers of Celiac disease

Call a doctor if it's recurring. Some people may have chronic diarrhea due to malabsorption of a nutrient, such as lactose intolerance; consult a physician. Other signs of illness that need medical attention include appearance of blood, mucus, or worms; severe abdominal pain; or diarrhea accompanied by vomiting or fever.

WHO'S AFFECTED?

- 10% of people over age 40 and in 50% of people over age 60
- In the U.S., 10 to 25% of people who have diverticulosis get diverticulitis
- People who eat low-fiber diets
- People who live in developed or industrialized countries, such as the U.S., Canada, England, and Australia

DIVERTICU-LITIS

FOODS THAT HEAL

Berries

Bananas

Figs

Bran

Brown rice

Black beans

Split peas

Artichokes

Water

Broth

Diets lacking in dietary fiber, which are common in industrialized countries, can cause constipation, which may provoke unnatural contractions of the large intestine, which in turn leads to the formation of diverticula. This condition, called diverticulosis, can develop into diverticulitis when the diverticula become inflamed or infected. The specific cause remains unknown, but the disease mostly affects people who are over age 60 and overweight. It can be painful and may lead to complications such as abscesses, intestinal obstruction, or perforation of the

Old School
People with diverticulitis must avoid nuts and seeds.

New Wisdom
There is no scientific evidence to support the association between nuts and seeds diverticulitis.

intestinal wall. In addition to abdominal cramps and pain, other symptoms include gas, fever, and rectal bleeding. Constipation may alternate with diarrhea.

The type of care you receive depends on the severity of your symptoms. Talk to your doctor about what to expect and treatment options, which range from home care and liquid diets to different types of surgery.

Nutrition Connection

These dietary guidelines can help prevent or delay diverticulosis and diverticulitis. Try the following:

Eat more fiber, rich fruits, vegetables and whole grains. Diverticulitis is known to be less common among vegetarians than those who include meat in their diet, as vegetarian diets are typically higher in fiber-rich foods, such as berries, apples, pears, bananas, figs, bran, brown rice, barley, lentils, black beans, split peas, and artichokes. However, it is important to increase fiber intake gradually. If you have diverticular disease, do not start taking fiber supplements without first talking with your doctor.

QUICK TIP:
Go "exotic" once a month

Once a month, add a new type of grain to your diet. This will help slowly introduce more fiber to your diet, which helps diverticulitis. Mix in some amaranth, bulgur, or wheatberries into steamed carrots and broccoli, toss with olive oil and a bit of Parmesan or feta cheese, maybe throw in a can of tuna or a couple of ounces of cut-up chicken, and you've got dinner.

Drink fluids. Along with a high-fiber diet, at least eight glasses of clear liquids like water, tea, or broth every day produces bulky, soft stools that move easily through the intestinal tract. Not enough fluids can lead to constipation.

Keep notes. Make note of foods that cause inflammation or pain and avoid them.

Beyond the Diet

Diverticulosis sufferers should keep track of their symptoms and follow these recommendations:

Go to the bathroom when you have to. If you have diverticular disease, constipation can increase your risk of a diverticulitis flare-up because it increases pressure within your colon.

Exercise. Exercise reduces pressure inside your colon and encourages normal bowel movements.

ECZEMA

FOODS THAT HARM
Milk, eggs, nuts, or any other foods that trigger or worsen eczema

FOODS THAT HEAL
Apricots
Carrots
Mangoes
Bananas
Squash
Green leafy vegetables
Legumes
Salmon
Flaxseed
Canola oil
Brown rice
Wheat germ

Eczema is an itchy, scaly rash often caused by sensitivity to foods, certain chemicals, or environmental conditions such as dryness. The rash is not always a true allergic reaction, but an immune system reaction to a normally harmless substance. Symptoms can appear anywhere from a few minutes to several hours after exposure to the offending food or substance. Eczema runs in families, often along with a tendency to develop asthma, hay fever, or hives.

The most common type of eczema is atopic dermatitis; the term "atopic" refers to a personal and family tendency to develop eczema, asthma, or hay fever. Other types include contact dermatitis, which occurs after a substance damages the skin, and seborrheic eczema, which is better known as dandruff, or greasy, scaly patches on the skin or scalp.

Nutrition Connection

While some foods may help alleviate eczema, some foods may trigger it. Note these guidelines:

Test for allergies. Common culprits include eggs, dairy products, seafood, walnuts, and pecans. Cow's milk can cause eczema in babies and small children; goat's milk or soy milk may be better tolerated. Many children outgrow their sensitivities by the age of six, but others have lifelong recurrences.

Consume more antioxidants. Dryness may cause eczema by triggering the formation of free radicals and therefore may be countered by antioxidants such as beta-carotene. Brightly colored fruits and vegetables including apricots, squash, mangoes, carrots, pumpkin, and sweet potatoes are good choices.

Eat foods rich in essential fatty acids. Foods like vegetable oils, fatty fish, and flaxseed may decrease swelling by helping to generate hormone-like substances

- An estimated 10 to 20 percent of infants and young children in the U.S.
- Worldwide, about 7% of people have some form of eczema during their lives
- Those who have asthma and hay fever

- More than 2 million North Americans are affected by epilepsy
- 10% of people who have Alzheimer's disease
- 50% of children with both mental retardation and cerebral palsy

QUICK TIP: Drink oolong tea
Three cups of oolong tea may help relieve the symptoms of eczema. The polyphenols in the tea suppress allergic responses.

called prostaglandins, which reduce inflammation.

Get lots of vitamin B6. Some researchers believe a diet rich in vitamin B6 protects against sensitivity rashes. Good sources include oily fish, meats, legumes, bananas, brown rice, wheat germ, and leafy green vegetables.

Beyond the Diet

There are many potential causes of eczema that don't pertain to food. Here are some general recommendations to avoid flare-ups:

Avoid known triggers. If your rash becomes worse in either hot or very cold weather, avoid extremes of temperature. Buy soaps, detergents, and toilet papers that are free of dyes and perfumes.

Evaluate external causes. Common offenders include nickel, which is often used for making costume jewelry; latex, which is used in household and industrial rubber gloves; woolen clothing; skin care products based on lanolin, the natural oil that is found in wool; and acrylic adhesives, used in applying acrylic nails or in sneakers.

EMPHYSEMA

See Respiratory Disorders, page 332

EPILEPSY

FOODS THAT HARM
Alcohol
Any foods that trigger attacks or interact with anticonvulsants

Epilepsy refers to recurrent seizures triggered by abnormal electrical impulses in the brain. Some seizures are so mild and fleeting that they are barely noticeable; others last for several minutes, during which the person falls down and is seized by convulsive movements. The frequency of seizures also varies from person to person.

Neurologists generally discount any link between diet and epilepsy, but there are exceptions. Those with epilepsy who have migraine headaches that are triggered by certain foods often cease to have seizures when those foods are eliminated. Some diabetics suffer seizures when their blood sugar levels drop suddenly. Large amounts of alcohol consumed in a short time can cause seizures. There have been rare reports of aspartame triggering seizures in people with epilepsy.

Another exception: The ketogenic diet has helped halt seizures in the 20% of children whose attacks cannot be controlled by drugs.

Nutrition Connection

There is no one set diet for those with epilepsy, but some of these nutritional approaches may be helpful in controlling the disease:

Consider the ketogenic diet for children. Neurologists at Johns Hopkins Hospital have refined a dietary treatment for severe epilepsy. The ketogenic diet causes the body to break down fats instead of carbohydrates for energy. For children, the diet begins with 2 to 3 days of fasting in a hospital, and then the foods are introduced gradually. It provides about 75% of the calories generally recommended for healthy children, most of them from fats. A small amount of protein is added to allow for at least some growth, but carbohydrates are kept to a minimum. Fluid intake is restricted. The diet must be carefully tailored and then followed exactly, as even small changes can cause seizures. Although difficult, there's a payoff: Most can resume a normal diet and still be seizure-free after 2 to 3 years.

Make diet changes. Adults can also try the ketogenic diet if they don't respond to drugs. But this diet isn't recommended for adults because of its very restrictive nature. Johns Hopkins researchers have also developed a modified Atkins diet, which is a low-carbohydrate, high-fat diet. Studies have shown that the diet lowers seizure rates in nearly half of adults who try it. Speak to your doctor before changing your diet.

Beyond the Diet

People with epilepsy can lead a fulfilling life. Keep the seizures under control by following these guidelines:

Stay on top of your medications. Although dealing with side effects can be difficult, it is imperative to take the right doses as frequently as directed by your doctor. If the side effects bother you, speak to your doctor.

Get good sleep. Not getting enough rest can trigger a seizure. Aim for 7 to 8 hours a night.

Wear a medical alert bracelet. This can alert medical personnel effectively and save your life.

Inquire about other therapies. Depending on your situation, surgery or other therapies may be advisable. Speak to your doctor about your options.

22% of stroke patients may develop epilepsy.

EYE PROBLEMS

FOODS THAT HARM
Red meat, butter, and other foods with saturated fats

FOODS THAT HEAL
Carrots
Corn
Red pepper
Dark leafy greens like kale or collard greens
Fish

WHO'S AFFECTED?
- People age 50 and older
- Smokers
- People with a family history of eye problems
- People with diabetes
- Sun worshippers

While it may seem like deteriorating vision is an inevitable part of aging, eating an antioxidant-rich diet can prevent or combat many eye problems.

Age-related macular degeneration (ARMD) is one of the most common causes of blindness in seniors. It entails a gradual, painless deterioration of the macula, the tissue in the central portion of the retina. The first symptom is usually blurring of central vision but eventually side vision can also become limited.

Cataracts develop when the lens, the transparent membrane that allows light to enter the eye, yellows. This hinders the passage of light rays, making your vision hazy, cloudy, or blurry. It's like looking through a frosty or fogged-up window. Cataracts can develop in one or both eyes, and most are the result of getting older. During middle age, however, cataracts are often small and don't impair vision. As they grow, your ability to see things clearly diminishes and reading and driving, especially at night, become more difficult. If untreated, the lens may become completely opaque, resulting in blindness.

QUICK TIP:
Start your day with fruit

Whether your breakfast staple is eggs, cereal, or pancakes, add a vision-saving burst of antioxidants to your morning meal with a glass of orange or tomato juice, grapefruit, kiwi, strawberries, or cantaloupe.

Nutrition Connection

Choose antioxidant-rich vegetables and fruits. While carrots are good for your eyes, you'll get more peeper-protecting antioxidant vitamins such as A, C and E, lutein, and zeaxanthin from dark leafy greens, corn, and red pepper.

Maintain a healthy weight. Carrying around too many pounds may increase your risk for cataracts. Eat a healthy diet, watch your calorie intake, and exercise to lose weight and keep the pounds off.

Take a multivitamin every day. A major study suggested that if every American at risk for ARMD took daily supplements of antioxidant vitamins and zinc, more than 300,000 people could avoid the associated vision loss over the next five years. Other studies found that women who took vitamin C supplements for at least 10 years were 77% less likely to show initial signs of cataracts than those who took no supplemental C.

Eat fish at least twice a week. A study from Australia involving more than 3,500 older adults found that eating fish just one to three times per month appeared to protect them against ARMD.

Cut back on saturated fats. Research shows that a diet high in saturated fats, including foods (such as fatty red meat, butter, and cheese) increases the risk of ARMD. Scientists theorize that saturated fats may clog the arteries in the retina in the same way that they contribute to atherosclerosis in larger blood vessels.

Beyond the Diet

Shade your eyes. Wear sunglasses and a wide-brimmed hat or cap to protect your eyes from ultraviolet rays, which may contribute to the development of age-related eye problems.

Stay slim and active. Being severely overweight may cause these diseases to progress more rapidly. You can reduce your risk of ARMD by 54% if you are active (even walking or gardening) 1 to 2 hours a day.

Keep your blood pressure and cholesterol low. High blood pressure and high cholesterol increase your risk of developing ARMD.

Quit smoking. If you don't, your chances of developing cataracts increase.

FEVER

FOODS THAT HEAL
- Water
- Fruit juice
- Chicken broth, or soup
- Herbal teas
- Bananas
- Rice
- Applesauce
- Toast
- Eggs
- Rice cereals

Although normal body temperature is generally thought of as 98.6°F (37°C), human temperature may vary over the course of the day by as much as two degrees. Most people can feel a difference in their body temperature that they will call a fever once it reaches about 101°F (38.5°C).

Fever is not a disease in itself but a symptom of an underlying problem, most commonly an infection. A fever is often accompanied by other symptoms, such as sweating, shivering, thirst, flushed skin, nausea, vomiting, and diarrhea. A fever alone does not necessarily require treatment. It is one of the body's natural ways of fighting disease and should not be suppressed unless very high or accompanied by other symptoms.

Nutrition Connection

The following dietary tips will help alleviate a fever:

Drink lots of fluids. Sweating, diarrhea, and vomiting may all accompany a fever, which can cause dehydration. Drink at least eight glasses of fluid daily. This includes water, fruit juice, herbal teas, and even frozen fruit juice bars.

Quickly add fluids for babies. Note that infants may get dehydrated very quickly

because they have a large body surface in proportion to their fluid volume. When babies have high temperatures, parents should give frequent bottles of plain water or a commercial infant rehydration product. You can easily make your own rehydrating solution by dissolving ½ cup (118 mL) of baby rice cereal in 2 cups (473 mL) of water with ¼ Tbsp (4 mL) of salt. The mixture should be thick but pourable and drinkable.

Don't starve a fever. If you feel like eating, eat. There is no medical basis for the saying "Feed a cold and starve a fever." If anything, you need more calories than normal if you have a raised temperature because your metabolic rate rises as the fever rises.

Try the BRAT diet. Eat bananas, rice, applesauce, and toast for fever-related diarrhea. When diarrhea is a problem, solid foods should be avoided until the bowels stabilize. Then, small servings of bland foods, such as ripe bananas, applesauce, white toast dipped in chicken or beef broth, chicken-rice soup, rice cereals, or boiled or poached eggs can be eaten.

Beyond the Diet

Several strategies can help address fever. Here are a few suggestions:

Let low-grade fever work itself out. According to some experts, aggressive treatment of a fever may interfere with the body's immune response. Keep in mind that many viruses and bacteria thrive at normal body temperatures, and thus a fever may be the body's way of dealing with the virus.

Try over-the-counter (OTC) medications. OTC drugs such as acetaminophen

WHO'S AFFECTED?
- People with illnesses such as the cold and flu
- Those with a bacterial infection
- Sufferers of heat exhaustion or extreme sunburn
- People who take certain medications, such as antibiotics or blood pressure drugs

Old School
You must do all it takes to bring down a child's temperature.

New Wisdom
Making a feverish child comfortable is much more important than reducing fever.

or aspirin are recommended for lowering high fevers. However, aspirin should not be given to anyone under the age of 18 without a doctor's approval; if given during a viral infection, aspirin increases the risk of developing Reye's syndrome, a potentially life-threatening disease affecting the brain and liver.

Get enough rest. Sleep and rest help the body recuperate and fight off viruses.

Stay cool, but don't get cold. Keep the room temperature comfortable, but avoid making conditions too cool, which may cause shivers and in turn raise body temperature.

If the fever is persistent, see a doctor. In general, a child or an adult under 60 with a fever above 103°F (39.5°C) should seek immediate medical attention. Any fever of 101°F (38.5°C) that lasts longer than 3 days, or or is higher than that and is accompanied by severe headache, nausea, vomiting, a stiff neck, a change in alertness, or hypersensitivity to light requires medical attention.

Don't delay treatment for infants and the elderly. Infants under 3 months of age with a fever higher than 100°F (38°C) and adults over 60 with a fever over 102°F (39°C) need medical attention.

WHO'S AFFECTED?

- African American women
- Women ages 40 to 50
- Identical twins of women with fibroids
- Women who took birth control pills at 13 to 16 years of age

FIBROIDS

FOODS THAT HARM
Beer

FOODS THAT HEAL
Dairy products
Broccoli
Spinach
Swiss chard
Brussels sprouts
Oranges

FOODS TO LIMIT
Breads, pastas, and other foods made with white flour

Uterine fibroids are benign (non-cancerous) tumors of the uterus and are the leading cause for hysterectomies in the United States. Fibroids are common in women during their childbearing years and can cause heavy menstrual bleeding, longer-lasting periods, cramping, lower back pain, pain during intercourse, and bleeding between periods.

Researchers are still working on determining what causes fibroids. The current thinking is that hormones, especially estrogens and progesterone, play a role.

Nutrition Connection

These dietary tips will help minimize the impact of fibroids:

Reduce high-carb foods. Researchers who study fibroids say that eating too many refined carbs (breads, pastas, and other foods made with white flour; sugary treats) leads to high, prolonged levels of blood glucose. That can lead to higher blood levels of estradiol, a potent estrogen, which could theoretically fuel the development of fibroids.

Get milk. Milk and other dairy products substantially lower the risk for developing fibroids.

Gobble oranges. Women who eat a couple of oranges a day have a lower fibroid risk than women who ate fewer oranges. But OJ is no substitute for the real deal—drinking it doesn't lower a woman's risk.

Graze on green veggies. Eating more than a serving a day of green vegetables slashes fibroid risk by 50%.

Abstain from beer. Women who have one or more beers a day increase their fibroid risk by 50%.

Drop a few pounds. Women who have fibroids tend to be overweight. Being obese ups your risk by 20%.

Beyond the Diet

Some nondietary guidelines will reduce and help manage fibroids, including:

Check your blood pressure. The Nurses' Health Study, one of the largest studies on women's health, points to a link between high blood pressure and fibroid development.

Do some deep breathing. Stress could raise progesterone levels and increase fibroid development.

FLATULENCE

FOODS THAT HARM

Carbonated drinks

Chewing gum

Bran

Milk, for those who are
   lactose intolerant

FOODS THAT HEAL

Peppermint, chamomile, fennel,
   or ginger tea

Yogurt

Anise

Rosemary

Bay leaf

Kombu seaweed

FOODS TO LIMIT

Kidney beans and other dried beans

Brussels sprouts

Cauliflower

Onions

Corn

Asparagus

Bran

Sorbitol

Excessive gas, or flatulence, causes uncomfortable abdominal bloating, which can be relieved by bringing the gas up from the stomach (burping) or expelling it through the anus. Although it is embarrassing, this experience is the completely natural result of intestinal bacteria acting on undigested carbohydrates and proteins. The average person has more than 14 to 23 episodes a day, most of which pass unnoticed. It's only when certain malodorous gases are released that the problem becomes unpleasant. Flatulence seems to worsen with age, and some individuals are simply more susceptible to gas than others.

Nutrition Connection

Passing gas can be an uncomfortable side effect of a well-intentioned move toward a healthier, high-fiber diet. However, incorporating some dietary changes can help decrease gas:

Gulp less air when eating. Eating smaller portions, chewing food thoroughly, and not gulping liquids can help minimize episodes. Avoiding carbonated beverages can also help.

Drink herbal tea. A cup of peppermint, chamomile, or fennel tea after a meal sometimes helps improve digestion and reduce flatulence. Ginger tea can also help.

Try yogurt. Some people find that eating yogurt made with live cultures cuts down on gas production.

Soak dried beans first. Except for lentils and split peas, which do not need to be presoaked, soaking dried beans for at least 4 hours (preferably 8 or more hours) before cooking them in plenty of water helps to reduce the indigestible sugars, raffinose and stachyose, that cause gas.

Avoid vegetables from the cabbage family. Although chock-full of healthy nutrients, brussels sprouts, broccoli, cauliflower, and other members of the cabbage plant family cause flatulence in many people. Other vegetables that may cause excessive gas include onions, corn, and asparagus. However, you may be able to reduce gas by adding spices such as anise, ginger, rosemary, bay leaf, and fennel seeds to these foods during cooking. Some cooks add kombu seaweed, available in Asian markets and natural food stores, to cooking water for the same purpose.

Increase fiber intake very gradually. If you're interested in increasing fiber intake, nutritionists suggest taking it slow. They also recommend avoiding bran and high-fiber laxatives.

Check nutrient levels. Sorbitol, fructose, and other sweeteners can cause flatulence in some people, as can high doses of vitamin C.

Beyond the Diet

You can reduce the amount of flatulence your body produces with these simple tips:

Avoid habits that encourage swallowing air. Don't chew gum or drink through a straw, which promotes swallowing air.

Try gas-reducing enzyme products. Products made from natural enzymes are available in pharmacies as drops or tablets to helps reduce flatulence. Add a few drops on gas-producing food or take a tablet before a meal.

Talk to your doctor. Sometimes flatulence is a sign of a more serious medical disorder: If the problem is severe and persists, it could be a symptom of food allergies, Crohn's disease, lactose intolerance, or irritable bowel syndrome.

FOOD POISONING

FOODS THAT HARM
  Raw or undercooked food, such as eggs with runny yolk, mayonnaise, mousses, and unbaked cake batters
  Leftovers

FOODS THAT HEAL
  Water
  Diluted juice
  Ginger ale
  Bananas
  Rice
  Applesauce
  Dry toast
  Mashed potatoes
  Chicken broth

FOODS TO LIMIT
  Dairy products
  Diuretics, such as caffeine and alcohol
  Highly seasoned foods

The term *food poisoning* applies to an illness (most often gastroenteritis, but occasionally nervous system complications) that comes from eating food with bacteria, viruses, toxins, or parasites.

Contamination of foods can occur at any point of food processing or production, including harvesting, packing, transporting, and displaying food for sale. Most cases of food poisoning are caused by bacterial contamination. The microorganisms that are most often responsible are *Clostridium botulinum*, *Clostridium perfringens*, *Escherichia coli*, *Listeria monocytogenes*, Salmonella strains, and *Staphylococcus aureus*.

Food poisoning usually causes nausea and vomiting, diarrhea, cramps, headache, and sometimes fever and prostration. Double vision and difficulty in speaking, chewing, swallowing, and breathing are symptoms of botulism, a rare but particularly grave form of food poisoning. If you see any of these symptoms in someone, call for immediate medical attention. The infection can be serious in vulnerable people, especially infants, young children, people with chronic illness (including AIDS and other immune system disorders), and the elderly. Call a doctor if someone you know in these groups exhibits symptoms.

Nutrition Connection

The following recommendations can help support the body during its recovery from food poisoning:

Prevent fluid depletion. Replace much-needed fluids and electrolytes. Sip a mixture of apple juice and water, or weak tea. Sipping ginger ale can help to calm any surges of nausea. Chicken broth with rice is a palatable rehydration remedy; the broth replaces fluid as well as sodium and potassium, to restore the balance of electrolytes, and the rice has a binding effect on the bowel.

Avoid dairy products. Dairy may worsen diarrhea.

Don't tax your digestive system. Wait until your stomach is ready to handle food.

Eat bland foods when you're ready. When you're confident that your system has settled down, reintroduce foods such as bananas, rice, applesauce, and toast. Then try other bland foods, such as soft-cooked chicken and mashed potatoes. Avoid fresh fruits for a few days.

Beyond the Diet

Once you treat the food-borne illness, it's helpful to know how to prevent future episodes. Follow these guidelines for recovery and food safety precautions:

Let nature run its course. If you're a healthy adult, your body will rid itself of the organisms that cause food poisoning through vomiting and diarrhea. Most cases will clear up without medical help.

Rest. Food poisoning, along with dehydration, may cause weakness.

Seek medical care if it's serious. Very severe cases may require antibiotics. If you cannot drink fluids and have diarrhea, fluids may be given intravenously.

Practice food safety when cooking. Before you cook or handle food, use hot, soapy water to wash your hands, utensils, and preparation surfaces, such as chopping boards. Keep raw foods separate from cooked foods, and be especially careful when handling meat, fish, shellfish, and poultry; foods of animal origin are most prone to contamination. Make sure raw foods don't contaminate cooked foods in any way, or don't let cooked foods touch surfaces with traces of raw food. Keep washing your hands throughout cooking.

Cook foods thoroughly. Use a food thermometer to check that foods have cooked to a safe temperature. Cook pork

WHO'S AFFECTED?

- People who are susceptible, such as pregnant women, the elderly, and people with chronic diseases
- Roughly 48 million Americans and 11 million Canadians get sick each year each year

G

and ground beef to an internal temperature of 160°F (71°C); steaks, roasts, and fish to at least 145°F (63°C); and chicken to 165°F (74°C).

Wash sponges after use. Use hot water and soap to wash sponges and dishcloths after every use. This will help prevent cross-contamination and the spread of bacteria.

Keep cold foods cold and hot foods hot. If you don't intend to eat food immediately after preparing it, refrigerate or freeze it. Never leave food for longer than 2 hours at temperatures between 45°F (7°C) and 140°F (60°C), which are ideal for bacterial growth. When defrosting food, don't leave it out at room temperature; rather, defrost it in the refrigerator or use the microwave.

Do not buy anything in or use food from dented or bulging cans. Dented cans may indicate botulism. Bulging is most likely caused by the pressure of gases produced by bacterial metabolism.

When in doubt, toss it out. Discard food that smells bad or is discolored. Even tasting a little bit is risky and will not tell you if a food is unsafe.

QUICK TIP: Thermometer know-how

1. Take the temperature of thin foods like burgers within one minute of removal from heat, or larger cuts like roast after 5 to 10 minutes.

2. Insert the thermometer stem or indicator into the thickest part of the food, away from bone, fat, or gristle.

3. Leave the thermometer in food for at least 30 seconds before reading temperature.

4. When food has an irregular shape, like some beef roasts, check the temperature in several places.

5. Always wash the thermometer stem thoroughly in hot, soapy water after each use.

GALLSTONES

FOODS THAT HEAL
Tomatoes
Salmon
Brown rice
Whole wheat bread
Barley
Avocado
Olive oil
Walnuts
Flaxseeds

FOODS TO LIMIT
Red meat, butter, and foods
  with saturated fat
Processed foods that contain
  trans fat
Sugary foods, such as cookies
  and soft drinks

The gallbladder stores and concentrates bile, a fluid produced by the liver to digest fats in the small intestine. Bile fluid contains high levels of cholesterol and the pigment bilirubin, both of which can form stones.

For many, gallstones are symptomless and do not require treatment. For others, however, the presence of gallstones can cause pain in the upper right abdomen when the gallbladder contracts to release bile after a meal, and can cause inflammation of the gallbladder (cholecystitis) that brings on sudden, severe pain extending to the back and under the right shoulder blade, with fever, chills, and vomiting. If stones obstruct the flow of bile, the skin and the whites of the eyes become jaundiced. Left untreated, stones can lodge in the bile duct and cause inflammation of the liver or pancreas.

Nutrition Connection

These guidelines and strategies can help:

Eat right. Monitor foods to avoid any that cause discomfort. Diets should include plenty of whole grains with lots of fruits and vegetables, moderate servings of protein, and small amounts of fat. It is best to avoid alcohol. Also, eat more foods with vitamins C, E, and calcium. Such foods include tomatoes, salmon, and nuts.

Always eat breakfast. A substantial breakfast causes the gallbladder to empty itself and flush out any small stones and stagnant bile.

Consume small, frequent meals. Small meals can help spur the gallbladder to empty stones and bile, while eating 5 to 6 meals spaced throughout the day encourages routine gallbladder function.

Avoid extreme dieting. Bile is likely to form stones after you fast. Seek a weight loss program that helps you lose weight without long restrictive periods.

To prevent gallstones, eat a high-fiber diet. A variety of fruits and vegetables and whole grains may help prevent gallstones from forming.

Bump up unsaturated fats. Sources of polyunsaturated fat such as walnuts, flaxseeds, and salmon, and foods rich in monounsaturated fat, such as olive oil and avocado, may also prevent gallstones.

Limit fatty and sugary foods. Foods rich in saturated fat, and trans fat, such as red meat, chicken skin, butter, cheese, and processed foods, may increase the risk of gallstone formation. Sugar foods, such as cakes and cookies, can also be a problem.

Beyond the Diet

Try these tips to help deal with existing gallstones or to prevent them from forming in the first place:

Maintain a healthy weight. A large clinical study showed that being even moderately overweight increases the risk of developing gallstones. Obesity is a major risk factor, especially for women.

Consider supplements. Those who do not get enough vitamins C or E or calcium in their diet may have an increased risk. Speak to your doctor before taking any supplements; as in most cases, it's best to get your vitamins and minerals from foods.

Talk to your doctor about treatment. For frequent painful attacks, the usual treatment is the surgical removal of the gallbladder, called cholecystectomy. The procedure can be performed by conventional surgery or by laparoscopy, which involves a tiny incision and a brief hospital stay. Another option is a procedure called lithotripsy, which uses shock waves to break up the gallstones.

QUICK TIP:
Drop pounds slowly

Shedding extra pounds is good for your health, but keep the weight loss at a slow, steady pace of about 1 to 2 pounds a week. Rapid weight loss increases your risk of getting gallstones.

WHO'S AFFECTED?

- 10 to 15% of North Americans have gallstones, including more than 20 million Americans annually
- Women are twice as likely as men to develop gallstones
- People who are moderately overweight or obese
- People who crash crash diet often

GASTRITIS

See Indigestion and Heartburn, page 289

GASTRO-ENTERITIS

See Food Poisoning, page 275

GERD (GAS-TROESOPHA-GEAL REFLUX DISEASE

See Indigestion and Heartburn, page 289

See Indigestion and Heartburn, page 289

QUICK TIP:
Avoid overheating

Recent research has found that external heat, such as warm summer days, may play a role in triggering gout attacks. So stay cool to stay pain-free.

WHO'S AFFECTED?

- Between 2 and % of North Americans
- More men than women are affected, but prevalence increases with age for both groups, especially for women after menopause
- Those who have a family history
- Those who are overweight, drink too much alcohol, or eat too many foods rich in purines
- Those who have had an organ transplant

GOUT

FOODS THAT HARM
Organ meats
Game meats
Anchovies
Sardines
Herring

FOODS THAT HEAL
Water
Fruit juice
Herbal teas
Vegetable broth
Soy

FOODS TO LIMIT
Cauliflower
Asparagus
Dried beans and peas
Oats
Whole grain cereals
Wheat germ and wheat bran
Mushrooms
Poultry
Alcohol

Marked by swelling, inflammation, and excruciating tenderness in the joints, gout most commonly affects the joints at the base of the big toe, other foot joints, knees, ankles, wrists, and fingers. The slightest touch—even that of a bedsheet—may be un-bearably painful during an attack of gout.

Long known as "the disease of kings" or "rich man's disease," gout has been associated with overindulgence and high living, as well as obesity. But in actuality, gout is a type of arthritis that is caused by an inherited defect in the kidney's ability to excrete uric acid.

Nutrition Connection

To reinforce the beneficial effect of drug treatment, people with gout should make dietary changes to help reduce their production of uric acid. The following are general guidelines:

Avoid foods that are high in purines. Foods with a high content of naturally occurring chemicals called purines promote overproduction of uric acid in people with a tendency for gout. Steer clear of high-purine foods such as anchovies, sardines, liver, kidney, brains, herring, mackerel, scallops, and game.

Limit foods with a moderate level of purines. Such foods include whole grain cereals, wheat germ and wheat bran, oatmeal, dried beans and peas, nuts, asparagus, cauliflower, and mushrooms. These may be taken in moderation.

Limit your intake of meat, fish and poultry. Because meat products are high in purines, you'll need to more closely monitor the amount of these foods you eat. About 4 to 6 oz (113 to 170 g) is recommended per day.

Eat more plant-based proteins. Add more plant-based sources of protein such as soy. These foods contain the essential protein you need without the purines contained in meat products.

Consume plenty of liquids. Try to drink at least 2 qt (2 L) a day to dilute urine and prevent kidney stone formation.

Limit or avoid alcohol. Any alcohol can interfere with the elimination of uric acid. Gout sufferers should drink only distilled alcohols in small amounts.

Avoid low-carb diets. High-protein, low-carbohydrate diets should be avoided since these diets encourage the formation of ketones, metabolic by-products that hamper the body's ability to excrete uric acid.

Lose weight gradually. Although losing weight—especially fat around the abdomen—often prevents future gout attacks, weight loss should be gradual because a rapid reduction can raise blood levels of uric acid and provoke gout. People with gout should avoid skipping meals; fasting also increases the blood levels of uric acid.

Beyond the Diet

Colchicine, a drug derived from the autumn crocus flower, is one of the most effective gout medications, but it can also cause severe nausea and diarrhea. Follow these suggestions to keep gout under control:

Possibly modify your drug therapy. Sometimes gout is brought on by using aspirin or diuretics for high blood pressure. These medicines may interfere with normal kidney function and the elimination of uric acid.

Address other health issues. Gout sufferers also may have hypertension, heart disease, diabetes, and high blood cholesterol. Talk to your doctor about the best ways to manage your unique situation.

HALITOSIS

FOODS THAT HARM
  Garlic
  Onions

FOODS THAT HEAL
  Water
  Red bell pepper
  Broccoli
  Fennel seeds
  Chewing gum with xylitol

WHO'S AFFECTED?
• People with dental problems, sinusitis, diabetes, chronic bronchitis, and other underlying conditions

Everyone can have bad breath once in a while, particularly after eating a meal laced with odiferous garlic or onions. But when it happens regularly, you might have a chronic underlying problem. Halitosis has many causes, including poor dental hygiene, gum disease, denture problems, dry mouth, or an infection of some kind.

Treatment starts with attending carefully to brushing and flossing your teeth regularly, or making sure dentures are cleaned properly. If odor still persists, a trip to the dentist for evaluation is in order, and if you get an all-clear on your oral health, visit your physician to rule out other problems, which could include sinusitis, diabetes, strep throat, chronic bronchitis, or other diseases.

QUICK TIP:
Chew on fennel seeds

Chewing on a pinch of fennel seeds after meals can help freshen your breath.

Nutrition Connection

Your breath is what you eat. For either occasional halitosis or chronic bad breath, here are a few guidelines:

Drink plenty of water. Quaffing a big glass of water after every meal will help flush out the bits of food that stenchproducing bacteria thrive on. Water also helps you produce saliva, which helps the mouth cleanse itself.

Chew sugar-free gum. Chewing gum sweetened with xylitol—a natural, low-calorie sugar—helps cleanse breath because xylitol curbs the growth of bacteria in the mouth. The gum itself helps loosen trapped food particles and increases saliva production. For best results, chew for at least five minutes after every meal.

Reach for raw veggies. Those rich in vitamin C, such as broccoli and red bell pepper, are particularly good fighters of bad breath, because they create an unfriendly environment for bacteria. What's more, eating raw, crunchy vegetables helps remove food particles stuck between teeth.

Beyond the Diet

Some lifestyle choices affects your breath. Here's what you should do to freshen up:

Enforce a tobacco taboo. A mouth that smells like an ashtray is yet another reason to stop smoking.

Launder those dentures. Improperly cleaned dentures house smelly bacteria, fungi and food particles, which cause bad breath.

Brush your tongue. When you brush your teeth, pass your soft toothbrush over your tongue a few times to dislodge bacteria. Some people use tongue scraper tools, but there's little evidence that they're any more effective than simple brushing.

HAY FEVER

FOODS THAT HARM
Artichokes
Chamomile tea
Endives
Escarole
Tarragon
Beer and wine
Sourdough bread
Blue cheese
Dried fruit
Mushrooms
Sausages
Sauerkraut
Soy sauce
Vinegar
Honey
Bee pollen capsules

FOODS THAT HEAL
Salmon
Herring
Flaxseeds

Hay fever is a seasonal allergy characterized by sneezing, tearing eyes, and itchiness triggered by the inhalation of pollen or, less commonly, molds. Medically known as seasonal or allergic rhinitis, the term *hay fever* is a misnomer. Although symptoms may occur during the haying season, hay itself is not the culprit nor is there a fever.

Although foods aren't ordinarily associated with hay fever, people with certain types of seasonal allergies may experience symptoms after eating particular foods. For example, plants in the sunflower family have antigens that cross-react with members of the ragweed family. Thus, a person whose hay fever symptoms are triggered by ragweed may react to eating any herbs and vegetables in the sunflower family.

Similarly, people sensitive to mold spores may have an issue eating foods and beverages that harbor molds.

Nutrition Connection

There is no special diet to alleviate hay fever symptoms, aside from avoiding foods that may trigger flare-ups.

Avoid foods in the sunflower plant family. If ragweed triggers hay fever flare-ups for you, avoid foods in this family. They include artichokes, chamomile tea, chicory, dandelions, endives, escarole, Jerusalem artichokes, salsify, safflower (found in vegetable oils and margarines), sunflower seeds and oil, tansy (used in some herbal medicines and folk remedies), and tarragon.

Avoid fermented foods if you're allergic to mold. These include alcoholic beverages, especially beer, wine, and other drinks made by fermentation; breads made with lots of yeast or the sourdough varieties; cheeses, especially blue cheese; dried fruits, including raisins and others that are allowed to dry outdoors; mushrooms of all kinds; processed meats and fish, including hot dogs, sausages, and smoked fish; sauerkraut and other fermented or pickled foods, including soy sauce; and vinegar and vinegary products, such as salad dressings, mayonnaise, ketchup, and pickles.

Watch out for honey. Contaminants or pollens in some foods can also trigger the onset of hay fever symptoms. This is especially true of honey, which may harbor bits of pollen, and bee pollen capsules, a food supplement and natural remedy.

Eat more omega-3s. Some reports suggest that eating fatty fish and other foods that are high in omega-3 fatty acids such as salmon, herring, and flaxseeds.

Beyond the Diet

Take over-the-counter (OTC) allergy medications. Drugs such as Benadryl, Claritin, and Zyrtec can provide considerable relief from mild to moderate hay fever symptoms.

Try a nasal rinse. Rinsing your nasal passageways with a water and salt solution helps to relieve nasal congestion and keep the pathway clear by flushing out mucus and allergens from your nose and sinuses. A neti pot or a squeeze bottle can be found at your local drugstore.

WHO'S AFFECTED?

- 10 to 30% of all adults in North America

40% of all children in the United States suffer from hay fever.

Talk to your doctor. For severe hay fever flare-ups, a doctor may prescribe nasal or oral corticosteroids, or leukotriene modifiers that block immune system chemicals that cause allergy symptoms.

HEARTBURN

See Indigestion and Heartburn, page 289

- Overweight people
- Those ages 45 to 65
- Pregnant women

HEMORRHOIDS

FOODS THAT HEAL
  Water
  Black beans
  Lima beans
  Barley
  Bran flakes
  Raspberries
  Apples
  Pears
  Oats
  Flaxseeds

FOODS TO LIMIT
  Red meat

Hemorrhoids are enlarged blood vessels found in the anal canal. They can be either internal or external. Hemorrhoids are an all-too-familiar problem for millions of people—and have been since the dawn of time.

Nutrition Connection

Drink lots of water. This softens the stool, which can relieve pain, bleeding, and prolapse (when hemorrhoids protrude outside the anal canal at the rectum).

Fill up on fiber. Women should aim for 21 to 25 g of fiber a day; men should get 30 to 38 g a day. Be sure to eat at least two servings of a high-fiber food such as beans, whole grains, berries, apples, and pears (with the skin on) at every meal. Adding freshly ground flax seeds to cereals, smoothies, and yogurt is another way to add more fiber to your diet.

> **QUICK TIP:**
> **Add a fiber supplement**
>
> Incorporating a fiber supplement containing psyllium helps prevent hemorrhoids.

Beyond the Diet

Go when nature calls. Delaying a bowel movement can make it harder to pass later on, which exacerbates hemorrhoids.

Don't strain. Forcing out a bowel movement creates pressure that makes hemorrhoids worse. Relax, breathe, and let things pass naturally.

But don't dally. When you peruse a book or magazine while sitting on the commode, you also place pressure on hemorrhoids.

Take exercise breaks. Spread exercise breaks throughout your day, especially if you sit for a living, as many people do.

Avoid lifting. If you can forgo picking up heavy objects, do so. If you can't, be sure to exhale while you're lifting and don't hold your breath.

Sleep on your side, especially if you're pregnant. This relieves pressure on the blood vessels in your pelvic region and may prevent hemorrhoids from enlarging.

HEPATITIS

FOODS THAT HARM
  Alcohol
  Raw shellfish
  Sweets

FOODS THAT HEAL
  Lean meat
  Poultry
  Fish
  Eggs
  Dairy
  Legumes
  Whole grains

FOODS TO LIMIT
  Fried and fatty foods

Hepatitis refers to the inflammation of the liver, which is commonly caused by a virus, but can also occur after taking certain drugs or after exposure to poisons. It damages liver cells and may lead to cirrhosis, in which the function of the liver is seriously and irreversibly impaired. Hepatitis A and E are typically caused by food contaminated by fecal matter and go away on their own after a few weeks or months. Hepatitis B, C, and D are typically caused by exposure to infected blood , and are more serious.

Nutrition Connection

With a nutritious, well-balanced diet and rest, hepatitis A resolves itself. But appetite loss and nausea are common symptoms. Here are some dietary guidelines that may help. These can also help ease symptoms of other forms of hepatitis, as well.

Try to have breakfast. Often, appetite decreases and nausea increases as the day progresses. Breakfast may be the best-tolerated meal.

Eat a diet high in protein. When recovering from hepatitis, a person should consume a healthy diet with sufficient protein daily from both animal and vegetable sources. The best sources are lean meat, poultry, fish, eggs, dairy products, and a combination of legumes and grains.

Graze during the day. If the appetite is poor, intersperse several small meals a day with a nutritious snack (such as a milk shake or an enriched liquid drink). Fried and very fatty foods, which are difficult to digest, should be avoided; a small amount of fat is acceptable, however, to provide needed calories and add flavor. Usually, the fats in dairy products and eggs are easier to digest than those in fatty meats and fried foods.

Avoid sweets and alcohol. Because sweets may squelch the appetite for more nutritious foods, it is best to avoid them. Alcohol should not be consumed, because it places added stress on an already sick liver.

Beyond the Diet

In addition to nutritional guidelines, follow these tips for treating hepatitis:

Maintain good hygiene. Because hepatitis A and E can be contracted through contaminated food and water, be sure to always wash your hands after using the bathroom and before handling food. And avoid drinking or using tap water to brush your teeth when traveling in regions where heptatitis A or E outbreaks occur.

Seek medications. Talk to your doctor about treatments for chronic hepatitis B, C, or D.

> ## QUICK TIP:
> ### Eat cooked shellfish
>
> Don't go raw. Cooking oysters and other shellfish destroys the bacteria that can contaminate them and cause hepatitis.

HERPES

FOODS THAT HEAL
- Lean meat
- Fish
- Yogurt
- Milk
- Whole grains
- Fresh fruit and vegetables

FOODS TO LIMIT
- Alcohol
- Caffeinated drinks

A common and highly contagious infectious disease, herpes is caused by strains of the herpes simplex virus and is noted by painful and itchy blisters. Type 1 herpes,

WHO'S AFFECTED?
- Most people have herpes simplex virus type 1
- 16.2% of Americans have herpes simplex type 2 (HSV-2)
- HSV-2 affects those who have had many sexual partners

or oral herpes, causes cold sores or fever blisters around the mouth. In some cases, this type of herpes infects the eyes and can result in blindness or, even more seriously, can spread to the brain and result in life-threatening herpes encephalitis. Type 2, or genital herpes, is sexually transmitted and causes sores in the genital and anal areas. Engaging in oral sex with an infected person can cause mouth and throat blisters that are difficult to differentiate from type 1 herpes.

Regardless of the type or location, herpes blisters usually rupture into open weeping sores that crust over and eventually heal within a few days or weeks. Some people also experience a mild fever, swollen lymph nodes, and fatigue. Even after healing, the virus remains dormant in the body; some

20.9% of American women have type 2 herpes, almost twice as many as men at 11.5%.

people never have another attack, while others have repeated but milder eruptions sporadically throughout their lives.

Recurrences may be triggered by hormonal changes, physical or emotional stress, fever, exposure to the sun, or other environmental factors.

Nutrition Connection

Certain foods and drugs precipitate recurrences in susceptible people. Keep notes of those items and avoid them while bolstering your immune system through diet. Follow these tips:

Eat a nutritious diet. To help prevent recurrences, strengthen your immune system to resist disease by eating a well-balanced diet with plenty of whole grains, fresh fruits and vegetables, and protein.

Eat foods rich in lysine. Foods high in the amino acid lysine, found in meat, fish, milk, and dairy products, may help to reduce the frequency of herpes attacks. The supplement version can also help; some natural medicine advocates recommend taking 500 to 1,000 mg of L-lysine daily on an empty stomach. It can be found in natural food stores. Discuss with your doctor before taking.

Eat yogurt. Anecdotal evidence suggests that *Lactobacillus acidophilus*, a healthy bacteria found in certain yogurts containing live or "active" cultures and also sold in capsule form, may help prevent recurrences of cold sores. You may need to take supplements to get a therapeutic dose.

Avoid excessive alcohol and caffeine. In large amounts, alcoholic and caffeinated drinks can suppress the immune system.

Beyond the Diet

If you have frequent attacks, analyze your lifestyle and try to figure out what specific triggers may have precipitated them. Here are some suggestions:

Don't smoke. Smoking weakens the immune system.

Avoid the sun. Sun exposure can trigger outbreaks of cold sores. Always wear sunscreen.

Balance your lifestyle. Regular exercise alleviates stress that can cause outbreak and adequate rest ensures a healthy immune system.

Pre-empt an outbreak. If you have a warning symptom before an outbreak, of oral herpes, prompt use of aspirin and ice packs sometimes prevents the recurrence. Once the lesions appear, compresses of cold water or milk may ease the discomfort.

Ease inflammation. For genital outbreaks, warm baths or saltwater compresses can help soothe the area. Keep the infected area clean and dry. Wash your hands after contact with the sores to avoid spreading infection to other parts of your body.

Look into medications. In more severe herpes cases, doctors prescribe acyclovir, an antiviral medication that can be taken orally or used as a cream. Acyclovir can shorten the duration of an attack and help prevent a recurrence.

Protect others. Avoid kissing anyone, sharing dishes or utensils, or having sex during outbreaks. A pregnant woman who has had herpes should inform her obstetrician immediately. An active infection may be transmitted to the baby during delivery and can cause blindness, retardation, even death. A cesarean delivery can prevent transmission.

HIATAL HERNIA

See Indigestion and Heartburn, page 289

HIVES

FOODS THAT HARM
Yellow food color no. 5 (tartrazine)
Shellfish
Nuts
Berries
Apricots
Grapes
Dried fruits
Tea

FOODS THAT HEAL
Poultry
Seafood
Seeds
Fortified and enriched cereals
and breads

Medically known as urticaria, hives are the itchy red welts that develop as a result of reactions to foods, medications, and other provoking substances.

If hives are accompanied by swelling of the throat and difficulty breathing, speaking, or swallowing, seek immediate medical help. These symptoms may signal anaphylaxis, a potentially fatal medical emergency.

Nutrition Connection

Avoid trigger foods. This is the best way to prevent a hives outbreak. Some common causes are shellfish, nuts, and berries. A person who is allergic to aspirin (acetylsalicylic acid) should also be wary of foods that contain natural salicylates. These include apricots, berries, grapes, raisins and other dried fruits, tea, and foods processed with vinegar.

Keep a food diary. If you get hives repeatedly, start a food diary; once you identify the suspect foods, eliminate them from your regular diet, then reintroduce one at a time.

WHO'S AFFECTED?
- 15 to 24% of Americans will experience acute hives or angioedema (swelling that occurs in the tissue just below the skin, especially around the lips and eyes) at some point in their lives
- People who have allergies such as hay fever
- People with infections from colds or by bacteria or fungi
- People with lupus, thyroid disease, and a type of vasculitis

- Women, especially during the 6 months after being pregnant or having a baby
- People ages 30 to 60
- People with a family history of thyroid disease
- People with autoimmune disorders

Eat foods that are high in niacin. Since hives and other allergy symptoms are triggered by the release of histamines, it may be useful to increase consumption of foods that are high in niacin (vitamin B3), which is believed to inhibit histamine release. Good sources of niacin include poultry, seafood, seeds and nuts, whole grains, and fortified and enriched cereals and breads. However, note that some foods that are good sources of niacin are among those that tend to provoke an allergy.

Check food labels to avoid tartrazine. Although food additives are often blamed for causing allergic reactions, only tartrazine (yellow no. 5), a common coloring agent, has been found to cause hives—and in fewer than one out of 10,000 people. All product labels must list food colorants; people who are sensitive to tartrazine should read labels on food products, medications, and vitamin supplements.

Beyond the Diet

Take these steps to pin down the causes of hives and to avoid future attacks:

Avoid trigger situations. Emotional stress; exposure to sunshine, heat, or cold (even ice cubes in drinks); and viral infections can all cause hives.

Take antihistamines. These medications can block histamines that produce the symptoms of hives. Your doctor may recommend a drug such as Claritin, Allegra, Zyrtec, or Clarinex or a combination of antihistamines and other drugs such as corticosteroids. Apply medicated lotions. Ask your doctor or a dermatologist about lotions to reduce itching and relieve inflammation.

Talk to your doctor. He or she may recommend allergy testing and be able to prescribe special medications for severe outbreaks.

HYPER-THYROIDISM

FOODS THAT HARM
Caffeinated drinks

FOODS THAT HEAL
Dairy products
Soy products
Collard greens
Mustard greens

Hyperthyroidism, in which an overactive thyroid produces too much hormone, is the opposite of hypothyroidism (see page 288). Instead of everything in your body slowing down, it speeds up. The predominant symptoms are nervousness and jitteriness, and eventually a sense of fatigue prevails. People with overactive thyroids also experience unusual hunger, weight loss, muscle weakness, and rapid heartbeat. They find heat hard to bear and sweat excessively. Treatment is aimed at the cause and involves reducing hormone production either by giving radioactive iodine or antithyroid drugs or by surgery to remove all or parts of the thyroid.

Nutrition Connection

While changing your diet won't prevent or reverse hyperthyroidism, you can help ease some of the symptoms by following these guidelines:

Avoid caffeine. Additional stimulation is the last thing someone with hyperthyroidism needs.

Maintain an adequate intake of calcium and vitamin D. Because hyperthyroidism may contribute to thinning bones, it's important to get enough calcium every day to help prevent osteoporosis (1,000 to 1,200 mg a day) and vitamin D (600 to 800 international units (IUs) a day). Good food sources include dairy products, soy products, and dark leafy greens like collard and mustard greens.

Beyond the Diet

To address concerns about hyperthyroidism, follow these tips:

See an eye doctor. Anyone whose hyperthyroidism is accompanied by bulging eyes should be closely followed by an ophthalmologist.

Avoid cold medicines. Because some cold medicines contain stimulants, they could overstimulate people with overactive thyroid or strain their heart.

HYPO-GLYCEMIA

FOODS THAT HEAL
Apples
Lentils
Barley
Oats

FOODS TO LIMIT
Alcohol
Sugary foods, such as candy

Hypoglycemia, also known as low blood sugar, is characterized by low levels of glucose, the body's main source of energy. It occurs when the amount of insulin in the blood exceeds the amount needed to metabolize the available glucose in the body. The condition may occur when a person with diabetes takes too much insulin, but it can also happen under other circumstances, such as overconsumption of alcohol; taking large amounts of aspirin or acetaminophen, beta-blockers, and

some antipsychotic drugs; or when tumors develop that secrete insulin.

Symptoms include confusion, abnormal behavior, double vision, heart palpitations, shakiness, anxiety, sweating, and hunger. While less common, the person may have a seizure or lose consciousness.

One condition called reactive hypoglycemia occurs when blood sugar levels plummet 1 to 2 hours after a meal. Symptoms include dizziness, headache, trembling, palpitations, and irritability. This uncommon condition can only be diagnosed by monitoring blood glucose levels after ingestion of a known dose of glucose.

Nutrition Connection

Prevent episodes of hypoglycemia with these dietary tips:

Eat small, frequent meals that are balanced. An even mix of carbohydrates, fats, and proteins will help your body metabolize the foods slowly. Because they take longer than sugars to be digested and converted into glucose, they allow for a steady release of energy.

Eat foods rich in fiber. Include foods that are higher in soluble fiber such as lentils, oats, barley, apples, and citrus fruits since they are absorbed more slowly. Choose whole grains (such as whole wheat

WHO'S AFFECTED?
- Those who have diabetes
- People with liver disease or insulinoma, a tumor in the pancreas
- Those who drink excessive amounts of alcohol

bread) over refined grains (such as white bread or pasta) as often as possible.

Eat foods with a low glycemic index (GI), or load (GL). GI and GL are measurements of how readily foods are converted to blood glucose. For more information, see page 262. Focus on foods that help blood sugar levels remain stable. They include apples, kidney beans, lentils, oats, barley, and bran.

Avoid sweets. Candies, cookies, and anything loaded with sugar can be a potential problem. Consumed by themselves, they spike up your blood glucose levels and cause the body to pump out more insulin, which eventually leads to hypoglycemia.

Avoid excessive drinking. Excessive alcohol consumption can cause hypoglycemia because the body's breakdown of alcohol interferes with the liver's efforts to raise blood glucose. This type of hypoglycemia can be very serious or even fatal.

Address insulin reactions as soon as possible. A serious type of hypoglycemia occurs when someone with diabetes takes more insulin than is needed to metabolize the available glucose. The onset of symptoms of an insulin reaction—hunger, tingling sensations, sweating, faintness, impaired vision, mood changes, palpitations, and a cold, clammy sensation—can be reversed by immediately eating a tablespoonful of sugar or honey, sucking on a hard candy, or drinking a small glass (about ½ cup or 125 mL) of orange juice or a smal sugary drink.

Beyond the Diet

Hypoglycemia may require medical attention. A doctor can run tests to determine the cause of hypoglycemia and then treat the condition or the underlying medical problem. Sepsis, obesity, alcohol abuse, and hormonal changes can be an underlying cause of hypoglycemia.

WHO'S AFFECTED?

- People over age 50 may have hyperthyroidism
- Females, especially after pregnancy
- People with autoimmune disorders
- Anyone who has a family history of thyroid problems
- People who've had radiation treatments to the neck
- Anyone who's been treated with radioactive iodine or antithyroid medications

HYPO-THYROIDISM

FOODS THAT HARM
Walnuts
Soybean flour

FOODS THAT HEAL
Carrots
Sweet potato
Papaya
Cantaloupe
Spinach
Turnip greens

Hypothyroidism is a condition in which the thyroid gland in your neck isn't producing enough hormones. An underactive thyroid slows metabolism, causing weight gain and lethargy. Symptoms such as fatigue, weight gain, hair loss, and poor memory are often dismissed as normal signs of aging. People with a sluggish thyroid feel cold, even on hot days, and develop dry skin and thinning hair. Nails grow slowly and become brittle. Women often develop menstrual irregularities; constipation is another common problem.

WARNING! FOOD-DRUG INTERACTION
If you're taking a synthetic thyroid hormone, limit dietary fiber. Certain foods (walnuts, soybean flour), supplements (iron, calcium), and medications (some antacids, ulcer medications, and cholesterol drugs) can have the same effect. To avoid potential interactions, eat these foods or use these products several hours before or after you take your thyroid medication.

13.5 million people with an underactive thyroid are undiagnosed.

A simple blood test performed by your doctor will sort out whether or not your thyroid is functioning normally. Treatment usually requires lifelong hormone replacement.

Nutrition Connection

These measures can help control hypothyroidism:

Eat more beta-carotene–rich foods. The hormone thyroxine that is used to treat hypothyroidism accelerates the conversion of beta-carotene to vitamin A in the body. People with hypothyroidism may need a higher intake of beta-carotene to meet vitamin A needs. The best sources: deep yellow or orange fruits and vegetables, and dark green vegetables.

Cook your broccoli. Certain vegetables, mainly cabbage, broccoli, and other cruciferous vegetables, contain substances known as goitrogens, which block the effects of thyroid hormones. Cooking these foods inactivates the goitrogens.

Beyond the Diet

Don't mess with your meds. Even when your symptoms go away, you need to continue to take your medication to maintain adequate levels and to enable your doctor to monitor the medication's effectiveness. Consult your doctor before making any changes to your medication.

Watch calories and exercise. Thyroid disorders and medications can cause weight gain so be vigilant to limit any unwanted pounds.

IMPOTENCE

See Sex Drive, Dimished, page 337

INDIGESTION AND HEARTBURN

FOODS THAT HARM
Fatty foods

FOODS THAT HEAL
Small meals at regular intervals

FOODS TO LIMIT
Alcohol
Caffeine and other caffeinated drinks
Chocolate
Spicy foods
Peppermint
Tomatoes
Pickles
Vinegar
Citrus fruits

Many North Americans have indigestion occasionally, but for some, it is a daily trial. Indigestion is a general term to describe discomfort in the upper abdomen after a meal. It's not a disease itself, but a description of symptoms.

Although indigestion is often used to describe heartburn, these are two different conditions. Heartburn is the burning, painful sensation in the chest that occurs

WHO'S AFFECTED?
- More than 31 million Americans and 5 million Canadians experience heartburn once a week
- Those who have GERD (gastroesophageal reflux disease)
- Pregnant women, the obese, and the elderly

when stomach acid and other contents flow backward, or reflux, into the esophagus.

When acid reflux and heartburn occur at least twice a week, a person may be diagnosed with Gastroesophageal Reflux Disease, or GERD. Over time, GERD damages the lining of the esophagus and may even cause a precancerous condition known as Barrett's esophagus. People with GERD may require stronger medications or surgery to treat symptoms.

Indigestion can be caused by GERD, peptic ulcer disease, gastritis, cancer, or abnormality of the pancreas or bile ducts. Heartburn may be caused by obesity and pregnancy, both of which increase pressure on the stomach and force fluids up into the esophagus. Another possible cause of heartburn is a hiatal hernia, which develops when the upper part of the stomach protrudes through the hiatus, the opening where the esophagus meets the stomach.

Nutrition Connection

Dietary tactics and modifications can alleviate symptoms of indigestion and heartburn. Here are several recommendations:

Eat small, frequent meals. You may be able to digest five to six smaller meals better than three large ones. Avoid eating within 2 hours of bedtime.

Eat a balanced, low-fat diet. The stomach will digest a low-fat diet that offers a balance of protein, starches, and fiber-rich vegetables and fruits more easily than fatty foods, which take longer to digest and thus slow down the rate of food emptying from the stomach.

Avoid acidic foods and drinks. Coffee, including decaffeinated brands, promotes high acid production; so do tea, cola drinks, and other sources of caffeine. Acidic foods include citrus fruit, tomatoes, pickles, and anything made with vinegar.

Avoid spicy foods. Omit from your diet other foods that tend to irritate your stomach or provoke bouts of indigestion. Avoid curries, hot peppers, and any other offenders that cause discomfort.

Avoid foods that relax the diaphragmatic muscle. Chocolate or peppermint worsens indigestion by relaxing the sphincter muscle connecting the esophagus to the stomach.

Limit alcohol intake. Alcohol can irritate the stomach lining.

Dine earlier in the evening. If you give yourself at least 3 hours between dinner and bedtime, your stomach is more likely to be empty when it's time to lie down, so reflux is less likely to occur.

Chew nonmint gum for dessert. In the case of GERD, chewing gum stimulates you to produce more saliva, which contains bicarbonate. Gum chewing also increases your rate of swallowing. The saliva then neutralizes the acid in the esophagus—so you're activating nature's own antacid system. However, mint gums may cause the lower esophagus to relax, potentially allowing more stomach acid to rise.

Beyond the Diet

Indigestion and heartburn caused by reflux can usually be controlled with a few lifestyle changes. The following tips can help:

Exercise. In addition to contributing to overall health, exercise helps reduce stress, a potential cause of indigestion.

Don't smoke. Smoking increases stomach acid levels, and nicotine relaxes the sphincter muscle, which causes acid reflux.

Sit up straight after meals. Bending over or lying down increases pressure on the stomach and promotes acid reflux.

Maintain a healthy weight. Extra weight around the abdomen pushes up your stomach and causes acid reflux in your esophagus.

Don't wear tight-fitting clothes. Clothes that are too snug around the waist place additional pressure on your stomach.

Elevate your head at bedtime. If heartburn strikes frequently at night, raising the head 3 to 6 in (8 to 15 cm) can help symptoms.

Sleep on your left side. This helps reduce pressure on your stomach, which is likely to reduce the chance of reflux.

Track your triggers. You have to know which foods trigger your symptoms— foods that work well for one person may cause problems for another. Common foods that trigger GERD include chocolate, caffeinated beverages, and alcohol. Keep a journal to note your symptoms; as you list foods and beverages for each meal, also note what else is going on. Write down symptoms and their frequency. Your diary should also note all medications taken, including supplements. Your doctor should review this diary to help identify specific contributing factors.

Take an antacid. An over-the-counter antacid can soothe heartburn and indigestion symptoms. However, the use of antacids to treat heartburn by neutralizing stomach acid is questionable. The problem is not too much acid, but acid in the wrong place. If they do help, follow instructions and never take them for longer than recommended. Overuse may cause diarrhea or constipation.

Talk to your doctor. If all else fails, speak to your physician, who may run some tests or take x-rays to determine whether you have GERD or to rule out other diseases. Prescription-strength drugs, which include H-2 receptor blockers and proton pump inhibitors, may be suggested.

INFERTILITY

FOODS THAT HEAL
  Enriched or fortified breakfast
    cereals
  Brussels sprouts
  Broccoli
  Turnip greens
  Yogurt
  Legumes
  Lean meat
  Fish
  Orange juice

FOODS TO LIMIT
  Coffee and other caffeinated drinks
    (for women)
  Alcohol

WHO'S AFFECTED?
• Between 8.5 to 15% of North American couples

Infertility is defined as the inability to achieve a pregnancy after at least 1 year of trying. Many couples assume that infertility rests with the woman, but men are just as likely to be infertile.

The leading cause of female infertility is the failure to ovulate, which may be influenced by the diet, hormonal imbalances, and other factors. Both women who are very thin and those who are markedly overweight often do not ovulate because the amount of body fat is closely associated with estrogen levels.

A low sperm count is the major cause of male infertility, and for unknown reasons,

33% of cases are attributable to the male, 33% to the female. (The remaining 33 % are either both or the cause can't be identified.)

men worldwide are producing fewer sperm than a few decades ago. Some scientists believe certain pesticides, which have estrogen-like effects, may be linked to the declining count. Alcohol and tobacco use lower sperm production and should be avoided if there is difficulty conceiving.

Nutrition Connection

While nutrition is not a leading cause of infertility, it's important for both men and women to consume a healthful diet to enhance the chance of conceiving and delivering a healthy baby.

Eat a balanced diet that's rich in essential nutrients. Using oral contraceptives for 5 years or more may cause reduced reserves of vitamins B6, B12, C, and E, as well as calcium, zinc, and other minerals. Inadequate zinc intake may also lower male fertility. And even for men who are not deficient, evidence suggests that vitamin B12 (found in all animal products) may improve sperm count and motility. Eat foods rich in these nutrients—fruits and vegetables for vitamin C; milk and low-fat yogurt for calcium; and fortified breads and cereals, lean meat, poultry,

and seafood for the B vitamins as well as iron, zinc, and other minerals.

Eat foods rich in folate or take supplements. Doctors advise women who are pregnant, or who may become pregnant, to consume lots of folate-rich foods or take folic acid supplements to lessen the risk of having children with neural tube defects such as spina bifida. Good dietary sources of folate include fortified breakfast cereals, leafy greens, legumes, and orange juice.

Limit alcohol. Alcohol is known to reduce fertility in both women and men.

Limit coffee. Researchers at Johns Hopkins University found that women who drank more than three cups of coffee a day reduced their chances of conceiving in any given month by 25%.

Go for B12. Other evidence suggests that vitamin B12 (found in all animal products) may improve sperm count and motility, even in men who are not B12 deficient.

Beyond the Diet

Treatment of infertility depends on many factors, including ages of both partners, the length of infertility, and personal preferences. With a little advice and technology, a couple may be able to conceive. Here are general suggestions and approaches:

Avoid smoking. Smoking reduces fertility in both women and men.

Maintain a healthy weight. Any woman who is considering becoming pregnant should try to achieve her ideal weight before conception. Women who are underweight at conception may have anemia during pregnancy, and the baby may be more at risk for health problems. An overweight woman should diet before trying to conceive; this also lowers her risk of developing high blood pressure or diabetes during pregnancy.

Talk to your doctor or see a fertility specialist. See a doctor to determine the cause of infertility. Depending on the cause, fertility drugs, assisted reproductive technology, or surgery may be recommended.

INFLAMMATORY BOWEL DISEASE

FOODS THAT HARM
Dairy, fried foods, artificial sweeteners, or any other trigger foods
Alcohol
Caffeinated beverages

FOODS THAT HEAL
Water
Bananas
Rice
Applesauce
Toast
White meat
Poultry

FOODS TO LIMIT
Bran
Whole grains
Nuts
Dried fruits

Inflammatory bowel disease (IBD) is an umbrella term for chronic conditions marked by gastrointestinal tract inflammation. Two of the most common conditions are ulcerative colitis and Crohn's disease. Ulcerative colitis is more localized than Crohn's disease but in both cases, the immune system responds abnormally to normal substances in the intestines, such as food and bacteria. To fight off the invader, your body sends white blood cells into the lining of the intestines, and the result is chronic inflammation, which causes symptoms such as bloody stools, cramping, diarrhea, and appetite loss.

Nutrition Connection

While diet doesn't cause IBD and can't cure it, some foods may ease symptoms while others may trigger flare-ups. These are different for each person, so you may need to do a little detective work to tailor an eating plan that works for you. The following suggestions may help:

Eat 5 to 6 smaller meals. Spacing smaller meals throughout the day, rather than having three large meals, puts less strain on your intestinal tract.

Drink lots of fluids but avoid alcohol. This can help prevent dehydration, kidney problems, or gallstones. Alcohol can worsen intestinal bleeding, lowers the body's immunity, and may contribute to malnutrition. Taking in liquid at the same time as food, though, may sometimes cause diarrhea, so do your drinking in between meals.

Identify your trigger foods. Try eliminating any foods that seem to create problems, such as dairy, fried foods, artificial sweeteners, or spices. Add them back in one at a time, and keep a diary of symptoms.

Stick to your safe foods. While these are different for everyone, most people find that the classic BRAT (bananas, rice, applesauce, toast) diet works to soothe symptoms. Chicken, turkey, and other white meat is also usually well tolerated.

Limit foods high in fiber. High-fiber foods are often improperly digested and passed through to the colon where they can be digested by bacteria. This may cause bacterial overgrowth, which in turn can exacerbate the disease, irritate the intestines, and make diarrhea worse. In-soluble fiber, such as that found in bran, whole grains, nuts, and dried fruits, tends to be more irritating than soluble fiber, such as that found in oats.

Discuss other ways of obtaining nutrition. The most severe cases of Crohn's may require total parenteral nutrition (TPN), in which all nutrients are given intravenously. TPN is most beneficial for patients who need to rest their intestinal tract or are unable to absorb nutrients from eating. This approach also benefits children whose growth is being stunted by inadequate nutrition. Because it can be administered at home, TPN allows for a more normal lifestyle.

Beyond the Diet

Because ulcerative colitis is usually local-ized to the colon, surgery to remove the colon is considered a cure. For patients with Crohn's disease, however, while surgery to remove diseased parts of the bowel may provide some relief, the disease usually recurs. Some medications, such as 5-ASA medications and corticosteroids, are used to treat both conditions. In addition, try the following:

Stop smoking. Smoking is a risk factor for Crohn's disease and can actually worsen your symptoms. Ask your doctor for help in quitting.

Practice relaxation techniques. Stress can worsen IBD symptoms, so mind-body exercises such as yoga, meditation, and tai chi can be helpful.

Move your body. Although exercise is the last thing you may feel like doing, try to be more active. Doing so eases stress in addition to helping maintain overall health.

Consider hypnosis. At least one study suggests that hypnotherapy can help reduce IBD symptoms.

Get psychological support. Depression and anxiety are common among people with IBD, especially children. Cognitive behavioral therapy can help deal with symptoms and improve your coping skills.

Talk to your doctor about taking supplements. Even Crohn's patients who maintain a normal diet may develop nutritional deficiencies because of poor nutrient absorption. High-dose vitamins should only be taken under a doctor's supervision; for example, those who develop vitamin B12 deficiency often need to take it by injection if they lack the intestinal substances to metabolize it. Patients with severe symptoms or those who have had extensive surgery may need a special high-calorie liquid formula, either as a nutritional supplement or as a meal replacement. In unusual cases, an elemental diet—a low-fat, easy-to-digest formula—may be prescribed.

INSOMNIA

FOODS THAT HARM
Alcohol
Coffee and other caffeinated drinks

FOODS THAT HEAL
Milk and honey
Turkey sandwich
Banana

There's more to insomnia than just trouble falling asleep. Some people fall asleep just fine, but wake up in the middle of the night and can't get back to sleep. Others sleep through the night but wake too early in the morning. And still others appear to sleep through the night with no problem, but never wake rested.

Insomnia can be one of the symptoms of anxiety, depression, or stress, or it can be caused by a medical problem. Overcoming the underlying cause of these disorders is essential to improving the quality of sleep, but attention to nutrition and other aspects of sleep hygiene can also help.

Nutrition Connection

Better nutrition and a few tips can help you sleep better. Here's how:

Sip warm milk and honey. Milk contains sleep-inducing tryptophan, which works by increasing the amount of serotonin, a natural sedative, in the brain. But you need carbs—like honey—to get tryptophan into your brain. A turkey sandwich provides another sleep-inducing combination of tryptophan and carbohydrates. A banana with milk gives you vitamin B6, which helps convert tryptophan to serotonin.

Watch your nighttime eating and drinking. A light snack at bedtime can promote sleep, but too much food can cause digestive discomfort that leads to wakefulness People who suffer from heartburn or acid reflux should especially avoid late, heavy meals that delay the emptying of the stomach. Stop drinking any fluids a couple of hours before bed to reduce the chances of having to get up in the night.

Avoid caffeine and alcohol. Caffeine is known to affect the quality of sleep so it's best to cut it out about 8 hours before bed. Alcohol may make you sleepy but it can disrupt REM sleep and also dehydrate you, leaving you more tired the next day.

Beyond the Diet

Manage stress. If anxiety is keeping you up at night, try yoga, meditation, or a journal.

Check your medications. Many medications can interfere with sleep, including beta-blockers, thyroid medication, decongestants, corticosteroids, medications with caffeine, and certain antidepressants like the selective serotonin reuptake inhibitors (SSRIs). Talk to your doctor about changing dosages or medication.

Create a bedtime ritual. Go to sleep and get up at about the same times every day, and follow the same bedtime preparations each night, such as a reading in bed, or listening to soothing music. But avoid scary movies or novels.

Take a hot bath. A study published in the journal *Sleep* found that women with in-

WHO'S AFFECTED?
- Women
- Anyone under a lot of stress
- People with depression
- Those who are overweight and obese, especially if they have sleep apnea
- People who have pain such as from arthritis, heartburn, a sore back, headache, or fibromyalgia

QUICK TIP:
Try the herb valerian

Valerian that is brewed into a tea or taken as a capsule or tincture can reduce the time it takes to fall asleep and produce a deep, satisfying rest. Melatonin can also help induce sleep.

somnia who took a hot bath for about 90 to 120 minutes slept much better that night.

Make your bedroom sleep friendly. Keep it dark, quiet, and cool. Use your bedroom only for sleeping and sex, not for working or watching TV. Avoid late-night news casts, scary movies, and Stephen King novels.

INTERSTITIAL CYSTITIS

WHO'S AFFECTED?
- Young and middle-age women
- People who have experienced bladder trauma or surgery
- People who have experienced spinal cord trauma

FOODS THAT HARM
Hot peppers
Coffee
Cranberry juice
Artificial sweeteners

FOODS THAT HEAL
Water
Fresh fruits and vegetables
Dairy products

FOODS TO LIMIT
Processed foods containing preservatives and other chemicals

Interstitial cystitis (IC) is a chronic, severely debilitating disease that affects the bladder. Its symptoms include urgent and frequent urination, pelvic pain, and painful intercourse; its causes are unknown. The problems can come and go, flare-ups are common, and the condition usually lasts a lifetime. Typically, IC is diagnosed only after ruling out a variety of other conditions, including sexually transmitted diseases, bladder cancer, and bladder infections. And because doctors often misdiagnose IC as an infection, years can elapse before the condition is accurately diagnosed.

Nutrition Connection

Here are some food strategies to help alleviate the symptoms of IC:

Try an elimination diet. Many foods are reported to worsen symptoms, but people react differently to different foods. Rather than eliminating suspected food triggers from your diet all at once, try eliminating one at a time for several days, and note whether or not your symptoms got better. Some common triggers include coffee, cranberry juice, and hot peppers.

Avoid trigger foods. Once you've identified your food triggers, be especially careful not to eat them when you're starting a new drug therapy.

Consider going organic. Since many people with IC are sensitive to food additives, including preservatives, artificial sweeteners and flavorings, and other chemicals, try to buy fresh organic food whenever you can.

Beyond the Diet

Find a drug regime that works. Medications used to treat IC include ibuprofen, tricyclic antidepressants, diphenhydramine, and pentosan polysulfate, the only drug specifically approved by the FDA to treat IC.

Get some PT. Physical therapy can be extremely helpful for some IC symptoms, particularly if you also experience pelvic pain. Seek out a therapist who is experienced in treating people with IC.

IRON OVERLOAD

FOODS THAT HARM
   Iron supplements and iron-rich
      multivitamins
   Alcohol (if there is liver damage)
   High doses of vitamin C
   Raw shellfish

FOODS TO LIMIT
   Iron-rich foods, such as lean red
      meats and organ meats
   Dark green leafy vegetables

Hemachromatosis is the most common form of iron overload disease and can be inherited or caused by anemia or alcoholism. Left untreated, it can cause irreversible damage to the body.

Hemachromatosis causes the body to absorb and store excess iron. The body stores the excess in muscles and vital organs, specifically the liver, heart, and pancreas. An iron overload does not produce symptoms until a harmful amount has accumulated in the body. The symptoms and signs often surface in middle age, and they include a ruddy complexion, fatigue, joint and intestinal pain, and an irregular heartbeat. As the liver becomes damaged, jaundice may develop. Unless treated, the damage can lead to serious conditions such as cancer, heart disease, and liver disease.

Nutrition Connection

The main focus in dealing with hemachromatosis should be avoiding excess iron intake and foods that increase iron absorption.

Avoid eating foods high in vitamin C with iron-rich plant foods. For those who are predisposed to store extra iron, this combination may be harmful. Consume the vitamin C items between meals.

Be careful with multivitamins and supplements. Unless prescribed by a doctor, supplements containing iron and large doses of vitamin C should not be taken. Some experts advise that anyone who is contemplating taking a vitamin C supplement should first have a blood test to measure iron levels.

Avoid alcohol. Alcohol may cause liver damage.

Avoid raw shellfish. Those with hereditary hemachromatosis are prone to infections, particularly ones caused by bacteria in raw shellfish.

Beyond the Diet

If anyone in your family has hemochromatosis, it's important to get screened by a physician who can help you manage the disease before it inflicts any damage to your organs. Make note of the following steps:

Receive an in-depth diagnosis. Your doctor may run blood tests to diagnose an iron overload. In some cases, a test for a gene mutation or a liver biopsy may be necessary.

Look at blood removal. This safe and effective treatment, which is just like donating blood, involves periodic removal of 1 pt (0.5 L) or so of blood, which reduces iron levels by forcing the body to use some of its stores to make new red blood cells.

WHO'S AFFECTED?
- About 43 million Americans of Northern European descent carry the single or double copies of the hemachromatosis gene and are susceptible to developing the disease
- 100,000 Canadians of Northern European descent have hereditary hemachromatosis
- Secondary hemachromatosis affects people who have anemia, alcoholism, and other disorders

10 years or more of taking iron supplements or having blood transfusions may lead people to suffer iron overload.

INTERACTION WARNING:
When Food and Medicine Don't Mix

In our body, drugs share the same route of absorption and metabolism as nutrients, which creates the potential for interactions. Foods can affect drug action in many ways. The most common interaction is when foods interfere with absorption, which can make a drug less effective. Nutrients or other components of food can also interfere with a drug's metabolism, or how it is broken down in the body, and vice versa.

FOOD-DRUG INTERACTIONS

Here are some of the most common prescription and over-the-counter medications that may interact with everyday foods. Talk with your doctor if you have any concerns about medications that you're taking.

DRUGS	EFFECTS AND PRECAUTIONS
Antibiotics	
Cephalosporins, penicillin	Take on an empty stomach to speed absorption of drugs.
Ciprofloxacin	Avoid dairy products, caffeine, and supplements that contain calcium, iron, or zinc for 2 hours before and after taking the medication.
Erythromycin	Don't take with fruit juice or wine, which decrease the drug's effectiveness.
Sulfa drugs	These increase the risk of vitamin B12 deficiency.
Tetracycline	Dairy products decrease the drug's efficacy. It lowers vitamin C absorption.
Anticoagulants	
Warfarin	Foods high in vitamin K can reduce the drug's effectiveness. Do not increase or decrease the usual intake of broccoli, spinach, kale, brussels sprouts, or cabbage.
Anticonvulsants	
Dilantin, phenobarbital	These increase the risk of anemia and nerve problems due to a deficiency of folate and other B vitamins.
Antidepressants	
Fluoxetine	Reduces appetite and can lead to excessive weight loss.
Lithium	A low-salt diet increases the risk of lithium toxicity; excessive salt reduces drug's efficacy.
MAO inhibitors	Foods high in tyramine (aged cheeses, processed meats, legumes, wine, beer, among others) can bring on a hypertensive crisis.
Tricyclics	Many foods, especially legumes, meat, fish, and foods high in vitamin C, reduce absorption of the drugs.
Asthma Drugs	
Pseudoephedrine	Avoid caffeine, which increases feelings of anxiety and nervousness.
Theophylline	Charbroiled foods and a high-protein diet reduce absorption. Caffeine increases the risk of drug toxicity.
Cholesterol-Lowering Drugs	
Cholestyramine	It increases the excretion of folate and vitamins A, D, E, and K.
Gemfibrozil	Avoid fatty foods, which decrease the drug's efficacy.

DRUGS	EFFECTS AND PRECAUTIONS
Heartburn and Ulcer Medications Antacids	These interfere with the absorption of many minerals; for maximum benefit, take medication 1 hour after eating.
Cimetidine, famotidine, sucralfate	Avoid high-protein foods, caffeine, and other items that increase stomach acidity.
Antihypertensives, Heart Medications ACE inhibitors	Take on an empty stomach to improve the absorption of the drugs.
Alpha-blockers	Avoid caffeine, which increases the risk of an irregular heartbeat.
Beta-blockers	Take on an empty stomach; food, especially meat, increases the drugs' effects and can cause dizziness and low blood pressure.
Digitalis	Avoid taking with milk and high-fiber foods, which reduce absorption. Digitalis increases potassium loss.
Diuretics	These increase the risk of potassium deficiency.
Potassium-sparing diuretics	Unless a doctor advises otherwise, don't take diuretics with potassium supplements or salt substitutes, which can cause potassium overload.
Thiazide diuretics	These increase the reaction of MSG.
Hormone Preparations Oral contraceptives	Salty foods increase fluid retention. Drugs reduce the absorption of folate, vitamin B6, and other nutrients; increase intake of foods high in these nutrients to avoid deficiencies.
Steroids	Salty foods increase fluid retention. Increase intake of foods high in calcium, vitamin K, potassium, and protein to avoid deficiencies.
Thyroid drugs	Iodine-rich foods lower the drugs' efficacy.
Laxatives Mineral oils	Overuse can cause a deficiency of vitamins A, D, E, and K.
Painkillers Aspirin and stronger non-steroidal anti-inflammatory drugs	Always take with food to lower the risk of gastrointestinal irritation; avoid taking with alcohol, which increases the risk of bleeding. Frequent use of these drugs lowers the absorption of folate and vitamin C.
Codeine	Increase fiber and water intake to avoid constipation.
Sleeping Pills, Tranquilizers Benzodiazepines	Never take with alcohol. Caffeine increases anxiety and reduces the drugs' efficacy.

THE BOTTOM LINE

- Some food-drug interactions affect the efficacy of medications and absorption of nutrients.
- A few of these interactions can cause serious illness or even death.
- Refer to the chart and talk with your doctor.

I

IRRITABLE BOWEL SYNDROME

WHO'S AFFECTED?

- More than 37 million Americans and 5 million Canadians
- Occurs more in women than men, especially during menstrual periods
- People with a family history of IBS

FOODS THAT HARM
Fatty and fried foods
Sugar alcohols such as sorbitol, lactitol, mannitol, and maltitol

FOODS THAT HEAL
Water
Whole grain breads and cereals
Berries
Lentils
Artichokes
Bananas

Irritable bowel syndrome (IBS) is often characterized by abnormal muscle contractions in the intestines, resulting in too little or too much fluid in the bowel. Symptoms vary markedly from one person to another.

Some people experience urgent diarrhea. Others experience the type called spastic colon, with alternating bouts of diarrhea and constipation as well as abdominal pain, cramps, bloating, gas, and nausea, particularly after eating.

There are no tests for IBS, which is diagnosed by ruling out colitis, cancer, and other diseases. Although it may be aggravated by food intolerances or allergies, no specific cause has been established. It may be worsened by stress and emotional conflict, but it is not a psychological disorder.

Nutrition Connection

Various dietary factors can play a major role in exacerbating or calming IBS. While both the trigger foods and effects vary from person to person, these general guidelines will help eliminate some discomfort and some of the other symptoms:

Eat several small meals. Avoid eating large meals and instead space meals out over the course of a day. This can reduce the increase in bowel contractions and diarrhea.

Eat slowly. Eating too quickly may increase swallowed air, which promotes irritating intestinal gas. Also, poorly chewed foods can be more difficult to digest.

Drink lots of water. To maintain adequate fluid, drink at least eight glasses of water or other beverages daily, but avoid such potential bowel irritants as alcohol and caffeine.

Avoid fatty foods. Most doctors advise against eating fried and other fatty foods because fat is the most difficult nutrient to digest.

Closely monitor fiber intake. Whole grain products and other high-fiber foods can pose problems for some IBS sufferers who have chronic diarrhea. On the other hand, if constipation is the predominant symptom, a diet that includes ample fresh fruits and vegetables, whole grain breads and cereals, nuts and seeds, and other high-fiber foods is usually recommended.

Consider psyllium seeds. For persistent constipation, ask your doctor about taking ground psyllium seeds or another high-fiber laxative. Avoid chronic laxative use, which can lead to vitamin and nutritional deficiencies.

Avoid sugar alcohols. The sugar substitutes sorbitol, lactitol, mannitol, and malti-

QUICK TIP:
Take peppermint oil capsules
Take one or two enteric-coated capsules of peppermint oil between meals. The oil should not be taken by people suffering from acid reflux disease.

tol are used in a variety of foods and can trigger IBS symptoms in some people. For others, the lactose in dairy products and possibly fructose can exacerbate symptoms.

Know which fiber you need. Insoluble fiber helps to bulk up stools and ease elimination, relieving IBS-associated constipation. Foods high in soluble fiber absorb water and are helpful for bouts of diarrhea.

Consider probiotics. Recent research has found that probiotics may help relieve the symptoms of IBS. Probiotics have been shown to normalize bowel function in those suffering from IBS (For more information about probiotics, see page 16.)

Beyond the Diet

Because IBS differs from person to person, it's essential to develop an individualized regimen to treat your symptoms. Beyond the dietary modifications described above, try the following:

Track your triggers. The first step in learning to control IBS symptoms is recognizing the factors that may trigger symptoms. A diary that records IBS symptoms along with all foods and beverages ingested and stressful events can help pinpoint possible culprits.

De-stress. It is common for stress to exacerbate IBS symptoms, so it is important to make an effort to develop effective relaxation techniques, such as meditation, yoga, and biofeedback.

Exercise. Being active can be very therapeutic for people with IBS because it helps reduce stress: It can also normalize bowel function if constipation is a problem.

Look to medications for relief. A doctor may prescribe medications to quell abnormal muscle contractions and alleviate diarrhea. Some recent research suggests that bacterial overgrowth in the bowel may be a cause of IBS. In one study, 78% of those with IBS were found to have bacterial overgrowth in the small intestine, and antibiotics eliminated the disease in half of those who got rid of the overgrowth.

20% of all adults are affected by irritable bowel syndrome.

JAUNDICE

FOODS THAT HARM
Alcohol

FOODS THAT HEAL
Lean meat
Poultry
Fish
Eggs
Dairy products
Quinoa
Lentils

FOODS TO LIMIT
Fatty and fried foods
Sugary foods

WHO'S AFFECTED?

- Those who have liver disease, such as hepatitis, cirrhosis, or cancer
- Those with blood disorders, such as hemolytic anemia
- Those with genetic syndromes, such as Gilbert's syndrome
- Those who have blockage of bile ducts
- Infants

A yellowing of the skin and the whites of the eyes is the hallmark of jaundice. This condition typically occurs when bilirubin, a by-product of bile, builds up in the blood.

There are three general types of jaundice: The most common variety is hepatitis, an inflammation of the liver, or another liver disorder. Obstructive jaundice usually results from gallstones or another gallbladder disease. And the least common type involves some sort of abnormality in bilirubin metabolism. Several other rare forms of jaundice are inherited disorders.

Newborns also develop infant jaundice during the first few days of life, typically caused by a liver that is not fully functional. There are usually no other symptoms, and the condition often clears up within a week as the liver matures.

Nutrition Connection

Some types of jaundice resolve themselves with the help of a nutritious, well-balanced diet, although it may take several weeks. The following guidelines will help:

Eat small, frequent meals. Several small meals a day may be more manageable, as those who have jaundice often experience a decrease in appetite and an increase in nausea as the day progresses. In such cases, eat as much as possible at breakfast, then intersperse smaller meals throughout the day with a nutritious snack, such as a milk shake or an enriched liquid drink.

Eat a diet high in protein if you suffer from hepatitis. Consume a healthy diet with sufficient protein daily, from both animal and vegetable sources. The best sources are lean meat, poultry, fish, eggs, dairy products, and a combination of legumes, such as lentils and grain products, such as quinoa.

Avoid fatty foods. Fried and very fatty foods are difficult to digest. A small amount of fat is acceptable to provide needed calories and add flavor, so opt for fats in dairy and eggs, which are easier to digest than fatty meats or fried foods.

Avoid alcohol. Alcohol places added stress on an already sick liver. It may be tolerated after recovery, but some liver disorders mandate total abstinence from alcohol for life.

Avoid sweets. Because they may squelch the appetite for more nutritious foods, it is best to avoid sweets.

60% of all newborns have jaundice.

WHO'S AFFECTED?

- Anyone who crosses two or more time zones can suffer the effects of jet lag

Beyond the Diet

Treatment and lifestyle changes will vary. Many conditions can cause jaundice, so it's best to consult a medical professional.

JET LAG

FOODS THAT HEAL
Water
Cucumber
Celery
Watermelon
Grapes
Papaya

FOODS TO LIMIT
Alcohol
Caffeine

Jet lag occurs when your body's internal clock becomes disrupted after you cross time zones. It causes fatigue, insomnia, "brain fog," and even constipation or diarrhea in some people. By adjusting your diet ahead of time through a series of feasting and fasting, you can trick your body to be on the right time.

Nutrition Connection

Lose the booze. Eschew alcoholic drinks the day before your flight, during the flight, and the day after the flight. Alcohol can dehydrate you and also disrupts your sleeping schedule.

Ditch the caffeine. As with alcohol, caffeine dehydrates you and disrupts sleep, plus it can put nervous fliers even more on edge. Don't drink caffeinated beverages the day before, during the flight, or just after your flight.

Eat your water. In addition to drinking lots of water, bring watery fruits and vegetables, such as cucumbers, celery, watermelon, grapes, and papaya, as snacks.

Alternate fasting and feasting. The late Charles F. Ehret, PhD, who was a senior scientist and circadian rhythm expert at the Argonne National Laboratory in Lemont, Illinois, developed a 4-day anti–jet lag diet that featured alternating days of feasting and fasting. That diet was tested in 2002 on 186 National Guard personnel who were deployed nine time zones away. Of the volunteers, 134 used the diet and 52 did not. The dieters had significantly less jet lag than the nondieters.

Beyond the Diet

Ease the symptoms of jet lag with these guidelines:

Prepare in advance. If your trip will last longer than a few days, start to adjust your body clock to the new time zone before you leave.

QUICK TIP: Try melatonin

A 2005 MIT study suggests that taking a dose of 0.3 mg to 5 mg can ease jet lag for people crossing five or more time zones.

Harness the sun. Sunlight helps you reset your body clock when you've reached your destination.

Take an air stroll. Make sure to walk around the plane every hour or so and jiggle your legs frequently. Stretch your body as often as you can.

KIDNEY DISEASE

FOODS THAT HARM
Salty foods, such as pickles

FOODS THAT HEAL
Water
Cranberry juice
Lemon juice

FOODS TO LIMIT
Berries
Soybeans
Beet greens
Quinoa
Chocolate
Tea

Kidney disease may be either a primary condition, such as kidney stones, or a consequence of other disorders, such as hypertension, atherosclerosis, or diabetes—all of which can severely damage the organ's blood vessels. Older men are susceptible to kidney infections stemming from enlargement of the prostate. Pregnant women and people with diabetes are vulnerable to infections of the urinary tract. Side effects from drugs are common and preventable causes of serious kidney disorders.

Kidney stones form when crystalline minerals and acid salts stick together and form clumps in the kidneys. This common

WHO'S AFFECTED?
- More than 12 million North Americans
- Men with prostate enlargement
- Pregnant women
- Those taking some prescription medications

K

condition occurs when your urine contains more of these substances than the fluids in the urine can dilute. Symptoms include intense pain in the side and back, below the ribs; pain when urinating; pink, red, or brown urine; or urinating more than usual.

Inflammation of the kidney—known medically as nephritis—may result from a bacterial infection or a number of other causes, including side effects of drugs. Kidney infections, like stones, require a doctor's intervention and must be treated with antibiotics.

10% of people ages 20 and older in the U.S. have chronic kidney disease.

Kidney failure may be either a temporary response to acute shock or injury or a severe long-term state necessitating drastic treatment. Acute kidney failure may be caused by severe infection, burns, poisoning (including drug effects or interactions), surgery, or kidney injury. When the problem is resolved, function usually returns to normal. Chronic kidney failure may be caused by untreated hypertension, poorly controlled diabetes, or an inborn condition. Severe chronic, or endstage, kidney failure requires regular dialysis—in which a machine removes waste products from the blood—or where possible, a kidney transplant.

Old School
People with kidney stones should cut down on calcium-rich foods.

New Wisdom
Adequate calcium intake actually reduces the risk of calcium oxalate stones.

Nutrition Connection

Diet is crucial in treating kidney problems. If you have a serious kidney disorder, your doctor will probably refer you to a clinical dietitian for advice concerning changes to your diet. The allowable types and portions of foods differ, depending upon the type and severity of the kidney disorder. Here are some basic guidelines:

Drink lots of fluids to prevent kidney problems. Healthy people can prevent kidney disorders by drinking plenty of liquids to flush the urinary system and replace lost fluids. If you have had kidney stones, regardless of the type of stone, it's essential to drink enough liquids to maintain fluid balance and flush away the minerals that accumulate to form stones. People who have had nephritis and are prone to urinary tract infections may benefit from a daily glass of cranberry juice, which helps prevent recurrences. Lemon juice, which contains citric acid, has been shown to decrease urinary calcium excretion.

Limit foods high in oxalates but don't reduce essential minerals if you have kidney stones. Most kidney stones contain calcium oxalate. Although it's not entirely clear that reducing your intake of calcium-rich or oxalate-rich foods reduces the risk of forming stones, you may want to limit them somewhat. Oxalate-rich foods include berries, soybeans, dark green leafy vegetables like beet greens, whole grains like quinoa, chocolate, and tea. Protein is also known to play a role in the formation of stones, possibly by increasing the acidity of urine. However, eliminating all of these foods depletes the diet of essential vitamins and minerals, so don't take a drastic approach.

Follow these general recommendations, in case of kidney failure. Restrict phosphorus, potassium, protein, and salt. Fluids must be monitored: too little, and the electrolytes are out of balance; too much, fluid retention causes edema and electrolyte problems and contributes to high blood pressure and perhaps congestive heart failure. Protein consumption needs must be adjusted as kidney function, dialysis, or stress levels change. Studies show that if protein intake is limited to about 0.5 g per pound (1 g per kg) of body weight per day, the patient on dialysis will receive the essential amino acids but reduce the risk of further kidney damage. Proteins from fish, egg whites, and legume and grain combinations are preferable to those in meat because they contain less saturated fat.

Seek specialized care. Kidney failure requires highly specialized medical care. No changes in diet should be made without a doctor's approval.

Beyond the Diet

In addition to dietary changes, the following considerations may be part of preventing or managing kidney disease:

Seek help sooner, rather than later. If you suspect you have kidney stones, see a doctor right away.

Watch your medications. Acetaminophen, aspirin, and other nonsteroidal anti-inflammatory drugs (NSAIDs) are among the nonprescription drugs that can damage kidneys. Combining aspirin and acetaminophen is especially damaging.

Recurrence of kidney stones can be prevented with medications that address the specific types of mineral stone your body is prone to making. Talk to your doctor.

LACTOSE INTOLERANCE

FOODS THAT HARM
Milk
Soft cheeses

FOODS THAT HEAL
Lactose-free dairy products
Broccoli
Fortified and enriched breads
Fortified and enriched juices
Canned salmon
Pinto beans
Rhubarb
Spinach

FOODS TO LIMIT
Yogurt
Hard cheeses

WHO'S AFFECTED?
- More than 37 million North Americans

Lactose intolerance, the inability to digest milk sugar, is very common. Lactose is the natural sugar found in milk and milk products. If you don't have enough enzymes to break down the lactose in the food you eat, you will experience a variety of unpleasant symptoms such as gas, bloating, diarrhea, and cramps.

Lactose intolerance should not be confused with milk allergy, which is hypersensitivity to the proteins in dairy products. If you are allergic to milk, consuming a lactose-reduced product will not prevent a reaction.

Nutrition Connection

You can control symptoms of lactose intolerance by choosing a diet that limits dairy products. Here are general guidelines:

Read labels carefully. Lactose is found in dairy products, including milk, yogurt, and cheese. Such dairy products can be an ingredient or component of various food products such as cookies, breads, processed meats, hot dogs, some artificial sweeteners, and even some medications. When reading labels, look for milk, milk solids, cream, whey, cheese flavors, curds, and nonfat milk powder.

Eat lactose-reduced products. For people with more severe intolerance who still want dairy products, grocery stores sell lactose-free dairy products.

70% of people of African and Asian descent are partly or entirely lactose intolerant after 4 years of age.

Stick to low-lactose foods. Most lactose-intolerant people can consume cultured dairy products such as yogurt because the bacteria used in fermentation use up most of the lactose for fuel. Others include hard cheeses, such as cheddar, edam, and gouda.

Try slowly adding milk to your diet. Most lactose-intolerant people can consume some milk without much discomfort. Try ¼ cup of milk and gradually increase the amount. You'll find, in time, your tolerance will increase. Additionally, drink milk with meals, never on an empty stomach.

Get calcium from other sources. If you are very intolerant, other calcium-rich foods include broccoli, fortified and enriched breads and juices, canned salmon, pinto beans, rhubarb, and spinach.

Eat foods rich in vitamin D. Since D is also needed for strong bones, eat eggs, salmon, and yogurt if you can't consume foods rich in calcium, since both nutrients are needed for strong bones. Talk to your doctor about adding a supplement.

Beyond the Diet

Although there is no cure for lactose intolerance, there are ways you can still enjoy dairy products without suffering the symptoms. Here are some recommendations:

Take enzymes. Pharmacies carry enzyme drops that can be added to milk and enzyme tablets that can be taken before eating dishes containing dairy products, to help your body break down lactose.

Consider probiotics. Probiotics are living organisms found in foods such as yogurt and kefir. You can also look for probiotics in supplement form.

Avoid lactose filler. If you're severely lactose intolerant, avoid medications containing a lactose filler. Ask your doctor if substitute drugs are available.

LUPUS

FOODS THAT HARM
- Alfalfa
- Celery
- Parsnips
- Parsley
- Lemons
- Limes
- Mushrooms
- Smoked foods
- Grapefruit

FOODS THAT HEAL
- Broccoli
- Cabbage
- Cauliflower
- Spinach
- Milk
- Fortified soy and rice beverages
- Salmon
- Mackerel
- Herring

Nuts
Flaxseeds
Wheat germ

FOODS TO LIMIT
Fatty high-protein foods, especially
animal products

Lupus is a chronic autoimmune disease;
the most common type of the ailment is
called systemic lupus erythematosus (or
SLE). Symptoms include arthritic joint
pain, debilitating fatigue, and dry mouth;
a telltale sign is a rash on the face that
resembles butterfly wings. Lupus can also
damage organs throughout the body, particularly the kidneys. Although a mild disease for many, for some people, lupus can
be serious and even life threatening.

Lupus is believed to be caused by a
genetic predisposition, triggered by environmental factors, such as a virus; it may
be worsened by other factors, such as sun
exposure, infection, stress, and certain
foods and drugs.

Nutrition Connection

Because lupus is an inflammatory disease, it helps to increase your intake of
foods that fight and reduce inflammation
and support overall health. However, it's
important to be aware of foods that may
interact with certain medications. Here
are some guidelines, but discuss
any issues with your doctor or a
dietician:

Go for variety. Eat a variety of
foods that are rich in antioxidants
and nutrients. Foods such as broccoli, cabbage, and cauliflower
contain indoles which alter the
metabolism of estrogen in a way that has
a positive impact on lupus. Eating a colorful variety of fruits, vegetables, and whole
grains can also protect lupus sufferers

from heart disease in addition to providing essential nutrients.

Add omega-3s. Eat foods rich in
omega-3 fatty acids, especially oily fish,
which have anti-inflammatory effects and
may help relieve the joint pain, soreness,
and stiffness associated with lupus. Good
sources of omega-3 fatty acids include
salmon, mackerel, herring, walnuts, flaxseeds, and flax oil.

Find sources of vitamin D. Because
most people with lupus need to avoid exposure to the sun, they should make sure
their diet provides adequate amounts of
vitamin D. Good sources include milk and
fortified soy and rice beverages. Vitamin
D supplements are likely required.

Seek calcium. Because steroids increase
your risk of osteoporosis, consume plenty
of calcium-rich dairy products, fish with
bones, and dark green leafy vegetables,
like kale and spinnach. Supplements may
be required.

Eat foods rich in vitamin E. Preliminary
animal studies have found that vitamin E
may slow the progress of lupus. The best
food sources of vitamin E include nuts,
seeds, oils, and wheat germ. Talk to your
doctor before taking vitamin E in supplement form.

Avoid alfalfa in any form. Even herbal
supplements containing alfalfa worsen
lupus symptoms; other legumes may have
a similar effect.

20% of people with lupus have a parent or sibling who already has or will develop lupus.

**Avoid or limit mushrooms and some
smoked foods.** These may also cause problems for lupus sufferers.

Avoid foods containing psoralens. The majority of those with lupus experience worsening of symptoms when exposed to the sun or unshielded fluorescent light. Avoid foods containing psoralens, such as celery, parsnips, parsley, lemons, and limes, which heighten photosensitivity.

Limit high-protein, high-fat foods. Many lupus sufferers note an improvement after they decrease the consumption of fatty high-protein foods, especially animal products. Some experts recommend a vegetarian diet that allows eggs, skim milk, and other low-fat dairy products.

Beyond the Diet

The following recommendations may help prevent or manage lupus flare-ups:

Rest. The constant fatigue from lupus can take a toll. Get plenty of rest and sleep as necessary to let your body recuperate.

Protect yourself from the sun. Avoid UV light by wearing a hat and protective clothing, and always use sunscreen.

Exercise regularly. In addition to promoting overall well-being, exercise can help you recover from a flare-up, reduce your chances of getting heart disease, and fight depression.

Don't smoke. Smoking can lead to coronary artery disease. For those with lupus, smoking can greatly increase the risk of damaging your heart.

Stick to a medication regimen. Your doctor may prescribe NSAIDs or aspirin, antimalarial drugs, corticosteroids, or immune suppressors.

MEMORY LOSS

FOODS THAT HEAL
- Lean meat
- Whole grains
- Beans
- Oranges
- Cantaloupes
- Eggs
- Nuts and seeds
- Spinach
- Soybeans

Mild lapses in memory are common with age, and simple forgetfulness such as losing objects is relatively benign. Age-related memory loss may result from shrinkage of the brain's nerves, diminished production of brain chemicals, or restricted blood flow to brain tissue. Profound memory loss is a universal symptom of dementia or Alzheimer's disease. Genetic factors, head injuries, viruses, and cardiovascular disease may contribute to Alzheimer's disease.

Nutrition Connection

Some dietary factors can play a role in preventing memory loss. Consider these guidelines:

Eat a balanced diet. Protective brain nutrients include complex carbohydrates found in whole grains and breads, and B vitamins found in meat, which help ensure

WARNING! FOOD-DRUG INTERACTION

Some medications that lupus sufferers take may interact with various foods. Watch out for:

- **Grapefruit.** Although generally rcommended for most lupus patients, do not consume grapefruit or grapefruit juice if you are taking cyclosporine, a powerful immune system suppressor. Grapefruit can dramatically increase the body's ability to absorb cyclosporine, leading to severe toxicity.

- **Sodium.** If you are taking corticosteroids, cut back on salt. It will increase water retention and contribute to steroid-induced high blood pressure.

healthy nerve transmission and sufficient quantities of neurotransmitters.

Get plenty of beta-carotene and vitamin C. There is some evidence that high levels of beta-carotene and vitamin C found in oranges, cantaloupes, and many other fruits and vegetables, are associated with superior memory performance in people 65 or older. These antioxidants may delay brain aging and enhance mental longevity and fitness by combating free radicals in the brain.

Consume lots of vitamin E. In one large study, more than 4,000 people performed tests designed to assess their ability to remember facts. Those classified as having poor memory were more likely than others to have low blood levels of vitamin E, found in eggs and nuts and seeds. Other studies have found vitamin E helpful in slowing the progression of Alzheimer's disease.

Get enough iron. Studies have shown that children score better on tests of memory when their iron deficiency is corrected. Lean meat, dark leafy greens like spinach, and soybeans are good sources of iron.

Beyond the Diet

Consider these suggestions that support overall well-being and may play a hand in preserving memory:

Exercise. Exercise can help preserve brain longevity and sustain memory.

Keep learning. Take up a new hobby or do crossword puzzles. These tactics may help your mental function.

Consider supplements. Supplements such as vitamin C, beta-carotene, folate, gingko, sage oil, and phosphatidylserine—also called PS, Soy-PS, or PtdSer—may help prevent or delay memory loss, but more studies are needed. Speak to your doctor or dietitian before taking supplements.

Investigate other underlying conditions. If you have persistent episodes of memory loss, your doctor may run tests to rule out any underlying health conditions. If you're taking medications that may be causing memory loss, your physician may be able to suggest an alternative.

MENOPAUSE

FOODS THAT HEAL
Fortified and enriched cereals
Spinach
Tofu and other soy products
Nuts and seeds, especially flaxseeds
Vegetable oil

FOODS TO LIMIT
Alcohol
Coffee and other caffeinated drinks
Chocolate
Spicy foods

Doctors define menopause as the point when a woman has gone 12 months without a monthly menstrual period. The process is a result of a progressive decline in levels of the hormone estrogen. The beginning of this time of change is referred to as perimenopause, while the period after menopause is called postmenopause. Although menopause used to be viewed

M

as the beginning of old age, a majority of women today in developed countries can expect to live more than a third of their lives after menopause. It is a biological process, not a medical illness.

During menopause, fluctuations in estrogen levels can cause symptoms like hot flashes, night sweats, insomnia, vaginal dryness, difficulty concentrating, and weight gain. Some women experience few or no symptoms of menopause, while others experience severe symptoms that cause them extreme discomfort.

Menopause can also affect a woman's risk of developing certain diseases. Before menopause, a woman's hormones protect her from developing heart disease, but with the onset of menopause that protection is lost. By about 55 years of age,

QUICK TIP:
Eat ground flaxseed a day

Grind 1 to 2 Tbsp (15 to 30 mL) seeds and add to cereal, yogurt, or oatmeal. Flaxseed contains omega-3 fatty acids that support heart health and provide lignans.

women die of heart disease at approximately the same rate as men. In addition, the gradual loss of bone mass that most women experience from the age of 30 onward is drastically accelerated at menopause. This bone thinning, or osteoporosis, increases the risk of fractures, which can lead to disability and pain.

To treat milder symptoms, and to avoid development of chronic disease, women are encouraged to adopt a healthy lifestyle and to try other approaches, which can include dietary change, exercise, and herbal remedies.

Nutrition Connection

A healthy diet can help ease the symptoms of menopause and reduce the risk of chronic disease. Here are some helpful dietary strategies:

Eat foods known to reduce menopausal symptoms. Follow a diet high in whole grains, fruits, and vegetables, and low in saturated fats. It will provide you with plenty of fiber, vitamins, minerals, and bioflavonoids—all important for long-term health and to help minimize menopausal symptoms. High-fiber foods such as flaxseed also contain lignans, a phytoestrogen that helps reduce hot flashes.

Watch out for trigger foods. There are foods that can worsen symptoms like hot flashes, insomnia, and mood swings. Some common culprits are coffee, tea, chocolate, colas, alcohol, and spicy foods.

Include soy foods. Studies have shown that soy foods can help ease hot flashes. Soy foods contain a type of phytoestrogen called isoflavones, which have a weak estrogenic effect in the body. Soy foods include tofu, soybeans, soy beverages, soy nuts, and soy protein. While soy foods are safe enough, the safety and efficacy of isoflavone supplements have not been demonstrated.

Vitamin E may help. For some women, vitamin E, found in nuts, seeds, vegetable oils, green leafy vegetables, like spinach and fortified and enriched cereals, helps tame mild hot flashes. Talk to your doctor about supplements; more than 400 mg daily is not recommended.

Beyond the Diet

Some lifestyle adjustments can help you deal more easily with menopause. Here are some recommendations:

Exercise regularly. Regular exercise may help minimize mood swings and hot flashes. At least 30 minutes of exercise four to five times a week is recommended.

Learn relaxation techniques. Deep breathing, guided imagery, and yoga can all help relieve menopausal symptoms.

Consider herbs or medication. Although there have not been large clinical studies to establish efficacy for herbal remedies, you can try some of the more popular ones: black cohosh, which has been shown to help decrease depression, irritability, and insomnia; chasteberry, which helps manage fluid retention, hot flashes, and anxiety; and St. John's wort, which may help manage mild to moderate depression. Medications may also offer relief from symptoms.

MENSTRUAL PROBLEMS

FOODS THAT HARM
Fatty and highly refined foods

FOODS THAT HEAL
Apples
Pears
Whole grain and fortified and
   enriched cereals
Lean meat
Green leafy vegetables
Sunflower seeds
Nuts
Lentils
Dairy products
Soybeans
Figs
Salmon
Avocados
Potatoes
Raspberry leaf tea
Chamomile tea

FOODS TO LIMIT
Alcohol
Salty foods

Premenstrual syndrome (PMS) is the most common menstrual problem and is associated with more than 150 symptoms, most notably cramps, bloating, irritability, breast tenderness, food cravings, headache, and constipation. PMS seems to be caused by hormonal changes during the latter half of the menstrual cycle.

Other problems include heavy and irregular bleeding, which tends to occur at the beginning and end of a woman's reproductive years, and missed periods, which is most likely caused by pregnancy. However, the menstrual cycle may also be interrupted by hormonal imbalances related to obesity, diabetes, thyroid disease, a change in contraceptive pills, or an eating disorder such as anorexia nervosa. Women involved in high-level athletic training are prone to menstrual problems, because they lack the critical amount of body fat to maintain adequate estrogen levels.

Nutrition Connection

Many of the following suggestions are for PMS, which is the most common complaint, but a doctor, gynecologist, or a dietitian can help address other menstrual issues:

Eat a balanced diet. Eat regular, moderate meals, spaced throughout the day, with whole grains, legumes, vegetables, and fruits. Carbohydrate-rich foods can help by increasing production of serotonin, a brain chemical that regulates mood.

Eat foods that have a low glycemic load. Foods with a lower glycemic load (page 262) such as fiber-rich apples and pears are best because they raise blood sugar levels more slowly, helping to control appetite and possibly cravings.

WHO'S AFFECTED?
- Women in their reproductive years
- Three out of four menstruating women experience some form of premenstrual syndrome (PMS)
- 8% of women in the United States with PMS have symptoms that meet the diagnostic criteria for premenstrual dysphoric disorder, a more severe, disabling form of PMS

Avoid foods that may exacerbate PMS. Fats, highly refined foods, and caffeinated drinks should be avoided, and sodium intake should be reduced. Alcohol can trigger or worsen many symptoms and so should be avoided in the days before menstrual periods.

67% of women lose sleep during their menstrual cycle every month. Doctors attribute this form of insomnia to a rapid drop in the hormone progesterone.

Get more calcium. Calcium may help reduce mood disturbances, cramping, and bloating resulting from PMS. Some researchers believe PMS symptoms may be the result of low calcium levels, the symptoms of which are like the symptoms of PMS. Calcium sources include dairy products, fortified soy beverages, canned salmon or sardines, and leafy greens.

Add more magnesium. Women with PMS often have low magnesium levels, which may predispose them to PMS-induced headaches and depression. Foods rich in magnesium include sunflower seeds, nuts, lentils and legumes, whole grains, soybeans, figs, and green vegetables.

Boost vitamin B6. Foods rich in vitamin B6 may help alleviate PMS symptoms. Vitamin B6 may help stimulate production of serotonin and reduce anxiety and depression caused by PMS. Best food sources are beef, pork, chicken, fish, whole grain cereals, bananas, avocados, and potatoes. However, if you take supplements, do not exceed the upper limit for adults of 100 mg per day. Excess has been associated with nerve damage.

Indulge cravings carefully. It's okay to indulge in a piece of chocolate occasionally, but eating large amounts of sugary foods adds empty calories and can worsen the craving for sweets by disrupting normal blood sugar levels. Opt for healthier, fiber-rich snacks, such as whole grain crackers or fruit, which are metabolized at a slower rate than sweets and also help to prevent the constipation that some women experience as part of PMS.

Try herbal teas for painful cramps. Raspberry leaf tea contains a substance that is thought to relax the uterus and ease cramping. Chamomile tea also has anti-spasmodic action.

Try evening primrose oil. This oil, available in capsules and in liquid form, contains an essential fatty acid called gamma linolenic acid (GLA). This acid blocks the inflammatory prostaglandins that contribute to cramps and breast tenderness.

Eat lots of iron-rich foods if you bleed a lot. Although heavy bleeding is rarely a sign of a more serious condition, excessive blood flow may result in a loss of iron, increasing the risk of anemia. An adult woman needs 18 mg of iron daily. Good sources are red meat, legumes, fortified cereals, leafy green vegetables, and dried fruits. To help the body absorb iron better, foods rich in vitamin C should be eaten at the same meal.

Beyond the Diet

The following strategies can help address your menstrual issues:

Exercise. Women who exercise regularly are less likely to suffer from PMS.

Take a warm bath or use a heating pad. Both actions can help soothe cramps.

Take an anti-inflammatory. Prostaglandins, hormonelike substances that cause uterine contractions, play a part in causing menstrual cramps. Aspirin, ibuprofen, and other nonsteroidal anti-inflammatory drugs (NSAIDs) can block prostaglandin production and alleviate menstrual cramps.

Problematic periods. A woman who experiences persistently heavy or irregular periods should see a gynecologist to determine if she has a problem requiring treatment. In some instances, painful periods are related to other conditions, such as fibroid tumors or endometriosis. A woman may also be approaching menopause or have weight issues that lead to missed periods.

METABOLIC SYNDROME

See Diabetes, page 260

MIGRAINES AND OTHER HEADACHES

FOODS THAT HARM
Individual trigger foods such as aged cheeses, processed meats, fermented foods and more

FOODS TO LIMIT
Coffee and other caffeinated drinks

Headaches afflict about 70% of adults at least occasionally and provoke millions of North Americans each year to seek medical relief. Most headaches are transient and caused by tension or a temporary condition, such as a cold or the flu, but some reflect a serious underlying problem. Recurrent headaches warrant medical attention to diagnose the type and determine the best treatment.

A migraine is a one-sided, severe, throbbing or pulsating headache often accompanied by sensitivity to light and sound as well as by nausea and vomiting.

Cluster headaches, the most incapacitating of all headaches, last from 15 minutes to 3 hours and typically occurs in clusters. Often starting during sleep, they cause excruciating, stabbing pain on one side of the head, usually behind or around one eye.

Tension headaches are the most common type and are caused by muscle contractions or an imbalance of natural chemicals in the brain.

Headaches also may be due to sinusitis, an inflammation of the lining of the sinus cavities. Another type, called rebound headaches, can result from overuse of over-the-counter analgesics, prescription

WHO'S AFFECTED?

- 29.5 million Americans are affected by migraines
- Women are affected by migraines three times as often as men
- Men, especially heavy smokers or those who frequently drink alcohol, are more commonly affected by cluster headaches

pain medications and sedatives, and caffeine (which is a common ingredient in such drugs). Dental problems can cause very severe one-sided headaches, too.

The many other factors that can cause headaches include squinting for hours in bright sun, eyestrain, hunger, excessive alcohol consumption, and too little or too much sleep.

5 to 10% of children and adolescents are affected by migraines.

Nutrition Connection

The key to minimizing or avoiding headaches is to avoid the elements that cause them, some of them dietary. Here are some factors to consider:

Avoid common dietary triggers. Many foods, additives, and other dietary components can cause migraines, but the triggers vary greatly from one person to another. Keep a food diary, note what foods seem to prompt symptoms, and then eliminate them. Some common ones include: dairy products, such as aged cheeses; sourdough and other yeasty breads; fermented foods, including pickles; some legumes, especially dried beans, lentils, and soy products; nuts, seeds, and peanut butter; chocolate and cocoa; organ meats and meats that are salted, dried, cured, smoked, or contain nitrites; sardines and anchovies; many fruits, including avocados, bananas, citrus fruits, figs, grapes, pineapples, raspberries, red plums, and raisins; alcohol, especially red wine; seasonings and flavor enhancers, especially artificial sweeteners, ginger, and molasses; sulfites used as preservatives in wine and dried fruits; and monosodium glutamate (MSG).

Keep blood sugar steady. Eat regular meals, because hunger or low blood sugar can trigger a headache.

Use coffee to your advantage. The caffeine in coffee and other beverages—as well as in many over-the-counter analgesic drugs—can play a dual role in migraines. Regular and excessive ingestion can contribute to the frequency of the headaches. On the other hand, once you are completely off caffeine, you may be able to use it to fend off an impending attack, because it constricts dilated blood vessels. At the first sign of an aura or a pain, drink a cup of strong coffee or a cola, take two aspirin, and lie down in a dark, quiet room. The episode may pass within an hour or so.

Beyond the Diet

Headaches may be best managed by figuring out the causes and then avoiding them. Consider the following:

Try muscle relaxation techniques. Meditation, yoga, biofeedback, or guided imagery may all be helpful.

Take feverfew for migraines. Take one or two capsules of freeze-dried feverfew daily to reduce headache episodes. Research shows that regular feverfew intake decreases the frequency and intensity of migraine headaches and accompanying nausea. It cannot, however, stop an attack that has already started. Start slowly; feverfew can produce allergic reactions in some people. If you have no side effects, you can continue this regimen indefinitely.

Consider medications. A number of medications are available to treat migraines. Medications used to treat other headaches include acetaminophen, aspirin, ibuprofen, and naproxen. For rebound headaches, stop using drugs that contain caffeine.

MOOD DISORDERS

FOODS THAT HARM
Foods with additives, if allergic

FOODS THAT HEAL
Turkey
Milk
Eggs
Pasta
Breads
Kale
Orange juice
Corn
Asparagus
Tuna
Salmon

FOODS TO LIMIT
Caffeine
Alcohol
Sugary foods

The term *mood disorders* describes basic forms of mental illness, including different types of depression, such as postpartum depression and dysthymia; bipolar disorder, characterized by mood swings that range from depression to mania; and seasonal affective disorder (SAD), in which people are sad and moody throughout the winter months.

Nutrition Connection

While the links between diet and mood disorders are not firmly established, there has been a lot of research on the effects of certain foods and nutrients on the brain chemicals that control your mood. The following are general tips:

Consume more tryptophan. The amino acid tryptophan is used by the brain to produce serotonin, which is believed to influence mood. Food sources include turkey, milk, and eggs.

Add more carbs. Meals that are especially rich in carbs have been associated with a calming, relaxing effect. Carbohydrate-rich foods allow tryptophan to enter the brain. Feel-good food choices include pasta, breads, grains, cereals, fruits, and juices.

Lean on leafy greens. Many depressed people are deficient in folate. This essential mineral is abundant in green leafy vegetables like kale. Other sources include orange juice, lentils, corn, asparagus, peas, nuts, and seeds.

Feast on fish. Aim to eat fish three times a week or more. Researchers found that people who ate fish less than once a week had a 31% higher incidence of mild to moderate depression than people who ate fish more often.

Limit caffeine. The best-known mood-altering dietary item is caffeine, a stimulant found in coffee, tea, colas, and chocolate. While a cup of coffee may be a welcome eye-opener, too much caffeine causes palpitations, sleeplessness, and anxiety.

Limit or avoid alcohol. Second to caffeine as the most often used mood-

WHO'S AFFECTED?
- 4.3% of Americans are classified as having severe mood disorders
- Women are 50% more likely than men to experience a mood disorder over their lifetime

altering substance, alcohol is a depressant that slows down certain physiological processes. Because alcohol also interferes with sleep, it can cause irritability, anxiety, and depression.

Don't skip meals. Besides the types of food you eat, when and how much you eat can also affect your mood. Eating small amounts of food frequently through the day can keep your energy levels and mood more constant.

A NOTE ABOUT FOOD ALLERGIES

There is no evidence that food allergies, including the much-disputed "yeast sensitivity," cause emotional or behavioral changes. In some rare cases, children do have intolerances to certain food additives and these can manifest as behavioral problems. Discuss your questions with your pediatrician.

50.9% of those with mood disorders in the U.S. are receiving treatment.

Limit sugary foods. Foods made with refined sugar may have some effect on children's activity. Refined sugars enter the bloodstream quickly and produce high glucose levels that trigger adrenaline, followed by a sugar "crash."

Beyond the Diet

A combination of medication and therapy works best to address mood disorders. The following are general recommendations:

See a doctor. If you suspect that you have a mood disorder, talk to your doctor. He or she may be able to prescribe medications or refer you to a psychotherapist.

Soak up some light therapy. For those who experience SAD, light therapy or phototherapy can be effective.

Ask about medications. If any mood disorders are severe, a doctor may prescribe antidepressants, such as sertraline, paroxetine, or fluoxetine, among others. Those suffering from bipolar disorder may be prescribed mood stabilizers, such as lithium, anticonvulsants, antipsychotics, and antianxietry drugs.

Look into psychotherapy. Therapies such as cognitive behavioral therapy, family therapy, and group therapy may help an individual and his or her family better manage the disorder. Also, electroconvulsive therapy may be an option.

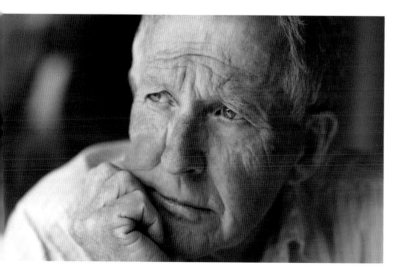

MOTION SICKNESS

FOODS THAT HEAL
Ginger
Saltines or other dry crackers
Ginger ale
Water

FOODS TO LIMIT
Alcohol
Fried and other fatty foods
Salty foods
Dairy products
Caffeinated drinks

For unknown reasons, certain people are especially sensitive to movement. Motion sickness is a fairly common condition that makes people feel sick to their stomachs when they're in moving cars, boats, trains, and airplanes.

Nutrition Connection

Common sense plays a big role when it comes to eating to ease motion sickness. You don't want to eat a heavy meal before you travel, for example. Here are some other guidelines to follow:

Add ginger to proteins. The root ginger, an essential spice for many Asian cuisines, has a scientifically proven track record for helping calm nausea and vomiting. Add about 1 Tbsp or so of chopped ginger per serving to simple fish, eggs, chicken, or turkey dishes as your pretravel meal. Bring cold ginger ale or iced ginger tea with you to sip as you travel.

Skip the chips—and milk. Eating salty foods and dairy products can worsen motion sickness, as can heavy, fatty meals.

Munch on dry crackers. These are easy on your queasy tummy.

Stay well hydrated. To maintain adequate fluid levels, drink at least eight glasses of water, ginger ale, or iced tea for 24 hours before you travel. Avoid alcohol and caffeine, which are dehydrating.

Beyond the Diet

Some proven techniques for avoiding motion sickness include:

Sit in the front. If you experience motion sickness on a car trip, try to ride in the front seat, or drive.

Skip the reading. Reading or using electronic gadgets while in a car or other moving vehicle makes many people experience motion sickness.

Get plenty of air. Keep air vents positioned toward your face or keep a window open, if possible.

Face the front. Choose a seat that faces the front on a train, and choose a seat as close to the front as possible on a boat or airplane. Request a window seat when you're flying.

Stay in the middle. When you're aboard a ship, stay in the center of the boat and focus on the horizon. Avoid going below decks when you're feeling queasy.

WHO'S AFFECTED?
- Those with inner-ear problems
- Those sensitive to movement

QUICK TIP:
Take ginger capsules

Take 250 mg of powdered gingerroot three times a day as needed for nausea symptoms.

MULTIPLE SCLEROSIS

WHO'S AFFECTED?

- About 300,000 to 425,000 North Americans
- Women are twice as likely as men to get multiple sclerosis
- White people whose family originated in Northern Europe have the highest risk

FOODS THAT HEAL

Prune juice

Berries

Whole grain breads and cereals

Split peas

Artichokes

Nuts

Papaya

Milk

Fish

Cranberry juice

Water

FOODS TO LIMIT

Alcohol

Spicy foods

Multiple sclerosis (MS) is a chronic, often disabling disease of the central nervous system that most often strikes people between the ages of 20 and 40. MS is characterized by the gradual destruction of the myelin sheaths that insulate the nerve fibers, thus robbing nerves of the ability to transmit impulses. Although the symptoms vary depending on the sites where myelin is destroyed in the brain and spinal cord, most people suffer abnormal fatigue, impaired vision, slurred speech, loss of balance and muscle coordination, difficulty chewing and swallowing, tremors, bladder and bowel problems, and, in severe cases, paralysis.

Nutrition Connection

The main role of diet for those with MS is to help control symptoms such as fatigue, constipation, urinary tract infections, and problems with chewing and swallowing. Here are guidelines to discuss with your doctor or dietician:

Think low-fat, high-fiber. A low-fat, high-fiber diet that contains fruits, vegetables, and whole grains can be helpful in managing MS by providing energy and nutrients to maintain and repair tissues, to fight infections, and to keep the risk of constipation low. Some foods include prune juice, bran cereal, raspberries, strawberries, whole wheat pastas, whole grain breads and cereals, barley, bran flakes, split peas, lentils, artichokes, peas, and broccoli.

Eat foods rich in antioxidants. Some scientists believe that free radical damage can promote the progression of MS. Antioxidants are believed to counter the effect of these free radicals, so it is prudent to include antioxidant-rich foods in your daily diet. These include fruits and vegetables for vitamin C and beta-carotene, such as oranges, carrots and papaya; vegetable oils, nuts, and seeds for vitamin E; and whole grains, nuts, and seafood for selenium.

Get plenty of vitamin D. Some studies suggest that vitamin D might prevent progression of the disease or may play other protective roles. In addition, people with MS are at risk for osteoporosis, and vitamin D plays an important role in lowering this risk. Good food sources include milk, fortified soy and rice beverages, fatty fish, and margarine.

Increase fluid intake. Constipation is aggravated by an inadequate fluid intake. Also, urinary tract infections are often a problem for people with MS, particularly when they have to undergo frequent catheterizations. Drinking cranberry juice may

QUICK TIP:
Regulate your temp

Heat worsens multiple sclerosis symptoms in many people, so make sure your air conditioners are working well in summer, avoid hot tubs, and choose swimming pools that aren't kept too warm.

help by increasing urinary acidity and creating a hostile environment for bacteria.

Avoid caffeine. If urinary incontinence is a problem, people with MS should avoid caffeinated drinks, such as coffee, tea, and colas, and save chocolate (it also contains caffeine) for an occasional treat. Caffeine has a diuretic effect and irritates the bladder.

Eat small, frequent meals. This helps to provide a constant source of energy.

Don't skip breakfast. A nutritious breakfast provides an important energy boost to start the day.

Avoid problem foods. Some people with MS have problems with bowel incontinence, which may be worsened by diet. Try eliminating suspect items such as coffee, alcohol, and spicy foods from the diet for a few days; then reintroduce them one at a time to see if the problem recurs.

Be careful with food textures. Modify food preparations to address difficulties with chewing and swallowing. For example, substitute shakes, yogurt, fruit and vegetable purees, thick soups, and puddings for firm or dry dishes.

Be wary of unproven diets. Some physicians as well as MS support groups advocate the Swank diet (named for the professor who proposed it in 1950), which eliminates most animal fats. This diet was evaluated for many years, with inconclusive results. Other diets that have

been proposed for treating MS are riskier, because they may lead to unbalanced or inadequate nutrition. Among them are liquid diets, crash diets, raw food diets, diets that restrict intake of pectin and fructose, and gluten-free regimens. None of these have been proven effective.

Look into vitamin therapy. Vitamin therapy has been promoted as helpful for people with MS. Studies suggest that vitamin D may lower the risk of developing MS. Your doctor can help determine the right dosage for you.

200 new cases of multiple sclerosis are diagnosed each week in the U.S.

Beyond the Diet

Although there is no cure, and living with MS can be difficult, these lifestyle adjustments may help to manage MS a little easier:

Don't smoke. MS sufferers often experience diarrhea or incontinence. Because nicotine can (among many other health effects) stimulate the bowel, which worsens these symptoms, it is important not to smoke.

Exercise. For those with mild to moderate MS, regular aerobic exercise can improve strength, muscle tone, balance, and coordination. It also helps relieve stress and symptoms of depression.

Rest. Address fatigue by getting plenty of sleep at night.

Watch your weight. It is especially important to maintain an appropriate weight related to height. Excess weight can add to mobility problems and can fatigue and strain the respiratory and circulatory systems. Being underweight is also undesirable, because it may decrease resistance to infection and increase the risk of developing pressure sores and other skin ulcers.

Seek emotional support. Stay connected to your friends and family, and talk to your doctor who may be able to recommend a therapist, counselor, or support group in your area for those dealing with MS.

MUSCLE CRAMPS

FOODS THAT HEAL
Bananas
Tomato juice
Milk
Water
Oranges
Melons

FOODS TO LIMIT
Caffeine

Cramps are painful spasms that mainly affect muscles in the legs and feet. A cramp generally lasts a few minutes and then ends on its own, although massage and stretching can hasten the process and certain foods may help to prevent its recurrence. Cramps can be the result of overuse, dehydration, lack of certain minerals, or blood flow to your muscles. Muscle cramps are more rarely caused by an injury, such as a pinched nerve.

Nutrition Connection

You can ward off cramps or lessen their severity by following these guidelines:

Drink plenty of water. Water maintains circulation and helps flush lactic acid and other cramp-causing waste products from the muscles. Most folks need about six to eight glasses of water a day. Drink more when exercising—about 16 oz (473 mL) for every hour of exercise.

Eat lots of high-potassium foods. A daily serving of a high-potassium food—a handful of dried fruits; a glass of tomato juice, citrus juice, or milk; a slice of melon, an orange, or a banana—can help to banish leg cramps and prevent their recurrence.

Avoid caffeine. Caffeine and nicotine constrict blood vessels, decreasing the circulation to the muscles and contributing to cramps. If cramps are a problem and you smoke, make every effort to quit—and switch to decaffeinated beverages if you haven't already done so.

Beyond the Diet

A few simple tips can help avoid cramps or diminish cramp pain:

Shut it down. If you're cramping during an exercise, it's time to stop. Ease the pain by gently massaging and stretching the affected area.

Curl your toes. The best remedy is regular exercise to tone the muscles and improve the circulation. One of the most common places for cramps to occur is the leg muscles. To relieve or prevent leg cramping, try curling and uncurling the toes a dozen times in quick succession; alternatively, straighten the leg, bend the foot upward, and then extend the foot and point the toes a dozen times in quick succession. Repeat these exercises throughout the day.

Go hot or cold. For tender muscles, apply a cold pack for about 10 minutes. For tight or tense muscles, apply a heat compress for about 10 minutes.

NAIL PROBLEMS

FOODS THAT HEAL

Lean meat

Poultry

Fish, especially salmon and
  mackeral

Citrus fruits

Dried apricots

Dark green leafy vegetables

Fortified and enriched cereals and
  breads

Legumes

Peas

Flaxseed oil

Most nail problems stem from abuse—
everything from picking and biting to
overuse of polish removers, glues, and
other harmful chemicals. In some instances, however, unhealthy nails actually
reflect a nutritional deficiency or an underlying medical problem.

Nutrition Connection

Here are a few guidelines for healthy nails:

Bulk up on protein. To make keratin, a
strong protein that's a major component in
skin, hair, and nails, the body needs high-
quality protein from lean meat, poultry,
fish, seafood, and other animal products.
A combination of grain products and legumes will also supply complete protein.

Add iron-rich foods. A common nutrition-related nail problem involves iron-
deficiency or other anemias, in which the
blood does not deliver adequate nutrients
to the nails. Increasing the consumption
of iron-rich foods—lean meat, poultry,
eggs, seafood, dried apricots, and fortified
and enriched cereals and breads—may be
enough to cure mild iron-deficiency ane-

mia. A doctor should be consulted, however, to determine whether the anemia is
caused by other nutritional deficiencies
or to chronic hidden bleeding. Never self-
treat with iron supplements; they can
lead to toxicity and many other serious
problems.

Check C levels. Vitamin C helps the human body absorb iron from plant sources.
Thus, a balanced diet should include
citrus fruits and a variety of other fresh
fruits and vegetables.

Try folate. Some types of anemia that
affect the nails are caused by a deficiency
of folate, an essential B vitamin. Whole
grains, legumes, dark green leafy vegetables, peas, nuts, and orange juice are
good sources of folate and other important
B vitamins.

Add more essential fatty acids. If your
nails are brittle or flaking, the solution
may be increasing your levels of essential
fatty acids. These are found in foods such
as fatty fish and flaxseeds.

**Make your nails as strong as a horse's
hooves.** Long ago, veterinarians discovered that biotin strengthened horses'
hooves, which are also made from
keratin. Swiss researchers
found that people who took
2.5 mg of biotin a day for
5.5 months had firmer,
harder nails. In a U.S.
study, 63% of people
taking biotin for brittle
nails experienced an
improvement.

Beyond the Diet

Keep your nails hydrated. Rub a
small amount of petroleum jelly, castor
oil, or olive oil into your cuticle and the
skin surrounding your nails every evening
before you go to bed or whenever your
nails feel dry.

WHO'S AFFECTED?

- Those who
  overuse harsh nail
  products
- People with
  nutritional
  deficiencies, such
  as protein or iron
- Those with
  underlying
  medication
  conditions such as
  lung disorders or
  infections

Old School
Gelatin, calcium, or zinc
supplements aid nail health.

New Wisdom
Gelatin lacks the amino acids
to give nails strength. And
nails contain very little
calcium or zinc.

Wear rubber gloves whenever you do housework or wash dishes. Most household chores, from gardening to scrubbing the bathroom to washing dishes, are murderous on your nails. To protect your digits from dirt and harsh cleaners, cover them with vinyl gloves whenever it's chore time.

NEURALGIA

WHO'S AFFECTED?

- About 800,000 Americans and 97,000 Canadians
- People with arthritis, diabetes, syphilis, or cancer

FOODS THAT HARM
Alcohol

FOODS THAT HEAL
Lean meat
Poultry
Fish
Spinach
Potatoes
Nuts and seeds
Wheat germ
Vegetable oils

Neuralgia is any type of throbbing pain that extends along the course of one or more of the peripheral nerves. In some cases, doctors can't find a cause; in others, the cause is an infection or underlying disease, such as arthritis, diabetes, or syphilis. Tumors, both cancerous and benign, can cause neuralgia, as do structural problems in which nerves become compressed or pinched. Sciatica, the throbbing pain that can extend from the lower back and buttocks to the feet, is one of the most common examples. Various medications, as well as arsenic and other toxins, can also produce neuralgia.

Nutrition Connection

Maintain vitamin B12 levels. A deficiency of vitamin B12, found in all animal products such as poultry and beef, can lead to degeneration of the spinal cord and widespread neuralgia as well as pernicious anemia.

Keep up vitamin B6. The long-term use of hydralazine (a powerful antihypertensive medication) or isoniazid (used to treat tuberculosis) can result in vitamin B6 deficiency, manifested by sensory loss and neuralgia. Anyone taking these drugs should follow a diet that provides extra B6. Good sources include lean meat, poultry, fish, spinach, sweet and white potatoes, watermelon, bananas, and prunes. A doctor may prescribe B6 supplements. Self-treating with high doses, however, can also damage sensory nerves.

Pump up vitamin E. In rare cases, malabsorption problems resulting in low vitamin E levels can cause a type of neuralgia. Good dietary sources include nuts, seeds, wheat germ, vegetable oils, fortified and enriched cereals, eggs, poultry, and seafood. Doctors may also give supplements of 30 to 100 mg a day.

Decrease alcohol consumption. Deficiencies of the B-complex vitamins can result in neuralgia involving numerous nerves throughout the body, a condition known as polyneuralgia or polyneuropathy. This condition often occurs in alcoholics, whose diets are generally poor.

Beyond the Diet

Medicate to ease pain. Various medications can be used to control the pain associated with neuralgia.

Investigate other treatments. Other treatments may include physical therapy, nerve ablation, or local injections of pain-relieving medications.

OBESITY

FOODS THAT HEAL
- Chickpeas
- Carrots
- Zucchini
- Broccoli
- Fish
- Chicken
- Beans
- Low-fat milk and other dairy products
- Whole wheat pasta

FOODS TO LIMIT
- Alcohol
- Sugary desserts
- Salty processed snack foods

Being overweight is the most common nutrition-related health problem in North America, affecting more than 60% of all adults. Of these, more than 24% of Canadians and 35% of Americans are considered obese and are consequently at increased risk for an early death.

Obesity can cause physical problems such as shortness of breath, skin chafing, and difficulty moving around, making it hard to enjoy a normal life. Obese people have an increased risk of coronary heart disease, high blood pressure, stroke, diabetes, and certain types of cancer. Other health consequences include damage to the weight-bearing joints. This leads to osteoarthritis and disability, which perpetuate the vicious circle by restricting movement, leading to further weight gain.

Nutrition Connection

Eating too much is the key factor in obesity and weight gain. Here are some food-related guidelines to help drop the pounds:

Limit calories. A diet providing about 1,500 calories a day for a woman and 2,000 for a man is a reasonable approach. Combined with a moderate exercise program, it should allow a loss of 1 to 2 lb (0.45 to 0.90 kg) a week. Watch empty calories. No foods need to be totally forbidden, but empty calories—those that don't provide any nutrition—such as those in alcohol, sugary desserts, and high-fat, high-salt snack foods should be limited.

Eat breakfast every day. Skipping breakfast is a lot like skipping rope: Neither gets you anywhere. Although lots of people think they'll cut calories by cutting breakfast, the opposite is true. One national U.S. health and nutrition survey found that men who eat breakfast weigh about 6 lb (2.7 kg) less than men who skip it; women weigh 9 lb (4 kg) less.

Eat high-fiber foods. Eat a bowl of brown rice topped with chickpeas and sautéed vegetables for lunch, and it's likely you won't want another bite until supper. High-fiber foods like these have few calories, little fat, and lots of bulk, which keeps you full. They're also digested slowly. A great way to get a good dose of fiber is to start your day with high-fiber cereal.

WHO'S AFFECTED?

- 35.7% of Americans and 24% of Canadians
- 20% of American children; 9% of Canadian children

85,000 new cancer cases per year are related to obesity.

Head for the salad bar. Greens and raw vegetables like carrots, zucchini, and broccoli are remarkably low in calories but high in water and slow-digesting fiber, so they tend to fill you up. But avoid creamy dressings, croutons, cheese, nuts, and other toppings that can add extra calories. Researchers have also found that people who eat a vegetarian diet weigh an average of 3 to 20% less than meat eaters.

Nosh on protein. Make it a point to eat some protein from fish, chicken, or beans with every meal (and every snack, too). Studies have shown that people on high-protein diets that are also rich in low-glycemic carbohydrates (such as fruits and vegetables, beans, and whole-wheat pasta) are less hungry and lose more weight than people on low-protein, high-carbohydrate diets.

Try low-fat dairy. People deficient in calcium tend to be hungrier. Enjoy low-fat dairy foods like milk, cheese, and yogurt to stay full and speed ftat loss.

Eat healthy nuts. Large studies have found that people who eat moderate portions of nuts regularly have a lower body mass index than those who don't. The healthy fat in nuts helps people feel full.

Avoid fad diets. Very low calorie diets or fad diets tend to lead to the yo-yo phenomenon, in which people lose weight, then quickly regain all they've lost and more. The additional weight is often even harder to shed.

Beyond the Diet

While maintaining a healthy diet is the primary way to ward off obesity, several other tips can help, including:

Buddy up. The studies are unequivocal: People who attend support groups as part of a comprehensive weight loss program lose more weight than those who go it alone. Even less formal forms of support can help. Among those who embarked on the program with friends in a University of Pennsylvania study, 95% completed the program compared to only 76% of those who dieted solo.

Move more. If you're trying to lose weight, more activity is better. An hour or even 90 minutes of moderate exercise, or 30 minutes of vigorous activity such as jogging, strenuous aerobics, or fast-paced cycling, is ideal. Of course, anything you do is better than nothing, and consistency counts.

Keep a journal. The biggest challenge is not losing weight but keeping it off. Most dieters regain all the weight they've lost within 5 years. Weighing yourself regularly and keeping track of your progress has been shown to help you maintain your results. Writing down what you've eaten and when you've exercised can not only keep you accountable, but it can help you uncover habits that may sabotage your weight loss.

Dodge obesogens. Chemical compounds that can disrupt metabolism, obesogens may lead to obesity. Bisphenol-A (BPA) in plastic bottles, high-fructose corn syrup in processed foods, and some pesticides and medications, including selective serotonin reuptake inhibitors (SSRIs), are all potential obesogens.

QUICK TIP:
Assess Your Weight

Body mass index (BMI) takes into account your height and weight to determine if your weight is healthy. Find a BMI calculator online. If your BMI is 25 to 29.9, you're overweight; 30 or more, you're obese. Another measure that's good to know is your waist circumference. An increased risk of developing heart disease, diabetes, and other health problems comes with a waist circumference greater than 35 in (88 cm) for women and greater than 40 in (102 cm) for men.

OSTEOPOROSIS

FOODS THAT HARM
- Coffee and other caffeinated drinks
- Salty foods
- High levels of protein

FOODS THAT HEAL
- Low-fat milk and other dairy foods
- Tofu
- Romaine lettuce

Cabbage

Kale

Fortified soy or rice beverages

Flaxseed

Eggs

Citrus fruit

Melons

Berries

FOODS TO LIMIT

Spinach

Throughout life, our bones are in a state of constant renewal, called remodeling. While some bone cells are breaking down and being reabsorbed, others are forming to take their place. When reabsorbing occurs faster than formation, the bones become weak and extremely porous. Fractures can occur with little or no pressure. This condition is called osteoporosis. Lack of estrogen appears to be its key contributing factor, but a falling off of androgens—the male hormones—is also involved, coupled with an inadequate intake of calcium and vitamin D.

Nutrition Connection

Consume enough calcium. The recommendation for calcium is 1,000 mg per day for men up to 70, and 1,200 mg per day for women older than 50 and men older than 70. Foods especially rich in calcium include milk and dairy products, fortified soy and rice beverages, dried beans and peas, tofu, canned fish eaten with the bones, nuts, and dark green leafy vegetables. The darker the greens, the more calcium they contain. An exception is spinach; it is high in oxalic acid, which inhibits calcium absorption.

Don't forget vitamin D. Just as important as calcium is vitamin D; the body needs it in order to absorb calcium. The RDA for adults up to 70 years old is 600 IU (15 mcg) and for those older than 70, 800 IU (20 mcg). The main source of vitamin D is sunlight—try to get about 10 minutes a day—but it can also be obtained from milk, fortified soy and rice beverages, egg yolks and fatty fish like mackerel. If your doctor recomments a calcium supplement, look for calcium citrate, the most easily absorbed. Because vitamin D is found in so few foods, a supplement is likely advisable.

Go green for vitamin K. Both the Nurses' Health Study and the Framingham Heart Study found that people who consume the most vitamin K have a lower risk of hip fractures than those who consume less. Vitamin K can be found in leafy green vegetables, green peas, broccoli, brussels sprouts, cabbage, kale, and beef liver.

Slip in some soy. Studies suggest that soy may play a role in prevention of osteoporosis as it contains isoflavones, a type of plant estrogen that may help conserve bone mass, particularly during perimenopause and menopause.

Add flaxseed. A study of postmenopausal women suggests that flaxseed, which is high in lignans, may retain bone mass, elevate antioxidant status, and help prevent urinary loss of calcium.

WHO'S AFFECTED?

- 44 million Americans and 1.4 million Canadians
- Post-menopausal women
- Those age 50 and older
- Women with surgically removed ovaries
- Women with menstrual irregularities
- Smokers
- Those with anorexia
- Those with kidney diseases
- Users of steroid-based medication

50% of all women older than 50 will break a bone because of osteoporosis.

Don't forget vitamin C. Studies have linked higher intakes of vitamin C with higher bone density. Vitamin C also helps to form the connective tissue that holds bones together. Some of the best food sources are fruits and vegetables, especially citrus fruits, berries, melons, and peppers.

Avoid bone-zapping foods. Caffeinated drinks such as coffee, tea, or colas; sodium; and high levels of protein can all cause calcium to be excreted.

Beyond the Diet

Other changes can strengthen bones and help you monitor your risk for osteoporosis. Here are a few guidelines:

Get regular weight-bearing exercise. Walking, jogging, aerobics, tennis, and dancing are all excellent for helping to maintain bones. Shoot for at least 30 minutes a day.

Seek scans. Many doctors recommend a baseline bone density scan for women when menstrual periods become irregular.

Watch medications that can affect the levels of calcium in the body. Antacids containing aluminum can promote calcium excretion. Calcium is also lost during long-term use of other drugs, including certain antibiotics, diuretics, and steroids.

PARKINSON'S DISEASE

FOODS THAT HEAL
Broccoli
Spinach
Whole grain cereals and breads
Soft or pureed foods

FOODS TO LIMIT
High-protein foods, if taking
medications such as levodopa

Parkinson's disease is a chronic and progressive nerve disorder that causes uncontrollable shaking or trembling (tremors), a fixed staring expression, muscle rigidity, stooped posture, and an abnormal gait. The disease varies from one person to another; some people develop speech problems and difficulty swallowing, while others suffer progressive dementia. Parkinson's affects men and women equally and generally develops after the age of 50.

Nutrition Connection

Although there are no nutritional treatments for Parkinson's disease, diet helps to increase the effectiveness of treatment with levodopa, which is a medication patients often take to control the tremors and muscle spasms, and manage such problems as constipation and difficulty in chewing and swallowing. Here's how:

Make treatments more effective. To be its most effective, some physicians advise taking levodopa 20 to 30 minutes before meals, but if this provokes nausea, it can be taken with a carbohydrate snack, such as crackers or bread. Protein delays the absorption of levodopa, so avoid high-protein diets while on the medication. Some doctors suggest eating the day's protein in the evening, when it's less likely to create problems.

Control other symptoms. Constipation can be minimized by consuming ample fresh fruits and vegetables, whole grain cereals and breads, and other high-fiber foods, as well as drinking 6 to 8 glasses of water or other fluids daily.

Put easy-to-chew foods on the menu. Those with advanced Parkinson's often have trouble chewing and swallowing food, because the tongue and facial muscles are affected. Meals should emphasize foods that are easy to chew and swallow. These include cooked cereals or well-moistened dry cereals, poached or scrambled eggs, soups, mashed potatoes, rice, soft-cooked pasta, tender chicken or turkey, well-cooked boneless fish, pureed or mashed vegetables and fruits, custard,

WHO'S AFFECTED?
- About 1.2 million North Americans
- Those with head injuries

yogurt, and juices. If eating is tiring, try smaller but more frequent meals.

Consider vitamin K. Some initial research has shown that vitamin K can improve cellular energy production and possibly ward off the Parkinson's symptom of diminished energy distribution among brain cells. Sources of vitamin K include green vegetables, such as broccoli and spinach.

Beyond the Diet

There is no cure for Parkinson's, but various medications, especially levodopa, can reduce symptoms and slow the progression. Here are some other guidelines for easing the symptoms:

Make time for fitness. Exercise promotes healthy bowel function and is advised for anyone with Parkinson's disease, because it preserves muscle tone and strength.

Ease digestion. Sit up straight and tilt your head slightly forward when swallowing. Take small bites, chew thoroughly, and swallow everything before taking another bite. Sip a liquid between bites to help wash food down.

PEPTIC ULCERS

FOODS THAT HARM
Coffee, including decaffeinated, and other sources of caffeine
Alcohol
Peppermint
Tomatoes
Black pepper
Chile peppers
Garlic
Cloves

FOODS THAT HEAL
Lean meat
Poultry
Fortified and enriched breads and cereals
Dried fruits
Legumes
Yogurt
Licorice

FOODS TO LIMIT
Fatty foods
Milk

WHO'S AFFECTED?
- More than 5 million Americans and 600,000 Canadians are diagnosed with peptic ulcers
- Those with a family history of ulcers

All sores that erode mucous membranes or the skin and penetrate the underlying muscle are referred to as ulcers. Those that occur in the lower part of the esophagus, the stomach, or the duodenum are known more specifically as peptic ulcers, because they form in areas exposed to stomach acids and the digestive enzyme pepsin. Peptic ulcers are one of the most common disorders diagnosed in North America today, and men and women are equally affected.

A person with an ulcer may describe the pain as gnawing or burning and can often pinpoint it's exact spot. The pain usually occurs 2 to 3 hours after eating, is worse when the stomach is empty, and can be relieved by eating a small amount of food or taking an antacid. Some people never have ulcer pain; however, they may develop intestinal bleeding, heartburn, bloating, and

20% to 50% of the populations in industrialized countries have the *Helicobacter pylori* bacterium.

gas, as well as nausea and vomiting.

Although excess acid secretion plays a role, most ulcers develop when a common bacterium, called *Helicobacter pylori,* infects the intestinal tract. Smoking, emotional stress, and heavy drinking can also contribute to a person's risk of ulcers, and some people may have a hereditary predisposition. Ulcers frequently occur in people subjected to extreme physical stress, such as serious burns or surgery.

Nutrition Connection

There are several ways to reduce the pain from ulcers and avoid them in the future, including:

Avoid trigger foods. Triggers vary from person to person, but common offenders are coffee (including decaffeinated), caffeine in beverages and chocolate, alcohol, peppermint, and tomato-based products.

Avoid raiding the fridge at night. Late-evening snacks should be avoided, because they stimulate acid secretion during sleep. It is also wise to avoid eating large quantities of food at one time.

Reduce fat and dairy. Fatty foods can slow down stomach emptying and stimulate acid release. Milk and dairy products

temporarily relieve pain but can cause a rebound in acid secretion.

Turn down the spice. Foods and seasonings that stimulate gastric acid secretion such as black pepper, garlic, cloves, and chili powder should be limited or avoided by people for whom they cause problems. Citrus juices may cause discomfort for some people.

Eat iron-rich foods. Bleeding from untreated ulcers can lead to iron-deficiency anemia. People with anemia should eat iron-rich foods, including lean meat, poultry, enriched or fortified breads and cereals, dried fruit, and dried beans and other legumes.

Spoon some yogurt. Yogurt with live lactobacilli and bifidobacteria during treatment can reduce symptoms.

Check out licorice. One home remedy that seems to work well is a form of licorice called deglycyrrhizinated licorice (DGL). DGL is sold in wafer form at health food stores. Follow the dosage instructions.

Sip aloe vera juice. This is another home remedy. Drink a ½ cup three times a day.

Beyond the Diet

Stop smoking. Smoking is one factor closely linked to poor healing and ulcer recurrence. Cigarette smokers often continue to suffer from ulcers until they quit.

Stop harmful medications. People with ulcers caused by NSAID use must discontinue the offending drug.

Exercise to raise your endorphin level. Regular exercise promotes the release of endorphins, brain chemicals that dull pain and elevate mood.

Check medications. A major cause of ulcers is the heavy use of drugs like aspirin, ibuprofen, naproxen, and other nonsteroidal anti-inflammatory drugs (NSAIDs).

Don't rely on baking soda. Many people self-treat ulcer pain with over-the-counter drugs or with home remedies concocted from baking soda (sodium bicarbonate) to neutralize stomach acid. But long-term use of antacids containing aluminum hydroxide can prevent the body from absorbing phosphorus and result in the loss of bone minerals.

PMS

See Menstrual Problems, page 311

PNEUMONIA

See Respiratory Disorders, page 332

POLYCYSTIC OVARY SYNDROME

FOODS THAT HARM
   High-glycemic foods such as white bread and refined cereals

FOODS THAT HEAL
   Apples
   Pears
   Berries
   Lima beans
   Pinto beans
   Pigeon peas
   Whole grains

FOODS TO LIMIT
   Alcohol

Polycystic ovary syndrome (PCOS) is a complicated female hormone disorder. It occurs when women have high levels of male hormones and their female hormones don't cycle properly. Experts also point to a connection with insulin resistance, infertility, and cancers of the breast, prostate, and colon. There may also be a genetic component. Women who have PCOS tend to have high blood pressure, low HDL levels, elevated triglycerides levels, and high fasting blood sugars and are at higher risk for developing type 2 diabetes and heart disease.

Nutrition Connection

The dietary approach to treating PCOS is similar to what doctors recommend for people with type 2 diabetes. Women with PCOS may experience a tougher time losing weight, possibly because high levels of male hormones can increase the appetite. Follow these guidlines:

Lose just a little weight. A weight loss of just 5% can improve insulin resistance, and that can improve PCOS.

Increase fiber intake. Adding more fiber to your diet can help you feel fuller longer and help avoid binges. Choose foods such as an apples, pears, berries, lima beans, pinto beans, and pigeon peas.

Be vigilant about portion control. Serving sizes that are too big often cause too many calories to slip in to the diet.

Study glycemic index and load levels. The glycemic index and glycemic load (see pages 262-263) indicates the effects that foods have on increasing your blood sugar and insulin levels. Avoid high-glycemic foods, such as white bread and refined cereals, and choose low-glycemic foods, such as legumes, whole grains, and many vegetables and fruits, to help reduce cravings and make it easier to stick to a healthy diet plan.

WHO'S AFFECTED?

- 4% to 18% of women
- Obese women
- Women who have excessive body hair
- Premenopausal women
- Women with irregular periods
- Women with immediate family members who have the condition

P

Beyond the Diet

To combat PCOS, diet, exercise, and weight loss are key along with these guidelines:

Start walking. A 10-minute walk, maybe around the block, is a great way to get more active.

45% of women with PCOS have severe depression.

Address stress and depression. Many symptoms trigger stressful feelings. Those feelings can make you feel worse and neglect the self-care you need to improve your condition. It's a vicious cycle.

Consider cognitive behavioral therapy. This short-term talk therapy teaches coping skills and helps you control unhelpful behaviors. In a 2009 study, eight weekly sessions plus three family sessions helped teens with PCOS lose weight and slash their depression scores.

Address depression. If you have PCOS, you're also at much higher risk for depression than other women. Try meditation, yoga, or other relaxation techniques and ask your doctor whether a referral to a psychopharmacologist is appropriate.

PROSTATE PROBLEMS

FOODS THAT HEAL
Tomatoes and tomato products
Red grapefruit
Watermelons
Brazil nuts
Salmon
Trout
Arctic char
Wheat bran and wheat germ
Oats
Brown rice
Soy products
Broccoli
Cauliflower
Cabbage
Whole grains
Water

FOODS TO LIMIT
Fatty foods, especially animal products
Caffeine

The prostate, a walnut-size gland located just below the bladder, is the source of many male urinary problems, including cancer, benign enlargement, and inflammation (prostatitis). Urinary tract infections, lifestyle habits, and a high-fat diet seem to predispose a man to some of these problems.

As men age, the prostate tends to enlarge, a condition called benign prostatic hypertrophy (BPH). About one-third of all men over 50 experience this noncancerous enlargement that can cause severe obstruction of urinary flow.

Prostate cancer is the second most common type of cancer among American men, and more than 28,000 American men die of the ailment per year. If treated in an early stage, it is highly curable.

Nutrition Connection

Follow these guidelines for better prostate health:

Mix in foods with lycopene. A recent study of nearly 48,000 men found that this substance—found in such foods as tomatoes, red grapefruit, and watermelon—appears to reduce the risk of prostate cancer. Cooking appears to release more of the lycopene in tomatoes, so tomato-based pasta sauces and soups may be especially beneficial. Lycopene is fat soluble so is better absorbed when eaten with a little fat.

Go nuts. The selenium in nuts may protect against prostate cancer. This antioxidant is found in nuts, especially Brazil nuts, seafood, some meats, fish, wheat bran, wheat germ, oats, and brown rice.

Seek out soy. Soy products can help prevent prostate enlargement, may help protect against prostate cancer, and may slow tumor growth. This effect is attributed to isoflavones, plant chemicals that help lower dihydrotestosterone (DHT), a male hormone that stimulates the overgrowth of prostate tissue.

Be oily. A diet that is high in saturated animal fats has been linked to an increased incidence of prostate cancer. However, oily fish such as salmon, trout, and Artic char are high in omega-3 fat's which seem to reduce the risk of prostate cancer.

Dish out plenty of veggies. Vegetables from the cruciferous family such as broccoli, cabbage, and cauliflower contain isothiocyanates, which are phytochemicals that appear to protect against cancer.

Eat whole grains. Whole grains offer fiber, selenium, vitamin E, and phytochemicals, all of which play a role in the prevention of cancer.

Drink plenty of fluids. Anyone with an enlarged prostate should drink plenty of water and other nonalcoholic fluids and reduce the intake of caffeine.

Beyond the Diet

Some nondiet changes can help reduce the risk of prostate cancer or may slow its progress. They are:

Reduce zinc intake. According to research led by the National Institutes of Health, zinc takers had twice the risk of prostate cancer.

Exercise. Get 30 minutes of moderate aerobic activity six days a week.

Reduce stress. Spend a total of about an hour a day practicing stress-reduction techniques, such as deep breathing, guided imagery, and stretching. You don't have to get all zen in one sitting. Ten minutes here and there works.

PSORIASIS

FOODS THAT HARM
Products with gluten for those who are allergic

FOODS THAT HEAL
Asparagus
Spinach
Avocados
Chickpeas
Lentils
Flaxseeds
Oranges
Salmon
Mackerel
Herring

R

Psoriasis is an unsightly, tough-to-treat skin condition marked by red, raised, and scaly-looking patches of skin that seem to appear and disappear for no good reason. It's actually an immune disorder. Psoriasis occurs when your body's T-cells, which are supposed to destroy germs as they enter your system, instead destroy healthy skin cells. In addition, about 15% of those with psoriasis will have some arthritis pain. Scientists aren't sure what the connection between the two ailments might be but speculate that it may have to do with an immune response that's also felt in the tendons and ligaments.

16% of people with psoriasis are allergic to gliadin, a gluten protein.

Nutrition Connection

Boosting your immune system with a healthy diet can help diminish the effects of psoriasis. Here's how:

Find folic acid. Some studies suggest that people with psoriasis are deficient in the B-vitamin called folate, or folic acid. So liberally lace your diet with plenty of folate-rich foods, which include asparagus, spinach, broccoli, avocados, oranges, chickpeas, and lentils.

Befriend flax. Flaxseeds and flaxseed oil are rich in anti-inflammatory essential fatty acids that may calm skin conditions like psoriasis.

Opt for omega-3s. A British study found that people who ate 5.5 oz (156 g) of fatty fish a day (think salmon, mackerel, herring, and sardines) experienced improved psoriasis symptoms.

Beyond the Diet

Other ways to ease symptoms include:

Get tested for allergies. Ask your doctor to refer you for testing to see if you're allergic or sensitive to gluten.

Stop smoking. One 2007 study found that the more someone smokes, the greater the chance that person has of developing psoriasis.

Relax in the tub. Add up to 3 cups of Epsom salts to a lukewarm tub. Epsom salts contain magnesium, which helps heal psoriasis by removing the scales and reducing the itch.

Soak up some sun. Vitamin D helps your body fight psoriasis. During the winter, or on rainy days, take 1000 IU of vitamin D.

Try tea tree. Dilute tea tree oil in a little olive oil and massage into psoriasis patches several times a day. This home remedy relieves itching and softens scaly skin.

RESPIRATORY DISORDERS

FOODS THAT HARM
- Alcohol
- Fatty fried food

FOODS THAT HEAL
- Tomatoes
- Cantaloupes
- Green leafy vegetables
- Lean meat
- Oysters
- Yogurt
- Whole grain
- Garlic
- Chiles
- Horseradish

FOODS TO LIMIT

Milk

Beans

Legumes

Cabbage

Brussels sprouts

Broccoli

Onions

Respiratory disorders range from colds and flu (see page 252), which are usually minor infections, to chronic diseases, such as asthma (see page 231), which are much more problematic. Any condition that affects the passage of air to and from the lungs should be taken seriously.

Four of the more common respiratory disorders are: bronchitis, an inflammation of the tubes that carry air to and from the lungs, which is marked by a relentless cough and thick phlegm; emphysema, also known as chronic obstructive pulmonary disease, which causes shortness of breath and is usually a consequence of smoking; pneumonia, caused by viruses, bacteria, fungi, parasites, or toxic substances, which leads to a cough, fever, chills, and chest pain; and sinusitis, an inflammation of the membranes lining the sinus cavities, which results in a stuffed-up feeling and a deep, dull headache.

Nutrition Connection

A nutritious and well-balanced diet can help prevent or reduce the severity of bronchitis, pneumonia, and other lung infections. Follow these guidelines:

Drink plenty of fluids. Adequate fluid intake, particularly of warm liquids like chicken broth or hot tea, helps to thin mucus and make breathing easier. Hot tea contains theophylline, a compound believed to ease breathing by relaxing the smooth muscles in the walls of the airways.

Fill your plate with antioxidant foods. Vitamins A, and C, beta-carotene, and other antioxidants help protect lung tissue from the cellular damage caused by free radicals; build and repair epithelial tissues, which protect the respiratory system from bacteria; and help build immunity against lung disease. Tomatoes, cantaloupes, and green leafy vegetables are great sources of these vitamins.

Balance zinc content. Zinc, found in lean meat, oysters, yogurt, and whole grain products, is important for boosting immunity, especially against upper respiratory infections. But consuming more than 40 mg per day can depress your immune system, making you more susceptible to infection.

Spice it up. Some foods, herbs, and spices, are natural decongestants. These include garlic, onions, chiles, horseradish, ginger, thyme, cumin, cloves, and cinnamon.

Limit milk. In one study, patients with chronic sinusitis reported improvement after eliminating milk products from their diets.

WHO'S AFFECTED?
- Smokers
- Those exposed to dust or chemicals

5+ apples a week was strongly associated with increased lung function, according to researchers.

Reduce fatty, fried food. Fats, like those in fried food remain in the stomach longer because they require more time to digest and may crowd the lungs longer than other types of foods, making those with emphysema feel uncomfortable.

Pass on the gas. Anything that causes gas and bloating should also be limited because it may make breathing difficult. common offenders include beans and

INFLAMMATION:
Eat to Quell the Dangers

Inflammation is your body's alarm system. Sort of like how an ankle swells when you twist it, other parts of your body—even internal ones—will swell in response to injury, exposure to chemicals, or viruses. Doctors are just now beginning to understand that inflammation can have several other health consequences. Research has led experts to believe that inflammation plays a role in heart disease, cancer, and diabetes.

However, certain foods may help heal inflammation:

Berries and cherries. These sweet fruits help reduce inflammation by neutralizing free radicals in the body and may also help stop tissue inflammation.

Bran cereal. Fiber from bran cereal is associated with less inflammation in women with type 2 diabetes. And the Physicians' Health Study found that doctors who ate whole grain cereal every day were 28% less likely to have heart failure over 24 years—an effect that may be linked to reduced inflammation.

Bright vegetables. Choose deep orange, red, or yellow vegetables, which are full of carotenoids, anti-inflammatory antioxidants.

Chamomile. Germans use chamomile as a universal healer, referring to it as *alles zutraut*, or "capable of anything." As an anti-inflammatory, chamomile works like an NSAID—think ibuprofen or aspirin.

Chicken soup. When a researcher from the Nebraska Medical Center tested chicken soup in the lab, he found that it could reduce inflammation and congestion caused by virus-fighting immune system agents called neutrophils by about 75%. Canned chicken soup worked, too.

Cloves. An aromatic spice common in Indian cooking, cloves contain an anti-inflammatory chemical called eugenol. In recent animal studies, this chemical inhibited COX-2, an enzyme that spurs inflammation.

Flaxseed. Flaxseed is rich in alpha linolenic-acid, which the body uses to make the same type of omega-3 fatty acids you get from fish. Like fish, it guards against inflammation in the body.

Ginger. Ginger has been used for thousands of years to help with a variety of ailments, from stomachaches to arthritis to heart conditions because of its anti-inflammatory effect. It may play a role in preventing and slowing the growth of cancer as well easing migraines by blocking inflammatory substances called prostaglandins.

Green tea. Used for centuries for a variety of medicinal purposes, green tea is an excellent source of polyphenols, which may help reduce free radicals in the body that can cause inflammation.

Nuts. An excellent source of vitamin E, consuming nuts together with fish oil seems to boost the body's ability to fight inflammation beyond what either nutrient would do on its own, according to two animal studies.

Olive oil. Olive oil contains antioxidants called polyphenols, which research suggests help to reduce inflammation in the blood vessels and in the brain. Look for virgin olive oil—it retains more of the polyphenols than heavily processed variants.

Orange juice. When researchers fed volunteers either glucose-sweetened water or OJ, the sweet water triggered an inflammatory response but the OJ did not. The researchers credit the effect to the juice's vitamin C content and various flavonoids. Choose 100% juice made from frozen concentrate, which has more vitamin C than fresh squeezed after four weeks of storage.

Pomegranates. These fruits are especially high in antioxidants, such as ellagic acid, that reduce inflammation. That may explain why pomegrantes have been shown in studies to reverse the progression of coronary heart disease.

Sage. This anti-inflammatory herb has also been shown in some research to boost memory and reduce swelling.

Salmon. Salmon is packed with omega-3 fatty acids—a family of fats that helps, put the brakes on inflammation. Studies suggest that increasing your intake of omega-3 fatty acids can help quell symptoms of rheumatoid arthritis.

Soy. Soy is packed with isoflavones, plant hormones with anti-inflammatory properties. An Oklahoma State study found that people with knee pain reported less discomfort and used fewer pain meds after eating soy protein every day for 3 months.

Turmeric. Curcumin, the chemical responsible for turmeric's yellow color, helps to quell the inflammation that contributes to cancer growth. Scientists are also studying curcumin's anti-inflammatory effect on cystic fibrosis.

Wine. Vino drinking has been linked to a lower risk of heart disease and it could be due to an anti-inflammatory effect. But don't overdo it. Heavy drinking has been linked to cancer.

THE BOTTOM LINE

- Inflammation can lead to chronic conditions including diabetes and cancer.
- Inflammation of internal organs and the circulatory system has been linked to heart disease.
- Many foods, including nuts, fruits, and spices can help cool inflammation.

- About 14 million Americans and 1.5 million Canadians
- Caucasian women, particularly during menopause
- People with fair skin
- Adults between the ages of 30 and 60

other legumes, cabbage, brussels sprouts, broccoli, and onions.

Eat small, frequent meals. People with emphysema generally feel better if they eat smaller, more frequent meals. Consuming too much at one time can increase the volume in the stomach and crowd the already distended lungs.

Slow down. To further avoid gas and ease digestion, don't rush; have small servings and eat slowly.

Avoid alcohol. Alcohol lowers immunity and should be avoided during any infection. Because chronic bronchitis and emphysema predispose a person to develop lung infections, it's a good idea to abstain from all alcoholic beverages.

Beyond the Diet

Here are some tips that can help ease the symptoms of respiratory ailments:

Quit smoking. Smoking is by far the leading cause of chronic respiratory disorders, including chronic bronchitis, emphysema, and lung cancer. Also try to avoid secondhand smoke and air pollutants.

Try aromatherapy. A soothing means of relieving lung problems is to inhale the steam from a bowl of hot water that contains a few drops of highly concentrated essential oils. A combination of eucalyptus, thyme, pine, and lavender oils is often recommended to ease bronchitis. Eucalyptus oil is particularly good for relieving the feeling of congestion and may be helpful to people with emphysema.

Humidify. Heat and dry air can produce swollen, dry nasal membranes that are predisposed to sinusitis. A humidifier may be a simple solution.

ROSACEA

FOODS THAT HEAL
Cucumbers
Iced water

FOODS TO LIMIT
Specific trigger foods, such as alcohol and spicy foods

Rosacea is a chronic skin disease that usually affects the face and sometimes the eyes. People who have rosacea experience redness and pimples; in later stages, the skin can thicken. Though its causes are not known, doctors suspect that there may be a tendency to inherit rosacea.

Nutrition Connection

Follow these dietary recommendations to avoid flare-ups:

Chill out. Eating cool foods—from both a spice and temperature standpoint—can help tamp down rosacea flare-ups. Instead of that tortilla soup with jalapeño sauce, opt for a cool cucumber salad.

Stay hydrated. Drinking plenty of iced water or other noncaffeinated beverages can lead to fewer flare-ups. Drink even more in the summer or when you're exercising.

Keep a food diary. Take note of the time of day you eat, what you're eating, and even how you're feeling emotionally and what you're doing. This is the most effective way to get a handle on foods that trigger your flare-ups. Common trigger foods include alcohol and spicy foods.

> **QUICK TIP: Dodge the wind**
>
> Avoid exercising outdoors on windy days—wind can trigger flare-ups.

Beyond the Diet

Follow these lifestyle tips to help decrease the severity of rosacea:

Don't smoke. Smoking can cause flushing, so here's another reason to quit the nasty habit.

Seek shade. 81% of people with rosacea report that sun exposure triggers flare-ups.

Just say "ohm." Stress can easily set off flare-ups—in fact, 79% of rosacea sufferers say that stress is a trigger for them. Consider learning meditation techniques, take a yoga class, or just sit quietly and breathe deeply for 10 minutes while you're going through stressful times.

Cleanse skin gently. Just as certain foods can triggers rosacea, so can certain skin care products. In particular, avoid cosmetic products made with known potential triggers, which include alcohol, witch hazel, peppermint, eucalyptus oil, clove oil, menthol, and salicylic acid. Also steer clear of products that have fragrance, and instead use unscented skin care products.

SEX DRIVE, DIMINISHED

FOODS THAT HARM
Alcohol

FOODS THAT HEAL
Citrus fruits
Low-fat milk and other dairy products
Green leafy vegetables
Wheat germ
Beef
Poultry
Liver

Fortified and enriched cereals
Oysters
Pine nuts
Beans
Garlic

FOODS TO LIMIT
Saturated fats

Some people vouch for the effect of foods on their sex drive, but extravagant claims for aphrodisiacs are not borne out by scientific studies. While sexual function may be our physical response to a cascade of hormones, sexual drive is basically maintained by an active mind in a healthy body.

Nutrition Connection

A healthy sex life depends on good nutrition. Good nerve function, healthy hormone levels, and an unobstructed blood flow to the pelvic area are essential to sexual performance. To keep these systems in working order, follow these guidelines:

Be complex with carbs. A diet should be based on legumes, grain products, and other unrefined carbohydrates, with plenty of fruits and vegetables and modest levels of protein. Particularly important are citrus fruits for vitamin C to strengthen blood vessel walls, and low-fat dairy products, fortified and enriched cereals, whole grains, and green vegetables for riboflavin to maintain the mucous membranes that line the female reproductive tract.

WHO'S AFFECTED?
- Men older than 45
- Postmenopausal women
- Those dealing with stress

QUICK TIP:
Make pesto and pasta

Pesto contains pine nuts, great sources of arginine. Arginine helps open blood vessels so blood flow improves.

Consume more zinc. It is known that zinc is tied to sexual function, although its importance to the sex drive has yet to be explained. Without enough zinc, sexual development in children is delayed, and men, can't make sperm. Zinc is found abundantly in foods of animal origin, including seafood (especially oysters), meat, poultry, and liver, as well as in eggs, milk, beans, nuts, wheat germ, and whole grains.

Eat a diet low in saturated fats. Plaques similar to atherosclerotic ones develop on the myriad tiny vessels in the penis if you eat too much saturated fat. Without free-flowing circulation, the penis cannot physically respond to messages from the sex drive.

Curb alcohol consumption. Alcohol's effect on sexual function was neatly stated by William Shakespeare, who noted that wine "provokes the desire, but takes away the performance." Alcohol can actually cause impotence and shrink the testes in men who drink heavily.

Pump up iron. In some cases, iron-deficiency anemia may be responsible for fatigue and loss of desire. A diet that includes meat, fish and shellfish, nuts and seeds, legumes, enriched or fortified grains and cereals, leafy greens, and dried fruits helps to replenish iron stores.

Mix in some garlic. High in an ingredient called allicin, garlic can help stimulate circulation and blood flow to sexual organs in both men and women.

Beyond the Diet

Get moving. Fatigue and depression are common culprits in sexual complaints. These conditions are often linked, and both may be helped by a program of regular exercise, which stimulates the production of endorphins.

WHO'S AFFECTED?

- About 30% of people will contract the ailment sometime in their lives
- Anyone who's had chicken pox
- Those older than 50
- People with suppressed immune systems

Stop smoking. Nicotine is an enemy of the arteries. Nicotine not only promotes the formation of atherosclerotic plaque in the penile blood vessels but also constricts them.

SINUSITIS

See Respiratory Disorders, page 332

SHINGLES

FOODS THAT HEAL
Nuts and seeds
Wheat germ
Vegetable oils
Seafood
Lean meat
Chicken
Milk
Yogurt
Beans
Whole grains

Shingles is an encore presentation of the chicken pox attack you had as a child. This very painful nerve condition is caused by the same varicella zoster virus that causes chicken pox. Although the virus remains dormant in most people, shingles can occur when the virus is reactivated in the nerve pathways.

Scientists don't know exactly what "wakes up" the hibernating shingles virus, but they believe advancing age, a weakened immune system, some medications (such as cortisone-type drugs or immune-suppressing medications), emotional stress, or recovery from surgery can trigger it.

Nutrition Connection

Some doctors believe that good nutrition may help prevent postherpetic neuralgia, a long-term complication of shingles. Here's what to do:

Get plenty of E and C. Vitamin E, an antioxidant found in nuts, seeds, wheat germ, and vegetable oils, and the bioflavonoids found in melons, peppers, and other fruits and vegetables that are high in vitamin C may help prevent the inflammation associated with postherpetic neuralgia and supports your immune system.

Load up on zinc. Zinc-rich foods like seafood, meat, poultry, milk, yogurt, beans, nuts, and whole grains also strengthen your immute system. Pain may also be eased with applications of an ointment that contains capsaicin.

Beyond the Diet

Exercise to prevent stress. Stress can trigger shingles, and exercise can help reduce stress. Try walking briskly for half an hour a day, or take up swimming, biking, or yoga.

Soothe your skin. To promote healing (and relaxation), add a few drops of rose, lavender, bergamot, or tea tree oil to your warm bath. Mix them in a carrier oil, such as vegetable oil first.

Numb the pain. Calendula lotion or ointment applied to blisters several times a day eases pain. Or apply a paste made of two crushed aspirin tablets and 2 Tbsp (30 mL) of rubbing alcohol three times a day to soothe throbbing nerves.

Add supplements. Taking vitamins regularly may keep your immune system strong and therefore less likely to succumb to shingles. And for relief from posttherpetic neuralgia, ask your doctor about vitamin B12 injections, which can strengthen the tissue that covers your nerves.

SLEEP DISORDERS

See Insomnia, page 295

SORE THROAT

FOODS THAT HARM
- Alcohol
- Caffeine

FOODS THAT HEAL
- Lemon
- Honey
- Yogurt
- Eggs
- Seafood
- Lean meat
- Whole grains
- Fruit juice
- Water
- Tea

A raw, stinging throat can often be the first sign of a viral upper respiratory infection, such as a cold or flu, laryngitis, or less commonly, a bacterial infection such as strep throat. In children, swollen and infected tonsils can cause a sore throat; among adults, smoking is a common cause of mild, chronic throat pain. Respiratory viruses and strep organisms spread easily from one person to another, but attention to hygiene and good nutrition helps prevent many episodes.

Nutrition Connection

Prevent that initial sore throat from becoming a more serious condition by following these guidelines:

WHO'S AFFECTED?
- Those with allergies
- Children, up to teen years
- Elderly
- People with compromised immune systems
- Those who live or work in crowded conditions

Eat plenty of fruits and vegetables. Eat 5 to 10 servings of fruits and vegetables a day, which would provide more than adequate amounts of vitamin C, beta-carotene, and other essential vitamins and minerals. These are instrumental in building immunity. Good sources include lemons and berries.

Try zinc lozenges. Several studies have demonstrated that zinc lozenges can shorten the duration or severity of a sore throat. A diet that provides adequate zinc strengthens the body's immune defenses. Good sources include yogurt and other dairy products, oysters and other seafood, lean meat, eggs, and grains. But don't overdo it; getting more than 40 mg of zinc per day for an extended period of time can weaken your immune system.

Avoid alcohol and caffeine. Alcohol, which reduces immunity and irritates inflamed mucous membranes, should be avoided until the sore throat clears up. It's also a good idea to cut down on, or eliminate, caffeine; its diuretic effect increases the loss of body fluids and results in drier membranes and thicker mucus.

Switch to a liquid diet. Nonalcoholic fluids, whether hot or cold, can alleviate painful swallowing. Some doctors even advise temporarily switching to a liquid diet to maintain nutrition without exacerbating throat pain. Good choices include water, tea, fruit juices, broths and soups, and semiliquid foods such as custards, puddings, and gelatin.

Mix in some honey. The amber stuff coats the throat and has mild antibacterial properties. Stir 1 to 3 tsp (5 to 15 mL) of honey into 1 cup (237 mL) of warm water and gargle two or three times a day.

Beyond the Diet

Gargle with salt water. Home sore throat remedies abound, and many are useful in alleviating symptoms. The most time-honored favorite is to gargle with salty warm water. You can make an alternative gargle by adding 2 tsp (10 mL) of cider vinegar to ½ cup (118 mL) of warm water.

STRESS

FOODS THAT HEAL
- Whole grains
- Seafood
- Lean meat
- Poultry
- Milk
- Eggs
- Nuts
- Herbal tea

FOODS TO LIMIT
- Alcohol
- Caffeinated beverages like coffee, tea, cocoa, and soda
- Fatty foods
- Hot or spicy foods

While physical stress is often episodic, emotional stress is part of daily life. Our bodies react to stress with the fight-or-flight response, which floods the body with adrenaline and other hormones that raise blood pressure, speed up the heartbeat, tense muscles, and put other systems on

QUICK TIP:
Sip some lemon tea

Lemons are loaded with vitamin C and can be soothing and beneficial for sore throats when made into a hot drink. Squeeze the juice of a lemon into a cup of boiling water and add a little honey.

alert. Metabolism quickens to provide extra energy; digestion stops as blood is diverted from the intestines to the muscles.

Chronic stress sets the stage for decreased immunity and increased vulnerability to illnesses, ranging from the common cold to heart attacks and cancer.

Nutrition Connection

Battle stress with a healthy diet. Prolonged stress, whether psychological or physical, plays havoc with digestion and nutritional needs. Food provides energy while vitamins and minerals helps your body maintain resistance to infection under stress.

Zap stress with zinc. Foods high in zinc such as seafood, meat, poultry, milk, eggs, whole grains, and nuts also help to keep your immune system healthy.

Eat several small meals. When under stress, some people are always hungry and binge on food; others have to force themselves to eat. Because stress interferes with digestion, it's better to eat four to six small meals spaced throughout the day instead of the traditional three large ones.

Go ahead, eat carbs. Carbohydrate-rich meals can increase levels of serotonin, a brain chemical that is known to induce a feeling of calm. Studies have shown that stress-prone individuals who eat a diet higher in carbohydrates and lower in protein had less stress-induced depression.

Eat breakfast. If you are running on empty, stress can be hard to handle.

Munch slowly. Eating quickly is often associated with digestive upset and this—coupled with stress—can make your food difficult to digest.

Don't diet. Changing eating habits is stressful at the best of times.

Limit caffeine and alcohol. They can affect your mood and sleep patterns. Alcohol can also heighten feelings of depression. If you drink coffee, choose decaf. Try herbal teas such as chamomile and peppermint, which have a calming effect. Or substitute low-fat milk, fruit juice, sparkling water, or a noncaffeinated soda for caffeinated soda.

Avoid fatty or spicy foods. Fatty foods are difficult to digest and may trigger indigestion and heartburn when you are in a stressful period. Many people also find that hot or spicy foods cause them problems during times of stress.

Beyond the Diet

In addition to a healthy diet, other ways to reduce stress include:

Exercise regularly. Exercise increases the production of endorphins, brain chemicals that lift mood.

Find your inner peace. Learn a relaxation technique, such as yoga, meditation, or deep-breathing exercises. Or simply sit quietly with your eyes closed for a few minutes.

Prioritize what matters. Make a things-to-do list for the day and arrange the items by importance. Focus on one item at a time and then move undone ones to the next day's list.

Pet a pooch (or cat). Research suggests that stroking an animal can help lower your stress and your blood pressure.

WHO'S AFFECTED?
- 75% of adults report moderate to high levels of stress within the past month
- 80% of U.S. workers feel stressed on the job
- About 24% of Canadians reported they felt extremely or quite stressed on a daily basis

Tap into your social support. Reach out, share your problems with a family member, friend, or counselor, and ask for support. Several studies have shown that a support network can help reduce stress by creating a feeling of security and increasing your self-worth.

Tune in. Music is a surprisingly effective way to calm down. Music can lower blood pressure and heart rate, increase endorphin levels, and decrease stress hormones.

Consider a multivitamin. Studies have shown that chronically stressed people have depressed levels of nutrients in their body, which may be corrected by taking a multivitamin and mineral supplement. Although there is no pill that will make stress go away or make it easier to cope, if you are not eating well during a difficult period, try taking a multivitamin and mineral supplement to help fortify your body.

STROKE

FOODS THAT HARM
Red meat, butter and other foods
   with saturated fats
Palm and coconut oil
Salty foods

FOODS THAT HEAL
Oats
Lentils
Flaxseeds
Whole grains
Grapes
Nuts
Red wine
Apples
Berries
Trout
Mackerel
Walnuts
Canola oil
Soybeans
Green leafy vegetables
Low-fat dairy products
Garlic
Onions

A stroke occurs when a clot blocks blood flow to a part of the brain. Most of these clots form in an artery that is already narrowed by atherosclerosis, either in the brain itself or, more commonly, in the carotid artery in the neck. The warning signs of a stroke include sudden weakness or numbness of the face, arm, and leg on one side of the body; difficulty speaking or understanding others; dimness or impaired vision in one eye; and unexplained dizziness, unsteadiness, or a sudden fall. Immediate treatment is critical, even if the symptoms disappear, as in the case of a ministroke (transient ischemic attack), a common prelude to a full-blown stroke. Prompt treatment may be lifesaving, and it may also minimize permanent damage, which can include impaired movement, speech, vision, and mental function.

Nutrition Connection

Many of the same nutritional recommendations made for people who have heart disease, high blood pressure, and elevated blood cholesterol levels apply to people who are at risk for, or who have had, a stroke:

Adopt a diet that is low in fats. A good starting point is to reduce your consumption of fats, especially saturated animal fats, trans fats and tropical (palm and coconut) oils.

Boost fiber. Foods that are high in soluble fibers, especially oats, lentils, and flax, can help control cholesterol levels and reduce the risk of atherosclerosis, which narrows the arteries and sets the stage for developing the blood clots that block the flow of blood to the brain.

WHO'S AFFECTED?

- About 795,000 Americans and 50,000 Canadians have a stroke each year
- Those with high blood pressure or diabetes
- Smokers
- African Americans
- People who have atrial fibrillation
- Women who take birth control pills
- Those with a family history of stroke

Go whole. Eating whole grains is important for stroke protection since data suggest a whole grain–based diet may reduce the risk for this condition.

Find foods that smooth blood flow. Preliminary evidence suggests that resveratrol, a phytochemical found in grapes, nuts, and red wine, may inhibit blood clots and also help relax blood vessels. Population-based studies suggest that dietary flavonoids, particularly quercetin, found in apples and berries may reduce fat deposits in arteries that can block blood flow to the brain.

Get lots of omega-3s. A number of other foods appear to lower the risk of a stroke. Some fish, for example, are rich in omega-3 fatty acids, which help to prevent blood clots by reducing the stickiness of blood platelets. Doctors recommend eating salmon, trout, mackerel, sardines, or other oily cold-water fish two or three times a week. Other good sources of omega-3 fatty acids include walnuts and walnut oil, canola (rapeseed) oil, flaxseed oil, soybeans, and leafy greens.

Get milk and other dairy products. Low-fat dairy contains calcium, potassium, magnesium, and vitamin D, all nutrients that can help lower blood pressure, a major risk factor for strokes.

Eat plenty of garlic and onions. Garlic and onions appear to decrease the tendency of the blood to clot, and they also boost the body's natural clot-dissolving mechanism.

Reduce salt. Anyone who has high blood pressure, or a family history of this disease or of strokes, should limit salt intake.

Limit alcohol. Numerous studies link excessive alcohol use, defined as more than two drinks a day for men and one for women, to an increased incidence of stroke; the risk is compounded if the person also smokes. The best approach is to abstain completely from smoking and to use alcohol in moderation.

Beyond the Diet

Get your blood pressure checked. Failure to detect and control high blood pressure is the leading cause of avoidable strokes.

Exercise. Regular exercise is helpful in reducing the risk of a stroke and heart attack by helping control weight and blood cholesterol levels. It also promotes an enhanced sense of well-being. Shoot for at least 30 minutes a day.

Cheer up! A new study by researchers at the University of Michigan found that optimistic people had a reduced risk of stroke. Optimism's protective effect could be explained by the fact that optimistic people tend to make healthier choices about exercise and diet, say researchers. But it is also possible that positive thinking has a direct impact on biology.

TAKE THIS AT-HOME TEST

Those with atrial fibrillation—or irregular heartbeat—are five to seven times more likely to have a stroke than those without the condition. However, the condition is often undiagnosed. A simple test, though, may help determine if you have afib. Place a finger on your neck or wrist and tap your foot to the rhythm of your pulse for a minute. If the beat is so irregular you can't tap along, relax for an hour and check again. If it's still very uneven, tell your doctor. In several studies, this test alerted doctors to more than 90% of people with afib, which was confirmed by heart monitoring.

ULCERATIVE COLITIS

See Inflammatory Bowel Disease, page 293

WHO'S AFFECTED?

- About 8.8 million Americans and 975,000 Canadians
- Women have a greater than 50% chance of having a UTI during their life
- 3% of girls and 1% of boys before age 11

URINARY TRACT INFECTIONS

FOODS THAT HARM
Coffee, tea, cola or other caffeinated drinks
Alcohol
Spicy food

FOODS THAT HEAL
Cranberries and cranberry juice
Water and caffeine-free drinks
Oranges
Tomatoes
Broccoli
Yogurt

Also known as bacterial cystitis, urinary tract infections (UTIs) mostly affect the bladder, but some may involve the kidneys, the ureters (the tubes that carry urine to the bladder), and the urethra (the tube through which urine exits the body). The most common symptom is an urgent need to urinate, even when the bladder is not full. Urination may be accompanied by pain or burning and, in severe cases, small amounts of blood. There may also be a low-grade fever and an ache in the lower back.

Most urinary infections are caused by *E. coli* bacteria, organisms that live in the intestinal tract but that can travel to the bladder. Chlamydia, a sexually transmitted organism, is another cause of UTIs.

Women are more vulnerable to urinary infections because the female urethra is shorter than that of males and its location provides a convenient entryway for bacteria.

Nutrition Connection

Antibiotics are needed to cure bacterial urinary infections, but dietary approaches can speed healing and help prevent recurrences, including:

Drink plenty of water. Doctors advise drinking at least 8 to 10 glasses of fluids a day to increase the flow of urine and to flush out infectious material.

Ditch caffeine and alcohol. Avoid coffee, tea, colas, and alcoholic drinks, because these increase bladder irritation.

Skip spices for a while. Some people find that spicy foods also aggravate the urinary tract.

Drink cranberry juice. Cranberry juice is a favorite home remedy and one that is supported by research. Cranberries and blueberries contain substances that speed the elimination of bacteria by preventing them from sticking to the bladder wall.

Pump up vitamin C. Eating fresh fruits and vegetables that contain vitamin C, such as oranges, tomatoes, and broccoli, helps strengthen the immune system, fight infection, and acidify the urine.

Go for yogurt. Consuming probiotics may be helpful since they are thought to inhibit the growth of microorganisms that cause UTIs. These beneficial bacteria, found in some yogurts, are also thought to foster the growth of friendly flora in the body, which may be reduced by antibiotic therapy.

Beyond the Diet

Many doctors recommend the following tactics:

Be free flowing. Wear loose-fitting white cotton underwear and panty hose that have cotton crotches.

Don't douche. Avoid douching and using vaginal deodorants, which can cause bladder irritation.

Check your diaphragm. If you use a diaphragm, ask your doctor to check the size. One that is even slightly too large can irritate the urethra and bladder.

Sip before sex. Drink a glass of water and urinate before sexual intercourse, and within an hour afterward to flush out the urinary tract.

Go front to back. After a bowel movement, wipe from the front to the back to reduce the risk of carrying intestinal bacteria to the urethra.

VARICOSE VEINS

FOODS THAT HEAL

Oranges and other citrus fruits

Berries

Broccoli

Red pepper

Whole grain cereals

Whole wheat pasta

Popcorn

Grapes

Varicose veins are blood vessels that appear ropey, swollen, and purple. They occur most often in the legs, but may show up elsewhere on the body. They occur when a valve in the veins that keeps blood moving forward malfunctions. That allows blood to pool in the veins, which enlarges them.

Any condition that places pressure on the leg veins, including obesity, constipation, pregnancy, or standing for long periods, can contribute to varicose veins.

Doctors aren't always certain what causes them, but they believe that some people inherit a tendency to the condition. Having a history of deep vein thrombosis (in which a blood clot forms in a large vein in the leg) may also be a cause.

Nutrition Connection

Because obesity is a risk factor for varicose veins, maintaining a healthy diet rich in fruits, vegetables, lean proteins, whole grains, and healthy fats is essential for helping prevent the problem. Here's how:

Hit high C. Vitamin C strengthens blood vessels and protects them from free radical damage. High-C fruits and veggies include red pepper, broccoli, citrus fruits, and berries.

Feast on fiber. Reduces strain during bowel movements, which decreases pressure on blood vessels in the legs. Think whole grain cereal, whole wheat pasta, beans, lentils, and popcorn.

Make flavonoids your friend. Flavonoids are antioxidants found in a variety of fruits and vegetables. They have various beneficial actions on blood vessels and play a role in helping protect against cardiovascular disease. At least one small study showed that the flavonoid hesperidin, found in oranges, improved varicose veins.

QUICK TIP: Wedge in oranges

Oranges are one of the most perfect foods to combat varicose veins. They're full of vitamin C, fiber, and flavanoids, all of which help strengthen blood vessels.

Pick some berries. Blueberries, blackberries, and grapes contain antioxidant compounds that help reduce blood vessel leakage and protect vessels from free radical damage.

Beyond the Diet

Some simple daily changes can help prevent varicose veins. Follow these guidelines:

Stand down. If you have varicose veins, or have a family history, avoid prolonged standing. If your job keeps you on your feet, be sure to take frequent breaks to elevate your feet for 10 minutes or so.

Exercise aerobically. A good brisk 20-minute walk is one of the best things you can do for your varicose veins. When you walk, you pump blood back to your heart every time you contract your leg muscles.

Do some leg lifts. While standing, raise yourself on the balls of your feet and then lower your heel back down. Do this calf exercise for 10 minutes several times a day to help your blood vessels force blood upward.

YEAST INFECTIONS

FOODS THAT HARM
   Sugary foods

FOODS THAT HEAL
   Yogurt with live, active cultures
   Sauerkraut
   Tempeh
   Kefir
   Miso
   Cherries
   Grapes
   Apricots

The moist, dark areas of your body—the mouth, vagina, and rectum—are full of beneficial bacteria that help protect against infection as well as fungi that normally cause no problems. But certain conditions change that balance, killing off beneficial bacteria that keep yeast populations in check. Common culprits include pregnancy and diabetes, both of which can change the acidity of the vagina, making it more vulnerable to infection, and antibiotics, which can wipe out the good bacteria that protect the body from more harmful bacteria. The result? Fungus of the Candida variety, the type behind most yeast infections, can take over. Oral thrush, a white, itchy, sensitive rash in the mouth, and vaginal yeast infections, with their burning itch and discharge, commonly crop up as a result.

Yeast infections can be stubborn, recurring even after successful treatment with medicines and antifungal creams. For that reason, prevention is the best option, and you can start with that yogurt in the refrigerator. Eating foods that strengthen the immune system is also smart because they may help fortify your body against many types of infection, so you might avoid the antibiotics that make you vulnerable to yeast infections.

Nutrition Connection

Follow these tips to reduce your chance of getting a yeast infection:

Enjoy yogurt. Yogurt is cultured with lactobacillus, a "friendly" bacteria that inhibits the growth of *Candida albicans* and also makes it harder for it to adhere to the vaginal walls. Make sure you choose yogurt with live, active cultures, particularly *L. acidophilus*. Avoid sweetened yogurts, because sugar can worsen a yeast infection.

Get some garlic. Garlic is a powerful bacteria fighter. But only recently have scientists discovered that garlic's little bulbs are packed with antioxidants, so eating plenty of garlic should also help keep your immune system running at full steam. Garlic is most effective when eaten raw, so chop some and add it to salads, salsa, and pasta dishes.

Try some fermented foods. Foods like sauerkraut, tempeh (a fermented soy product), kefir (a yogurtlike drink), and miso contain probiotics that in theory could work against the candida fungus in the same way as lactobacillus does.

Ditch the sweet stuff. Yeasts love sugars—in fact, they thrive on them. To starve the troublemakers, make a conscious effort to cut back. That means avoiding fruit juices, sweetened breakfast cereals, ice cream, and desserts as well as anything made with high-fructose corn syrup, like soft drinks and packaged cookies or candy. Try to satisfy your sweet tooth with fruits like cherries, grapes, and fresh apricots or, better yet, have some sweet, crunchy carrots.

Beyond the Diet

Rinse out thrush. Gargling with a warm salt-water rinse: ½ tsp (2.5 mL) of salt to 1 cup (237 mL) of warm water can speed healing and help kill the yeast.

Keep dry and airy down below. Dry yourself off after bathing, don't wear tight panties, and change out of a wet swimsuit as soon as you can. Candida thrive in warm, moist environments.

Stick with cotton. Undies made of synthetic fabrics increase sweating in the genital area.

Avoid soap and fragranced cleansers. These can irritate sensitive skin as can feminine hygiene products.

AGES & STAGES:
Pregnancy & Breastfeeding

At no other time in a woman's life is good nutrition more essential than during pregnancy and the time spent breastfeeding. In the best-case scenario she should evaluate her eating habits before trying to conceive. Women who are too thin are at risk for having babies with low birth weights, while women who are overweight have a greater risk of gestational diabetes and giving birth to an oversized baby. Infants who are either too small or too large at birth are at risk for serious problems, including respiratory disorders.

This is also the time to abstain from alcohol consumption, because alcohol causes the most harm to a fetus during the first trimester of a pregnancy. Fetal alcohol syndrome may cause mental deficiency, facial and heart malformations, an undersized head, and retarded growth.

WHILE PREGNANT: EAT FOR YOU—NOT TWO

The recommended weight gain for a woman of average weight experiencing an average pregnancy is approximately 25 to 35 lb (11 to 16 kg). Women who are underweight at conception may need to gain as much as 40 lb (18 kg), and women who are overweight may be advised to gain no more than 15 to 25 lb (6.8 to 11 kg). Obese woman should not try to lose weight during pregnancy; to do so exposes her fetus to numerous hazards.

Most women need to add approximately 300 calories to their daily diet during the last two trimesters to support normal fetal growth. This is a relatively small amount, despite the saying about "eating for two." When eating for pregnancy, follow these guidelines:

Don't cut back on protein. The average nonpregnant woman needs about 50 to 60 g of protein a day, but most women in North America eat more than that. So, although it's true that you need more protein while pregnant or breastfeeding, the average woman does not need to increase protein intake—just don't cut back. And make your protein choices lean. Good sources include lean meat, poultry, eggs, cheese, and a combination of grains and legumes, all of which also provide other vitamins and minerals.

Increase calcium consumption. A woman in her childbearing years needs 1,000 mg of calcium a day (pregnant teenagers should aim even higher—1,300 mg). Because many North American women do not get enough calcium, it's a good idea to increase consumption of calcium-rich foods before becoming pregnant. This is especially important for women under 30, whose bones are still increasing in density.

One cup (237 mL) of milk has about 300 mg of calcium—almost a third of the way toward the recommended 1,000 mg. One oz (28 g) of cheese contains about 200

Old School
One glass of beer a day increases a mother's supply of breast milk.

New Wisdom
Beer or alcohol doesn't boost milk production. Stick to just one drink per day while breastfeeding.

mg, while ½ cup (118 mL) of yogurt contains about 230 mg. If you're dairy-free, you can get about the same amount of calcium from 2 cups (473 mL) of baked beans, 4 oz (113 g) of canned salmon with the bones, 3 cups (710 mL) of cooked broccoli, $\frac{2}{3}$ cup (156 mL) of tofu, or ¾ cup (177 mL) of almonds. If your doctor recommends calcium supplements, consume them with meals to increase absorption and reduce intestinal upset.

Double up (almost) on iron. A woman's iron requirement almost doubles during pregnancy, going from 18 mg to 27 mg daily. Iron-rich foods include red meat, fish, poultry, fortified or enriched breads and cereals, legumes, eggs, dried fruits, and leafy green vegetables. The heme iron in animal products is absorbed more efficiently than the nonheme iron in plants and eggs. Absorption of nonheme iron can be increased by eating an iron-rich food together with one that is high in vitamin C, such as orange juice.

Even a well-balanced diet provides only about 12 mg to 15 mg of iron a day, and if a woman's iron stores are low when pregnancy begins, she risks developing anemia. Most women need to take an iron supplement during pregnancy. These supplements are absorbed best if they are taken between meals with liquids other than coffee, tea, and milk, which decrease the absorption of iron.

Ensure adequate folate consumption. Adequate folate, or folic acid, can help prevent birth defects, especially those involving the brain and spinal cord. The Recommended Dietary Allowance (RDA) calls for 400 mcg (micrograms) of folate for women who are not pregnant; this increases to 600 mcg during pregnancy and then changes to 500 mcg during breastfeeding.

Because the most critical period for folate consumption is during the first 4 to 6 weeks of pregnancy, when the fetal central nervous system is being formed, women planning to become pregnant are generally advised by their doctors to take a supplement before conceiving. Good dietary sources include green leafy vegetables, orange juice, lentils, peas, beans, asparagus, liver, fortified flour, and pasta.

Bump up fiber. Pregnancy is a good time to add a little fiber since constipation is very common. Eat lots of fruits, vegetables, and whole grains, and drink lots of fluids.

Cut back on caffeine. One study found that pregnant women who consumed more than 200 mg of caffeine per day faced twice the risk of miscarriage. Some evidence suggests that high levels of caffeine may delay conception. Yet other studies have failed to find any association between caffeine consumption and birth defects or premature birth. To be prudent, limit caffeine intake to under 300 mg per day. One cup (237 mL) of filter drip coffee has about 200 mg of caffeine and 1 cup (237 mL) of black tea has about 100 mg. Consult with your doctor on an acceptable amount of caffeine.

Avoid toxins. Mercury is an established environmental pollutant with known toxicity in humans. Pregnant women and women who may become pregnant should avoid king mackerel, tilefish, shark, swordfish, and fresh tuna. Also steer clear of foods that may be contaminated by *Listeria monocytogenes*, bacteria that are widespread in our environment and can cause listeriosis, which is especially dangerous for pregnant women and may even cause miscarriage. Such foods include:

- Hot dogs and luncheon or deli meats unless they are reheated until steaming hot or to an internal temperature of 160°F (71°C)
- Soft cheeses such as feta, brie, and camembert; especially if unpasteurized; blue-veined cheeses; and Mexican-style cheeses such as *queso blanco fresco*
- Pâté or meat spreads, as well as smoked seafood, unless it is an ingredient in a cooked dish
- Raw or unpasteurized milk, or foods that contain unpasteurized milk
- Raw meats, raw fish, raw poultry or eggs, and unpasteurized cider

WHILE BREASTFEEDING: MAINTAIN HEALTHY HABITS

Breastfeeding provides exactly the right amount of nutrition for baby to grow, helps mom regain her prebaby weight, and protects both mother and baby from disease. Plus it's an amazing bonding experience for mom and baby. Decrease iron consumption to 9 mg daily while breastfeeding, but don't cut back on calories. In fact, most women need 500 calories more per day than normal to ensure an adequate milk supply. Drink lots of water, cut back on alcohol and caffeine, watch out for contaminants like mercury or pesticides, and eat a healthy variety of fresh foods. Prenatal vitamins may help to fill in any nutritional gaps, especially of calcium, vitamin D, and DHA.

When a woman stops nursing is largely a matter of personal preference: Some mothers wean their babies after only a few weeks or months, while others continue for a year or more. An adequate alternative to breast milk is commercial infant formula, which provides comparable nutrition but lacks some of the unique benefits of breast milk.

THE BOTTOM LINE

- While pregnant, gain weight gradually and don't believe the saying that you're "eating for two."
- Increase protein, iron, and calcium while pregnant.
- Folate is an essential nutrient that helps healthy development of the baby.
- Reduce caffeine consumption while pregnant.

AGES & STAGES: Infant

New parents probably worry more about feeding their baby than any other aspect of early child care. How do I know if the baby is getting enough? Too much? Should I give the baby vitamins? When do I start solid food?

Parents quickly learn that almost everyone is eager to answer such questions—grandparents, neighbors, even strangers in the supermarket. As might be expected, however, much of the advice is conflicting and adds to a parent's feelings of confusion and uncertainty. So take a deep breath and calm down. Rest assured in the knowledge that if your baby is growing and developing at a normal pace, he's getting enough to eat.

Then, just follow along through these three stages:

0 TO 3 MONTHS: BREASTFEEDING AND FORMULA

On average, most babies double their birth weight in 4 to 5 months, and triple it by the time of their first birthday. Although it varies, breastfed babies generally nurse every 2 to 4 hours for the first month or so. Experts promote "on demand" feeding—in other words, babies should be fed whenever they are hungry for the first 4 or 5 months. Some babies may be sleepy or disinterested in food; a baby who is not feeding at least six to eight times a day may need to be stimulated to consume more. A baby who has regular stools and produces six or more wet diapers a day is most likely getting plenty of food. Here's how to ensure proper nutrition the first few months of life:

Breastfeed for better health. Breast milk provides the best and most complete food to achieve optimal health, growth, and development for full-term infants. In fact, the World Health Organization recommends that a full-term, healthy infant should be exclusively breastfed up to 6 months of age (premature and low-birth-weight babies may need specialized formula in addition to breast milk). Even if you can only breastfeed for a few days, it's worth doing. Colostrum, the breast fluid that is secreted in the first few days after birth, is rich in antibodies, which increase the baby's resistance to infection.

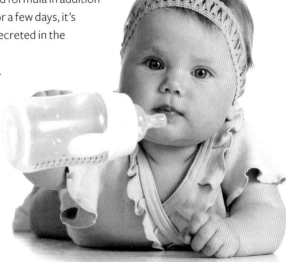

Supplement vitamin D and iron. However, a daily supplement of vitamin D (400 IU) is recommended in the United States and Canada for breastfed babies and should be continued until an adequate amount of vitamin D is consumed through diet.

Bottle-feed as an alternative. Although more than half of all North American women breastfeed for at least the first few weeks, many mothers elect to bottle-feed. Commercial infant formulas provide all the essential nutrients, and, when used according to the manufacturers' instructions, babies thrive on them. Choose an iron-fortified formula. Babies under one year of age should not be given regular cow's milk because it is difficult for them to digest and may provoke an allergic reaction. The cow's milk in most infant formulas is modified to make it easier to digest. Despite this precaution, some babies may require a soy or rice formula.

Sterilize bottles, discard old formula. Bottle-feeding requires more work than nursing. Bottles, nipples, and other equipment must be sterilized. Some formulas are premixed; others are concentrated or powdered, and must be mixed with sterile water. Formula mixed in advance should be refrigerated but not longer than 24 hours; after that, it should be discarded. Any formula that is left in the baby's bottle after a feeding should be discarded; if not, there is a possibility it could be contaminated by microorganisms entering through the nipple opening.

4 TO 6 MONTHS: SOLID FOODS

There is no specific age at which to start solid foods, but for most babies, 4 to 6 months is about right. Starting too early can be harmful because the digestive system may not be able to handle solid foods yet. Also, the early introduction of solid foods may increase the risk of developing food allergies. An infant who is thriving solely on breast milk can generally wait until he is 5 or 6 months old; after that, nursing alone may not provide adequate calories and the nutrients that a baby needs for normal growth. Here's how to start:

Expect messy first feedings. The first solid food must be easy to digest and unlikely to provoke an allergic reaction. Infant rice cereal is a good choice. For the first few feedings, put a very small amount on the spoon, gently touch the baby's lips to encourage him to open his mouth, and place the cereal at the back of the tongue. Don't expect these feedings to go smoothly. A baby usually does a lot of spitting, sputtering, and protesting.

Add iron and other supplements. Beginning at 4 to 6 months of age, babies usually require additional iron, which is typically provided by an iron-fortified cereal. Fluoride supplementation may be required for some infants after 6 months. Babies of vegan mothers may require a B12 supplement. Check with your pediatrician to see if supplements are needed.

Start with milk. The baby should be hungry but not ravenous. Some experts suggest starting the feeding with a few minutes of nursing or bottle-feeding, then offering a small amount of the moistened cereal—no more than a tsp or two—and finishing with the milk. After a few sessions, you can start with the cereal, then gradually increase the amount of solid foods as you reduce the amount of milk.

QUICK TIP:
Practice dental health early

Don't let a baby fall asleep while nursing or sucking a bottle; this allows milk to pool in the mouth, and the sugar (lactose) in it can cause extensive tooth decay. Offering a little water at the end of a feeding rinses any remaining milk from the baby's mouth. The gums and emerging teeth can be wiped gently with a gauze-wrapped finger.

Begin slowly. Introduce one new food at a time, and wait at least 3 days between each new food. If you use home-cooked foods, make sure that they're thoroughly pureed. In addition to rice cereal, try some single-ingredient cereals like oatmeal and barley, strained vegetables and fruits. Potentially allergenic foods, such as eggs, citrus, and peanut products, should be delayed until the baby is a year older, or even later if there is a family history of allergies. Withdraw any food that provokes a rash, runny nose, unusual fussiness, diarrhea, or any other sign of a possible allergic reaction or food intolerance.

7 TO 12 MONTHS: SELF-FEEDING

When they are about 7 or 8 months old, most babies have developed enough eye-hand coordination to pick up finger food and maneuver it into their mouths. The teeth are also beginning to come in at this age. Giving a baby a teething biscuit or cracker to chew on can ease gum soreness as well as provide practice in self-feeding. To help your baby start to feed himself, follow these suggestions:

Think bite-size. Good first solid foods could include dry cereals, ripe bananas or peaches, cooked carrots and peas, cubed cheese, cooked pasta, and cooked boiled or roasted chicken. All foods should be cut into pieces large enough to hold but small enough so that they don't lodge in the throat and cause choking. Never leave your baby unsupervised while feeding.

Pull up a chair. As soon as the baby can sit in a high chair, he should be included at family meals and start eating many of the same foods, even though they may need mashing or cutting into small pieces. Give the child a spoon, but don't be disappointed if he prefers using his hands. At this stage, it's more important for the baby to become integrated into family activities and master self-feeding than to learn proper table manners. These will come eventually, especially if the parents and older siblings set a good example.

Old School
Vegetables should be introduced to baby's diet before fruits in order to increase the acceptance of vegetables.

New Wisdom
It doesn't matter in what order you introduce fruits and vegetables.

THE BOTTOM LINE

- Breastfeeding provides all the essential nutrients a child needs for about the first 6 months of life.
- Breastfed babies may need a vitamin D supplement.
- Growing babies that have regular bowel movements are eating enough.
- Use iron-fortified formula for bottle-fed babies.
- Carefully sanitize bottle and nipples, and discard formula after 24 hours.
- At about 4 to 6 months old, introduce one or two new foods per week.
- When a child is old enough to sit and eat more solid foods, set him or her at the table with the rest of the family.

FOODS FOR THE FIRST YEAR

During the first 3 months of life, breast milk or formula provides all the nutrients a newborn needs. The following chart summarizes the generally accepted guidelines for introducing new foods to babies under 1 year of age. It should be noted, however, that all babies are different; consequently, the timing varies considerably from one baby to another. Check with your pediatrician when your baby is ready.

FIRST MONTH
Breast milk; enough for weight gain and to yield regular soft stools and six or more wet diapers a day. Formula, 2 to 4 oz (60 to 118 mL) per feeding (every 2 to 4 hours).

SECOND AND THIRD MONTHS
Breast milk and formula; 4 to 5 oz (118–148 mL) each feeding; six feedings a day.

Milk and Dairy	Cereal and Other Starchy Foods	Vegetables and Fruits	Meat and Meat Alternatives	Occasional Foods and Foods to Avoid
4 TO 6 MONTHS Total intake: About 30 to 40 oz (887 to 1,183 mL) of breast milk or formula per day, plus small amounts of new foods—start with 1 to 2 tsp (5 to 10 mL) and work up—at two or three feedings a day.				
5 to 6 oz (148 to 177 mL) breast milk or formula per feeding five or six times a day.	Iron-fortified single-ingredient baby cereals.			Avoid honey in the first year due to its link to botulism in infants, and egg white to reduce risk of egg allergy.
6 TO 9 MONTHS Total intake: 28 to 36 oz (828 to 1,064 mL) of breast milk or formula; 2 to 4 oz (60 to 118 mL) of cereal and/or pureed baby food at each of the baby's three meals.				
6 to 8 oz (177 to 237 mL) breast milk or formula per feeding four or five times each day.	Iron-fortified baby cereals (mixed grains is okay). **Daily intake:** ¼ to ½ oz (59 to 118 mL) starchy food over three meals.	Plain, cooked mashed vegetables; plain, soft, mashed fruits. **Daily intake:** Four ¼-oz to ½-oz (59 to 118 mL) servings of fruits and vegetables.	Plain, or pureed meat or poultry; cooked egg yolk; mashed legumes, lentils, and tofu. **Daily intake:** Two ½- to ¾-oz (14 to 21 g) portions.	
9 TO 12 MONTHS Total intake: 20 to 30 oz (591 to 887 mL) of breast milk or formula; 750 to 900 total calories needed per day divided into three meals and two snacks.				
6 to 8 oz (177 to 237 mL) per feeding three to four times a day; yogurt; cheese; cottage cheese .	Soft breads; dry unsweetened cereals; crackers; cooked pasta and rice. **Daily intake:** ½ oz to ¾ oz (118 to 177 mL) total a day.	Soft, bite-size pieces of cooked vegetables; mashed potatoes; soft, ripe, peeled fruit or canned fruits. **Daily intake:** Six ¼-oz (59-mL) servings a day.	Minced or diced lean tender meats, poultry, fish; soft, whole legumes or lentils; diced tofu. **Daily intake:** Total of 2 oz (57 g) of meat a day.	May use moderate amounts of butter (unsalted) and small amounts of jam on bread, toast, and crackers. Do not give peanut butter, which can cause choking. Spices and seasonings can also be added.

AGES & STAGES: Childhood

Between the ages of 2 and 20, the human body changes continuously and dramatically. Muscles grow stronger, bones grow longer, height may more than double, and weight can increase as much as fivefold. The most striking changes take place during puberty, which usually occurs between the ages of 10 and 15 in girls and between the ages of 12 and 19 in boys. Sexual development and maturity take place at this time, which results in a startling physical transformation.

Children need energy for all the growing years: typically 1,300 calories a day for a 2-year-old, 1,700 for a 5-year-old, 2,200 for a 16-year-old girl, and 2,800 for a 16-year-old boy.

The amount of food that a child needs varies according to height, build, gender, and activity level. Left to themselves, most children will usually eat the amount of food that's right for them; however, it is up to the parents to make sure that their children have the right foods available to choose from. Don't fall into the age-old trap of forcing them to eat more food than they want or need. Yesterday's notion of "cleaning your plate" can lead to overeating and weight problems in some cases, or to a lifelong dislike of particular foods. Parents may find it better to serve smaller portions in the first place or to allow children to serve themselves.

> **QUICK TIP:**
> **Recruit kids as sous chefs**
>
> You can involve children in family meals by having them help out with simple mealtime tasks, such as peeling potatoes, preparing salads, or setting the table. If mealtime is a pleasant event, children may practice healthful eating habits later on in life.

TODDLERS (1 TO 4 YEARS): ADJUSTING APPETITE

In most children, appetite slackens as the growth rate slows after the first year; it will then vary throughout childhood, depending on whether the child is going through a period of slow or rapid growth. It is perfectly normal for a young child to eat ravenously one day and then show little interest in food the following day. Choking hazards are still an issue at this age. Don't give them whole nuts or other foods they may choke on.

Follow these suggestions for guiding your toddler to a healthy diet:

Serve several small meals. After the first year, children can eat most of the dishes prepared for the rest of the family. Toddlers, however, have high energy requirements and small stomachs, so they may need five or six small meals or snacks a day. Schedule a toddler's snacks so they don't interfere with food intake during meals. An interval of about an hour and a half is usually enough.

Ride out odd preferences. Toddlers often go on food jags—for example, eliminating everything that's white or green. Such food rituals are often short-lived, although they can be annoying or worrisome if they get out of hand. Respect the child's preferences without giving in to every whim; offer a reasonable alternative.

SCHOOL-AGE CHILDREN (5 TO 9 YEARS): BALANCE AND VARIETY

Children need a wide variety of foods. Carbohydrates—breads, cereals, fruits, and vegetables—should make up the major part of the diet. Protein foods can include meat, fish, milk, soy products (such as bean curd), and combinations of grains and legumes. Milk is an important source of calories, minerals, and vitamins. Children 5 to 9 years old should have two to three milk-product servings every day (some of the milk may be in the form of cheese or yogurt). You can switch from whole to skim or 2% milk at this stage. Grilled and baked foods are preferable to fried and fatty ones for children of all ages.

Include dietary fats. We all need a certain amount of fat for important body functions. Several vitamins (A, D, E, and K) can be absorbed only in the presence of fat, and fats are necessary for the production of other body chemicals, including the hormones that transform boys and girls into men and women. Despite the benefits of fat intake, excessive fat intake in childhood may lead to obesity and many adult diseases. The current recommendation for fat intake is similar in the United States and Canada. Children should consume a diet containing no more than 30% of energy as fat and no more than 10% of energy as saturated fat.

Pump up iron. Iron is an essential mineral for normal growth and development for a child. Unfortunately, many children have inadequate stores of iron because of insufficient intake of iron-rich foods. Foods that contain heme iron, which is easily absorbed, include meat, eggs, fish, poultry, and seafood. While breakfast cereals, legumes, grains, breads, seeds, nuts, dried fruits, and dark green leafy vegetables contain the nonheme variety, which is poorly absorbed. Children should have a variety of iron-containing foods in their diet. In addition, the consumption of vitamin C–rich foods improves the absorption of dietary iron.

QUICK TIP: Sneak in vegetables

Many parents have a battle when it comes to getting children to eat vegetables, but you can win children over by appealing to their taste for bright colors and interesting textures. Choose crisp, raw carrot sticks and other attractive crunchy veggies. Substitute minced vegetables (zucchini, eggplant, mushrooms) for ground meat in spaghetti sauce, or chop chickpeas with grains and other vegetables to make veggie burgers.

FOOD FOR GROWING UP

As children grow, their nutritional needs change; some needs vary between the sexes. The chart below gives an overview of the Recommended Dietary Allowances (RDAs) of certain nutrients for children from ages 1 to 18.

AGES		1-3	4-8	9-13	14-18
Vitamin A (mcg)	Boys	300	400	600	900
	Girls	300	400	600	700
Vitamin D (mcg)		5*	5*	5*	5*
Vitamin E (mg)		6	7	11	15
Vitamin C (mg)		15	25	45	65–75
Niacin (mg)	Boys	6	8	12	16
	Girls	6	8	12	14
Thiamine (mg)	Boys	0.5	0.6	0.9	1.2
	Girls	0.5	0.6	0.9	1.0
Riboflavin (mg)	Boys	0.5	0.6	0.9	1.3
	Girls	0.5	0.6	0.9	1.0
Folate (mcg)		150	200	300	400
Vitamin B6 (mg)	Boys	0.5	0.6	1.0	1.3
	Girls	0.5	0.6	1.0	1.2
Vitamin B12 (mcg)		0.9	1.2	1.8	2.4
Calcium (mg)		500*	800*	1,300*	1,300*
Iron (mg)	Boys	7	10	8	11
	Girls	7	10	8	15
Zinc (mg)	Boys	3	5	8	11
	Girls	3	5	8	9

Asterisks (*) represent daily Adequate Intake (AI). The term *Adequate Intake* is used rather than RDA when scientific evidence is insufficient to estimate an average requirement.

TWEENS AND TEENS (10 TO 16 YEARS): FUELING FOR FAST GROWTH

Eating patterns change with the onset of the adolescent growth spurt. Teenagers usually develop voracious appetites to match their need for additional energy. Adolescents need more of everything to keep up with the massive teenage growth spurt: calories and protein for growth and to build muscles; and protein, calcium, phosphorus, and vitamin D for bone formation. For many the demands of school and social life mean that they eat meals away from home. Suddenly, they are responsible for choosing the major part of their diet. Some may not make the best choices. Others may use food to establish an identity, such as by becoming a vegetarian, without knowing how to maintain proper nutrition. Both obesity and eating disorders can plague adolescents. A sensitive approach is necessary in order to help an adolescent maintain a positive self-image and professional help may be necessary. Here's how to keep them healthy:

Build bone. Calcium is important for forming strong, healthy bones during adolescence and preventing osteoporosis later in life. Youths 10 to 16 years old need 3 to 4 milk-product servings a day—the equivalent of 2 cups (473 mL) of milk and 1 to 2 oz (28 to 57 g, or two slices) of cheese, or 3 to 4 cups (710 to 946 mL) of yogurt—every day. If teens are not drinking milk, they can try a smoothie, fortified soy beverages, cheese on a sandwich, or even chocolate milk.

Emphasize simple swaps. Teenagers often prefer snacks loaded with fat, sugar, and salt: potato chips, french fries, hamburgers, hot dogs, pizza, and candy bars. These are high in sodium and strike a poor balance between calories and nutrition. Encourage some easy-to-remember swaps. For example, ask your teen to choose grilled chicken over breaded, sandwiches with lean meats, or a slice of vegetarian pizza.

Set out healthy snacks. You can generally keep your teenager out of nutritional danger by providing snacks that are high in vitamins, minerals, and protein but low in sugar, fat, and salt. This means buying healthful snack foods, such as fresh and dried fruits, juices, raw vegetables, nuts, cheese, whole grain crackers, unadulterated popcorn, and yogurt. Set them on the kitchen table and place them front and center in the refrigerator so they're handy for your on-the-go teen.

THE BOTTOM LINE

- Set a good example for your child to copy. Share mealtimes and eat the same healthy foods.
- Discourage snacking on sweets and fatty foods. Keep plenty of healthy foods, such as fruits, raw vegetables, low-fat crackers, and yogurt, around for children to eat between meals.
- Allow children to follow their natural appetites when deciding how much to eat.

A GROWING EPIDEMIC: OBESITY

In North America, children are becoming obese (defined as being 20% or more above desirable weight) or overweight in growing numbers and at earlier ages. Overweight children may become overweight adults. The consequence: high blood pressure, high cholesterol, type 2 diabetes, some cancers, sleeping disorders, and orthopedic problems. To keep your kids at a healthy weight, limit foods high in saturated fat after they turn two; give them more fruits, vegetables, and whole grains; encourage them to get at least 60 minutes of physical activity every day; and foster a positive body image.

AGES & STAGES: Seniors

Thanks to modern medicine and all of the healthy-living information out there, the elderly—those 65 and older—are now the fastest-growing segment of the population worldwide. Seniors are often committed to taking better care of themselves, but as you get into your 70s and 80s, it's not always easy to eat right, especially if you live alone. When you don't have a family to cook for, and aren't all that hungry to begin with, reaching for a bag of chips or a frozen dinner may seem way more convenient than sitting down to a well-balanced meal.

Well, ditch the excuses. As you get older, healthy eating habits become even more important, helping to combat debilitating conditions like osteoporosis, diabetes, and heart disease. In fact, one study found that as much as half of all health problems in the elderly are related to poor diet. With that in mind, we put together some simple tips that'll help you eat right and get all the good-for-you, health-boosting nutrients you need, without too much effort.

EAT LESS, BUT MAKE THOSE CALORIES COUNT

As you get older, your metabolism slows down (those stubborn extra inches around your middle may have been your first clue), which means you don't need to consume as many calories in a day.

But while you may be eating less, you need to boost the healthfulness of your meals. Meals should be chock-full of essential nutrients. Particularly important for seniors are calcium, vitamin D, B12, protein, and fiber. The good news: Studies have found that those who eat less actually live longer, not only because they maintain a more healthy body weight, but also because they may be producing fewer damaging free radicals.

COLOR YOUR PLATE

Liven up the dinner hour by creating a plate that looks bright and beautiful, loaded with fresh, healthy foods. Your body needs at least five servings of fruits and vegetables a day to reduce your risk of heart disease, lower your blood pressure and cancer risk, protect your eyesight, and more.

SPICE UP YOUR MENU

No, you're not imagining things—food may taste blander to you than it did once upon a time. That's because your sense of smell and taste start to diminish in your later years, so dishes that may have once tickled your taste buds may now fall flat. Of course, that does nothing to help with a diminished appetite.

Unfortunately, adding salt will just boost your blood pressure, which you definitely don't want. Instead, get creative with spices and seasonings. You can add cinnamon to your morning oatmeal, garlic powder and dried basil to your vegetable soup, and oregano, thyme, rosemary, and sage to everything from baked chicken breasts to roasted potatoes.

CUT DOWN ON RED MEAT AND POULTRY

The Japanese have the longest life expectancy in the world, especially those who live in the Okinawan Islands. What's their secret? A diet loaded with healthy grains, vegetables, fish, and soy, but very scant on meat, poultry, and dairy. Similarly, certain religious groups that follow a vegetarian diet also seem to have a longer life expectancy.

It makes sense when you think about it: Those who consume little red meat and poultry usually weigh less, consume fewer bad fats, and eat more antioxidant-rich vegetables and fruits.

DRINK SIX TO EIGHT GLASSES OF FLUID A DAY

You know that water is good for you and that you should be drinking it more often, but for a variety of reasons, seniors often neglect to replenish their H_2O. Thanks to bladder-control problems that come with advanced age, you may not want to drink too many fluids, for fear you'll be running off to the bathroom every 10 minutes. Plus, your sensitivity to thirst diminishes, so you may not even be aware when your body is in desperate need of water.

All of these issues make you more susceptible to dehydration, which can cause you to become dizzy, fatigued, even confused. It can also contribute to constipation and even kidney problems. So be sure that you're getting at least six to eight glasses of liquid every day. You may even want to purchase two or three refillable BPA-free plastic water bottles that you can keep around your house and in your car to remind you to rehydrate, and make it more convenient to do so.

HAVE A COCKTAIL

Sitting down to a healthy meal is that much more enjoyable with a nice glass of wine or even a cold beer. The best part: a little bit of imbibing with a meal actually aids digestion. Also, according to research, red wine has been shown to have powerful antiaging effects, thanks to an ingredient called resveratrol. Of course, you don't want to go overboard—just one glass will do. Plus, you'll want to check with your doctor to make sure that alcohol won't interact negatively with any medications you're taking.

BEST FOODS FOR SENIORS

Aim to incorporate these foods into your diet every day:

Spinach. Calcium is essential to help maintain good bone health and prevent osteoporosis. Those over 70 need at least 1,200 mg a day, which is a lot. Luckily, it's in a number of healthy foods, including dark green leafy vegetables like spinach—just 1 cup (237 mL) of cooked spinach gives you about 250 mg of calcium.

Milk. In order for your body to absorb calcium, you need a daily supply of vitamin D. Often, you get that dose from exposure to sunlight, but if you find you spend a lot of time indoors, you'll need to supplement. Milk is fortified with vitamin D, so a glass or two every day will give you some of what you need.

Salmon. Omega-3 fatty acids, found in fish oils, are pretty much like a fountain of youth for the elderly. Not only do they prevent heart attack, but studies also found they can reduce your risk of macular degeneration and vision loss, as well as protect against Alzheimer's disease. Researchers recommend eating fish high in omega-3 fatty acids but low in mercury—like salmon, trout, mackerel, herring, and sardines—a few times a week.

Berries. A recent study found that blueberries and strawberries may actually slow down mental decline in the elderly. Apparently, the flavonoids, abundant in berries, have powerful antioxidant properties that reduce the organ inflammation often blamed for cognitive impairment in seniors.

Beans. Legumes are packed with soluble fiber, known to help lower your bad cholesterol and blood sugar and help to curb constipation. As you get older, your digestive system slows down, so you'll need to consume even more fiber to help move things along. Beans are a staple in any vegetarian diet because in addition to all that fiber, they're also full of protein and B vitamins, but with little saturated fat.

Whole grains. Another high-fiber food, whole grains have the added benefit of protecting against heart disease, diabetes, metabolic syndrome and cancer. If your doctor is concerned about you losing weight, whole grain bread and crackers are a tasty, healthy way to help pack on pounds.

Cantaloupe. High in potassium, this sweet melon should be a diet staple for seniors. Not only does it lower blood pressure, it also helps build muscle strength.

THE BOTTOM LINE

- To ward off debilitating diseases such as diabetes and cancer, seniors need to be more aware of their diets.
- Seniors may eat less, but they need to make sure their meals supply the essential nutrients for this stage of life.
- Nutrients especially important during the senior years include calcium, vitamin D, B12, protein, and fiber.
- Properly hydrating with six to eight glasses of water a day can help keep bodily functions running smoothly.

GLOSSARY

Adipocyte—A fat cell.

Aflatoxin—A toxin produced by molds that grow mainly on peanuts, cottonseed, and corn.

Ajoenes—Phytochemicals, found in garlic, that reduce LDL ("bad") cholesterol and possess anticlotting, anticancer, and antifungal activity, according to some studies.

Albumin—A protein found in most animal and many plant tissues that coagulates on heating.

Allicin—A chemical that forms when garlic is crushed or cut and helps reduce LDL cholesterol levels. Responsible for garlic's pungent smell, allicin produces numerous sulfur compounds, possibly with antibacterial properties.

Allyl sulfides—Sulfur compounds, found in garlic, onions, leeks, scallions, and other members of the onion family, that help lower the risk of heart disease, stimulate the immune system, and are under review for their potential to fight cancer.

Alpha-carotene—Like beta-carotene, alpha-carotene is an antioxidant carotenoid and a precursor to vitamin A. It is found in apricots, carrots, pumpkins, and sweet potatoes.

Alpha-linolenic acid—An essential fatty acid linked to a wide range of health benefits. It cannot be made in the body and must therefore be obtained from foods. ALA is important for the maintenance of cell membranes and for creating substances in the body that protect against inflammatory conditions. ALA converts in the human body into two omega-3 fatty acids: EPA (eicosapentaenoic acid) and DHA (docosahexaenoic acid) and is found in canola oil, soybean oil, flaxseed, and walnuts. Smaller amounts are also found in dark green leafy vegetables.

Amino acids—The building blocks of protein. Twenty amino acids are necessary for proper human growth and function. Nine amino acids are termed essential, because they must be provided in the diet; the body produces the remaining 11 as they are needed.

Anthocyanins—Responsible for the red and blue pigments found in certain fruits and vegetables, anthocyanins are flavonoids with the potential to suppress tumor cell growth, to lower LDL ("bad") cholesterol levels, and to prevent blood from forming clots. They are found in apples, berries, cherries, cranberries, black currants, red and purple grapes, plums, and pomegranates.

Antigen—A foreign substance that stimulates the body to defend itself with an immune response.

Antioxidant—A substance that can reduce the damage from free radicals, which steal electrons from normal cells, damaging them in the process. Antioxidants replace the missing electron. Common antioxidants include vitamins C and E, beta-carotene, lutein, lycopene, anthocyanins, and isoflavones, and are found in a wide variety of fruits, vegetables, nuts, and seeds. Antioxidants are beneficial in a host of ailments, including heart disease, cancer, dementia, and macular degeneration.

Arteriosclerosis—The stiffening and hardening of the arterial walls.

Bacteria—Single-celled micro-organisms that are found in air, food, water, soil, and in other living creatures, including humans. "Friendly" bacteria prevent infections and synthesize certain vitamins; others cause disease.

Basal metabolic rate—The energy required by the human body to maintain vital processes during a 24-hour period.

Beta-carotene—One of the most studied of the carotenoids, beta-carotene is a potent antioxidant plentiful in red, orange, and yellow plant foods (as well as in dark green vegetables where the orange color is masked by chlorophyll). It is converted by the body into vitamin A. Food sources include: apricots, carrots, brussels sprouts, dark leafy greens, pumpkin, spinach, sweet potatoes, and winter squash.

Beta-glucan—A type of soluble dietary fiber that helps to lower serum cholesterol levels. It is found in oats, oat bran, barley, brown rice bran, and shiitake mushrooms.

Beta-sitosterol—A plant sterol similar in structure to cholesterol, beta-sitosterol may help to manage benign prostatic hyperplasia (BPH), as well as protect against high cholesterol and cancer. It is found in avocados, corn oil, rice bran, seeds, soy foods, and wheat germ.

B vitamins—Although not chemically related to one another, many of the B vitamins occur in the same foods, and most perform closely linked tasks within the body, mostly by helping enzymes carry out their work. B vitamins are known either by numbers or names, or both: B1, thiamine; B2, riboflavin; B3, niacin; B5, pantothenic acid; B6, pyridoxine; B12, cobalamin; biotin; and folate.

Boron—This bone-nourishing mineral is thought to enhance the body's ability to use calcium, magnesium, and vitamin D. It is found in beans and nuts.

Bromelain—An enzyme derived from pineapples, bromelain is believed to have anti-inflammatory and pain-reducing properties.

Calorie—The basic unit of measurement for the energy value of food and the energy needs of the body. It is defined as the energy needed to raise the temperature of 1 g of water by 1 degree Celsius. Because 1 calorie is minuscule, values are usually expressed as units of 1,000 calories, properly written as kilocalories (kcal). One kilocalorie is what we commonly refer to as a food calorie.

Carotenoids—Pigments that give certain produce their characteristic orange, yellow, and red colors. They may possess potent antioxidant properties to fight heart disease, certain types of cancer, as well as degenerative eye diseases such as cataracts and macular degeneration. To date, more than 600 carotenoids have been identified, including alpha-carotene, beta carotene, beta-cryptoxanthin, lutein, lycopene, and zeaxanthin.

Catechins—A powerful antioxidant found in green tea and other foods, catechins increase metabolism and the rate at which the liver burns fat.

E. coli—Short for *Escherichia coli*, *E. coli* is the name of several types of bacteria. Some types of *E. coli* are harmless, but some strains can cause diarrhea and other symptoms. Harmful types of *E. coli* can be passed through food, water, and contact with infected animals or people. Washing hands, cooking meat thoroughly, washing produce, and avoiding cross-contamination between meat and produce can help prevent *E. coli*-related illness.

Cellulose—One of the main ingredients of plant cell walls, this indigestible carbohydrate is an important source of insoluble fiber.

Chlorophyll—The green pigment of leaves and plants, chlorophyll not only helps to freshen breath but it may also help to prevent DNA damage to cells. Sources include dark leafy greens, kiwifruit, parsley, peas, and peppers.

Coenzymes—Compounds that work with enzymes to promote biological processes. A coenzyme may be a vitamin, contain a vitamin, or be manufactured in the body from a vitamin.

Collagen—Fibrous protein that helps hold cells and tissue together.

Complementary proteins—Proteins that lack one or more of the essential amino acids but which when paired can supply a complete protein. For example, grains are high in the essential amino acid methionine, but they lack lysine. This essential amino acid is plentiful in dried beans, peanuts, and other legumes, which are deficient in methionine. So by combining a grain food with a legume, a complete range of amino acids can be obtained.

Complete protein—Contains all the essential amino acids. It is found in single animal foods; it can also be constructed by combining two or more complementary plant foods.

Complex carbohydrates—Fiber and starch in legumes, vegetables, and grains are complex carbohydrates. A diet that emphasizes complex carbohydrates can help protect against cardiovascular disease, improve blood sugar levels, relieve diarrhea, and ease insomnia. Sources include fruits, grains, legumes, potatoes, and rice.

Cruciferous vegetables—A family of phytochemical-rich vegetables named for their cross-shaped flowers, cruciferous vegetables are touted for their compounds that exhibit cancer-fighting activity in laboratory studies. Cruciferous vegetables include bok choy, broccoli, brussels sprouts, cabbage, cauliflower, kale, mustard greens, radishes, rutabaga, turnips, and watercress.

Deoxyribonucleic acid (DNA)—The basic genetic material of all cells, DNA is the "genetic blueprint" that causes characteristics to be passed on from one generation to the next.

DHA—An omega-3 fatty acid, DHA (docosahexaenoic acid) is important for all phases of the human life cycle. A major building block of human brain tissue and the primary structural fatty acid in the gray matter of the brain and the retina, DHA is vital for brain and eye health. Studies indicate that DHA may have cardiovascular benefits as well as neurological benefits. Although the body has enzymes that convert alpha-linolenic acid to DHA, you get it more efficiently by eating oily fatty fish such as herring, mackerel, salmon, sardines, and trout.

Electrolytes—Substances that separate into ions that conduct electricity when fused or dissolved in fluids. In the human body, sodium, potassium, chloride, and other minerals are electrolytes essential for nerve and muscle function and for maintaining the fluid balance as well as the acid-alkali balance of cells and tissues.

Ellagic acid—A phenolic compound with potent antioxidant capabilities, ellagic acid is thought to fight cancer by inducing cancer cell death as well as by neutralizing carcinogens such as tobacco smoke or air pollution. Sources include apples, apricots, berries, grapes, pomegranates, and walnuts.

Endorphins—Natural painkillers made by the brain, with effects similar to those of opium-based drugs, such as morphine.

Enzymes—Protein molecules that are catalysts for many of the chemical reactions that take place in the body.

EPA—An omega-3 fatty acid, eicosapentaenoic acid (EPA) is linked to cardiovascular and anticancer benefits, and may help improve inflammatory conditions such as rheumatoid arthritis. Although the body has enzymes that convert alpha-linolenic acid to EPA, you get it much more directly and more efficiently by eating oily fatty fish.

Epinephrine—Also called adrenaline, this is an adrenal hormone that prepares the body to react to stressful situations.

Essential fatty acids (EFAs)—The building blocks of necessary fats, EFAs must be obtained through foods. They help form cell membranes, aid in immune function, and produce important hormones. Food sources include canola oil, fatty fish (such as herring, mackerel, salmon, sardines, and trout), flaxseed oil, sunflower seeds, walnuts, and wheat germ.

Fiber, insoluble—Composed of the indigestible parts of plants, insoluble fiber adds bulk to stools, which eases elimination. Insoluble fiber may promote satiety as well. Sources include fruits and vegetables, wheat bran, and whole grains.

Fiber, soluble—Soluble fiber forms a gel-like mass around food particles, slowing down the rate of digestion and absorption as well as preventing cholesterol from being absorbed. Pectin and beta-glucan are two types of soluble fiber that are particularly beneficial for lowering cholesterol levels. Soluble fiber also helps to manage diarrhea and may regulate levels of blood glucose as well. Sources include apples, barley, beans and lentils, citrus fruits, dried peas, flax, oats, and psyllium.

Flavonoids—Powerful antioxidants, flavonoids are phytochemicals linked to a reduced risk of cardiovascular disease and may impede the development of cancer. The free-radical scavenging properties of flavonoids are thought to inhibit clot formation, act as natural antibiotics, slow age-related decline in memory function, bolster blood vessels, and improve the potency of immune cells. Some important flavonoid compounds include anthocyanins, hesperidin, isoflavones, quercetin, and resveratrol. They are found in fruits, grains, tea, vegetables, and wine.

Free radicals—Unstable, highly reactive molecules that are the products of metabolism and also form as a result of environmental pollution such as cigarette smoke. Free radicals contribute to "oxidative stress," which is implicated in premature aging as well as the onset of many diseases.

Fructooligosaccharides (FOS)—Indigestible carbohydrate compounds, fructooligosaccharides are thought to encourage the growth of friendly bacteria in the body and may reduce the amount of toxins produced by unfriendly flora in the colon. They are found in asparagus, bananas, garlic, Jerusalem artichokes, and onions.

Genistein—A potent isoflavone with estrogenlike activity, genistein may help balance hormones and might reduce the risk for hormone-related cancer, such as prostate cancer, as well as help prevent fibrocystic breasts and premenstrual syndrome. It is found primarily in soy products.

Glucose—A simple sugar (monosaccharide) that is the body's prime energy source. Blood levels of glucose are regulated by several hormones, including insulin.

Gluten—A protein in barley, buckwheat, oats, rye, and wheat. Certain people, particularly those with celiac disease, have an intolerance to it and experience an adverse gastrointestinal reaction necessitating the avoidance of foods made with these grains.

Glycogen—A form of glucose stored in the liver and muscles, which is converted back into glucose when needed.

Goitrogens—When eaten in large quantities, goitrogens in uncooked foods have the potential to interfere with the absorption of iodine and slow thyroid function. Goitrogens are primarily found in cabbage, turnips, mustard greens, and radishes, but in relatively small quantities.

Heme iron—A mineral found in animal foods such as red meat, pork, and eggs; the body absorbs about four times as much heme iron as nonheme iron, which is found in plants.

Hemoglobin—The iron-containing pigment in our red blood cells that carries oxygen.

Hesperidin—A flavonoid found in citrus fruits and juices, hesperidin may improve the integrity of capillary linings.

High-density lipoproteins (HDLs)—The smallest and "heaviest" lipoproteins, they retrieve cholesterol from the tissues and transport it to the liver to be removed from the body; called "good cholesterol," because high blood levels of HDLs are considered desirable in lowering heart disease risk.

High-fructose corn syrup—High-fructose corn syrup (HFCS) is a sweetener made from corn that is found in sodas, breads, frozen foods, and many other processed foods. Research has linked large amounts of added sugar to a variety of health problems, including heart disease and obesity. Because HFCS is one of the most common types of added sugar, many people have been concerned about potential adverse effects. Although no links between HFCS and disease have been proven, some research has suggested that it may upset human metabolism and encourage overeating.

Histamine—A chemical in the body's immune defense, it is released during allergic reactions to cause swelling, itching, rash, and sneezing.

Homocysteine—A compound that results from the breakdown of methionine, an essential amino acid.

Hormones—Chemicals secreted by the endocrine glands that serve as molecular messengers triggering a host of body activities, including growth, development, and reproduction.

Hydrogenation—A process used by many manufacturers to make liquid oil more solid (as in the manufacturing of spreads). This process lengthens shelf life and provides the stability of many baked goods and processed foods. However, the process of hydrogenation creates trans-fatty acids, which raise LDL cholesterol (the "bad" cholesterol) and also lower HDL cholesterol (the "good" cholesterol), increasing the risk of heart disease.

Incomplete proteins—Proteins, usually from plant sources, that lack one or more essential amino acids.

Indoles—Partially responsible for the strong taste of broccoli and brussels sprouts, indoles are a class of glucosinolate phytochemicals present in cruciferous vegetables and may stimulate cancer-fighting enzymes.

Indole-3 carbinol—A well-studied compound and a member of the glucosinolate phytochemical family, indole-3-carbinol is particularly abundant in broccoli and other cruciferous vegetables. It may offer protection against hormone-dependent cancers, such as breast cancer.

Insulin—A hormone produced by the pancreas that regulates carbohydrate metabolism. Insulin causes cells in the liver, muscle, and fat tissue to take up glucose from the blood. Insulin resistance, which leads to type 2 diabetes, occurs when insulin is no longer effective at removing blood glucose.

Isoflavones—Found primarily in soy foods, isoflavones are a major class of phytoestrogens, plant chemicals with mild estrogen activity. Genistein and daidzein are the most prominent isoflavones. Soy isoflavones are under investigation for their potential to ease menopause symptoms and to protect against osteoporosis-related fractures, Alzheimer's disease, high cholesterol, and hormone-dependent cancers, such as breast and prostate cancer.

Ketones—Potentially toxic waste products produced from the body's partial burning of fatty acids for fuel.

Lecithin—A phospholipid constituent of cell membranes and lipoproteins, lecithin is a natural emulsifier that helps stabilize cholesterol in the bile. Lecithin is not an essential nutrient, because it is synthesized by the liver.

Lentinan—A polysaccharide (carbohydrate compound) extracted from shiitake mushrooms, lentinan may have the potential to enhance immunity, as well as to protect against cancer, high blood pressure, and high cholesterol.

Lignans—Phytoestrogens with mild estrogenlike activity. They may have antitumor effects, antimicrobial benefits, and provide relief from PMS and protection against osteoporosis. Food sources include ground flaxseeds, flaxseed oil, soy foods, and grains.

Limonene—A phytochemical found in lemons, limes, and oranges. Now under review for its ability to inhibit tumors and protect the lungs from disease.

Linoleic acid—One of the omega-6 essential fatty acids.

Linolenic acid—One of the omega-3 essential fatty acids.

Lipid—A fatty compound made of hydrogen, carbon, and oxygen, lipids are insoluble in water. The chemical family includes fats, fatty acids, cholesterol, oils, and waxes.

Lipoprotein—A combination of a lipid and a protein that can transport cholesterol in the bloodstream. The main types are high density (HDL), low density (LDL), and very low density (VLDL).

Low-density lipoproteins (LDLs)—These abundant, so-called "bad" lipoproteins carry most of the circulating cholesterol; high levels are associated with atherosclerosis and heart disease since this form of cholesterol builds up on artery walls.

Lutein—Lutein is a pigment in the carotenoid family that is linked to a reduced risk for macular degeneration and cataracts. Lutein is found in green leafy vegetables such as collard greens, kale, spinach, and watercress, as well as corn and egg yolks.

Lycopene—A powerful antioxidant that lends red color to numerous foods, lycopene is particularly abundant in tomatoes and tomato products. Studies have shown lycopene to be protective against prostate cancer, lung cancer, and heart disease.

Macronutrients—The vital energy-yielding nutrients—carbohydrate, protein, and fat—that make up the bulk of our food and work in harmony with micronutrients to keep the body fit and functioning well.

Metabolism—The collective term for the body's physical and chemical processes that are needed to maintain life, including derivation of energy from food.

Micronutrients—Required in small amounts from the diet, vitamins and minerals are non-caloric essential nutrients known as micronutrients. They are critical for normal growth, development, and good health. Micronutrients promote and regulate chemical reactions vital for life and participate in all body processes, such as deriving energy from macronutrients, transmitting nerve impulses, and battling infections.

Monoterpenes—A family of phytochemicals that includes limonene, monoterpenes are under review for their ability to detoxify carcinogens, hinder cancer cell growth, and improve cholesterol levels. Food sources include cherries, citrus fruits, caraway, dill, and spearmint.

Monounsaturated fat—Found in olive oil, canola oil, peanut oil, some margarine, avocado, nuts, and seeds, heart-healthy monounsaturated fat is not easily damaged by oxidation, so is less likely than saturated fat and trans fats to clog arteries. When consumed in place of saturated and trans fats, monounsaturated fats help lower LDL cholesterol levels. These fats are part of the Mediterranean diet, associated with lower rates of heart disease and cancer.

Neurotransmitters—Chemicals released from nerve endings that relay messages from one cell to another.

Nitrates—Nitrogen-containing compounds that occur naturally in certain foods, nitrates are used as preservatives in some meat products, as fertilizers, and in vasodilator drugs.

Nitrites—Compounds that are produced in the body by the action of bacteria on nitrates, nitrites are also used as meat preservatives.

Nitrosamines—Compounds that are formed in food or in the body through the reaction of nitrites with amines. They are regarded as carcinogens, although no definite link has been established between nitrosamines and cancer in humans.

Oleic acid—When consumed in place of saturated fat, this monounsaturated fat is linked to healthier cholesterol levels. Food sources include avocados, canola oil, and olive oil.

Oxalates—Found in the greatest quantities in green vegetables, oxalates are compounds that bind calcium, iron, and zinc, blocking their absorption in the body. In addition, people prone to kidney stones should avoid foods high in oxalates since the compounds may fuel the formation of certain types of kidney stones. Food sources include beet greens, chocolate, chard, cranberries, nuts, parsley, rhubarb, spinach, strawberries, tea, and wheat bran.

Oxidation—A chemical process in which food is burned with oxygen to release energy.

Pasteurization—The process of heating milk or other fluids to destroy microorganisms that might cause disease.

Pectin—A soluble fiber that helps to lower artery-damaging LDL cholesterol. Pectin may also be useful for managing diarrhea and diabetes. Sources include apples, apricots, bananas, carrots, figs, kiwifruits, and sweet potatoes.

Peristalsis—Wavelike muscle contractions that help food and fluids move along through the digestive tract.

Phenylketonuria (PKU)—A condition caused by a genetic defect that prevents metabolism of the amino acid phenylalanine. People with PKU must follow a phenylalanine-free diet and avoid the artificial sweetener aspartame.

Phytochemicals—Naturally occurring plant chemicals that offer protection against a variety of diseases.

Phytoestrogens—Compounds found in plants that exhibit estrogenlike activity and may lower the risk of hormone-related cancers, as well as relieve fibrocystic breasts, osteoarthritis, and symptoms of perimenopause and menopause. The two major classes of phytoestrogens are isoflavones and lignans. Food sources include beans and soy.

Plasma—The clear yellow fluid that makes up about 55% of the blood and carries cells, platelets, and vital nutrients throughout the body.

Platelets—Disc-shaped cells, manufactured in the bone marrow, that are needed for blood coagulation.

Polyphenols—A class of antioxidants, polyphenol phytochemicals are under review for their potential to suppress tumor growth, detoxify carcinogens, interfere with the damaging effects of high estrogen levels, lower the risk of stroke, and prevent plaque buildup in the arteries. Sources include fruits, vegetables, tea, and red wine.

Polyunsaturated fats—Fats containing a high percentage of fatty acids that lack hydrogen atoms and have extra carbon bonds. They are liquid at room temperature (corn and sunflower oils, for instance) unless hydrogen is added. When hydrogen is added, these fats become more like saturated fats and have an adverse effect on blood cholesterol.

Prebiotics—These type of foods act as a food supply to probiotics. Prebiotic properties are found in onions, garlic, leeks, chicory, Jerusalem artichokes, legumes, and whole grains. They're also available in tablet form as a dietary supplement, and food manufacturers have started adding prebiotics to some processed foods.

Probiotics—"Good" bacteria that live in our digestive systems, combat "bad" bacteria, and help maintain the health of the cells that line the gastrointestinal tract. There are many different probiotics with *Lactobacillus acidophilus*, *L. rhamnosus GG*, and bifidobacteria, among those more commonly studied. Probiotics are found primarily in yogurt and are beneficial in the treatment of diarrhea, inflammatory bowel diseases, urinary tract infections, vaginal infections, asthma, obesity, and some cancers.

Prostaglandins—Hormonelike chemicals involved in many body processes, including hypersensitivity (allergy) reactions, platelet aggregation (blood clotting), inflammation, pain sensitivity, and smooth muscle contraction.

Psyllium—The seed stalk of the plantain, which is similar to the banana, psyllium absorbs water and becomes almost like a mucous. Psyllium helps to promote bowel movements and can also absorb the water that leads to diarrhea. Because of the way psyllium moves through the digestive system, it also can help cleanse the bowels. Psyllium comes in many different forms, including capsule as a supplement, powdered, and chopped. It can be added to liquids or sprinkled over foods.

Purines—Compounds that form uric acid when metabolized, purines are found in a number of foods, particularly high-protein foods, such as organ meats. Caffeine (in coffee and tea), theobromine (in chocolate), and theophylline (in tea) are related compounds. People prone to gout or kidney stones should avoid purines.

Pyridoxine—One of the B vitamins, more commonly called B6, this vitamin is essential for protein metabolism and the production of red blood cells. It is important for a healthy nervous and immune system. Food sources include meat, fish, whole grains, avocado, banana, and potatoes.

Quercetin—A potent flavonoid linked to a reduced risk of cancer, cardiovascular disease, and cataracts. Red onions, apples, grapes, red wine, and berries are rich sources of quercetin.

Resveratrol—A phytochemical particularly abundant in the skin of red grapes, resveratrol is under review for its potential to improve cholesterol levels, prevent atherosclerosis, and reduce the risks for stroke and cancer. Sources include red and purple grape juice, and red wine.

Ribonucleic acid (RNA)—A substance present in every cell that translates the information contained in DNA into instructions telling the cell which proteins to synthesize.

Salicylates—Compounds related to salicylic acid that are used for making aspirin and other painkillers and as a preservative. Naturally occurring salicylates in fruits or vegetables may produce allergic reactions in people who are sensitive to aspirin.

Salmonella—A bacterium that is a frequent cause of food poisoning.

Saturated fat—Fat found in animal products such as meat, poultry, and full-fat dairy products, as well as tropical oils such as palm and coconut. They are linked to an increased risk of heart disease, certain cancers, and other diseases.

Serotonin—A neurotransmitter that helps promote sleep and regulates many body processes, including pain perception and the secretion of pituitary hormones.

Stanols—Found naturally in vegetables, nuts, and seeds, stanols are compounds that help lower cholesterol by reducing the amount you absorb from food. In addition, stanols may be added to margarines and other food to boost its health benefits.

Sucrose—Better known as table sugar, sucrose is composed of glucose and fructose. It is obtained from sugarcane and sugar beets; it's also present in honey, fruits, and vegetables.

Sulforaphane—A notable sulfur compound, sulforaphane may increase the activity of cancer-fighting enzymes in the body, reduce tumor growth, block carcinogens from initiating cancer, and fight hormone-related cancer. Best food sources include broccoli and cabbage.

Tannins—Also called proanthocyanidins, tannins may detoxify carcinogens and scavenge harmful free radicals. Tannins in cranberries may protect against urinary tract infections. Note also that tannins reduce iron bioavailability. Sources include blackberries, blueberries, cranberries, grapes, lentils, tea, and wine.

Tartrazine—Also identified as E102, tartrazine is a yellow dye widely used in soft drinks, sweets, and sauces. It acts as an allergen and can cause nettle rash (urticaria), dermatitis, asthma, or rhinitis.

Toxin—Any substance that when introduced into the body is capable of causing an adverse effect.

Trans-fatty acids—Fats that are formed when vegetable oils are processed (hydrogenated) to improve their stability and to make them more solid. A food that lists "hydrogenated vegetable oil" on its ingredient list contains trans fatty acids. Growing concern about these acids is based on research that -suggests high intakes of trans fatty acids may contribute to heart disease by elevating LDL ("bad") cholesterol and reducing HDL ("good") cholesterol. Some margarines (especially stick margarines), solid shortenings, snack foods, commercial frying fats (used in many fast-food establishments), and commercial baked goods are the major sources of trans fats.

Triglycerides—The most common form of dietary and body fat; high blood triglyceride levels have been linked to heart disease.

Tryptophan—An essential amino acid, tryptophan is converted by the body into the B vitamin niacin. Tryptophan stimulates production of serotonin, a neurotransmitter that supports mental health. Complex carbohydrates enhance the absorption and use of tryptophan in the brain.

Uric acid—A nitrogen-containing waste product of protein metabolism, uric acid causes gout when it builds up.

Xylitol — A plant-derived sugar that bacteria just can't metabolize, xylitol is the sweetener for non-sugar gums. Xylitol helps block the cavity-causing process when bacteria creates acid.

Zeaxanthin—Zeaxanthin is a pigment in the carotenoid family that is linked to a reduced risk for macular degeneration and cataracts. Zeaxanthin is found in greens, red peppers, and corn.

INDEX

FOODS
THAT
HARM
FOODS
THAT
HEAL

COOKBOOK

*More Than 250 Delicious Recipes
to Beat Disease and Live Longer*

CONSULTANTS: FRAN BERKOFF, RD, AND KATHLEEN HANUSCHAK, RD

Reader's
digest

The Reader's Digest Association, Inc.
New York, NY • Montreal

ABOUT THIS BOOK

An all-new cookbook companion to the mega-selling food guide

Welcome to *Foods That Harm, Foods That Heal Cookbook!* This companion to the best-selling *Foods That Harm, Foods That Heal* will help you take all of its knowledge about nutrition, healing foods, and harmful foods and put it to use every day, so you and your family can lead healthier, happier lives.

The first edition of the pioneering *Foods That Harm, Foods That Heal,* published in 1997, introduced readers to the explosion of research on the links between nutrition and health and the benefits of whole foods. Subsequent editions—including the latest, published in 2013—expanded on that information to highlight new healing compounds as well as introduce you to new foods and explore the connections that certain foods have to specific ailments.

Knowledge is power, but it only goes so far. You need to know how to put that knowledge to work for you, and that's where *Foods That Harm, Foods That Heal Cookbook* comes in. It is your practical, daily guide. Loaded with 250 recipes plus meal plans for more than 100 ailments, this cookbook gives you the tools you need to get more "foods that heal" into your diet and "foods that harm" out of it.

Foods That Harm, Foods That Heal Cookbook is divided into three sections: Foods, Recipes, and Ailments. The first part of the book is an A-to-Z directory of almost 150 foods along with selected lists of "What They Heal," "How They Harm," and the nutrients they provide. You'll find serving sizes and calorie amounts (for your information only—no need to measure, count, or calculate!), along with advice on how to buy the best products, keep them fresh, and prepare them simply. You'll also find special sidebars about foods that you should enjoy "In Moderation Only," along with tips on how to make them healthier when you do indulge.

Recipes make up the next section. Organized by categories, including Breakfasts, Soups and Stews, Sandwiches and Light Meals, Salads, Entrées, Sides, Snacks, Desserts, and Drinks, they are quick, easy-to-make, and delicious. Each recipe features at least three healing foods and a list of some of the ailments it can heal.

In the third section, you'll find an alphabetical listing of more than 100 ailments—from a common sore throat to debilitating conditions such as multiple sclerosis. For each ailment, we show you which foods can cause or exacerbate that condition, and which can help prevent or treat it. For example, those with arthritis should seek out foods rich in omega-3s, such as fish and flaxseed, but avoid red meat, butter, and other foods with saturated fat. The centerpiece of each entry is a sample daily meal plan with recipes. You'll see exactly what to eat, how to eat it, and when to eat it to maximize the healing benefits. In addition, we provide a list of more healing food recipes and eating tips (in the order they appear in the book) to make it easy for you to plan future menus.

So what are you waiting for? Get out your measuring cups, preheat the oven, and start to cook up a healthier diet.

Introduction:
Cooking to Heal What Ails You..............1

PART 1
Foods

An A-to-Z Guide to Healing Foods

PART 2
Recipes
250 Delicious Recipes for Good Health

Breakfasts

Soups and Stews

Sandwiches and Light Meals

Salads

Entrées

Desserts

Drinks

PART 3
Ailments
Daily Meal Plans to Heal What Ails You

INTRODUCTION: COOKING TO HEAL WHAT AILS YOU

Cooking up healthier meals starts with an understanding of basic nutrition. In this section, you'll get an overview of what you need to know. From there, you'll learn tips to perfect your cooking techniques and get advice on choosing the healthiest method for the foods you're preparing.

Nutrition Know-How

Are fats all bad for you? Is vitamin D a cure-all? And what are phytochemicals, anyway? New research is published every day about the effects of nutrients on our health, and it's easy to become confused by all the details. But the basics are simple. We need two main types of nutrients: macronutrients (carbohydrates, fat, and protein), which we need in large amounts; and micronutrients (vitamins, minerals, and other substances), which we need in smaller amounts. Here's a breakdown of the nutrients you'll hear more about throughout the book.

Carbohydrates

Despite the bad rap they've gotten over the years—thanks to low-carb diets such as Atkins and South Beach—carbs are your body's primary source of energy. They should make up 45% to 65% of children's, teens', and adults' total calories; pregnant and lactating women need even more. Breads, pastas, and cereals are what most people think of as carbohydrates; however, fruits and vegetables (including beans) are carbs, too.

All carbohydrates are made up of different types of sugars that the body breaks down into glucose or blood sugar. Glucose is essential for the proper functioning of your brain, nervous system, muscles, and various organs. Carbohydrates are divided into two groups: simple and complex.

Simple carbohydrates, or sugars, are made of just one or two sugars. They form a short chain that breaks down quickly for a burst of energy that doesn't last long. Some simple sugars are naturally occurring, such as those found in a variety of fruits, some vegetables, and honey. Processed sugars include table sugar, brown sugar, molasses, and high-fructose corn syrup. Sodas, baked snacks, jams, ice cream, and sweets all contain simple carbs that add calories but don't offer much, if anything, in the way of nutrition.

Complex carbohydrates, or starches, are made of longer chains of sugars. These types of carbohydrates are harder to break down and provide longer-lasting energy. Starches are naturally found in most grains, vegetables, and legumes. Unprocessed whole grains are the healthiest; they retain fiber and other major nutrients that can help reduce your risk of heart disease. Refined grains—such as white bread, sugary cereal, white rice, and white pasta—lack fiber and many essential nutrients, and boost heart attack risk by up to 30%. You should aim to make at least half of the grains you eat whole grain. Look for products with at least 3 g of fiber per serving and for the first ingredient to be a whole grain such as:

- Bran
- Brown rice
- Bulgur
- Kasha
- Oats
- Quinoa
- Rye
- Whole wheat

In addition to unprocessed grains, get plenty of legumes, beans, and raw or slightly cooked vegetables and fruits.

Fats

They're not all bad; in fact, fats are essential to health. They are necessary for growth and development in children, the production of sex hormones and prostaglandins (chemical messengers), the formation and function of cell membranes, and the transport and absorption of fat-soluble vitamins such as A, D, E, and K. Some fats, like those found in fish and olive oil, actually lower your risk of heart disease. But the key is to choose the right fats and limit your consumption. Adults should restrict their fat intake to 20% to 35% of each day's calories.

As with carbohydrates, the type of fats you eat is more important than the total amount. Fats fall into two main categories: saturated and unsaturated. Most foods naturally contain both but are higher in one. Many commercially produced foods are made with trans fats, which are rarely found in nature.

Saturated fats generally come from animal sources and include meat, poultry, butter, cheese, and coconut and palm oils. A diet high in saturated fats can raise your risk for heart disease and some types of cancer. Experts recommend that no more than 10% of your daily calories come from saturated fat, especially animal fats.

Unsaturated fats tend to be healthier and may lower cholesterol and blood pressure. Unsaturated fats are divided into two groups: monounsaturated and polyunsaturated. Polys are further broken down into omega-3 and omega-6 fats. Each type affects your health in different ways.

- **Monounsaturated fats:** MUFAs, for short, should be the predominant source of fat in your diet. They improve cholesterol levels, thus lowering your risk of heart disease. Major food sources include olives, nuts, avocados, and olive, canola, and peanut oil.
- **Omega-3 fats:** These are another healthy fat that should be a part of your regular diet. Research shows that people who consume just 1 or 2 servings of omega-3-rich fish per week lower their risk of a fatal heart attack by an average of 36%.

These fats are also important for proper brain function. Omega-3s are found in fatty fish—including salmon, mackerel, herring, and sardines—as well as flaxseed, walnuts, canola oil, and some newer products such as omega-3-rich eggs.

- **Omega-6 fats:** These types of fats can have an opposite effect, increasing your risk of heart disease and some types of cancer if you consume too much. Omega-6 food sources include safflower, sunflower, and corn oils, and some nuts and seeds. While opinions vary on the optimal ratio of omega-3 to omega-6, experts agree that we tend to eat far more omega-6 fats than we need and too few omega-3s.

Trans fats are man-made fats created when a vegetable oil undergoes hydrogenation, a process that lengthens the shelf life of food. The result is that polyunsaturated vegetable oils act like saturated fats, raising LDL (bad) cholesterol levels. Experts recommend that you consume as few trans fats as possible. Trans fats are found in products that list partially hydrogenated vegetable oils in their ingredient lists, such as margarines, crackers, cookies, and commercially fried foods.

Proteins

They are the building blocks that every cell in the human body requires for growth or repair. The antibodies that protect us from disease, the enzymes needed for digestion and metabolism, and hormones like insulin are all proteins. While protein is linked to so many essential functions, you need only 10% to 12% of your daily calories to come from proteins to meet your body's requirements.

Proteins are made up of amino acids. The human body requires 20 different amino acids to build all the proteins it needs. Of those, 11 can be made in the body, but the other nine, referred to as essential amino acids, must come from the diet. With the exception of oils and pure sugar, all foods contain at least some protein, but its quality varies according to the amino acids it provides. Animal protein provides all nine essential amino acids and is therefore referred to as complete, or high-quality, protein. Unfortunately, many animal proteins also come with relatively high amounts of saturated fat. Plant proteins lack one or more of the essential amino acids. To get complete proteins from plants, you need to combine foods such as a grain with a legume. Most North Americans, though, eat too much protein rather than not enough.

Vitamins

To date, 13 vitamins essential to human health have been discovered. They are classified as fat- or water-soluble, according to how they are absorbed and stored in the body. Fat-soluble vitamins (A, D, E, and K) need fat in order to be absorbed. Because the body can store fat-soluble vitamins in the liver and fatty tissue, toxic amounts may build up if a person takes high doses of these supplements. Overdosing is unlikely to happen if you get your vitamins from food. The B vitamins and C are water-soluble so they are more easily absorbed. However, the body stores only a small amount and excretes the rest in urine, so they need to be consumed more often.

Minerals

All minerals are vital to health. Because the body is unable to make them on its own, they must be provided by food. Some minerals, such as calcium, phosphorus, and magnesium, are needed in greater

quantities and your body is able to store larger amounts. Others, such as iron, fluoride, selenium, iodine, zinc, and potassium, are stored in small amounts and you don't need as much of them.

Phytochemicals

These plant chemicals include antioxidants, polyphenols, flavonoids, and a whole host of hard-to-pronounce substances. While they are not technically nutrients, research has shown that many phytochemicals play a critical role in your health. Polyphenols that include the subgroup flavonoids may help prevent heart disease and cancer and lower blood pressure. Carotenoids, such as beta-carotene, lycopene, and lutein, may reduce the risk of some cancers and have powerful antioxidant effects. Allyl sulfides, found in garlic and onions, help strengthen the immune system.

QUICK TIP: Get a vitamin boost

Add shredded or pureed veggies to pasta sauces or soups for an extra dose of nutrients.

While phytochemicals play a wide variety of roles in the body, most research has focused on their potential as antioxidants, which are molecules that stabilize free radicals. Free radicals, unstable molecules that can damage healthy cells, are created every time a cell in your body uses oxygen to derive energy from digested food. Thus, by neutralizing free radicals, antioxidants help prevent cardiovascular disease and cancer, among other ailments. Researchers have identified hundreds of substances that act as antioxidants in our foods, including vitamins C and E, selenium, and carotenoids such as beta-carotene and lycopene.

In order to get all of these nutrients without going overboard on calories, the key is to choose nutrient-dense foods—those with a high proportion of nutrients to calories—and keep your portions reasonable. (See "Portion Patrol" at left.) Remember, even when we list a particular food as being healing for a condition, that doesn't mean you should eat as much as you can of that food.

Smart Shopping

Now that you know the basics of good nutrition, it's time to start shopping. In Part 1 of this book, Foods, you'll see specific buying tips for each food to ensure that you choose the freshest and most nutritious items. You'll also learn how to store each food to prevent it from spoiling and losing nutrients. Here are some general guidelines on how to find the healthiest foods.

What to Avoid

For our ancestors, getting food was fraught with danger, whether they were hunting wild animals or gathering plants they hoped weren't poisonous. Luckily, our modern-day food supply is generally safe. But there are still a few things you may be concerned about.

Pesticides and other chemicals, including fertilizers used on crops, antibiotics and hormones given to livestock, and environmental pollutants such as mercury and PCBs (polychlorinated biphenyls), may cause birth defects, neurological damage, and even cancer in high doses. In the United States and Canada, these chemicals are heavily regulated, and the trace amounts found in our food are unlikely to be enough to affect our health. But it's not a bad idea to limit your exposure to them as much as possible.

Additives include preservatives to prevent spoilage; emulsifiers to prevent water and fat from separating; thickeners; vitamins and minerals (either to replace nutrients lost in processing or to increase nutritional value); sweeteners (both natural and artificial); salt; flavorings to improve taste; and dyes to make everything from candies to soft drinks more visually appealing. Additives are carefully regulated and generally safe to eat, but they are rarely nutritious. The most common additives are sugar, corn syrup, sodium, and trans fats, which can contribute to obesity, high blood pressure, heart disease, and many other health problems. And some additives, such as artificial colorings and saccharin, have been identified by the Center for Science in the Public Interest and other nonprofit groups as ones that may be linked to cancer. So it's best to avoid additives, especially artificial ones, as much as possible.

Foodborne pathogens such as bacteria, viruses, parasites, and toxins can cause different diseases, and food can be contaminated at any point from harvesting to transporting to processing to displaying for sale. While farms, food manufacturers, and restaurants are all subject to inspection by government agencies, it's impossible to completely avoid contamination. But proper food storage and preparation can reduce your risk.

What to Look for

While the lists of pesticides, additives, and other chemicals to avoid can sound very scary, just a few precautions can help to lower your exposure:

Eat a wide variety of foods. Doing so helps keep you from overeating any one type of food that may have high levels of a particular chemical.

Eat plenty of fresh fruits and vegetables. They're rich in fiber and antioxidants that may help protect the body from carcinogens.

Eat whole foods with minimal processing. The less that's been done to get a food from the farm to your table, the fewer additives and other chemicals it's likely to have. In addition to fresh fruits and vegetables, choose fresh fish and meats rather than canned or boxed foods. (Frozen foods, on the other hand, frequently are free of additives.)

Read food labels. Look for shorter ingredient lists and those with ingredients you recognize. And choose products with the lowest amounts of trans fats, saturated fats, sodium, and sugar (which can often be listed as "corn syrup" or any ingredient that ends in "-ose").

Consider buying organically grown foods. Organic foods are grown or processed without the use of any synthetic chemicals. (See "Organic Foods" below.)

How to Store Foods

Of all the potential dangers lurking in your food, bacteria, viruses, and other foodborne pathogens are the most likely to cause acute illnesses like food poisoning. Luckily, there are many things you can do to protect yourself.

ORGANIC FOODS

Organic foods are typically more expensive, so it makes sense to shop selectively. Although there is no evidence that fruits and vegetables with higher residues of pesticides or other chemicals (as identified by nonprofit research groups such as Consumers Union and the Environmental Working Group) pose a hazard, selecting the organic versions of these foods is a logical place to start:

- Apples
- Strawberries
- Spinach
- Imported grapes
- Potatoes
- Lettuce
- Celery
- Peaches
- Imported nectarines
- Sweet bell peppers
- Domestic blueberries
- Kale and collard greens

These foods tend to have a low residue so you don't need to buy organic:

- Onions
- Pineapples
- Asparagus
- Mangoes
- Cabbage
- Sweet potatoes
- Mushrooms
- Avocados
- Sweet peas
- Eggplants
- Cantaloupes
- Kiwis
- Watermelons
- Grapefruits

Finally, consider organic meat. While most people worry about produce, animals actually accumulate residues from the foods they eat, which is stored in their fat. So you may want to buy organic hamburger, steak, pork chops, and lamb to avoid a more concentrated exposure.

- Refrigerate or freeze all perishables within two hours of purchase. If the weather is hot, reduce that time to one hour and use a cooler if possible for high-risk foods, which include meat, fish, shellfish, poultry, eggs, dairy products, mayonnaise mixtures, and moist foods such as poultry stuffing.
- Store grains, flours, and nuts in plastic, metal, or glass containers with tight-fitting lids. Whole grain flours and nuts should be stored in the refrigerator or freezer; other flours and grains should be stored in a dry place between 50°F and 70°F (10°C to 21°C).
- Store tightly sealed oils in a dark cupboard or the refrigerator.
- Most produce is best stored at about 50°F (10°C). If refrigerated, put it in the crisper section.
- Cook frozen vegetables straight from the freezer; don't thaw them first.
- Store meats and fish in the coldest part of the refrigerator, or freeze them. Defrost frozen meat, poultry, and fish on the bottom shelf of the refrigerator. If using the microwave to defrost, cook immediately.
- Fresh milk and cream should be stored in paper cartons, rather than plastic or glass, and should be tightly sealed.
- Store spices and dried herbs in tightly sealed containers in a dark place away from sunlight.
- To store fresh herbs, wash them and stand them upright in a glass containing 1 to 2 in (2.5 to 5 cm) of cold water. Cover with a plastic bag and refrigerate.

Healthy Cooking Basics

You could choose the healthiest foods possible, but depending on the method you use to cook them, you could negate many or all of their benefits. Eating a diet rich in foods that heal requires learning to cook in the healthiest ways possible to maximize the benefits. Forget frying, and give some of these methods a try for your next meal:

Steaming

It takes just as long as other cooking methods and retains more nutritional goodness and flavor from foods. A Chinese study found that broccoli retained more vitamin C when it was steamed as compared to microwaving, boiling, or stir-frying.

Use a flat steamer basket. You'll have more space for food. Bring the water to a rolling boil and spread the vegetables out in a single layer. Cover with a tight-fitting lid to retain the heat. Be sure that the pan containing the water doesn't boil dry.

Try it for fish and chicken. Steaming isn't just for veggies. It's an ideal cooking method for delicate foods like fish, too. You can line the basket with cabbage leaves to prevent sticking.

Don't use salt. Although food can be seasoned before steaming, wait until it's done before sprinkling on the salt, as it will draw out the moisture and nutrients.

Add flavor. Toss thick slices of onions, chopped vegetables such as celery or fennel, lemon slices, or fresh herb sprigs into the boiling water. Their flavors will waft upward and seep into the food as it cooks.

Put it in a packet. You can steam foods in a packet made from parchment paper or aluminum foil. Load your ingredients (traditionally some fish, vegetables, and seasonings of your choosing) into the packets, crimp the edges, and grill or bake until done. The packets will puff up due to steam generated as the food cooks, so open carefully and examine contents for doneness before serving.

Use your microwave. Place freshly washed vegetables in a glass bowl and cover with plastic wrap that has a few holes poked into it. Cooking times will vary depending on the power level and quantity of food, so follow the manufacturer's instructions.

Boiling

Like steaming, boiling is a good method to cook vegetables, meats, and fish quickly without adding any extra fat. Unfortunately, boiling can cause foods, especially vegetables, to lose nutrients. Here's how to preserve them:

Leave skins on root vegetables. Vitamins and minerals are often concentrated in and near the skin. Just make sure you scrub vegetables thoroughly before cooking.

Think big. Chop and slice vegetables into larger pieces to reduce the surface area exposed, thereby minimizing nutrient loss. Cook vegetables whole whenever possible, then slice or chop them after cooking if needed.

Use little water. Cook vegetables in the minimum amount of water. Water-soluble vitamins leach out into cooking water and vanish down the drain when the water is discarded.

Be quick. Cook vegetables only as long as necessary. Long cooking times destroy vitamins that are susceptible to heat.

Give veggies the right dunk. Root vegetables such as potatoes should be covered with cold unsalted water and simmered to cook them through. Leafy green vegetables should be plunged into a large quantity of boiling water and cooked just until their color is bright, to preserve taste and nutrients.

Skip the salt. If you're not in a rush, don't add salt before boiling water. Salted water boils at a slightly higher temperature than plain water so food cooks faster, but increases sodium in your dish.

Braising

Braising is a moist-heat cooking method that requires food to be browned first, and then cooked low and slow in a heavy pot with a tight-fitting lid either on a stovetop or in the oven. Slow cookers are another option for delivering similar results. Whatever equipment you choose, this method is a foolproof way to lock in flavor and render lean cuts of meat tender and delicious when you follow these key rules:

Avoid peeking. Braised dishes lose a lot of heat when you take the top off. Instead, rely on a timer to make sure you're stirring at regular intervals and not extending the cooking time longer than necessary.

Use minimal liquids. Follow recipes closely and don't add extra liquid. Most vegetables and meats give off their own liquids, and the braising process retains moisture. Too much liquid will dilute the flavor.

Cook ahead if you can. Refrigerating your dish overnight will make it easy to remove fat; simply scoop off congealed fat before reheating. Most braised dishes, especially those with complex spices, actually taste better the next day.

Stir-frying

Lean cuts of meat and poultry are perfect for stir-frying, as are firm-textured fish, shellfish, vegetables, and cooked rice and noodles. Because cooking is quick, the flavors, colors, and nutrients are retained. As long as you use only a little oil, stir-frying is a healthy way to prepare foods.

Choose the right oil. You need to use oil that can withstand a high cooking temperature. Good choices are peanut, corn, canola, or sunflower oils. Don't use olive oil because it has a low smoke point and will burn. For the same reason, toasted sesame oil should be sprinkled over a stir-fry toward the end of cooking.

Make your own seasoning. Avoid pre-made stir-fry sauces because they are often high in sodium and added sugars, as well as preservatives. To make your own sauce, whisk together ½ cup homemade chicken stock, 3 Tbsp reduced-sodium soy sauce, 1 Tbsp rice wine vinegar, 1 tsp toasted sesame oil, 1 tsp minced garlic, 1 tsp minced ginger and ½ tsp red pepper flakes. If you want the sauce to thicken as it cooks, dissolve 1 tsp cornstarch in 1 Tbsp of cold water and add it to the mix before using.

Be prepared. Stir-fries cook quickly, so it's essential to have all your ingredients cut up, measured, and marinated before you start cooking.

Heat first. Get a wok or large, deep-based frying pan very hot before adding oil to ensure an even heat. Use about 1 to 2 Tbsp of oil and swirl it around. When it starts to sizzle, you're ready to start cooking. Because hot oil can spit, use a long-handled spatula for stirring.

Go in order. Cook protein foods first and transfer to a plate before cooking vegetables. Start with veggies that require the longest cooking time, such as carrots, and add tender ones, such as bean sprouts, last. In the final few minutes of cooking, toss cooked protein and seasoning sauces into the wok and mix gently until ingredients are thoroughly combined and heated.

Grilling

This popular summertime activity gives intense flavor to meat, vegetables, and even fruit because of grilling's very high temperatures—four to six times higher than can be reached in an oven. The high heat, however, can cause the outside of food to become charred before the inside is cooked through. That's why grilling is best for quick-cooking foods, such as fish, as well as thin cuts of meat and poultry. It is also an excellent method of preparing many vegetables, including eggplant, onion, zucchini, peppers, and mushrooms, and even fruits like peaches, mangoes, pineapple, and bananas. In general, pregrill preparation requires little more than a light brushing of oil to prevent food from sticking to the grill or drying out. Marinating food before grilling also helps and adds flavor without much fat. One downside: Cancer-causing substances can form when fat from meat drips onto hot coals; the resulting smoke deposits those substances on the food. To minimize risks, take the following steps:

Defrost first. Trying to cook frozen meat tends to burn the surface and can lead to dry and tough results.

Avoid chill. If time allows, let meat sit at room temperature for a half hour or so before putting it on the grill, for more even cooking.

Trim the fat. Choose lean cuts and trim all visible fat from meat. Keep meat portions thin so they don't have to spend as long on the grill.

Cover the grill with punctured aluminum foil. The foil protects food from smoke and flames.

Grill for a finishing touch. You can avoid the struggle of making sure your meat is properly cooked through if you partly bake the food in the oven beforehand. Finish it off with a few minutes on the grill for a crusty exterior and succulent interior.

Rely on indirect heat. Don't place the heat source directly under the meat. For example, place coals slightly to the side so the fat doesn't drip on them. When using a gas grill, turn one set of burners off, place meat over the cool side, and cover to cook. Indirect heat is also a good way to ensure more even cooking.

Avoid flare-ups. Burning juice or fat can produce harmful smoke. If smoke from dripping fat is heavy, move the food to another section of the grill or reduce the heat.

Slice off charred parts. It's not always possible to cook meat until it is done without charring it. When that happens, just don't eat those pieces.

Roasting

Roasting is a term for a dry-heat cooking method that can be done at either high or lower temperatures in the oven. It browns food and produces a distinct caramelized flavor, and it's a good option for meat, poultry, and vegetables.

Use the convection. With a fan designed to circulate the air inside, a convection oven allows you to roast foods at a lower temperature with faster results. To convert recipes developed for a conventional oven, lower the heat about 50°F (10°C) and expect your dish to be done about 25% sooner.

Flip the bird. When roasting poultry, consider starting your bird breast side down for juicier results.

Coat lightly. To help foods brown properly and to lock in rich, intense flavors, lightly coat them with oil beforehand. For vegetables and cut meat, place in a plastic bag with oil, seal, and toss to coat.

Use a rack. Elevate meat or poultry on a rack in the pan so it doesn't simmer in the fat drippings. Also, consider using wine or lemon juice to baste the meat instead of pan drippings.

Skim the drippings. If you want to make a quick pan gravy, use a bulb baster to extract the flavorful drippings from the pan. Simply insert the tip beneath the layer of fat that floats on the surface. To remove fat from pan drippings, drop an ice cube into the cooled liquid. The fat will harden around the ice cube and can be easily removed.

Give it a rest. To ensure your finished roast or poultry is moist and juicy, cover your dish loosely with foil and let sit for 15 minutes before slicing or carving. This allows time for the natural juices to seep back into the meat or bird. Carve any earlier and the resulting slices are far more likely to be tough and dry.

Microwaving

There's a lot more that you can do with a microwave beyond heating leftovers and making popcorn. Some models now have built-in sensors that measure the amount of steam in the oven to gauge how long your food needs to cook. Others have incorporated convection oven technology to provide better roasting options. Regardless of these advances, even the most basic microwave ovens are great for boiling water, softening butter and cream cheese, and steaming vegetables. Here's how to make your microwave work for you:

Cook in glass. Or use other microwave-safe dishes.

Opt for undercooking. When in doubt, always slightly undercook the food, then stir (if appropriate) and allow it to rest for a few minutes. You can always return it to the microwave if it needs a little more cooking.

Keep it covered. Most food heats more evenly in microwave ovens when it is covered, and plastic wrap is ideal for that job. It also prevents food from drying out or splashing the inside of the oven.

Don't let plastic wrap touch your food.
Poke a few holes in the top before cooking to release the steam; otherwise, the plastic will deflate onto the food as the steam escapes.

Baking

For healthier versions of cakes, cookies, and pies, you can usually cut the amount of fat in recipes by at least one-third and sugar by up to one-half without substantially jeopardizing texture and flavor. Here are more ways to bake up healthier treats:

Use fruit. You can substitute applesauce, strained prunes, mashed bananas, and other pureed fruits for at least some of the fat in cookie and cake recipes without affecting the taste and texture. While adapting your particular recipes may require some trial and error, in general you should plan to replace the butter you remove from a dish with half as much fruit puree. For example, if you are taking ⅔ cup of butter out, use ⅓ cup of fruit puree instead. When oil is called for, use ¾ of the amount in fruit puree. Since the fruit is sweet, you may be able to use less sugar, too.

Swap sugar for spices. Fruit contains its own sugar, so you can use even less added sugar in fruit pies and other fruit-filled baked goods. Experiment to see how low you can go. For more flavor without the calories, add an extra dash of ground cinnamon or allspice.

Use two flours. Replace half of the all-purpose flour in recipes with the same amount of whole wheat pastry flour for a fiber boost. If you don't have whole wheat pastry flour, try replacing ⅓ of the all-purpose flour with rolled oats in recipes that don't already call for oats. Whirl the flour and oats together in a food processor for a finer texture.

Consider crust options. One easy way to cut the fat content in a crusty dessert

is to use a low-fat graham cracker crust or make a deep-dish crustless pie or cobbler. If you can't bear to part with a flaky crusted pie, make a single-crust pie versus a double. For a real change of pace, put the crust on top instead of the bottom.

Cut the yolks. In general, you can safely replace half the egg yolks. This increases protein and decreases fat and cholesterol. One exception: any recipe that calls for you to beat the yolks and whites separately.

Lighten up toppings and fillings. Substitute condensed skim milk for cream in frostings and pie fillings. Similarly, try strained yogurt cheese instead of high-fat cream cheese for toppings and fillings. Fruit and fruit sauces are good low-calorie toppings.

FOODS

An A-to-Z Guide to Healing Foods

Most of us tend to eat the same foods over and over again. Even if they're healthy choices, the wider the variety of foods you eat, the more healthy compounds you're likely to get and the more enjoyable eating will be. This section is going to introduce an array of new foods and, along with your old favorites, help you pinpoint the ones that can boost your health and heal any ailments you may have.

Each entry includes a list of the ailments or the parts of your body that the food may affect. These lists are not meant to be comprehensive—some foods, like beans and legumes, are jam-packed with anti-inflammatory compounds that protect against cancer, heart disease, and diabetes. But they also stop food cravings, help build bone, boost immunity, and offer many other benefits we couldn't fit on these pages. The ailments that a food may heal or harm are listed roughly in order of how much they may boost or hurt health. This treatment allows you to weigh the possible ben-

efits of a food versus its potential risks. One such example: One such example: Spinach is rich in anti-oxidants that may help prevent cancer, blindness, and birth defects. However, it can also contribute to kidney and bladder stones and interfere with blood-thinning drugs.

In addition to the healthful and potentially harmful effects of specific foods, you'll get calorie info based on typical serving sizes (just to give you an idea, no need to measure!) and find out how to buy and store foods to maintain freshness. (Most foods are available year-round but if there's an optimal time to buy fresh produce, we've noted it here.) Plus, you'll see important food-drug interaction warnings and get ideas on quick and easy ways to incorporate each food into your diet, including delicious recipes from Part 2 to try.

So, get ready to take your taste buds on an exciting adventure as you discover new foods and new ways to prepare your favorites for better health!

ACORN SQUASH

See Squash, page 108

ALMONDS

See Nuts and Seeds, page 76

APPLES

Typical serving size: 1 medium (182 g), 95 calories

HOW THEY HARM

Pesticide residues
Bacterial infection
Allergies

WHAT THEY HEAL

Alzheimer's disease
Colon cancer
High blood pressure
Weight gain
Blood sugar swings
Cardiovascular disease
High cholesterol
Teeth and gums

NUTRIENTS

Fiber
Flavonoids (antioxidants)
Procyanidins (cancer-fighting antioxidant)
Quercetin (antioxidant)
Vitamin C

QUICK TIP:
Bake your way healthy

Golden Delicious, MacIntosh, and Granny Smith are some of the favored varieties for baking. Save Red Delicious and Gala for snacking.

BUYING

Choose apples that are:
- smaller
- firm with no soft spots

Avoid apples that are:
- larger
- discolored
- have soft spots, bruises, or worm holes

STORING

Where: Refrigerator.
How: In plastic bags. Remove any that begin to decay immediately.
For how long: 6 weeks.

COOKING

- Layer apple slices with cashew butter on a toasted whole wheat English muffin.
- Serve apple wedges on a vegetable crudités platter.
- Roast apple chunks with chicken wings.

RECIPES TO TRY

- Pasta with Cabbage, Apples, and Leeks
- Herbed Chicken and Apple Burgers
- Fruity Brussels Sprouts

ALCOHOL, BEER, AND WINE

While studies show there are some benefits to moderate drinking, alcohol is addictive, and overindulging can negate those benefits or worse. It may increase your risk of developing cancer or heart disease, cause liver damage, and affect blood sugar in people with diabetes. Pregnant women should avoid alcohol because of potential adverse effects on the unborn child. Drinking too much may also interfere with vitamin and mineral absorption, as well as provoke mood swings, aggression, and hangovers.

To enjoy some of the benefits alcohol has to offer—relaxation, higher HDL (good) cholesterol levels, less chance of having a heart attack, and maybe even stronger bones— stick to about 8 servings a week (no more than two a day for men, one for women).

KEEP IT HEALTHY

Avoid mixing alcohol and medication. It can cause a host of symptoms, including drowsiness, fainting, nausea, vomiting, and headaches.

Chase a drink with water. If you're out for the evening and know you're going to have several drinks, sip a glass of water in between. You'll drink less and being well hydrated may curb any aftereffects.

Don't drink on an empty stomach. It can cause spikes in blood sugar.

Choose low-cal mixers. Diet sodas or juices, club soda, or sparkling water will cut your calorie and alcohol intake.

WHAT'S IN THE GLASS?

You'll make smarter drinking decisions when you have a little information. The drinks below are organized from least healthy to healthiest.

	SERVING SIZE	ALCOHOL VOLUME	CALORIES	BOTTOM LINE
Frozen drinks such as piña coladas, daiquiris	10 oz (300 mL)	10%	375-770	A low alcohol content, but a serious calorie wallop
Creamy mixed drinks like white Russians, mudslides	5 oz (150 mL)	17.7%	275-465	Basically these are desserts in a glass
Martini	4 oz (120 mL)	43%	220-260	Get a dose of healthy fats by adding olives
Margarita	8 oz (225 mL)	10%	280-340	Syrups or homemade blends can add sugar and calories
Clear drinks like vodka tonics	6 oz (180 mL)	14%	150-175	Calorie-free mixes like tonic cut calories and alcohol
Sparkling wine/champagne	5 oz (150 mL)	13%	105-120	Similar benefits as red and white wine
Stouts/dark beer	12 oz (355 mL)	7%	130-190	More flavonoids, but also more calories than lighter beer
Mimosa, Bloody Mary	5 oz (150 mL)	6%	90-120	Vitamin C and minerals from juice mixers
Regular beer	12 oz (355 mL)	5%	150	Some healthy compounds
Light beer	12 oz (355 mL)	5%	95-140	Some healthy compounds and fewer calories
White wine	5 oz (150 mL)	11.5%	90-120	Healthy flavonoids
Red wine	5 oz (150 mL)	11.5%	95-125	Resveratrol and 8 times more healthy flavonoids than white
Wine spritzer	8 oz (225 mL)	6%	75-100	Healthy flavonoids with fewer calories

APRICOTS

Typical serving size: 3 medium (115 g), 51 calories; ¼ cup dried (33 g), 78 calories

HOW THEY HARM
Allergies
Cavities

WHAT THEY HEAL
Cancer
High cholesterol
High blood pressure
Nerves and muscles
Eyes

NUTRIENTS
Beta-carotene
Iron
Pectin (soluble fiber)
Potassium
Vitamin C

BUYING

Choose apricots that are:
- plump
- golden orange
- slightly soft

Avoid apricots that are:
- pale yellow or greenish-yellow
- very firm
- shriveled
- bruised

QUICK TIP: Skip the pit
Doctors warn that apricot pits in any form should not be ingested because eating them could cause cyanide poisoning.

Best time to buy: summer

When buying dried apricots, avoid ones that are brown, which means they've been treated with sulfites.

STORING

Where: Refrigerator when ripe. To help them ripen, place apricots in a paper bag with an apple.
How: Unwashed, in a paper or plastic bag.
For how long: 2 days.

COOKING

- Broil halves sprinkled with brown sugar and cinnamon; top with Greek yogurt.
- Toss chopped dried apricots into a wild rice pilaf.
- Mix all-fruit apricot spread with grated ginger as a glaze for grilled shrimp.

RECIPES TO TRY

- Turkey Bacon and Apricot Bites
- Wheat Berry Salad with Dried Apricots
- Fruit Salad with Spiced Coconut

ARTICHOKES

Typical serving size: 1 medium, cooked (120 g), 64 calories

HOW THEY HARM
Allergies

WHAT THEY HEAL
Skin cancer
Indigestion

NUTRIENTS

Fiber

Folate

Silymarin (anticancer compound)

BUYING

Choose artichokes that:
- are firm without "give"
- are compact and heavy for their size
- have thick, green, fresh-looking scales
- squeak when squeezed

Avoid artichokes that have:
- thin stalks
- large areas of brown on the scales
- spreading scales
- grayish-black discoloration
- mold
- worm injury

Best time to buy: spring

STORING

Where: Refrigerator.

How: Unwashed, in a plastic bag.

For how long: 1 week. For maximum taste and tenderness, cook as soon as possible.

COOKING

- Toss thinly sliced raw baby artichokes into a mixed green salad.
- Top bruschetta with sliced marinated artichoke hearts and grated parmesan.
- Stir frozen artichoke hearts into a chicken stew about 10 minutes before the end of cooking time.

RECIPES TO TRY

- Orange Chicken with Artichokes and Sun-Dried Tomatoes
- Artichokes with Lentils and Lima Beans
- Warm Artichoke and Bean Dip

ASPARAGUS

Typical serving size: ½ cup cooked (90 g), 20 calories

HOW IT HARMS

Gout

WHAT IT HEALS

Cancer

Aging

Cognitive decline

Edema

Stress

NUTRIENTS

Asparagine (natural diuretic)

Chromium

Folate

Vitamin C

Vitamin K

BUYING

Choose asparagus that are:
- firm, yet tender
- smooth and round
- deep green on the stalks
- purplish on closed, compact tips
- narrow in diameter (thicker ones are less tender)

Avoid asparagus with:
- open and spread-out tips
- mold or decay
- ridges up and down the spear
- excessive sand

A

Asparagus is best eaten the day it is purchased, because the flavor lessens with each passing day.

Best time to buy: early spring

STORING

Where: Crisper drawer of refrigerator.
How: Store stalks with bottoms wrapped in a damp paper towel. If you don't have a crisper, put them in plastic bags and place them in the coldest part of the refrigerator.
For how long: 3 to 4 days.

COOKING

- Grill lightly oiled spears until browned.
- Stir-fry pieces until crisp-tender, drizzle with Thai peanut sauce.
- Bake spears coated with olive oil and grated parmesan cheese.

RECIPES TO TRY

- Asparagus, Egg, and Ham Sandwiches
- Asparagus and Chicken Stir-Fry
- Salmon and Asparagus Farfalle with Walnut-Feta Sauce
- Open-Faced Grilled Vegetable Sandwich
- Beef, Scallion, and Asparagus Roll-Ups

AVOCADOS

Typical serving size: ½ cup cubed (75 g), 120 calories

HOW THEY HARM

- Weight gain
- Allergies

WHAT THEY HEAL

- High cholesterol
- Cardiovascular disease
- Cancer
- Blood sugar swings
- Insulin resistance
- Hair

NUTRIENTS

- Fiber
- Folate
- Magnesium
- Monounsaturated fat
- Potassium
- Sterols (cholesterol-lowering compounds)
- Vitamin B6
- Vitamin E

BUYING

Choose avocados that are:
- slightly firm, but yield to gentle pressure if you're planning to use immediately
- firm if you're planning on using them later

Avoid avocados with:
- bruises
- hard or soft spots

STORING

Where: At room temperature to ripen; in the refrigerator when ripe.

How: In a paper bag to ripen, uncut.
For how long: 2 to 5 days to ripen; 2 to 3 days in fridge.

To retain a fresh green color, avocados should either be eaten immediately or should be sprinkled with lemon or lime juice or white vinegar.

COOKING

- Avocados are best eaten raw.
- Serve sliced avocado with huevos rancheros.
- Layer slices with sliced red onion, tomato, and lettuce on whole grain toast.
- Stuff avocado half with chicken salad dressed with salsa.

RECIPES TO TRY

- Individual Breakfast Tortilla
- Shrimp Seviche with Avocado and Pumpkin Seeds
- Papaya and Avocado Salad

BANANAS

Typical serving size: ½ cup sliced (75 g), 67 calories; 1 medium (7 to 8 in or 17 to 20 cm long) (118 g), 105 calories

HOW THEY HARM

Allergies

WHAT THEY HEAL

Stress, anxiety, and depression
High blood pressure
Blood sugar swings
Muscles
Teething pain
Sleeplessness

NUTRIENTS

Fiber
Potassium
Tryptophan
Vitamin B6
Vitamin C

BUYING

Choose bananas that are:
- firm
- free of bruises
- solid yellow and speckled with brown if you're planning to use immediately
- unripe (with green tips or practically no yellow color) if you're planning to use later

Avoid bananas that:
- have brown spots
- are very soft
- have a strong odor

STORING

Where: Refrigerator when ripe. To ripen, leave at room temperature for a couple of days.
How: In the peel. The peel may turn brown in the refrigerator, but the fruit will not change.
For how long: 3 to 5 days.

COOKING

- Top sliced bananas with low-fat yogurt and a sprinkle of low-fat granola.
- Add slices to chicken curry.
- Drizzle lengthwise halves with honey, cinnamon, and chopped walnuts.
- Serve chunks atop mango sorbet.

RECIPES TO TRY:

- Grilled Fruit en Brochette
- Cauliflower Salad with Cashews
- Banana-Peanut Bread
- Chocolate Banana Soufflés

BARLEY

See also Grains, page 57

Typical serving size: ½ cup cooked (79 g), 97 calories

HOW IT HARMS

Allergies

WHAT IT HEALS

Cardiovascular disease
Weight gain
Blood sugar swings
Anemia
Muscles and nerves

NUTRIENTS

Fiber
Niacin
Selenium
Thiamine

BUYING

Choose:

- pearl, scotch, or pot barley for use in soups and casseroles
- scotch or pot barley for more dietary fiber
- barley meal when making breads
- whole barley for the nutrition (you can often find whole, hull-less barley in the natural foods section)

STORING

Where: Refrigerator or freezer.
How: In an airtight container.
For how long: 6 months.

COOKING

- Toss cooled cooked barley with chopped canned beets, red onion, and a dollop of plain yogurt.

- Serve warm cooked barley with honey and milk for breakfast.
- Toss ¼ cup cooked barley into banana bread batter for extra nutrients and fiber.

RECIPES TO TRY

- Barley and Beet Salad
- Broccoli and Pearl Barley Salad

BEANS AND OTHER LEGUMES

See also Lentils, page 70; Peanuts and Peanut Butter, page 88; Peas and Pea Pods, page 89; Soy, page 105

Typical serving size: ½ cup (86 to 128 g), 108 to 143 calories

HOW THEY HARM

Nutrient absorption
Gout
Favism (in susceptible people)
Allergies
Drug interaction
Flatulence

WHAT THEY HEAL

Cardiovascular disease
High cholesterol
Cancer
Diabetes
Weight gain

NUTRIENTS

Calcium

Copper

Fiber

Folate

Iron

Isoflavones (phytochemical that protects against heart disease)

Magnesium

Manganese

Phosphorous

Phytosterols (anticancer and cholesterol-lowering compounds)

Potassium

Protein

Saponins (cholesterol-lowering compounds)

Thiamin

Zinc

BUYING

Choose beans that:

- are firm, clean, and whole (dried)
- have a bright color and slight sheen (dried)

Avoid beans that are:

- cracked or chipped (dried)
- in cans with dents
- past the sell-by date

STORING

Where: Cool, dry place away from direct sunlight.

How: In an airtight container.

For how long: Up to 1 year.

BEAN COUNTING

When planning meals with beans, here's how to judge the amount of beans you'll need:

15 oz (425 mL) canned beans = 1½ cups cooked beans, drained

1 lb dry beans = 6 cups cooked beans, drained

1 lb dry beans = 2 cups dry beans

1 cup dry beans = 3 cups cooked beans, drained

You can store cooked beans in an airtight container in the refrigerator for up to 3 days or in the freezer for several months.

COOKING

- Soak dried beans in water for at least 12 hours before cooking.
- Rinse canned beans before using.
- Simmer brown lentils in vegetable broth with carrots, celery, and onions for a quick soup.
- Toss drained and rinsed cannellini beans with canned tuna, scallions, olive oil, and lemon juice.

RECIPES TO TRY

- Italian White Bean Spread
- Lentil Soup with Canadian Bacon
- Couscous-Stuffed Peppers

BEAN SPROUTS

Typical serving size: 1 cup (104 g), 31 calories

HOW THEY HARM

Bacterial infection

Lupus

WHAT THEY HEAL

Cancer

NUTRIENTS

Calcium

Fiber

Iron

Protein

Sulforaphane (anticancer compound)

Vitamin C

WARNING!
FOOD-DRUG INTERACTION

If you take a monoamine oxidase (MAO) inhibitor to treat depression, you should avoid fava beans; the combination can raise blood pressure.

BUYING

Choose sprouts that:
- are crisp with the buds attached
- have firm, white roots that are slightly moist

Avoid sprouts that are:
- musty smelling
- slimy
- dark

STORING

Where: Crisper drawer of refrigerator.

How: Wash the sprouts thoroughly with water to remove any dirt, then place them in a plastic bag.

For how long: 3 days. Rinsing daily under cold water may extend their life. Sprouts can be frozen for up to 1 year if you're going to cook them in the future.

COOKING

- Add bean sprouts to coleslaw.
- Sprinkle sprouts on chili.
- Blend a handful of sprouts in a smoothie.

RECIPES TO TRY

- Crab and Avocado Salad
- Sesame Greens and Bean Sprouts

QUICK TIP:
Avoid sprouts if indicated

Children, the elderly, and people with weak immune systems should avoid eating sprouts because they have been associated with outbreaks of salmonella and *E.coli* infection. Alfalfa sprouts can also prompt a flare-up of symptoms in people with lupus. You can reduce risk of illness by cooking sprouts before eating them.

BEEF AND VEAL

Typical serving size: 3 oz (90 g), calories vary depending on the cut (see charts on page 23 and 24)

HOW THEY HARM
Cardiovascular disease
Cancer
Bacterial infection
Hormones

WHAT THEY HEAL
Anemia
Weight gain
Bones, muscles, cartilage, skin, and blood

NUTRIENTS
Iron
Phosphorous
Potassium
Protein
Selenium
Vitamin B6
Vitamin B12
Vitamin D
Zinc

BUYING

- When buying raw meat, select it just before checking out at the register.
- If available, put the packages of raw meat in disposable plastic bags, to contain any leaks.

Choose:
- lean cuts (see charts on pages 23 and 24)
- bright red beef (maroon if vacuum packed)
- whitish veal with pink highlights
- beef and veal that is firm to the touch

WHAT'S IN THE BEEF?

Choose the leanest cuts for the dish you want to make. The following all contain 10 grams or less of total fat per 3-oz (90-g) serving, and are organized first by cooking method, then from least to most fatty.

CUT	CALORIES & FAT PER 3-OUNCE (90-G) PORTION		AVERAGE SIZE	TOTAL TIME	BEST COOKING METHOD	DONENESS GUIDELINE
Top round steak	169	4.2 g	¾-1 in (1.5-2.5 cm)	1¼-1¾ hr	Braise by covering with liquid, covering dish, and either simmering on stove top or baking in 325°F (160°C) oven	Cook until beef is fork-tender
			1-1½ in (2.5-3.5 cm)	1¾ - 2½ hr		
Shank cross cuts	171	5.4 g	Varies	Varies		
Arm pot roast	179	6.5 g	2½-4 lb (1.25-2 kg)	2-3 hr		
First half of a brisket	181	6.8 g	2½-3 lb (1.25-1.5 kg)	2½-3 hr		
Top sirloin steak	156	4.9 g	¾ in (1.5 cm)	9-12 min	Broil; position broiler pan so that meat is approximately 3-4 in (7.5-10 cm) from the heat	Cook until internal temperature reaches 145°F (63°C) (medium-rare) or 160°F (71°C) (medium)
			1½ in (3.5 cm)	26-31 min		
T-bone steak	150	6.3 g	¾ in (1.5 cm)	10-13 min		
			1 in (2.5 cm)	15-20 min		
Top loin steak (such as strip or New York steak)	164	6.5 g	¾ in (1.5 cm)	9-11 min		
			1 in (2.5 cm)	13-17 min		
Tenderloin steak	160	7 g	1 in (2.5 cm)	13-16 min		
			1½ in (3.5 cm)	18-22 min		
Flank steak	172	7.9 g	1½-2 lb (750 g-1 kg)	13-18 min		
Shoulder steak (chuck tender)	160	8 g	¾ in (1.5 cm)	10-13 min		
			1 in (2.5 cm)	16-21 min		
Rib-eye steak	170	10 g	1 in (2.5 cm)	14-18 min		
Eye-round roast	142	4.1 g	2-3 lb (1-1.5 kg)	1½ - 1¾ hr	Roast at 325°F (160°C)	Remove from oven when internal temperature reaches 145°F (63°C) (medium-rare) or 160°F (71°C) (medium)
Round tip roast	154	6.4 g	4-6 lb (2-3 kg)	2-2½ hr (medium-rare)		
				2½ hr (medium)		
Tri-tip roast	184	9.2 g	1½-2 lb (750 g-1 kg)	30-40 min (medium-rare)	Roast at 425°F (220°C)	
				40-45 mins (medium)		
95% lean ground beef	154	6.4 g	Varies	10-15 min	Pan-brown	Until completely brown

QUICK TIP: Skim excess fat

A quick way to remove fat from pan drippings is to drop an ice cube into the cooled liquid. The fat will harden around the ice cube and can be easily removed.

Avoid:

- ground beef that contains pink slime (listed on labels as Lean Finely Textured Beef)
- products with damaged packaging or excess moisture

STORING

Where: Refrigerator or freezer.

How: In original packaging if possible. Otherwise, tightly wrap in plastic wrap or freezer paper. If freezing longer than 2 months, overwrap these packages with airtight heavy-duty foil, plastic wrap, or freezer paper or place the package inside a plastic bag.

For how long: 1 to 2 days for fresh hamburger, ground beef or veal, and stew meats (3 to 4 months frozen); 3 to 5 days for fresh steaks, chops, and roasts (4 to 6 months for frozen chops, 6 to 12 months for frozen steaks and roasts).

COOKING

- Start with 4 oz (125 g) of raw meat to end up with 3 oz (90 g) cooked.
- Trim all visible fat from your meat. Reduce fat further by broiling, grilling, or roasting on a rack (so fat can drip away).
- Cook ground beef until it reaches 160°F (71°C). Don't eat ground beef patties that are still pink in the middle.
- Chill soups and stews so that the congealed fat can be removed easily, and then reheat the dishes before serving.
- Layer thinly sliced cold roast beef on mini rye toast spread with horseradish and plain yogurt for an appetizer.
- Stir-fry thin strips of boneless beef top sirloin with red bell pepper, garlic, spinach, and a splash of balsamic vinegar.

WHAT'S THE BEST CUT OF VEAL?

The following cuts all contain 10 grams or less of total fat per 3-oz (90-g) serving, and are organized first by cooking method, then from least to most fatty. Trim all visible fat before you cook.

CUT	CALORIES & FAT PER 3-OZ (90 G) PORTION		AVERAGE SIZE	TOTAL TIME	BEST COOKING METHOD	DONENESS GUIDELINE
Round steak	179	5.4 g	¼ in (0.5 cm) thick	30 min	Braise by covering with liquid, covering dish, and either simmering on stove top or baking in 325°F (160°C) oven	Cook until veal is fork-tender
			½ in (1 cm) thick	45 min		
Shoulder (chuck, arm or blade roast)	201	8.7 g	¼ in (0.5 cm) thick	30 min		
			½ in (1 cm) thick	45 min		
Sirloin	173	5.5 g	3-4 lb (1.5-2 kg)	1 ¾-2 ½ hr	Roast at 325°F (160°C)	Cook until internal temperature reaches 145°F (63°C) (medium-rare) or 160°F (71°C) (medium)
Loin	192	7.8 g				
Rib (chop)	180	10 g	1 in (2.5 cm) thick	14 min	Broil; position broiler pan so that meat is approximately 3-4 in (7.5-10 cm) from the heat	

- Roast chunks of marinated veal round steak with cherry tomatoes and pearl onions.

RECIPES TO TRY

- Caraway-Coated Pepper Steak with Cherry Sauce
- Pot Roast with Root Vegetables
- Beef-Fillet Salad with Mustard Vinaigrette
- Tuscan Veal Chops
- Beef in Lettuce Wraps

BEETS

Typical serving size: ½ cup boiled, sliced (68 g), 29 calories

HOW THEY HARM

Kidney stones and gout (beet greens can aggravate these conditions)

Discolored urine and stools

WHAT THEY HEAL

Cancer

Cardiovascular disease

Dementia

High blood pressure

Constipation

Eyes and nerves

NUTRIENTS

Beta-carotene

Calcium

Fiber

Folate

Iron

Potassium

Protein

Vitamin B6

Vitamin C

Vitamin K

BUYING

Choose beets that:
- are small, with greens still attached
- have unblemished skin
- have sturdy, unwilted greens

Avoid beets that are:
- elongated with round, scaly areas around the top surface
- wilted, flabby, rough, or shriveled

Best time to buy: summer and autumn

Beets are also available canned and pre-cooked for easier preparation.

STORING

Where: Refrigerator.

How: Trim each beet, but leave about 1 inch (2.5 cm) of the stem. Place in a plastic bag.

For how long: 2 weeks.

The greens (which are rich in nutrients) wilt quickly, so use them within a day or two.

COOKING

- Boil beets unpeeled to retain nutrients and deep red color.
- Add shredded raw beets to salads.
- Stir finely chopped beet greens into vegetable soup shortly before the end of cooking.
- Stir-fry matchstick-cut beet slices with sliced red cabbage.
- Cook and serve beet greens, the most nutritious part of the vegetable, like spinach or Swiss chard.

RECIPES TO TRY

- Raspberry-Beet Smoothie
- Balsamic Beets with Toasted Pecans
- Barley and Beet Salad
- Orange Beets

BERRIES

See also Cranberries, page 45

Typical serving size: ½ cup (62 to 76 g), 25 to 42 calories

HOW THEY HARM

Allergies
Kidney and bladder stones
Pesticide residue
Intestinal irritation
Dark stools

WHAT THEY HEAL

Cancer
Diabetes
Memory loss
High cholesterol
High blood pressure
Birth defects
Macular degeneration
Constipation
Skin

NUTRIENTS

Anthocyanins (antioxidant)
Ellagic acid (cancer-fighting
   substance)
Fiber
Folate
Pectin (soluble fiber)
Potassium
Vitamin C

BUYING

Choose berries that are:
- firm
- plump
- deep in color

Avoid berries that are:
- soft or watery
- mushy
- moldy
- dehydrated looking or wrinkled
- in containers with juice stains

Best time to buy: summer

STORING

Where: Crisper drawer of refrigerator.
How: In original container (remove any moldy or deformed berries first).
For how long: 1 day to 1 week depending on ripeness (raspberries spoil faster; blueberries tend to last the longest).

COOKING

- Wash berries just before eating or recipe preparation.
- Top strawberry halves with a dollop of part-skim ricotta cheese whipped with grated orange peel.
- Toss blueberries into a spinach salad.
- Stir raspberries into oatmeal.

RECIPES TO TRY

- Blueberry and Cranberry Granola
- Lemony Blueberry Cheesecake Bars
- Mixed Berry and Stone Fruit Soup
- Peach and Blackberry Phyllo Pizzas
- Broccoli Salad with Almonds and Dried Cranberries

BLACKBERRIES

See Berries, page 26

BLUEBERRIES

See Berries, page 26

BRAN

Typical serving size: 1 Tbsp (7 g), 14 calories

HOW IT HARMS

- Irritable bowel syndrome (can aggravate symptoms in people with this condition)
- Mineral absorption (in raw bran only)

WHAT IT HEALS

- Cancer
- Heart attack risk
- Weight gain
- Diverticulitis
- Diabetes
- Constipation
- Hemorrhoids

NUTRIENTS

- Fiber

BUYING

Choose bran that is:
- in a well-sealed container
- from a store that has a high product turnover because bran can go rancid

Avoid bran that:
- contains any clumps

You can find wheat and oat bran in the cereal or baking section of grocery and natural food stores.

STORING

Where: Dark, dry, cool place.
How: In a tightly sealed container.
For how long: Up to 6 months in the refrigerator; up to 1 year in the freezer.

COOKING

- Replace ¼ cup (50 mL) flour with bran in quick bread or muffin recipes.
- Coat fish fillets with bran before sautéeing.
- Add bran to a fruit smoothie.

RECIPES TO TRY

- Pear Rhubarb Muffins
- Toasted Oat-Raisin Bread

QUICK TIP:
Add a little at a time

Gradually increase your intake of bran until your body gets used to it, and drink plenty of water. This will prevent gastrointestinal problems like bloating and gas.

BREAD

See also Grains, page 57

Typical serving size: 1 slice (about 26 g), see chart on page 29 for calories

HOW IT HARMS

- Celiac disease (causes symptoms in people with this disease)
- Allergies
- Diabetes (white bread)
- Fat storage (white bread)
- High blood pressure (high-sodium bread)

WHAT IT HEALS

- Diabetes (whole grain bread)
- Weight gain (whole grain bread)
- Anemia (fortified or enriched bread)

NUTRIENTS

- Fiber (whole grain bread)
- Folate
- Iron
- Niacin
- Riboflavin
- Thiamine

BUYING

Choose breads that:
- are made with whole grains
- contain at least 3 g of fiber per serving
- are 100% whole wheat

Avoid breads that:
- list sugar in any form as one of the first four ingredients

STORING

Where: At room temperature or in freezer, if you plan to keep it beyond its "best before" date or if you think it will become moldy. Don't store bread in the fridge. A single day in the fridge is equivalent to 3 days at room temperature.

How: In its wrapper.

For how long: You'll see the "best before" date on the plastic tie or wrapper. In the freezer, 3 months.

Eat crusty bread and rolls the day you buy them, because they become stale quickly.

COOKING

- Make French toast with (day-old) raisin bread.
- Cut dried rye bread into croutons to garnish a red cabbage salad.
- Serve minestrone over a slice of dry whole wheat bread.

RECIPES TO TRY

- Tomato Biscuits
- Multigrain Seeded Loaf
- Carrot-Flecked Corn Bread
- Cod with Gremolata Crust

WHAT KIND OF BREAD IS HEALTHIEST?

Choose the highest-fiber breads that are appropriate for your dishes. Here's a guide to some of the most common types, listed in order from most to least grams of fiber per 2-oz (60-g) serving.

TYPE	CALORIES PER 2-OZ (60 G) SERVING	GRAMS OF FIBER PER 2-OZ (60 G) SERVING	DESCRIPTION	BEST FOR
Multigrain	149	4.2	Made with a combination of flours and added ingredients, including sprouts and seeds; nutrition facts often comparable to whole wheat bread	All-purpose bread; use leftovers in casseroles and to make bread crumbs
Pita (6.5 in or 17 cm in diameter, whole wheat)	149	4.1	Flat, leavened bread that puffs up during baking and then flattens out to leave a hollow middle, or pocket	Pairing with Middle Eastern dips and salads; excellent base for personal pizzas; cut into wedges and bake until crisp as an alternative to chips
Tortilla (corn: 3 tortillas 6 in or 15 cm in diameter)	120	4	Unleavened Mexican bread made of corn or wheat flour, salt, and water	Mexican dishes and wrap-style sandwiches; thick flour tortillas can make a base for personal pizzas or appetizers
(wheat: 8 to 10 in or 20 to 25 cm in diameter)	187	4		
Whole Wheat	138	3.8	Yeast bread made with whole wheat flour	All-purpose bread; use leftovers in casseroles and to make bread crumbs
Rye	145	3.3	Heavy and dense; may be seasoned with caraway seeds; most softer, deli-type rye breads are made with more wheat flour than rye	All-purpose sandwich bread; pairs well with Eastern European–style dishes like sauerkraut and a variety of sausages
Corn bread	175	1.3	Cornmeal-based quick bread; may be savory or slightly sweet depending on recipe	Stuffing, pairing with Southwestern dishes; slather with equal parts butter and honey for a decadent snack
Foccacia	160	1.1	Disc-shaped yeast bread made from a dough similar to pizza; traditionally flavored with olive oil, onions, garlic, and herbs	Pairing with soups and salads; toss bite-size pieces with olive oil and toast in the oven to make croutons
Challah	170	1	Rich, moist yeast bread usually formed into a distinct braided shape and brushed with egg white for a shiny exterior	French toast, bread pudding; pulse leftover bread in food processor for fresh bread crumbs
French (baguette)	150	1	A long, narrow loaf; crusty exterior	Crostini-style appetizers; use leftover slices in casseroles
Sourdough	140	1	White-flour bread leavened with a fermented wild yeast culture known as a starter	All-purpose bread; pairs well with strong flavors, especially assertive cheeses

BROCCOLI

Typical serving size: ½ cup cooked, chopped (78 g), 27 calories; ½ cup raw, chopped (44 g), 15 calories

HOW IT HARMS

Bloating and flatulence

WHAT IT HEALS

Bladder cancer
Colorectal cancer
Breast cancer
Lung cancer
Cardiovascular disease
Bone health
Colds
Skin
Weight gain

NUTRIENTS

Antioxidants
Beta-carotene
Calcium
Fiber
Folate
Potassium
Sulforaphane (anticancer compound)
Vitamin C

BUYING

Choose broccoli bunches with:
- florets that are dark green, purplish, or bluish green
- tightly closed buds
- stalks that are very firm and slender

Avoid bunches that have:
- pale or yellowing florets
- bendable or rubbery stalks
- open, flowering, discolored, or water-soaked bud clusters
- tough, woody stems

STORING

Where: Crisper drawer of refrigerator.
How: Unwashed in an open plastic bag.
For how long: A day or two after purchasing.

COOKING

- Steam, cook in the microwave, or stir-fry with a little broth or water to preserve vitamin and mineral content.
- Cut an X in the bottom of each stalk for more even cooking.
- Cooked broccoli should be tender enough so that it can be pierced with a sharp knife, and still remain crisp and bright green in color.
- Stir-fry broccoli chunks with garlic and teriyaki sauce.
- Roast florets coated with oil and curry powder on a baking sheet until browned.
- Simmer chopped broccoli in chicken broth until tender; puree for soup.

RECIPES TO TRY

- One-Egg Omelet with Chopped Broccoli, Tomatoes and Cheddar
- Orange Beef with Broccoli and Jicama
- Vegetable Pot Pie
- Pasta Primavera
- Orange-Walnut Broccoli

BRUSSELS SPROUTS

Typical serving size: 1 cup cooked (155 g), 65 calories

HOW THEY HARM

Bloating and flatulence

WHAT THEY HEAL

Cancer

Cardiovascular disease

High blood pressure

Birth defects

Digestion

Cataracts

Weight gain

NUTRIENTS

Beta-carotene

Fiber

Folate

Phytochemicals

Potassium

Vitamin C

BUYING

Choose brussels sprouts that are:
- small, firm, compact sprouts
- bright green in color
- unblemished
- displayed in stores chilled

Avoid brussels sprouts that have:
- yellow or wilted leaves
- a strong, cabbage-like odor
- a puffy or soft feel

Best time to buy: autumn

STORING

Where: Refrigerator.

How: Do not wash or trim sprouts before storing them in a plastic bag. Remove any yellow or wilted outer leaves. For sprouts packaged in a cellophane-covered container, take off the wrapping, examine them, remove any that are in bad condition, return them to container, and re-cover with cellophane.

For how long: 3 to 5 days.

COOKING

- Cut an X in the bottom of the stem for even cooking when using the sprouts whole.
- Make a slaw with shaved brussels sprouts.
- Roast brussels sprouts with pork loin and carrot chunks.
- Sprinkle shredded cheddar cheese over cooked brussels sprouts.

RECIPES TO TRY

- Braised Chicken with Winter Vegetables
- Fruity Brussels Sprouts
- Brussels Sprouts with Caraway Seeds

BUCKWHEAT

See Grains, page 57

BULGUR

See Grains, page 57

BUTTERNUT SQUASH

See Squash, page 108

BUTTER AND MARGARINE

Butter and margarine are both high in calories—one tablespoon has more than 100 calories—and they both contain fats that may be harmful to your heart. So it's important to use both in moderation and choose the one that will be most satisfying to you.

KEEP IT HEALTHY

Make it soft. Buy soft trans fat free margarines in tubs. The softer your spread, the less you'll use.

Combine it with other ingredients. You can reduce the amount of butter or margarine you need to use by boosting flavor with herbs, spices, or low-fat ingredients. Top baked potatoes with chives and blended low-fat cottage cheese. When making cakes, cut the amount of butter or margarine by one-third to one-half and add about half a cup of applesauce for moisture.

Halve it with olive oil. Beat a soft stick of butter until it is smooth. Then slowly beat in ¼ to ½ cup olive oil. You've just significantly cut the amount of saturated fat while adding loads of healthy monounsaturated fat.

Choose margarine with plant sterols. Research has shown that these types of margarines actually improve cholesterol levels.

CABBAGE

Typical serving size: ½ cup cooked, shredded (75 g), 17 calories; 1 cup raw, chopped (89 g), 22 calories

HOW IT HARMS

Bloating and flatulence

High in calories (some coleslaw and sauerkraut)

Sulfites (sauerkraut and other prepared foods

WHAT IT HEALS

Colon cancer

Breast cancer

Cancers of the uterus and ovaries

Diabetes

Weight gain

NUTRIENTS

Beta-carotene

Fiber

Folate

Indoles (anticancer compound)

Potassium

Sulphoraphane (anticancer compound)

Vitamin C

Vitamin K

BUYING

Choose cabbage that has:

- a tight, heavy head
- a vibrant green or red color, depending on type

Avoid cabbage that has:

- wilted, discolored, or dried outer leaves
- large blemishes
- separation of the leaves from the core

STORING

Where: Refrigerator.

How: Unwashed and covered loosely with a plastic bag.

For how long: Up to 2 weeks for fresh, uncut heads; 5 to 6 days for sliced cabbage.

To prevent discoloration, rub cut surfaces with lemon juice.

COOKING

- Cook cabbage quickly in an uncovered pan with as little water as possible to minimize odor. Overcooking can destroy the cabbage's stores of vitamin C.
- Stir-fry sliced green cabbage with scallions and grated ginger until golden.
- Use shredded savoy cabbage as a base for shrimp salad.
- Add slices of napa cabbage to beef noodle soup.

RECIPES TO TRY

- Pork Chops and Cabbage
- Pasta with Cabbage, Apples and Leeks
- Thai-Style Beef Sandwich
- Brown Rice with Cabbage and Chickpeas
- Napa Cabbage Slaw with Peanut Dressing

IN MODERATION ONLY

CAKES, COOKIES, AND PASTRIES

The combination of fat and sugar in these foods makes them nearly irresistible—no wonder they're high on most people's list of favorite foods. Research has shown that this combo actually turns on pleasure sensors in the brain, making you desire more. Unfortunately these tasty treats offer little to no nutritional value, and eating too many of them can lead to weight gain (some desserts can have as many as 1,500 calories), diabetes, and high cholesterol. Additionally, most packaged baked goods are loaded with trans fats, man-made fats that contribute to heart disease. About the only upside to these foods are the mood and energy boosts they provide, However, both are short lived. But don't try to deprive yourself of these foods entirely, it will only make you crave them more. Instead, indulge wisely.

KEEP IT HEALTHY

Go for small portions. You'll still enjoy the pleasures of these foods without all the fat and calories.

Make your own. Cut down on sugar and find healthy substitutes for unhealthy fat with the Healthy Baking tips on page 11.

CANTALOUPE

See Melons, page 34

CARROTS

Typical serving size: ½ cup raw, chopped (64 g), 26 calories; ½ cup cooked, sliced (78 g), 27 calories

HOW THEY HARM

Skin yellowing

WHAT THEY HEAL

High cholesterol

Diabetes

Cancer

Macular degeneration

Cataracts

Night blindness

NUTRIENTS

Beta-carotene

Fiber

Potassium

BUYING

Choose carrots that have:

- bright green tops
- firm bodies, small to medium size
- smooth, even color without cracks

QUICK TIP:
Cook for more nutrition

Cooking increases carrots' nutritional value because it breaks down the tough cellular walls that encase the beta-carotene.

Avoid carrots that have:

- large green areas at the top
- soft spots
- wilted leaves

STORING

Where: Crisper drawer of refrigerator.

How: In perforated plastic bags without green tops; keep carrots away from apples and pears.

For how long: Up to 2 weeks.

COOKING

- Add a pat of butter or a tablespoon of olive oil to cooked carrots for better beta-carotene absorption.
- Stir ½ cup shredded carrot into oatmeal raisin cookie dough.
- Roast carrots tossed in soy sauce and honey until golden brown.
- Add shredded carrots and minced chives to scrambled eggs.

RECIPES TO TRY

- Carrot Cake with Cream Cheese Glaze
- Flank Steak with Carrots and Red Pepper
- Tuna and Carrot Sandwich on Rye
- Braised Carrot, Celery, and Fennel

CANDIES

While chocolate (especially dark chocolate) provides some health benefits (see page 42) and sugarless gum may help prevent cavities, the only thing other types of candy have to offer is sugar. While you may enjoy a quick energy burst, the jolt can have an equally negative effect. The rapid rise in blood sugar from eating candy causes insulin levels to spike. And when your blood sugar crashes after a high, you're likely to feel hungry and tired. Sweets and sugary foods also form an acid bath that is corrosive to tooth enamel and create an environment where destructive, cavity-causing bacteria flourish. The one group that actually benefits from candy in small amounts is people who have hypoglycemia, when they experience severe drops in blood glucose. It's unlikely that anyone can swear off candy forever, so enjoy it only occasionally.

KEEP IT HEALTHY

Pick your favorites. Don't waste the calories on candy that's just so-so. When you do indulge, make sure it's a type you really love and then savor it.

Have sugarless gum. It's calorie-free and may help stimulate saliva flow to flush food particles out of your mouth.

Chew, don't suck. Candies that linger in the mouth longer are more damaging to teeth than those quickly swallowed. However, be careful of chewy caramels and other candies that leave sticky particles behind.

Go nuts. You can minimize blood sugar spikes by choosing candy with nuts in it.

CAULIFLOWER

Typical serving size: ½ cup cooked (62 g), 14 calories; ½ cup raw (50 g), 13 calories

HOW IT HARMS

Bloating and flatulence

WHAT IT HEALS

Cancer

Weight gain

NUTRIENTS

Bioflavonoids (anticancer compounds)

Fiber

Folate

Indoles (anticancer compounds)

Potassium

Vitamin B6

Vitamin C

BUYING

Choose cauliflower that has:

- a firm head
- compact florets
- a snowy, white color
- crisp, green leaves

Avoid cauliflower that has:

- brown spots
- loose sections

Best time to buy: autumn

STORING

Where: Crisper drawer of refrigerator.
How: In a plastic bag.
For how long: Up to 5 days.

COOKING

- Boil or steam cauliflower in a minimum amount of water to retain flavor and nutrients.
- Stir-fry cauliflower florets with smoked paprika and garlic.
- Simmer cauliflower in some chicken broth until tender; puree.
- Sauté cauliflower florets and garlic in olive oil until golden; toss with whole-wheat pasta and slivered green olives.

RECIPES TO TRY

- Spiced Cauliflower with Peas
- Cauliflower and Spinach Casserole
- Vegetable Pot Pie
- Cauliflower Salad with Cashews
- Broccoli and Cauliflower with Cream Sauce

CELERIAC

(also known as Celery Root)

Typical serving size: ½ cup cooked (78 g), 21 calories

WHAT IT HEALS

Weight gain
Cardiovascular disease

NUTRIENTS

Fiber
Phosphorous
Potassium
Vitamin B6
Vitamin C
Vitamin K

BUYING

Choose celeriacs that are:
- small- to medium-size
- firm
- heavy for their size
- smooth

Avoid celeriacs that:
- have soft spots

Best time to buy: autumn and winter

STORING

Where: Refrigerator.
How: In an unsealed plastic bag.
For how long: Up to 1 week. If it turns soft, do not eat.

COOKING

- Place peeled celeriac in some water with a squeeze of lemon juice immediately after cutting, to prevent it from changing color.
- Add shredded celeriac in place of celery in potato salad.
- Cook shredded celeriac with a wild rice pilaf.
- Layer sliced celeriac with potatoes in a gratin.

RECIPES TO TRY

- Ham and Celeriac Pitas
- Sweet Potato and Celery Root Puree
- Pot Roast with Root Vegetables

CEREALS

Not all cereals are created equally. While more than 90% of all commercial cereals are enriched or fortified with various vitamins and minerals—especially iron, niacin, thiamine, vitamin B6, and folic acid—many are high in sugar, and some are also high in salt. Even if you choose whole grain varieties, they can have too much sugar and salt. Granola types can also be high in fat from added oils. In addition, it's very easy to pour out much larger portions than recommended, so you could end up consuming more calories than you think. But if you take the time to read labels and keep portion size in check, cereal can be a healthy way to start your day.

KEEP IT HEALTHY

Read carefully. Some cereals are low in calories and sugar when consumed in small servings. Pay extra attention to the serving size, which often varies from one box to the next.

Start with whole grain varieties or ones with bran added. Check the ingredient list. Whole grain or bran should be at the top.

Look for high-fiber cereals. Aim for at least 4 g per serving.

Keep salt and sugar in check. A serving should have no more than 240 mg of sodium and 13 g of sugar.

CELERY

Typical serving size: ½ cup raw, diced (60 g), 9 calories

WHAT IT HEALS

Weight gain

High blood pressure

Inflammation

Cancer

NUTRIENTS

Beta-carotene

Fiber

Folate

Phthalides (compounds that may lower blood pressure)

Phytochemicals

Potassium

BUYING

Look for celery stalks that are:

- light green
- crisp
- firm
- uniform in color
- have dark leaves

Avoid celery stalks that are:

- bruised
- browning
- hollow

STORING

Where: Refrigerator.

How: Wrap the stalks loosely in plastic wrap.

For how long: 1 week.

COOKING

- Fill ribs with cashew butter and sprinkle dried cranberries on top.
- Scatter thinly sliced celery over tacos.
- Add minced celery to meat loaf.
- Add the leaves to soups, salads, and other dishes enhanced by the flavor of celery.

RECIPES TO TRY

- Spicy Vegetable Cocktail
- Honey-Roasted Rack of Lamb
- Three-Bean Salad with Manchego Cheese
- Shellfish Salad with Herbed Lemon Dressing

**WARNING!
FOOD-DRUG
INTERACTION**
Tyramine—found in aged cheeses such as cheddar, blue cheese, and camembert—also interacts with monoamine oxidase (MAO) inhibitors, drugs sometimes used to treat depression, and can cause a life-threatening rise in blood pressure.

CHEESE

See also Milk and Dairy Products, page 39

Typical serving size: Varies; see chart on page 50

HOW IT HARMS

High in saturated fat and sodium
Migraines
Allergies
Bacterial infection
Drug interaction

WHAT IT HEALS

Diabetes
Metabolic syndrome
Bones
Muscles
Tooth decay

NUTRIENTS

Calcium
Phosphorous
Potassium
Protein
Vitamin B12

BUYING

Choose cheese that:
- contains the words "pasteurized milk" in the ingredient list
- has uniformity in color and texture
- is within the "use-by" date noted on the packaging

Avoid cheese that:
- is missing or has an incomplete label, or does not contain a factory seal

Take advantage of the broad range of low-fat cheeses on the market. Production methods have improved to allow for smoother texture and better taste.

STORING

Where: Crisper drawer of refrigerator.
How: Wrap hard cheese such as parmesan or gouda in waxed paper, then in plastic wrap; wrap blue cheeses and semihard cheeses in plastic wrap; and keep fresh cheeses (like mozzarella or feta) in their packaging in water and change the water every couple of days.
For how long: Hard cheeses up to several months; softer cheeses from 1 to 3 weeks after opening; large pieces of cheese tend to keep longer than shredded cheese.

COOKING

- Puree low-fat cottage cheese in a blender, then season to taste with salt-free herb blend.

WHICH CHEESE SHOULD YOU CHOOSE?

Keep calories and fat in check while selecting the best type of cheese for the dishes you're creating. The cheeses here are organized from least to most fatty.

TYPE	CALORIES PER 1-OZ (30 G) SERVING	FAT PER 1-OZ (30 G) SERVING	DESCRIPTION	BEST FOR
Cottage cheese (low-fat)	81 per 4 oz (125 g) serving	1.2 g per 4 oz (125 g) serving	Technically a mild-flavored cheese curd that is not pressed or cured	Lasagna, jello salads, and desserts, as well as pairing with fresh fruit
Mozzarella (part-skim)	72	4.5 g	Mild, semisoft unripened white cheese; fresh mozzarella is sold in a brine solution; low-moisture mozzarella can be refrigerated for up to a month	Italian-style dishes and salads
Feta (sheep milk)	75	6 g	Compressed curds are cut into blocks and soaked in a brine solution; crumbles easily; salty, tangy flavor	Mediterranean-style dishes, salads
Brie	95	7.8 g	Pale, creamy cheese under a rind of edible white mold; soft texture; flavor becomes stronger with age	Appetizers and cheese plates
Gouda	101	7.8 g	Yellow semihard cheese that develops a nutty sweetness as it ages; young cheeses (aged less than 6 months) are noticeably softer and creamier	Appetizers and cheese plates
Swiss	106	7.8 g	Pale yellow to off-white cheese that may or may not have holes depending on the variety; in general, flavors become more pronounced with age; most young cheeses (aged less than 6 months) are noticeably softer and creamier	Sandwiches and fondue (gruyere and emmental)
Blue	100	8 g	Creamy white and streaked with blue-green ribbons of mold; soft and often crumbly texture; flavor can be strong or mild depending on variety	Fruit, salads, pasta dishes
Monterey jack	100	8 g	Mild, semihard white cheese sometimes marbled with colby (sold as colby jack) or hot peppers (pepper jack); excellent melting cheese	Fruit, Mexican-style dishes, dips
Parmesan	122	8.1 g	Hard, dry, and sharply flavored cheese sold in wedges or already grated	Italian-style dishes
Havarti	110	9 g	Buttery semisoft cheese, similar to swiss, that can be flavored with dill or caraway seeds	Grilled cheese sandwiches
Cheddar	113	9.3 g	Pale yellow to off-white; hard texture; sharp flavor becomes stronger with age	Macaroni and cheese; sandwiches with other strong flavors

- Replace grated parmesan with half the amount of intensely flavored grated romano for pastas and salads.
- Scatter crumbled reduced-fat feta cheese on veggie pita pizzas.

RECIPES TO TRY

- Huevos Rancheros
- Pumpkin Maple Cheesecake
- Turkey Braciole Stuffed with Provolone and Spinach
- Baked Pasta with Garlic and Greens
- Mediterranean Salad with Edamame

CHERRIES

Typical serving size: ½ cup fresh with pits (59 g), 37 calories; ¼ cup dried (40 g), 140 calories

HOW THEY HARM

Allergies

WHAT THEY HEAL

Inflammation

Cancer

High cholesterol

Gout

Arthritis

NUTRIENTS

Anthocyanins (antioxidant)

Beta-carotene

Pectin (soluble fiber)

Potassium

Quercetin (flavonoid)

Vitamin C

BUYING

Look for cherries that are:
- plump
- firm
- green stemmed

Avoid cherries that are:
- bruised

Best time to buy: early summer

STORING

Where: Refrigerator.

How: Unwashed, with stems attached in an open bag or container.

For how long: About 3 to 5 days; cherries spoil quickly, so eat them as soon as possible.

COOKING

- Stir quartered cherries into a wild rice pilaf just before serving.
- Fold pitted cherries into a Waldorf salad.
- Puree cherries and combine them with ice and cold seltzer for a refreshing drink.

RECIPES TO TRY

- Caraway-Coated Pepper Steak with Cherry Sauce
- Fruit Salad with Spiced Coconut
- Savory Cranberry Chutney
- Fruity Granola Mix

CHIA

See Nuts and Seeds, page 77

CHICKEN

See Poultry, page 96

CHICKPEAS

See Beans and Other Legumes, page 20

CHILES

Typical serving size: ½ cup raw, chopped (75 g), 30 calories; 2 Tbsp dried (4 g), 30 calories

HOW THEY HARM

Hemorrhoids

Gastric discomfort

WHAT THEY HEAL

Cancer

Blood clots

Nasal congestion

Weight gain

NUTRIENTS

Beta-carotene

Bioflavonoids (anticancer compounds)

Capsaicin (may prevent blood clots)

Vitamin C

BUYING

Choose chile peppers that have:
- smooth skin
- deep color

Avoid chiles that are:
- bruised or wrinkled
- mushy or have soft spots

Red varieties generally have a higher nutritional content than the green ones.

STORING

Where: Fresh, in the refrigerator; dried, in a cool dry place away from sunlight.

How: Fresh, in a plastic bag; dried, in an airtight container.

For how long: Fresh, up to 2 weeks; dried, up to 4 months.

COOKING

- Remove the white ribs and seeds from chiles for a milder flavor.
- Blend three or four tomatoes, cilantro, chopped onion, a couple of chiles, and a pinch of salt for instant fresh salsa.
- Mix some minced jalapeño chiles into hamburger patties.
- Add a pinch of dried red chiles to pasta salad.
- Include some minced serrano chiles in a marinade for flank steak.

RECIPES TO TRY

- Quinoa with Chiles and Cilantro
- Green Pork Chili

CHIPS AND CRACKERS

See Convenience and Processed Foods, page 47

CHOCOLATE

Typical serving size: Varies; in general, 1 oz (28 g), 150 calories

HOW IT HARMS

High in sugar and fat

Migraines

WHAT IT HEALS

High blood pressure

Cardiovascular disease

Mood disorders

NUTRIENTS

Epicatechin (disease-fighting flavonoids)

Procyanidins (disease-fighting flavonoids)

BUYING

Choose chocolate that:
- is dark, with at least 60% cocoa for the most antioxidants
- has a smooth shiny surface, if visible

Avoid chocolate that has:
- a whitish or gray coating (which indicates blooming)
- milk or white chocolate
- a long ingredient list

White chocolate is a mixture of cocoa butter, milk solids, and sugar. It has no cocoa solids and does not keep well. The darker the chocolate, the less fat and sugar it has.

STORING

Where: In a cool, dry place. Do not store in the refrigerator because this causes "blooming," or separation of cocoa butter from the chocolate.

How: In a tightly sealed container or bag.

For how long: Up to 1 year.

COOKING

- Use crunchy, unsweetened cocoa nibs in place of chocolate chips in baked goods.
- Substitute ½ cup unsweetened cocoa powder for the flour in pancake recipes.
- Dip slices of crystallized ginger into melted bittersweet chocolate.

RECIPES TO TRY

- Nutty Chocolate Chip Cookies
- Chocolate-Almond Biscotti
- Chocolate Banana Soufflés

CLAMS

See Shellfish, page 103

COFFEE

Drinking more than 400 to 500 mg a day of caffeine can pose a number of health problems. Some may just be annoying, like feeling jittery or making frequent trips to the bathroom. But others can be more serious. Caffeine prompts a temporary rise in blood pressure, increases calcium excretion, may interfere with conception, and may raise the risk of miscarriage. If you are susceptible to cardiac arrhythmias, have high blood pressure, suffer from migraines or headaches, are at risk for osteoporosis, are trying to conceive, or are pregnant, you should talk to your doctor about the effect that caffeine may have on you.

If you're not at risk for any of these serious health problems, go ahead and enjoy your cup of joe. Research shows that a moderate intake can reduce your risk of diabetes, Alzheimer's disease, colon cancer, Parkinson's disease, and skin cancer.

KEEP IT HEALTHY

Limit caffeine to less than 500 mg a day. That's the amount in about four 6-oz (180 mL) cups. Most coffee cups today are much bigger, so you may only get to have one or two cups a day. And don't forget to include other sources of caffeine, such as tea or soft drinks, in your tally.

Watch out for specialty coffee drinks. While a 6-oz (180 mL) cup of sugar-free black coffee has only 4 calories, coffee drinks with syrups and whipped cream often have more fat and calories than a rich dessert.

COCONUTS

Typical serving size: 1 cup raw, shredded (80 g), 283 calories

HOW THEY HARM

High cholesterol

WHAT THEY HEAL

Cravings
Digestion
Weight gain

NUTRIENTS

Fiber
Potassium

BUYING

Choose coconuts that have:
- a firm shell

Avoid coconuts with:
- dark or soft spots

STORING

Where: Refrigerator once it's cut.
How: Wrapped tightly in plastic.
For how long: Up to 5 days; whole coconuts can be kept at room temperature for up to a month.

COOKING

- Use reduced-fat coconut milk in place of cow's milk for french toast.
- Toss shredded fresh coconut in a

shrimp salad with lime dressing.
- Sprinkle shredded coconut on high-fiber breakfast cereal.
- Blend shredded raw coconut into smoothies.

RECIPES TO TRY

- Thai Roasted Shrimp
- Fruit Salad with Spiced Coconut
- Thai Coconut Rice

COLLARD GREENS

See Kale and Other Cooking Greens, page 65

CORN

Typical serving size: 1 medium ear (90 g), 77 calories; ½ cup kernels (82 g), 67 calories

HOW IT HARMS

Pellagra (a niacin or tryptophan deficiency)

WHAT IT HEALS

Cardiovascular disease
Cancer
Macular degeneration

NUTRIENTS

Ferulic acid (anticancer compound)
Fiber
Folate
Lutein (antioxidant)
Potassium
Thiamine

BUYING

Choose corn that has:
- moist, green husks
- shiny silks
- plump and healthy kernels all the way to the tip
- some heft for its size
- been frozen rather than canned
- no salt added, if you must buy canned

To check the condition of the kernels, don't strip the husk—it dries out the corn and leaves it susceptible to fungus. Instead, feel around the silk end for firm, plump kernels.

Avoid corn that:
- feels wrinkled, mushy, or dry

Best time to buy: summer

STORING

Where: Crisper drawer of refrigerator.
How: With husks attached.
For how long: Within 1 to 2 days.

COOKING

- Use plain popcorn in place of bread for a poultry stuffing recipe.
- Stir corn kernels into a vegetable casserole.
- Toss corn kernels into a salad made with cooked red quinoa, minced onion, cilantro, and some salsa.

RECIPES TO TRY

- Carrot-Flecked Corn Bread
- Sweet and Spicy Snack Mix
- Cod and Vegetable Stew
- Bulgur with Dried Cherries and Corn

CONDIMENTS

While condiments certainly add zest to food, they generally contribute little nutrition and sometimes add a lot of sugar, fat, sodium, cholesterol, or nitrites. Too much of those can lead to weight gain, high blood pressure, diabetes, heart disease, and even cancer. Used judiciously, though, condiments add variety and make food tastier.

KEEP IT HEALTHY

Stick to the good guys. Salsas, chutney, mustards, and hummus tend to be the lowest in fat and calories, although commercially prepared versions may still contain excess sugar or fat. Those made with cream, butter, egg yolk, and cheese tend to be the most unhealthy. Read labels carefully or make your own.

Buy modified versions. Many condiments are available in low-fat, nonfat, no-added-sugar, or other healthier options.

Check ingredients. If you have allergies or food intolerances, the culprits may be in these products, so read the labels carefully.

CRANBERRIES

See also Berries, page 26

Typical serving size: ½ cup whole (48 g), 22 calories; ¼ cup dried (30 g), 90 calories

HOW THEY HARM

Blood sugar spikes
Drug interaction

WHAT THEY HEAL

Urinary tract infections
Cardiovascular disease
Cancer

NUTRIENTS

Anthocyanins (antioxidants)
Fiber
Flavonols (plant chemical that prevents heart disease)
Proanthocyanidins (plant chemical that prevents heart disease)
Vitamin C

BUYING

Choose cranberries that are:
- firm
- brightly colored
- unsweetened
- bouncy when dropped
- fresh or frozen

Avoid cranberries that are:
- bruised or mushy
- dry or shriveled
- canned or sweetened

Best time to buy: autumn

STORING

Where: Fresh, in the refrigerator; dried, in a cool dark place or in the refrigerator.
How: In their original plastic packaging or tightly wrapped.
For how long: Fresh, up to 4 weeks; frozen, up to a year; dried, 6 months on a shelf or up to a year in the refrigerator.

WARNING! FOOD-DRUG INTERACTION

Do not drink cranberry juice if you are on the medication warfarin. The interaction between the juice and the drug may lead to bleeding.

COOKING

- Add dried cranberries to walnut biscotti dough.
- Stir some fresh cranberries into braised chicken about 10 minutes before cooking time is finished.
- Add some fresh cranberries to an apple cobbler or pie filling.

RECIPES TO TRY

- Rice-Stuffed Squash
- Savory Cranberry Chutney
- Cranberry-Peanut Cereal Bars
- Broccoli Salad with Almonds and Dried Cranberries

CUCUMBERS

Typical serving size: ½ cup sliced (52 g), 7 calories

WHAT THEY HEAL

Weight gain

NUTRIENTS

Folate

Potassium

BUYING

Choose cucumbers that are:
- firm
- brightly colored

Avoid cucumbers that have:
- soft spots, blemishes, or bruises
- wrinkled or dry looking skin

QUICK TIP: Snack on cucumbers in hot weather

The interior flesh of cucumbers is about 20 degrees cooler than the outside temperature even if they aren't chilled. And their high water content—about 95%—will keep you hydrated.

Best time to buy: summer

STORING

Where: Crisper drawer of refrigerator.

How: Unwashed and unpeeled; if peeled, wrap tightly in plastic wrap.

For how long: 1 to 2 days for unwaxed or peeled; up to 1 week for waxed.

COOKING

- If cucumber skin is waxed, peel before using.
- Layer thinly sliced cucumbers on cheese, ham, or turkey sandwiches.
- Puree peeled, seeded cucumber with plain yogurt, garlic, chopped dill, and a bit of ice water for a refreshing summer soup.
- Dip cucumber sticks in baba ghanoush.

RECIPES TO TRY

- Chunky Gazpacho with Garlicky Croutons
- Greek Lamb Kebabs
- Poached Salmon with Cucumber-Dill Sauce
- Minty Melon Cups
- Japanese Sushi Rolls

CONVENIENCE AND PROCESSED FOODS

Convenience foods that require little or no preparation—from ready-to-eat breakfast cereals and canned, dried, or frozen fruits and vegetables, to prepackaged heat-and-serve meals—are practically a necessity in our busy lifestyles. Unfortunately, many are much less healthy than home-cooked versions because of extra sugar, salt, and fat, all of which can have adverse health effects. They also tend to be loaded with artificial flavorings, emulsifiers, fillers, preservatives, and trans fats that can increase your risk for heart disease. And processing often strips vitamins and minerals from foods. But nutritious picks that help busy cooks put meals together quickly do exist; you just have to be a savvy shopper.

KEEP IT HEALTHY

Go for fresh options. Precut veggies and fruit and rotisserie chicken are quick healthy options. Just don't eat the skin on the chicken.

Boost nutrition. Add a fresh side salad to a meal consisting of processed food, like frozen lasagna, to provide a wide assortment of valuable nutrients.

Watch out for sauces. Vegetables and many fruits harvested and quick-frozen at their peak often have more vitamins than those picked before maturity, shipped long distances, and then placed on shelves. But you can undo those benefits if you choose varieties in high-calorie, high-fat sauces and syrups. Stick to plain varieties for the healthiest option.

Limit salt. Scan the nutrition panel carefully, and keep your daily intake under 2,300 mg of sodium.

Watch out for red-flag ingredients. Be wary of ingredient lists with the words "corn sweetener," "corn syrup," "corn syrup solids," "high-fructose corn syrup," "hydrogenated fats," or "vegetable shortening."

Choose whole grains. Look for packaged rice or noodle products made with brown rice or whole wheat pasta whenever possible. If you can't find prepackaged foods with whole wheat pasta or brown rice, cook some up separately and then add it to the dish. Along with more fiber, it will increase the amount of food you have, so the sodium, sugar, and fat per serving will be less.

DATES

Typical serving size: 5 to 6 dates (40 g), 126 calories

HOW THEY HARM

Weight gain

Tooth decay

Drug interaction

WHAT THEY HEAL

Cancer

Bone loss

Cardiovascular disease

High blood pressure

NUTRIENTS

Calcium

Fiber

Iron

Magnesium

Manganese

Niacin

Polyphenols (anticancer compounds)

Potassium

Vitamin B6

BUYING

Choose dates that are:

- shiny
- uniformly colored

QUICK TIP:
Refresh your dates

If they've been stored for an extended period of time, immerse them in hot water (about 80°F or 30°C) for about 20 to 30 minutes, allowing water to absorb to improve texture and taste. Remove, pat dry with a paper towel.

Avoid dates that are:

- cracked
- discolored or have yellow or brown blemishes

Fresh dates are classified according to their moisture content, falling into three categories: soft, semisoft, and dry. Most varieties in North America are semisoft, which are marketed fresh, as well as dried after part of their moisture has been evaporated.

Best time to buy: autumn

STORING

Where: At room temperature.
How: In an airtight container.
For how long: Several months. Refrigerated dates last up to 1 year.

COOKING

- Blend a couple of dates into a smoothie in place of other sweeteners and for added fiber.
- Stuff dates with whole blanched almonds and drizzle with melted white chocolate.
- Stir some chopped dates into tabbouleh salad.
- Create a sweet and sour sauce for sautéed chicken breasts by deglazing the skillet with sherry vinegar and chopped dates.

RECIPES TO TRY

- Hot Cereal with Apples and Dates
- Fruity Brussels Sprouts
- Chewy Date-Walnut Bars

DUCK

See Poultry, page 96

EDAMAME

See Soy, page 105

EGGPLANTS

Typical serving size: ½ cup cooked (50 g), 18 calories (with no fat added)

HOW THEY HARM

Fat and calorie magnet

WHAT THEY HEAL

Weight gain

NUTRIENTS

Fiber

Anthocyanins (antioxidants)

BUYING

Choose eggplants that are:
- firm with thin skin
- smaller
- heavy for their size
- deep purple to light violet or white

Avoid eggplants that are:
- cracked or discolored
- bruised or shriveled
- yellowish or have blue or brown streaks

STORING

Where: Crisper drawer of refrigerator.
How: Whole, no container or bag needed.
For how long: 5 to 7 days.

COOKING

- Eggplants' spongy texture causes them to soak up more fat and calories than potatoes. For healthier cooking, use a preparation that requires minimal fat, such as broiling, baking, roasting, or stewing. If sautéing, use a nonstick pan and little oil.
- Grill baby eggplant slices, then spread with ricotta cheese, pesto, and finely chopped tomato. Roll into tubes.
- Grill eggplant wedges, then toss in a bowl with hoisin sauce and chile paste just to coat.
- Stir-fry eggplant cubes in olive oil with chopped onion, zucchini, and tomato.
- Slice eggplant into thin slivers and use in place of noodles in lasagna.
- Cut eggplant in half and roast until soft. Scoop out the insides and mix with a bit of olive oil, salt, pepper, a crushed garlic clove, and a squeeze of lemon for a quick baba ghanoush.
- Use it in place of meat in stews, casseroles, and sandwiches.

RECIPES TO TRY

- Penne with Fresh Tomato Sauce and Grilled Eggplant
- Rustic Grilled Vegetable and Rigatoni Salad
- Grilled Eggplant Sandwiches with Red Pepper–Walnut Sauce

QUICK TIP:
Sprinkle with salt

To eliminate bitterness in some eggplants, sprinkle cubed or sliced eggplant with salt. Let it stand for half an hour, then drain it and blot it dry. The salt draws out excess moisture and reduces bitterness.

EGGS

Typical serving size: 1 large (50 g), 75 Calories

HOW THEY HARM

Allergies

Bacterial infection

WHAT THEY HEAL

Cardiovascular disease

Cancer

Cataracts and macular degeneration

Memory

NUTRIENTS

Beta-carotene

Choline

Iron

Lutein

Protein

Vitamin B12

Vitamin D

Vitamin E

Zeaxanthin (antioxidant)

Zinc

BUYING

Choose eggs that are:

- enhanced with omega-3s (they're lower in saturated fat and higher in vitamin E than regular eggs)
- brown or white—they're equally nutritious (free-range eggs may have slightly higher levels of carotenoids)

Avoid eggs that are:

- cracked or stuck to the bottom
- past the "use-by" date

STORING

Where: In the main part of the refrigerator, not on the inside of the door.

QUICK TIP:
Limit eggs if indicated

Doctors recommend that people with high cholesterol eat no more than three yolks a week. People with diabetes should limit consumption, too.

How: In its carton with the pointed end of the egg down.

For how long: Up to 3 weeks. (Eggs age more in 1 day at room temperature than in 1 week in the refrigerator.)

COOKING

- To be certain that eggs have been cooked long enough, boil them for at least 4 minutes, poach them for 5 minutes, or fry them for 3 minutes. Both the yolk and the white should be firm. Omelets and scrambled eggs should be cooked until firm and not runny.
- Refrigerate hard-cooked eggs for up to a week for quick, easy snacks or sandwich fillings.
- Stir-fry leftover cooked noodles or rice with leftover veggies and a beaten egg for a quick meal.
- Top steamed asparagus with a poached egg and a sprinkling of parmesan cheese.

RECIPES TO TRY

- Asparagus, Egg, and Ham Sandwiches
- Mushroom and Bell Pepper Frittata
- Zucchini-Carrot Crustless Quiche Squares
- Fried Rice with Tofu and Vegetables

FENNEL

Typical serving size: 1 cup sliced (87 g), 25 calories

HOW IT HARMS
Skin irritation

WHAT IT HEALS
Weight gain
High blood pressure
High cholesterol
High blood sugar
Cancer

NUTRIENTS
Beta-carotene
Calcium
Fiber
Folate
Iron
Potassium
Vitamin C

BUYING
Choose fennel that has:
- firm bulbs
- bright green stalks and leaves

Avoid fennel that is:
- blemished
- soft or has mushy spots

Best time to buy: autumn to early spring

STORING
Where: Crisper drawer of refrigerator.
How: Unwashed in a sealed plastic bag.
For how long: Up to 5 days.

COOKING
- All parts of the plant are edible. It can be prepared raw in salads, or braised or sautéed as a side dish.
- Marinate shrimp in cracked fennel seeds, lemon juice, and olive oil before grilling.
- Dip fennel wedges into hummus.
- Sauté fennel and sweet onion wedges until browned, then season with balsamic vinegar.
- Use in place of celery in stews and soups.

RECIPES TO TRY
- Braised Carrot, Celery, and Fennel
- Grilled Oysters with Fennel and Spinach
- Warm Kasha and Seafood Salad
- Sicilian Pasta Salad

FIGS

Typical serving size: 2 small (80 g), 60 calories; ¼ cup dried (50 g), 124 calories

HOW THEY HARM
Diarrhea
Tooth decay
Canker sores

WHAT THEY HEAL
Cardiovascular disease
High cholesterol
Diabetes
Cancer
Bone loss
Constipation

NUTRIENTS
Calcium
Fiber
Iron
Manganese
Pectin (soluble fiber)
Potassium
Vitamin B6

BUYING

Choose figs that are:

- ripe and unblemished
- a deep purple
- soft, but not mushy

Avoid figs that are:

- moldy or smell fermented
- mushy or blemished

Best time to buy: late summer to early autumn

STORING

Where: Refrigerator.
How: In a paper towel–lined container.
For how long: Within 2 days.

COOKING

- Macerate quartered dried figs in orange juice.
- Use chopped dried figs in place of raisins.
- Bake halved fresh figs with fresh pineapple wedges sprinkled with cinnamon.

RECIPES TO TRY

- Sesame Fig Bars
- Nutty Muesli
- Fresh Figs with Raspberries and Rose Cream
- Grilled Fruit en Brochette

QUICK TIP: Pick the sweetest

Fig connoisseurs say to look for a drip of moisture at the hole on the bottom of the fruit.

FISH

See also Shellfish, page 103

Typical serving size: About the size of a deck of cards, or 3 oz (85 g); calories vary depending on variety (see chart on page 53)

HOW IT HARMS

Pollutants

Parasites

Bacteria and viruses

WHAT IT HEALS

Cardiovascular disease

Stroke

Inflammation

Memory loss

Macular degeneration

NUTRIENTS

Calcium (canned salmon and sardines with bones)

Magnesium

Niacin

Omega-3 fatty acids

Protein

Vitamin A (oily fish such as salmon)

Vitamin D (oily fish such as salmon)

Vitamin B12

Zinc

BUYING

Shop at a busy fish counter—it means faster turnover and fresher fish. Or look for markets that keep fish covered (both top and bottom) with ice. The best sources of omega-3 fats are oily cold-water fish such as salmon, mackerel, trout, sardines, herring, and anchovies. You'll also find them in halibut, bluefish, ocean perch, bass, red snapper, and smelts. Limit your intake of large bottom-feeders such as tuna, shark, king mackerel, tilefish, and

WHICH TYPE OF FISH OR SHELLFISH TO CHOOSE?

In general, cook fish for 10 minutes for every inch of thickness, or until it flakes easily with a fork. Before cooking clams, oysters, and mussels, discard any that don't close with a light tap on the shell; cook until the shells open, and avoid eating any that do not open during cooking. When preparing lobster, scallops, shrimp and squid, cook just until firm; longer cooking times can result in a tough, chewy texture. Octopus traditionally requires a longer cooking time, usually at least an hour, to become tender. Because most of the fat in fish is healthy (as noted on the chart below), don't shy away from fatty types.

TYPE	CALORIES PER 3 OZ (90 G) COOKED PORTION	FAT PER 3 OZ (90 G) COOKED PORTION	BEST FOR
Anchovies	162	9*g	Pizza and pasta dishes; due to their intense flavor, smaller portions are more typical
Bass	124	4g	Fillets and paired with a wide variety of dishes; excellent grilled, pan-seared, or roasted
Catfish	115	6.5g	Fillets and paired with Southern foods; excellent when pan-seared or baked
Clams	126	1.7g	Steaming and eating right out of the shell; also great in soups and pasta dishes
Cod (Pacific)	89	0.7g	Fillets; excellent when pan-seared or baked with a topping to prevent dryness
Crab (blue)	87	1.5g	Crab cakes, pasta dishes, salads
Halibut	119	2.5g	Fillets or fish tacos; excellent either grilled or broiled
Herring	173	9.9*g	Appetizers; if pickled, choose herring in wine sauce versus cream sauce for less fat and fewer calories (calories listed do not include any sauce)
Lobster	76	0.7g	Steaming and eating right out of the shell; also great in soups, risottos, salads, and pasta dishes
Mackerel	223	15.1*g	Fillets and paired with other strong flavors, such as garlic and olives; great when grilled (whole), pan-seared, or roasted
Mussels	146	3.8g	Steaming and eating right out of the shell; also great in pasta dishes
Octopus	139	1.8g	Mediterranean and Asian dishes; to save time, look for chopped, frozen octopus
Oysters	139	3.9g	Eating raw right out of the shell; also great in soups and stuffing
Red snapper	109	1.5g	Fillets and paired with Caribbean dishes; best grilled, pan-seared, or roasted
Salmon	155	6.9*g	Fillets and paired with a wide variety of dishes; excellent grilled, pan-seared, or smoked; choose wild salmon when feasible
Sardines	136	7.9*g	Appetizers; typically sold in smaller cans
Scallops	150	1g	Main dishes and appetizers; best pan-seared or broiled
Shrimp	84	0.9g	Main dishes and appetizers; excellent in most cooking methods, including pan-seared, baked, grilled, steamed, and boiled
Squid	60	1.5g	Main dishes and appetizers; best when cooked very briefly
Tilapia	109	2.2g	Fillets and when well-seasoned to compensate for its mild flavor; excellent pan-seared or baked
Trout	162	7.2*g	Main dishes and appetizers; excellent pan-seared, baked, or smoked
Tuna (chunk, light)	99	0.7g	Casserole and pasta dishes; opt for tuna packed in water

* High in omega-3 fatty acids

swordfish because they tend to be high in mercury.

Choose fish that has:
- bright, bulging, and clear eyes (whole fish)
- bright red gills (whole fish)
- bright, glossy skin with tight scales (whole fish)
- moist, resilient skin (fillets)
- firm flesh
- a fresh, briny odor

Avoid fish that has:
- gray or cloudy eyes (whole fish)
- grayish or pink gills (whole fish)
- any discoloration (fillets)
- gaps in the flesh (fillets)
- a fishy odor

When buying canned fish, choose those packed in water rather than oil. For tuna, go with the light or albacore variety.

STORING

Where: In the coldest part of the refrigerator, or in the freezer.
How: Wrapped in plastic wrap.
For how long: Fresh, 1 to 2 days; frozen, within 3 months for fatty fish, and 6 months for lean fish.

COOKING

- Serve slivers of smoked whitefish with a spinach salad.
- Brush grilled halibut with teriyaki sauce.
- Crumble drained canned salmon into a pasta salad.

RECIPES TO TRY

- Roasted Mackerel with Cherry Tomatoes and Potatoes
- Monkfish and Mussel Kebabs

**WARNING!
FOOD-DRUG
INTERACTION**

Because the lignans in flax are phytoestrogens, it may affect drugs such as Tamoxifen that are used to treat hormone-sensitive conditions. While some research suggests that it helps these conditions, more studies are needed. Talk to your doctor before eating flax while on Tamoxifen, or if you have hormone-sensitive ailments such as breast or uterine cancer, endometriosis, or fibroids.

- Snapper and Snaps in a Packet
- Grilled Salmon Salad
- Tossed Tuna Salad Niçoise

FLAX

See also Nuts and Seeds, page 77

Typical serving size: 1 to 2 Tbsp, ground (7 to 14 g), 33 to 66 calories

HOW IT HARMS

Fetus and nursing infants (check with doctor if pregnant or nursing)
Bleeding problems (avoid if you have a bleeding disorder)
Drug interaction

WHAT IT HEALS

Cardiovascular disease
High cholesterol
Menopause symptoms
Cancer
Constipation

NUTRIENTS

Alpha linolenic acid (ALA—a heart healthy omega-3 fatty acid)
Fiber
Lignans (phytoestrogens)

BUYING

In the grocery, you can find flaxseeds and flaxmeal in the same aisle as flour. Flaxseed oil is often found in the pharmacy section.

Choose flaxseeds that are:
- whole (grind them in a blender or coffee grinder as needed)
- from a store with a high turnover, if ground
- refrigerated, if ground
- vacuum-packed, if ground

Avoid flaxseeds that:
- are not in an opaque container
- don't come with a "use-by" date

STORING

Where: In the refrigerator or freezer, especially if ground.

How: In an airtight, opaque container in the fridge if whole or in oil form; in the freezer if ground.

For how long: Up to 1 year if whole; if ground, a few weeks in the freezer or until the best-before date on the package.

If flaxseed tastes bitter or smells sharp or fishy, throw it away.

COOKING

- Replace 2 Tbsp of flour in cookie recipes with an equal amount of flaxmeal.
- Use flaxmeal to bread fish or chicken cutlets to be baked or sautéed.
- Spread corn on the cob with a blend of flaxseed oil and Cajun seasoning.
- Add ground flax to muffin or pancake batter.
- Sprinkle ground flax onto oatmeal.

RECIPES TO TRY

- Broccoli Salad with Almonds and Dried Cranberries
- Berry-Flaxseed Smoothie
- Chicken-Kale Soup with Roasted Pepper Puree
- Cranberry-Peanut Cereal Bar
- Whole Wheat Flaxseed Bread

FLOUR

See Grains, page 57

GARLIC

See also Herbs and Spices, page 61

Typical serving size: 3 cloves (9 g), 12 calories

HOW IT HARMS

Bleeding problems
Stomach irritation
Drug interaction

WHAT IT HEALS

High blood pressure
Atherosclerosis
Cardiovascular disease
Diabetes
Colon and rectal cancer
Infections
Tick bites

NUTRIENTS

Allicin
Antibacterial, antifungal, and antiviral compounds

BUYING

Choose garlic that:
- is dry
- has lots of papery sheath covering it
- looks and feels plump and firm
- is white or off-white

Avoid garlic that is:
- shriveled
- moldy
- mushy
- sprouting

WARNING! FOOD-DRUG INTERACTION
Garlic may interfere with the effectiveness of saquinavir, a drug used to treat HIV infection.

Best time to buy: late summer

STORING

Where: In a cool, dark, and dry place with plenty of circulation or a clay garlic holder; not in the refrigerator.
How: In its papery covering.
For how long: Several weeks.

QUICK TIP:
Prepare before cooking

To activate garlic's full nutritional power, it should be chopped or crushed and then left to stand for 10 minutes before cooking. This allows allicin and its potent derivatives to be activated.

COOKING

- Boil peeled garlic cloves with potatoes to season the mash.
- Stir-fry spinach with extra-virgin olive oil and plenty of minced garlic.
- Wrap a whole head of garlic in foil and bake in the oven for 30 minutes for a soft spread for breads or potatoes.
- Sauté garlic and add it to tomato sauce, or mince it and add it raw.

RECIPES TO TRY

- Braised Mixed Greens with Dried Currants
- Roasted Tomatoes with Garlic and Herbs
- Turkey, Spinach, and Rice in Roasted Garlic Broth
- Bok Choy, Tofu, and Mushroom Stir-Fry
- Romaine Lettuce with Chunky Tomato Vinaigrette

GINGER

Typical serving size: 1 tsp or 1-in (2.5-cm) diameter slice, raw (2 g), 2 calories; 1 tsp ground (2 g), 6 calories

HOW IT HARMS

Bleeding problems
Miscarriage
Inflamed mouth and mucous membranes
Drug interaction

WHAT IT HEALS

Motion sickness and nausea
Pain
Cancer
Flatulence

NUTRIENTS

Beta ionone (cancer-fighting compound)
Gingerols (phenol compound)
Shogaols (phenol compound)

BUYING

Fresh ginger can be found at any supermarket, but dried and powdered forms are readily available, as are ginger juices and teas.

Choose ginger that:
- is plump and firm
- has smooth skin
- has a spicy fragrance

Avoid ginger that is:
- withered
- cracked
- moldy
- blemished

Remedy your cold naturally

Here's a comforting way to relieve congestion: Make ginger tea by simmering one or two slices of fresh ginger root in water for 10 minutes; add a pinch of cinnamon for extra flavor.

STORING

Where: In the refrigerator or freezer.
How: Unpeeled and dry, in a sealed plastic bag with all the air pressed out.
For how long: 2 weeks in the refrigerator; up to 2 months in the freezer.

COOKING

- Sauté minced ginger with broccoli and a little olive oil for an antioxidant feast.
- Add grated fresh ginger to butternut squash soup.
- Top baked tilapia with grated ginger, soy sauce, and a few drops of canola oil.
- Whisk grated ginger into a salad dressing of canola oil and rice wine vinegar.

RECIPES TO TRY

- Chicken Breast with Peaches and Ginger
- Jerk Turkey Breast with Ginger Barbecue Sauce
- Shrimp and Vegetable Stir-Fry
- Pork, Pear, and Potato Salad
- Fruit Parfait with Ginger Tea Cream

GRAINS

See also Barley, page 20; Bran, page 27; Oats, page 78; Quinoa, page 98; Rice, page 101; Wheat and Wheat Germ, page 115

Typical serving size: ½ cup cooked whole grains, 73 to 151 calories

HOW THEY HARM

- Cardiovascular disease (refined grains)
- Atherosclerosis (refined grains)
- Diabetes (refined grains)
- Celiac disease

WHAT THEY HEAL

- Diabetes (whole grains)
- Cardiovascular disease (whole grains)
- Cancer (whole grains)
- Digestive health (whole grains)
- Diverticular disease (whole grains)
- Anemia (whole grain and enriched flours)

NUTRIENTS

- B vitamins (whole grains and enriched)
- Complex carbohydrates (whole grains)
- Fiber (whole grains)
- Folate (enriched)
- Iron (whole grains and enriched)
- Magnesium (whole grains)
- Vitamin E (whole grains)
- Zinc (whole grains)

BUYING

Choose grains that:

- are unrefined; look for the words "whole wheat flour" as the first ingredient on breads and cereals
- have a "100% Whole Grains" label

WARNING! FOOD-DRUG INTERACTION

Consuming ginger while on medications that slow bleeding such as warfarin may cause bleeding and bruises. If you are on these medications, do not eat ginger.

RECIPES TO TRY

- Warm Kasha and Seafood Salad
- Multigrain Seeded Loaf
- Buckwheat Pancakes with Fruit Sauce
- Whole Wheat Pasta with Sausage and Greens
- Wheat Berry Salad with Dried Apricots

GRAPEFRUITS

Typical serving size: ½ grapefruit (123 g), 52 calories; or ¾ cup (177 mL) juice, 70 calories

HOW THEY HARM

Allergies
Canker sores
Drug interaction

WHAT THEY HEAL

High cholesterol
Cancer
Weight gain
Inflammation

NUTRIENTS

Beta-carotene (pink and red varieties)
Bioflavonoids
Fiber
Limonoids (cancer fighters)
Lycopene (antioxidant)
Monoterpenes (cancer fighters)
Pectin (soluble fiber)
Phenolic acid (cancer fighter)
Potassium
Terpenes (cancer fighters)
Vitamin C

If you have a gluten sensitivity, you can find flours made from all sorts of grains, nuts, and other foods, including potato, almonds, rice, chickpeas, and buckwheat.

Avoid grains that are:
- refined
- labeled wheat flour

STORING

Where: In a cool, dry place, in the refrigerator, or in the freezer.
How: In an airtight container or in bags with the air pressed out.
For how long: 2 to 6 months.

COOKING

- Add some cooked roasted buckwheat groats (kasha) to a bean or lentil salad.
- Replace ½ cup of the flour in muffin recipes with rolled oats.
- Serve grits as a side dish instead of mashed potatoes.
- Stuff bell peppers with seasoned cooked millet.

WARNING! FOOD-DRUG INTERACTION

Grapefruit juice can enhance the effects of certain medications, possibly resulting in adverse effects. Drugs to watch out for include those for high blood pressure, anxiety, depression, elevated lipids, and more. As a precaution, it is best to avoid taking any drug with grapefruit juice until you have asked your doctor or pharmacist if it is safe to do so.

BUYING

Choose grapefruits that are:
- firm
- heavy for their size
- bright and colorful

Avoid grapefruits that are:
- wrinkled
- bruised
- have blemishes

Best time to buy: winter

STORING

Where: At room temperature or in the crisper drawer of the refrigerator.
How: Unpeeled or cut.
For how long: Up to 1 week at room temperature; 2 to 3 weeks in the fridge.

COOKING

- Add grapefruit wedges to a smoothie.
- Dip wedges into melted bittersweet chocolate.
- Stir-fry boneless chicken breast cubes with garlic and cumin, add grapefruit chunks and toss until heated.

RECIPES TO TRY

- Tropical Fruit Salad
- Roast Pork and Quinoa Salad
- Chicken Salad with Citrus

QUICK TIP: Serve it warm

Turn this typical warm weather breakfast fruit into a toasty treat. Cut a grapefruit in half and discard the center membrane and seeds. Sprinkle with sugar and cinnamon and broil until browned.

GRAPES AND RAISINS

Typical serving size: ½ cup or about 15 grapes (46 g), 31 calories; 1 oz or about 55 raisins (28 g), 85 calories

HOW THEY HARM

Asthma attacks in sulfur-sensitive people
Allergies in people with aspirin allergies

WHAT THEY HEAL

Cardiovascular disease
Cancer
Muscle cramps
Anemia

NUTRIENTS

Anthocyanins (antioxidants)
Ellagic acid (anticancer compound)
Iron
Potassium
Quercetin (antioxidant)
Resveratrol (anticancer compound)
Vitamin C

European table grapes have more nutrients, such as vitamin C, than American varieties. Red and purple varieties have more nutrients, such as anthocyanins and resveratrol, than green.

BUYING

Choose grapes that are:
- plump
- without blemishes
- uniform in color

Avoid grapes that are:
- wrinkled or brownish
- white where the stem meets the fruit

Buy raisins in single-serving boxes to limit portion size and keep calories reasonable.

Best time to buy: summer

STORING

Where: Refrigerator.
How: Unwashed, in a ventilated plastic bag.
For how long: Up to 1 week.

COOKING

- Sauté red grapes with chard or kale.
- Freeze grapes on a tray, then store in a freezer-proof container for quick snacks.
- Add dark raisins to a tossed green salad.
- Add golden raisins to braised pork.

RECIPES TO TRY

- Fruit Salad with Spiced Coconut
- Rice Salad with Chicken and Grapes
- Turkey Braciole Stuffed with Provolone and Spinach
- Brown Rice with Cabbage and Chickpeas

GREEN BEANS

See Beans and Other Legumes, page 20; Peas and Pea Pods, page 89

GUAVAS

Typical serving size: 1 medium (90 g), 45 calories

HOW THEY HARM

Allergies

WHAT THEY HEAL

Cancer
Cardiovascular disease
Constipation
Weight gain

NUTRIENTS

Vitamin C
Pectin (soluble fiber)
Potassium

BUYING

Choose guavas that:

- are firm but not hard (skin yields slightly when pressed)
- have a fragrant, musky aroma

Avoid guavas that:

- are wrinkled
- are bruised
- smell fermented

Best time to buy: late autumn and early winter

STORING

Where: Counter, if unripe; crisper drawer of refrigerator, if ripe.
How: Unwrapped.
For how long: Up to 4 days when ripe.

To hasten ripening, place the guava in a brown paper bag with a banana or an apple.

COOKING

- Toss chopped guavas into an arugula salad.
- Simmer chopped guavas with brown sugar and cinnamon.
- Add guava chunks to a smoothie.

RECIPES TO TRY

- Guavas and Plums with Vanilla Syrup
- Fresh Fruit Soup

HERBS AND SPICES

See also Garlic, page 54; Ginger, page 56

Typical serving size: varies according to recipe, negligible calories

HOW THEY HARM

Allergies

Pesticides

WHAT THEY HEAL

Digestion

Bloating and flatulence

Inflammation

High blood pressure

Colds and flus

Cancer

Nausea and motion sickness

Fainting

Stomach cramps

NUTRIENTS

See chart on page 62

BUYING

Choose:

- whole spices to grind at home for the freshest, most pungent flavor
- organic herbs to avoid pesticides
- herbs that smell robust

Avoid:

- herbs with brown spots
- herbs that smell moldy
- herbs that are limp

Spices are sold bottled in supermarkets and, less expensively, in bulk-food stores and ethnic markets.

STORING

Where: Dark, dry cupboard for spices and dried herbs; refrigerator for fresh herbs.

How: In airtight containers for spices and dried herbs. For fresh herbs, snip ends and stand them in a glass of water; change water daily.

For how long: About 1 year for spices and dried herbs; up to 1 week for fresh herbs.

COOKING

- Add chopped fresh mint to cucumber salad.
- Stir chopped fresh cilantro into hummus.
- Add a handful of chopped fresh parsley to tossed salad.
- Create a Moroccan spice blend with equal parts of ground cinnamon, coriander, and cumin.
- Sprinkle oregano on grilled zucchini slices brushed with olive oil.
- Season stir-fried shrimp with crushed fennel seeds and garlic.

RECIPES TO TRY

- Roasted Pork with Pomegranate Sauce
- Fruit Salad with Spiced Coconut
- Fruity Granola Mix
- Minty Melon Cups
- Herb-Buttered Turnips

WHICH HERBS AND SPICES SHOULD YOU USE?

Both fresh and dried herbs provide a wide variety of active phytochemicals that promote health and protect against chronic disease. Discover the healing power of nine popular herbs and spices and how to get more of them into your diet.

TYPE	HOW THEY HEAL	HOW TO USE IN COOKING
Cayenne	Helps break up nasal and sinus congestion	Add a dash of ground cayenne to any dish that needs a little heat. For an extra kick, try a light dusting on popcorn or party mix. Excellent as part of a spice rub mix.
Cinnamon	Aids digestion and may help fight infection due to anti-inflammatory and antimicrobial properties	Use cinnamon's distinct warm flavor as a complement to sweet desserts and drinks, including mulled cider and Mexican hot chocolate. Also used in Greek and Moroccan cooking to add balance to savory dishes.
Clove	Contains eugenol, which may help curb toothache pain	Add a dash of ground cloves alongside other warming spices, including cinnamon, nutmeg, ginger, and allspice in cookies, pies, and other baked goods.
Cumin	May protect eyes and cardiovascular system against diabetes-related damage	Use ground cumin alongside dried coriander in Mexican and Indian cooking; also pairs nicely with sautéed onions and canned beans (add a squirt of fresh lime to balance cumin's earthy notes); for maximum flavor, toast lightly just before using to release fragrant oils.
Mint	Aids digestion by calming upset stomach; relieves gas	Brew as a tea by steeping fresh or dried leaves in hot water; chop fresh mint and add to fruit salads, beverages and desserts, as well as traditional Mediterranean and Middle Eastern dishes such as tabbouleh and cucumber-laced tzatziki sauce.
Oregano	A member of the mint family, oregano may help improve symptoms of a sinus infection as part of a steam inhalation therapy	Add fresh or dried oregano to Italian and Mediterranean dishes; pairs well with tomatoes and garlic (add a splash of lemon or vinegar to the combination to highlight oregano's herbal qualities). One teaspoon dried oregano is roughly equal to 1 Tbsp fresh; reserve fresh oregano for dishes that are seasoned just before serving, as heat quickly dissipates the flavor.
Rosemary	Distinct piney scent was once thought to aid memory; today research indicates it may help relieve asthma and allergy symptoms	Use chopped fresh rosemary along with garlic in marinades, dressings and side dishes for a classic Mediterranean combination; especially good tucked inside roasted fish or poultry, or chopped and scattered over roasted potatoes. The herb's tough, woody stems are excellent to use as skewers when grilling fish and other delicate proteins.
Thyme	Reduces inflammation and helps fight infection; excellent in mouthwashes and natural cough drops	Keep this versatile herb in your pantry for dressing up a wide variety of sauces and sides; complements poultry, seafood, potato, and egg dishes.
Turmeric	A relative of ginger; has anti-inflammatory compounds that may fight pain and swelling associated with arthritis	Use a teaspoon when cooking curry sauces and rice dishes; add a dash when assembling potato salads or mixing up egg recipes to impart a distinct yellow hue to the finished dish.

HONEY

See Sugar and Other Sweeteners, page 62

HONEYDEW

See Melons, page 73

HUMMUS

See Condiments, page 45

ICE CREAM

This creamy frozen treat is another one of those fat-sugar combos—like cakes, cookies, and pastries—that's just so hard to say no to, especially during summer months. Along with loads of calories, ice cream contains big helpings of saturated fat, which is bad for your heart and your waistline. Its redeeming qualities are a healthy dose of calcium and protein. To enjoy the good while limiting the bad, keep portions small, indulge only occasionally, and follow these guidelines.

KEEP IT HEALTHY

Opt for alternatives, such as fruit sorbets or low-fat frozen yogurt. Just be sure to read labels carefully—some of these products may have more sugar and calories.

Look for slow-churned or double-churned. These types of light or reduced-fat ice cream contain up to half the fat and two-thirds the calories of original and have a creamier texture.

Choose cones wisely. A sugar cone contains 60 calories, while a chocolate-dipped waffle cone has more than 200. And avoid high-calorie toppings like candy.

Top it with fruit. The fiber will fill you up so you'll be satisfied with less. Nuts are another option; just watch the portion size since they're high in calories.

JICAMA

Typical serving size: ½ cup sliced (60 g), 23 calories

HOW IT HARMS
Allergies

WHAT IT HEALS
Cardiovascular disease
Stroke
Weight gain
High blood sugar
Constipation
Skin
Cataracts

NUTRIENTS
Fiber
Potassium
Vitamin C

BUYING

Choose jicama:
- between 1 and 2 lb (500 g and 1 kg); larger ones may be less sweet
- with firm, smooth, slightly shiny skin
- that is heavy for its size

Avoid jicama that is:
- blemished or cracked
- moldy
- discolored

Best time to buy: late autumn through spring

STORING

Where: Refrigerator.
How: Uncut, in a plastic bag; cut, wrapped in plastic.
For how long: Uncut, 2 to 3 weeks; cut, up to 1 week.

- Season jicama sticks with lime juice and chili powder.
- Eat it with a dip, diced in a salad, or added to stir-fries.
- Top jicama slices with tapenade for an appetizer.
- Shred jicama and add it to slaws. It's a great topping for fish tacos.

COOKING

- Peel jicama and remove the fibrous white area just beneath the skin.

RECIPES TO TRY

- Orange Beef with Broccoli and Jicama
- Avocado, Jicama, and Orange Salad
- Jamaican Jerked Chicken Salad

IN MODERATION ONLY

JAMS, JELLIES, AND OTHER SPREADS

High in sugar, jams and jellies are no substitute for the abundant nutrition found naturally in fruits. In fact, most of the vitamin C and other key nutrients are destroyed during the intense cooking process involved in producing them. Low-calorie, reduced-sugar jams aren't much better because they're often sweetened with concentrated fruit juice, fructose, and corn syrup and thickened with starches, giving you only empty calories. Soft spread-cheese-based products contain only trace amounts of vitamin A and calcium and are high in sodium, fat, and cholesterol. Chocolate and marshmallow spreads are just spreadable sugar. About the only upside to these products is the quick boost of energy they provide. But that's really only helpful for people prone to hypoglycemia. So whenever possible, choose the real thing—sliced strawberries with peanut butter for a sandwich, cheese slices on crackers, or melted dark chocolate—instead of the processed stuff. But when you can't, follow these guidelines.

KEEP IT HEALTHY

Go for all-fruit. Choose preserves made of 100% fruit.

Skip additives. That includes added oils, salt, sugar, and preservatives.

Measure how much you use. And use the least amount possible. A tablespoon (15 mL) of regular jelly has about 60 calories and 11 g of sugar.

JUICES

Even if you choose the healthiest juices, they still contain a lot of calories because of the natural fruit sugar. Canned or bottled vegetable juices tend to have less sugar than fruit juices but more salt, which can increase blood pressure. Fruit juice should not be given to infants under 6 months old because it can cause diarrhea, poor weight gain or delayed development, and tooth decay. If consumed in moderation, drinking juice can be an easy way to get more of the recommended 5 to 10 servings of fruits and vegetables. About 4 oz (125 mL) of juice is equal to 1 serving. Since juice lacks fiber and other compounds found in whole pieces of fruit and vegetables, it's best to make only 2 or 3 of your fruit servings from juice. And when you do, choose wisely.

KEEP IT HEALTHY

Strive for 100%. Look for juices labeled "100% juice" for the most nutrients.

Go unsweetened. Choose juices that do not have added sugars.

Look for plant sterols. These cholesterol-lowering compounds that have been used in margarine are now showing up in orange juice.

Step away from "fruit drinks" and "fruit punch." They contain extra sugar (usually corn syrup) and other additives with less actual fruit juice.

KALE AND OTHER COOKING GREENS

See also Spinach, page 107

Typical serving size: ½ cup cooked, chopped (65 g), 18 calories

HOW THEY HARM

Bloating and flatulence

WHAT THEY HEAL

Cardiovascular disease
Cancer
Eye conditions
Bone health

NUTRIENTS

Beta-carotene
Bioflavonoids
Calcium
Carotenoids
Fiber
Folate
Indoles (anticancer compounds)
Iron
Lutein (antioxidant)
Magnesium
Potassium
Vitamin C

BUYING

Choose kale that has:
- crisp edges
- deep color
- small to medium size leaves

Avoid kale that has:

- wilted leaves
- yellowed or brown leaves

STORING

Where: Refrigerator.
How: Rinsed, slightly damp, wrapped in a paper towel, and in a plastic bag.
For how long: Within 3 days.

COOKING

- Simmer finely chopped mustard greens in vegetable soup.
- Add some chopped Italian lacinato kale to marinara sauce for pasta.
- Stuff blanched collard green leaves instead of cabbage leaves.

RECIPES TO TRY

- Summer Greens Scramble
- Baked Pasta with Garlic and Greens
- Chicken-Kale Soup with Roasted Pepper Puree

KETCHUP

See Condiments, page 45

KIWI

Typical serving size: 1 large kiwi or ½ cup sliced (90 g), 56 calories

WHAT THEY HEAL

High blood pressure
High cholesterol
Cancer
Macular degeneration
Weight gain

NUTRIENTS

Lutein (antioxidant)
Pectin (soluble fiber)
Phytochemicals
Potassium
Vitamin C
Vitamin E
Zeaxanthin (antioxidant)

BUYING

Choose kiwis that:

- are firm, but give to slight pressure
- have rough, fuzzy skin

Avoid kiwis that are:

- blemished
- wrinkled

STORING

Where: Room temperature, or in the refrigerator.
How: Unpeeled and uncut.
For how long: About 1 week at room temperature; up to 4 weeks in the fridge.

COOKING

- Kiwi skin is edible if it is de-fuzzed.
- Toss chunks with strawberries and chopped fresh mint.
- Grill unpeeled halved kiwi to serve with grilled pork chops.
- Serve kiwi slices over lemon yogurt.

RECIPES TO TRY

- Tropical Fruit Salad
- Jamaican Jerked Chicken Salad

QUICK TIP:
Tenderize meat with kiwis

Rub meat with a cut kiwi and wait 30 to 60 minutes before cooking to tenderize.

KOHLRABI

Typical serving size: 1 cup raw, chopped (135 g), 36 calories

HOW IT HARMS
Bloating and flatulence

WHAT IT HEALS
Cancer
Cardiovascular disease

NUTRIENTS
Bioflavonoids
Fiber
Indoles (anticancer compounds)
Iron
Isothiocyanates (anticancer compounds)
Potassium
Vitamin C

BUYING
Choose kohlrabi with:
- a diameter of less than 3 in (7.5 cm) (larger ones can be tough and woody)
- thin rinds
- fresh tops

Avoid kohlrabi with:
- blemishes
- cracks

STORING
Where: Crisper drawer of refrigerator.
How: Remove leaf stems and place in a sealed plastic bag.
For how long: Several weeks.

COOKING
- Simmer chunks of kohlrabi with green split peas to puree for soup.
- Stir-fry chopped kohlrabi with a slice of diced bacon until crisp-tender.
- Serve raw kohlrabi sticks on a veggie platter with dip.

RECIPES TO TRY
- Maple-Glazed Chicken with Root Vegetables

LAMB

Typical serving size: 3 oz (85 g), 160-200 calories, depending on cut

HOW IT HARMS
Weight gain

WHAT IT HEALS
Muscles
Anemia
Immunity

NUTRIENTS
Conjugated linoleic acid (fatty acids that improve cholesterol levels)
Iron
Phosphorous
Potassium
Protein
Vitamin B12
Zinc

BUYING
Look for lamb that is:
- firm
- red colored with some white marbling

Avoid lamb that:
- has holes in its packaging
- is past the "use-by" date

LEEKS

Typical serving size: 1 raw (89 g), 50 calories

HOW THEY HARM

Flatulence

WHAT THEY HEAL

Cancer
High cholesterol
High blood pressure

NUTRIENTS

Beta-carotene
Kaempferol (anticancer compound)

STORING

Where: In the refrigerator at 40°F (4°C) or below, or in the freezer.

How: In its original packaging and covered to prevent cross-contamination (overwrap tightly when freezing).

For how long: 1 to 2 days for ground lamb or stew meat in the fridge (3 to 4 months in the freezer); 3 to 5 days for lamb chops, roasts, and steaks in the fridge (6 to 9 months in the freezer).

COOKING

- Sauté thinly sliced lamb with slivered onions and curry powder.
- Stuff a pita bread half with sliced roast lamb, cucumber, plain yogurt, and fresh dill.
- Marinate skewered chunks of lamb, onion, and bell pepper in lemon-garlic salad dressing before grilling.

RECIPES TO TRY

- Skillet Okra and Lamb
- Lamb Burgers with Fruit Relish
- Savory Lamb Stew with Sweet Potatoes
- Greek Lamb Kebabs

BUYING

Choose leeks that have:
- firm, crisp stalks
- as much white and light green regions as possible

Avoid leeks that have:
- yellow or withered tops

STORING

Where: Refrigerator.
How: Unwashed, in a plastic bag.
For how long: Up to 2 weeks.

COOKING

- Serve steamed whole leeks with cheddar cheese sauce.
- Roast chunks of leeks with brussels sprouts tossed in canola oil and sprinkled with sesame seeds.
- Toss sliced raw leeks with beets in reduced-fat ranch dressing.
- Chop green tops of leeks and add to soups and stocks.

RECIPES TO TRY

- Lentil and Rice Paella with Clams
- Pasta with Cabbage, Apples, and Leeks
- Vegetable Stock

LEGUMES

See Beans and Legumes, page 20

LEMONS AND LIMES

Typical serving size: ½ cup sectioned and peeled (106 g), 31 calories

HOW THEY HARM

Skin irritation

Fungicides and pesticides

Sun sensitivity

Canker sores

Tooth enamel damage

WHAT THEY HEAL

High cholesterol

Cancer

Cardiovascular disease

Kidney stones

Varicose vein pain

Dry mouth

NUTRIENTS

Bioflavonoids (anticancer compound)

Limonene (in the zest; cholesterol-lowering compound)

Rutin (flavonoid)

Vitamin C

BUYING

Look for lemons and limes that are:
- not waxed
- heavy for their size
- bright skinned

Avoid lemons and limes that have:
- bruises or wrinkles
- large blemishes or discoloration
- soft spots

STORING

Where: At room temperature or in the crisper drawer of refrigerator.

How: In a plastic bag in the refrigerator.

For how long: Several days at room temperature; about 2 weeks in the refrigerator.

COOKING

- Macerate sliced strawberries in lemon juice and a sprinkling of sugar.
- Stuff a halved lemon and bouquet garni into the chicken cavity before roasting.
- Toss grated lime peel and juice with hot cooked quinoa.
- Freeze lemon or lime juice mixed with the grated peel in small resealable freezer bags for convenience.
- Use lime juice as a salt substitute for meat and fish dishes.

RECIPES TO TRY

- Scallops Florentine
- Trout with Lemon-Mushroom Stuffing
- Shellfish Salad with Herbed Lemon Dressing
- Grilled Chicken Sandwiches with Basil Mayonnaise
- Angel Food Cake with Strawberries

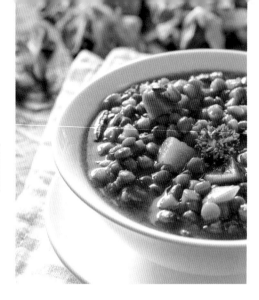

LENTILS

See also Beans and Other Legumes, page 20

Typical serving size: ½ cup cooked (99 g), 115 calories

HOW THEY HARM

Bloating and flatulence

WHAT THEY HEAL

High cholesterol
Blood sugar spikes
Weight gain
Constipation
Anemia
Cardiovascular disease
Reproductive health
Cancer

NUTRIENTS

B vitamins
Fiber
Folate
Iron
Magnesium
Niacin
Potassium
Protein

BUYING

Choose lentils that are:
- uniform size
- brightly colored

Avoid lentils that are:
- not in clear packaging
- cracked, shriveled, or have holes

The common khaki-colored lentils are widely available in supermarkets; the more delicate green and red lentils may be harder to find.

STORING

Where: A cool, dry place.
How: In an airtight container.
For how long: Up to 6 months. Cooked lentils may be stored in a sealed container in the refrigerator for up to 1 week.

COOKING

- Sort through lentils before cooking and discard any that are shriveled.
- Don't mix new lentils with older ones, because older lentils will take longer to cook.
- Red lentils cook faster than the khaki ones.
- Coarsely grind cooked seasoned lentils in a food processor, then shape into patties for frying or grilling.
- Use lentils in place of beans in minestrone.
- Toss cooked lentils with cooked rotini pasta and shredded provolone cheese.

RECIPES TO TRY

- Lentil and Rice Paella with Clams
- Artichokes with Lentils and Lima Beans
- Lentil Soup with Canadian Bacon

LETTUCE AND OTHER SALAD GREENS

See also Spinach, page 107

Typical serving size: 1 cup (20 to 55 g depending on variety), 4 to 10 calories

HOW THEY HARM
Food poisoning

WHAT THEY HEAL
Cancer
Cardiovascular disease
Weight gain

NUTRIENTS
Antioxidants
Beta-carotene
Calcium
Folate
Iron
Potassium
Vitamin C

Amounts vary from one variety to another, with dark green or other deeply colored leaves being more nutritious than paler varieties. Arugula, watercress, escarole, and mache are some of the most nutritious varieties.

BUYING

Look for lettuce with:
- fresh, crisp leaves
- good, bright color

Avoid lettuce with:
- decay like wilting or sliminess
- blemishes
- tip burn, a tan or brown area around the margins of the leaves
- very hard or irregular shaped heads
- insect damage

STORING

Where: Crisper drawer of the refrigerator.
How: Discard brown and wilted leaves, separate leaves and rinse, spin them dry, and layer between sheets of paper towel.
For how long: Up to 1 week; if using within 3 days, you can store greens in a plastic bag in the refrigerator.

COOKING

- Pair romaine lettuce with apples, pecans, blue cheese and cider vinaigrette.
- Try arugula with beets, walnuts, feta cheese, and red wine vinaigrette.
- Stir-fry sliced romaine lettuce with some Chinese black beans and grated ginger as a side dish.
- Make a pureed soup by blending simmered lettuce, garlic, thyme, and chicken broth; garnish with grated parmesan.
- Braise sliced escarole with raisins, garlic, balsamic vinegar, and a pinch of ground red pepper.

QUICK TIP: Dress your salad with a little oil

Oil enhances the absorption of beta-carotene, which is plentiful in arugula and romaine varieties of lettuce. Beta-carotene plays an important role in preventing cancer and vision loss.

RECIPES TO TRY

- Watermelon and Feta Salad
- Asian Chicken Salad
- Buckwheat Noodles with Tofu and Green Vegetables
- Endive, Apple, and Watercress Salad
- Salmon and Fennel Lettuce Wraps

LIMES

See Lemons and Limes, page 69

LIVER

See Organ Meats, page 83

LOBSTER

See Shellfish, page 103

MANGOES

Typical serving size: ½ cup sliced (83 g), 54 calories

WHAT THEY HEAL

Cancer
High blood pressure
High cholesterol
Weight gain

NUTRIENTS

Beta-carotene
Pectin (soluble fiber)
Potassium
Vitamin C

BUYING

Look for mangoes that:

- yield slightly when gently pressed
- emit a fruity aroma
- have a green or yellow-green color with a red blush

Avoid mangoes that:

- have large dark spots
- are completely green
- have shriveled skin

Best time to buy: summer

STORING

Where: At room temperature and out of the sun until ripened; in refrigerator, once ripe.
How: In a plastic bag if cut.
For how long: 1 to 2 weeks uncut; no more than 3 days once cut.

COOKING

- Use mangoes in any recipe that calls for peaches.
- Sprinkle mango chunks with toasted coconut.
- Add mango chunks to a pork stir-fry.

RECIPES TO TRY

- Broiled Salmon with Avocado-Mango Salsa
- Fruit Salad with Spiced Coconut
- Indian-Style Turkey Burger
- Fish Tacos
- Yogurt Parfait

MARGARINE

See Butter and Margarine, page 32

MELONS

Typical serving size: ½ cup diced (78 to 85 g), 23 to 31 calories, depending on type

HOW THEY HARM

Bacterial infection

WHAT THEY HEAL

Cancer
Cardiovascular disease
High blood cholesterol
Weight gain

NUTRIENTS

Beta-carotene
Bioflavonoids and carotenoids (anticancer compounds)
Fiber
Lycopene (antioxidant in watermelons)
Potassium
Vitamin C

BUYING

Look for melons that:
- are whole to preserve nutritional content
- have a smooth, slightly sunken scar near where the stem was
- have a deep, intense fragrance

QUICK TIP: **Keep 'em juicy**

When storing slices of cantaloupe or honeydew, keep the seeds intact if possible. This will prevent the fruit from drying out.

- rattle when shaken or produce a slightly hollow sound when thumped

Avoid melons that:
- are lopsided or have a flat side
- have cracks, soft spots, or dark bruises
- have stems on the scar

Best time to buy: summer to early autumn

STORING

Where: Crisper drawer of refrigerator.
How: Whole and unwashed; in a sealed container if cut.
For how long: 5 to 7 days; the riper they are, the shorter they will keep. Toss cut melons that have been left at room temperature for more than 4 hours.

COOKING

- Before cutting, scrub the skin with a clean vegetable brush under running water and blot it dry.
- Add finely chopped watermelon to barbecue sauce.
- Grill sliced honeydew melon with Cajun seasoned catfish fillets.
- Stir cantaloupe cubes into chicken salad.

RECIPES TO TRY

- Crab Cakes with Melon Relish
- Chicken-Melon Salad
- Cantaloupe and Orange Soup
- Fruit Parfait with Ginger Tea Cream

MILK AND DAIRY PRODUCTS

See also Butter and Margarine, page 32; Cheese, page 38; Ice Cream, page 63; Yogurt, page 116

Typical serving size: 1 cup (236 mL), calories vary (see chart below)

HOW THEY HARM

High cholesterol (whole milk and milk products)

Lactose intolerance

Allergies

Acne

WHAT THEY HEAL

Bone loss

Insulin resistance

High blood pressure

NUTRIENTS

Calcium

Magnesium

Potassium

Protein

Riboflavin

Vitamin B12

Vitamin D

BUYING

Choose milk:
- dated several days in the future (the date on the carton indicates the last day on which the milk can be sold)
- in a cardboard or opaque container

Avoid milk:
- on or past its "use-by" date
- in a clear or translucent container

STORING

Where: Toward the back of the refrigerator.

How: A temperature just above freezing is ideal, but milk should not be frozen.

WHICH MILK SHOULD YOU DRINK?

In recent years, some new milk options have popped up in grocery stores, and they're not all created equally. Here's what you need to know to find the best milk for you.

		PER FLUID 8-OZ SERVING					
		CALORIES	TOTAL FAT (G)	SAT FAT (G)	CALCIUM (MG)	PROTEIN (G)	VITAMIN D (IU)
	Whole (3.25% milk fat)	149	7.9	4.6	276	7.7	124*
	Reduced-fat (2% milk fat)	122	4.8	3.1	293	8	120*
	Low-fat (1% milk fat)	102	2.4	1.5	305	8.2	117*
	Skim (0% milk fat)	83	0	0	299	8.3	115*
	Buttermilk (low-fat)	98	2.2	1.3	284	8.1	0
LACTOSE-FREE	Almond milk (unsweetened)	40	3	0	450*	1	100*
	Soymilk (original and vanilla)	104	3.6	0.5	299*	6.3	104*
	Rice milk (unsweetened)	113	2.3	0	283*	0.7	101*
	Coconut milk (unsweetened)	80	5	5	300*	1	120*

*Indicates nutrient added to the milk during processing; may vary according to brand

For how long: 1 to 5 days beyond "use-by" date.

COOKING

- Freeze cubes of milk mixed with an equal amount of orange juice; process cubes in a food processor to make sherbet.
- Cook rice in milk instead of water for a creamy side dish.
- Simmer sliced red potatoes and onions in milk for a quick soup; season with dill and black pepper.

RECIPES TO TRY

- Chai
- Macaroni and Cheese with Spinach
- Potato Salad with Sun-Dried Tomatoes, Scallions, and Basil

QUICK TIP: Try dry milk

To boost calcium, add nonfat dry milk (from a sprinkling up to ¼ cup) when baking or to soups, casseroles, stews, egg dishes, meatloaf, and mashed potatoes. A ¼ cup (125 g) of dry milk has 210 mg of calcium.

MUSHROOMS AND TRUFFLES

Typical serving size: ½ cup raw, sliced (35 g), 8 calories; ½ cup cooked (78 g), 22 calories

HOW THEY HARM

May be poisonous

WHAT THEY HEAL

Cardiovascular disease
High blood pressure
High cholesterol
Prostate and breast cancer
Immunity
Weight gain

NUTRIENTS

Chitin (cholesterol-lowering fiber)
Lentinan (phytochemical that may
  help boost immunity)
Niacin
Potassium
Selenium

BUYING

Choose mushrooms that are:
- firm buttons
- large; the largest of any variety have the most flavor

Avoid mushrooms with:
- bruises

STORING

Where: Crisper drawer of refrigerator.
How: In a paper bag.
For how long: 5 days.

COOKING

- Rinse mushrooms only before using them. Do not peel them or remove the stalks.
- Squeeze a little lemon juice on mushrooms to retain their color.
- Mix sautéed chopped mushrooms into turkey meat loaf.
- Grill portobello mushroom caps mounded with wild rice stuffing.
- Sprinkle truffle oil over sautéed mushrooms as a bruschetta topping.

RECIPES TO TRY

- Mushroom and Bell Pepper Frittata
- Trout with Lemon-Mushroom Stuffing
- Bok Choy, Tofu, and Mushroom Stir-Fry
- Baked Rice with Wild Mushrooms and Cheese
- Vegetable-Stuffed Mushrooms

MUSTARD GREENS

See Kale and Other Cooking Greens, page 65

NECTARINES

See Peaches and Nectarines, page 87

NUTS AND SEEDS

See also Flax, page 54; Peanuts and Peanut Butter, page 88

Typical serving size: 1 oz (28g), calories vary (see chart on page 77)

HOW THEY HARM

High in fat and calories
Allergies
Dehydration (chia seeds)

WHAT THEY HEAL

Diabetes
Cardiovascular disease
High cholesterol
Cancer
Low energy
Constipation
Anemia
Weight gain

NUTRIENTS

Calcium
Fiber
Flavonoids
Folate
Iron
Magnesium
Manganese
Monounsaturated fats
Omega-3 fatty acids
Potassium
Protein
Selenium
Vitamin E
Zinc

BUYING

Choose nuts or seeds that are:
- plump
- uniform in color and size

WHICH NUT AND SEED IS BEST?

While these little gems are high in fat and calories, most of it is healthy poly-unsaturated and monounsaturated fat. To keep your waistline from expanding as you enjoy all the good nutrition in nuts and seeds, keep an eye on your portions. Here are guidelines for serving sizes and how many calories they pack.

TYPE	AVERAGE NUMBER OR AMOUNT PER OUNCE	CALORIES PER 1-OZ (30 G) SERVING	FAT PER 1-OZ (30 G) SERVING	BEST FOR
Almond	24	163	14 g	Use sliced or chopped to add light crunch to salads, baked goods; whirl smoked almonds with roasted peppers and a splash of vinegar for a quick and easy vegetable dip.
Brazil nut	9	192	19 g	General snacking and pesto; try tossing toasted, chopped nuts with roasted asparagus.
Cashew	16-18	156	12.4 g	Curries and stir-fries; use as an alternative to peanuts; to make a dairy-free "cream sauce" that you can season countless ways, soak raw cashews overnight in enough water to cover them and then puree until smooth.
Hazelnut	20	178	17.2 g	Italian dishes and desserts; for an easy and elegant side dish, toss green beans with a little cooked chopped bacon and toasted hazelnuts.
Macadamia	10-12	200	21 g	Desserts; toast with sweetened coconut and sprinkle over fresh pineapple.
Pecan	20 halves	196	20.4 g	Desserts and breakfast dishes; chop and mix with raisins and chopped dried apples for an easy addition to your oatmeal routine.
Pine nut	3 Tbsp	190	19.3 g	Pesto and pasta dishes; use sparingly as they are more expensive than many nuts; store in freezer to extend freshness.
Pistachio	47	158	12.6 g	Italian dishes and salads; try dried apricots dipped in melted dark chocolate and then chopped pistachios.
Pumpkin seed	3 Tbsp	160	12.6 g	Trail mixes and Mexican dishes (including mole sauce); scatter a small handful over rice pilaf for an attractive (and flavorful) garnish. Also sold as pepitas.
Sesame seed	3 Tbsp	162	14 g	Asian dishes and general baking; make an easy gourmet crust by pressing sesame seeds into salmon or tuna fillets before pan searing.
Sunflower seed (shelled)	¼ cup	150	11 g	General snacking; use as a coating for cheese balls or add to granola mix for a classic combination.
Walnut	14 halves	185	18.5 g	General baking and salads; chop finely and use to coat boneless, skinless chicken breasts before oven roasting.

Avoid nuts or seeds that are:
- moldy
- close to or past their "use-by" date

STORING

Where: Cool, dry place when unopened, in the refrigerator once opened.
How: In an airtight container or sealed plastic bag.
For how long: Up to 6 months.

COOKING

- Sprinkle lemon-pepper seasoning over hot roasted sunflower seeds.
- Scatter chopped walnuts over a chicken stir-fry.
- Scatter pistachios over a salad of watercress, sliced orange, and red onion.
- Sprinkle sesame seeds into tuna salad.
- Puree raw almonds, roasted red peppers, and garlic as a sandwich spread.

RECIPES TO TRY

- Pasta with Walnut Cream Sauce
- Spiced Almonds
- Blueberry and Cranberry Granola
- Cauliflower Salad with Cashews
- Balsamic Beets with Toasted Pecans

OATS

See also Grains, page 57

Typical serving size: ½ cup cooked with water (117 g), 83 calories

HOW THEY HARM

Blood sugar spikes (instant oatmeal)

WHAT THEY HEAL

Cardiovascular disease
High cholesterol
High blood pressure
Diabetes
Constipation
Weight gain

NUTRIENTS

Beta-glucan (soluble fiber that can help lower cholesterol)
Calcium
Folate
Iron
Manganese
Polyphenols and saponins (antioxidants)
Protein
Thiamine
Vitamin E

BUYING

Choose:
- steel-cut or whole oat products

Avoid:
- flavored or instant oatmeal

STORING

Where: A cool, dry place or freezer.
How: In an airtight container; in a plastic bag with the air squeezed out if freezing.
For how long: About a year.

COOKING

- Stir ¼ cup steel-cut oats into a beef stew to thicken.
- Sprinkle rolled oats atop quick bread loaves before baking.
- Serve cooked oats topped with a poached egg.
- Use rolled oats instead of breadcrumbs in meat loaf, or to coat chicken or fish patties before cooking.

RECIPES TO TRY

- Hot Cereal with Apples and Dates
- Multigrain Pancakes or Waffles
- Spinach Stuffed Meat loaf
- Chewy Oatmeal Raisin Cookies
- Cherry Crisp

OILS

See also Olives and Olive Oil, page 80

Typical serving size: 1 Tbsp (15 mL), 120 calories

HOW THEY HARM

High in saturated fat (coconut, palm kernel, and palm oil)
Bacterial infection

WHAT THEY HEAL

High cholesterol
Hormone production
Nutrient absorption

NUTRIENTS

Monosaturated and omega-3 fats

BUYING

Choose:
- single-source oils, such as pure canola or pure olive

Avoid:
- blended oils

STORING

Where: A cool, dark place.
How: In original container.
For how long: About 6 months.

COOKING

- Choose canola oil for sautéeing or stir-frying.

- Use olive oil in a carrot muffin recipe.
- Drizzle roasted sesame oil over zucchini wedges after they're grilled.

RECIPES TO TRY

- Romaine Lettuce with Chunky Tomato Vinaigrette
- Buckwheat Noodles with Tofu and Green Vegetables
- Walnut Shortbread

OKRA

Typical serving size: ½ cup cooked (80 g), 18 calories

WHAT IT HEALS

High cholesterol
Constipation
Weight gain

NUTRIENTS

Beta-carotene
Fiber
Folate
Magnesium
Pectin (soluble fiber)
Potassium
Thiamine
Vitamin C

BUYING

Choose okra with:
- firm pods
- bright green color
- shallow ridges in pods

Avoid okra with:
- yellow or black discoloration
- shriveling
- any bruising, pitting, or decay

STORING

Where: Crisper drawer of refrigerator.
How: Unwashed and loosely wrapped in a perforated plastic bag.
For how long: 3 days.

COOKING

- Sauté baby okra in canola oil and garlic until crisp-tender, toss with teriyaki sauce.
- Bake whole baby okra flavored with olive oil, fine bread crumbs, garlic, and parmesan cheese.
- Use sliced okra in a chicken potpie filling.

RECIPES TO TRY

- Savory Lamb Stew with Sweet Potatoes
- Skillet Okra and Lamb

QUICK TIP:
Use as a thickener

Okra is high in starch, pectin, and soluble fiber, which help thicken soups and stews when it is cooked. As okra cooks, its fats are released and naturally thicken the soups and stews.

OLIVES AND OLIVE OIL

See also Oils, page 79

Typical serving size: 4 small olives (13 g), 16 calories; 1 Tbsp oil (15 mL), 120 calories

HOW THEY HARM

Blood pressure (olives)

WHAT THEY HEAL

High blood cholesterol
Cancer
Inflammation
Immunity
Weight gain

NUTRIENTS

Lignans (compounds that may protect against cancer)
Monounsaturated fats
Phytochemicals
Vitamin E

BUYING

Choose:
- oils that are minimally processed, such as extra-virgin or cold-pressed
- low-sodium varieties of canned olives

Avoid:
- olives that are soft or mushy

STORING

Where: Refrigerator for olives; dark, cool place for oil.
How: In an airtight container.
For how long: Up to 2 months for olives; several years for oil (if the oil turns cloudy, toss it).

COOKING

- Stir slivered ripe olives into risotto.
- Toss hot spaghetti with extra-virgin olive oil and garlic.
- Add minced green olives to egg salad.

RECIPES TO TRY

- Green Beans with Tomatoes and Olives
- Penne with Fresh Tomato Sauce and Grilled Eggplant
- Grilled Salmon with Sautéed Greens
- Linguine with Clams
- Tuna and Cannellini Salad with Lemon

ONIONS

Typical serving size: ½ cup raw (80 g), 32 calories

HOW THEY HARM

Bloating and flatulence

WHAT THEY HEAL

Lung cancer and other cancers
Heart attacks
High cholesterol
High blood sugar
Bacterial infections

NUTRIENTS

Beta-carotene
Chromium
Flavonoids
Potassium
Vitamin C

BUYING

Choose onions that:
- are firm
- have crackly, dry skin
- have a mild odor

QUICK TIP: Go raw

Cooking onions at a high heat significantly reduces the benefits of diallyl sulfide, their cancer-protective phytochemical. For the biggest health boost, enjoy fresh raw onions. Mincing (or even chewing) the onion helps to release its phytochemical power.

- have fresh, crisp, green tops that extend 2 to 3 in (5 to 7.5 cm) up from the root (spring onions/scallions)

Avoid onions that:
- feel soft
- have black spots
- have green sprouts showing at the top
- have a strong, oniony smell
- have yellowing, wilted, discolored, or decayed tops (spring onions/scallions)

STORING

Where: A cool, dry place away from direct light and away from potatoes. Store scallions and cut onions in the refrigerator.

How: With skin on for whole onions; tightly wrapped in plastic if cut; in a plastic bag for scallions.

For how long: 3 to 4 weeks uncut; 2 to 3 days cut; 3 days for scallions (use them before they begin to soften).

COOKING

- Broil pita bread topped with sautéed onions and grated swiss cheese until bubbly.
- Stir sliced scallions into scrambled eggs.
- Marinate slivers of sweet onion in cider vinegar in the refrigerator for several hours to make quick pickled onions.

RECIPES TO TRY

- Pineapple-Chipotle Chicken
- Herbed Turkey Meatballs and Fusilli
- Spinach Salad with Chickpeas
- Tuscan Bean Soup
- Sloppy Joes

ORANGES AND TANGERINES

Typical serving size: 1 medium orange (131 g), 63 calories; 1 medium tangerine (109 g), 50 calories; ½ cup juice (4 fl oz, 120 mL), 52 calories

HOW THEY HARM

Allergies
Tooth enamel erosion
Drug interaction
Canker sores

WHAT THEY HEAL

Cancer, including thyroid cancer
High blood pressure
High cholesterol
Inflammation
Weight gain

NUTRIENTS

Beta-carotene
Bioflavonoids
Fiber
Folate
Nobiletin (flavonoid that may have anti-inflammatory actions)
Potassium
Thiamine
Vitamin C

BUYING

Choose oranges that:
- are firm
- are heavy for their size
- have bright orange skin

Avoid oranges that:
- have bruised, wrinkled skin
- are discolored
- are canned

Best time to buy: winter and spring

STORING

Where: At room temperature, or crisper drawer of refrigerator (preferred spot for tangerines).
How: Unpeeled.
For how long: Up to 2 weeks.

COOKING

- Mix orange chunks with cottage cheese and mint.
- Quickly sauté orange slices as a topping for vanilla ice cream.
- Simmer tangerine sections, sliced pears, brown sugar, and a pinch of cloves in a saucepan to make a compote to serve with yogurt or on toast.
- Grill tangerine sections with sea scallops threaded on skewers.

QUICK TIP:
Don't be a perfect peeler

Eat the orange with the pith, the spongy white layer between the zest and the pulp. Although bitter, the pith stores a good amount of the fruit's fiber and antioxidant plant chemicals.

RECIPES TO TRY

- Orange Beef with Broccoli and Jicama
- Cantaloupe and Orange Soup
- Orange and Pomegranate Compote
- Asian Chicken Salad
- Orange Beets

ORGAN MEATS

Typical serving size: 3 to 4 oz (85 to 115 g), 165 to 216 calories

HOW THEY HARM

Toxins
Gout
High cholesterol
Vitamin A toxicity
Creutzfeldt-Jakob disease risk

WHAT THEY HEAL

Anemia
Vitamin B12 deficiency
Protein deficiency

NUTRIENTS

Folate
Iron
Niacin
Potassium
Protein
Vitamin B12
Zinc

BUYING

Choose organ meat that:
- is from a local butcher
- has the Safe Food Handling label on the package when buying at a supermarket
- is tightly wrapped and cold to the touch
- is shiny
- has a pleasant smell

Avoid organ meat that is:
- soaking in a large amount of liquid

STORING

Where: In the coldest part of the refrigerator or the meat drawer or bin.
How: Loosely wrapped.
For how long: 1 to 2 days (3 to 4 months if frozen).

COOKING

- Sauté chicken livers and minced onion, mash, and use as a sandwich spread.
- Add some finely chopped beef tripe to chili.
- Sauté veal sweetbread with chopped bacon.

RECIPES TO TRY

- Calf's Liver with Rigatoni

OYSTERS

See Shellfish, page 103

PAPAYAS

Typical serving size: 1 medium (304 g), 119 calories

HOW THEY HARM
Allergies

WHAT THEY HEAL
Cardiovascular disease
Colon cancer
Inflammation
Arthritis
Macular degeneration

NUTRIENTS
Beta-carotene
Fiber
Folate
Potassium
Vitamin C
Vitamin E

BUYING
Choose papaya that:
- have reddish-orange skin
- are slightly soft to the touch or yield to gentle pressure

Avoid papayas with:
- blemished skin
- large dark spots
- mold or are soft
- leaking at the stem end

STORING
Where: At room temperature to ripen; in the refrigerator when ripe.
How: Uncut in a plastic bag.
For how long: Up to 3 days.

COOKING
- Prepare a salad with shredded green papaya and ginger vinaigrette.
- Add papaya chunks to chicken curry.
- Top 2% Greek yogurt with papaya chunks and finely chopped roasted peanuts.

RECIPES TO TRY
- Papaya and Avocado Salad

PARSNIPS

Typical serving size: 1 cup cooked (156 g), 111 calories

HOW THEY HARM
Allergies

WHAT THEY HEAL
High cholesterol
Weight gain
Constipation
Cancer
Birth defects

NUTRIENTS
Fiber
Folate
Potassium
Vitamin C
Vitamin K

BUYING
Choose parsnips that are:
- firm and dry without pits
- about the size of a medium carrot

Avoid parsnips that are:
- very large
- covered with roots
- soft and shrunken or have moist spots

Best time to buy: autumn and winter

STORING

Where: In the refrigerator.
How: Unwashed with tops removed and in an unsealed bag.
For how long: 3 weeks or more.

COOKING

- Don't peel them. The most nutritious part of a parsnip is just below the surface of the skin.
- To bring out their sweetness, accent parsnips with nutmeg, ginger, mace, or cinnamon.
- Boil parsnip and carrot chunks until tender, drain and mash.
- Add chunks of parsnip to shepherd's pie.
- Make latkes from grated parsnip instead of potato.

RECIPES TO TRY

- Honey-Roasted Rack of Lamb
- Braised Chicken with Winter Vegetables
- Carrot and Parsnip Puree
- Roasted Root Vegetables

QUICK TIP: Beware of allergies

You might want to avoid parsnips if you have a history of allergies to birch pollen as well as foods like walnuts, figs, carrots, and parsley. Symptoms in sensitive people usually include a slight swelling and itching of the lips and mouth.

PASSION FRUIT

Typical serving size: 1 medium (18 g), 17 calories

HOW IT HARMS
Bloating and flatulence

WHAT IT HEALS
Vision
Immunity
Constipation
Weight gain

NUTRIENTS
Fiber
Vitamin A
Vitamin C

BUYING

Choose passion fruit that are:
- heavy and firm
- red, purple, or yellow
- wrinkled
- fragrant

Avoid passion fruit that is:
- lightweight or feels hollow

Best time to buy: winter and spring

STORING

Where: In the refrigerator when ripe (ripen smooth-skinned passion fruit at room temperature).
How: In a plastic bag.
For how long: Up to 7 days.

COOKING

- Seeds are edible, but if you'd like to remove them, strain the pulp and juice through a cheesecloth or another non-aluminum sieve.

- Spoon passion fruit over grilled bananas.
- Dollop passion fruit over sautéed chicken breasts.
- Add some passion fruit to an apple crumble.

RECIPES TO TRY

- Berry Salad with Passion Fruit
- Kiwi-Passion Fruit Salad

PASTA

Typical serving size: ½ cup (70 g), about 110 calories

HOW IT HARMS

Weight gain (white pasta)
Diabetes (white pasta)

WHAT IT HEALS

Mood
Diabetes (whole grain pasta)
Cardiovascular disease (whole grain pasta)
Colon cancer

NUTRIENTS

Fiber
Iron
Niacin
Thiamine

BUYING

Choose pasta that is:
- whole wheat
- high fiber

Avoid pasta that is:
- white

STORING TIPS

Where: A cool, dry place for dried pasta; refrigerator for fresh pasta.
How: Sealed container for dried; airtight container for fresh.
For how long: Indefinitely for dried; within a few days of purchase for fresh.

COOKING

- Simmer orzo pasta in chicken broth and Italian herb seasoning for a side dish.
- Fill an omelet with some leftover sauced pasta.
- Toss cooked whole grain spaghetti with bottled Thai peanut sauce and cilantro.

QUICK TIP:
Pick diabetes-friendly pasta

If you have diabetes, you'll minimize blood sugar spikes if you choose whole grain pasta, which contains three times the fiber of white pasta. Other options are the new higher protein pastas that are enriched with soy flour and milk solids and have a lower glycemic index (see page 354).

RECIPES TO TRY

- Whole Wheat Pasta with Sausage and Greens
- Linguine with Clams
- Farfalle with Winter Squash Sauce
- Penne with Fresh Tomato Sauce and Grilled Eggplant
- Sicilian Pasta Salad

PEACHES AND NECTARINES

Typical serving size: 1 medium peach (98 g), 38 calories; 1 medium nectarine (142 g), 62 calories

HOW THEY HARM

Allergies

Cyanide poisoning (pit only)

WHAT THEY HEAL

High cholesterol

Cancer

Weight gain

Constipation

NUTRIENTS

Beta-carotene

Carotenoids (antioxidants)

Fiber

Pectin (soluble fiber)

Potassium

BUYING

Choose peaches or nectarines that are:

- yellow or creamy with a rosy blush
- moderately firm
- fragrant

Avoid peaches or nectarines with:

- green undertones
- wrinkled skin or bruises, or ones that are rock hard
- tan circles on their skin

Best time to buy: spring, summer, early autumn

STORING

Where: Refrigerator when ripe; at room temperature if unripe.

How: Uncut if ripe; in a paper bag to ripen.

For how long: 3 or 4 days when ripe; 2 or 3 days to ripen.

COOKING

- Make salsa with peaches or nectarines in place of tomatoes.
- Stir chunks of peaches or nectarines into pancake batter.
- Top grilled peach or nectarine halves with a dollop of whipped ricotta cheese and honey.

RECIPES TO TRY

- Chicken Breast with Peaches and Ginger
- Peach and Blackberry Phyllo Pizzas
- Wheat Germ Smoothie
- Mixed Berry and Stone Fruit Soup
- Watermelon and Feta Salad

PEANUTS AND PEANUT BUTTER

See also Other Beans and Legumes, page 20

Typical serving size: 1 oz (28 g) peanuts, 166 calories; 2 Tbsp peanut butter (32 g), 188 calories

HOW THEY HARM

High in trans fats (peanut butter)

Allergies

WHAT THEY HEAL

Diabetes

High blood pressure

Cardiovascular disease

Low energy

Weight control

NUTRIENTS

Fiber

Folate

Magnesium

Monosaturated fats

Potassium

Sterols (plant compounds that improve cholesterol)

Vitamin E

BUYING

Choose:
- unsalted peanuts
- fresh-ground peanut butter

Avoid:
- peanuts that are moldy or have an "off" taste
- peanut butter with added sugar, salt, or trans fats (hydrogenated ingredients)

STORING

Where: Refrigerator or freezer (nuts only).

How: Tightly sealed container.

For how long: Up to 1 year for peanut butter in the fridge, up to 2 weeks if it's fresh ground; about 3 months for shelled nuts in the fridge, up to 6 in the freezer.

Nuts still in their shells can be kept in a cool, dry place, but keeping them in the fridge will help them last up to 9 months.

COOKING

- Scatter chopped roasted peanuts over roasted sweet potato sticks.
- Toss chopped roasted peanuts with corn kernels, bell pepper, and onion for a salad.
- Spread peanut butter over a pork tenderloin before roasting.

RECIPES TO TRY

- Whole Wheat Noodles with Peanut Sauce and Chicken
- Bulgur with Dried Cherries and Corn
- Banana-Peanut Bread
- Asian Peanut Dip
- No-Bake Flaxseed-Nut Bars

PEARS

Typical serving size: 1 medium (166 g), 96 calories

HOW THEY HARM

Allergies

Tooth decay (dried pears)

WHAT THEY HEAL

High cholesterol

Constipation

High blood pressure

Diabetes

NUTRIENTS

Antioxidants

Fiber

Pectin (soluble fiber)

Potassium

Vitamin C

BUYING

Choose pears that:
- have a smooth skin
- yield slightly to the touch at the stem
- have a slight fragrance

Avoid pears that:
- are dark or bruised

STORING

Where: Room temperature until ripe, then refrigerator.

How: Uncut.

For how long: A few days.

COOKING

- Make a salsa with chopped pears, basil, and orange juice.
- Use pears instead of apples in pastry recipes.
- Grill pear halves with agave nectar and nutmeg.

RECIPES TO TRY

- Pear Rhubarb Muffins
- Buckwheat Pancakes with Fruit Sauce
- Grilled Fruit en Brochette
- Minty Melon Cups
- Pork, Pear, and Potato Salad

PEAS AND PEA PODS

See also Beans and Other Legumes, page 20

Typical serving size: ½ cup green peas (49 g), 73 calories; 10 pea pods (34 g), 14 calories

HOW THEY HARM

Gout

WHAT THEY HEAL

Cancer

Constipation

High cholesterol

Macular degeneration

NUTRIENTS

Coumestrol (anticancer compound)

Fiber

Iron

Lutein (antioxidant)

Pectin (soluble fiber)

Protein

Vitamin C

BUYING

Choose fresh peas that are:
- less developed and have flatter pods
- firm
- bright green

Avoid peas that are:
- decaying
- wilted

If you can't get fresh peas, choose frozen over canned.

STORING

Where: Refrigerator.
How: Unwashed in a perforated plastic bag or unsealed container.
For how long: 3 to 5 days.

COOKING

- Cook peas in as little water as possible until just tender to minimize the loss of vitamins.
- Stir fresh or frozen baby peas and basil into a cheese risotto.
- Simmer fresh or frozen baby peas and chopped onion in chicken broth until tender; puree for soup.
- Serve pea pods with hummus for dipping.
- Add pods with the peas to soup stock for added flavor and nutrition.

RECIPES TO TRY

- Asparagus and Chicken Stir-Fry
- Snapper and Snaps in a Packet Spanish Rice
- Scallops Florentine
- Bulgur with Spring Vegetables
- Spiced Cauliflower with Peas

PECANS

See Nuts and Seeds, page 77

PEPPER, GROUND

See Herbs and Spices, page 61

PEPPERS

Typical serving size: ½ cup chopped (75 g), 20 calories

HOW THEY HARM

Digestion
Joint function
Pesticides
Canker sores

WHAT THEY HEAL

Cancer
Cardiovascular disease
Macular degeneration
Immunity

NUTRIENTS

Antioxidants
Beta-carotene
Bioflavonoids (anticancer compounds)
Folate
Lutein (antioxidant)
Phenolic acid (anticancer compound)
Sterols (cholesterol-lowering compound)
Vitamin B6
Vitamin C
Zeaxanthin (antioxidant)

BUYING

Choose peppers that:
- feel heavy for their size
- have smooth, unwrinkled skin

Avoid peppers that:
- have soft or dark spots
- are dull, shriveled, or pitted

Best time to buy: summer and early autumn

STORING

Where: Refrigerator.
How: In a plastic bag.
For how long: About 5 days.

COOKING

- Mix chopped green bell peppers into turkey meat loaf.
- Stuff Anaheim peppers with seasoned ground beef, then braise in marinara sauce.
- Stir some minced fresh cayenne pepper into a pasta salad.

RECIPES TO TRY

- Flank Steak Roll with Carrots and Red Peppers
- Grilled Eggplant Sandwiches with Red Pepper–Walnut Sauce
- Beef, Onion, and Pepper Fajitas
- Couscous-Stuffed Peppers
- Basil-Scented Sautéed Vegetables

PERSIMMONS

Typical serving size: 1 medium (5 to 6 cm) (168 g), 118 calories

HOW THEY HARM
Bloating and flatulence

WHAT THEY HEAL
Cancer
Immunity
High blood pressure
Digestion
Weight gain

NUTRIENTS
Fiber
Potassium
Vitamin A
Vitamin C

BUYING

Choose:
- Hachiya varieties that are very soft
- Fuyu varieties that are crisper
- plump, well-rounded fruit with leaf still attached
- deeply colored fruit with glossy skin

Avoid persimmons with:
- blemishes
- cracks
- bruises
- yellow patches (which indicate unripe fruit)

STORING

Where: Refrigerator if ripe; room temperature if unripe.
How: Inside a plastic bag if ripe; in a paper bag with an apple to ripen.
For how long: Up to 3 days in the fridge; 1 to 3 days to ripen.

Store puréed persimmon flesh in the freezer for up to 6 months.

COOKING

- Toss slices of ripe persimmon into an escarole and walnut salad.
- Add chopped persimmon to a bread pudding.
- Stir persimmon chunks into oatmeal with maple syrup.

RECIPES TO TRY

- Nutty Muesli
- Cauliflower Salad with Cashews

PINEAPPLES

Typical serving size: 1 cup diced (155g), 78 calories

HOW THEY HARM

Allergies
Canker sores

WHAT THEY HEAL

Cancer
Blood clots
Inflammation
Metabolism

NUTRIENTS

Bromelain (anti-inflammatory)
Ferulic acid (plant chemical that protects against cancer)
Fiber
Manganese
Potassium
Vitamin C

BUYING

Choose pineapples that:
- exude a fragrant odor
- have light yellow or white flesh
- are dense and heavy for their size
- have green, fresh-looking leaves
- make a dull, solid sound when thumped

Avoid pineapples with:
- brown patches
- bruises and soft spots on the base

When buying canned pineapple, choose 100% fruit juice over pineapple in heavy syrup.

Best time to buy: summer

STORING

Where: Refrigerator if cut; on the counter if whole.
How: In an airtight container when cut.
For how long: 3 days in the fridge if cut; a few days at room temperature if whole.

COOKING

- Blend crushed pineapple with part-skim ricotta cheese for a spread.
- Freeze the juice from no-sugar-added canned pineapple in ice pop trays for snacks.
- Stir some pineapple chunks into a three-bean salad.
- Add pineapple to stews or marinades for a natural tenderizer.

RECIPES TO TRY

- Jamaican Jerked Chicken Salad
- Pineapple-Chipotle Chicken
- Twice-Baked Stuffed Sweet Potatoes
- Grilled Fruit en Brochette

PLUMS AND PRUNES

> **Typical serving size:** 1 medium plum (66 g), 40 calories; ¼ cup prunes (40 g), 122 calories

HOW THEY HARM

Allergies

Cyanide poisoning (pit only)

Tooth decay (prunes)

WHAT THEY HEAL

Cancer

Weight gain

Constipation

Bone loss

NUTRIENTS

Anthocyanins (antioxidant)

Fiber

Iron

Isatin (a natural laxative)

Potassium

Riboflavin

Vitamin C

Vitamin K

BUYING

Choose plums that:

- are brightly colored
- yield slightly to the touch

Avoid plums that are:

- too soft or too hard
- bruised or discolored
- shriveled or have skin breaks
- leaky

Best time to buy: late spring to early autumn

STORING

Where: At room temperature to ripen; in refrigerator when ripe.

How: In a paper bag to ripen for plums; in an airtight container in a cool, dark place for prunes.

For how long: 2 to 3 days for plums; up to 6 months for prunes.

COOKING

- Blend a plum and yogurt smoothie.
- Add plum slices to a skillet of sautéed chicken.
- Simmer prunes in spiced red wine until tender.

RECIPES TO TRY

- Buckwheat Pancakes with Fruit Sauce
- Mixed Berry and Stone Fruit Soup
- Guavas and Plums with Vanilla Syrup

POME-GRANATES

Typical serving size: ½ cup arils (seeds) (87 g), 59 calories

HOW THEY HARM
Drug interaction

WHAT THEY HEAL
Prostate cancer
High cholesterol
High blood pressure
Erectile dysfunction

NUTRIENTS
Anthocyanins (antioxidant)
Copper
Ellagic acid (antioxidant)
Fiber
Folate
Potassium
Vitamin C

BUYING
Choose pomegranates that:
- are heavy for their size
- have a bright, fresh color
- have thin, yet tough skin

Avoid pomegranates with:
- blemishes or broken skin
- mold around the crown

Best time to buy: autumn and early winter

STORING
Where: A cool, dark place or in the refrigerator.
How: Unpeeled.
For how long: 2 weeks in a cool place; up to 2 months in the fridge. Seeds can be frozen for up to 1 year.

COOKING
- Make a spritzer with pomegranate juice and sparkling apple cider.
- Add pomegranate seeds to poultry stuffing.
- Scatter pomegranate seeds over roasted brussels sprouts.

RECIPES TO TRY
- Bulgur with Dried Cherries and Corn
- Creamy Citrus and Vanilla Rice Pudding
- Roasted Pork with Pomegranate Sauce
- Orange and Pomegranate Compote

PORK

See also Smoked and Cured Meats, page 104

Typical serving size: 3 oz (85 g), 105 to 180 calories, depending on cut

HOW IT HARMS
High blood pressure (cured or smoked products)
Parasites

WHAT IT HEALS
Bones
Muscles
Heart and nervous system function
Anemia
Immunity

NUTRIENTS
Iron
Protein
Selenium
Thiamin
Vitamin B12
Zinc

WARNING!
FOOD-DRUG INTERACTION

Eating pomegranates or drinking pomegranate juice can affect how the liver processes medications and increase their side effects. Such medications include fluoxetine, codeine, and ondansetron. Also, some heart medications, such as ACE inhibitors, can be affected by pomegranates as well. Taking blood pressure medication and pomegranates could possible cause your blood pressure to go too low.

BUYING

Choose pork that is:
- smooth and pink
- lean
- fresh (check date stamp on packages, which reflects the last date of sale)

Avoid pork that is:
- gray or damp looking

STORING

Where: Refrigerator.

How: In original package and wrapped if uncooked; in a sealed container if cooked.

For how long: Up to 3 days uncooked (1 week for bacon), 5 days cooked. Freeze bacon for up to 1 month.

COOKING

- Braise pork shoulder in dark beer, tomato puree, sliced onion, and Cajun seasoning.
- Stir-fry thin slices of pork tenderloin with Granny Smith apples and sage.
- Add some crumbled bacon to navy bean soup.

RECIPES TO TRY

- Pork Chops and Cabbage
- Ham and Celeriac Pitas
- Green Pork Chili
- Spinach-Stuffed Meat Loaf
- Roast Pork and Quinoa Salad

QUICK TIP: Cook to perfection

Cook pork tenderloin, chops, and roasts to an internal temperature of 145°F (63°C). When using ground pork to make meatballs or patties, cook them until they reach 160°F (71°C).

POTATOES

Typical serving size: 1 medium (154 g), 140 calories

HOW THEY HARM

Toxic risk (green and sprouted potatoes)

Digestion (if sensitive to night shade)

Joint function (if sensitive to night shade)

Diabetes (depending on preparation)

WHAT THEY HEAL

Cancer

Hypertension

NUTRIENTS

Chlorogenic acid (anticancer compound)

Fiber

Kukoamines (compounds that may lower blood pressure)

Magnesium

Potassium

Vitamin B6

Vitamin C

BUYING

Choose potatoes that:
- are firm and blemish free

Avoid potatoes that have:
- bald spots (except new potatoes)
- wrinkles or cracks
- sprouted
- a green tinge

STORING

Where: In a cool, dark place, but not in the refrigerator or near onions.

How: Uncut and unpeeled.

For how long: Up to 2 weeks.

COOKING

- Don't remove the skin. Fiber is in the skin, and many of the nutrients are near the surface.
- Scrub them under water with a vegetable brush.
- Baking, steaming, or microwaving preserves the maximum amount of nutrients.
- Roast cubed potatoes in extra-virgin olive oil, garlic, and rosemary until crisp.
- Toss cooked marble-size red potatoes in Greek yogurt and chopped dill for a quick salad.
- Simmer cubed potatoes with Mexican seasoning, canned diced tomatoes and enough water to cover until tender.

RECIPES TO TRY

- Pot Roast with Root Vegetables
- Braised Chicken with Winter Vegetables
- Potato Salad with Sun-Dried Tomatoes, Scallions, and Basil
- New Potatoes with Nori
- Mashed Turnips with Carrots and Potatoes

POULTRY

See also Smoked and Cured Meats, page 104

Typical serving size: 3 oz (85 g), calories vary (see chart on page 97)

HOW IT HARMS

Bacterial contamination

WHAT IT HEALS

Anemia
Cardiovascular disease
Immunity
Bones and muscles

NUTRIENTS

Iron
Niacin
Phosphorous
Potassium
Protein
Vitamin B6
Vitamin B12
Zinc

BUYING

Choose poultry that:

- has a current date stamp (for rotisserie chicken, check time stamps to see when it was prepared, and purchase within 2 to 4 hours after)
- has white to deep yellow colored fat
- is skinless for less fat

Avoid poultry with:

- rough, dry, or bruised skin
- gray or pasty-colored fat

STORING

Where: Coldest part of the refrigerator or freezer.
How: Securely wrapped.
For how long: Up to 3 days in fridge if cooked or raw; 2 months if frozen raw, 1 month if frozen cooked.

WHICH TYPE OF POULTRY IS HEALTHIEST?

Choose the leanest cuts and cook your poultry to perfection with this guide, organized from least to most fatty.

CUT	CALORIES & FAT PER 3-OZ (90-G) COOKED PORTION		AVERAGE SIZE	TOTAL TIME	BEST COOKING METHOD	DONENESS GUIDELINE
Turkey breast	110	0.5 g	4-6 lb (2-3 kg)	1 ½ - 2 ¼ hr	Roast at 325°F (160°C)	Until internal temperature is 165°F (74°C)
Ground turkey, extra-lean	120	1.5 g	Varies	Varies with amount and size of skillet	Brown in skillet over medium-high heat	
Chicken tenders	139	3.0 g	2 oz (60 g) each	15-20 min	Roast at 350°F (180°C)	
				4-6 min per side	Grill	
Chicken breast (boneless, skinless)			4-6 oz (125-175 g)	20-30 min	Roast at 350°F (180°C)	
				6-8 min per side	Grill	
Chicken breast (bone-in, skinless)			6-8 oz (175-250 g) oz each	30-40 min	Roast at 350°F (180°C)	
				10-15 min per side	Grill	
Duck, breast (boneless skinless)	144	6 g	8-10 oz (250-300g)	12 min	Roast at 425°F (220°C)	
Chicken thigh (boneless, skinless)	176	9.2 g	3-5 oz (90-150 g)	20-30 min	Roast at 350°F (180°C)	
				6-8 min per side	Roast at 350°F (180°C)	

COOKING

- Remove the skin after cooking to reduce fat and calories while maximizing flavor.
- Dip boneless chicken breast strips into buttermilk, then coat in crushed bran cereal and bake.
- Stir-fry chicken chunks with peanuts and Chinese pea pods.
- Slow-cook turkey drumsticks with chunks of onion, carrot, and celery in chicken broth.

RECIPES TO TRY

- Curried Chicken Salad Sandwiches
- Turkey, Spinach, and Rice in Roasted Garlic Broth
- Pesto Chicken Spirals with Roasted Peppers
- Herbed Turkey Meatballs and Fusilli
- Grilled Duck Breast with Polenta

PRUNES

See Plums and Prunes, page 93

PUMPKINS

Typical serving size: 1 cup cooked, mashed (245 g), 49 calories

HOW THEY HARM

Choking hazard (seeds)

WHAT THEY HEAL

Cancer

High blood pressure

Crohn's disease

NUTRIENTS

Beta-carotene

B vitamins (seeds)

Fiber

Iron

Potassium

Vitamin C

Vitamin E (seeds)

BUYING

Choose pumpkins that:
- have a hard, tough rind with the stem attached
- are heavy for their size
- are free of decay

Avoid pumpkins that:
- are used for jack-o-lanterns
- have cuts or punctures
- have sunken or moldy spots

STORING

Where: In a cool, dry place.

How: Uncut.

For how long: About 1 month.

COOKING

- Bake pumpkin pie filling in oiled custard cups for individual puddings.
- Roast pumpkin seeds and add them to trail mix.

QUICK TIP:

Try it for Crohn's disease

There's no one diet that seems to work for people living with the inflammatory problems associated with Crohn's disease. However, pumpkins and pumpkin seeds tend to be well tolerated by most.

- Simmer a quick soup with canned pumpkin, evaporated fat-free milk, cumin, and garlic.

RECIPES TO TRY

- Shrimp Seviche with Avocado and Pumpkin Seeds
- Broccoli and Pearl Barley Salad
- Whole Wheat Pumpkin Rolls
- Sweet and Spicy Snack Mix

QUINOA

See also Grains, p 57

Typical serving size: ½ cup cooked (93 g), 111 calories

HOW IT HARMS

Kidney stones

WHAT IT HEALS

Celiac disease

Cancer

Cardiovascular disease

Diabetes

Weight gain

NUTRIENTS

B vitamins

Complex carbohydrates

Fiber

Folate
Iron
Lysine (amino acid)
Magnesium
Niacin
Phosphorous
Potassium
Protein
Quercetin (antioxidant)
Saponins (phytochemicals that help prevent heart disease and cancer)
Thiamine
Zinc
Vitamin E

BUYING

Look for quinoa:
- in white, red, and black varieties (darker colors tend to have a stronger, earthy flavor while lighter colors are more mild)
- in health food stores and supermarkets, next to rice

STORING

Where: In a cool, dark place.
How: In an airtight package.
For how long: Up to 6 months, or freeze indefinitely.

COOKING

- Rinse thoroughly in a mesh strainer before cooking.
- Flavor cooked quinoa with a spoonful of pesto.
- Stir some cooked quinoa into a sweet potato salad.
- Use quinoa instead of rice to stuff bell peppers.

RECIPES TO TRY

- Roast Pork and Quinoa Salad
- Springtime Quinoa
- Quinoa with Chiles and Cilantro

RADISHES

Typical serving size: 5 medium raw (23 g), 5 calories

HOW THEY HARM

Bloating and flatulence
Allergies

WHAT THEY HEAL

Weight gain
Cancer

NUTRIENTS

Folate
Iron
Potassium
Vitamin C

BUYING

Choose radishes that:
- are brightly colored
- feel solid
- have crisp greens, if attached

Avoid radishes that are:
- really big (red globe radishes)
- blemished

Best time to buy: spring to early summer

STORING

Where: Refrigerator.
How: Remove any attached greens and place in plastic bags.
For how long: About 2 weeks.

COOKING

- Dip radishes into baba ghanoush.
- Add sliced radishes to a vegetable stir-fry.

- Dip raw radishes into extra-virgin olive oil, coarsely ground black pepper, and sea salt.

RECIPES TO TRY

- Warm Kasha and Seafood Salad
- Pork, Pear, and Potato Salad

RAISINS

See Grapes and Raisins, page 59

RASPBERRIES

See Berries, page 26

RHUBARB

Typical serving size: ½ cup diced (122 g), 26 calories

HOW IT HARMS

Poisonous (leaves)

Mineral absorption

Kidney stones

Gallstones

WHAT IT HEALS

Cancer

High blood pressure

NUTRIENTS

Fiber

Polyphenols (anticancer compounds)

Potassium

Vitamin C

BUYING

Choose rhubarb with:

- firm stalks
- no blemishes
- red flesh

Avoid rhubarb that is:

- green-fleshed
- discolored or scarred
- wilted, flabby, or mushy

Best time to buy: spring

STORING

Where: Crisper drawer of refrigerator or in the freezer.

How: Cut off the leaves, if any, and discard. Wash stalks in cold water, pat dry, and place them in a plastic bag. Cut into ½-in (1 cm) pieces if freezing.

For how long: One week in the fridge; up to 1 year in the freezer. Do not use if the stalks become mushy or discolored.

COOKING

- Baking rhubarb for 20 minutes releases high levels of polyphenols.
- Simmer sliced rhubarb, raisins, honey, vinegar, and ginger to make a chutney.
- Cook a chopped stalk of rhubarb with curried lentils.
- Roast chunks of rhubarb sprinkled with brown sugar just until crisp-tender.
- Stew to make a sauce to complement poultry, meats, pork, and desserts.

RECIPES TO TRY

- Pear Rhubarb Muffins
- Rhubarb-Blackberry Crumble

RICE

See also Grains, page 57

Typical serving size: ½ cup cooked
(93g), 85 to 120 calories

HOW IT HARMS

Blood sugar spikes (white rice)

WHAT IT HEALS

Colon cancer (brown rice)

Diarrhea

Diabetes (brown rice)

Celiac disease

NUTRIENTS

B vitamins

Fiber (brown rice)

Lysine (especially wild rice)

Magnesium

Phytochemicals

Protein (especially wild rice)

Vitamin E (brown rice)

BUYING

Choose rice that is:

- brown
- short, medium, or long varieties
- covered and dry, if buying in bulk

Avoid rice that is:

- white

STORING

Where: Refrigerator or freezer for brown
rice; a cool, dry cupboard for white rice.
How: In an airtight container.
For how long: Up to 6 months for brown
rice; 1 year for white. To store cooked
rice, let it cool, then place it in an airtight container in the coldest part of the
refrigerator for no more than 5 days or
in the freezer for up to 6 months.

COOKING

- Scatter leftover cooked brown rice
  over a vegetable frittata.
- Cook wild rice in apple juice.
- Toss cooled cooked rice with chopped
  tomatoes and basil in Italian dressing.

RECIPES TO TRY

- Snapper and Snaps in a Packet
- Rice Salad with Chicken and Grapes
- Japanese Sushi Rolls
- Creamy Citrus and Vanilla Rice
  Pudding

QUICK TIP: Get the right rice

Long-grain rice such as basmati is
fragrant and delicate, making it a
nice complement to curries and
other spicy dishes. Instant rice is
good for quick meals and works well
in casseroles, side dishes, and soups.
Wild rice, a very distant cousin of
rice, is technically a water grass. It
works well in pilafs, soups, and
stuffings. Choose arborio rice for
risotto because of its creamy texture.

RYE

See Grains, page 57

SAUSAGES

See Smoked and Cured Meats, page 104

SALT AND SODIUM

You need 1,300 to 1,500 mg of sodium per day for your body to function. North Americans typically consume 4,000 to 7,000 mg per day. Some people are more salt-sensitive than others, and they will get the biggest payoff from cutting back on salt. Everyone can benefit, though. Along with contributing to high blood pressure in sensitive individuals, a high-salt diet may increase your risk of kidney stones by stealing calcium from your body. Here's how to cut your intake down to only the essential amount.

KEEP IT HEALTHY

Hide your salt shaker. Don't add salt at the table. Taste your food first instead of salting out of habit. Cut the amount of salt in recipes by half—you probably won't even notice the difference. One teaspoon provides more than 2,000 mg of sodium.

Limit processed and preserved foods. Everyday food items like cereals, cold cuts, canned soups, canned vegetables, prepackaged meals, and baked goods are bursting with sodium. It's also found in MSG (monosodium glutamate); meat tenderizers; sauces and condiments such as ketchup, soy sauce, salad dressings, chili sauce, and steak sauce; soups; cured or smoked foods; olives; and pickles.

Choose low-sodium or no-salt-added canned foods. Whenever possible, rinse canned foods with water before cooking to remove more sodium. This works well with canned beans.

Season with sodium-free herbs and spices. Good choices include garlic powder or fresh garlic, onion flakes, dry mustard, coriander, lemon, mint, cumin, chili powder, curry, rosemary, thyme, basil, bay leaves, ginger, hot peppers, black pepper, chives, and parsley.

Use kosher salt. The grains are larger so it tastes saltier and you can use it more sparingly.

Opt for the least processed option. Eat fresh or frozen fish instead of canned or dried varieties. Choose sliced roast beef or chicken over bologna, salami, or other processed meat.

SEAWEED

Typical serving size: ½ cup (40 g), 20 calories

HOW IT HARMS

High in sodium

WHAT IT HEALS

Thyroid function

Muscles

Immunity

Metabolism

NUTRIENTS

Beta-carotene

Folate

Iodine

Protein

Vitamin A

BUYING

Look:
- in Asian markets and natural food stores

STORING

Where: Cool cupboard, if dried; refrigerator, if fresh.

How: Well wrapped in an airtight container.

For how long: Up to 1 year, if dried; up to 1 to 2 days, if fresh.

COOKING

- Sprinkle snipped dried dulse over Manhattan clam chowder.
- Toss sliced fresh wakame with thinly sliced cucumbers, rice wine vinegar and a sprinkling of sugar for a salad.
- Add some ready-to-eat dried wakame to the filling of a vegetable omelet.

RECIPES TO TRY

- Warm Kasha and Seafood Salad
- Japanese Sushi Rolls
- New Potatoes with Nori
- Miso Soup with Tofu

SHELLFISH

Typical serving size: 2 to 3 oz shelled (56 g to 85 g), calories vary (see chart on page 53)

HOW IT HARMS

Allergies

WHAT IT HEALS

Cancer

Weight gain

Cardiovascular disease

Anemia

Thyroid function

NUTRIENTS

Iodine

Iron

Omega-3 fatty acids

Protein

Selenium

Vitamin B12

BUYING

Buy shellfish that:
- is well covered with ice, or for lobsters, in aerated tanks with circulating water
- smells briny

QUICK TIP:
Try lemon instead of butter

A simple squeeze of lemon juice can be enough to flavor shellfish as long as it hasn't been overcooked.

STORING

Where: On the bottom shelf in the back of the refrigerator.

How: In a shallow pan on a bed of ice.

For how long: 24 hours from purchase. Purchased frozen shellfish can be kept frozen for up to 6 months.

COOKING

- Make a salad with slices of grilled squid, tomatoes, red onions, and ripe olives.
- Season stir-fried shrimp with Thai peanut sauce.
- Marinate soft-shell crabs in Italian dressing for one 1 hour before grilling.

RECIPES TO TRY

- Pan-Seared Scallops with Oranges and Sun-Dried Tomatoes
- Thai Roasted Shrimp
- Shellfish Salad with Herbed Lemon Dressing
- Crab Cakes with Melon Relish
- Oysters with Tomato Salsa

Avoid shellfish that:
- smells like iodine
- smells fishy

Most shrimp are trimmed and frozen in bulk at sea, then thawed for sale. Shrimp processed in this way should be labeled "previously frozen."

IN MODERATION ONLY

SMOKED AND CURED MEATS

You might want to skip the deli line the next time you go food shopping. The reddish-pink color of cured meats, including cold cuts, is due to the presence of nitrites, chemicals that may cause cancer. These types of meat also tend to have a high sodium content that can increase blood pressure. Aside from some protein, these foods offer little nutritionally so they're best consumed infrequently.

KEEP IT HEALTHY

Look for lower-sodium options. Even these will be high in sodium; some brands still top 460 g per serving. So limit the quantity and frequency that you eat these types of food.

Select the least processed meats. Choose sliced roast beef or chicken over bologna, salami, or other processed meat.

Go color free. Lean cuts of white meat such as turkey breast have less fat and are a healthier option to most cold cuts.

SHRIMP

See Shellfish, page 103

SOY

See also Beans and Other Legumes,
page 20

Typical serving size: Varies (see chart
on page 106)

HOW IT HARMS
Cancer risk
Thyroid function

WHAT IT HEALS
Cardiovascular disease
Breast and prostate cancers
Osteoporosis
Menopause

NUTRIENTS
Calcium
Essential amino acids (only plant
   product to contain all of them)
Isoflavones (potential anticancer
   compounds)
Protein

BUYING
Look for:
- edamame (green soy beans) in the
  pod in the produce section, if fresh, or
  shelled in the frozen food section, if
  frozen
- tofu in the produce or refrigerated
  (dairy) section
- soy flour with other flours
- soymilk in the dairy section

Avoid soy products with:
- lots of salt, sugar, or other additives

STORING
Where: Edamame and tofu, in the refrigerator or freezer; low-fat soy flour,
and shelf-stable soymilk in a cupboard;
full-fat soy flour, in the freezer; regular
soymilk, in the refrigerator.
How: In airtight packages or containers.
For how long: Edamame, up to 5 days;
tofu, before "use-by" date; low-fat soy
flour, up to 1 year; full-fat soy flour, up to
1 year; soymilk, 7 to 10 days after opening or as indicated on the label.

COOKING
- Simmer rice in miso broth in place of
  water.
- Use thinly sliced soft tofu to replace
  half of the cheese in a lasagna recipe.
- Add some steamed edamame to a
  three-bean salad.

RECIPES TO TRY
- Mediterranean Salad with Edamame
- Edamame Hummus with Pita Crisps
- Miso Soup with Tofu
- Bok Choy, Tofu, and Mushroom
  Stir-Fry

QUICK TIP:
Pair it with vitamin C

The iron in soy products is not
well absorbed. To improve
absorption, add foods high in
vitamin C—such as orange juice,
tomatoes, peppers, strawberries,
or melons—to your meal.

WHAT'S THE DIFFERENCE BETWEEN SOY PRODUCTS?

Most soy foods contain some amount of isoflavones, which are plant-based, estrogen-like nutrients that may play a role in fighting heart disease and osteoporosis. However, ingesting high amounts of isoflavones may be problematic for people with some types of cancer and other hormone-sensitive conditions. Talk with your doctor about including soy foods in your diet. This chart lists products from highest to lowest isoflavone content.

TYPE	WHAT IT IS	HOW IT'S USED	TYPICAL SERVING SIZE	ISOFLAVONE CONTENT (MG PER SERVING)
Edamame	Japanese name for young soybeans	Steamed and served in the pod, sometimes sprinkled with salt and a squirt of fresh lemon	½ cup	160
Soy flour, full-fat	Made from roasted soybeans that have been finely ground; rich in protein	Substitute up to ¼ all-purpose flour with soy flour in recipes; makes baked goods brown faster, so adjust baking time accordingly.	¼ cup	107
Soy flour, low-fat		As an egg substitute in baking, mix 1 Tbsp soy flour with 1 Tbsp cold water; can be used to make homemade soymilk (mix with water, heat, and strain it)	¼ cup	79
Tempeh	Made from cooked soybeans that have been pressed into a cake; firm texture and subtle, nutty flavor	Use in salads, sandwiches, burgers, chili-style dishes, and stir-fries as an alternative to chicken, pork, or beef	4 oz (125 g)	54
Tofu, soft	Versatile, high-protein pressed soymilk curds; moisture content determines softness; good source of calcium when made with calcium sulfate; virtually flavorless	May be grilled, baked, or fried in a variety of sweet and savory dishes; for best results, always drain regular tofu by pressing the blocks between paper towels before slicing	4 oz (125 g)	37
Tofu, firm			4 oz (125 g)	28
Soymilk	Processed beverage; available sweetened or flavored	Use as you would regular milk in most recipes; scalds easily so always stir when heating; doesn't set as easily in pudding and pie recipes, so experiment by adding small amount of cornstarch to soymilk before heating	8 oz (250 g)	24
Miso	Rich, salty Japanese condiment made from fermented soybeans and grains (usually rice or barley); it comes in a paste, concentrated broth, or freeze-dried; darker-colored miso indicates stronger flavors	Use in soups, marinades, and salad dressings; to preserve nutrients, do not boil	1 tsp	2
Soy cheese	Processed soymilk product designed to resemble dairy-based cheeses	Use in recipes as you would regular cheese; melting times and consistency may vary by brand	1 oz (30 g)	2
Meat analogues	Term used to describe processed meatless foods that are often made from soy and designed to resemble common meats	Use tofu hot dogs and sausages, meatless crumbles and burgers, as well as soy-based chicken chunks and strips in place of animal protein, especially in saucy dishes where spices are the dominant flavor	Varies	Varies*
Non-dairy soy frozen desserts	Term used to describe processed soymilk product designed to resemble ice cream	Use in frozen dessert recipes as you would regular ice cream; variety of brands and flavors are available	½ cup	Varies
Soy sauce	Salty brown liquid made from fermented soybeans and grains (usually rice or barley)	Traditionally used throughout Asia as an all-purpose seasoning; salt-sensitive people should use lower-sodium soy sauce when available	1 Tbsp	None

*These processed products have proprietary blends so isoflavone content isn't standard.

SOFT DRINKS

Apart from a quick energy boost from the caffeine or sugar, soft drinks and soda pop offer little to no nutritional value. The extra sugar in sodas can lead to weight gain and tooth decay, and many contain acids that erode tooth enamel. Research suggests that one soda a day increases a child's chances of becoming obese by 60%. Colas also contain large amounts of phosphates, which may impair calcium absorption. Even worse is that kids are likely to drink less milk if they're consuming soda. While diet soft drinks have fewer calories, they may still contribute to weight gain by tricking your taste buds into craving more sugar, and they contain artificial sweeteners and caffeine. The one time when soda can actually benefit you is if you have an upset stomach. Ginger ale or cola can help to quell nausea and provide energy for people unable to take solid food.

KEEP IT HEALTHY

Choose a healthier fizz. Carbonated drinks are refreshing, so try sparkling water, club soda, or sodium-free seltzer.

Mix your own soft drink. Combine 100% fruit juice with one of the carbonated beverages above for an energy boost with less sugar and no caffeine.

Shrink the serving size. Choose the smallest portion or share with a friend.

SPICES

See Herbs and Spices, page 61

SPINACH

See also Kale and Other Cooking Greens, page 65; Lettuce and Other Salad Greens, page 71

Typical serving size: 1 cup raw (30 g), 7 calories; ½ cup cooked (90 g), 21 calories

HOW IT HARMS

Mineral absorption

Kidney and bladder stones

Drug interaction

WHAT IT HEALS

Macular degeneration

Cancer

Congenital neurological birth defects

Anemia

Bone health

NUTRIENTS

Bioflavonoids

Folate

Lutein (antioxidant)

Potassium

Riboflavin

Vitamin A

Vitamin B6

Vitamin C

Vitamin K

Zeaxanthin (antioxidant)

WARNING! FOOD-DRUG INTERACTION

Spinach may interfere with blood-thinning drugs. If your physician has prescribed blood-thinning medication such as heparin and warfarin (Coumadin), it is wise to moderate your intake of vitamin K–rich foods, such as spinach. Excess vitamin K can counteract the effects of these drugs.

BUYING

Choose spinach that:
- has dark green leaves
- is crisp and fresh
- has no added sauce, if frozen

Avoid spinach that:
- is wilted or yellowing
- has signs of insect damage, holes in leaves

STORING

Where: Crisper drawer of refrigerator.
How: In a plastic bag.
For how long: Up to 5 days.

COOKING

- To maximize nutrients in spinach, don't overcook it. Instead, lightly steam or stir-fry to preserve vitamin content, texture, and flavor.
- Scatter chopped cooked spinach over cheese pizza.
- Season cooked spinach with soy sauce and grated ginger.
- Drain cooked pasta in a colander filled with baby spinach leaves, return the pasta and spinach to the pot, and toss with olive oil, grated romano cheese and dried red chile.

QUICK TIP: Ditch the dirt

To effectively remove dirt and sand from spinach, submerge it in a bowl of cold water. Let the sand fall to the bottom, then remove and rinse the leaves. Dry them if making a salad. If you are cooking the spinach, the water left on the leaves may be just about the right amount with which to steam it.

RECIPES TO TRY

- Flank Steak Roll with Carrots and Red Peppers
- Turkey Braciola Stuffed with Provolone and Spinach
- Scallops Florentine
- Cauliflower and Spinach Casserole
- Spinach, Sweet Potato, and Shiitake Salad

SQUASH

(includes summer squash, such as chayote, patty pan, yellow crooknecks and straightnecks, and zucchini, and winter squash, such as acorn, banana, butternut, delicata, dumpling, hubbard, spaghetti, and turban)

See also Zucchini, page 117

Typical serving size: ½ cup slices, cooked (90 g), 18 calories

WHAT IT HEALS

Vision
Bone growth
Cell functions
Immunity
Constipation
High cholesterol
Weight gain

NUTRIENTS

Beta-carotene (especially winter varieties)
B vitamins
Fiber
Folate
Iron
Potassium
Vitamin C

BUYING

Choose squash with:
- firm, unblemished skin or rind
- dull, brown stems (winter variety)
- long necks and smaller bottoms (butternut squash)
- shiny skin (summer variety)

Avoid:
- summer squash with pitted skin or spongy texture
- winter squash that gives when pressed hard
- winter squash with shiny green stems

STORING

Where: Crisper drawer of refrigerator for summer varieties; in a cool, dark place for winter ones.

How: Uncut.

For how long: Up to 1 week for summer squash; several months for winter ones. If any soft or discolored spots develop on the squash, cut them away and discard before eating.

COOKING

- Summer squash can be eaten raw. If it is cooked, stir-frying or steaming minimizes nutrient loss and keeps the vegetable from becoming too mushy.
- To avoid making dishes watery because of its high water content, lightly salt summer squash slices or pieces and place them on absorbent paper towels; rinse before adding them to the recipe.

QUICK TIP: Baked is better

You'll retain more nutrients if you bake or steam winter squash instead of boiling it.

- Microwave small hard-shell squash, pierced several times with a knife, for 10 minutes on high power for easy peeling.
- Simmer chopped acorn or hubbard squash in a marinara sauce.
- Stir-fry slices of delicata squash with chopped leeks.

RECIPES TO TRY

- Broccoli and Pearl Barley Salad
- Roasted Pork with Pomegranate Sauce
- Cider-Baked Acorn Squash with Apple Stuffing
- Fruity Butternut Squash Casserole with Papaya
- Ginger Butternut Squash Soup

STRAWBERRIES

See Berries, page 26

SUGAR AND OTHER SWEETENERS

One healthy change every American should make is eating less sugar. We consume about 22 teaspoons of added sugar a day (that is, sugar added during preparation, not sugar that occurs naturally in fruit and other foods)—about 355 empty calories that can show up on your waistline and can increase your risk for diabetes and heart disease. This is sugars—that has been added during processing or preparation or at the table, not sugar that occurs naturally in foods like fruit. Despite some claims, brown sugar, honey, and molasses aren't any healthier than white sugar. Even some agave products, which have been hailed as more healthful alternatives because of their low glycemic index, actually cause blood sugar swings. And all of these sweeteners encourage the growth of oral bacteria that can lead to cavities. While it's unrealistic to think you can eliminate sugar entirely, you can make smarter choices.

KEEP IT HEALTHY

Monitor your intake. It's amazing how quickly it adds up. Aim to consume under 40 g (about 10 tsp) of added sugar a day. That's about one can of Coke.

Satisfy your sweet tooth with whole foods. Natural sugars found in fruits and some vegetables make them a good option.

Consider calorie-free alternatives. Artificial sweeteners such as aspartame and sucralose (Splenda) have virtually no calories. While they may sound like a perfect choice if you're trying to lose weight, some research suggests that they may not be as helpful as expected and could contribute to weight gain, so use them wisely. They may be a good alternative for people with diabetes because they generally don't raise blood sugar. They also don't promote tooth decay.

Be cautious with sugar alcohols. Used in chewing gums, candies, ice cream, and many baked goods, sweeteners such as sorbitol, xylitol, maltitol, and lactitol provide fewer calories than sugar, do not promote tooth decay, and do not cause sudden jumps in blood glucose. However, they can produce a laxative effect in some people.

Brush afterward. More dangerous than the amount of sugar is the length of time the sugar remains in contact with the teeth.

SWEET POTATOES AND YAMS

Typical serving size: ½ cup baked (2.4 oz or 68 g); 80 to 90 calories

WHAT IT HEALS

High blood pressure
Eyes and skin
Immunity
Cardiovascular disease
Diabetes
Prostate and breast cancer
High blood sugar
High cholesterol
Insulin resistance

NUTRIENTS

Beta-carotene
Carotenoids
Chlorogenic acid (anticancer compound)
Fiber
Potassium
Vitamin C

BUYING

Choose yams and sweet potatoes that are:
- firm and smooth

Avoid yams and sweet potatoes that have:
- wrinkles or bruises
- sprouts or decay

STORING

Where: In a dry, cool place such as a cellar, pantry, or garage.
How: Unwashed, uncut.
For how long: 1 month; stored at room temperature, 1 week.

COOKING

- Scrub the potatoes but don't peel them, to retain more fiber and nutrients.
- Mash cooked yams or sweet potatoes with grated ginger and roasted sesame oil.
- Top roasted, split yams or sweet potatoes with chili.
- Make a soup with chunks of yam or sweet potato, chicken chunks, and chopped kale in broth.

RECIPES TO TRY

- Savory Lamb Stew with Sweet Potatoes
- Cod and Vegetable Stew
- Black Bean and Sweet Potato Burritos
- Twice-Baked Stuffed Sweet Potatoes

QUICK TIP:
Lighten up traditional recipes

For candied sweet potatoes, use thickened apple juice as a glaze, instead of sugar, and substitute pineapples for marshmallows.

TANGERINES

See Oranges and Tangerines, page 82

TEA

Typical serving size: 6 fl oz (177 mL), 2 calories

HOW IT HARMS

Iron absorption

Increased urination

Insomnia

Migraines

WHAT IT HEALS

Weight gain

Stroke

Diabetes

Cardiovascular disease

Cancer

Asthma

Dental health

Diarrhea

NUTRIENTS

Antioxidants

Catechins (especially green and white varieties; compounds that may help with weight loss)

Epigallocatechin gallate (compounds that may protect against diabetes, heart disease, and cancer)

Flavonoids

Flouride

L-theanine (chemical that boosts immunity)

Phenols

Tannins (compounds that protect teeth)

Theophyllines (compounds that may help with respiratory problems)

BUYING

Choose tea:

- in whole leaf form, when available, for best flavor and healing properties
- in bags that are made from unbleached natural fiber
- that's unsweetened

Avoid tea:

- flavored with fruit syrups and sweetened with sugar, including commercial iced teas

STORING

Where: In a cool spot.
How: In a metal container.
For how long: Up to 1 year.

COOKING

- Stir a spoonful of matcha, powdered green tea, into scrambled eggs.
- Add some cold brewed red rooibos tea to a berry smoothie.
- Use cold brewed black tea to replace water or milk in muffin recipes.

RECIPES TO TRY

- Earl Grey Chicken
- Napa Cabbage Slaw with Peanut Dressing
- Melon Berry Compote with Green Tea and Lime
- Chai

TOFU

See Soy, page 105

TOMATOES

HOW THEY HARM

Indigestion and heartburn
Allergies
Headaches
Canker sores

WHAT THEY HEAL

Cancer
Cardiovascular disease

NUTRIENTS

Chlorogenic acid (anticancer compound)
Folate
Lycopene (antioxidant)
Potassium
Salicylates (anticlotting effects)
Vitamin C

BUYING

Choose tomatoes that:
- have deep red color and shiny, firm skin
- are vine ripened
- have reduced or no sodium added, for canned or jarred tomatoes

Avoid tomatoes that are:
- wrinkled or blemished
- pale colored
- have signs of insect or worm damage

STORING

Where: At room temperature for fresh tomatoes; in a cool cupboard if canned or jarred.
How: Out of direct sunlight.
For how long: 1 week if fresh; 1 year if canned or jarred.

COOKING

- Top a pizza with sliced tomatoes.
- Add some finely chopped tomatoes to corn bread batter before baking.
- Use sliced tomatoes instead of pineapple in an upside-down cake recipe.

RECIPES TO TRY

- Orange Chicken with Artichokes and Sun-Dried Tomatoes
- Roasted Mackerel with Cherry Tomatoes and Potatoes
- Fusilli with Pan-Roasted Vegetables
- Tomato Biscuits

TURKEY

See Poultry, page 96

TURNIPS

HOW THEY HARM

Bloating and flatulence
Thyroid function

WHAT THEY HEAL

Cancer
High cholesterol
Vision
Bones
Immunity

NUTRIENTS

Beta-carotene (turnip greens)
Calcium
Fiber
Lysine (may help with cold sores)
Potassium
Vitamin C

BUYING

Choose turnips that:

- are firm
- feel heavy for their size
- have smooth skin
- are no more than 3 in (7.5 cm) in diameter
- have brightly colored and fresh greens

Avoid turnips that:

- are mushy
- have sunken brown spots
- have wilted or yellow greens

Best time to buy: winter

STORING

Where: Crisper drawer of refrigerator.
How: In a plastic bag.
For how long: Up to 2 weeks.

COOKING

- Small turnips of about 2 inches (5 cm) in diameter may only need to be well scrubbed, not peeled, before cooking.
- Shred turnips and use in coleslaw.
- Add matchstick-cut turnips to a vegetable stir-fry.
- Roast turnip chunks with carrot, onion, and walnuts.
- Replace half of the potatoes in a gratin recipe with turnips.

RECIPES TO TRY

- Herb-Buttered Turnips
- Basil-Scented Sautéed Vegetables
- Mashed Turnips with Carrots and Potatoes

VINEGAR

Typical serving size: 1 Tbsp, 3 to 14 calories, depending on variety

HOW IT HARMS

Allergies

WHAT IT HEALS

Weight gain

NUTRIENTS

Trace amount of some minerals such as manganese, potassium, iron, and magnesium, depending on the variety

BUYING

Choose:

- inexpensive white vinegar for making pickles
- sherry vinegar for vinaigrettes
- rice wine vinegar for sushi
- a shop that offers samples of different vinegars before buying

STORING

Where: In a cool dark cabinet.
How: In a sealed bottle or jar.
For how long: Indefinitely if unopened; up to 6 months when opened.

COOKING

- Add fresh herbs or fruit to distilled, cider, or wine vinegars to make flavored vinegars.
- Use white wine vinegar in recipes calling for lemon juice.
- Use sherry wine vinegar to dress a three-bean salad.
- Marinate beef chuck in cider vinegar for several hours before roasting.

RECIPES TO TRY

- Brussels Sprouts with Caraway Seeds
- Napa Cabbage Slaw with Peanut Dressing
- Buffalo Chicken Fingers

WALNUTS

See Nuts and Seeds, page 76

WATERCRESS

See Lettuce and Other Salad Greens, page 73

WATERMELON

See Melons, page 73

WHEAT AND WHEAT GERM

See also Grains, page 57

Typical serving size: 2 Tbsp wheat germ (14 g), 54 calories

HOW THEY HARM

High blood sugar (refined wheat)
Allergies

WHAT THEY HEAL

High cholesterol
Gastrointestinal distress
Weight gain
Cardiovascular disease

High blood pressure
Inflammation
Anemia

NUTRIENTS

B vitamins
Copper
Fiber
Folate
Iron
Magnesium
Manganese
Phosphorous
Sterols (cholesterol-lowering compounds)
Protein
Thiamine
Vitamin E
Zinc

BUYING

Choose:
- products labeled "100% whole wheat"

Avoid:
- refined products

STORING

Where: In the refrigerator; defatted wheat germ can be kept in the cupboard.
How: In an airtight container.
For how long: 6 to 8 months.

COOKING

- Cook wheat berries for a grain side dish.
- Sprinkle toasted wheat germ over creamy soups before serving.
- Toss some wheat germ into a salad.

RECIPES TO TRY

- Whole Wheat Noodles with Peanut Sauce and Chicken
- Macaroni and Cheese with Spinach
- Wheat Berry Salad with Dried Apricots

WRAPS AND TORTILLAS

See Bread, page 28

YAMS

See Sweet Potatoes and Yams, page 111

YOGURT

See also Milk and Dairy Products, page 74

Typical serving size: 6 oz, 80 to 160 calories, depending on brand and type

HOW IT HARMS

Phenylketonuria

WHAT IT HEALS

Digestion
Bone health
High blood pressure

NUTRIENTS

Calcium
Live or "active" bacteria
Phosphorus
Protein

BUYING

Choose yogurt that is:
- plain
- low-fat or nonfat

Avoid yogurt with:
- fruit added
- sweeteners or flavoring

STORING

Where: Refrigerator.
How: In its container.
For how long: Within a week of the "use-by" date.

COOKING

- Use 2% Greek yogurt in recipes calling for sour cream.
- Blend a dip with plain yogurt, sun-dried tomatoes, garlic, and salt-free seasoning mix.
- Replace buttermilk in baked goods with yogurt thinned with milk or water.

RECIPES TO TRY

- Mackerel Tandoori Style
- Lobster Salad with Lime Dressing
- Tomato Biscuits
- Carrot Soup with Dill
- Strawberry-Yogurt Smoothie

YUCCA

(also known as cassava or manioc)

Typical serving size: ½ cup raw (103 g), 165 calories

HOW IT HARMS

Bloating and flatulence

WHAT IT HEALS

Immunity
Collagen production
Digestion
Celiac disease
Gluten intolerance

NUTRIENTS

Fiber
Vitamin C

BUYING

Choose yucca that is:
- firm

Avoid yucca that is:
- blemished
- soft

STORING

Where: In a dry, cool, dark place.
How: Unwashed, uncut.
For how long: 1 week uncut. You can also peel yucca, place it in water, and refrigerate it for up to 3 days; or peel, wrap, and freeze it for up to about 3 months.

COOKING

- Bake yucca sticks coated with olive oil and garlic until browned and crispy.
- Top a shepherd's pie with mashed cooked yucca.
- Toss a salad of cooked yucca cubes with corn kernels, red bell pepper, scallions. and cilantro in lime dressing.

RECIPES TO TRY

- Shrimp and Yucca Salad
- Baked Yucca Chips

ZUCCHINI

See also Squash, page 108

Typical serving size: 1 cup raw, chopped (124 g), 20 calories

WHAT IT HEALS

High cholesterol
Weight gain

NUTRIENTS

Fiber
Folate
Potassium
Vitamin C

BUYING

Choose zucchini that are:
- firm
- heavy for their size
- small, about 6 to 9 in (15 to 22.5 cm) long

Avoid zucchini that are:
- blemished
- bruised
- moldy

Best time to buy: summer

STORING

Where: Crisper drawer of refrigerator.
How: In a plastic bag.
For how long: Up to 1 week.

COOKING

- Coarsely shred zucchini, place in a cold skillet, and cook until it's wilted; drain and sprinkle with parmesan cheese.
- Make a gratin of thinly sliced zucchini and fine dry bread crumbs drizzled with olive oil.
- Toss a salad of grilled zucchini strips, tomatoes, olives, and crumbled feta cheese.

RECIPES TO TRY

- Zucchini Frittata
- Monkfish and Mussel Kebabs
- Beef and Blue Cheese Burgers
- Couscous-Stuffed Peppers
- Zucchini-Carrot Crustless Quiche Squares

RECIPES

250 Delicious Recipes for Good Health

Healthy eating doesn't have to be time-consuming, expensive, bland, or boring. In this section, you're going to discover simple ways to get more foods that heal into your diet. It's easy when every recipe contains at least three healing foods—some have many more. (We've listed just the ones that are most abundant on these pages.) These recipes are packed with nutrients, but they don't have endless lists of ingredients. The foods you'll use, however, are specially selected to enhance the flavor of each dish without making preparation difficult. You'll be amazed at how tasty healthy cuisine can be.

More than 250 recipes cover Breakfasts, Soups and Stews, Sandwiches and Light Meals, Salads, Entrées, Sides, Snacks, Desserts, and Drinks—you can eat healthy all day long and keep your taste buds entertained with new dishes. While some of the recipes may seem exotic and use foods you're not familiar with, you'll also find some old favorites that have been made over to provide more nutrients with less fat, calories, sugar, and sodium. There's something for everyone.

In addition to the healing foods, each recipe features a list of the ailments it may help. Again, this is not intended to be a complete listing but just a guide to help you identify recipes that address the health issues you face. For instance, fish and tomatoes are bursting with antioxidants that help prevent cancer, lower cholesterol, and combat mood disorders; you'll find them both in the Tuna and Tomato Pizzas. But these same ingredients may also benefit Alzheimer's disease, eye problems, and many other health issues that we didn't have room to put on these pages. Plus, we go beyond the ingredients to make sure that the sodium, saturated fat, fiber, and levels of other nutrients in each recipe are appropriate for the ailments listed.

Planning and preparing dishes that boost your health and improve your life just got easier and tastier. Bon appétit!

NUTTY MUESLI

Serves 6

Prep Time: 15 minutes plus soaking

Healing Foods: bulgur, oats, nuts and seeds, persimmons, passion fruit

Ailments It Heals: atherosclerosis, chronic fatigue syndrome, lactose intolerance, neuralgia

½ cup bulgur

1 cup water

1½ cups rolled oats

1 cup apple juice

½ cup slivered unblanched almonds

¼ cup pine nuts

2 Tbsp shelled raw sunflower seeds

10 dried apricots, diced

10 dried figs, stalks removed, then diced

¼ cup brown sugar

2 green apples, cored and coarsely grated

1 large or 2 small persimmons, peeled and diced plus extra for serving

1 passion fruit

Few drops of pure almond essence (optional)

Pomegranate seeds or blueberries

1. In large bowl, combine bulgur with water and stir to combine. Cover and soak for 30 minutes to soften bulgur. Drain well in sieve and return to bowl.

2. Add oats, apple juice, almonds, pine nuts, sunflower seeds, apricots, figs, sugar, apples, and persimmon. Fold into bulgur.

3. Cut passion fruit in half. Place sieve over bowl of muesli, and spoon passion fruit pulp and seeds into it. Press until juice has gone through sieve and only seeds are left behind. Discard seeds.

4. Add almond essence, if using, and a little more apple juice if needed to make a moist but not sloppy consistency. Keep, tightly covered, in fridge until ready to eat. It can be kept for up to 2 days. To serve, stir muesli well, then top with pomegranate seeds or blueberries, whichever is in season, plus additional persimmon.

Per serving: 369 calories, 8 g protein, 62 g carbohydrates, 10 g fiber, 11 g total fat, 1 g saturated fat, 0 mg cholesterol, 25 mg sodium

BLUEBERRY AND CRANBERRY GRANOLA

Serves 8

Prep Time: 10 minutes

Cook Time: 40 minutes plus cooling

Healing Foods: oats, wheat germ, nuts and seeds, blueberries, cranberries

Ailments It Heals: cardiovascular disease, colds and flu, peptic ulcers, urinary tract infections

2¾ cups oats

½ cup wheat germ

7 Tbsp millet flakes

2 Tbsp slivered almonds

2 Tbsp sunflower seeds

1 Tbsp sesame seeds

½ cup dried blueberries

½ cup dried cranberries

1 Tbsp soft light brown sugar

2 Tbsp maple syrup

2 Tbsp canola oil

2 Tbsp orange juice

1. Preheat oven to 325°F (160°C). In large bowl, combine oats, wheat germ, millet flakes, almonds, sunflower seeds, sesame seeds, dried berries, and sugar. Stir until well mixed.

2. In measuring cup, whisk together maple syrup, oil, and orange juice. Pour slowly into dry ingredients, stirring until liquid is evenly distributed and coats everything lightly.

3. In nonstick roasting pan, spread out mixture evenly. Bake, stirring every 10 minutes to encourage even browning, for 30 to 40 minutes, or until slightly crisp and lightly brown.

4. Remove roasting pan from oven and leave granola to cool. Store in airtight container up to 2 weeks. Serve with plain yogurt, milk, or fruit juice.

Per serving: 307 calories, 8 g protein, 48 g carbohydrates, 7 g fiber, 9 g total fat, 1 g saturated fat, 0 mg cholesterol, 22 mg sodium

HOT CEREAL WITH APPLES AND DATES

Serves 4
Prep Time: 10 minutes
Cook Time: 10 minutes
Healing Foods: milk, apple, oats, bulgur, dates
Ailments It Heals: AIDS and HIV infections, constipation, hemmorrhoids, menstrual problems, PCOS, stroke

1½ cups low-fat milk
1½ cups water
1 cup unpeeled chopped apple (¼ in or 0.5 cm pieces)
½ cup old-fashioned oats
½ cup coarse bulgur
3 dates, pitted and snipped
½ tsp ground cinnamon

Stir together milk, water, apple, oats, bulgur, dates, and cinnamon in medium saucepan and heat, stir-

ring frequently, until boiling. Cover, reduce the heat to low, and cook, stirring occasionally, for 10 minutes, or until grains are tender.

Per serving: 185 calories, 7 g protein, 37 g carbohydrates, 6 g fiber, 2 g total fat, 1 g saturated fat, 5 mg cholesterol, 44 mg sodium

ASPARAGUS, EGG, AND HAM SANDWICHES

Serves 4
Prep Time: 15 minutes
Cook Time: 8 minutes
Healing Foods: asparagus, eggs, tomatoes, cheese
Ailments It Heals: anemia, mood disorders, psoriasis

24 thin stalks asparagus or 12 thick stalks, trimmed
4 slices seven-grain bread
4 tsp Dijon mustard
8 slices 97% fat-free ham
2 hard-cooked eggs, peeled and sliced
8 thin slices tomatoes
2 slices provolone cheese, cut into thin strips

1. Preheat broiler.

2. In skillet of simmering water, cook asparagus for 3 to 4 minutes, or until crisp-tender. Drain well.

3. Place bread slices on baking sheet. Broil 3 to 4 in (7.5 to 10 cm) from heat for 1 minute each side, or until bread is toasted.

4. On each bread slice, spread 1 tsp mustard, then arrange 2 slices of ham, 6 thin or 3 thick asparagus spears, half of 1 sliced egg, 2 tomato slices, and a quarter of the provolone strips.

5. Broil sandwiches for 1 to 2 minutes, or until cheese is melted and golden brown and sandwich is heated through.

Per serving: 199 calories, 15 g protein, 17 g carbohydrates, 3 g fiber, 9 g total fat, 4 g saturated fat, 128 mg cholesterol, 738 mg sodium

SPINACH AND GOAT CHEESE OMELET

Serves 1
Prep Time: 10 minutes
Cook Time: 2 minutes
Healing Foods: spinach, cheese, eggs
Ailments It Heals: ADHD, bleeding problems, celiac disease, hyperthyroidism, menopause

 2 cups baby spinach, rinsed
 2 Tbsp crumbled goat cheese or feta cheese
 1 Tbsp chopped scallion
 1 large egg
 2 large egg whites
 ¼ tsp hot red-pepper sauce, such as Tabasco
 1 tsp olive oil
Pinch of salt
Pinch of ground black pepper

1. Bring about 1 in (2.5 cm) of water to a boil in large saucepan. Drop in spinach and cook for 30 seconds, or just until wilted. Drain, press out liquid, and chop coarsely. (Alternatively, place spinach in microwave-safe bowl, cover with vented plastic wrap, and microwave on high for 1 to 2 minutes.) Place spinach in small bowl. Stir in cheese and scallion.

2. Stir egg, egg whites, hot sauce, salt, and black pepper briskly with fork in medium bowl. Heat oil in 7- to 10-in (18 to 25 cm) nonstick skillet over medium-high heat until hot. Tilt skillet to spread oil over surface. Pour in egg mixture. Immediately stir with heat-resistant rubber spatula or fork for a few seconds. Then use spatula to push cooked portions at edges toward the center, tilting skillet to allow uncooked egg mixture to fill in areas around edges. Sprinkle spinach mixture over omelet. Continue to cook until almost set and bottom is golden. The entire cooking process should take about 1 minute.

3. Use spatula to fold one-third of omelet over filling. Tip skillet and, using spatula as a guide, slide omelet onto plate so that it lands, folded in thirds, seam side down.

Per omelet: 235 calories, 20 g protein, 4 g carbohydrates, 1 g fiber, 15 g total fat, 6 g saturated fat, 228 mg cholesterol, 471 mg sodium

ONE-EGG OMELET WITH CHOPPED BROCCOLI, TOMATOES, AND CHEDDAR

Serves 4
Prep Time: 10 minutes
Cook Time: 12 minutes
Healing Foods: broccoli, tomatoes, eggs, cheese
Ailments It Heals: anorexia, cancer, hepatitis, jet lag

1½ cups chopped broccoli florets
2 Tbsp water
¼ cup chopped tomato
1 Tbsp chopped fresh basil or cilantro
1 tsp extra-virgin olive oil
1 clove garlic, crushed or grated
¼ tsp coarse salt
⅛ tsp ground black pepper
4 large eggs
1 oz (30 g) shredded cheddar cheese

1. In small covered saucepan over medium-low heat, cook broccoli in water for 4 minutes, or until broccoli is fork-tender. Drain off excess moisture, then add tomato, basil or cilantro, oil, garlic, salt, and pepper. Stir to blend. Keep warm over low heat.

2. Heat small heavy nonstick skillet over medium heat until hot enough that a drop of water sizzles. Coat with cooking spray. Beat 1 egg until frothy and add to pan, tilting pan to let egg run to edges. Cook, undisturbed, for 2 minutes, or until egg is set along edges and center is moist but not runny.

3. Slide egg "pancake" onto plate. Place ¼ cup of the broccoli mixture on half of egg and top with one-quarter of the cheese. Fold egg over to make omelet. Repeat with remaining eggs.

Per serving: 129 calories, 9 g protein, 4 g carbohydrates, 1 g fiber, 7 g total fat, 3 g saturated fat, 188 mg cholesterol, 269 mg sodium

MUSHROOM AND BELL PEPPER FRITTATA

Serves 4
Prep Time: 10 minutes
Cook Time: 26 minutes
Healing Foods: peppers, mushrooms, eggs, cheese, basil
Ailments It Heals: alcoholism, diabetes, osteoporosis, stress

2 Tbsp olive oil
1 red or orange bell pepper, seeded and cut into ¼-in (0.5 cm) slices
1 yellow bell pepper, seeded and cut into ¼-in (0.5 cm) slices
2 cups sliced mushrooms
8 large eggs
¼ tsp salt
¼ tsp ground black pepper
⅓ cup grated parmesan cheese
10 fresh basil leaves, torn in small pieces

1. In large nonstick skillet over medium-high heat, heat oil. Add bell peppers. Sauté until softened, about 4 minutes. Add mushrooms. Sauté for 5 minutes, or until vegetables are lightly browned. Reduce heat to medium.

2. In medium bowl, stir together eggs, salt, and black pepper. Pour into skillet, spreading evenly. Cook, stirring frequently, for 3 to 4 minutes, or until soft-scrambled. Reduce heat to medium-low. Stir in cheese and basil. Smooth top. Cook for 5 minutes. Cover and cook for 8 minutes, or until eggs are firm and bottom is browned.

3. To serve, loosen frittata around edge with spatula. Invert onto large plate. Cut into 4 equal wedges. Serve warm or at room temperature.

Per serving: 269 calories, 17 g protein, 8 g carbohydrates, 2 g fiber, 19 g total fat, 5 g saturated fat, 430 mg cholesterol, 397 mg sodium

ZUCCHINI FRITTATA

Serves 6
Prep Time: 5 minutes
Cook Time: 15 minutes
Healing Foods: eggs, garlic, zucchini, peppers
Ailments It Heals: Alzheimer's disease, hepatitis, jaundice, kidney disease

- 4 eggs
- 4 egg whites
- ¼ cup grated parmesan cheese
- ¼ tsp salt
- 2 Tbsp olive oil
- 1 clove garlic, minced
- 2 small zucchini, shredded
- 2 roasted red bell peppers, cut into thin strips

1. Preheat oven to 400°F (200°F). In medium bowl, whisk together eggs, egg whites, cheese, and salt.

2. Heat oil in large ovenproof nonstick skillet over medium heat. Add garlic and cook for 1 minute, or just until tender. Add zucchini and peppers and cook for 1 minute. Pour in egg mixture and cook for 3 minutes, or until bottom of frittata is set.

3. Bake for 10 minutes, until set.

Per serving: 138 calories, 9 g protein, 5 g carbohydrates, 1 g fiber, 9 g total fat, 2 g saturated fat, 144 mg cholesterol, 331 mg sodium

HUEVOS RANCHEROS

Serves 4
Prep Time: 15 minutes plus 30 minutes for marinating
Cook Time: 13 minutes
Healing Foods: tomatoes, chiles, eggs, cheese
Ailments It Heals: colds and flu, cystic fibrosis, respiratory disorders

Salsa
- 5 medium tomatoes, finely chopped
- 1 mild fresh red chile, seeded and finely chopped
- 1 small red onion, finely chopped
- 1 small clove garlic, finely chopped
- 2 Tbsp finely chopped fresh cilantro
- 1 Tbsp olive oil
- 2 tsp lime juice

Salt and pepper

Eggs
- 4 (10 in or 25 cm) flour tortillas
- 1 tsp vinegar
- 4 eggs

Garnish
- 2 oz (60 g) coarsely grated reduced-fat cheddar cheese
- 6 Tbsp low-fat sour cream

4 scallions, chopped
Chopped fresh cilantro
Lime wedges

1. To make salsa: Place tomatoes in bowl and stir in chile, red onion, garlic, and cilantro. Add oil and lime juice to taste. Set aside to marinate for about 30 minutes, then season lightly with salt and pepper to taste.

2. Preheat oven 350°F (180°C). Stack tortillas and wrap in foil. Place in oven to warm for 7 to 10 minutes.

3. To make eggs: Meanwhile, half-fill large skillet with water. Heat until just starting to simmer, then reduce heat so water does not boil. Add vinegar. Break eggs into water, one at a time, and poach for 3 minutes. Toward the end of cooking, spoon water over yolks. When cooked, remove eggs with slotted spoon and drain on paper towel–lined plate.

4. Place warmed tortillas on 4 plates. Spoon over a little salsa, then put eggs on top and season with salt and pepper to taste. Put cheese, sour cream, scallions, chopped cilantro, and lime wedges into small bowls, and serve, along with the remaining salsa.

Per serving: 459 calories, 20 g protein, 55 g carbohydrates, 5 g fiber, 19 g total fat, 7 g saturated fat, 231 mg cholesterol, 554 mg sodium

INDIVIDUAL BREAKFAST TORTILLA

Serves 1
Prep Time: 12 minutes
Cook Time: 3 minutes
Healing Foods: eggs, beans, tomatoes, avocados
Ailments It Heals: diabetes, gallstones, sex drive (diminished)

1 large egg
⅛ tsp chili powder
1 corn or whole grain tortilla (6 in or 15 cm)
1 Tbsp shredded monterey jack, provolone, or cheddar cheese
2 Tbsp cooked or canned black beans, drained and mashed with a fork
1 thin slice tomato, halved
1 tsp chopped fresh cilantro
1 thin slice avocado
1½ tsp fat-free sour cream

1. Whisk together egg and chili powder in small bowl until well-blended.

2. Heat small heavy skillet over medium heat until hot enough that a drop of water sizzles. Coat with cooking spray and pour in egg. Cook, stirring with rubber spatula, for about 15 seconds, or until set. Transfer to plate and keep warm. Wipe out skillet and respray.

3. Increase heat to medium-high. Heat tortilla in skillet, turning, for 1 minute, or until heated. Turn, sprinkle with the cheese, and heat for 10 seconds, or until melted. Transfer to serving plate.

4. Spread beans on half of tortilla. Add egg, tomato, cilantro, avocado, and sour cream. Fold the tortilla to make a "sandwich."

Per tortilla: 238 calories, 12 g protein, 25 g carbohydrates, 5 g fiber, 10 g total fat, 3 g saturated fat, 188 mg cholesterol, 229 mg sodium

SUMMER GREENS SCRAMBLE

Serves 4
Prep Time: 10 minutes
Cook Time: 11 minutes
Healing Foods: kale, eggs, cumin
Ailments It Heals: ADHD, celiac disease, mood disorders, osteoporosis

- 2 cups shredded, stemmed fresh kale
- 5 large eggs
- 5 large egg whites
- ¼ tsp ground cumin
- ¼ tsp salt
- ¼ cup chopped lean deli ham
- 2 scallions, trimmed and thinly sliced

1. In large saucepan of boiling salted water, cook kale, 3 to 5 minutes, or until tender. Drain. Rinse under cold water. Drain well.

2. In large bowl, whisk together eggs, egg whites, cumin, and salt.

3. Coat large nonstick skillet with cooking spray. Heat over medium heat. Add egg mixture. Cook, stirring constantly, for 2 to 3 minutes, or until eggs start to thicken slightly. Stir in kale, ham, and scallions. Cook, stirring occasionally, for 2 to 3 minutes, or until eggs are soft-scrambled.

Per serving: 145 calories, 15 g protein, 5 g carbohydrates, 1 g fiber, 7 g total fat, 2 g saturated fat, 270 mg cholesterol, 385 mg sodium

BERRY SALAD WITH PASSION FRUIT

Serves 6
Prep Time: 10 minutes
Healing Foods: strawberries, raspberries, blackberries, blueberries, passion fruit
Ailments It Heals: cancer, colds & flu, irritable bowel syndrome, PCOS

- 4 cups ripe strawberries, hulled and cut in half
- 1 cup fresh red raspberries
- 1 cup fresh blackberries
- ½ cup fresh blueberries
- ½ cup mixed fresh red currants and black currants, removed from their stalks (optional)
- 2 passion fruits
- 3 Tbsp sugar, or to taste
- 1 Tbsp fresh lime or lemon juice

1. In large serving bowl, combine strawberries, raspberries, blackberries, blueberries, and red and black currants, if using.

2. Cut each passion fruit in half. Holding strainer over bowl of berries, spoon passion fruit and seeds into strainer. Press flesh and seeds with back of spoon to squeeze all of juice through strainer onto berries. Reserve a few seeds left in strainer and discard the rest.

3. Add sugar and lime juice to berries. Gently toss. Sprinkle with reserved passion fruit seeds. Serve salad immediately, or cover and chill briefly.

Per serving: 89 calories, 1 g protein, 22 g carbohydrates, 6 g fiber, 1 g total fat, 0 g saturated fat, 0 mg cholesterol, 4 mg sodium

YOGURT PARFAIT

Serves 1
Prep Time: 5 minutes
Healing Foods: yogurt, berries, mangoes, coconuts
Ailments It Heals: osteoporosis, peptic ulcers, shingles, urinary tract infections

¾ cup nonfat plain or artificially sweetened yogurt
¼ cup mixed berries
¼ cup mango
¼ cup low-fat granola
1 Tbsp shredded coconut

In tall parfait glass, layer one-third of the yogurt, half of the fruit, all of the granola, another one-third of the yogurt, the remaining fruit, and the remaining yogurt. Top with coconut.

Per serving: 250 calories, 13 g protein, 44 g carbohydrates, 4 g fiber, 4 g total fat, 3 g saturated fat, 5 mg cholesterol, 210 mg sodium

BLUEBERRY OATMEAL MUFFINS

Makes 12
Prep Time: 25 minutes
Cook Time: 22 minutes
Healing Foods: wheat, oats, blueberries
Ailments It Heals: constipation, diabetes, diverticulitis, hypoglycemia, irritable bowel syndrome, varicose veins

¾ cup plus 2 Tbsp whole wheat flour
¾ cup all-purpose flour
1½ tsp baking powder
½ tsp baking soda
¼ tsp salt
1 tsp ground cinnamon
1 cup plus 2 Tbsp old-fashioned rolled oats
1 large egg
2 large egg whites
½ cup maple syrup
¾ cup low-fat buttermilk
3 Tbsp canola oil
2 tsp grated orange zest
1 Tbsp orange juice
1 tsp vanilla extract
1½ cups fresh blueberries, rinsed and patted dry

1. Preheat oven to 400°F (200°C). Coat 12 standard-size muffin cups with cooking spray or insert paper liners.

2. In large bowl, whisk together flours, baking powder, baking soda, salt, and cinnamon. Stir in 1 cup rolled oats.

3. In medium bowl, whisk egg, egg whites, and syrup until smooth. Add buttermilk, oil, zest, orange juice, and vanilla and whisk until blended. Add to flour mixture and mix with rubber spatula just until dry ingredients are moistened. Fold in blueberries. Spoon batter into muffin cups, filling them almost to the top. Sprinkle tops with remaining 2 Tbsp rolled oats.

4. Bake for 18 to 22 minutes, or until muffins are lightly browned and tops spring back when touched lightly. Loosen edges of muffins, turn out onto wire rack, and let cool slightly before serving.

Per muffin: 180 calories, 5 g protein, 30 g carbohydrates, 3 g fiber, 5 g total fat, 0 g saturated fat, 18 mg cholesterol, 190 mg sodium

PEAR RHUBARB MUFFINS

Makes 12
Prep Time: 10 minutes
Cook Time: 30 minutes
Healing Foods: pears, rhubarb, wheat, oats, ginger
Ailments It Heals: atherosclerosis, cardiovascular disease, cholesterol (high), hemorrhoids, PCOS

3.5 oz (100 g) dried pears, cut into ¼ in (0.5 cm) cubes, tough parts removed
3.5 oz (100 g) rhubarb stalks, trimmed and chopped into ½ in (1 cm) lengths
1 cup low-fat milk
1 Tbsp soft brown sugar
2 Tbsp honey
2 Tbsp light olive oil
1 tsp baking soda
⅔ cup whole wheat flour
⅔ cup self-rising flour
⅔ cup oat bran
1 tsp baking powder
1 tsp ground cinnamon
1 tsp ground nutmeg
2 tsp ground ginger

1. Preheat oven to 375°F (190°C). Coat 12 standard-size muffin cups with cooking spray or insert paper liners.

2. In large saucepan, add pears, rhubarb, milk, sugar, honey, and oil. Bring to a boil, then reduce heat to low and simmer for 2 minutes, or until rhubarb has softened. Mixture will look curdled, but this is normal. Add baking soda and stir until frothy.

3. In large bowl, combine flours, oat bran, baking powder, cinnamon, nutmeg, and ginger and stir to combine. Add fruit mixture and stir gently until just combined. Spoon into prepared muffin cups and bake for 30 minutes, or until muffins are brown and risen. Allow to cool slightly on a wire rack before serving.

Per muffin: 132 calories, 3 g protein, 26 g carbohydrates, 3 g fiber, 4 g total fat, 1 g saturated fat, 2 mg cholesterol, 250 mg sodium

CARROT GINGER YOGURT MUFFINS

Per muffin: 118 calories, 4 g protein, 22 g carbohydrates, 3 g fiber, 2 g fat, 0 g saturated fat, 16 mg cholesterol, 186 mg sodium

Makes 12

Prep Time: 10 minutes

Cook Time: 25 minutes plus cooling

Healing Foods: flour, ginger, chia, oats, carrots, apples, yogurt

Ailments It Heals: arthritis, blood pressure, hives, interstitial cystitis

- 1 cup whole wheat flour
- 1 tsp ground ginger
- 1½ tsp baking soda
- ½ cup brown sugar
- ¼ cup chia seeds or flaxseed
- ½ cup rolled oats, plus extra to sprinkle
- 2 packed cups finely grated carrots (2 medium carrots)
- 1 packed cup grated apples (1 medium apple)
- 1 egg
- ½ cup low-fat plain yogurt
- ½ tsp vanilla extract

1. Preheat oven to 350°F (180°C). Coat 12 standard-size muffin cups with cooking spray or insert paper liners.

2. In large bowl, sift flour, ginger, and baking soda. Add sugar, chia seeds, and oats. Mix to combine, then mix in carrots and apples. Make a well in center of mixture.

3. In small bowl, whisk together egg and yogurt. Stir in vanilla. Add to well in large bowl and stir together until mixture is just combined (do not overstir).

4. Spoon evenly into muffin tin. Sprinkle each with extra oats.

5. Cook for 20 to 25 minutes, or until golden brown on top and a wooden pick inserted in center comes out clean. Cool in tin for 10 minutes, then transfer to wire rack.

BUCKWHEAT PANCAKES WITH FRUIT SAUCE

Serves 5

Prep Time: 5 minutes

Cook Time: 20 minutes

Healing Foods: apples, buckwheat, eggs

Ailments It Heals: cardiovascular disease, cirrhosis, cholesterol (high), hypoglycemia, stroke

- 3 apples, pears, or plums, cored and sliced
- ⅓ cup pure maple syrup
- 1 cup buckwheat flour
- ⅓ cup brown rice flour
- 2 Tbsp brown sugar
- 1 tsp baking powder
- ½ tsp baking soda
- ½ tsp salt
- ½ tsp ground cinnamon
- ¾ cup milk
- 2 Tbsp canola oil
- 2 eggs

1. Coat nonstick skillet with cooking spray and heat over medium heat. Add apples and cook, turning, for 5 minutes, or until just tender. Add syrup and reduce heat to low to keep warm.

2. In large bowl, mix together flours, sugar, baking powder, baking soda, salt, and cinnamon. In measuring cup, whisk together milk, oil, and eggs. Stir into flour mixture just until blended.

3. Coat griddle or nonstick skillet with cooking spray and heat over medium heat. Drop 2 Tbsp batter onto griddle to form pancake. Cook for 3 minutes, or until browned on bottom and bubbles form on top. Turn and cook for 3 minutes, or until browned on bottom and firm to the touch. Place on plate and cover to keep warm. Repeat with remaining batter. Serve with fruit syrup.

Per serving: 328 calories, 7 g protein, 54 g carbohydrates, 7 g fiber, 10 g total fat, 2 g saturated fat, 88 mg cholesterol, 283 mg sodium

MULTIGRAIN PANCAKES OR WAFFLES

Serves 8
Prep Time: 20 minutes
Cook Time: 15 to 20 minutes
Healing Foods: oats, wheat and wheat germ, eggs, strawberries
Ailments It Heals: depression, diabetes, muscle cramps, prostate problems

2	cups low-fat buttermilk
½	cup old-fashioned rolled oats
⅔	cup whole wheat flour
⅔	cup all-purpose flour
⅔	cup toasted wheat germ
1½	tsp baking powder
½	tsp baking soda
¼	tsp salt
1	tsp ground cinnamon
2	large eggs
¼	cup firmly packed brown sugar
1	Tbsp canola oil
2	tsp vanilla extract
1	cup maple syrup, warmed
1½	cups sliced strawberries or blueberries

1. Mix buttermilk and oats in small bowl. Let stand for 15 minutes.

2. In large bowl, whisk whole wheat flour, all-purpose flour, wheat germ, baking powder, baking soda, salt, and cinnamon.

3. In medium bowl, whisk eggs, sugar, oil, and vanilla. Add buttermilk mixture. Add this mixture to flour mixture and mix with rubber spatula just until flour mixture is moistened.

4. To make pancakes: Coat large nonstick skillet with cooking spray and heat over medium heat. Spoon about ¼ cup batter for each pancake into skillet. Cook for 3 minutes, or until bottoms are golden and small bubbles start to form on top. Flip the pancakes and cook for 1 to 2 minutes, or until browned and cooked through. (Adjust heat as necessary for even browning.) Keep the pancakes warm in 200°F (100°C) oven while you finish cooking remaining batter.

5. To make waffles: Coat waffle iron with cooking spray and heat iron. Spoon in enough batter to cover three-quarters of surface. Close iron and cook for 4 to 5 minutes, or until waffles are crisp and golden brown. Keep waffles warm in 200°F (100°C) oven while you finish cooking remaining batter.

6. Top with maple syrup and strawberries or blueberries. Wrap any leftover pancakes or waffles individually in plastic wrap, and refrigerate for up to 2 days or freeze for up to 1 month. Reheat in a toaster or toaster oven.

Per serving: 292 calories, 8 g protein, 60 g carbohydrates, 3 g fiber, 3 g total fat, 1 g saturated fat, 56 mg cholesterol, 331 mg sodium

BERRY-FLAXSEED SMOOTHIE

Serves 2
Prep Time: 5 minutes
Healing Foods: flax, yogurt, berries, bananas
Ailments It Heals: cardiovascular disease, hay fever, irritable bowel syndrome, lupus, multiple sclerosis, osteoporosis

2 Tbsp whole flaxseeds
½ cup orange juice
½ cup nonfat vanilla yogurt
1 cup unsweetened frozen mixed berries or blueberries
1 small banana, sliced

In dry blender, place flaxseeds, cover, and blend until ground into fine powder. Add orange juice, yogurt, mixed berries (or blueberries), and banana. Cover and blend until smooth and creamy.

Per serving: 200 calories, 5 g protein, 36 g carbohydrates, 7 g fiber, 5 g total fat, 0 g saturated fat, 1 mg cholesterol, 33 mg sodium.

RASPBERRY-BEET SMOOTHIE

Serves 4
Prep Time: 10 minutes
Healing Foods: beets, raspberries, yogurt
Ailments It Heals: asthma, menstrual problems, PCOS, urinary tract infections

2 cooked beets, cooled and coarsely chopped
2 oz (60 g) fresh or frozen raspberries
1 cup cranberry juice, chilled
1 cup low-fat plain yogurt
Chilled raspberries for garnish (optional)

1. In food processor or blender, puree beets, raspberries, and cranberry juice until smooth.

2. Pour through strainer into large pitcher. Whisk in most of the yogurt.

3. Pour into 4 glasses and top with remaining yogurt. Garnish with extra raspberries, if using. Serve immediately.

Per serving: 90 calories, 4 g protein, 18 g carbohydrates, 2 g fiber, 1 g total fat, 1 g saturated fat, 5 mg cholesterol, 75 mg sodium

STRAWBERRY-YOGURT SMOOTHIE

Serves 4
Prep Time: 10 minutes
Healing Foods: strawberries, yogurt, oranges
Ailments It Heals: blood pressure, flatulence, infertility, sore throat, urinary tract infections, yeast infections

4 cups ripe strawberries
1 cup plain low-fat yogurt
½ cup fresh orange juice
1 Tbsp sugar, or to taste
4 small strawberries with leaves, optional
4 thin round slices unpeeled orange, optional

1. Rinse and drain strawberries and place in food processor or blender. Add yogurt, orange juice, and sugar. Process on highest speed until well-blended puree forms, about 15 seconds, stopping to scrape down sides of container once or twice. Taste and sweeten with more sugar, if you wish.

2. For a very smooth beverage, strain mixture, using wooden spoon to push the drink through a sieve. Discard strawberry seeds.

3. Pour into 4 tall glasses and serve immediately. If you wish to decorate the drinks, slit strawberries and orange slices halfway through centers. Attach one berry and one orange slice to rim of each glass.

Per serving: 108 calories, 4 g protein, 21 g carbohydrates, 4 g fiber, 2 g total fat, 1 g saturated fat, 5 mg cholesterol, 45 mg sodium

WHEAT GERM SMOOTHIE

Serves 2
Prep Time: 5 minutes
Healing Foods: bananas, yogurt, peaches, wheat germ
Ailments It Heals: colds and flu, lupus, neuralgia, prostate problems, sex drive (diminished)

1   ripe medium banana, frozen and cut into chunks
1   cup low-fat or nonfat vanilla yogurt
1   cup fresh or frozen peaches
¼   cup fresh orange juice
¼   cup wheat germ
Skim milk
Peach or banana slices and wheat germ, for garnish

In blender, combine banana, yogurt, peaches, orange juice, and wheat germ. Blend until smooth, adding skim milk for desired consistency. Serve in 2 tall glasses. Garnish with sprinkle of wheat germ and a peach or banana slice.

Per serving: 220 calories, 10 g protein, 38 g carbohydrates, 7 g fiber, 3 g total fat, 1 g saturated fat, 8 mg cholesterol, 83 mg sodium

SAVORY LAMB STEW WITH SWEET POTATOES

Serves 4
Prep Time: 15 minutes
Cook Time: 55 minutes
Healing Foods: lamb, sweet potatoes, peanut butter, okra
Ailments It Heals: ADHD, cystic fibrosis, dental problems, neuralgia

3   tsp olive oil
1   lb (500 g) well-trimmed lean leg of lamb, cut into 1-in (2.5 cm) chunks
1   medium onion, finely chopped
4   cloves garlic, minced
⅓   cup plus 1½ cups water
1   cup canned crushed tomatoes
1   lb (500 g) sweet potatoes, peeled and cut into ½-in (1 cm) chunks
2   Tbsp creamy peanut butter
½   tsp salt
½   tsp cayenne pepper
10 oz (300 g) frozen cut or whole okra, thawed

1. Preheat oven to 350°F (180°C). In large nonstick Dutch oven or flameproof casserole, heat 2 tsp oil over medium-high heat. Add lamb and sauté for 5 minutes, or until browned. With slotted spoon, transfer lamb to plate.

2. Reduce heat to medium and add remaining 1 tsp oil, onion, and garlic. Cook for 2 minutes. Stir in ⅓ cup water and cook until onion is golden brown and tender, about 5 to 8 minutes.

3. Stir in tomatoes, sweet potatoes, peanut butter, salt, cayenne, and 1½ cups water. Bring to a boil.

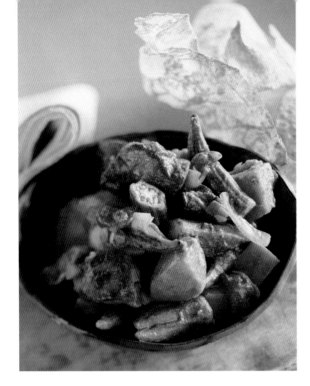

2 Tbsp olive oil
1 lb (500 g) pork tenderloin, cut into 1-in
   (2.5 cm) chunks
2 Tbsp flour
6 scallions, thinly sliced
3 cloves garlic, minced
1 large green bell pepper, cut into ½-in
   (1 cm) chunks
1 pickled jalapeño chile pepper, finely chopped
4.5 oz (140 g) chopped mild green chiles
¼ tsp salt
½ tsp ground coriander
1¼ cups water
1½ cups packed cilantro sprigs, chopped
1½ cups frozen peas, thawed
2 Tbsp fresh lime juice
1 red bell pepper, slivered

Return lamb to pan. Cover, transfer to oven, and bake for 25 minutes.

4. Stir in okra, return pan to oven, and bake for 15 minutes, or until lamb and okra are tender.

Per serving: 364 calories, 29 g protein, 32 g carbohydrate, 7 g fiber, 14 g total fat, 3 g saturated fat, 74 mg cholesterol, 618 mg sodium

GREEN PORK CHILI

Serves 4
Prep Time: 15 minutes
Cook Time: 35 minutes plus stand time
Healing Foods: pork, peppers, chiles, cilantro, peas
Ailments It Heals: bleeding problems, depression, menstrual problems, shingles

1. Preheat oven to 350°F (180°C). In nonstick Dutch oven or flameproof casserole, heat oil over medium heat. Dredge pork in flour, shaking off excess. Sauté pork for 4 minutes, or until golden brown. With slotted spoon, transfer pork to plate.

2. Add scallions and garlic to pan and cook for 1 minute, or until scallions are tender. Add green bell pepper and jalapeño and cook for 4 minutes, or until bell pepper is crisp-tender. Stir in green chiles, salt, coriander, water, and half the cilantro. Bring to a boil.

3. Return pork to pan. Cover, place in oven, and bake for 25 minutes, or until pork is tender.

4. Stir in peas, lime juice, and remaining cilantro. Cover and let stand for 3 minutes. Serve topped with red bell pepper.

Per serving: 287 calories, 28 g protein, 20 g carbohydrate, 5 g fiber, 10 g total fat, 2 g saturated fat, 74 mg cholesterol, 338 mg sodium

LENTIL SOUP WITH CANADIAN BACON

Serves 8
Prep Time: 10 minutes
Cook Time: 50 minutes
Healing Foods: olive oil, carrots, celery, tomatoes, lentils, yogurt
Ailments It Heals: atherosclerosis, constipation, irritable bowel syndrome, jaundice, memory loss

6	tsp olive oil
3	oz (90 g) sliced Canadian bacon, cut into matchsticks
3	carrots, sliced
2	celery stalks, sliced
1	onion, chopped
2	cloves garlic, minced
1	tsp chili powder
½	tsp dried oregano
½	tsp ground cumin
½	tsp salt
28	oz (796 mL) crushed tomatoes, with juice
1½	cups lentils, sorted and rinsed
6	cups water
2	cups low-fat plain yogurt

1. In stockpot, heat 1 tsp oil over medium heat. Add bacon and cook, stirring constantly, for 3 minutes, or until well browned. Transfer to a plate.

2. Add remaining 5 tsp oil to stockpot and heat. Add carrots, celery, and onion and cook, stirring, for 5 minutes, or until well browned. Add garlic, chili powder, oregano, cumin, and salt. Cook for 2 minutes, stirring constantly.

3. Add tomatoes with juice, lentils, and water and bring to a boil. Reduce heat to medium-low, partially cover, and simmer for 30 to 40 minutes, or until the lentils are tender.

4. To serve, ladle soup into 8 bowls and top each with ¼ cup yogurt and a few strips of bacon.

Per serving: 256 calories, 15 g protein, 38 g carbohydrates, 9 g fiber, 6 g total fat, 1 g saturated fat, 9 mg cholesterol, 506 mg sodium

BASIC CHICKEN STOCK

Makes 5 cups
Prep Time: 10 minutes
Cook Time: 2 hours 10 minutes plus cooling
Healing Foods: chicken, onions, carrots, celery
Ailments It Heals: burns, diarrhea, fever, respiratory disorders

1	chicken carcass, bones from 4 chicken pieces, or 1 leg with thigh
1	onion, quartered
1	large carrot, coarsely chopped
1	celery stalk, cut into chunks
7	cups water
1	bay leaf
1	parsley sprig
1	thyme sprig
8	whole black peppercorns
½	tsp salt

1. Break up whole chicken bones; leave leg whole. In large saucepan over medium-high heat, combine bones or chicken, onion, carrot, and celery. Add water and bring to boil, skimming off foam.

2. Add bay leaf, parsley, thyme, peppercorns, and salt. Reduce heat, cover, and simmer for 2 hours.

3. Strain stock through sieve into heatproof bowl, discarding solids. Let cool, then refrigerate until cold and remove fat with spoon. Use refrigerated stock within 3 days or frozen stock within 3 months.

Per serving: 20 calories, 2 g protein, 1 g carbohydrate, 0 g fiber, .5 g total fat, 0 g saturated fat, 6 mg cholesterol, 247 mg sodium

CHICKEN-KALE SOUP WITH ROASTED PEPPER PUREE

Serves 4

Prep Time: 10 minutes

Cook Time: 20 minutes

Healing Foods: chicken, peppers, flax, kale

Ailments It Heals: colds and flu, eye problems, mood disorders, nail problems

4 cups water

1¼ lb (625 g) boneless skinless chicken thighs, cut into 1-in (2.5 cm) chunks

4 carrots, thinly sliced

3 large red onions, cut into ½-in (1 cm) chunks

5 cloves garlic, minced, plus 1 whole clove garlic

2 Tbsp finely chopped fresh ginger

1 tsp cayenne pepper

¾ tsp salt

2 red bell peppers, cut lengthwise into flat panels

1 Tbsp hulled roasted pumpkin seeds

1 Tbsp flaxseed oil

¾ cup orzo

8 cups shredded kale

1. In large saucepan or stockpot, combine water, chicken, carrots, onions, minced garlic, ginger, cayenne, and salt. Bring to a boil over high heat. Reduce to a simmer, partially cover, and cook for 25 minutes.

2. Meanwhile, preheat broiler. Place bell pepper pieces, skin side up, on broiler pan and broil 6 in (15 cm) from heat for 10 minutes, or until skin is well charred. When cool enough to handle, peel peppers and transfer them to food processor along with pumpkin seeds, flaxseed oil, and whole garlic clove. Process until pureed.

3. Add orzo to soup, and cook, uncovered, for 5 minutes. Stir in kale and cook for 5 minutes, or until kale and orzo are tender.

4. Serve soup with a dollop of roasted pepper puree on top.

Per serving: 439 calories, 35 g protein, 43 g carbohydrate, 8 g fiber, 15 g total fat, 3 g saturated fat, 94 mg cholesterol, 641 mg sodium

QUICK CHICKEN NOODLE SOUP

Serves 6

Prep Time: 10 minutes

Cook Time: 25 minutes

Healing Foods: chicken, garlic, carrots, peppers, pasta

Ailments It Heals: colds and flu, inflammatory bowel disease, jaundice, Parkinson's disease, sore throat

- 2 Tbsp olive oil
- ¾ lb (375 g) boneless skinless chicken breasts, cut into 1-in (2.5 cm) pieces
- 1 large onion, chopped
- 2 cloves garlic, chopped
- 2 carrots, chopped
- 1 red bell pepper, chopped
- 1 tsp dried thyme
- 32 oz (1 L) chicken broth
- 1 cup water
- 8 oz (250 g) whole grain spaghetti, broken into 2-in (5 cm) pieces

1. In large saucepan, heat oil over high heat. Add chicken and cook, stirring, for 5 minutes, or until browned. With slotted spoon, transfer to bowl.

2. Add onion to saucepan and cook for 5 minutes, or until lightly browned. Add garlic, carrots, bell pepper, and thyme. Cook, stirring, for 3 minutes, or until lightly browned. Add broth, water, chicken, and any drippings in the bowl and bring to a boil. Add spaghetti and cook for 8 minutes, or until tender.

Per serving: 275 calories, 20 g protein, 37 g carbohydrates, 4 g fiber, 6 g total fat, 1 g saturated fat, 33 mg cholesterol, 345 mg sodium

TURKEY, SPINACH, AND RICE IN ROASTED GARLIC BROTH

Serves 4

Prep Time: 15 minutes

Cook Time: 1 hour

Healing Foods: garlic, turkey, spinach

Ailments It Heals: arthritis, circulatory disorders, stroke

- 2 medium whole heads garlic, unpeeled
- 2 Tbsp tomato paste
- 29 oz (825 mL) reduced-sodium, fat-free chicken or turkey broth
- 1 cup cooked turkey cubes
- 1 cup cooked long-grain white rice
- ¾ lb (375 g) spinach, stemmed and coarsely chopped
- ¼ tsp ground black pepper
- ¼ tsp hot-pepper flakes, or to taste
- 1 Tbsp fresh-squeezed lemon juice

1. Preheat oven to 400°F (200°C).

2. Cut top third off garlic heads. Wrap each head in foil. Bake for 50 minutes, or until very soft. Let cool. Remove foil. Squeeze out pulp into small bowl.

3. In large saucepan, stir together garlic pulp and tomato paste. Stir in broth. Bring to a boil. Add turkey, rice, spinach, black pepper, and pepper flakes. Simmer, uncovered, for 8 minutes. Just before serving, stir in lemon juice.

Per serving: 197 calories, 19 g protein, 24 g carbohydrates, 3 g fiber, 4 g total fat, 1 g saturated fat, 30 mg cholesterol, 208 mg sodium

COD AND VEGETABLE STEW

Serves 4

Prep Time: 15 minutes

Cook Time: 25 minutes

Healing Foods: onions, garlic, peppers, sweet potatoes, peas, fish

Ailments It Heals: AIDS and HIV infection, burns, cholesterol (high), obesity

2	Tbsp olive oil
2	medium onions, finely chopped
3	cloves garlic, thinly sliced
1	large red bell pepper, cut into matchsticks
1	lb (500 g) sweet potatoes, peeled and cut into ½-in (1 cm) chunks
1⅓	cups water
¾	tsp salt
½	tsp dried thyme
1½	cups frozen peas
1	cup frozen corn kernels
1½	lb (750 g) boneless skinless cod fillet, cut into bite-size pieces

1. In large skillet or Dutch oven, heat oil over medium heat. Add onions and garlic and cook, stirring frequently, for 5 minutes, or until onion is light golden.

2. Add bell pepper and sweet potatoes. Cover and cook for 5 minutes, or until sweet potatoes begin to soften. Stir in water, salt, and thyme and bring to a boil. Reduce to a simmer, cover, and cook for 5 minutes, or until sweet potatoes are tender. Stir in peas and corn.

3. Place cod on top of vegetables. Cover and cook for 7 minutes, or until fish is cooked through but still tender.

Per serving: 396 calories, 36 g protein, 42 g carbohydrate, 8 g fiber, 9 g total fat, 1 g saturated fat, 73 mg cholesterol, 584 mg sodium

VEGETABLE STOCK

Makes 12 cups

Prep Time: 20 minutes

Cook Time: 1 hour 10 minutes plus cooling

Healing Foods: leeks, mushrooms, celeriac, parsnips, ginger

Ailments It Heals: diabetes, fever, gout, sore throat

2	Tbsp vegetable oil
3	large leeks with tops, rinsed and sliced
2	large carrots, scrubbed and coarsely chopped
1	medium onion, coarsely chopped
4	cloves garlic, crushed with the flat of a knife
14	cups water
8	oz (250 g) fresh mushrooms, halved
1	small celeriac, peeled and sliced
3	celery stalks with leaves, coarsely chopped
2	medium parsnips, peeled and thickly sliced
10	parsley sprigs
1½	Tbsp minced fresh ginger
2	bay leaves
¾	tsp dried marjoram
3	Tbsp tomato paste
½	tsp salt

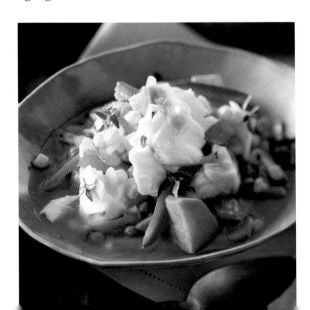

1. In 6-quart (6-L) stockpot, heat oil over medium-high heat. Add leeks, carrots, onion, and garlic and sauté, stirring occasionally, for 10 minutes, or just until tender.

2. Add water, mushrooms, celeriac, celery, parsnips, parsley, ginger, bay leaves, marjoram, tomato paste, and salt. Increase heat to high and bring to boil, then reduce heat and simmer, uncovered, for 1 hour.

3. Strain stock through a large sieve into heatproof bowl, discarding solids. When cool, cover and refrigerate up to 3 days or freeze up to 3 months.

Per serving: 5 calories, 0 g protein, 1 g carbohydrates, 0 g fiber, 0 g total fat, 0 g saturated fat, 0 mg cholesterol, 110 mg sodium

1. In medium saucepan, heat oil over medium heat. Add onion and garlic. Sauté for 5 minutes, or until softened. Add broth, carrots, and thyme. Simmer, uncovered, for 40 minutes, or until vegetables are very tender.

2. In batches, puree soup in blender. Add salt and pepper. To serve hot, ladle into 4 bowls and garnish each bowl with yogurt and dill. To serve cold, remove from heat and let cool to room temperature. Cover and refrigerate until cold. Garnish just before serving.

Per serving: 135 calories, 6 g protein, 20 g carbohydrates, 5 g fiber, 4 g total fat, 0 g saturated fat, 1 mg cholesterol, 628 mg sodium

CARROT SOUP WITH DILL

Serves 4
Prep Time: 10 minutes
Cook Time: 45 minutes
Healing Foods: carrots, yogurt, dill
Ailments It Heals: dental problems, hypothyroidism, interstitial cystitis, obesity

1   Tbsp vegetable oil
1   onion, coarsely chopped
1   clove garlic, minced
29 oz (825 mL) reduced-sodium, fat-free chicken broth
4   cups carrots (about 1¼ lb or 625 g), peeled and coarsely chopped
½   tsp dried thyme, crumbled
Salt to taste
White pepper to taste
¼   cup low-fat plain yogurt
1   Tbsp finely chopped dill

CELERIAC AND SPINACH SOUP

Serves 4
Prep Time: 15 minutes
Cook Time: 20 minutes
Healing Foods: onions, garlic, celeriac, spinach
Ailments It Heals: fibroids, lactose intolerance, psoriasis

1 large onion, thinly sliced
1 clove garlic, crushed
1 celeriac (about 1¼ lb or 625 g), peeled and
 grated
4 cups boiling water
1 reduced-sodium vegetable bouillon cube,
 crumbled, or 2 tsp vegetable bouillon
 powder
1 lb (500 g) fresh spinach, washed and trimmed
Pinch of nutmeg
Salt and ground black pepper
2 Tbsp fat-free half-and-half
Fresh chives

1. Coat large saucepan with cooking spray and heat over medium-high heat. Add onion and garlic, and cook until onion is softened but not browned, about 5 minutes. Add celeriac. Pour in water and add bouillon cube or powder. Bring to a boil, then reduce heat to low and cover pan. Cook until celeriac is tender, about 10 minutes.

2. Add spinach and stir well. Increase heat and bring soup to a boil, then remove pan from heat. Cool slightly, then puree it, in batches, in blender or food processor until smooth. (Alternatively, puree soup in pan using handheld blender.) Soup will be fairly thick.

3. Reheat soup, if necessary, then stir in nutmeg, salt, and pepper. Ladle into 4 bowls. Swirl a spoonful of half-and-half into each portion and garnish with fresh chives. Serve immediately.

Per serving: 95 calories, 5 g protein, 20 g carbohydrates, 5 g fiber, 1 g total fat, saturated fat, 0 mg cholesterol, 232 mg sodium

GINGER BUTTERNUT SQUASH SOUP

Serves 4
Prep Time: 20 minutes
Cook Time: 45 minutes plus cooling
Healing Foods: turmeric, butternut squash, apples, ginger
Ailments It Heals: atherosclerosis, eczema, memory loss, motion sickness

2 Tbsp olive oil
1 large onion, chopped
2 cloves garlic, minced
1 tsp turmeric
1 butternut squash (about 2 lb or 1 kg), peeled, seeded, and cubed
4 cups vegetable or chicken broth
2 large apples, peeled, cored, and chopped
1 Tbsp grated fresh ginger or 1 tsp ground ginger
¼ tsp salt

1. In large saucepan, heat oil over medium heat. Add onion and cook, stirring, for 4 minutes, or until lightly browned. Stir in garlic and turmeric and cook for 1 minute. Add squash and broth and bring to a boil.

2. Reduce heat to low, cover, and simmer for 20 minutes, or until squash is just tender. Add apples, ginger, and salt and cook for 10 to 20 minutes, or until squash and apples are very tender. Remove from heat and let cool for about 10 minutes.

3. Working in batches, place the mixture in a food processor or blender and process until smooth.

Per serving: 267 calories, 4 g protein, 51 g carbohydrates, 6 g fiber, 8 g total fat, 1 g saturated fat, 0 mg cholesterol, 617 mg sodium

BROCCOLI POTATO SOUP

Serves 4

Prep Time: 20 minutes

Cook Time: 1 hour 40 minutes

Healing Foods: broccoli, potatoes, yogurt

Ailments It Heals: hyperthyroidism, infertility, Parkinson's disease, urinary tract infections

- 1 bulb garlic
- 1 bunch broccoli
- 2 Tbsp olive oil
- 1 large onion, chopped
- 32 oz (1L) vegetable or chicken broth
- 1 russet potato, peeled and chopped
- 1 cup water
- ½ cup low-fat plain yogurt

1. Preheat oven to 400°F (200°F). Cut top ¼ in (0.5 cm) off garlic to expose cloves. Wrap in a double thickness of foil and bake for 1 hour, or until very tender and browned.

2. Meanwhile, remove florets from broccoli and chop coarsely. Peel and chop stalks.

3. In large saucepan, heat oil over medium heat. Add onion and cook for 5 minutes, or until lightly browned. Add 3 cups broth, potato, and broccoli. Bring to a boil, then reduce heat to low, cover, and simmer for 30 minutes, or until broccoli stalks and potato are very tender.

4. Squeeze garlic into food processor. Add hot broccoli mixture and puree until smooth. Return to saucepan and add water and remaining broth. Simmer for 10 minutes, to blend flavors. Top each serving with a dollop of yogurt.

Per serving: 247 calories, 9 g protein, 37 g carbohydrates, 7 g fiber, 8 total fat, 1 g saturated fat, 2 mg cholesterol, 512 mg sodium

MISO SOUP WITH TOFU

Serves 4

Prep Time: 5 minutes plus standing

Cook Time: 10 minutes

Healing Foods: seaweed, mushrooms, tofu

Ailments It Heals: fever, menopause, sore throat, yeast infections

- 4 cups water
- 1 piece (about 3½ in or 8.5 cm) kombu or kelp
- ¼ cup dried bonito flakes
- 3 Tbsp light or dark miso
- 6 shiitake mushrooms, stems removed, thinly sliced
- 8 oz (250 g) soft tofu, cut into ½-in (1 cm) cubes
- 1 scallion, trimmed and finely chopped

1. In medium soup pot, add water and kombu and bring almost to a boil.

2. Meanwhile, wrap bonito flakes in a clean coffee filter or tea ball. When water is just under a boil, remove pot from heat and add wrapped bonito flakes. Let stand for 5 minutes. Remove and discard kombu and bonito.

3. In small bowl, whisk together miso and a few Tbsp of soup broth until miso dissolves. Stir back into soup pot along with mushrooms, tofu, and scallion. Heat over low heat for 2 minutes. Let stand for 2 minutes before serving.

Per serving: 82 calories, 8 g protein, 4 g carbohydrates, 1 g fiber, 4 g total fat, 1 g saturated fat, 0 mg cholesterol, 563 mg sodium

THREE-BEAN CHILI

Serves 8
Prep Time: 10 minutes
Cook Time: 7 hours 15 minutes
Healing Foods: carrots, celery, tomatoes, chiles, beans, peppers
Ailments It Heals: AIDS and HIV infections, burns, cancer, cardiovascular disease, constipation, diverticulitis

3 carrots, sliced
3 celery stalks, sliced
2 cloves garlic, minced
1 large onion, chopped
28 oz (796 mL), crushed tomatoes
16 oz (455 mL) salsa
2 tsp chili powder
1 tsp ground cumin
15.5 oz (440 mL) kidney beans, drained and rinsed
15 oz (425 mL) black beans, drained and rinsed
15 oz (425 mL) white beans, drained and rinsed
1 green bell pepper, chopped
1 red bell pepper, chopped

1. In a 3½- to 4-quart (3½- to 4-L) slow cooker, place carrots, celery, garlic, onion, tomatoes, salsa, chili powder, and cumin. Cover and cook on high for 5 to 7 hours, or until vegetables are tender.

2. Stir in beans and bell peppers and cook, uncovered, on high for 15 minutes, or until chili thickens slightly and peppers are tender.

Per serving: 299 calories, 19 g protein, 58 g carbohydrates, 16 g fiber, 2 g total fat, 0 g saturated fat, 0 mg cholesterol, 712 mg sodium

TUSCAN BEAN SOUP

Serves 6
Prep Time: 15 minutes
Cook Time: 30 minutes
Healing Foods: onions, carrots, celery, tomatoes, beans
Ailments It Heals: atherosclerosis, celiac disease, colds and flu, hemorrhoids, obesity, PCOS

1 Tbsp olive oil
2 medium onions, coarsely chopped
2 medium carrots, coarsely chopped
2 celery ribs, chopped
29 oz (825 mL) reduced-sodium chicken broth
28 oz (796 mL), crushed tomatoes in puree
½ cup chopped fresh basil
2 Tbsp chopped fresh oregano, or 1 tsp dried
15.5 oz (440 mL) red kidney beans
15.5 oz (440 mL) cannellini beans
15.5 oz (440 mL) chickpeas
6 Tbsp freshly grated parmesan cheese

1. In large nonstick Dutch oven, heat oil over medium-high heat. Add onions, carrots, and celery and sauté for 5 minutes, or until soft. Add broth,

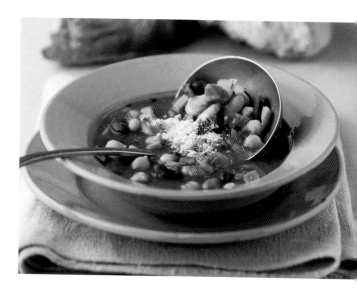

tomatoes in puree, basil, and oregano. Bring to a boil. Reduce heat to medium-low, partially cover, and cook for 10 minutes.

2. Put kidney and cannellini beans and chickpeas in colander. Rinse and drain. Stir into soup. Cook for 10 minutes, or until flavors develop. Remove from heat.

3. Very coarsely puree about one-fourth of soup using immersion blender. Or transfer about 2 cups soup to food processor, very coarsely puree, and return to pot. Serve 2 cups soup per person topped with 1 Tbsp parmesan.

Per serving: 290 calories, 15 g protein, 45 g carbohydrates, 10 g fiber, 6 g total fat, 1 g saturated fat, 4 mg cholesterol, 605 mg sodium

CHUNKY GAZPACHO WITH GARLICKY CROUTONS

Serves 4

Prep Time: 20 minutes plus chilling
Cook Time: 15 minutes
Healing Foods: garlic, tomatoes, cucumbers, peppers
Ailments It Heals: chronic fatigue syndrome, respiratory disorders, rosacea

2   cloves garlic, peeled
4   slices French bread (1 in or 2.5 cm thick)
1   tsp ground black pepper
½   tsp salt
½   cup coarsely chopped red onion
28   oz (796 mL) no-salt-added diced tomatoes
¼   cup seasoned dry bread crumbs
¼   cup chopped parsley

3   Tbsp red wine vinegar
1   Tbsp olive oil
2   medium cucumbers, peeled and chopped
2   medium green bell peppers, chopped
2   medium red bell peppers, chopped

1. Preheat oven to 350°F (180°C). Cut 1 garlic clove in half and rub cut sides on inside of large bowl and on both sides of bread slices. Tear bread into 1-in (2.5 cm) pieces. Put in large bowl and lightly coat with cooking spray. Sprinkle with ½ tsp black pepper and ¼ tsp salt. Toss to coat and transfer to baking sheet. Bake for 15 minutes, or until golden. Cool croutons completely.

2. Pulse onion and remaining garlic clove in food processor or blender until finely chopped. Add half of tomatoes and all their juice. Puree. Add bread crumbs, parsley, vinegar, oil, and remaining ½ tsp black pepper and ¼ tsp salt. Process just until blended and pour into large nonreactive bowl.

3. Stir remaining tomatoes into tomato mixture with half of cucumbers and half of green and red peppers. Refrigerate for 1 hour, until chilled. Ladle into bowls and top with remaining cucumber, green and red peppers, and croutons.

Per serving: 250 calories, 8 g protein, 46 g carbohydrates, 6 g fiber, 5 g total fat, 1 g saturated fat, 0 mg cholesterol, 730 mg sodium

CANTALOUPE AND ORANGE SOUP

Serves 6
Prep Time: 20 minutes plus chilling time
Healing Foods: oranges, cantaloupe, honey, yogurt, raspberries
Ailments It Heals: blood pressure, colds and flu, gout, memory loss, muscle cramps, osteoporosis

- 3 large orange
- 1 large cantaloupe, halved and seeded
- 2 cups orange juice
- Juice of 1 lime
- 1 Tbsp honey
- 1 cup fat-free plain yogurt
- 1 cup fresh raspberries

1. Finely grate zest from 1 or 2 oranges, according to taste, and reserve. With a sharp knife, peel cantaloupe. Cut flesh into chunks and place in food processor or blender. Peel and section oranges, then cut sections into pieces and add to melon. Puree until smooth.

2. Strain puree through medium-gauge sieve into large bowl, pressing fruit through sieve with back of wooden spoon.

3. Stir in orange juice, lime juice, honey, and yogurt until blended. Cover bowl and refrigerate for at least 2 hours.

4. Serve soup garnished with orange zest and fresh raspberries.

Per serving: 161 calories, 5 g protein, 37 g carbohydrate, 4 g fiber, 1 g total fat, 0 g saturated fat, 1 mg cholesterol, 54 mg sodium

BEEF IN LETTUCE WRAPS

Serves 4
Prep Time: 5 minutes
Cook Time: 11 minutes
Healing Foods: beef, carrots, lettuce
Ailments It Heals: anemia, eczema, herpes, osteoporosis

- 3 Tbsp hoisin sauce
- 2 Tbsp wine vinegar
- 1 Tbsp soy sauce
- 1 tsp toasted sesame oil
- ½ tsp ground ginger
- 1 lb (500 g) lean ground beef
- 4 scallions, chopped
- 2 carrots, shredded
- 1 clove garlic, minced
- 12 Bibb or Boston lettuce leaves

1. In small bowl, whisk together hoisin sauce, vinegar, soy sauce, oil, and ginger.

2. In nonstick skillet over medium heat, cook beef for 5 minutes, or until browned. Add scallions, carrots, and garlic and cook for 3 minutes, or until tender. Stir in the hoisin mixture and cook for 3 minutes, or until thickened and flavors are blended.

3. Place 3 lettuce leaves on each of 4 plates and fill with beef mixture.

Per serving: 201 calories, 24 g protein, 13 g carbohydrates, 3 g fiber, 6 g total fat, 2 g saturated fat, 61 mg cholesterol, 619 mg sodium

BEEF, ONION, AND PEPPER FAJITAS

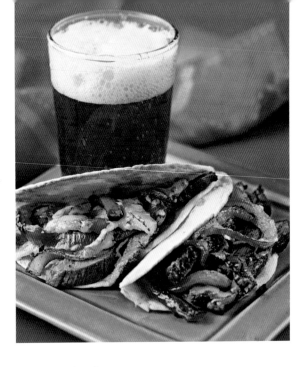

Serves 8

Prep Time: 15 minutes plus marinating

Cook Time: 13 minutes

Healing Foods: beef, onions, peppers, garlic, chiles

Ailments It Heals: hepatitis, memory loss, nail problems

1   flank steak (about 1 lb or 500 g)
1   red onion, sliced
1   small red bell pepper, seeded and cut into thin strips
1   small green bell pepper, seeded and cut into thin strips
1   small yellow bell pepper, seeded and cut into thin strips
4   cloves garlic, minced
½   cup fresh lime juice
2   Tbsp olive oil
2   Tbsp balsamic vinegar
1   tsp ground cumin
½   tsp salt
¼   tsp ground black pepper
1   serrano or jalapeño chile pepper, seeded and finely chopped (wear gloves when handling; they burn)
8   flour tortillas (6 in or 15 cm), warmed following package directions
¼   lb (125 g) monterey jack cheese, shredded

1. In shallow baking dish, combine steak, onion, and bell peppers. In small bowl, whisk together garlic, lime juice, oil, vinegar, cumin, salt, black pepper, and chile pepper. Pour over steak mixture. Toss to coat. Refrigerate, covered, for 1 to 2 hours.

2. Preheat broiler.

3. Broil steak on broiler-pan rack 4 in (10 cm) from heat 2 minutes each side. Add onion and bell peppers to rack. Spoon remaining marinade over steak and vegetables. Broil, turning meat and vegetables occasionally, for 6 to 8 minutes, or until meat is cooked to desired doneness and vegetables are crisp-tender. Let meat stand for 5 minutes.

4. Cut meat diagonally across grain into thin slices. Place meat, onion, and peppers on warmed tortillas, dividing equally. Top with cheese. Place under broiler for 30 seconds, or just until cheese melts. Fold tortillas over filling and serve.

Per serving: 293 calories, 18 g protein, 24 g carbohydrates, 2 g fiber, 14 g total fat, 6 g saturated fat, 40 mg cholesterol, 411 mg sodium

BEEF AND BLUE CHEESE BURGERS

Serves 4
Prep Time: 15 minutes plus soaking
Cook Time: 10 minutes
Healing Foods: beef, zucchini, cheese, spinach, wheat
Ailments It Heals: anemia, bleeding, burns, neuralgia

8	oz (250 g) 95% lean ground beef
1	large egg white, lightly beaten
1	cup shredded zucchini (½ small)
⅓	cup finely chopped onion (½ small)
⅔	cup whole wheat panko (Japanese-style bread crumbs) or fresh whole wheat bread crumbs
1	Tbsp Worcestershire sauce
2	tsp dijon mustard
¼	tsp salt
¼	tsp ground black pepper
¼	cup crumbled blue cheese
1	cup thinly sliced sweet onion or red onion
2	cups baby spinach or arugula, washed and dried
1	medium tomato, sliced
4	100% whole wheat English muffins, split

1. In large bowl, mix beef, egg white, zucchini, onion, panko, Worcestershire sauce, mustard, salt, and pepper. Form into 8 patties, ¼ in (0.5 cm) thick. Place about 1 Tbsp cheese on each of 4 patties and place a second patty on top to enclose cheese. Press to seal in cheese and form into ½-in-thick (1 cm) patties.

2. Place onion in medium bowl, cover with ice water, and soak for 10 to 20 minutes. Drain.

3. Preheat grill to medium-high. Lightly oil grill grate by rubbing it with a piece of oil-soaked paper towel (use tongs to hold paper towel when working over a hot grill). Grill patties for 5 minutes per side, or until browned and cooked through (an instant-read thermometer inserted in center should register 160°F or 71°C). About 1 minute before patties are done, place muffins, cut side down, on grill for 30 to 60 seconds, or until lightly toasted.

4. To assemble burgers, divide spinach and tomato slices among muffin bottoms. Add patties and top with onion slices. Replace muffin tops. One serving is 1 patty with 1 English muffin and garnishes.

Per serving: 322 calories, 23 g protein, 43 g carbohydrates, 7 g fiber, 7 g total fat, 3 g saturated fat, 41 mg cholesterol, 909 mg sodium

SLOPPY JOES

Serves 4
Prep Time: 10 minutes
Cook Time: 15 minutes
Healing Foods: onions, beef, tomatoes, chiles, carrots, cabbage
Ailments It Heals: ADHD, jaundice, Parkinson's disease

1	Tbsp vegetable oil
1	medium onion, finely chopped
1	celery rib, finely chopped
1	small green bell pepper, finely chopped
1	lb (500 g) lean (95%) ground beef
4	sandwich buns, split
14.5	oz (410 mL) no-salt-added stewed tomatoes
½	cup chili sauce
2	tsp Worcestershire sauce
½	tsp ground black pepper
2	tsp cider vinegar
1	large carrot, cut into very thin matchsticks
¼	small head cabbage, slivered

1. Put rack in middle of oven and preheat to 350°F (180°C). In large nonstick skillet, heat oil over medium-high heat. Add onion, celery, and green pepper and sauté for 5 minutes, or until tender. Add ground beef and cook, breaking up meat with spoon, for 4 minutes, or until meat is no longer pink.

2. Meanwhile, put buns cut side up on baking sheet and heat in oven for 4 minutes, or until toasted.

3. Add tomatoes (with juice), chili sauce, Worcestershire, and black pepper to skillet. Cook, stirring often, for 4 minutes, or until flavors blend. Stir in vinegar.

4. Transfer buns to 4 plates. Spoon mixture on bottom of each bun. Top with several strips of carrot and cabbage. Cover with top of bun.

Per serving: 396 calories, 31 g protein, 42 g carbohydrates, 5 g fiber, 11 g total fat, 3 g saturated fat, 51 mg cholesterol, 767 mg sodium

THAI-STYLE BEEF SANDWICH

Serves 4
Prep Time: 10 minutes plus marinating and standing
Cook Time: 8 minutes
Healing Foods: limes, beef, cabbage, carrots, herbs and spices
Ailments It Heals: acne, alcoholism, arthritis, hepatitis, prostate problems

 2 Tbsp tomato paste
 ½ cup fresh lime juice (about 3 limes)
 1½ tsp ground coriander
 1 lb (500 g) well-trimmed flank steak
 1 tsp sugar
 ½ tsp salt
 ¾ tsp red-pepper flakes
 3 cups packed shredded green cabbage (about 12 oz or 375 g)
 2 carrots, shredded
 1 large red bell pepper, cut into matchsticks
 ¾ cup chopped cilantro
 ⅓ cup chopped fresh mint
 4 whole grain rolls, halved crosswise

1. In shallow nonaluminum pan, stir together the tomato paste, ¼ cup lime juice, and coriander. Add flank steak, turning to coat. Refrigerate for 30 minutes.

2. In large bowl, whisk together sugar, salt, pepper flakes, and remaining ¼ cup lime juice. Add cabbage, carrots, bell pepper, cilantro, and mint and toss well to combine. Refrigerate until serving time.

3. Preheat broiler. Remove steak from marinade. Broil 6 in (15 cm) from heat for 4 minutes per side for medium-rare, brushing any remaining marinade over steak. Let stand for 10 minutes before thinly slicing across the grain on the diagonal.

4. To serve, place cabbage slaw on bottom half of each cut roll. Top with ribbons of sliced steak.

Per serving: 396 calories, 32 g protein, 48 g carbohydrates, 9 g fiber, 10 g total fat, 3 g saturated fat, 70 mg cholesterol, 723 mg sodium

LAMB BURGERS WITH FRUIT RELISH

Serves 4
Prep Time: 20 minutes
Cook Time: 10 minutes
Healing Foods: lamb, wheat, oranges
Ailments It Heals: anemia, multiple sclerosis, stress

1 lb (500 g) lean ground lamb
1 medium carrot, peeled and grated
1 small onion, finely chopped
½ cup fresh whole wheat bread crumbs
Pinch of freshly grated nutmeg
2 tsp fresh thyme leaves or 1 tsp dried
Salt and ground black pepper
1 large egg, beaten
2 tsp olive oil
1 orange
½ cup fresh or thawed frozen raspberries
2 tsp sugar
4 whole wheat English muffins
Shredded lettuce to garnish

1. Preheat grill or oven broiler. Put lamb into large bowl. Add carrot, onion, bread crumbs, nutmeg, and thyme. Season with salt and pepper to taste. Mix well. Add egg and use your hands to mix ingredients together thoroughly.

2. Divide mixture into 4 patties. Brush both sides of burgers with oil, then put in grill pan. Cook for 4 to 5 minutes on each side, depending on thickness.

3. Meanwhile, cut peel and pith from orange with sharp knife. Working over a bowl to catch juice, cut between membranes to release segments. Roughly chop segments and add to juice. Add raspberries and sugar, lightly crushing fruit with fork to mix relish together.

4. Split English muffins and toast lightly. Put a burger on each muffin and add some lettuce to garnish and a good spoonful of relish. Serve with remaining relish.

Per serving: 370 calories, 26 g protein, 40 g carbohydrates, 6 g fiber, 12 g total fat, 4 g saturated fat, 121 mg cholesterol, 328 mg sodium

HAM AND CELERIAC PITAS

Serves 6
Prep Time: 15 minutes
Cook Time: 2 minutes
Healing Foods: celeriac, carrots, pork, onions, olives
Ailments It Heals: chronic fatigue syndrome, eye problems, hypothyroidism, memory loss, peptic ulcers

¼ cup Greek yogurt
½ tsp whole grain mustard
2 Tbsp mayonnaise
1 small celeriac
2 carrots
5 oz (150 g) thickly sliced lean low-sodium smoked ham, cut into ½-in (1 cm) pieces
1 small red onion, thinly sliced
8 pitted green olives, pimiento-stuffed if desired, halved
⅓ cup currants
2 Tbsp chopped fresh parsley
6 pita breads
1 Romaine lettuce heart, finely shredded
Fresh parsley sprigs to garnish

1. In medium-size bowl, mix together yogurt, mustard, and mayonnaise.

CURRIED CHICKEN SALAD SANDWICHES

Serves 4

Prep Time: 10 minutes

Healing Foods: yogurt, curry, chicken, apples, celery

Ailments It Heals: burns, colds and flu, jet lag

¼ cup low-fat plain yogurt

2 Tbsp low-fat canola mayonnaise

1½ tsp curry powder

1 tsp honey

¼ tsp salt

2 cups chopped cooked chicken

1 apple, cored and chopped

2 celery stalks, chopped

4 lettuce leaves

2 whole grain pita breads (8 in or 20 cm), halved

2. Preheat grill to high. Peel and coarsely grate the celeriac and carrots. Add to the bowl of dressing and mix well. Add the ham, onion, olives, currants, and chopped parsley and mix everything together.

3. Warm the pita breads on the grill for about 1 minute on each side. Cut each one across in half to make 2 pockets of bread. Divide the lettuce among the pita pockets, then add the ham and celeriac salad. Garnish with parsley sprigs and serve.

Per serving: 303 calories, 12 g protein, 46 g carbohydrates, 3 g fiber, 8 g total fat, 2 g saturated fat, 16 mg cholesterol, 797 mg sodium

1. In large bowl, whisk together yogurt, mayonnaise, curry powder, honey, and salt. Add the chicken, apple, and celery.

2. Place a lettuce leaf in each pita half and fill with one-quarter of the chicken salad.

Per serving: 253 calories, 23 g protein, 27 g carbohydrates, 4 g fiber, 6 g total fat, 1 g saturated fat, 53 mg cholesterol, 440 mg sodium

GRILLED CHICKEN SANDWICHES WITH BASIL MAYONNAISE

Serves 4

Prep Time: 10 minutes
Cook Time: 7 minutes
Healing Foods: lemons, basil, chicken, salad greens, tomatoes
Ailments It Heals: Alzheimer's disease, hyperthyroidism, obesity

- 1 large lemon
- 1/3 cup reduced-fat mayonnaise
- 2 Tbsp chopped fresh basil or 2 tsp dried
- 4 boneless, skinless chicken breast halves (4 oz or 125 g each)
- 1 Tbsp lemon-pepper seasoning
- 4 sandwich rolls (2 oz or 60 g each), split
- 1 small bunch watercress or arugula, trimmed
- 2 medium tomatoes, sliced

1. Grate zest from lemon into small bowl. Squeeze juice into measuring cup. Combine mayonnaise and basil with zest. Sprinkle chicken with lemon-pepper seasoning.

2. Generously coat nonstick ridged grill pan with cooking spray and set over medium-high heat until hot but not smoking. Cook chicken for 4 minutes, or until grill marks appear. Turn chicken and sprinkle with lemon juice. Cook for 3 minutes, or until juices run clear.

3. Cut chicken into thin slices. Spread rolls evenly with basil mayonnaise. Layer bottoms of rolls with half of watercress, all of tomato and chicken, then remaining watercress. Cover with tops of rolls.

Per serving: 378 calories, 33 g protein, 38 g carbohydrates, 4 g fiber, 11 g total fat, 2 g saturated fat, 66 mg cholesterol, 614 mg sodium

HERBED CHICKEN AND APPLE BURGERS

Serves 4

Prep Time: 20 minutes plus chilling
Cook Time: 10 minutes
Healing Foods: chicken, apples, herbs, wheat, watercress
Ailments It Heals: diabetes, hypoglycemia, Parkinson's disease, PCOS

- 1 lb (500 g) ground chicken
- 1 large red onion, finely chopped
- 1/4 cup plain dry bread crumbs
- 2 large green apples, such as Granny Smith (for a tart taste) or Golden Delicious (for a sweet taste), peeled and coarsely grated
- 1 Tbsp chopped fresh sage leaves
- 1 Tbsp fresh thyme leaves
- 1/4 tsp salt
- 1/4 tsp ground black pepper
- 1/4 cup dijon mustard
- 1 Tbsp honey
- 4 whole wheat hamburger buns, split
- 3 oz (90 g) watercress sprigs, large stalks discarded

1. In large bowl, place chicken, onion, bread crumbs, apples, sage, thyme, salt, and pepper. Using your hands, mix ingredients together until evenly distributed. Wet your hands, then divide mixture into 4 equal portions and shape each into a burger about 4 in (10 cm) in diameter and 1½ in (4 cm) thick. Chill burgers for 1 hour to firm up meat and make it easier to hold together while it cooks.

2. Preheat grill or broiler to high. Place burgers on rack about 6 in (15 cm) from source of heat. Grill or broil about 5 minutes per side, turning once, until golden brown on both sides and still juicy but cooked through completely or until the burger reaches an internal temperature of 165°F or 74°C.

3. Meanwhile, mix mustard and honey in small cup. On flat surface, open 4 buns with soft cut sides up. Spread cut sides of tops and bottoms with honey mustard. Pile one-fourth of the watercress on bottom of each bun.

4. Place cooked burger on top of watercress. Cover with top of bun and serve immediately.

Per serving: 364 calories, 34 g protein, 49 g carbohydrates, 6 g fiber, 5 g total fat, 1 g saturated fat, 64 mg cholesterol, 872 mg sodium

INDIAN-STYLE TURKEY BURGERS

Serves 4

Prep Time: 10 minutes

Cook Time: 18 minutes

Healing Foods: garlic, ginger, peppers, curry, mangoes, turkey, yogurt

Ailments It Heals: anemia, depression, mood disorders

1	Tbsp olive oil
1	large red onion, finely chopped,
3	cloves garlic, minced
2	Tbsp minced fresh ginger
1	red bell pepper, diced
1½	tsp curry powder
½	cup tomato juice
4	Tbsp chopped mango chutney
1	lb (500 g) lean ground turkey breast
⅓	cup plain low-fat yogurt
¼	cup chopped cilantro
1	slice firm white sandwich bread, crumbled
¼	tsp salt

1. In small skillet, heat oil over medium heat. Add onion, garlic, and ginger and cook, stirring frequently, for 5 minutes, or until onion is lightly browned. Measure out ½ cup onion-ginger mixture and transfer to large bowl.

2. To remaining mixture in skillet, add bell pepper and cook for 4 minutes, or until crisp-tender. Stir in 1 tsp curry powder and cook for 1 minute. Stir in tomato juice and 2 Tbsp chutney and bring to a boil. Boil for 1 minute.

3. To bowl with reserved onion-ginger mixture, add turkey, yogurt, cilantro, crumbled bread, salt, and remaining ½ tsp curry powder and 2 Tbsp chutney. Gently shape mixture into 4 patties.

4. Preheat broiler. Broil patties 6 in (15 cm) from heat for 3½ minutes per side, until cooked through or until the burger reaches an internal temperature of 165°F or 74°C. Serve burgers with the sautéed pepper mixture on top.

Per serving: 288 calories, 31 g protein, 28 g carbohydrates, 2 g fiber, 5 g total fat, 1 g saturated fat, 72 mg cholesterol, 540 mg sodium

TURKEY COBB SALAD SANDWICHES

Serves 4

Prep Time: 15 minutes

Cook Time: 5 minutes

Healing Foods: chives, avocado, salad greens, turkey, tomatoes

Ailments It Heals: hives, insomnia, mood disorders

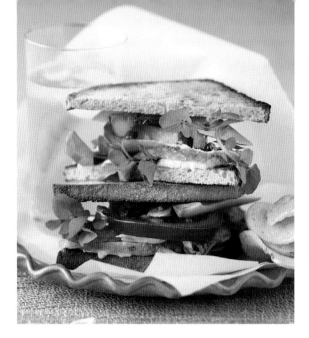

¼ cup nonfat mayonnaise
¼ cup blue cheese, crumbled
2 Tbsp snipped fresh chives
4 slices lean low-sodium bacon
8 slices whole wheat bread, toasted
4 oz (125 g) watercress, tough stems trimmed
12 oz (375 g) fresh-roasted turkey breast slices
2 medium tomatoes, sliced
4 scallions, thinly sliced
1 small avocado, peeled, pitted, and thinly sliced

1. In small bowl, combine mayonnaise, blue cheese, and chives.

2. In medium skillet over medium-high heat, cook bacon until crisp. Transfer to paper towels to drain, then tear into small pieces.

3. Spread blue cheese mixture evenly on bread. Layer 4 slices with watercress, turkey, tomatoes, scallions, avocado, and bacon. Top with remaining bread and cut sandwiches diagonally in half.

Per serving: 450 calories, 37 g protein, 39 g carbohydrates, 7 g fiber, 14 g total fat, 4 g saturated fat, 85 mg cholesterol, 660 mg sodium

JAPANESE SUSHI ROLLS

Makes 32
Prep Time: 20 minutes plus cooling
Cook Time: 20 minutes
Healing Foods: rice, vinegar, cucumbers, fish, seaweed
Ailments It Heals: anorexia, jet lag, rosacea

10 oz (300 g) sushi rice
1 Tbsp fine granulated sugar
3 Tbsp rice wine vinegar
2 scallions, very finely chopped
1 cucumber, seeded and finely chopped
4 oz (125 g) smoked salmon
4 sheets sushi nori
2 tsp wasabi paste
Gari (pickled ginger)
Reduced-sodium soy sauce

1. In saucepan of boiling water, cook sushi rice according to packet instructions.

2. Meanwhile, place sugar and vinegar in small pan and heat gently until sugar dissolves. When rice is cooked, drizzle mixture over it, then add spring onions and cucumber and mix. Cover with tea towel and leave to cool.

3. Divide sushi rice into 4 equal portions. Cut salmon into strips about ½ in (1 cm) wide. Place a sheet of nori, shiny side down, on a bamboo mat or on a sheet of parchment paper on a board. Spread a portion of rice over nori, pressing it down evenly and leaving a ½ in (1 cm) space at top and bottom. Place one-quarter of salmon along middle of layer of rice, then spread salmon with ½ tsp wasabi paste.

4. Using the bamboo mat or the paper, roll up nori, rice, and salmon into a neat tube. Roll tightly to ensure rice sticks together and holds filling in place. Make 3 more rolls in the same way.

5. Using a wet knife, cut each roll across into 8 slices and stand them upright on a serving plate. Rinse knife between cuts. Garnish with pieces of gari and offer a small dish of soy sauce for dipping.

Per serving: 109 calories, 3 g protein, 23 g carbohydrates, 0 g fiber, 0 g total fat, 0 g saturated fat, 2 mg cholesterol, 187 mg sodium

SALMON AND FENNEL LETTUCE WRAPS

Serves 4
Prep Time: 15 minutes
Healing Foods: lemons, fish, fennel, lettuce
Ailments It Heals: cardiovascular disease, hay fever, stroke

- 3 Tbsp reduced-fat mayonnaise
- 1 Tbsp reduced-fat sour cream
- 2 Tbsp fresh lemon juice
- 1 Tbsp chopped fresh dill
- 12 oz (375 g) canned Alaskan pink or sockeye salmon, drained
- ½ fennel bulb, trimmed and finely chopped
- 4 large Boston lettuce leaves

1. In medium bowl, whisk together mayonnaise, sour cream, lemon juice, and dill. Stir in salmon and fennel.

2. For each wrap, start about 1 in (2.5 cm) up from bottom of lettuce leaf and mound one-fourth of salmon mixture in horizontal row along bottom third of lettuce.

3. Fold bottom of lettuce over filling, then fold in about 1 in (2.5 cm) of sides. Roll firmly away from you.

4. Cut each wrap in half on a diagonal.

Per serving: 179 calories, 21 g protein, 5 g carbohydrates, 1 g fiber, 8 g total fat, 2 g saturated fat, 39 mg cholesterol, 422 mg sodium

SALMON CAKE SANDWICHES

Serves 4
Prep Time: 15 minutes plus chilling
Cook Time: 6 minutes
Healing Foods: fish, wheat, lettuce, tomatoes
Ailments It Heals: cancer, lactose intolerance, menstrual problems, multiple sclerosis

- ¼ cup mild salsa
- 2 egg whites
- ¼ cup low-fat canola mayonnaise
- ½ tsp ground cumin
- ¼ to 1 tsp hot red-pepper sauce
- 2 pouches (7 oz or 200 g each) salmon, patted dry
- 1 cup fresh whole wheat bread crumbs
- 4 lettuce leaves
- 4 whole wheat sandwich rolls
- 1 large tomato, cut into 4 slices

1. Drain salsa by placing it in a sieve over a bowl for about 10 minutes. Shake sieve to release any remaining liquid.

2. Line baking sheet with parchment paper. In medium bowl, whisk egg whites. Stir in salsa, mayonnaise, cumin, and red-pepper sauce. Add salmon and bread crumbs and gently fold in just until combined. Shape mixture into 4 cakes, place on baking sheet, and refrigerate for at least 30 minutes.

3. Coat nonstick skillet with cooking spray. Add cakes and cook over medium heat, turning once, for 6 minutes, or until browned and crisp.

4. Place lettuce leaf on each roll. Top with salmon cake and tomato slice.

Per serving: 367 calories, 30 g protein, 39 g carbohydrates, 6 g fiber, 11 g total fat, 1 g saturated fat, 81 mg cholesterol, 779 mg sodium

ASIAN GRILLED TUNA BURGERS

Serves 4
Prep Time: 25 minutes
Cook Time: 5 minutes
Healing Foods: fish, peppers, cucumbers, limes
Ailments It Heals: AIDS and HIV infections, cholesterol (high), halitosis, sex drive (diminished),

12	oz (375 g) water-packed albacore tuna, drained
1	large egg
4	scallions, thinly sliced
½	cup chopped cilantro
3	Tbsp plain dried bread crumbs
2	Tbsp low-fat mayonnaise
1	Tbsp minced fresh ginger
2	tsp dark sesame oil
¼	tsp salt
1	red bell pepper, cut into matchsticks
1	cucumber, peeled, halved lengthwise, seeded, and cut into matchsticks
2	Tbsp reduced-sodium soy sauce
2	Tbsp fresh lime juice
2	tsp sugar

1. In large bowl, combine tuna, egg, scallions, cilantro, bread crumbs, mayonnaise, ginger, sesame oil, and salt. Stir until well combined.

2. Form mixture into four 4-in (10 cm) patties, a scant ½ in (1 cm) thick. (Patties can be made ahead and refrigerated for several hours.)

3. In medium bowl, combine bell pepper, cucumber, soy sauce, lime juice, and sugar.

4. Preheat broiler. Broil patties 4 in (10 cm) from heat, carefully turning once, for 2½ minutes per side, or until firm and lightly golden. Top the finished burgers with pepper-cucumber relish.

Per serving: 216 calories, 24 g protein, 13 g carbohydrates, 2 g fiber, 8 g total fat, 2 g saturated fat, 38 mg cholesterol, 862 mg sodium

TUNA AND CARROT SANDWICH ON RYE

Serves 2
Prep Time: 15 minutes
Healing Foods: carrots, lemons, olive oil, fish, rye
Ailments It Heals: eye problems, hyperthyroidism, mood disorders, rosacea

⅔	cup shredded carrot (1 medium)
2	tsp lemon juice
2	tsp extra-virgin olive oil
1	Tbsp chopped scallions
1	Tbsp chopped fresh dill or parsley
⅛	tsp salt, or to taste
3	oz (90 g) water-packed chunk light tuna, drained and flaked
¼	cup finely chopped celery
2	Tbsp reduced-fat mayonnaise
4	slices rye or pumpernickel bread
4	lettuce leaves, rinsed and dried

1. In small bowl, combine carrot, lemon juice, oil, scallions, dill or parsley, and salt. Mix with fork.

2. In another small bowl, mix tuna, celery, and 1 Tbsp of mayonnaise.

3. Spread remaining 1 Tbsp mayonnaise over bread slices. Spread half of tuna mixture over 2 bread slices. Top with carrot salad and lettuce. Set remaining bread slices over filling. Cut each sandwich in half. One serving equals 2 sandwich halves. Sandwiches will keep, well wrapped, in refrigerator or cooler packed with ice packs for up to 1 day.

Per serving: 303 calories, 17 g protein, 38 g carbohydrates, 5 g fiber, 9 g total fat, 2 g saturated fat, 13 mg cholesterol, 758 mg sodium

OPEN-FACED SARDINE SANDWICHES

Serves 2
Prep Time: 5 minutes
Cook Time: 5 minutes
Healing Foods: lemons, fish, cheese
Ailments It Heals: Alzheimer's disease, atherosclerosis, asthma, circulatory disorders

1 Tbsp low-fat canola mayonnaise
½ tsp fresh lemon juice
¼ tsp grated lemon zest
2 slices (each ¾ in or 1.5 cm thick) whole grain bread, such as 12-grain
1 small tomato, cut into 4 slices
3.75 oz (106 g) sardines in olive oil
2 slices (2 oz or 60 g) low-fat Jarlsberg cheese

1. Preheat the broiler. In a small bowl, combine the mayonnaise, lemon juice, and lemon zest. Spread half of the mixture onto each slice of bread.

2. Top each slice with 1/2 of the tomatoes, sardines, and cheese. Place on a broiler pan or baking sheet and broil until the cheese melts, about 3 minutes.

Per serving: 228 calories, 20 g protein, 17 g carbohydrates, 5 g fiber, 9 g total fat, 1 g saturated fat, 72 mg cholesterol, 637 mg sodium

FISH TACOS

Serves 4
Prep Time: 10 minutes plus standing
Cook Time: 7 minutes
Healing Foods: limes, fish, mangoes, lettuce
Ailments It Heals: cholesterol (high), chronic fatigue syndrome, jaundice, obesity, multiple sclerosis

1 Tbsp olive oil
2 cloves garlic, minced
1 tsp ground cumin
½ tsp salt
3 Tbsp lime juice
1½ lb (750 g) halibut fillets
1 ripe mango, peeled, seeded, and chopped
½ small red bell pepper, seeded and finely chopped
½ jalapeño chile pepper, seeded and finely chopped (wear gloves when handling; they burn)
¼ cup chopped cilantro (optional)
8 soft corn tortillas (6 in or 15 cm)
1 cup shredded lettuce

1. Preheat broiler. Coat broiler pan with cooking spray. In medium bowl, combine oil, garlic, cumin, salt, 1 Tbsp lime juice, and fish and toss to coat. Let stand 15 minutes.

2. In small bowl, combine mango, bell pepper, chile pepper, cilantro (if using), and remaining 2 Tbsp lime juice. Set salsa aside.

3. Wrap tortillas in foil. Remove fish from marinade and place on broiler pan. Broil for 3 to 6 minutes, or until opaque. Transfer to plate and place tortillas in oven for 1 minute, to warm slightly. Flake the fish.

4. Top tortillas with equal amounts of lettuce, fish, and salsa.

Per serving: 380 calories, 39 g protein, 36 g carbohydrates, 5 g fiber, 9 g total fat, 1 g saturated fat, 54 mg cholesterol, 430 mg sodium

CRAB CAKES WITH MELON RELISH

Serves 4

Prep Time: 10 minutes

Cook Time: 12 minutes

Healing Foods: limes, cantaloupe, tomatoes, shellfish, olive oil

Ailments It Heals: burns, cancer, psoriasis, respiratory disorders

¼ cup fresh lime juice
2 Tbsp honey
1 Tbsp plus 2 tsp dijon mustard
2 cups cantaloupe chunks (½ in or 1 cm)
1 green bell pepper, diced
1 cup cherry tomatoes, quartered
1 lb (500 g) lump crabmeat, picked over to remove any cartilage
4 scallions, thinly sliced
¼ tsp salt
2 egg whites
½ cup plain dry bread crumbs
2 Tbsp olive oil

1. In medium bowl, whisk together lime juice, honey, and 1 Tbsp mustard. Add cantaloupe, bell pepper, and tomatoes and toss to combine. Refrigerate until ready to serve.

2. In separate bowl, combine crabmeat, scallions, salt, and remaining 2 tsp mustard. Beat egg whites until stiff peaks form and gently fold into crabmeat mixture. Gently shape into 8 patties.

3. Dip patties in bread crumbs. In large nonstick skillet, heat 1 Tbsp oil over medium heat. Add 4 crab cakes and cook for 2 to 3 minutes per side, or until hot and cooked through. Transfer crab cakes to a plate. Repeat with remaining 1 Tbsp oil and 4 crab cakes. Serve crab cakes with melon relish alongside.

Per serving: 315 calories, 26 g protein, 32 g carbohydrates, 3 g fiber, 9 g total fat, 2 g saturated fat, 88 mg cholesterol, 768 mg sodium

GRILLED EGGPLANT SANDWICHES WITH RED PEPPER–WALNUT SAUCE

Serves 4
Prep Time: 20 minutes
Cook Time: 12 minutes
Healing Foods: nuts, peppers, eggplant, cheese
Ailments It Heals: Alzheimer's disease, eye problems, prostate problems

Red Pepper–Walnut Sauce
- ¼ cup walnuts
- 1 Tbsp fine dry unseasoned bread crumbs
- 1 clove garlic, minced (½ tsp)
- 1 tsp ground cumin
- ⅛ tsp red-pepper flakes
- Salt to taste
- 7 oz (200 g) roasted red peppers, drained and rinsed
- 1 tablespoon lemon juice

Sandwich
- 2 medium-large baby eggplants, cut crosswise into ⅜-in-thick (1 cm) slices
- Salt to taste
- Ground black pepper to taste
- 8 small slices sourdough bread, toasted if desired
- 4 oz (125 g) creamy goat cheese, cut into ⅜-in-thick (1 cm) slices
- ¾ cup arugula leaves, washed and dried

1. To make sauce: In food processor, combine walnuts, bread crumbs, garlic, cumin, red pepper, and salt. Process until walnuts are ground. Add roasted red peppers and lemon juice and process until smooth.

2. Preheat grill or broiler.

3. To make sandwich: Spritz both sides of eggplant slices with cooking spray and season with salt and pepper. Lightly oil grill or broiler rack by rubbing it with a piece of oil-soaked paper towel (use tongs to hold paper towel when working over a hot grill). Grill or broil eggplant for 4 to 6 minutes per side, or until very tender and browned.

4. Spread about 1½ Tbsp Red Pepper–Walnut Sauce over one side of each bread slice. Layer eggplant slices and goat cheese slices on 4 bread slices. Top with arugula. Set remaining bread slices on top and cut sandwiches in half. One serving is 2 sandwich halves. Sandwiches will keep, wrapped in plastic wrap or foil, in refrigerator or cooler packed with ice packs for up to 2 days.

Per serving: 425 calories, 16 g protein, 60 g carbohydrates, 7 g fiber, 18 g total fat, 6 g saturated fat, 13 mg cholesterol, 960 mg sodium

OPEN-FACED GRILLED VEGETABLE SANDWICH

Serves 4
Prep Time: 15 minutes
Cook Time: 14 minutes
Healing Foods: olive oil, mushrooms, asparagus, peppers, cheese
Ailments It Heals: cardiovascular disease, diabetes, kidney disease

- 2 Tbsp olive oil
- 1 Tbsp balsamic vinegar
- ¼ tsp salt
- ⅛ tsp ground black pepper

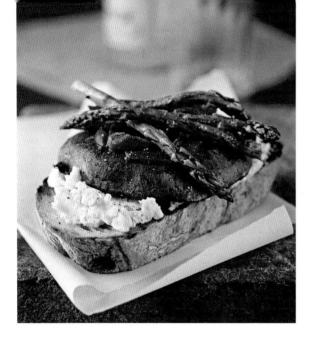

4 portobello mushrooms, stems removed
1 small bunch asparagus, trimmed and spears cut in half
1 large red bell pepper, halved and seeded
4 slices Italian bread
3 oz (90 g) goat cheese

1. Preheat grill or broiler.

2. In small bowl, whisk together oil, balsamic vinegar, salt, and black pepper. Brush mushrooms, asparagus, and bell pepper with oil mixture.

3. Grill or broil vegetables 4 in (10 cm) from heat, turning once, until tender, about 10 minutes for asparagus and bell pepper, and about 12 minutes for mushrooms. When cool enough to handle, peel and slice pepper.

4. Turn off grill or broiler. Place bread on grill or broiler rack for 2 minutes, or until warm. Spread goat cheese on bread. Place mushrooms on each slice. Top with bell pepper and asparagus. Serve warm.

Per serving: 274 calories, 11 g protein, 26 g carbohydrates, 4 g fiber, 15 g total fat, 6 g saturated fat, 17 mg cholesterol, 443 mg sodium

ZUCCHINI-CARROT CRUSTLESS QUICHE SQUARES

Serves 16
Prep Time: 15 minutes
Cook Time: 1 hour plus cooling
Healing Foods: zucchini, eggs, carrots, cheese
Ailments It Heals: ADHD, anemia, cystic fibrosis

1 tsp olive oil
1 large onion, finely chopped
1 large zucchini, cut into ½-in (1 cm) cubes
½ tsp salt
2 large eggs
¼ cup milk
3 medium carrots, peeled, grated, blotted dry
1 cup shredded cheddar cheese
1 Tbsp chopped dill

1. Heat oven to 375°F (190°C). Lightly coat 8-in (2 L) square or round baking pan with cooking spray. In large nonstick skillet, heat oil over medium heat. Add onion and sauté for 3 minutes, or until slightly softened. Add zucchini. Increase heat to medium-high and sauté for 7 to 10 minutes, or until zucchini is soft and all liquid has evaporated. Stir in ¼ tsp salt. Remove from heat.

2. In large bowl, beat eggs, milk, and remaining ¼ tsp salt. Add zucchini, carrots, cheese, and dill. Spread in prepared pan.

3. Bake for 45 minutes, or until quiche is just set in center. Transfer to wire rack. Let cool for at least 10 minutes before cutting. Serve warm.

Per serving: 54 calories, 3 g protein, 3 g carbohydrates, 1 g fiber, 3 g total fat, 2 g saturated fat, 35 mg cholesterol, 128 mg sodium

COUSCOUS-STUFFED PEPPERS

Serves 6

Prep Time: 20 minutes

Cook Time: 28 minutes

Healing Foods: peppers, zucchini, chickpeas, cheese

Ailments It Heals: cancer, cirrhosis, stress

6 large bell peppers (red, yellow, orange, or green)
1 Tbsp vegetable oil
1 small zucchini, finely chopped
2 cloves garlic, minced
1 Tbsp fresh-squeezed lemon juice
2 cups cooked couscous
15 oz (450 mL) chickpeas, drained and rinsed
1 ripe tomato, seeded and finely chopped
1 tsp dried oregano, crumbled
½ tsp salt
¼ tsp ground black pepper
½ cup crumbled feta cheese

1. Slice tops off peppers to make lids. Scoop out membranes and seeds and discard. In large saucepan of lightly salted boiling water, simmer peppers and lids, covered, for 5 minutes. Drain.

2. Preheat oven to 350°F (180°C).

3. In medium saucepan, heat oil over medium heat. Add zucchini and garlic and sauté for 2 minutes. Stir in lemon juice. Cook for 1 minute and remove from heat. Stir in couscous, chickpeas, tomato, oregano, salt, and black pepper. Stir in cheese. Fill each pepper with couscous mixture. Place upright in shallow baking dish. Cover with pepper tops.

4. Bake for 20 minutes, or just until filling is heated through.

Per serving: 207 calories, 8 g protein, 36 g carbohydrates, 7 g fiber, 4 g total fat, 1 g saturated fat, 3 mg cholesterol, 307 mg sodium

SALADS

BEEF-FILLET SALAD WITH MUSTARD VINAIGRETTE

Serves 4

Prep Time: 20 minutes

Cook Time: 45 minutes plus chilling, standing

Healing Foods: beef, vinegar, mustard, potatoes, green beans, peas, leeks

Ailments It Heals: ADHD, anemia, infertility

1 lb (500 g) beef fillet

1 tsp plus 1½ Tbsp olive oil

1 Tbsp red wine vinegar

1½ tsp dijon mustard

Pinch of sugar

Salt and ground black pepper

¾ lb (375 g) new potatoes, scrubbed

¼ lb (125 g) haricots verts (French green beans) or regular green beans, halved

½ cup shelled fresh or frozen peas

1 large leek, finely chopped

2 Tbsp snipped fresh chives

1. Preheat oven to 450°F (230°C). Rub fillet with 1 tsp oil and set on a rack in a roasting pan. Roast for 15 minutes for rare beef or up to 25 minutes for well done.

2. Meanwhile, in large mixing bowl, whisk together vinegar, mustard, sugar, salt, pepper, and 1½ Tbsp oil.

3. When beef is done, remove from oven and let stand for 5 minutes, then cut into thin slices against the grain. Add to bowl with dressing and let cool.

4. In saucepan of boiling water, cook potatoes for 15 minutes, or until tender. Drain well. When cool enough to handle, cut in half or into thick slices and add to bowl.

5. Drop green beans into another pan of boiling water and cook for 1 minute. Add peas and cook for 3 minutes, or until vegetables are tender. Drain vegetables and refresh briefly under cold running water, then add to bowl. Toss well. Cover and refrigerate for 30 minutes.

6. About 15 minutes before serving, remove salad from refrigerator and stir in leek and chives.

Per serving: 318 calories, 24 g protein, 25 g carbohydrates, 4 g fiber, 14 g total fat, 4 g saturated fat, 60 mg cholesterol, 117 mg sodium

PORK, PEAR AND POTATO SALAD

Serves 6

Prep Time: 35 minutes

Cook Time: 22 minutes

Healing Foods: pecans, potatoes, radishes, pears, salad greens, pork

Ailments It Heals: infertility, memory loss, menstrual problems, neuralgia

Salad

⅓ cup halved pecans

1½ lb (750 g) new potatoes (even sized), washed

2 Tbsp finely minced fresh ginger

2 tsp coarse mustard

2 tsp white wine vinegar

2 Tbsp canola oil

2 tsp hazelnut oil

Salt and ground black pepper

1 small daikon radish (Japanese white radish), peeled and thinly sliced

8 red radishes, cut into quarters

2 firm ripe pears

1 oak leaf lettuce or other greens, separated into leaves

1 bunch watercress, tough stalks discarded

12 oz (375 g) cooked roast pork loin, trimmed of fat and thinly sliced

1. Heat small skillet over medium-high heat and toast pecans for 6 to 7 minutes. Cool, then chop roughly. Set aside.

2. In saucepan of boiling water, cook potatoes for 15 minutes, or until tender. Drain. When cool enough to handle, cut into quarters and place in mixing bowl.

3. Put ginger in garlic crusher and press to squeeze out juice (this will have to be done in three or four batches). You need 2 tsp of this ginger juice. In small jar or container with a tight-fitting lid, add ginger, mustard, vinegar, oils, and salt and pepper to taste. Shake well to mix. Pour about one-third of dressing over warm potatoes and toss gently to coat. Leave to cool.

4. In another bowl, toss the daikon and red radishes with half of remaining dressing, to prevent them from browning. Halve pears lengthways and scoop out cores, then cut into long wedges. Toss with radishes.

5. Arrange lettuce leaves and watercress in shallow salad bowl. Add radish mixture to potatoes and gently mix together. Pile mixture onto the middle of the salad leaves and arrange pork slices on top.

6. Stir toasted pecans into remaining dressing and drizzle over top of salad. Serve immediately.

Per serving: 355 calories, 21 g protein, 34 g carbohydrates, 5 g fiber, 16 g total fat, 3 g saturated fat, 48 mg cholesterol, 93 mg sodium

ROAST PORK AND QUINOA SALAD

Serves 4
Prep Time: 25 minutes
Cook Time: 25 minutes
Healing Foods: mustard, lemons, pork, grains, grapefruits, salad greens
Ailments It Heals: AIDS and HIV infection, celiac disease, jaundice

¼ cup apricot jam
2 Tbsp dijon mustard
1 tsp grated lemon zest
2 Tbsp fresh lemon juice
1 tsp chili powder
1 lb (500 g) well-trimmed pork tenderloin
¾ tsp salt
2 cups water
1 cup quinoa, well rinsed
1 Tbsp olive oil
3 pink grapefruits
8 cups arugula (about 2 bunches)

1. Preheat oven to 400°F (200°C). In large bowl, whisk together jam, mustard, lemon zest, lemon juice, and ½ tsp chili powder. Measure out 3 Tbsp of jam mixture and reserve.

2. Place pork in small roasting pan. Rub with ¼ tsp salt and remaining ½ tsp chili powder. Roast for 15 minutes. Brush 3 Tbsp jam mixture over pork and roast for 10 minutes, or until cooked through but still juicy.

3. Meanwhile, in large saucepan, bring water to a boil. Add quinoa and remaining ½ tsp salt and return to a boil. Reduce to a simmer, cover, and cook for 12 minutes, or until tender. Drain.

4. Whisk oil with remaining jam mixture in bowl. Add quinoa, tossing to combine.

5. With paring knife, cut off skin from grapefruits. Working over a bowl to catch juice, cut between membranes to release sections. Add sections and ¼ cup grapefruit juice to bowl with quinoa.

6. Place quinoa salad on bed of arugula. Thinly slice pork and arrange on top.

Per serving: 450 calories, 31 g protein, 59 g carbohydrates, 5 g fiber, 10 g total fat, 2 g saturated fat, 65 mg cholesterol, 697 mg sodium

ASIAN CHICKEN SALAD

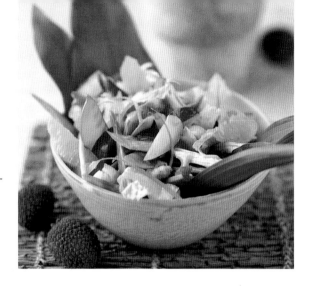

Serves 4

Prep Time: 20 minutes

Cook Time: 10 minutes

Healing Foods: lettuce, peas, oranges, plums, chicken, peanut butter

Ailments It Heals: acne, hepatitis, obesity

1	lb (500 g) romaine lettuce
4	oz (125 g) snow peas
20	oz (568 mL) canned lychees, drained and cut in half
1	large navel orange, peeled and cut into sections
1	red plum, pitted and sliced
4	scallions, thinly sliced
12	oz (375 g) boneless, skinless chicken breast halves
⅓	cup nonfat mayonnaise
3	Tbsp creamy peanut butter
1	clove garlic, minced

1. Finely shred lettuce and put into large salad bowl. Trim snow peas and remove strings with fingers. Cut peas in half on the diagonal and add to salad bowl. Add lychees, orange, plum, and scallions and toss to mix.

2. Coat nonstick ridged grill pan with cooking spray and set over medium-high heat for 2 minutes, or until hot. Grill chicken breasts for 4 minutes on each side, or until cooked through.

3. Meanwhile, in small measuring cup, whisk mayonnaise, peanut butter, and garlic until blended. Diagonally cut chicken into thin slices and add to salad bowl. Right before serving, drizzle salad with dressing and toss to coat.

Per serving: 378 calories, 27 g protein, 53 g carbohydrates, 7 g fiber, 9 g total fat, 2 g saturated fat, 49 mg cholesterol, 378 mg sodium

CHICKEN SALAD WITH CITRUS

Serves 4

Prep Time: 30 minutes

Healing Foods: oranges, grapefruits, chicken, olives, salad greens

Ailments It Heals: anemia, fibroids, prostate problems, varicose veins

3	navel oranges
2	ruby red grapefruits
3	Tbsp olive oil
1	Tbsp balsamic vinegar
2	tsp dijon mustard
½	tsp salt
2	generous cups shredded cooked chicken breasts or thighs, leftover or poached
½	cup kalamata olives, pitted and sliced
½	cup slivered red onion
2	bunches arugula, tough stems trimmed (about 6 cups)

1. With paring knife, cut off and discard skin, white pith, and outer membrane of oranges and grapefruits. Working over a bowl to catch juices, section oranges and grapefruits: Use paring knife to cut along both sides of each dividing membrane to release segments, transferring them to smaller bowl. Squeeze any juice left in membranes into bowl. Measure out 3 Tbsp of citrus juice and transfer to large salad bowl (reserve any extra juice for another use).

2. Whisk oil, vinegar, mustard, and salt into citrus juice in bowl. Add chicken, olives, onion, arugula, and orange and grapefruit sections and toss well.

Per serving: 385 calories, 27 g protein, 29 g carbohydrates, 5 g fiber, 19 g total fat, 3 g saturated fat, 70 mg cholesterol, 619 mg sodium

CHICKEN-MELON SALAD

Serves 4
Prep Time: 15 minutes
Cook Time: 13 minutes
Healing Foods: chicken, limes, salad greens, cantaloupe, tomato
Ailments It Heals: colds and flu, diabetes, hives, respiratory disorders

1 Tbsp chili powder
1 tsp dried oregano
1 lb (500 g) boneless, skinless chicken breasts
1 Tbsp olive oil
5 Tbsp fresh lime juice
½ tsp salt
2 corn tortillas (6-in or 15 cm diameter), cut into 8 wedges each
2 Tbsp light mayonnaise
2 tsp dijon mustard
2 bunches watercress, tough stems trimmed (about 6 cups)

3 cups cantaloupe chunks (½ in or 1 cm)
2 cups cherry tomatoes, halved
2 scallions, thinly sliced

1. Preheat oven to 450°F (230°C). In small bowl, stir together chili powder and oregano. Measure out 1 tsp of mixture and set aside. Rub remaining mixture into chicken.

2. In small bowl, whisk together oil, reserved 1 tsp spice mixture, 1 Tbsp lime juice, and ¼ tsp salt. Dip tortilla wedges into mixture. Transfer wedges to baking sheet and bake for 5 minutes, or until crisp. Remove from oven and preheat broiler.

3. Broil chicken 6 in (15 cm) from heat for 4 minutes per side, or until cooked through. When cool enough to handle, slice into bite-size pieces.

4. Meanwhile, in large bowl, whisk together mayonnaise, mustard, and remaining 4 Tbsp lime juice and ¼ tsp salt. Add chicken, watercress, cantaloupe, tomatoes, and scallions. Serve topped with tortilla wedges.

Per serving: 286 calories, 28 g protein, 23 g carbohydrates, 4 g fiber, 10 g total fat, 2 g saturated fat, 75 mg cholesterol, 616 mg sodium

JAMAICAN JERKED CHICKEN SALAD

Serves 4
Prep Time: 15 minutes
Cook Time: 8 minutes
Healing Foods: vinegar, chicken, pineapples, kiwi, peppers, jicama
Ailments It Heals: arthritis, chronic fatigue syndrome, colds and flu

3 cloves garlic, minced

1¼ tsp dried thyme

1 tsp ground black pepper

¾ tsp ground allspice

4 scallions, thinly sliced

¾ tsp salt

2 tsp dark brown sugar

4 Tbsp red wine vinegar

2 Tbsp dijon mustard

1 lb (500 g) boneless, skinless chicken breasts

1 Tbsp olive oil

2 cups pineapple chunks

4 kiwi, peeled and cut into wedges

1 large red bell pepper, cut into matchsticks

1 cup jicama matchsticks

1. In large bowl, stir together garlic, thyme, black pepper, allspice, half the scallions, and ½ tsp salt. Stir in brown sugar, 2 Tbsp vinegar, and 1 Tbsp mustard and mix well. Add chicken, rubbing mixture into chicken. Cover and set aside.

2. In separate bowl, whisk together oil and remaining 2 Tbsp vinegar, 1 Tbsp mustard, ¼ tsp salt. Add pineapple, kiwi, bell pepper, jicama, and remaining scallions. Toss to combine.

3. Preheat broiler. Broil chicken 6 in (15 cm) from heat for 4 minutes per side, or until cooked through. When cool enough to handle, slice chicken on diagonal. Add to bowl with salad and toss.

Per serving: 287 calories, 28 g protein, 31 g carbohydrates, 5.9 g fiber, 6 g total fat, 1 g saturated fat, 66 mg cholesterol, 701 mg sodium

WARM KASHA AND SEAFOOD SALAD

Serves 4

Prep Time: 15 minutes

Cook Time: 1 hour 15 minutes

Healing Foods: buckwheat, fish, cucumbers, peas, fennel, seaweed

Ailments It Heals: cancer, flatulence, sore throat

8 oz (250 g) kasha (toasted buckwheat)

2½ cups vegetable stock

3 Tbsp sunflower oil

2 Tbsp extra-virgin olive oil

1 Tbsp white wine vinegar

1 tsp dijon mustard

2 Tbsp chopped fresh mixed herbs, such as basil, marjoram, oregano, rosemary, sage, and thyme

14 oz (420 g) frozen mixed seafood, thawed

1 English cucumber, diced

7 oz (210 g) sugar snap peas, sliced

1 fennel bulb, about (8 oz or 250 g), halved and thinly sliced

4 oz (125 g) radishes, thinly sliced

1 sheet toasted nori

Salt and ground black pepper

1. Put kasha in nonstick saucepan, pour in stock, and bring to a boil. Cover and simmer for 5 minutes, or until kasha has absorbed the stock.

2. Stir in 2 Tbsp sunflower oil, cover, and cook for 10 minutes. Remove lid and fluff kasha with a fork, tossing and turning to separate grains. Cook over very low heat, uncovered, for 1 hour, tossing the kasha with a fork every 10 minutes to separate grains. When done, place in large salad bowl.

3. Meanwhile, in medium bowl, whisk together olive oil, vinegar, mustard, and mixed herbs until thoroughly mixed.

4. Heat remaining 1 Tbsp sunflower oil in wok or large frying pan. Add seafood and stir-fry over medium heat for 2 to 3 minutes, or until hot. Add hot seafood to kasha together with cucumber, sugar snap peas, fennel, and radishes. Drizzle dressing over top and toss gently to mix.

5. Snip nori into fine strips with scissors, sprinkle over salad, and serve immediately.

Per serving: 500 calories, 27 g protein, 56 g carbohydrates, 10 g fiber, 20 g total fat, 3 g saturated fat, 135 mg cholesterol, 682 mg sodium

GRILLED SALMON SALAD

Serves 4
Prep Time: 30 minutes plus marinating
Cook Time: 5 minutes
Healing Foods: cardamom, fish, salad greens, mangoes, papayas, oranges
Ailments It Heals: acne, cholesterol (high), psoriasis

  8 cardamom pods, crushed
  1 tsp cumin seeds
Finely grated zest and juice of 1 lime
Juice of 1 large orange
  1 Tbsp light soy sauce
  1 Tbsp honey
Salt and ground black pepper

  4 pieces (4 oz or 125 g each) skinless salmon fillet
  4 cups mixed salad leaves, such as oak leaf, red leaf lettuce, and baby chard, or use romaine
  1 mango, peeled and cut into 1-in (2.5 cm) cubes
  1 papaya, peeled, seeded, and cut into 1-in (2.5 cm) cubes
  1 orange, peeled and segmented

1. Heat small nonstick skillet over medium heat. Scrape seeds from cardamom pods and add to hot pan with cumin seeds. Toast for a few seconds to release aromas and remove seeds to shallow nonmetallic dish.

2. Add lime zest and juice, orange juice, soy sauce, and honey to seeds. Season lightly with salt and pepper. Lay salmon pieces in dish and turn to coat both sides. Cover and let marinate for 30 minutes.

3. Preheat grill or oven broiler. Lift salmon out of marinade, place on grill rack or broiler pan, and grill or broil for 4 to 5 minutes on one side only. The fillets should still be slightly translucent in the center. Meanwhile, pour marinade into small saucepan and bring just to a boil.

4. Arrange salad leaves in middle of 4 plates. Scatter mango and papaya cubes and orange segments over salad. Place cooked salmon on top of salad and drizzle with warm marinade. Serve immediately.

Per serving: 313 calories, 26 g protein, 30 g carbohydrates, 4 g fiber, 10 g total fat, 2 g saturated fat, 77 mg cholesterol, 223 mg sodium

TOSSED TUNA SALAD NIÇOISE

Serves 4
Prep Time: 15 minutes
Cook Time: 20 minutes
Healing Foods: potatoes, lemons, green beans, fish, tomatoes, salad greens
Ailments It Heals: Alzheimer's disease, hives, hyperthyroidism, mood disorders

1   lb (500 g) small red-skinned potatoes, cut into eighths
⅓   cup fresh lemon juice
2   Tbsp olive oil
2   Tbsp dijon mustard
½   tsp salt
12   oz (375 g) green beans, cut into 2-in (5 cm) lengths
2   tuna steaks (1 in or 2.5 cm thick, 1½ lb or 750 g total)
½   tsp ground black pepper
1   pint cherry tomatoes, halved
1   bunch watercress, tough stems trimmed
1   belgian endive, cut crosswise into ½-in (1 cm) slices

1. In large pot of boiling water, cook potatoes for 10 minutes, or until tender. Drain.

2. Meanwhile, in large bowl, whisk together lemon juice, oil, mustard, and ¼ tsp salt. Add potatoes while still warm, tossing to coat.

3. In vegetable steamer, steam green beans for 4 minutes, or until crisp-tender. Add to bowl with potatoes and toss to combine.

4. Meanwhile, preheat broiler. Place tuna on broiler pan and sprinkle with pepper and remaining ¼ tsp salt. Broil 6 in (15 cm) from heat for 3 minutes per side for medium-rare.

5. Add tomatoes, watercress, and endive to bowl,

tossing well. To serve, slice tuna and place on top.

Per serving: 427 calories, 41 g protein, 32 g carbohydrates, 6 g fiber, 15 g total fat, 3 g saturated fat, 58 mg cholesterol, 566 mg sodium

TUNA AND CANNELLINI SALAD WITH LEMON

Serves 4
Prep Time: 25 minutes
Healing Foods: beans, fish, lemons, salad greens, tomatoes
Ailments It Heals: depression, cholesterol (high), PCOS

DRESSING

3   Tbsp lemon juice
1   clove garlic, minced
¼   tsp salt, or to taste
⅛   tsp crushed red-pepper flakes
¼   cup extra-virgin olive oil
Ground black pepper

SALAD

19   oz (540 mL) cannellini beans, drained and rinsed
6   oz (175 g) water-packed chunk light tuna, drained and flaked
⅓   cup finely diced red onion
2   tsp chopped fresh rosemary
1½ tsp freshly grated lemon zest
6   cups arugula, washed, dried, and torn into bite-size pieces
1   cup cherry tomatoes, quartered

1. In small bowl, combine lemon juice, garlic, salt, and red pepper. Gradually whisk in the oil. Season to taste with pepper.

2. To make the salad: In medium bowl, combine beans, tuna, onion, rosemary, and lemon zest. Add ¼ cup dressing (save remaining dressing for the arugula). Toss to coat well. (The tuna-bean salad will keep, covered, in the refrigerator for up to 1 day.)

3. Just before serving, place arugula in large bowl. Add reserved dressing and toss to coat well. Divide arugula mixture among 4 plates. Top with tuna-bean salad and garnish with cherry tomatoes. One serving is 2/3 cup tuna-bean salad and 1½ cups arugula.

Per serving: 305 calories, 18 g protein, 25 g carbohydrates, 7 g fiber, 15 g total fat, 2 g saturated fat, 26 mg cholesterol, 500 mg sodium

SHRIMP AND YUCCA SALAD

Serves 4
Prep Time: 15 minutes
Cook Time: 15 minutes
Healing Foods: yucca, shrimp, garlic, green beans
Ailments It Heals: Alzheimer's disease, burns, cancer

1   bag (24 oz or 750 g) frozen yucca
1   Tbsp olive oil
1   lb (500 g) shrimp, peeled and deveined
2   cloves garlic, sliced thin
3   bunches scallions, cut into 1½-in (3.5 cm) pieces
½   lb (250 g) fresh string beans, steamed
Salt and ground black pepper

1. In large pot of boiling water, boil yucca for 10 minutes, or until soft. Do not overcook, or it will be mushy.

2. Remove and drain in colander. Cut into slices.

3. Heat large skillet or wok over high heat. When hot, add oil and coat pan. Add shrimp and cook, stirring, for 2 to 3 minutes, or until almost entirely pink. Add garlic and scallions and cook, stirring, for 2 minutes, or until scallions are bright green. Pour over yucca. Serve with string beans. Season to taste with salt and pepper.

Per serving: 429 calories, 19 g protein, 74 g carbohydrates, 5 g fiber, 6 g total fat, 1 g saturated fat, 143 mg cholesterol, 661 mg sodium

SHELLFISH SALAD WITH HERBED LEMON DRESSING

Serves 4
Prep Time: 15 minutes
Cook Time: 11 minutes
Healing Foods: shellfish, lemons, mustard, celery, peppers
Ailments It Heals: burns, halitosis, shingles

1   cup dry white wine
1   tsp dried tarragon
½   tsp dried oregano
1   dozen littleneck clams, well scrubbed
12 oz (375 g) large shrimp, shelled and deveined
8   oz (250 g) sea scallops, halved horizontally
½   cup fresh lemon juice
1   Tbsp olive oil
1½ tsp dijon mustard
2   celery stalks, halved lengthwise and cut crosswise into ¼-in (0.5 cm) slices
2   red bell peppers, diced
⅓   cup chopped parsley

1. In large saucepan, combine white wine, tarragon, and oregano and bring to a boil over high heat. Add clams, cover, and cook for 4 to 5 minutes, or until clams open (check after 3 minutes as some will open before others). Remove clams as they open (discard any that do not open). Reserve liquid in pan. When clams are cool enough to handle, remove clam meat and place in large bowl. Discard shells.

2. Heat liquid in pan over medium-low heat. Add shrimp and cook for 3 to 4 minutes, or until cooked through. With slotted spoon, remove shrimp, reserving liquid in pan. When shrimp are cool enough to handle, halve them horizontally and add to bowl with clams.

3. Heat liquid in pan over medium-low heat. Add scallops and cook for 2 minutes, or until cooked through. With slotted spoon, transfer scallops to bowl, reserving liquid in pan. Cool liquid to room temperature and measure out ½ cup.

4. In medium bowl, whisk together lemon juice, oil, mustard, and ½ cup reserved cooking liquid. Pour over shellfish. Add celery, bell peppers, and parsley and toss to combine. Chill salad until serving time.

Per serving: 208 calories, 30 g protein, 9 g carbohydrates, 1 g fiber, 6 g total fat, 1 g saturated fat, 138 mg cholesterol, 285 mg sodium

CRAB AND AVOCADO SALAD

Serves 6

Prep Time: 20 minutes

Cook Time: 15 minutes plus cooling

Healing Foods: bulgur, tomatoes, shellfish, avocados, apples, bean sprouts, lettuce

Ailments It Heals: atherosclerosis, chronic fatigue syndrome, menstrual problems

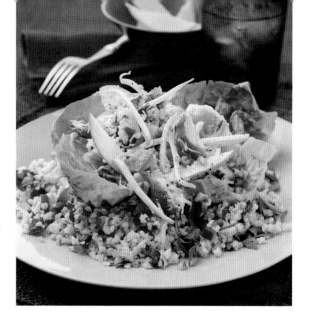

1	cup bulgur wheat
2½	cups boiling water
1	Tbsp olive oil
3	Tbsp chopped fresh flat-leaf parsley
1	Tbsp snipped fresh chives
2	medium tomatoes, diced
4	Tbsp lemon juice

Salt and ground black pepper

12	oz (375 g) fresh white crabmeat
2	avocados
2	crisp green apples
½	cup bean sprouts
3	Tbsp low-fat mayonnaise
3	Tbsp low-fat plain yogurt

Pinch of cayenne pepper

1	head butter (Bibb or Boston) lettuce, separated into leaves
¼	cup walnut halves, toasted and roughly chopped

1. Put bulgur wheat and boiling water in large saucepan. Bring to a boil over high heat, then reduce heat and simmer for 10 to 15 minutes, or until grains are just tender. Drain in a large sieve, pressing down well to squeeze out excess water. Let cool.

2. Combine oil, parsley, chives, diced tomatoes, and 3 Tbsp lemon juice in large mixing bowl. Add bulgur wheat and mix thoroughly, then season with salt and pepper to taste. Let stand at room temperature while preparing crab salad.

3. Pick over and flake crabmeat, discarding any fragments of shells. Place crabmeat in large bowl. Halve, pit, and peel avocados, then chop flesh and add to crab. Quarter and core apples, then thinly slice. Add apple slices and bean sprouts to crabmeat.

4. In small bowl, mix mayonnaise and yogurt until smooth. Add cayenne and remaining 1 Tbsp lemon juice and stir. Spoon into crab mixture and toss very gently until just combined.

5. Pile bulgur onto serving platter and arrange lettuce leaves on top. Spoon crab salad onto leaves and scatter walnuts over top. Serve immediately.

Per serving: 341 calories, 18 g protein, 39 g carbohydrates, 10 g fiber, 15 g total fat, 2 g saturated fat, 57 mg cholesterol, 254 mg sodium

LOBSTER SALAD WITH LIME DRESSING

Serves 4
Prep Time: 20 minutes
Cook Time: 15 minutes
Healing Foods: potatoes, peas, grapes, salad greens, lobster
Ailments It Heals: cardiovascular disease, depression, varicose veins, yeast infections

- ½ lb (250 g) baby red-skinned new potatoes, scrubbed
- 2 Tbsp low-fat mayonnaise
- 2 Tbsp low-fat plain yogurt
- Finely grated zest of 1 lime
- Salt and ground black pepper
- 2 small shallots, thinly sliced
- ½ cup snow peas, sliced
- ½ cup halved seedless red grapes
- ½ cup halved seedless green grapes
- 2 cups arugula, washed
- 1 cup watercress, washed
- 1 lb (500 g) cooked lobster meat

1. Put potatoes in a saucepan and cover with boiling water. Cook over medium-high heat for 15 minutes, or until just tender. Drain and leave to cool, then cut potatoes in half. Place in large bowl.

2. While potatoes are cooling, mix together mayonnaise, yogurt, and lime zest, and season with salt and pepper to taste.

3. Toss potatoes with shallots, snow peas, grapes, and lime dressing.

4. Arrange arugula on 4 large plates, and add watercress and potato salad. Scatter lobster on top.

Per serving: 219 calories, 26 g protein, 25 g carbohydrates, 2 g fiber, 2 g total fat, 0 g saturated fat, 81 mg cholesterol, 518 mg sodium

BARLEY AND BEET SALAD

Serves 5
Prep Time: 15 minutes
Cook Time: 45 minutes
Healing Foods: barley, olive oil, beets, dill
Ailments It Heals: AIDS and HIV infection, diabetes, gallstones

- 2½ cups water
- ½ cup pearl barley
- ½ tsp salt
- ⅓ cup extra-virgin olive oil
- 3 Tbsp red wine vinegar
- Ground black pepper to taste
- 1½ cups (8 oz or 250 g) diced cooked beets
- ½ cup chopped scallions
- ½ cup crumbled feta cheese
- 3 Tbsp chopped fresh dill

1. In small saucepan, combine water, barley, and ¼ tsp salt. Cover and simmer over medium-low heat for 40 to 45 minutes, or until tender. Transfer to large bowl and let cool.

2. In small bowl, whisk oil, vinegar, remaining ¼ tsp salt, and pepper. Add to barley along with beets, scallions, cheese, and dill. Toss to coat.

Per serving: 273 calories, 5 g protein, 23 g carbohydrates, 4 g fiber, 18 g total fat, 4 g saturated fat, 13 mg cholesterol, 444 mg sodium

BROCCOLI AND PEARL BARLEY SALAD

Serves 4
Prep Time: 15 minutes plus cooling
Cook Time: 30 minutes
Healing Foods: barley, broccoli, zucchini, peas, apricots, seeds
Ailments It Heals: hemorrhoids, hypoglycemia, lactose intolerance, obesity

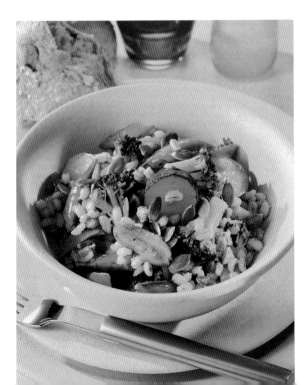

Spicy tomato dressing
- 3 Tbsp extra-virgin olive oil
- 1 Tbsp tomato paste

Juice of 1 lime
- 2 tsp ground cumin

Dash of Tabasco sauce
- 1 clove garlic, crushed
- 2 Tbsp chopped fresh coriander or flat-leaf parsley (optional)

Salad
- ⅔ cup pearl barley
- 3 cups cold water
- 7 oz (200 g) broccoli, cut into small florets
- 3 zucchini, thickly sliced
- 3.5 oz (100 g) sugar snap peas, halved
- ¼ cup dried apricots, thinly sliced

Salt and ground black pepper
- ¼ cup pepitas (pumpkin seeds)

1. In large bowl, whisk together oil, tomato paste, lime juice, cumin, Tabasco, garlic, and coriander or parsley, if using. Set dressing aside.

2. Rinse barley in one or two changes of water—do this in a bowl, swirling grains with your fingers and pouring off cloudy water. Drain barley in a sieve, then place in saucepan and pour in 3 cups water. Bring to a boil, then reduce heat and cover. Simmer very gently for 30 minutes, or until most of the water has been absorbed and grains are tender but still firm. Drain well.

3. While barley is cooking, bring a second pan of water to a boil. Add broccoli, zucchini, and peas and bring to a boil. Reduce heat and simmer for 3 to 4 minutes, or until just tender but still crisp. Drain well and rinse briefly with cold water to refresh and stop the cooking.

4. Stir apricots into dressing. Add barley and vegetables to dressing as soon as they are cooked, and mix well to coat. Check the seasoning, then cover and allow to cool until just warm.

5. Add pepitas to salad just before serving, warm or cold.

WHEAT BERRY SALAD WITH DRIED APRICOTS

Serves 6
Prep Time: 25 minutes
Cook Time: 1 hour 45 minutes
Healing Foods: wheat, apricots, olive oil, mint, almonds
Ailments It Heals: atherosclerosis, diabetes, nail problems

- ¾ cup hard wheat berries or spelt berries, rinsed
- ½ cup dried apricots, diced
- ¼ cup extra-virgin olive oil
- 3 Tbsp orange juice
- 2 Tbsp lemon juice
- ½ tsp honey
- ½ tsp ground cinnamon
- 1 clove garlic, minced
- ½ tsp salt, or to taste
- Ground black pepper to taste
- ½ cup chopped scallions
- ⅓ cup chopped fresh mint
- ⅓ cup slivered almonds or chopped peeled pistachios, toasted

1. In large saucepan, place wheat berries and cover generously with water. Bring to a simmer over medium-high heat. Reduce heat to medium-low, partially cover, and cook until wheat berries are tender, 1½ to 1¾ hours. (Add more water, if necessary.) Drain and rinse with cold running water.

2. Meanwhile, place apricots in small bowl. Cover with boiling water and let soak for 5 to 10 minutes. Drain.

3. In medium bowl or jar with tight-fitting lid, combine oil, orange juice, lemon juice, honey, cinnamon, garlic, salt, and pepper. Whisk or shake to blend.

4. In large bowl, combine wheat berries, apricots, scallions, and mint. Add orange juice dressing and toss to coat well. Just before serving, sprinkle with nuts. The salad will keep, covered, in the refrigerator for up to 2 days.

Per serving: 262 calories, 6 g protein, 32 g carbohydrates, 5 g fiber, 13 g total fat, 2 g saturated fat, 0 mg cholesterol, 200 mg sodium

ASIAN NOODLE SALAD

Serves 6
Prep Time: 15 minutes
Cook Time: 10 minutes
Healing Foods: wheat, peas, carrots, basil, peppers, peanuts
Ailments It Heals: anorexia, blood pressure, cirrhosis, eye problems

- 12 oz (375 g) whole wheat linguine
- ½ lb (250 g) snow peas, halved lengthwise
- 3 medium carrots, peeled, cut into 2-in (5 cm) lengths, and cut lengthwise into thin slices
- 2 cups packed fresh basil leaves
- ½ cup packed fresh mint leaves
- ¼ cup packed fresh cilantro leaves
- 2 cloves garlic
- 2 Tbsp dark sesame oil
- 1 Tbsp vegetable oil
- ¼ tsp red-pepper flakes
- ½ tsp salt

1 red bell pepper, seeded and cut into slivers
3 scallions, finely chopped
2 Tbsp chopped unsalted dry-roasted peanuts

1. Cook linguine in large pot of lightly salted boiling water until tender, following package directions. For last 2 minutes of cooking, add snow peas and carrots. Drain in colander. Rinse under cold running water. Drain well.

2. Meanwhile, in small food processor, combine basil, mint, cilantro, garlic, oils, pepper flakes, and ¼ tsp salt. Pulse until a paste forms.

3. In large bowl, combine linguine, snow peas, carrots, bell pepper, scallions, basil mixture, and remaining ¼ tsp salt. Serve at room temperature or chilled. Garnish with peanuts.

Per serving: 321 calories, 12 g protein, 52 g carbohydrates, 11 g fiber, 10 g total fat, 1 g saturated fat, 0 mg cholesterol, 355 mg sodium

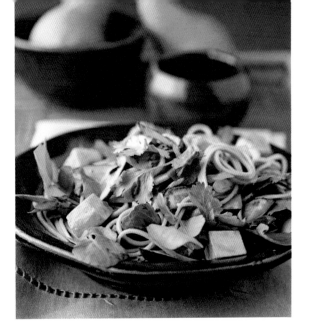

BUCKWHEAT NOODLES WITH TOFU AND GREEN VEGETABLES

Serves 4
Prep Time: 15 minutes
Cook Time: 15 minutes
Healing Foods: garlic, zucchini, tofu, buckwheat, salad greens
Ailments It Heals: atherosclerosis, diabetes, memory loss, menopause, menstrual problems, osteoporosis

1 Tbsp vegetable oil
4 scallions, chopped
4 cloves garlic, minced
1 medium zucchini, halved lengthwise and cut crosswise into ¼-in-thick (0.5 cm) slices
½ cup vegetable broth or reduced-sodium, fat-free chicken broth
2 Tbsp reduced-sodium soy sauce
2 tsp cornstarch
1 tsp dark sesame oil
6 oz (175 g) extra-firm tofu, cut in cubes
6 oz (175 g) buckwheat (soba) noodles
1 cup packed watercress, tough stems removed
2 Tbsp chopped cilantro
½ cup roasted unsalted soy nuts

1. In large nonstick skillet, heat oil over medium-high heat. Reserve some dark green parts of scallions for garnish. Add remaining scallions, garlic, and zucchini to skillet. Sauté for 5 minutes, or until softened.

2. In small bowl, whisk together broth, soy sauce, cornstarch, and sesame oil until smooth. Add to skillet along with tofu. Heat to a boil and cook, stirring constantly, for 1 to 2 minutes, or until sauce thickens. Remove from heat.

3. In large pot of lightly salted boiling water over medium-high heat, cook noodles until tender, following package directions. Reserve ¼ cup cooking liquid. Drain noodles and rinse under cold running water.

4. Combine noodles, zucchini-tofu mixture, reserved cooking liquid, watercress, and cilantro in large bowl. Toss gently. Divide into 4 portions. Garnish with reserved scallions, and soy nuts.

Per serving: 322 calories, 20 g protein, 45 g carbohydrates, 10 g fiber, 9 g total fat, 2 g saturated fat, 0 mg cholesterol, 647 mg sodium

RUSTIC GRILLED VEGETABLE AND RIGATONI SALAD

Serves 4

Prep Time: 15 minutes plus cooling and marinating

Cook Time: 27 minutes

Healing Foods: peppers, tomatoes, eggplant, vinegar, olive oil

Ailments It Heals: Alzheimer's disease, blood pressure, memory loss

- 8 oz (250 g) rigatoni
- 1 large red bell pepper, seeded and halved
- 2 medium tomatoes, cut into wedges
- 1 medium eggplant, trimmed and sliced lengthways
- 2 Tbsp balsamic vinegar or lemon juice
- 2 Tbsp olive oil
- 2 Tbsp chopped fresh basil
- 1 Tbsp chopped capers
- 1 large clove garlic, crushed (optional)
- ¼ cup grated parmesan cheese

Salt and ground black pepper

1. Cook rigatoni in boiling water for 10 to 12 minutes, or according to package directions, until al dente. Drain and rinse under cold running water, then drain thoroughly and set aside to cool.

2. Preheat broiler or grill to high. Broil or grill pepper halves, skin side up, for 5 to 10 minutes, or until blistered and blackened. Place in resealable plastic bag, then leave until cool enough to handle.

3. Broil or grill tomatoes and eggplant for 5 minutes, turning so that they cook evenly and removing pieces as they are ready. Place tomato wedges in large salad bowl. Set eggplant slices aside on plate to cool slightly.

4. Cut eggplant slices into 1-in (2.5 cm) strips and add to salad bowl. Peel peppers and cut into 1-in (2.5 cm) strips, then add to bowl. Mix in pasta.

5. In small bowl, mix vinegar or lemon juice, oil, basil, capers, garlic (if using), and cheese. Lightly toss with salad. Season lightly with salt and pepper. Set salad aside to marinate for about 30 minutes so that the flavors can infuse before serving.

Per serving: 242 calories, 8 g protein, 38 g carbohydrates, 4 g fiber, 7 g total fat, 2 g saturated fat, 5 mg cholesterol, 137 mg sodium

SICILIAN PASTA SALAD

Serves 4
Prep Time: 15 minutes
Cook Time: 10 minutes
Healing Foods: lemons, fennel, raisins, fish
Ailments It Heals: halitosis, lactose intolerance, menstrual problems

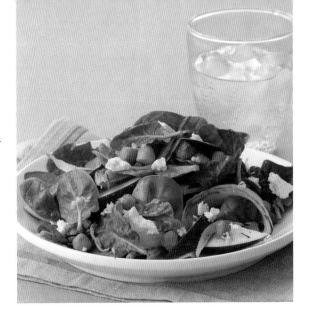

8 oz (250 g) medium pasta shells
½ cup fresh lemon juice
3 Tbsp tomato paste
1 tsp fennel seeds
½ tsp salt
1 fennel bulb, stalks removed (fronds reserved), bulb cut into ½-in (1 cm) chunks
⅓ cup raisins
13.5 oz (400 g) sardines packed in oil, drained

1. In large pot of boiling water, cook pasta according to package directions. Drain, reserving ½ cup of pasta cooking liquid.

2. Meanwhile, in large bowl, whisk together lemon juice, tomato paste, fennel seeds, and salt. Whisk in the reserved pasta liquid.

3. Add drained pasta, fennel chunks, and raisins to bowl and toss well.

4. Mince enough reserved fennel fronds to get ½ cup. Add minced fronds and sardines to bowl, and toss gently to combine. Serve at room temperature or chilled.

Per serving: 452 calories, 29 g protein, 61 g carbohydrates, 15 g fiber, 10 g total fat, 1 g saturated fat, 114 mg cholesterol, 830 mg sodium

SPINACH SALAD WITH CHICKPEAS

Serves 4
Prep Time: 10 minutes
Cook Time: 20 minutes
Healing Foods: onions, chickpeas, flax, spinach, apples
Ailments It Heals: eye problems, menopause, obesity, psoriasis, stroke

2 medium onions, cut into ½-in (1 cm) slices
15 oz (425 mL) chickpeas, drained, rinsed, and patted dry
¼ cup lemon juice
2 Tbsp flaxseed oil
1 Tbsp olive oil
1 clove garlic, minced
½ tsp salt
½ cup crumbled feta cheese
5 oz (150 g) baby spinach
2 apples, cored and sliced
2 Tbsp ground flaxseed

1. Preheat oven to 400°F (200°C). Coat baking sheet with sides with olive oil cooking spray. Add onion slices and coat each with spray. Roast for 10 minutes. Add chickpeas and roast for 10 minutes, or until onions are tender and browned.

2. Meanwhile, in measuring cup, whisk together lemon juice, oils, garlic, and salt. Stir in cheese.

3. Place spinach in large bowl and toss with onions, chickpeas, apples, and flaxseed. Drizzle with the vinaigrette.

Per serving: 292 calories, 9 g protein, 37 g carbohydrates, 10 g fiber, 14 g total fat, 3 g saturated fat, 8 mg cholesterol, 476 mg sodium

THREE-BEAN SALAD WITH MANCHEGO CHEESE

Serves 4

Prep Time: 15 minutes

Cook Time: 5 minutes

Healing Foods: peppers, green beans, corn, beans, cheese

Ailments It Heals: depression, diverticulitis, hemorrhoids

¼ cup red wine vinegar

2 Tbsp olive oil

1 Tbsp honey

1 chipotle pepper in adobo, finely chopped (2 tsp)

Salt to taste

12 oz (375 g) green beans, halved

1 cup frozen corn kernels

15 oz (425 mL) black beans, drained and rinsed

15 oz (425 mL) red kidney beans, drained and rinsed

1 celery stalk, diced

⅓ cup finely chopped red onion

4 oz (125 g) manchego or monterey jack cheese, cut into ¼-in-wide (0.5 cm) matchsticks

1. In large bowl, whisk together vinegar, oil, honey, chipotle, and salt.

2. Meanwhile, in large vegetable steamer, steam green beans for 5 minutes, or until crisp-tender. Add corn during the final minute of steaming. Transfer hot vegetables to bowl with dressing and toss to coat.

3. Add black beans, kidney beans, celery, onion, and cheese and toss to combine. Serve at room temperature or chilled.

Per serving: 404 calories, 20 g protein, 43 g carbohydrates, 10 g fiber, 18 g total fat, 8 g saturated fat, 30 mg cholesterol, 510 mg sodium

AVOCADO, JICAMA, AND ORANGE SALAD

Serves 6

Prep Time: 15 minutes plus chilling

Healing Foods: jicama, oranges, avocados, lettuce

Ailments It Heals: acne, diabetes, muscle cramps, psoriasis

3 Tbsp olive oil

1 Tbsp fresh-squeezed lime juice

1 clove garlic, minced

1½ tsp white wine vinegar

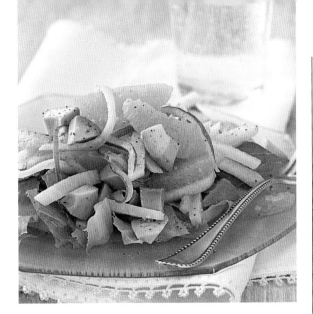

1/4 tsp ground cumin

1/8 tsp salt

Pinch of chili powder

8 oz (250 g) jicama, peeled and cut into 3 x 1/4-in (7.5 x 0.5 cm) strips

2 oranges, peeled and cut into sections

1 avocado, peeled, pitted, and cut into chunks

1/2 small red onion, thinly sliced crosswise

8 cups torn romaine lettuce

1. In small bowl, whisk together oil, lime juice, garlic, vinegar, cumin, salt, and chili powder to make vinaigrette.

2. In large bowl, toss together jicama, oranges, avocado, onion, and vinaigrette. Refrigerate for 15 minutes.

3. Serve salad on bed of romaine leaves.

Per serving: 156 calories, 3 g protein, 14 g carbohydrates, 7 g fiber, 12 g total fat, 2 g saturated fat, 0 mg cholesterol, 57 mg sodium

BROCCOLI SALAD WITH ALMONDS AND DRIED CRANBERRIES

Serves 6

Prep Time: 20 minutes

Healing Foods: vinegar, flax, broccoli, almonds, cranberries, cheese

Ailments It Heals: herpes, obesity, prostate problems

1/4 cup balsamic vinegar

2 Tbsp dijon mustard

2 Tbsp honey

1/4 tsp salt

1/4 tsp ground black pepper

2 Tbsp flaxseed oil

2 Tbsp extra-virgin olive oil

2 heads broccoli

1 small red onion, cut into thin wedges

1/2 cup whole almonds, toasted and coarsely chopped

1/2 cup dried cranberries

4 oz (125 g) chèvre goat cheese, crumbled

1. In large bowl, whisk together vinegar, mustard, honey, salt, and pepper. Whisk in oils until well blended. Set aside.

2. Remove florets from broccoli and add to bowl with vinaigrette. Trim ends of broccoli stalks and, with a vegetable peeler, peel off the thick outer layer. Shred stalks with a food processor or by hand.

3. Add shredded stalks, onion, almonds, and cranberries to bowl and toss to coat well. Top with cheese.

Per serving: 333 calories, 12 g protein, 33 g carbohydrates, 7 g fiber, 20 g total fat, 4 g saturated fat, 9 mg cholesterol, 303 mg sodium

CAULIFLOWER SALAD WITH CASHEWS

Serves 4

Prep Time: 15 minutes plus marinating

Cook Time: 5 minutes

Healing Foods: cauliflower, nuts and seeds, bananas, persimmons

Ailments It Heals: blood pressure, bulimia, irritable bowel syndrome, muscle cramps, prostate problems

10	oz (300 g) tiny cauliflower florets
⅓	cup cashew nuts, roughly chopped
1	tsp cumin seeds
2	Tbsp fresh thyme leaves
2	bananas

Juice of ½ lemon

1	Tbsp olive oil
3	persimmons, peeled and cut into small chunks
⅓	cup snipped fresh chives

Fresh thyme sprigs

1. Bring saucepan of water to a boil, add cauliflower, and bring back to a full rolling boil. Drain immediately in a colander and refresh under cold running water. Leave to drain thoroughly.

2. In heavy-bottom frying pan, roast cashews with cumin seeds and thyme for 30 to 60 seconds, or until cashews are lightly browned. Place in bowl and set aside to cool.

3. Slice bananas. Put in large bowl, add lemon juice, and toss to coat. Add cauliflower, nut mixture, and oil. Toss gently to mix.

4. Add persimmons and chives to bowl and fold in. Cover bowl with plastic wrap and let marinate for 15 to 30 minutes.

5. Spoon salad into shallow serving dish and garnish with thyme sprigs.

Per serving: 200 calories, 4 g protein, 30 g carbohydrates, 4 g fiber, 9 g total fat, 2 g saturated fat, 0 mg cholesterol, 24 mg sodium

FRUIT SALAD WITH SPICED COCONUT

Serves 6

Prep Time: 20 minutes plus chilling

Healing Foods: mangoes, cherries, grapes, strawberries, apricots, coconuts

Ailments It Heals: anorexia, constipation, eczema, PCOS

1	large mango, peeled and sliced
8	oz (250 g) cherries, pitted
3.5	oz (100 g) seedless green grapes
8	oz (250 g) strawberries, hulled and cut in half
3	large apricots, halved, stoned, and sliced
¾	cup unsweetened desiccated coconut
1	Tbsp sugar

Pinch of cayenne pepper

Pinch of mustard powder

1. In large serving bowl, place mango, cherries, grapes, strawberries, and apricots.

2. Finely grind the coconut in spice mill or with mortar and pestle. Add sugar, cayenne pepper, and mustard powder and mix well.

3. Add spiced coconut mixture to fruit and stir well to combine. Cover and refrigerate at least 2 hours, or overnight if time permits, to allow flavors to blend and develop.

Per serving: 181 calories, 2 g protein, 28 g carbohydrates, 4 g fiber, 8 g total fat, 6 g saturated fat, 0 mg cholesterol, 4 mg sodium

ENDIVE, APPLE, AND WATERCRESS SALAD

Serves 6

Prep Time: 10 minutes

Healing Foods: yogurt, salad greens, apples, almonds

Ailments It Heals: blood pressure, cancer, depression, fibroids, sex drive (diminished)

⅓ cup low-fat plain yogurt
1 Tbsp reduced-fat mayonnaise
2 tsp honey
1 tsp Dijon mustard
¼ tsp curry powder
⅛ tsp ground ginger
1 bunch watercress, tough stems removed
1 large endive, halved lengthwise and cut crosswise into ½-in-thick (1 cm) slices
1 McIntosh apple, halved, cored, and thinly sliced
2 Tbsp sliced or slivered almonds, toasted

1. In small bowl, whisk together yogurt, mayonnaise, honey, mustard, curry powder, and ginger to make dressing.

2. In large bowl, toss together watercress, endive, apple, and dressing. Top with almonds.

Per serving: 54 calories, 2 g protein, 8 g carbohydrates, 1 g fiber, 2 g total fat, 0 g saturated fat, 2 mg cholesterol, 62 mg sodium

MEDITERRANEAN SALAD WITH EDAMAME

Serves 8

Prep Time: 25 minutes

Cook Time: 4 minutes

Healing Foods: edamame, garlic, lettuce, tomatoes, olives, cheese

Ailments It Heals: atherosclerosis, Alzheimer's disease, hyperthyroidism, menopause, stroke

1 cup frozen shelled edamame beans
⅓ cup extra-virgin olive oil
3 Tbsp lemon juice
2 cloves garlic, minced
Salt to taste
¼ tsp sugar
Ground black pepper to taste
2 cups shredded romaine lettuce
2 cups cherry tomatoes, halved
1 cup sliced English cucumber
⅔ cup chopped scallions
½ cup pitted kalamata olives, halved
½ cup fresh mint leaves, washed, dried, and torn into ½-in (1 cm) pieces
½ cup fresh flat-leaf parsley leaves, washed, dried, and torn into ½-in (1 cm) pieces
1 cup crumbled feta cheese

1. Bring large saucepan of lightly salted water to a boil. Add edamame beans and cook, covered, over medium heat for 3 to 4 minutes, or until tender. Drain and rinse with cold running water.

2. In screw-top jar with tight-fitting lid, combine oil, lemon juice, garlic, salt, sugar, and pepper. Shake to blend.

3. In large bowl, combine lettuce, tomatoes, cucumber, scallions, olives, mint, parsley, and edamame beans. Just before serving, drizzle lemon dressing over salad and toss to coat well. Sprinkle each serving with cheese.

Per serving: 220 calories, 7 g protein, 10 g carbohydrates, 3 g fiber, 17 g total fat, 5 g saturated fat, 15 mg cholesterol, 427 mg sodium

PAPAYA AND AVOCADO SALAD

Serves 4
Prep Time: 15 minutes
Cook Time: 1 minute
Healing Foods: peppers, avocados, papayas, olive oil, seeds
Ailments It Heals: cirrhosis, diabetes, gallstones, hypothyroidism, multiple sclerosis

Salad

1 romaine lettuce head
2 scallions, thinly sliced
1 large orange or yellow bell pepper, seeded and cut into thin strips
1 medium avocado, peeled, pitted, and cut into 1-in (2.5 cm) slices
1 medium papaya, peeled, seeded, and cut into 1-in (2.5 cm) slices
Juice of 1 lime
1½ Tbsp olive oil
¼ tsp paprika
⅛ tsp ground cumin
1 tsp light brown sugar
4 Tbsp pumpkin seeds

1. Shred lettuce leaves and place in large shallow dish or on 4 individual dishes. Sprinkle scallions over lettuce.

2. Arrange peppers over lettuce. Scatter avocado and papaya over pepper.

3. In small bowl, whisk together lime juice, oil, paprika, cumin, and sugar. Pour over salad.

4. Heat small heavy saucepan over medium heat and add pumpkin seeds. Stir for 1 minute, or until lightly toasted. Sprinkle seeds over salad and serve.

Per serving: 242 calories, 8 g protein, 19 g carbohydrates, 5 g fiber, 17 g total fat, 3 g saturated fat, 0 mg cholesterol, 18 mg sodium

POTATO SALAD WITH SUN-DRIED TOMATOES, SCALLIONS, AND BASIL

Serves 6
Prep Time: 10 minutes
Cook Time: 15 minutes
Healing Foods: potatoes, onions, tomatoes
Ailments It Heals: jet lag, menstrual problems, prostate problems

1½ lb (750 g) small red potatoes, unpeeled and halved
2 Tbsp reduced-fat mayonnaise
2 tsp dijon mustard
¼ cup low-fat buttermilk
2 scallions, thinly sliced
¼ cup chopped sun-dried tomatoes (not oil-packed)

8 basil leaves, shredded or finely chopped

½ tsp salt

¼ tsp ground black pepper

1. In large pot of lightly salted boiling water, cook potatoes over medium-high heat for 10 to 15 minutes, or until tender. Drain well.

2. In small bowl, stir together mayonnaise and mustard. Stir in buttermilk.

3. In large bowl, combine potatoes, scallions, sundried tomatoes, basil, salt, and pepper. Add buttermilk dressing. Toss to coat.

Per serving: 103 calories, 4 g protein, 17 g carbohydrates, 3 g fiber, 2 g total fat, 0 g saturated fat, 2 mg cholesterol, 340 mg sodium

ROMAINE LETTUCE WITH CHUNKY TOMATO VINAIGRETTE

Serves 6

Prep Time: 12 minutes

Healing Foods: tomatoes, basil, olive oil, lettuce, cheese

Ailments It Heals: gout, osteoporosis, prostate problems, urinary tract infections

2 large ripe tomatoes, halved, seeded, and coarsely chopped

⅓ cup loosely packed fresh basil leaves

2 Tbsp ketchup

2 Tbsp olive oil

1 Tbsp balsamic vinegar

1 small clove garlic, minced

½ tsp salt

1 large head romaine lettuce, torn into bite-size pieces

¼ cup crumbled feta cheese

1. In food processor, combine tomatoes, basil, ketchup, oil, vinegar, garlic, and salt to make vinaigrette. Pulse until blended but still chunky.

2. In large bowl, toss romaine with vinaigrette. Sprinkle with cheese. Serve at once.

Per serving: 82 calories, 3 g protein, 5 g carbohydrates, 2 g fiber, 6 g total fat, 2 g saturated fat, 6 mg cholesterol, 237 mg sodium

SPINACH, SWEET POTATO, AND SHIITAKE SALAD

Serves 4

Prep Time: 10 minutes

Cook Time: 30 minutes

Healing Foods: sweet potatoes, nuts, olive oil, mushrooms, spinach

Ailments It Heals: alcoholism, depression, hypothyroidism, memory loss

1 lb (500 g) sweet potatoes, peeled, halved lengthwise, and cut crosswise into ½-in (1 cm) slices

⅓ cup walnuts

1 Tbsp plus 4 tsp olive oil

2 cloves garlic, slivered

12 oz (375 g) fresh shiitake mushrooms, stems discarded and caps thickly sliced

½ tsp salt

12 cups spinach leaves

½ cup red wine vinegar

1 Tbsp dijon mustard

1. Preheat oven to 400°F (200°C). Place sweet potatoes on lightly oiled baking sheet and bake for 15 to 20 minutes, or until tender. Toast walnuts in separate pan in oven for 5 to 7 minutes, or until crisp. When cool enough to handle, coarsely chop nuts.

2. In large skillet, heat 1 Tbsp oil over medium heat. Add garlic and cook for 30 seconds, or until fragrant.

3. Add half the mushrooms, sprinkle with ¼ tsp salt, and cook for 4 minutes, or until they begin to soften. Add remaining mushrooms and ¼ tsp salt, and cook for 5 minutes, or until mushrooms are tender.

4. Place spinach in large bowl. Add sweet potatoes and walnuts. Remove mushrooms from skillet with slotted spoon and add to bowl.

5. In same s til warm. Pour dressing over salad and toss to combine.

Per serving: 283 calories, 9 g protein, 32 g carbohydrates, 8 g fiber, 15 g total fat, 2 g saturated fat, 0 mg cholesterol, 524 mg sodium

- 3 Tbsp olive oil
- 2 Tbsp fresh-squeezed lemon juice
- ¼ tsp salt
- ¼ tsp ground black pepper
- 1 small watermelon (about 1 lb or 500 g)
- 2 large nectarines or peaches
- 6 cups mixed salad greens, including arugula, endive, and leaf lettuce
- 1 cup crumbled feta cheese
- 2 Tbsp toasted pumpkin seeds or sunflower seeds

WATERMELON AND FETA SALAD

Serves 4

Prep Time: 20 minutes

Healing Foods: watermelon, nectarines, salad greens, cheese, seeds

Ailments It Heals: bulimia, chronic fatigue syndrome, jet lag, prostate problems

1. In 2-cup jar or container with tight-fitting lid, place oil, lemon juice, salt, and pepper. Cover and shake until well blended.

2. Using serrated knife, cut watermelon into bite-size chunks, discarding rind and seeds. Toss into large salad bowl.

3. Cut nectarines in half (do not peel) and pit them. Place nectarines on cutting board, cut side down, and cut lengthwise into thin slices. Toss with watermelon. Tear salad greens into bite-size pieces, add to fruit, and toss to mix.

4. Crumble cheese over salad. Sprinkle seeds over top, drizzle with lemon dressing, and serve.

Per serving: 198 calories, 6 g protein, 13 g carbohydrates, 2 g fiber, 15 g total fat, 5 g saturated fat, 22 mg cholesterol, 386 mg sodium

CARAWAY-COATED PEPPER STEAK WITH CHERRY SAUCE

Serves 4

Prep Time: 20 minutes
Cook Time: 20 minutes
Healing Foods: seeds, beef, cherries
Ailments It Heals: anemia, shingles, yeast infections

1 Tbsp coarsely cracked black peppercorns
2 tsp caraway seeds
4 lean sirloin steaks (about 4 oz or 125 g each)
1 Tbsp olive oil
1 medium red onion, finely chopped
1 cup dry red wine
20 oz (600 g) frozen pitted sweet cherries, thawed, drained, and coarsely chopped
2 tsp dijon mustard
1 Tbsp red wine vinegar
½ tsp salt
¼ tsp ground ginger
¼ cup chopped parsley

1. In shallow bowl, combine peppercorns and caraway seeds. Dip steaks in spice mixture, pressing it into both sides.

2. In large nonstick skillet, heat oil over medium heat. Add steaks and cook for 3 minutes per side for medium-rare. Transfer steaks to platter and keep warm.

3. Add onion to skillet and sauté for 4 minutes, or until tender. Add wine, increase heat to high, and cook for 2 minutes. Stir in cherries, mustard, vinegar, salt, and ginger. Cook for 5 minutes, or until cherries are very tender.

4. Return steaks to skillet and cook for 1 minute per side to heat through. Transfer steaks to 4 plates. Stir parsley into sauce and spoon sauce over steaks.

Per serving: 351 calories, 27 g protein, 30 g carbohydrate, 4 g fiber, 10 g total fat, 3 g saturated fat, 69 mg cholesterol, 425 mg sodium

FLANK STEAK ROLL WITH CARROTS AND RED PEPPERS

Serves 6

Prep Time: 15 minutes plus marinating and standing
Cook Time: 40 minutes
Healing Foods: beef, spinach, onions, carrots, peppers
Ailments It Heals: hepatitis, memory loss, obesity

½ cup red wine
⅓ cup reduced-sodium soy sauce
2 Tbsp sugar
1 tsp garlic powder
1½ lb flank steak, butterflied
6 oz (175 g) fresh baby spinach leaves
4 scallions, coarsely chopped
⅛ tsp salt
2½ cups grated peeled carrots (1 lb or 500 g)
12 oz (375 g) roasted red peppers, drained

1. In large resealable plastic bag or container, combine red wine, soy sauce, sugar, and garlic powder. Add steak. Turn to coat. Refrigerate for at least 2 hours or up to 4 hours.

2. Meanwhile, rinse spinach and leave some water clinging to leaves. Place in large pot over medium

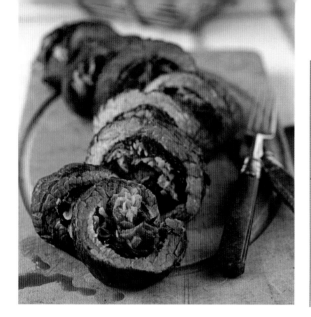

POT ROAST WITH ROOT VEGETABLES

Serves 6

Prep Time: 30 minutes

Cook Time: 3 hours 5 minutes plus resting

Healing Foods: beef, onions, potatoes, celeriac, turnips, carrots

Ailments It Heals: anemia, herpes, menstrual problems

heat. Cook, stirring often, for 1 minute, or just until wilted. Transfer to plate. Let cool.

3. Preheat oven to 375°F (190°C).

4. Remove meat from marinade. Pat dry and lay on work surface. Set marinade aside. Spread spinach in even layer over steak. Top with scallions. Sprinkle with salt. Layer carrots on top, then red peppers. Starting at one long side of steak, roll up meat tightly to enclose filling. Secure seam in several spots with wooden picks. Place roll, seam side down, in shallow baking pan. Brush top with marinade.

5. Roast for 15 minutes. Spoon any juices in pan over top of meat. Roast for 20 minutes longer for medium-rare, or until desired doneness. Let meat stand for 10 minutes.

6. Meanwhile, in small saucepan, boil remaining marinade just until it's thick enough to coat a spoon. Strain and set aside.

7. Cut meat diagonally into ¼-in-thick (0.5 cm) slices. Drizzle a little marinade on each plate. Top with steak slices.

Per serving: 229 calories, 21 g protein, 15 g carbohydrates, 2 g fiber, 9 g total fat, 4 g saturated fat, 48 mg cholesterol, 738 mg sodium

1   tsp extra-virgin olive oil

2   lb (1 kg) boneless beef chuck, about 3 in or 7.5 cm thick, trimmed of fat and tied

2   large onions, finely chopped

1   celery stalk, finely chopped

3   cloves garlic, crushed

1   cup dry red or white wine

1   cup canned chopped tomatoes

1   large carrot, grated, and 4 medium carrots, sliced

1   tsp chopped fresh thyme

2   cups beef stock, preferably homemade

21 oz (625 g) new potatoes, scrubbed and quartered

12 oz (375 g) celeriac, cut into 1-in (2.5 cm) cubes

12 oz (375 g) rutabaga, cut into 1-in (2.5 cm) cubes

Salt and ground black pepper

¼   cup chopped fresh parsley

1. Preheat oven to 325°F (160°C). Heat oil in large flameproof casserole dish. Add beef and brown over a medium-high heat for 6 to 8 minutes, or until well colored. Remove to plate.

2. Reduce heat to medium. Add onions, celery, and garlic and cook, stirring frequently, for 3 minutes, or until onions begin to soften. Add wine and let it bubble for about 1 minute, then add tomatoes and grated carrot. Cook for 2 minutes.

3. Return beef to casserole dish, together with any juices, and add thyme. Tuck a piece of foil around top of meat, turning back corners so it doesn't touch liquid, then cover with a tight-fitting lid. Transfer to oven and cook for 2½ hours.

4. About 20 minutes before end of cooking time, bring stock to a boil in deep saucepan with a lid. Add potatoes, celeriac, rutabaga, and sliced carrots. Cover and simmer gently for 12 to 15 minutes, or until just starting to become tender.

5. Remove beef from casserole dish and set aside. Remove any fat from cooking liquid. In blender, combine cooking liquid and vegetables from casserole dish. Puree until smooth. Season with salt and pepper to taste.

6. Drain potatoes and other root vegetables, reserving liquid. In casserole dish, layer half the root vegetables on bottom, put beef on top, and add remaining root vegetables and their cooking liquid. Pour pureed sauce over top. Cover casserole, return to oven, and cook for 20 minutes, or until root vegetables are tender.

7. Remove beef to carving board, cover, and let rest for 10 minutes. Keep vegetables and sauce warm. Carve beef and arrange on warmed plates with vegetables and sauce. Sprinkle with parsley and serve immediately.

Per serving: 393 calories, 39 g protein, 35 g carbohydrates, 7 g fiber, 8 g total fat, 3 g saturated fat, 98 mg cholesterol, 688 mg sodium

SPINACH-STUFFED MEAT LOAF

Serves 8
Prep Time: 45 minutes plus standing
Cook Time: 58 minutes
Healing Foods: onions, tomatoes, spinach, beef, pork, carrots
Ailments It Heals: bleeding problems, diabetes, Parkinson's disease, stress

1	tsp olive oil
2	large onions, finely chopped
6	cloves garlic, crushed, or to taste
24	oz (680 mL) chopped tomatoes
⅔	cup low-fat, reduced-sodium chicken broth
1	tsp dried mixed herbs (try basil, oregano, and thyme)

Salt and ground black pepper

1	lb (500 g) fresh spinach leaves
2	Tbsp low-fat plain yogurt
½	tsp freshly grated nutmeg
1	lb (500 g) lean (93%) ground beef
1	lb (500 g) lean ground pork
1	celery stalk, finely chopped
1	large carrot, grated
½	cup rolled oats
2	tsp chopped fresh thyme
5	Tbsp low-fat milk
1	egg, beaten
2	tsp dijon mustard

1. Heat oil in saucepan over medium heat. Add onions and garlic and cook for 5 minutes, or until onions are soft.

2. Transfer half of onion mixture to large bowl and set aside. Stir tomatoes (with their juice), broth, and mixed herbs into onions in saucepan. Season lightly with salt and pepper. Bring to a boil, then cover, reduce heat, and simmer sauce very gently.

3. Preheat oven to 350°F (180°C). Put spinach in large saucepan, cover with tight-fitting lid, and cook over high heat for 2 to 3 minutes, or until the leaves are wilted. Drain spinach, squeeze it dry with your hands, then chop it roughly and put into a bowl. Stir in yogurt and season with ¼ tsp nutmeg and salt and pepper to taste.

4. Put beef and pork into bowl with reserved onion mixture. Add celery, carrot, oats, thyme, milk, egg, mustard, and remaining ¼ tsp nutmeg. Season with salt and pepper. Mix ingredients together with your hands.

5. Lay large sheet of plastic wrap on work surface and place meat mixture in center. With a spatula, spread meat into a 9 x 7-in (23 x 18 cm) rectangle. Spread spinach mixture evenly over meat, leaving a ½-in (1 cm) border. Starting at a short end, roll up meat and spinach. Pat sides and place on nonstick baking sheet, discarding plastic wrap.

6. Place meat loaf, uncovered, in the center of oven and cook for 45 minutes, then remove and brush lightly with a little tomato sauce. Return to oven and cook for 5 minutes to set glaze and brown slightly. To check if meat loaf is cooked through, insert a skewer into the center and remove after a few seconds. It should feel very hot when lightly placed on the back of your hand. When meat loaf is ready, remove from oven, cover loosely with foil, and leave to stand for 10 minutes.

Per serving: 250 calories, 30 g protein, 17 g carbohydrates, 5 g fiber, 7 g total fat, 2 g saturated fat, 99 mg cholesterol, 380 mg sodium

ORANGE BEEF WITH BROCCOLI AND JICAMA

Serves 4
Prep Time: 20 minutes plus marinating
Cook Time: 11 minutes
Healing Foods: beef, broccoli, peppers, jicama
Ailments It Heals: anemia, hepatitis, herpes

12	oz (375 g) flank steak
2	tsp cornstarch
¼	cup dry sherry
2	Tbsp reduced-sodium soy sauce
¼	tsp baking soda
4	tsp olive oil
4	Tbsp finely slivered orange zest
¼	tsp crushed red-pepper flakes
5	cups broccoli florets and stems
1	red bell pepper, cut into matchsticks
4	scallions, thinly sliced
3	cloves garlic, minced
½	cup plus 1/3 cup water
1	cup jicama matchsticks

1. Halve flank steak lengthwise (with grain), then cut each piece crosswise (against grain) into thin slices.

2. In medium bowl, whisk together cornstarch, sherry, soy sauce, and baking soda until well combined. Add flank steak, tossing to coat. Refrigerate for 30 minutes.

3. In large nonstick skillet, heat 3 tsp oil over medium heat. Remove beef from marinade, reserving marinade. Add beef, 2 Tbsp orange zest, and pepper flakes and cook for 3 minutes, or until beef is just cooked through. Transfer beef to a plate.

4. Add remaining 1 tsp oil to skillet along with broccoli, bell pepper, scallions, and garlic. Cook for 3 minutes, or until broccoli begins to soften. Add ½ cup water and cook for 2 to 3 minutes, or until broccoli is crisp-tender.

5. Stir ⅓ cup water into reserved marinade and add to skillet. Bring to a boil and cook, stirring constantly, for 1 minute, or until sauce is slightly thickened. Return beef to skillet. Add jicama and cook for 1 minute, just until beef is heated through. Serve garnished with remaining 2 Tbsp orange zest.

Per serving: 255 calories, 23 g protein, 18 g carbohydrate, 6 g fiber, 10 g total fat, 2 g saturated fat, 53 mg cholesterol, 601 mg sodium

CALF'S LIVER WITH RIGATONI

Serves 6
Prep Time: 40 minutes
Cook Time: 20 minutes
Healing Foods: broccoli, liver, oranges, pasta,
Ailments It Heals: anemia, bleeding problems, dental problems, infertility, sex drive (diminished)

10 oz (300 g) calf's liver, trimmed
2 large oranges
14.5 oz (435 g) rigatoni, penne, or other pasta shapes
8 oz (250 g) broccoli, cut into 1-in (2.5 cm) pieces
2 Tbsp extra-virgin olive oil
1 clove garlic, crushed
1 small fresh red chile, seeded and finely chopped
4 Tbsp marsala or medium sherry
Salt and ground black pepper
1 tsp balsamic vinegar
2 tsp butter
1 tsp crushed roasted coriander seeds (optional)

1. Cut liver into strips about ½ in (1 cm) wide and 2 in (5 cm) long. Use citrus zester to take zest off one orange in short strips. Set strips aside. Peel and segment both oranges, working over a bowl to catch juice. Squeeze juice from peel, too. Set aside the 12 best segments, then squeeze remaining segments into juice bowl to get about 4 Tbsp juice in total.

2. Drop pasta into large saucepan of boiling water. When water returns to a boil, cook for 10 minutes. Add broccoli and cook for 2 to 3 minutes, or until pasta and broccoli are just tender.

3. Meanwhile, heat 1 Tbsp oil in frying pan large enough to cook liver in one layer. Sprinkle in garlic and chile and cook, stirring, over medium-high heat for 1 minute. Add liver and toss for 1 minute, or until browned. Add marsala (or sherry) and orange zest strips and juice and cook for 1 minute.

4. Drain pasta and broccoli and return them to saucepan off heat. Remove liver from sauce and add to pasta and broccoli. Add remaining 1 Tbsp oil and salt and pepper to taste. Toss well.

5. Bring sauce to a boil and boil to reduce by half, about 5 minutes. Stir in vinegar and butter to make sauce glossy. Add reserved orange segments

and warm through for 30 seconds, then spoon over liver, pasta, and broccoli and toss gently to combine. Sprinkle with coriander seeds, if using, and serve immediately.

Per serving: 418 calories, 21 g protein, 62 g carbohydrates, 4 g fiber, 9 g total fat, 2 g saturated fat, 133 mg cholesterol, 59 mg sodium

GREEK LAMB KEBABS

Serves 4

Prep Time: 20 minutes plus soaking

Cook Time: 8 minutes

Healing Foods: garlic, lamb, tomatoes, cabbage, mint, wheat

Ailments It Heals: ADHD, alcoholism, hepatitis, prostate problems

Kebabs

- 1 Tbsp olive oil
- 2 large cloves garlic, crushed

Juice of 1 lemon

- 1 Tbsp chopped fresh oregano
- 1 lb (500 g) boneless leg of lamb, trimmed of all fat and cut into 1-in (2.5 cm) cubes
- 4 white or whole wheat pita breads, cut into triangles

Salad

- 3 tomatoes, thickly sliced
- 1 small red onion, finely chopped
- ½ cup shredded green cabbage
- 4 Tbsp chopped fresh mint
- 1 cucumber, halved and thinly sliced

Juice of 1 lemon

- 2 tsp olive oil

Salt and ground black pepper

1. To make kebabs: Soak 4 wooden skewers in cold water for 30 minutes. Drain. Preheat grill or heat ridged cast-iron grill pan. Put oil, garlic, lemon juice, and oregano in bowl and stir to mix together. Add lamb and turn until very well coated. Thread cubes onto skewers.

2. Cook lamb on grill or grill pan, turning frequently, for 7 to 8 minutes, or until tender. Toward end of cooking, warm pita bread on grill or grill pan.

3. To make salad: In salad bowl, combine tomatoes, onion, cabbage, mint, cucumber, lemon juice, and oil and season to taste with salt and pepper. Toss together gently.

4. Serve kebabs with salad, and pita bread.

Per serving: 408 calories, 27 g protein, 46 g carbohydrates, 4 g fiber, 13 g total fat, 3 g saturated fat, 62 mg cholesterol, 389 mg sodium

HONEY-ROASTED RACK OF LAMB

Serves 4

Prep Time: 20 minutes plus standing

Cook Time: 40 minutes to 1 hour

Healing Foods: zucchini, parsnips, carrots, peppers, lamb

Ailments It Heals: anemia, burns, shingles

- 3 Tbsp honey
- 3 Tbsp lemon juice
- 3 Tbsp reduced-sodium soy sauce
- 2 cloves garlic, crushed
- 4 zucchini, cut into strips
- 4 parsnips, peeled and cut into strips
- 4 carrots, peeled and cut into strips
- 1 celery stalk, halved lengthways then cut into 4-in (10 cm) lengths

SKILLET OKRA AND LAMB

Serves 4
Prep Time: 10 minutes
Cook Time: 31 minutes
Healing Foods: onions, garlic, lamb, tomatoes, okra
Ailments It Heals: constipation, obesity, prostate problems

1   red bell pepper, cut into strips
6   sprigs fresh rosemary
2   cups lamb or beef stock
2   well-trimmed (frenched) lamb racks
      (8 cutlets each)

1   Tbsp olive oil
2   onions, finely chopped
2   cloves garlic, minced
½   lb (250 g) ground lamb
1   tomato, seeded and finely chopped
1   cup water
¼   cup tomato paste
¾   tsp salt
⅛   tsp ground black pepper
1   lb (500 g) okra, trimmed
2   Tbsp fresh-squeezed lemon juice
1   Tbsp finely chopped cilantro (optional)

1. Preheat oven to 400°F (200°C). In medium bowl, combine honey, lemon juice, soy sauce, and garlic. Set aside.

2. Lightly coat large baking dish with cooking spray. Add zucchini, parsnips, carrots, celery, and peppers and roast for 20 minutes, or until vegetables are lightly browned.

3. Top vegetables with rosemary and pour on stock. Arrange lamb racks on top of vegetables, baste with reserved honey sauce, and roast for 20 minutes for rare (lamb will be pink), 30 minutes for medium, or 40 minutes for well done. Continue basting with sauce occasionally while cooking.

4. Remove baking dish from oven and put lamb racks and vegetables on a platter. Cover and let rest for 10 minutes before carving meat.

5. Boil pan sauce and juices until they thicken slightly. Serve with lamb and vegetables.

Per serving: 435 calories, 42 g protein, 42 g carbohydrates, 7 g fiber, 11 g total fat, 5 g saturated fat, 109 mg cholesterol, 856 mg sodium

1. In large nonstick skillet, heat oil over medium heat. Add onions and sauté for 5 minutes, or until softened. Add garlic and sauté for 1 minute. Add lamb and cook, breaking up meat with wooden spoon, for 5 minutes, or until browned. Drain off any fat.

2. Stir in tomato, water, tomato paste, salt, and pepper. Top with okra and sprinkle with lemon juice. Cover and cook for 15 minutes, or until okra is tender. Uncover and simmer for 5 minutes to reduce liquid. Sprinkle with cilantro before serving, if desired.

Per serving: 245 calories, 15 g protein, 21 g carbohydrates, 6 g fiber, 12 g total fat, 4 g saturated fat, 41 mg cholesterol, 492 mg sodium

TUSCAN VEAL CHOPS

Per serving: 219 calories, 24 g protein, 16 g carbohydrates, 5 g fiber, 6 g total fat, 2 g saturated fat, 110 mg cholesterol, 501 mg sodium

Serves 2
Prep Time: 15 minutes
Cook Time: 15 minutes
Healing Foods: veal, carrots, tomatoes, green beans, onions
Ailments It Heals: anemia, lactose intolerance, obesity

2 bone-in rib or loin veal chops ($\frac{3}{4}$ in or 1.5 cm thick, about 5 oz or 150 g each)
$\frac{1}{4}$ tsp ground black pepper
1 large carrot, cut into matchsticks
1 medium tomato, cut into 8 wedges
4 oz (125 g) green beans
1 small red onion, thinly sliced
$\frac{1}{4}$ cup fat-free Italian dressing
2 Tbsp dry white wine
1 tsp chopped rosemary

1. Season chops on both sides with pepper. Put in shallow dish with carrot, tomato, green beans, and onion. In jar with tight-fitting lid, shake dressing and wine until mixed. Drizzle over chops and vegetables and toss to coat. Let stand at room temperature for 5 minutes.

2. Coat nonstick ridged grill pan or grill rack with cooking spray. Set grill pan over medium heat or preheat grill to medium. Cook or grill chops until golden brown but still slightly pink in center, about 7 minutes on each side for medium.

3. Meanwhile, coat large nonstick skillet with cooking spray. Transfer vegetables and any liquid remaining in dish to skillet and sprinkle with rosemary. Sauté over medium-high heat for 6 minutes, or just until vegetables are tender. To serve, divide vegetables evenly between 2 plates and top with veal chop.

PORK CHOPS AND CABBAGE

Serves 4
Prep Time: 20 minutes
Cook Time: 25 minutes
Healing Foods: pork, onions, cabbage, carrots
Ailments It Heals: alcoholism, celiac disease, herpes, osteoporosis, shingles

1 tsp dried thyme
$\frac{1}{4}$ tsp salt
$\frac{1}{4}$ tsp ground black pepper plus more to taste
1 lb (500 g) thin-cut boneless pork chops, trimmed
1 Tbsp canola oil
1 cup sliced onion (1 medium)
5 cups shredded green cabbage ($\frac{1}{2}$ medium head)
$\frac{1}{2}$ cup sliced carrots (2 medium)
$1\frac{3}{4}$ cups reduced-sodium chicken broth
$\frac{3}{4}$ cup water
2 tsp coarse-grain mustard
1 tsp apple cider vinegar

1. In small bowl, combine thyme, salt, and pepper. Rub mixture over pork chops. Heat 2 tsp oil in large nonstick skillet over medium heat. Add chops and cook for 2 to 3 minutes per side, or until browned and just cooked through. Transfer to plate, cover loosely with foil, and keep warm.

2. Add remaining 1 tsp oil to skillet. Add onion and cook over medium heat, stirring frequently, for 1 to 2 minutes, or until softened. Add cabbage and carrots and cook, stirring, for 2 minutes, or until cabbage is wilted. Add broth and water and bring to a simmer. Cover and cook for 10 to 15 minutes,

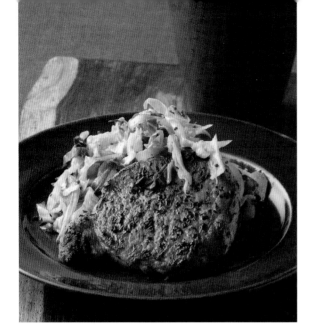

or until cabbage is tender. Stir in mustard and vinegar and season with pepper.

3. Serve pork chops over cabbage mixture.

Per serving: 224 calories, 24 g protein, 9 g carbohydrates, 3 g fiber, 10 g total fat, 2 g saturated fat, 57 mg cholesterol, 564 mg sodium

ROASTED PORK WITH POMEGRANATE SAUCE

Serves 4
Prep Time: 10 minutes
Cook Time: 51 minutes
Healing Foods: butternut squash, onions, pork, pomegranates
Ailments It Heals: alcoholism, burns, herpes

4 cups cubed (1 in or 2.5 cm pieces) peeled butternut squash (1 lb 2 oz or 560g)
2 cups whole shallots or cipollini onions, peeled

1 Tbsp plus 2 tsp olive oil
½ tsp salt
½ tsp ground black pepper
1 tsp ground cumin
1 tsp brown sugar
½ tsp ground coriander
¼ tsp cayenne pepper
1 lb (500 g) pork tenderloin, trimmed
¾ cup unsweetened pomegranate juice
¾ cup reduced-sodium chicken broth
3 Tbsp water
1 tsp cornstarch

1. Preheat oven to 425°F (220°C). Coat large roasting pan or baking sheet with sides with cooking spray.

2. In medium bowl, combine squash, shallots, 1 Tbsp oil, ¼ tsp salt, and ¼ tsp pepper and toss to coat. Spread vegetables in pan and bake for 15 minutes.

3. Meanwhile, in small bowl, mix cumin, brown sugar, coriander, cayenne, and remaining ¼ tsp salt and ¼ tsp pepper. Pat pork dry and rub with spice mixture.

4. Heat remaining 2 tsp oil in large nonstick skillet over medium-high heat. Add pork and cook, for 4 minutes, turning occasionally, until browned on all sides.

5. Stir vegetables and push them to sides of pan. Place pork in center. Bake, stirring vegetables occasionally, for 20 to 25 minutes, or until pork is just cooked through (an instant-read thermometer inserted in center should register 155°F or 68°C; temperature will rise to 160°F or 71°C during resting) and vegetables are tender.

6. Meanwhile, add pomegranate juice and chicken broth to skillet and bring to a boil. Boil for 10 minutes, or until reduced to ⅔ cup. In small bowl, mix 3 Tbsp water and cornstarch, then add to sauce and cook, stirring, for 1 minute, or until slightly thickened.

7. Transfer vegetables to a bowl and pork to a cutting board. Let pork rest for 5 minutes before carving. Cut into ½-in-thick (1 cm) slices and serve with vegetables and sauce.

Per serving: 316 calories, 27 g protein, 31 g carbohydrates, 4 g fiber, 11 g total fat, 3 g saturated fat, 65 mg cholesterol, 452 mg sodium

WHOLE WHEAT PASTA WITH SAUSAGE AND GREENS

Serves 6
Prep Time: 25 minutes
Cook Time: 23 minutes
Healing Foods: turkey, garlic, tomatoes, beans, pasta, cooking greens
Ailments It Heals: menstrual problems, obesity, sex drive (diminished)

1   link (4 oz or 125 g) hot Italian turkey sausage, casing removed
1   tsp olive oil
¾   cup chopped onion (1 small)
3   cloves garlic, minced
15   oz (425 mL) no-salt-added diced tomatoes
8   oz (225 mL) no-salt-added tomato sauce
15.5   oz (440 mL) cannellini beans, drained and rinsed
¼   cup water
Ground black pepper to taste
4   cups whole wheat pasta, fusilli, penne, or rigatoni
1   bunch (1 lb or 500 g) Swiss chard, stems trimmed, leaves washed, and torn into bite-size pieces
6   Tbsp grated parmesan cheese

1. Bring large pot of lightly salted water to a boil. In large nonstick skillet, cook sausage over me-dium heat, crumbling it with wooden spoon, for 3 to 5 minutes, or until browned. Transfer sausage to paper towel–lined plate to drain.

2. Add oil to skillet. Add onion and cook over medium heat, stirring often, for 1 to 2 minutes, or until softened. Add garlic and cook, stirring, for 10 to 20 seconds. Add diced tomatoes and mash with wooden spoon. Add tomato sauce, beans, water, and sausage. Bring to a simmer. Cook, uncovered, at a lively simmer over medium-low heat, stirring occasionally, for 10 to 15 minutes, or until flavors have blended. Season with pepper.

3. Meanwhile, add pasta to boiling water and cook for 5 minutes. Add Swiss chard and stir to immerse. Cook for 3 to 5 minutes, or until pasta is just tender and chard has wilted. Drain well and transfer to large bowl. Toss with the tomato mixture. Sprinkle each serving with cheese.

Per serving: 390 calories, 19 g protein, 65 g carbohydrates, 11 g fiber, 6 g total fat, 1 g saturated fat, 22 mg cholesterol, 409 mg sodium

ASPARAGUS AND CHICKEN STIR-FRY

Serves 4
Prep Time: 15 minutes
Cook Time: 10 minutes
Healing Foods: onions, chicken, asparagus, peas
Ailments It Heals: indigestion and heartburn, nail problems, peptic ulcers

1   Tbsp vegetable oil
3   scallions, thinly sliced
¾   lb (375 g) boneless, skinless chicken breasts, cut for stir-fry

12 oz (375 g) asparagus, trimmed and cut into
      long lengths on the diagonal
 8 oz (250 g) sugar snap peas or snow peas
½ cup chicken stock
½ tsp grated lemon zest, plus extra to garnish
 1 Tbsp light soy sauce
½ cup plus 1 Tbsp water
 1 tsp cornstarch

1. In wok or large frying pan, heat half of oil over medium heat. Add spring onions and stir-fry for 1 minute, or until just wilted. Add chicken and stir-fry for 3 minutes, or until chicken is no longer pink.

2. Add remaining oil and asparagus and toss for 2 minutes to coat.

3. Add peas, stock, lemon zest, soy sauce, and ½ cup water and bring to a boil. Reduce to a simmer and stir-fry for 2 minutes, or until chicken and asparagus are just cooked through.

4. Mix cornstarch with 1 Tbsp water to make smooth paste. Add to wok and stir until blended. Bring to a boil and cook, stirring constantly, for 1 minute, or until sauce is slightly thickened. Divide among bowls, garnish with extra lemon zest, and serve.

Per serving: 191 calories, 23 g protein, 12 g carbohydrates, 3 g fiber, 6 g total fat, 1 g saturated fat, 55 mg cholesterol, 270 mg sodium

BRAISED CHICKEN WITH WINTER VEGETABLES

Serves 4
Prep Time: 15 minutes plus soaking
Cook Time: 35 minutes
Healing Foods: mushrooms, chicken, leeks, potatoes, brussels sprouts
Ailments It Heals: hepatitis, hives, indigestion and heartburn, migraines and other headaches

½ cup dried shiitake mushrooms
 2 cups water
 8 skinless bone-in chicken thighs (about 5 oz or 150 g each)
 2 Tbsp flour
 3 tsp olive oil
 2 leeks, halved lengthwise, cut crosswise into 1-in (2.5 cm) lengths, and well washed
1½ lb (750 g) small red-skinned potatoes, cut into ½-in (1 cm) chunks
10 oz (300 g) frozen brussels sprouts
½ tsp salt
½ tsp dried thyme

1. Bring 1 cup of water to a boil. In small bowl, combine mushrooms and boiling water. Let stand for 20 minutes, or until softened. With your fingers, remove mushrooms from soaking liquid, reserving liquid. Trim any stems from mushrooms and thinly slice caps. Strain reserved liquid through a fine-meshed sieve or coffee filter and set aside.

2. Dredge chicken in flour, shaking off excess. In nonstick Dutch oven, heat 2 tsp oil over medium heat. Add chicken and cook for 3 minutes per side, or until golden brown. Transfer chicken to a plate.

3. Add leeks, mushrooms, and remaining 1 tsp oil to Dutch oven. Cook, stirring frequently, for 2 minutes, or until leeks are golden.

4. Add reserved soaking liquid, potatoes, brussels sprouts, salt, thyme, and remaining water to Dutch oven. Bring to a boil. Return chicken to pan and reduce to a simmer. Cover and cook, stirring occasionally for 25 minutes, or until chicken is cooked through and brussels sprouts and potatoes are tender.

Per serving: 501 calories, 48 g protein, 50 g carbohydrates, 6 g fiber, 12 g total fat, 3 g saturated fat, 172 mg cholesterol, 502 mg sodium

ORANGE CHICKEN WITH ARTICHOKES AND SUN-DRIED TOMATOES

Serves 4
Prep Time: 15 minutes
Cook Time: 12 minutes
Healing Foods: chicken, artichokes, tomatoes, rosemary
Ailments It Heals: diverticulitis, hepatitis, irritable bowel syndrome, memory loss

1 Tbsp extra-virgin olive oil
4 skinless, bone-in chicken breast halves (about 6 oz or 175 g each)
2 Tbsp whole wheat flour
3 cloves garlic, thinly sliced
1 cup low-sodium chicken stock
9 oz (275 g) frozen artichoke hearts, thawed and quartered
⅓ cup dry-pack sun-dried tomatoes, thinly sliced
½ tsp grated orange zest
¼ cup fresh orange juice
½ tsp chopped fresh or dried rosemary
½ tsp fine sea salt
¼ tsp ground black pepper

1. In large skillet, heat oil over medium-high heat. Dredge chicken in flour, add to skillet, and cook for 5 minutes, or until golden brown on both sides. Transfer to a plate.

2. Reduce heat to medium, add garlic to skillet, and cook for 2 minutes, or until golden brown.

3. Add stock, artichokes, tomatoes, orange zest, orange juice, rosemary, salt, and pepper and bring to a boil.

4. Return chicken to skillet and reduce heat to a simmer. Cover and cook for 5 minutes, or until chicken is cooked through.

Per serving: 237 calories, 28 g protein, 15 g carbohydrates, 5 g fiber, 7 g total fat, 1 g saturated fat, 73 mg cholesterol, 576 mg sodium

CHICKEN BREASTS WITH PEACHES AND GINGER

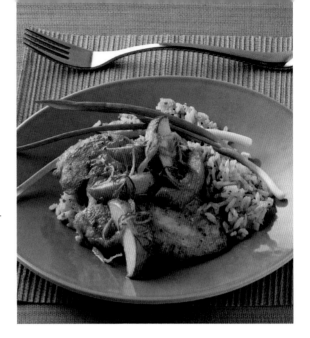

Serves 4

Prep Time: 25 minutes

Cook Time: 15 minutes

Healing Foods: onions, chicken, vinegar, ginger, peaches

Ailments It Heals: cancer, cholesterol (high), motion sickness

1 bunch scallions, trimmed

1 lb (500 g) boneless, skinless chicken breast halves, trimmed

¼ tsp salt or to taste

Ground black pepper to taste

2 tsp canola oil

3 Tbsp apple cider vinegar

2 Tbsp sugar

½ cup no-sugar-added peach juice or nectar, or apple juice

2 Tbsp grated fresh ginger

1¼ cups reduced-sodium chicken broth

1 large peach, peeled and sliced (½-in or 1 cm wedges)

2 tsp cornstarch

2 tsp water

1. Chop scallions, reserving all of white portions and ¼ cup of green portions separately.

2. If chicken pieces are large, cut them in half lengthwise so you have at least 4 pieces. Place chicken between 2 pieces of plastic wrap and pound with rolling pin or meat mallet into ½-in (1 cm) thickness. Season with salt and pepper.

3. Heat oil in large nonstick skillet over medium-high heat. Add chicken and cook for 3 to 3½ minutes per side, or until browned and no longer pink in center. Transfer to a plate.

4. Add vinegar and sugar to skillet. Stir to dissolve sugar. Cook, swirling skillet, for 30 to 60 seconds, or until syrup turns dark amber. Add scallion whites, peach juice, and ginger. Bring to a boil, stirring to scrape up any caramelized bits in skillet. Cook for 1 minute. Add broth and peach and return to a boil. Cook, turning peach slices from time to time, for 2 to 4 minutes, or until tender. Mix cornstarch and water and add to sauce. Cook, stirring, for 30 seconds, or until slightly thickened.

5. Reduce heat to low and return chicken and any accumulated juices to skillet. Simmer gently for 1 minute, or until chicken is heated through. Garnish with reserved scallion greens.

Per serving: 223 calories, 28 g protein, 17 g carbohydrates, 1 g fiber, 4 g total fat, 1 g saturated fat, 67 mg cholesterol, 275 mg sodium

EARL GREY CHICKEN

Serves 4
Prep Time: 15 minutes
Cook Time: 25 minutes
Healing Foods: tea, chicken, onions
Ailments It Heals: bleeding problems, jaundice, varicose veins

 6   cups water
 8   Earl Grey tea bags
 1   Tbsp fresh lemon juice
 4   boneless, skinless chicken breasts
     (about 1½ lb or 750 g)
 2   tsp olive oil
 ½   cup chopped onion
 1   clove garlic, minced
 1   cup chicken broth
 ¾   cup heavy cream
 ¼   tsp salt
 ⅛   tsp ground black pepper
 1   Tbsp chopped fresh oregano or parsley

1. Put water in deep sauté pan and bring to a boil. Turn off heat and add tea bags. Let steep for 5 minutes. Remove bags, squeezing to release any liquid.

2. Add lemon juice and return to a boil over high heat. Reduce heat to medium-low and barely simmer liquid (keep temperature at 160°F or 71°C). Add chicken, completely submerging it. Cook, uncovered, for 10 minutes, or until chicken is just barely pink in center. Remove from heat and let stand for 5 minutes.

3. Meanwhile, in small nonstick skillet, heat oil over medium heat. Add onion and garlic and cook for 4 minutes, or until tender.

4. Add broth, cream, and ¼ cup of poaching liquid. Raise heat to high and boil for 5 minutes, or until reduced to about half the original volume. Stir in salt and pepper.

5. Transfer chicken to platter or plates, and spoon sauce over top. Sprinkle with oregano (or parsley).

Per serving: 410 calories, 39 g protein, 10 g carbohydrates, 3 g fiber, 24 g total fat, 12 g saturated fat, 172 mg cholesterol, 603 mg sodium

MAPLE-GLAZED CHICKEN WITH ROOT VEGETABLES

Serves 4
Prep Time: 30 minutes
Cook Time: 58 minutes
Healing Foods: carrots, parsnips, celeriac, turnips, chicken
Ailments It Heals: acne, Alzheimer's disease, eye problems, hives

 4   cups assorted diced ½ x ¾-in (1 x 1.5 cm) peeled root vegetables, such as carrots, parsnips, celeriac, rutabaga, and/or turnips (1 lb 3 oz or 590 g)
 1   Tbsp olive oil
 ½   tsp salt
 ½   tsp ground black pepper
 2½ lb (1.25 kg) bone-in chicken thighs and/or drumsticks, skin removed and fat trimmed
 1   Tbsp dijon mustard
 1   Tbsp maple syrup
 2   tsp chopped fresh thyme or ¾ tsp dried
 ½   cup apple cider
 ½   cup reduced-sodium chicken broth

1. Preheat oven to 400°F (200°C). Coat large roasting pan with cooking spray.

2. Place vegetables in pan and toss with oil, ¼ tsp salt, and ¼ tsp pepper. Push vegetables toward sides of pan. Sprinkle chicken with remaining ¼ tsp salt and ¼ tsp pepper and place, skin side down, in center of pan. Bake, uncovered, for 15 minutes.

3. Meanwhile, in small bowl, combine mustard, syrup, and thyme.

4. Stir vegetables and turn chicken pieces. Brush chicken with mustard mixture. Bake, stirring vegetables occasionally, for 30 to 40 minutes, or until vegetables are glazed and tender and chicken is cooked through (an instant-read thermometer should register 165°F or 74°C). If either chicken or vegetables are done first, remove and keep warm. When finished baking, transfer to platter or individual plates.

5. Add apple cider and broth to roasting pan, place over 2 burners, and bring to a boil over medium-high heat. Boil for 2 to 3 minutes. Drizzle sauce over chicken and vegetables.

Per serving: 370 calories, 33 g protein, 24 g carbohydrates, 4 g fiber, 16 g total fat, 4 g saturated fat, 108 mg cholesterol, 568 mg sodium

PINEAPPLE-CHIPOTLE CHICKEN

Serves 4
Prep Time: 15 minutes
Cook Time: 27 minutes
Healing Foods: olive oil, chicken, peppers, ginger, pineapples, chiles
Ailments It Heals: arthritis, jaundice, motion sickness

1   Tbsp plus 2 tsp olive oil
4   boneless, skinless chicken breast halves (about 5 oz or 150 g each)

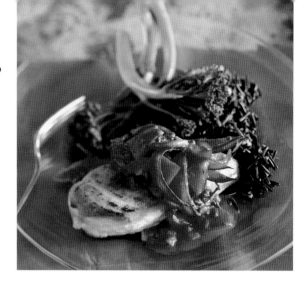

2   Tbsp flour
1   medium red onion, halved and sliced ½ in (1 cm) thick
3   cloves garlic, minced
1   red bell pepper, cut into ½-in (1 cm) chunks
¼   cup minced fresh ginger
2½ cups pineapple juice
¼   cup tomato paste
2   chipotle peppers in adobo, minced (4 tsp)
½   tsp salt

1. In large nonstick skillet, heat 1 Tbsp oil over medium heat. Dredge chicken in flour, shaking off excess. Add chicken to skillet and cook for 2 minutes per side, or until golden brown. Transfer to plate.

2. Add 2 tsp oil to skillet along with onion and garlic. Cook, stirring frequently, for 5 minutes, or until onion is tender.

3. Add bell pepper and ginger and cook for 3 minutes. Stir in pineapple juice, tomato paste, chipotle peppers, and salt. Bring to a boil. Boil for 5 minutes.

4. Return chicken to pan. Reduce heat to a simmer and cook for 10 minutes, or until chicken is cooked through.

Per serving: 350 calories, 36 g protein, 34 g carbohydrates, 2 g fiber, 8 g total fat, 1 g saturated fat, 82 mg cholesterol, 564 mg sodium

WHOLE WHEAT NOODLES WITH PEANUT SAUCE AND CHICKEN

Serves 8
Prep Time: 35 minutes
Cook Time: 9 minutes
Healing Foods: peanut butter, tofu, pasta, chicken, carrots, peppers, herbs and spices
Ailments It Heals: cardiovascular disease, cystic fibrosis, diabetes, infertility, multiple sclerosis

DRESSING

½ cup natural-style peanut butter
⅓ cup low-fat firm silken tofu
¼ cup reduced-sodium soy sauce
3 Tbsp lime juice
3 cloves garlic, minced
2 Tbsp firmly packed light brown sugar
¾ tsp crushed red-pepper flakes

SALAD

12 oz (375 g) whole wheat spaghetti
2 tsp toasted sesame oil
2½ cups shredded cooked skinless chicken breast
1 cup grated carrots (2 to 4 medium)
1 cup finely diced red bell pepper (1 small)
¾ cup grated seedless (English) cucumber (¼ medium)
⅓ cup coarsely chopped fresh cilantro leaves
¼ cup chopped scallions
3 Tbsp unsalted dry-roasted peanuts, chopped
Lime wedges

1. Bring a large pot of lightly salted water to a boil for cooking spaghetti.

2. To make dressing: In food processor, combine peanut butter, tofu, soy sauce, lime juice, garlic, sugar, and red pepper. Process until smooth and creamy, stopping once or twice to scrape down sides of work bowl.

3. To make salad: Cook spaghetti in boiling water, stirring often, for 6 to 9 minutes, or until al dente (or according to package directions). Drain and rinse with cold running water. Transfer to large bowl. Drizzle with oil and toss to coat.

4. Add chicken, carrots, and bell pepper to spaghetti. Add dressing and toss to coat. Sprinkle with cucumber, cilantro, scallions, and peanuts. Serve with lime wedges.

Per serving: 364 calories, 22 g protein, 43 g carbohydrates, 8 g fiber, 13 g total fat, 2 g saturated fat, 28 g cholesterol, 560 mg sodium

HERBED TURKEY MEATBALLS AND FUSILLI

Serves 4
Prep Time: 20 minutes
Cook Time: 22 minutes
Healing Foods: turkey, eggs, cheese, tomatoes, wheat
Ailments It Heals: atherosclerosis, cardiovascular disease, mood disorders, Parkinson's disease

2 Tbsp olive oil
1 medium onion, finely chopped
3 cloves garlic, minced
2 slices firm white sandwich bread, crumbled
¼ cup low-fat milk
1 lb (500 g) lean ground turkey breast
½ cup chopped parsley
1 large egg
⅓ cup grated parmesan cheese
¼ cup dried currants

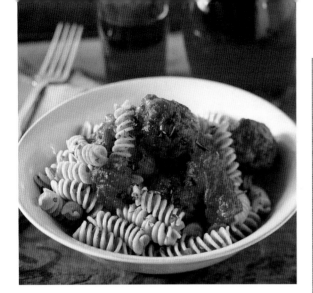

¾ tsp rubbed sage
Pinch of salt
2 Tbsp flour
28 oz (796 g) crushed tomatoes
3 strips (3 x ½-in or 7.5 x 1 cm each) orange zest
8 oz (250 g) whole wheat fusilli

1. In large skillet, heat 1 Tbsp oil over medium heat. Add onion and garlic and cook for 7 minutes, or until golden. Transfer to large bowl. Add bread and milk to bowl and let stand for 1 minute to soften bread.

2. Add turkey, parsley, egg, cheese, currants, sage, and salt to bowl and mix well. Shape mixture into 24 walnut-size meatballs. Dredge meatballs in flour, shaking off excess.

3. In same skillet, heat remaining 1 Tbsp oil over medium heat. Add meatballs and sauté for 3 minutes, or until golden brown. Add tomatoes and orange zest and bring to a boil. Reduce heat to a simmer, cover, and cook for 12 minutes, or until meatballs are cooked through.

4. Meanwhile, in a large pot of boiling water, cook fusilli according to package directions. Drain and toss in large bowl with meatballs and sauce.

Per serving: 579 calories, 46 g protein, 74 g carbohydrates, 10 g fiber, 13 g total fat, 3 g saturated fat, 130 mg cholesterol, 611 mg sodium

JERK TURKEY BREAST WITH GINGER BARBECUE SAUCE

Serves 6
Prep Time: 20 minutes plus marinating
Cook Time: 1 hour 40 minutes
Healing Foods: onions, chiles, allspice, turkey
Ailments It Heals: mood disorders, neuralgia, stroke

5 scallions, chopped
4 cloves garlic
1 onion, quartered
2 jalapeño chile peppers, seeded and deveined (wear gloves when handling)
1 piece (½ in or 1 cm) fresh ginger, peeled
¼ cup canola oil
2 Tbsp low-sodium soy sauce
2 tsp allspice
1 tsp dried thyme
1 bone-in turkey breast (6 lbs or 3 kg)
1 tsp salt
1 cup ginger ale
1 cup low-sodium barbecue sauce

1. In blender, combine green onions, garlic, onion, chile peppers, ginger, oil, soy sauce, allspice, and thyme. Blend until thick paste forms, then transfer to large bowl.

2. With tip of sharp knife, make several slits all over turkey breast. Add turkey to green onion mixture, turning to coat. Refrigerate for at least 4 hours, or overnight, turning occasionally.

3. Preheat gas grill on high until thermometer reaches maximum temperature. Turn off one burner and reduce heat on other burner(s) to medium. Remove turkey from marinade and sprinkle with salt. On lightly oiled grill rack, grill turkey

breast, skin side down, over unlit burner (using indirect heat), turning every 20 minutes, for 1 hour 40 minutes, or until an instant-read thermometer inserted into thickest part of breast registers 165°F (74°C). Remove to a cutting board and let rest for 10 minutes before slicing.

4. Meanwhile, in small pot, combine ginger ale and barbecue sauce and bring to a boil over medium-high heat. Reduce heat to medium-low and simmer for 18 to 20 minutes, or until thickened and reduced to about 1¾ cups.

Per serving: 398 calories, 57 g protein, 26 g carbohydrates, 1 g fiber, 6 g total fat, 1 g saturated fat, 141 mg cholesterol, 657 mg sodium

TURKEY BRACIOLA STUFFED WITH PROVOLONE AND SPINACH

Serves 4
Prep Time: 15 minutes
Cook Time: 15 minutes
Healing Foods: turkey, cheese, spinach, tomatoes, raisins
Ailments It Heals: cancer, diabetes, insomnia

- 8 turkey cutlets (1 lb or 500 g total)
- 1 tsp rubbed sage
- ¼ tsp salt
- 4 slices (4 oz or 25 g each) thinly sliced provolone cheese, halved
- 10 oz (300 g) frozen chopped spinach, thawed and squeezed dry
- 3 Tbsp flour

- 1 Tbsp olive oil
- 1¼ cups canned crushed tomatoes
- 1 tsp grated orange zest
- ¼ cup fresh orange juice
- 2 Tbsp dried currants or chopped raisins

1. Sprinkle one side of each cutlet with sage and salt. Lay 1 half-slice of provolone on top of sage. Top with spinach. Roll up cutlets and secure with wooden pick.

2. Dredge turkey rolls in flour, shaking off excess. In large nonstick skillet, heat oil over medium heat. Add turkey rolls and sauté for 2 minutes per side, or until golden brown.

3. Add tomatoes, orange zest, orange juice, and currants and bring to a boil. Reduce heat to a simmer, cover, and cook for 10 minutes, or until turkey is cooked through.

4. To serve, remove wooden picks and spoon sauce over turkey rolls.

Per serving: 329 calories, 39 g protein, 16 g carbohydrates, 3 g fiber, 12 g total fat, 6 g saturated fat, 90 mg cholesterol, 622 mg sodium

GRILLED DUCK BREAST WITH POLENTA

Serves 4
Prep Time: 15 minutes
Cook Time: 15 minutes
Healing Foods: turmeric, ginger, duck, peas, corn
Ailments It Heals: depression, mood disorders, nail problems

2 tsp turmeric

1 tsp salt

¾ tsp sugar

½ tsp ground ginger

4 boneless, skinless duck breast halves
   (about 5 oz or 150 g each)

1 Tbsp olive oil

¾ cup yellow cornmeal

2¼ cups cold water

1½ cups frozen peas

1½ cups frozen corn kernels

3 Tbsp mango chutney, finely chopped

1. In small bowl, stir together turmeric, ¼ tsp salt, sugar, and ginger. Rub mixture into both sides of duck breasts.

2. Preheat grill to medium-hot. Brush grill pan with oil. Add duck breasts, and cook for 3 minutes per side for medium-rare. (If cooking on stove, add oil to large skillet and cook duck breasts over medium-high heat.)

3. In small bowl, combine cornmeal and 1 cup cold water, stirring until smooth. In a medium saucepan, bring remaining 1¼ cups water to a boil over high heat. Stir in cornmeal mixture and remaining ¾ tsp salt. Reduce heat to low and cook, stirring frequently, for 7 minutes, or until polenta is thickened and tender.

4. Stir peas, corn, and chutney into saucepan and cook for 2 minutes, or until vegetables are heated through. Slice duck across grain on diagonal and serve alongside polenta.

Per serving: 415 calories, 35 g protein, 57 g carbohydrates, 5 g fiber, 5 g fat, 1 g saturated fat, 149 mg cholesterol, 920 mg sodium

BROILED SALMON WITH AVOCADO-MANGO SALSA

Serves 4

Prep Time: 15 minutes

Cook Time: 5 minutes

Healing Foods: herbs and spices, fish, mangoes, avocados, chickpeas, lettuce

Ailments It Heals: atherosclerosis, cardiovascular disease, cholesterol (high), circulatory disease, gallstones

2½ tsp paprika

2 tsp ground coriander

¼ tsp salt

4 4 oz (125 g) boneless, skinless salmon fillets

1 large mango, peeled and cut into ½-in (1 cm) chunks (about 1½ cups)

1 Hass avocado, peeled, pitted, and cut into ½-in (1 cm) chunks

1 cup canned chickpeas, drained and rinsed

⅓ cup chopped cilantro

1 tsp freshly grated lemon zest

2 Tbsp fresh lemon juice

2 tsp olive oil

6 cups mesclun or frisée lettuce, torn into bite-size pieces

1. In large bowl, stir together paprika, coriander, and salt. Measure out 2 tsp of mixture and sprinkle it over salmon, rubbing it into fish. Place salmon on broiler pan.

2. To remaining spice mixture in bowl, add mango, avocado, chickpeas, cilantro, lemon zest, lemon juice, and oil. Toss to combine.

3. Broil salmon 6 in (15 cm) from heat for 5 minutes for medium. Serve salmon and salsa on bed of lettuce.

Per serving: 430 calories, 27 g protein, 25 g carbohydrates, 7 g fiber, 26 g total fat, 5 g saturated fat, 60 mg cholesterol, 320 mg sodium

POACHED SALMON WITH CUCUMBER-DILL SAUCE

Serves 4
Prep Time: 10 minutes
Cook Time: 10 minutes
Healing Foods: fish, cucumbers, dill
Ailments It Heals: asthma, atherosclerosis, jet lag, obesity, rosacea

- 1½ cups water
- 1 cup dry white wine or reduced-sodium chicken broth
- 2 scallions, sliced
- 8 black peppercorns
- 4 salmon fillets (4 oz or 125 g each)
- ¾ cup nonfat sour cream
- ⅓ cup diced peeled cucumber
- 2 Tbsp snipped fresh dill
- 1 Tbsp fresh lemon juice
- ¼ tsp salt
- ⅛ tsp ground black pepper
- Fresh dill sprigs

1. Pour water into large nonstick skillet. Stir in wine, scallions, and peppercorns. Put salmon in skillet in single layer and bring just to a boil over high heat.

2. Reduce heat to medium-low, cover, and simmer for 6 minutes, or until fish flakes when tested with a fork.

3. Meanwhile, in medium bowl, stir sour cream, cucumber, dill, lemon juice, salt, and pepper to make sauce. Refrigerate if not serving immediately.

4. Carefully transfer fillets with slotted spatula to large platter. Garnish with fresh dill sprigs. Serve hot or chilled with sauce.

Per serving: 229 calories, 27 g protein, 5 g carbohydrates, 0 g fiber, 10 g total fat, 2 g saturated fat, 70 mg cholesterol, 229 mg sodium

GRILLED SALMON WITH SAUTÉED GREENS

Serves 4
Prep Time: 5 minutes
Cook Time: 11 minutes
Healing Foods: vinegar, fish, onions, spinach
Ailments It Heals: asthma, cardiovascular disease, cholesterol (high), stroke

- ¼ cup balsamic vinegar
- 2 Tbsp brown sugar
- 1 tsp mustard powder
- ½ tsp salt
- 1¼ lb (625 g) salmon, cut into 4 pieces
- 1 Tbsp olive oil
- 1 large red onion, cut into thin strips
- 8 oz (250 g) baby spinach

1. Preheat grill or broiler. In small bowl, combine vinegar, brown sugar, mustard, and salt. Brush half of mixture over salmon. Grill or broil for 4 to 5 minutes on each side, or until opaque, brushing with vinegar mixture after 2 minutes.

2. Meanwhile, heat oil in large skillet over medium heat. Add onion and cook for 2 minutes, or until lightly browned. Cover and cook for 2 minutes, or until tender. Add spinach and cook, stirring, for 1 minute, or until almost wilted. Add remaining vinegar mixture and cook, stirring, for 1 minute, or until spinach is wilted and sauce thickens slightly.

3. Divide spinach mixture equally among 4 dinner plates. Top each serving with a piece of salmon.

Per serving: 356 calories, 31 g protein, 13 g carbohydrates, 2 g fiber, 20 g total fat, 4 g saturated fat, 84 mg cholesterol, 428 mg sodium

SALMON AND ASPARAGUS FARFALLE WITH WALNUT-FETA SAUCE

Serves 4

Prep Time: 40 minutes

Cook Time: 28 minutes

Healing Foods: fish, olive oil, nuts, asparagus, cheese

Ailments It Heals: Alzheimer's disease, blood pressure, gallstones, hay fever, psoriasis

8 oz (250 g) boneless salmon fillet

¼ cup extra-virgin olive oil

¼ cup chopped walnuts

1 clove garlic, minced or crushed

12 oz (375 g) farfalle (bow-tie) or butterfly-shaped pasta

12 oz (375 g) asparagus, trimmed and cut into ½-in (1 cm) diagonals

½ cup crumbled mild goat's milk feta cheese (about 2 oz or 60 g)

2 Tbsp finely slivered fresh basil leaves

1. Heat 10-in (25 cm) nonstick skillet over medium-low heat until hot enough that a drop of water sizzles. Add salmon and cook on one side for 5 minutes. Turn with a wide spatula and cook for 3 to 5 minutes, or until center of thickest part of fish is opaque, depending on thickness. When cool enough to handle, remove and discard salmon skin and flake fish apart into ½-in (1 cm) pieces. Set aside.

2. Wipe out skillet and add oil, walnuts, and garlic. Cook over medium-low heat for 2 minutes, or until garlic sizzles and turns golden. (Do not leave unattended; walnuts burn quickly.) Remove from heat.

3. Bring large pot of water to a boil. Add pasta and cook, stirring occasionally, for 10 to 12 minutes, or until just cooked. Add asparagus and cook for 2 minutes, or until tender. Drain, reserving ½ cup of cooking water. Return pasta and asparagus to pot.

4. Reduce heat to medium-low. Add reserved cooking water, walnut mixture, salmon, and ¼ cup cheese to pot. Toss gently for 2 minutes, or until heated through and blended. Spoon into serving bowls and sprinkle the remaining ¼ cup cheese and basil on top.

Per serving: 623 calories, 29 g protein, 69 g carbohydrate, 5 g fiber, 27 g total fat, 5 g saturated fat, 38 mg cholesterol, 83 mg sodium

TUNA AND TOMATO PIZZAS

Per serving: 377 calories, 18 g protein, 58 g carbohydrates, 8 g fiber, 11 g fat, 1 g saturated fat, 25 mg cholesterol, 960 mg sodium

Serves 4

Prep Time: 10 minutes

Cook Time: 25 minutes

Healing Foods: onions, tomatoes, tuna, olives

Ailments It Heals: cancer, cholesterol (high), mood disorders

  3   tsp extra-virgin olive oil
  1   onion, finely chopped
14.5 oz (410 mL) canned chopped tomatoes with juice
  ½   tsp dried oregano
Pinch of sugar
Salt and ground black pepper
  2   ready-made thick pizza crusts (8 oz or 250 g each)
  2   Tbsp tomato paste
  6   oz (170 g) canned tuna in spring water, drained and flaked into chunks
  8   pitted black olives, sliced
Fresh basil leaves

1. Preheat oven to 425°F (220°C). In small pan, heat 1 tsp oil over medium heat. Add onion and cook for 4 minutes, or until softened. Add tomatoes (with juice), oregano, and sugar. Season with salt and pepper to taste. Simmer sauce for 10 minutes, stirring occasionally.

2. Put pizza crusts on 2 baking trays. Spread 1 Tbsp tomato paste on each. Spoon tomato sauce over each, then add tuna. Sprinkle evenly with capers and olives, and drizzle remaining 2 tsp oil over top.

3. Bake for 10 minutes, or until crusts are crisp and golden. Sprinkle with torn basil leaves and serve at once.

GRILLED TUNA STEAK WITH CORN AND ZUCCHINI

Serves 4

Prep Time: 20 minutes

Cook Time: 10 minutes

Healing Foods: fish, corn, tomatoes, zucchini, garlic, chiles

Ailments It Heals: cancer, cardiovascular disease, cholesterol (high)

  4   tuna steaks (1 in or 2.5 cm thick) (1½ lb or 750 g total)
  ½   tsp salt
  ¼   tsp ground black pepper
  ¼   cup apricot jam
  1   Tbsp dijon mustard
  1   ear corn, husked and cut into 8 equal pieces
  2   tomatoes, cored and each cut into 8 equal wedges
  2   medium zucchini, each quartered lengthwise and cut crosswise into ¼-in-thick (0.5 cm) slices
  2   cloves garlic, minced
  2   serrano chile peppers, seeded and finely chopped
  4   tsp olive oil

1. Preheat grill to medium-hot or preheat broiler.

2. Season tuna steaks with ¼ tsp salt and ⅛ tsp black pepper. In small cup, stir together jam and mustard. Spread one side of tuna steaks with half of jam mixture.

3. In center of each of four 12-in (30 cm) squares of foil, place corn, tomatoes, and zucchini, dividing equally. Sprinkle evenly with garlic, chile peppers, oil, and remaining ¼ tsp salt and ⅛ tsp black pepper. Fold edges of foil over to form tightly sealed packets.

4. Grill or broil tuna and foil packets 4 in (10 cm) from heat for 4 minutes. Turn tuna over. Spread with remaining jam mixture. Cook for 4 to 6 minutes, or until tuna is opaque in center and begins to flake when touched with fork. Carefully open vegetable packets and serve with tuna.

Per serving: 302 calories, 35 g protein, 27 g carbohydrates, 3 g fiber, 7 g total fat, 1 g saturated fat, 62 mg cholesterol, 458 mg sodium

COD WITH GREMOLATA CRUST

Serves 4
Prep Time: 20 minutes
Cook Time: 25 minutes
Healing Foods: lemons, fish, tomatoes, zucchini, potatoes
Ailments It Heals: cholesterol (high), chronic fatigue syndrome, hepatitis, jaundice

2 lemons
½ cup white bread crumbs
3 Tbsp chopped parsley
2 cloves garlic, crushed
Salt and ground black pepper
4 4 oz (125 g) skinless cod fillets
2 tsp coarse-grain mustard
3 plum tomatoes, quartered
1 large zucchini, thinly sliced diagonally
1 Tbsp olive oil
1 lb (500 g) potatoes, peeled and cut into chunks

1 tsp saffron threads
3 Tbsp low-fat milk

1. Preheat oven to 400°F (200°C). Finely grate zest and squeeze juice from one lemon, reserving juice. Mix zest with bread crumbs, parsley, and garlic. Season lightly with salt and pepper.

2. Place cod fillets in large ovenproof dish coated with cooking spray. Spread mustard evenly over top of fish, then sprinkle on reserved lemon juice. Arrange tomatoes and zucchini around fish. Cut remaining lemon into 4 wedges and place in dish.

3. Spoon bread crumb mixture over fish and press down lightly. Drizzle with oil. Bake for 25 minutes, or until fish flakes easily and topping is crisp.

4. Meanwhile, place potatoes in saucepan, cover with boiling water, and add saffron. Cook potatoes for 15 to 20 minutes, or until tender. Drain potatoes and mash with milk. Season lightly with salt and pepper. Serve fish with potatoes, tomatoes, and zucchini.

Per serving: 251 calories, 24 g protein, 28 g carbohydrates, 4 g fiber, 5 g total fat, 1 g saturated fat, 49 mg cholesterol, 174 mg sodium

MACKEREL TANDOORI STYLE

Serves 4
Prep Time: 20 minutes plus marinating
Cook Time: 39 minutes
Healing Foods: yogurt, ginger, fish, olive oil, onions, peppers
Ailments It Heals: atherosclerosis, cholesterol (high), nail problems, stroke

1 tsp ground cumin
¼ cup low-fat plain yogurt
1 Tbsp fresh lemon juice
2 tsp minced fresh ginger
1 clove garlic, peeled
2 tsp paprika
½ tsp salt
¼ tsp ground cardamom
¼ tsp cayenne pepper
4 mackerel fillets (about 6 oz or 175 g each), skin on, each cut crosswise in half
1 Tbsp plus 2 tsp olive oil
2 large onions, halved and thinly sliced
1½ tsp sugar
1 large red bell pepper, cut into matchsticks

1. In small skillet, toast cumin over low heat for 2 minutes, or until fragrant. Transfer to blender along with yogurt, lemon juice, ginger, garlic, paprika, salt, cardamom, and cayenne. Puree.

2. Place mackerel pieces, skin side down, in shallow ovenproof pan and make several diagonal slashes in mackerel flesh. Spread yogurt mixture over fish. Refrigerate for 2 hours or up to overnight.

3. About 30 minutes before serving time, remove fish from refrigerator. In large skillet, heat 1 Tbsp oil over medium heat. Add onions and sugar and cook, stirring frequently, for 20 minutes, or until onions are lightly browned. Add bell pepper and cook for 5 minutes, or until crisp-tender. Set aside.

4. Meanwhile, preheat oven to 450°F (230°C). Sprinkle mackerel with remaining 2 tsp oil and bake for 12 minutes, or until cooked through. Serve mackerel topped with the caramelized onion mixture.

Per serving: 414 calories, 29 g protein, 16 g carbohydrates, 2 g fiber, 26 g total fat, 5 g saturated fat, 100 mg cholesterol, 432 mg sodium

ROASTED MACKEREL WITH CHERRY TOMATOES AND POTATOES

Serves 4
Prep Time: 15 minutes
Cook Time: 40 minutes
Healing Foods: potatoes, tomatoes, paprika, fish
Ailments It Heals: asthma, atherosclerosis, cholesterol (high), eye problems, stroke

1 lb (500 g) small Yukon Gold or red-skinned potatoes, unpeeled, cut into ½-in (1 cm) wedges
1½ cups small cherry tomatoes
½ medium onion, cut into thin slices
1 clove garlic, thinly sliced
1 Tbsp extra-virgin olive oil
1½ tsp smoked paprika
¼ tsp ground black pepper
4 boneless, skinless mackerel fillets (4 oz or 125 g each)
1 Tbsp chopped flat-leaf parsley
1 lemon, cut into wedges

1. Preheat oven to 400°F (200°C).

2. In large shallow baking dish or roasting pan, toss potatoes, tomatoes, onion, garlic, and oil. Spread in single layer and sprinkle with 1 tsp paprika and ⅛ tsp pepper. Roast vegetables, turning once, for 30 minutes, or until lightly browned.

3. Remove pan from oven and increase temperature to 450°F (230°C). Arrange fish in a single layer, redistributing vegetables on top of and around fish. Sprinkle with remaining ½ tsp paprika and ⅛ tsp of pepper. Roast for 10 minutes, or until center of thickest part of fish is opaque, depending on thickness.

4. Sprinkle with parsley and serve with lemon wedges.

Per serving: 366 calories, 24 g protein, 23 g carbohydrate, 3 g fiber, 20 g total fat, 4 g saturated fat, 79 mg cholesterol, 114 mg sodium

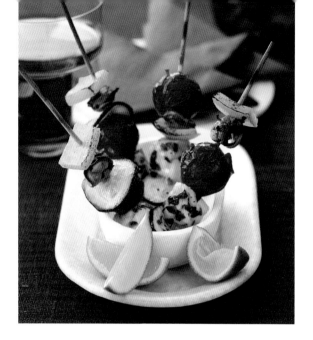

MONKFISH AND MUSSEL KEBABS

Serves 8
Prep Time: 20 minutes plus marinating
Cook Time: 10 minutes
Healing Foods: limes, fish, peppers, zucchini, tomatoes
Ailments It Heals: Alzheimer's disease, asthma, prostate problems, psoriasis, stroke

Finely grated zest and juice of 1 lemon
Juice of 1 lime
 1 Tbsp olive oil
 2 tsp honey
 1 clove garlic, crushed
 1 Tbsp chopped fresh oregano or marjoram
 1 Tbsp chopped parsley
Salt and ground black pepper
 7 oz (210 g) monkfish fillet, cut into 16 small cubes
16 shelled fresh mussels
 1 small yellow bell pepper, seeded and cut into 16 small chunks
 1 zucchini, cut into 16 thin slices
16 cherry tomatoes
Lime or lemon wedges

1. In shallow nonmetallic dish, whisk together lemon zest and juice, lime juice, oil, honey, garlic, chopped oregano (or marjoram), parsley, and salt and pepper to taste. Add monkfish and mussels. Turn seafood to coat all over with marinade. Cover and marinate in refrigerator for 1 hour.

2. Meanwhile, put 16 wooden skewers in warm water and leave to soak for 10 minutes. Drain. Preheat grill or oven broiler to medium-high.

3. Onto each skewer, thread 1 monkfish cube, 1 mussel, 1 bell pepper chunk, 1 zucchini slice, and a cherry tomato. (Reserve marinade.) Leave ends of skewers empty so they will be easy to hold.

4. Place kebabs on grill rack or broiler pan, and grill or broil for 8 to 10 minutes, or until monkfish is cooked and vegetables are just tender, turning occasionally and brushing frequently with reserved marinade. Serve hot, garnished with lime or lemon wedges. Each serving is 2 kebabs.

Per serving: 90 calories, 9 g protein, 7 g carbohydrates, 1 g fiber, 3 g total fat, 0 g saturated fat, 17 mg cholesterol, 84 mg sodium

SNAPPER AND SNAPS IN A PACKET

Serves 4
Prep Time: 10 minutes
Cook Time: 12 minutes
Healing Foods: peas, lemons, fish
Ailments It Heals: diabetes, eye problems, nail problems

3 cups sugar snap peas or snow peas
2 Tbsp lemon juice
2 tsp olive oil
Salt and ground black pepper to taste
4 red snapper fillets, 6 oz (175 g) each

1. Preheat oven to 400ºF (200°C) or prepare gas or charcoal grill.

2. In a large bowl, toss together peas, lemon juice, oil, salt, and pepper.

3. Coat four 15-in (38 cm) lengths of parchment paper (or foil) with cooking spray. Place each fillet on one half of the paper. Top with about 3/4 cup of pea mixture. Fold paper over fish and peas, and seal by folding over all edges.

4. Place packets on baking sheet and bake in oven, or place directly onto grill, and cook for 10 to 12 minutes.

Per serving: 233 calories, 37 g protein, 10 g carbohydrates, 2 g fiber, 5 g total fat, 1 g saturated fat, 63 mg cholesterol, 109 mg sodium

TROUT WITH LEMON-MUSHROOM STUFFING

Serves 4
Prep Time: 15 minutes
Cook Time: 52 minutes
Healing Foods: mushrooms, garlic, rice, fish, lemons
Ailments It Heals: Alzheimer's disease, cardiovascular disease, prostate problems

1 tsp olive oil
½ cup coarsely chopped carrots
8 oz (250 g) mushrooms, coarsely chopped
3 cloves garlic, minced
½ cup Texmati or jasmine rice
2 tsp grated lemon zest
¾ tsp salt
¼ tsp rosemary, minced
1¼ cups water
4 skin-on brook trout fillets (3 oz or 90 g each)
2 lemons, cut into 6 wedges each

1. In large nonstick skillet, heat oil over medium heat. Add carrots and cook for 4 minutes, or until crisp-tender. Add mushrooms and garlic and cook for 5 minutes, or until mixture is almost dry.

2. Stir in rice, lemon zest, ½ tsp salt, rosemary, and water and bring to a boil. Reduce heat to a simmer, cover, and cook for 17 minutes, or until rice is tender. Let stuffing cool to room temperature.

3. Preheat oven to 400°F (200°C). Coat 11 x 7-in (28 x 18 cm) baking pan with cooking spray. Spoon half of stuffing into pan. Place fillets skin side down on work surface. Place remaining stuffing on one half of each fillet and fold fillets over.

4. Place fillets on top of stuffing. Squeeze a wedge of lemon over each fillet and sprinkle with remaining ¼ tsp salt. Bake for 25 minutes, or until cooked through. Serve with remaining lemon wedges and additional stuffing from pan.

Per serving: 270 calories, 25 g protein, 24 g carbohydrates, 2 g fiber, 8 g total fat, 2 g saturated fat, 58 mg cholesterol, 478 mg sodium

LENTIL AND RICE PAELLA WITH CLAMS

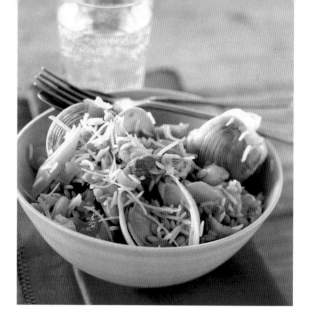

Serves 4
Prep Time: 20 minutes
Cook Time: 45 minutes
Healing Foods: leeks, garlic, carrots, lentils, clams
Ailments It Heals: constipation, eczema, hypoglycemia, sex drive (diminished)

1	Tbsp olive oil
2	large leeks, quartered lengthwise, thinly sliced crosswise, and well washed
5	cloves garlic, minced
3	large carrots, cut crosswise into ½-in (1 cm) slices
1	pickled jalapeño chile pepper, minced (wear gloves when handling)
⅔	cup lentils, picked over and rinsed
3	cups water
½	tsp salt
⅔	cup rice
1⅓	cups frozen lima beans
1	large tomato, coarsely chopped
2	tsp finely slivered lemon zest
18	littleneck clams, well scrubbed

1. In nonstick Dutch oven or flameproof casserole, heat oil over medium heat. Add leeks and garlic and cook, stirring frequently, for 7 minutes, or until leeks are tender.

2. Add carrots and chile pepper and cook for 5 minutes, or until carrots are crisp-tender.

3. Add lentils, stirring to coat. Add water and salt and bring to a boil over high heat. Reduce heat to a simmer, cover, and cook for 10 minutes.

4. Add rice, cover, and simmer for 10 minutes. Stir in lima beans, tomato, and lemon zest and cook for 2 minutes. Place clams on top of lentil-rice mixture. Cover and cook for 5 to 7 minutes, or until clams open (check after 3 minutes as some will open before others; discard any that do not open).

Per serving: 457 calories, 25 g protein, 79 g carbohydrates, 11 g fiber, 5 g total fat, 1 g saturated fat, 21 mg cholesterol, 464 mg sodium

LINGUINE WITH CLAMS

Serves 4
Prep Time: 15 minutes
Cook Time: 15 minutes
Healing Foods: carrots, garlic, clams, pasta
Ailments It Heals: cancer, cholesterol (high), diabetes

2 tsp olive oil
1 small onion, finely chopped
3 carrots, quartered lengthwise and thinly sliced crosswise
4 cloves garlic, minced
1 cup carrot juice
2 dozen littleneck clams, well scrubbed
8 oz (250 g) whole wheat linguine
¼ tsp salt
¼ cup chopped parsley
2 tsp unsalted butter

1. In large skillet, heat oil over low heat. Add onion, carrots, and garlic. Cook, stirring frequently, for 5 minutes, or until onion is tender.

2. Add carrot juice and bring to a boil. Add clams, cover, and cook for 5 minutes, or until clams open (check after 3 minutes as some will open before others). Remove clams as they open (discard any that do not open). Set skillet aside. When clams are cool enough to handle, remove clam meat and discard shells.

3. Meanwhile, in large pot of boiling water, cook linguine according to package directions. Drain.

4. Return carrot mixture to a boil and boil for 3 minutes. Stir in salt. Transfer to large bowl, add pasta, clam meat, parsley, and butter and toss well.

Per serving: 371 calories, 18 g protein, 60 g carbohydrates, 8 g fiber, 7 g total fat, 2 g saturated fat, 45 mg cholesterol, 291 mg sodium

PAN-SEARED SCALLOPS WITH ORANGES AND SUN-DRIED TOMATOES

Serves 6
Prep Time: 10 minutes
Cook Time: 20 minutes
Healing Foods: shellfish, tomatoes, oranges, basil
Ailments It Heals: cancer, urinary tract infections, varicose veins

2 tsp olive oil
1 lb (500 g) sea scallops
3 cloves garlic, sliced
¼ cup sliced oil-packed sun-dried tomatoes
1 cup dry white wine or sherry
1 cup vegetable broth
2 tsp fresh lemon juice
3 Tbsp fresh orange juice
2 Tbsp butter, cut into pieces
1 large navel orange, peeled, segmented, segments chopped
1½ Tbsp chopped fresh basil

1. In large, deep skillet, heat oil over medium-high heat. When very hot, add scallops and cook for 2 minutes per side, or just until lightly browned and barely translucent in center. Remove to a plate.

2. Add garlic, sun-dried tomatoes, and wine (or sherry) to skillet. Boil, scraping pan bottom occasionally, for 5 minutes, or until liquid is reduced by about half. Add broth and boil for 8 minutes, or until liquid is again reduced by about half.

3. Reduce heat to low and stir in lemon juice, orange juice, butter, orange segments, and 1 Tbsp basil. Simmer for 1 minute.

4. Divide sauce among bottoms of 6 small plates. Arrange scallops over sauce and sprinkle with remaining ½ Tbsp basil.

Per serving: 182 calories, 14 g protein, 10 g carbohydrates, 1 g fiber, 7 g total fat, 3 g saturated fat, 35 mg cholesterol, 214 mg sodium

SCALLOPS FLORENTINE

Serves 4
Prep Time: 10 minutes
Cook Time: 12 minutes
Healing Foods: spinach, olive oil, shellfish, garlic, peas
Ailments It Heals: cholesterol (high), hives, PCOS, shingles

- ¾ lb (375 g) fresh spinach
- 2 Tbsp olive oil
- 1½ lb (750 g) sea scallops
- 2 cloves garlic, minced
- 1 tsp grated lemon zest
- 1 cup reduced-sodium, fat-free chicken broth
- 1 cup frozen peas, thawed
- 1 Tbsp fresh-squeezed lemon juice
- ¼ tsp salt
- ¼ tsp ground black pepper

1. In steamer set over a pan of boiling water, steam spinach for 3 minutes, or just until wilted. Cool under cold running water. Squeeze dry.

2. In large nonstick skillet, heat oil over high heat. Add scallops. Sauté for 2 minutes per side, or until still slightly uncooked in center. Transfer to plate.

3. Lower heat to medium. Add garlic and lemon zest to skillet. Cook 30 seconds. Add chicken broth and peas. Simmer 3 minutes. Add spinach, scallops, lemon juice, salt, and pepper. Cook just until heated through. Serve in shallow bowls.

Per serving: 286 calories, 31 g protein, 13 g carbohydrates, 13 g total fat, 2 g saturated fat, 52 mg cholesterol, 4 g fiber, 550 mg sodium

SHRIMP AND VEGETABLE STIR-FRY

Serves 4
Prep Time: 20 minutes
Cook Time: 9 minutes
Healing Foods: ginger, shrimp, broccoli, peppers, peas, corn
Ailments It Heals: cancer, cystic fibrosis, prostate problems

- ⅔ cup water
- ⅓ cup light soy sauce
- 3 Tbsp white wine or orange juice
- 2 Tbsp cornstarch
- 1½ tsp grated peeled fresh ginger
- 1 Tbsp vegetable oil
- 2 cloves garlic, minced
- 1 lb (500 g) large shrimp, peeled and deveined
- 4 cups fresh broccoli florets
- 1 large red bell pepper, cut into strips
- 1 large yellow bell pepper, cut into strips
- 4 oz (125 g) snow peas
- ½ cup drained whole baby corn
- ½ cup sliced water chestnuts
- 4 scallions, cut diagonally into 2-in (5 cm) pieces

1. In small bowl, blend water, soy sauce, wine (or orange juice), cornstarch, and ginger until smooth. Set aside.

2. In large wok or large deep skillet, heat oil over medium-high heat until hot. Stir-fry garlic for 2 minutes, or until soft. Add shrimp and stir-fry for 3 minutes, or until pink. Remove shrimp with slotted spoon and set aside.

3. Add broccoli to wok and stir-fry for 2 minutes, or until bright green. Add bell peppers and snow peas and stir-fry for 1 minute, or until crisp-tender.

4. Return shrimp to wok. Add corn, water chestnuts, and scallions. Pour in reserved sauce mixture and stir-fry for 1 minute, or until sauce thickens and boils.

Per serving: 266 calories, 29 g protein, 23 g carbohydrates, 4 g fiber, 6 g total fat, 1 g saturated fat, 172 mg cholesterol, 992 mg sodium

SHRIMP SEVICHE WITH AVOCADO AND PUMPKIN SEEDS

Serves 4

Prep Time: 15 minutes plus cooling

Cook Time: 3 minutes

Healing Foods: shrimp, oranges, peppers, avocados, seeds

Ailments It Heals: burns, chronic fatigue syndrome, diabetes

1½ tsp ground coriander
¾ tsp salt
1½ lb (750 g) medium shrimp, shelled and deveined
2 tsp grated orange zest
2 cups orange juice
3 Tbsp fresh lime juice
¼ tsp cayenne pepper
1 red bell pepper, cut into matchsticks
¼ cup diced red onion
½ cup chopped cilantro
1 Hass avocado, peeled and cut into ½-in (1 cm) chunks
3 Tbsp hulled roasted pumpkin seeds

1. In large bowl, combine 1 tsp coriander and ¼ tsp salt. Add shrimp, tossing to coat.

2. In separate bowl, stir together orange zest, orange juice, lime juice, cayenne, and remaining ½ tsp salt and ½ tsp coriander. Stir in bell pepper, onion, and cilantro.

3. Preheat broiler. Broil shrimp 6 in (15 cm) from heat, turning once halfway through, for 3 minutes, or until cooked through. Transfer shrimp to bowl with orange mixture and toss to coat. Refrigerate for at least 2 hours, or until well chilled.

4. Serve chilled seviche topped with avocado and pumpkin seeds.

Per serving: 335 calories, 33 g protein, 23 g carbohydrates, 3 g fiber, 13 g total fat, 2 g saturated fat, 211 mg cholesterol, 650 mg sodium

THAI ROASTED SHRIMP

Serves 4
Prep Time: 5 minutes
Cook Time: 8 minutes
Healing Foods: coconuts, shrimp, tomatoes, rice
Ailments It Heals: cancer, celiac disease, respiratory disorders

- 14 oz (398 mL) light coconut milk
- 1 cup reduced-sodium vegetable or chicken broth
- 2 Tbsp reduced-sodium soy sauce
- ¼ to ½ tsp green curry paste
- 1 lb (500 g) shrimp, peeled and deveined
- 8 scallions, thinly sliced
- 1 large tomato, seeded and chopped
- 1 Tbsp lime juice
- 2 cups cooked brown rice or quinoa

1. In large saucepan, whisk together coconut milk, broth, soy sauce, and curry paste. Bring to a boil over medium-high heat. Add shrimp and scallions and cook for 5 minutes, or until shrimp is opaque.

2. Remove from heat and stir in tomato and lime juice. Serve over rice (or quinoa).

Per serving: 311 calories, 23 g protein, 31 g carbohydrates, 3 g fiber, 9 g total fat, 6 g saturated fat, 168 mg cholesterol, 516 mg sodium

BLACK BEAN AND SWEET POTATO BURRITOS

Serves 8
Prep Time: 25 minutes
Cook Time: 20 minutes
Healing Foods: sweet potatoes, tomatoes, beans, wheat, cheese
Ailments It Heals: constipation, diverticulitis, hemorrhoids

- 2 tsp canola oil
- 1 cup chopped onion (1 medium)
- 2 cloves garlic, minced
- 4 tsp ground cumin
- ½ tsp dried oregano
- ¾ cup vegetable broth or reduced-sodium chicken broth
- 1 medium sweet potato, peeled and diced (3 cups)
- 14.5 oz (410 mL) mild green chile–seasoned diced tomatoes with juice
- 15.5 oz (440 mL) black beans, drained and rinsed
- ¾ cup frozen corn
- ¼ cup chopped fresh cilantro
- 1 Tbsp fresh lime juice
- ⅛ tsp ground black pepper
- 8 whole wheat wraps or tortillas, (8-in or 20 cm each)
- 1 cup shredded pepper jack or monterey jack cheese
- ½ cup reduced-fat sour cream

1. Preheat oven to 325°F (160°C).

2. In large nonstick skillet, heat oil over medium heat. Add onion and cook, stirring often, for 2 to 3 minutes, or until softened. Add garlic, cumin, and oregano. Cook, stirring, for 10 to 20 seconds, or until fragrant. Add broth and sweet potato. Bring to a simmer. Cover and cook for 5 minutes. Add tomatoes (with juice), beans, and corn. Return to a simmer. Cover and cook for 5 to 10 minutes, or until sweet potato is tender. Mash about one-quarter of vegetable mixture with potato masher. Stir mashed and unmashed portions together. Stir in cilantro, lime juice, and pepper.

3. Meanwhile, enclose wraps (or tortillas) in foil and heat in oven for 10 to 15 minutes.

4. To serve, spoon about ⅔ cup of sweet potato filling down center of each tortilla. Sprinkle with about 2 Tbsp cheese. Fold in edges of wrap, then fold one side over filling and wrap up burrito. Serve with sour cream for dipping.

Per serving: 349 calories, 12 g protein, 47 g carbohydrates, 15 g fiber, 11 g total fat, 4 g saturated fat, 23 mg cholesterol, 562 mg sodium

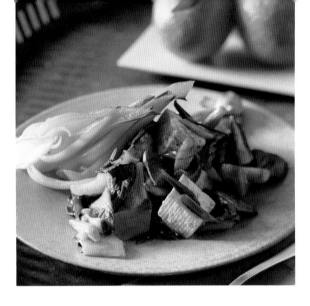

BOK CHOY, TOFU, AND MUSHROOM STIR-FRY

Serves 4
Prep Time: 15 minutes
Cook Time: 13 minutes
Healing Foods: tofu, ginger, garlic, mushrooms, cooking greens
Ailments It Heals: diabetes, menopause, osteoporosis, stroke

15   oz (450 g) extra-firm tofu
 3   Tbsp reduced-sodium soy sauce
 4   tsp dark brown sugar
1½   tsp cornstarch
 1   cup water
 4   tsp olive oil
 4   scallions, thinly sliced
 2   Tbsp minced fresh ginger
 3   cloves garlic, minced

 8   oz (250 g) fresh shiitake mushrooms, stems removed and caps quartered
 8   oz (250 g) button mushrooms, halved
¼   tsp salt
 1   large head bok choy, sliced crosswise into 1-in-wide (2.5 cm) strips

1. Halve tofu horizontally, then cut each piece into 12 squares or triangles. In small bowl, stir together soy sauce, brown sugar, cornstarch, and ½ cup water.

2. In large nonstick skillet, heat 2 tsp oil over medium heat. Add scallions, ginger, and garlic and cook for 1 minute, or until tender.

3. Stir in mushrooms. Add salt and remaining ½ cup water. Cover and cook, stirring occasionally, for 5 minutes, or until mushrooms are tender. Transfer to a bowl.

4. Add bok choy and remaining 2 tsp oil to skillet. Cook, stirring frequently for 5 minutes, or until bok choy is tender.

5. Return mushroom-scallion mixture to skillet and add tofu. Stir soy sauce mixture to recombine and add to skillet. Cook for 2 minutes, or until tofu is heated through and vegetables are coated with sauce.

Per serving: 240 calories, 20 g protein, 20 g carbohydrates, 4 g fiber, 11 g total fat, 1 g saturated fat, 0 mg cholesterol, 760 mg sodium

VEGETABLE POT PIE

Serves 6
Prep Time: 20 minutes
Cook Time: 55 minutes
Healing Foods: celery, onions, carrots, peppers, broccoli, cauliflower
Ailments It Heals: kidney disease, obesity, prostate problems

2 Tbsp butter
2 celery stalks, coarsely chopped
1 yellow onion, coarsely chopped
1 large carrot, peeled and cut into small chunks
1 small red bell pepper, seeded and coarsely chopped
¾ tsp dried thyme, crumbled
3 Tbsp all-purpose flour
1 cup vegetable broth or bouillon
1 cup broccoli florets
1 cup cauliflower florets
1 cup frozen pearl onions
2 oz (60 g) cheddar cheese, cut into small cubes
Pastry dough for one-crust 9-in (23 cm) pie

1. In large nonstick saucepan, melt butter over medium heat. Add celery, yellow onion, carrot, pepper, and thyme. Sauté for 10 minutes, or until vegetables are tender.

2. Stir in flour until well blended. Stir in broth. Increase heat to medium-high. Add broccoli, cauliflower, and pearl onions. Bring to boil, then lower heat and simmer, uncovered, for 15 minutes. Remove saucepan from heat. (If making filling ahead, let cool to room temperature, then cover and refrigerate.)

3. Preheat oven to 400°F (200°C).

4. Spread vegetable mixture in 9-in (23 cm) glass or ceramic pie plate. Top with cheese. Cover filling with pastry. Trim edges. (If crust is not lattice, cut 6 long slits in it, to vent steam.) Place dish on baking sheet.

6. Bake for 25 to 30 minutes, or until pastry is golden and filling is bubbly. Let stand for 10 minutes before serving.

Per serving: 296 calories, 7 g protein, 32 g carbohydrates, 4 g fiber, 17 g total fat, 8 g saturated fat, 27 mg cholesterol, 408 mg sodium

BAKED PASTA WITH GARLIC AND GREENS

Serves 8
Prep Time: 15 minutes
Cook Time: 50 minutes
Healing Foods: pasta, kale, tomatoes, cheese, olives
Ailments It Heals: Alzheimer's disease, arthritis, jet lag, osteoporosis

1 lb (500 g) penne or rigatoni pasta
1 Tbsp olive oil
6 cloves garlic, thinly sliced
10 oz (300 g) frozen kale or collard greens, thawed and well drained
3 cups prepared tomato sauce
1 cup part-skim ricotta cheese
1 cup shredded part-skim mozzarella cheese
Kalamata olives

1. Preheat oven to 350°F (180°C). Lightly coat 2-quart (2 L) baking dish with cooking spray.

2. In large pot of lightly salted boiling water, cook penne until tender, following package directions, and drain.

3. Meanwhile, in medium nonstick skillet, heat oil over medium-low heat. Add garlic. Sauté for 5 minutes, or until golden. Add kale and cook for 5 minutes. Transfer to large bowl. Stir in tomato sauce and ricotta cheese.

4. Add penne to bowl. Mix well. Scrape into baking dish. Top with mozzarella cheese. Cover with foil.

5. Bake for 25 minutes. Remove foil and bake for 10 minutes, or until lightly golden. Garnish with olives.

Per serving: 341 calories, 17 g protein, 53 g carbohydrates, 4 g fiber, 8 g total fat, 4 g saturated fat, 18 mg cholesterol, 810 mg sodium

FARFALLE WITH WINTER SQUASH SAUCE

Serves 4

Prep Time: 15 minutes

Cook Time: 15 minutes

Healing Foods: raisins, pasta, peppers, garlic, squash

Ailments It Heals: constipation, eye problems, Parkinson's disease

- ⅓ cup raisins
- 1 cup boiling water
- 8 oz (250 g) farfalle (bow-tie) pasta
- 1 Tbsp olive oil
- 1 large red bell pepper, diced
- 4 cloves garlic, minced
- 18 oz (510 g) winter squash puree, thawed
- 1 tsp rubbed sage
- ½ tsp salt
- ½ tsp ground black pepper
- 3 Tbsp reduced-fat cream cheese (Neufchâtel)
- ⅓ cup grated parmesan cheese

1. In small bowl, soak raisins in boiling water for 5 minutes, or until plump. In large pot of boiling water, cook pasta according to package directions. Drain, reserving ⅓ cup of cooking liquid.

2. Meanwhile, in large skillet, heat oil over medium heat. Add bell pepper and garlic. Cook, stirring frequently, for 5 minutes, or until pepper is tender. Add squash puree, sage, salt, and black pepper and cook until heated through.

3. Stir in raisins and their soaking liquid and cream cheese. Cook until cream cheese has melted. Transfer mixture to large bowl. Add pasta, reserved cooking liquid, and parmesan and toss to combine.

Per serving: 418 calories, 14 g protein, 73 g carbohydrates, 7 g fiber, 9 g total fat, 3 g saturated fat, 13 mg cholesterol, 469 mg sodium

FUSILLI WITH PAN-ROASTED VEGETABLES

Serves 4

Prep Time: 20 minutes

Cook Time: 25 minutes

Healing Foods: peppers, butternut squash, garlic, tomatoes, spinach, pasta

Ailments It Heals: cancer, cardiovascular disease, eye problems

- 2 Tbsp olive oil
- 1 large sweet onion, cut into thin wedges
- 1 yellow bell pepper, seeded and chopped
- 1 small butternut squash, 1¼ lb (625 g), peeled, seeded, and cut into 1-in (2.5 cm) chunks
- ½ tsp salt
- ¼ cup minced fresh basil
- 5 cloves garlic, minced

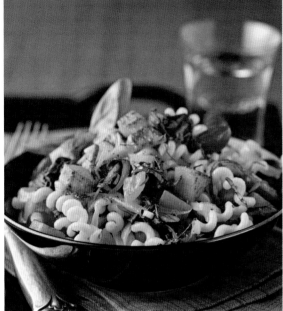

Per serving: 372 calories, 12 g protein, 66 g carbohydrates, 9 g fiber, 9 g total fat, 1 g saturated fat, 1 mg cholesterol, 485 mg sodium

MACARONI AND CHEESE WITH SPINACH

Serves 6

Prep Time: 15 minutes

Cook Time: 55 minutes

Healing Foods: milk, cheese, spinach, pasta, wheat germ

Ailments It Heals: ADHD, cystic fibrosis, interstitial cystitis, jet lag, Parkinson's disease

- 1 cup grape or cherry tomatoes, each cut in half
- 4 cups fresh baby spinach, tough stems removed
- 4 cups reduced-sodium, fat-free chicken broth
- 2 cups water
- 8 oz (250 g) fusilli whole wheat pasta

1. In large nonstick skillet, heat 1 Tbsp oil over medium heat. Add onion and bell pepper. Sauté for 5 minutes, or until softened. Add squash, ¼ tsp salt, basil, and half of garlic. Cover and cook, stirring occasionally, for 8 minutes. Increase heat to high. Cook, uncovered, stirring occasionally, for 5 to 7 minutes, or until vegetables brown slightly and squash is just tender. Transfer mixture to large bowl. Add tomatoes to bowl.

2. In same skillet, heat remaining 1 Tbsp oil over medium heat. Add spinach, remaining garlic, and ¼ tsp salt. Cook, stirring occasionally, for 2 minutes, or until spinach wilts. Add spinach to squash mixture.

3. Meanwhile, in large pot, bring broth and water to a boil. Add fusilli. Cook until tender, following package directions. Reserve ½ cup cooking liquid. Drain fusilli. Combine fusilli, squash mixture, and reserved cooking liquid and serve.

- 1 ¾ cups cold low-fat milk
- 3 Tbsp all-purpose flour
- 2 cups (6 oz or 170 g) grated extra-sharp cheddar cheese
- 1 cup 1% cottage cheese
- ⅛ tsp ground nutmeg
- ½ tsp salt, or to taste
- Ground black pepper to taste
- 10 oz (300 g) frozen spinach or 4 cups individually quick-frozen spinach
- 8 oz (250 g) whole wheat macaroni
- ¼ cup toasted wheat germ

1. Preheat oven to 400°F (200°C). Coat 8-in (20 cm) square baking dish (2-qt or 2 L capacity) with cooking spray. Bring large pot of lightly salted water to a boil for cooking macaroni.

2. Whisk ¼ cup milk with flour in small bowl until smooth. Set aside. In heavy medium saucepan, heat remaining 1½ cups milk over medium heat until steaming. Add flour mixture and cook, whisking constantly, for 2 to 3 minutes, or until sauce boils and thickens. Remove from heat. Add cheddar cheese, stirring until melted. Stir in cottage cheese, nutmeg, salt, and pepper.

3. Cook spinach according to package directions. Drain, refresh under cold water, and press out excess moisture.

4. Cook macaroni in boiling water, stirring often, for 4 to 5 minutes, or until not quite tender. (The macaroni will continue to cook during baking.) Drain, rinse with cold running water, then drain again.

5. In large bowl, mix macaroni with cheese sauce. Spread half of macaroni mixture in baking dish. Spoon spinach on top. Spread remaining macaroni mixture over spinach layer. Sprinkle with wheat germ.

6. Bake for 35 to 45 minutes, or until bubbly and golden.

Per serving: 357 calories, 22 g protein, 40 g carbohydrates, 6 g fiber, 12 g total fat, 7 g saturated fat, 35 mg cholesterol, 606 mg sodium

PASTA PRIMAVERA

Serves 4
Prep Time: 20 minutes
Cook Time: 18 minutes
Healing Foods: cauliflower, broccoli, pasta, mushrooms, tomatoes, milk
Ailments It Heals: alcoholism, hyperthyroidism, interstitial cystitis, jaundice

1⅓	cups small cauliflower florets
1⅓	cups small broccoli florets
7	oz (200 g) plain or spinach fettuccine
2	tsp olive oil
1	small red onion, diced
2	cloves garlic, minced
½	lb (250 g) mushrooms, thinly sliced
½	tsp salt
½	tsp dried rosemary, crumbled
1	medium tomato, cut into ½-in (1 cm) cubes
2	tsp flour
1	cup skim or low-fat milk
¼	cup grated parmesan cheese
¼	cup parsley

1. In large pot of boiling water, cook cauliflower and broccoli for 2 minutes to blanch. With slotted spoon, transfer vegetables to a plate.

2. Add fettuccine to boiling water and cook according to package directions. Drain and transfer to large serving bowl.

3. While fettuccine cooks, heat 1 tsp oil in large nonstick skillet over medium heat. Add onion and garlic and sauté for 5 minutes, or until tender. Add mushrooms and sauté for 3 minutes or until softened.

4. Add remaining 1 tsp oil to skillet and add cauliflower and broccoli, sprinkle with salt and rosemary, and sauté for 1 minute, or until vegetables are heated through. Add tomato and cook for 3 minutes, or until softened.

5. Sprinkle flour over vegetables, stirring to coat. Add milk and bring to a boil. Reduce to a simmer and cook, stirring, for 3 minutes, or until slightly thickened. Stir in cheese and parsley. Add to hot pasta, tossing until combined.

Per serving: 302 calories, 15 g protein, 49 g carbohydrates, 5 g fiber, 6 g total fat, 2 g saturated fat, 11 mg cholesterol, 467 mg sodium

PASTA WITH CABBAGE, APPLES, AND LEEKS

Serves 4

Prep Time: 20 minutes

Cook Time: 15 minutes

Healing Foods: leeks, cabbage, apples, vinegar, pasta

Ailments It Heals: cholesterol (high), lupus, osteoporosis

- 2 Tbsp olive oil
- 2 leeks, halved lengthwise, thinly sliced crosswise, and well washed
- 3 cups packed shredded green cabbage (about 12 oz or 340 g)
- 3 cloves garlic, minced
- 2 large red apples (unpeeled), cut into ½-in (1 cm) chunks
- ½ tsp salt
- ½ tsp ground black pepper
- 2 Tbsp cider vinegar
- 1 Tbsp dijon mustard
- 8 oz (250 g) farfalle (bow-tie) pasta

1. In large skillet, heat oil over medium heat. Add leeks, and cook, stirring frequently, for 5 minutes, or until tender. Add cabbage and garlic and increase heat to high. Cook, stirring frequently, for 5 minutes, or until cabbage is golden brown.

2. Add apples, salt, and pepper and cook for 2 minutes, or until apple is crisp-tender. Stir in vinegar and mustard and cook for 30 seconds to blend flavors.

3. Meanwhile, in large pot of boiling water, cook pasta according to package directions. Drain, reserving ½ cup of pasta cooking water. Transfer drained pasta to large bowl. Add cabbage-apple mixture and reserved pasta cooking water and toss to combine.

Per serving: 385 calories, 9 g protein, 70 g carbohydrates, 6 g fiber, 8 g total fat, 1 g saturated fat, 0 mg cholesterol, 411 mg sodium

PASTA WITH WALNUT CREAM SAUCE

Serves 4

Prep Time: 10 minutes

Cook Time: 10 minutes

Healing Foods: pasta, nuts, garlic, olive oil

Ailments It Heals: arthritis, cystic fibrosis, stress

- 8 oz (250 g) whole grain penne, fusilli, or farfalle (bow-tie) pasta
- 1 cup walnuts, toasted
- 1 to 3 cloves garlic, mashed
- ¼ cup basil leaves
- 2 Tbsp olive oil
- ½ cup low-fat evaporated milk
- ¼ cup grated parmesan cheese

1. Cook pasta according to package directions. Drain and place in large bowl.

2. Meanwhile, in food processor or blender, combine nuts, garlic, and basil. Process or blend until nuts are finely chopped. Add oil and milk and pulse until well blended.

3. Add sauce to bowl with hot pasta and sprinkle with cheese.

Per serving: 479 calories, 16 g protein, 49 g carbohydrates, 4 g fiber, 26 g total fat, 4 g saturated fat, 9 mg cholesterol, 115 mg sodium

PENNE WITH FRESH TOMATO SAUCE AND GRILLED EGGPLANT

Serves 4

Prep Time: 15 minutes plus standing
Cook Time: 18 minutes
Healing Foods: eggplants, garlic, tomatoes, pasta
Ailments It Heals: Alzheimer's disease, prostate problems, urinary tract infections

- 1 lb (500 g) eggplant, cut lengthwise into ¾-in-thick (2 cm) slices
- ½ tsp salt
- 2 Tbsp olive oil
- 4 cloves garlic, thinly sliced
- 1½ lb (750 g) ripe plum tomatoes, halved, seeded, and coarsely chopped
- 1 tsp chopped fresh oregano or ½ tsp dried, crumbled
- 2 tsp balsamic vinegar
- ½ tsp sugar
- 8 oz (250 g) penne pasta
- ¼ cup shaved or shredded parmesan cheese

1. Sprinkle eggplant slices with ¼ tsp salt. Let stand at least 30 minutes to draw out liquid.

2. Meanwhile, in large nonstick skillet, heat oil over medium-low heat. Add garlic. Cook, stirring, for 1 minute. Add tomatoes, oregano, and remaining ¼ tsp salt. Increase heat to medium and cook for 6 minutes, or just until tomatoes are softened. Stir in vinegar and sugar. Cook for 30 seconds longer.

3. Preheat grill or broiler. Rinse eggplant slices and pat dry. Lightly coat both sides of eggplant with olive oil cooking spray. Grill or broil eggplant 4 in (10 cm) from heat for 5 minutes on each side, or until softened and, if grilling, dark grill marks appear. Set aside to cool slightly.

4. Meanwhile, in large pot of lightly salted boiling water, cook penne until tender, following package directions. Drain. Toss with tomato mixture. Coarsely chop eggplant. Add to pasta mixture. Stir in parmesan. Serve hot or at room temperature.

Per serving: 362 calories, 13 g protein, 59 g carbohydrates, 7 g fiber, 10 g total fat, 2 g saturated fat, 4 mg cholesterol, 406 mg sodium

BULGUR WITH DRIED CHERRIES AND CORN

Serves 4
Prep Time: 20 minutes plus standing
Healing Foods: bulgur, tangerines, corn, cherries, peanuts
Ailments It Heals: acne, multiple sclerosis, varicose veins

1	cup medium-grain bulgur
2½	cups boiling water
1	tsp grated tangerine or orange zest
1	cup fresh tangerine or orange juice
2	Tbsp tomato paste
2	Tbsp pomegranate molasses
2	Tbsp olive oil
¾	tsp salt
1½	cups corn kernels
⅔	cup dried cherries
⅔	cup thinly sliced scallions
⅓	cup roasted peanuts, coarsely chopped

1. In large bowl, combine bulgur and boiling water. Let stand for 30 minutes at room temperature. Drain well.

2. Meanwhile, in large bowl, whisk together tangerine zest, tangerine juice, tomato paste, molasses, oil, and salt.

3. Add drained bulgur to bowl and fluff with a fork. Add corn, cherries, scallions, and peanuts, tossing to combine. Serve at room temperature or chilled.

Per serving: 433 calories, 10 g protein, 69 g carbohydrates, 10 g fiber, 14 g total fat, 2 g saturated fat, 0 mg cholesterol, 511 mg sodium

BULGUR WITH SPRING VEGETABLES

Serves 6
Prep Time: 15 minutes plus standing
Cook Time: 10 minutes
Healing Foods: bulgur, leeks, asparagus, peas
Ailments It Heals: circulatory disorders, depression, diabetes, respiratory disorders

1¼	cups bulgur
3½	cups boiling water
2	Tbsp olive oil
3	Tbsp fresh lemon juice
1	tsp salt
½	tsp ground black pepper
2	leeks, halved lengthwise, cut crosswise into 1-in (2.5 cm) pieces, and well washed
2	cloves garlic, minced
12	asparagus spears, cut into 2-in (5 cm) lengths
1	cup frozen peas
¼	cup chopped fresh mint

1. In large heatproof bowl, combine bulgur and boiling water. Let stand for 30 minutes, stirring after 15 minutes, until bulgur is tender. Drain well in large fine-meshed sieve.

2. In large bowl, whisk together 1 Tbsp oil, lemon juice, salt, and pepper. Add drained bulgur and fluff with a fork.

3. In medium skillet, heat remaining 1 Tbsp oil over low heat. Add leeks and garlic to skillet and cook for 5 minutes, or until leeks are tender. Transfer to bowl with bulgur.

4. In steamer set over a pan of boiling water, steam asparagus for 4 minutes, or until tender. Add peas during final 30 seconds of steaming. Add to bowl of bulgur along with mint and toss to combine. Serve at room temperature or chilled.

Per serving: 188 calories, 6 g protein, 32 g carbohydrates, 8 g fiber, 5 g total fat, 1 g saturated fat, 0 mg cholesterol, 330 mg sodium

QUINOA WITH CHILES AND CILANTRO

Serves 6

Prep Time: 15 minutes
Cook Time: 35 minutes
Healing Foods: quinoa, chiles, cilantro, seeds, limes
Ailments It Heals: AIDS and HIV infections, celiac disease, jaundice

- 1 cup quinoa
- 2 tsp canola oil
- 1 cup chopped onion (1 medium)
- 4 oz (125 g) chopped green chiles
- 2 cloves garlic, minced
- 1¾ cups reduced-sodium chicken broth or vegetable broth
- ¾ cup coarsely chopped fresh cilantro
- ½ cup chopped scallions
- ¼ cup pepitas (pumpkin seeds), toasted
- 2 Tbsp lime juice
- ¼ tsp salt, or to taste

1. In large dry skillet, toast quinoa over medium heat, stirring often, for 3 to 5 minutes, or until it crackles and becomes aromatic. Transfer to a fine sieve and rinse thoroughly.

2. Heat oil in large saucepan over medium heat. Add onion and cook, stirring often, for 2 to 3 minutes, or until softened. Add chiles and garlic. Cook, stirring, for 30 seconds. Add broth and quinoa and bring to a simmer. Reduce heat to low, cover, and cook for 20 to 25 minutes, or until quinoa is tender and most of liquid has been absorbed.

3. Add cilantro, scallions, pepitas, lime juice, and salt to quinoa. Mix gently and fluff with a fork.

Per serving: 182 calories, 7 g protein, 27 g carbohydrates, 4 g fiber, 6 g total fat, 1 g saturated fat, 0 mg cholesterol, 145 mg sodium

SPRINGTIME QUINOA

Serves 6

Prep Time: 10 minutes
Cook Time: 25 minutes
Healing Foods: quinoa, asparagus, peas
Ailments It Heals: bleeding problems, jaundice, migraines and other headaches, PCOS

- 1 cup quinoa, rinsed and drained
- ½ tsp salt
- 2 cups water
- 1 Tbsp olive oil
- 1 small red onion, halved and cut into thin slices
- ½ cup vegetable or chicken broth
- 1 lb (500 g) asparagus, cut into 2-in (5 cm) pieces
- 1 cup fresh peas

1. In small saucepan over high heat, bring quinoa, salt, and water to a boil. Reduce heat to low, cover, and simmer for 15 minutes, or until water is absorbed.

2. Meanwhile, in large nonstick skillet, heat oil over medium heat. Add onion and cook for 4 minutes, or until lightly browned. Add broth, asparagus, and peas and cook for 5 minutes, or until crisp-tender. Stir in quinoa.

Per serving: 171 calories, 8 g protein, 28 g carbohydrates, 5 g fiber, 4 g total fat, 1 g saturated fat, 0 mg cholesterol, 262 mg sodium

BAKED RICE WITH WILD MUSHROOMS AND CHEESE

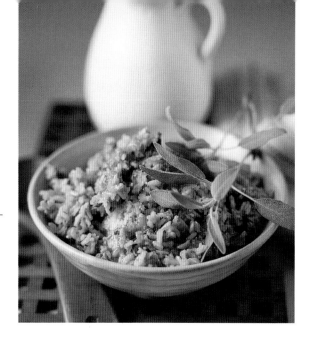

Serves 6

Prep Time: 20 minutes plus standing

Cook Time: 55 minutes

Healing Foods: mushrooms, tomatoes, rice, cheese

Ailments It Heals: cancer, cystic fibrosis, diverticulitis

⅓ cup dried porcini mushrooms

2½ cups hot water

⅓ cup sun-dried tomatoes (not oil-packed)

1 tsp olive oil

1 large onion, finely chopped

3 cloves garlic, minced

1 cup brown rice

1 tsp salt

½ tsp rubbed sage

½ tsp ground black pepper

½ cup shredded reduced-fat sharp cheddar cheese

2 Tbsp grated parmesan cheese

1. Place porcini in small bowl and pour 1 ½ cups hot water over them. Place sun-dried tomatoes in separate small bowl and pour remaining 1 cup hot water over them. Let both stand for 20 minutes, or until softened.

2. Scoop mushrooms out of soaking liquid. Finely chop mushrooms. Strain soaking liquid through fine-meshed sieve into bowl. Strain sun-dried tomato soaking liquid into same bowl and set aside. Coarsely chop tomatoes.

3. Preheat oven to 350°F (180°C). In medium saucepan, heat oil and 3 Tbsp mushroom-tomato soaking liquid over medium heat. Add onion and garlic and cook for 7 minutes, or until onion is golden. Add rice, stirring to coat. Add mushrooms, tomatoes, salt, sage, and pepper. Stir until well combined.

4. Transfer mixture to 8-in (2 L) square glass baking dish. Pour remaining soaking liquid on top and stir to combine. Cover with foil and bake for 45 minutes, or until rice is tender and liquid is absorbed. Sprinkle with cheeses.

Per serving: 199 calories, 9 g protein, 33 g carbohydrates, 3 g fiber, 4 g total fat, 2 g saturated fat, 5 mg cholesterol, 518 mg sodium

BROWN RICE WITH CABBAGE AND CHICKPEAS

Serves 4
Prep Time: 15 minutes
Cook Time: 47 minutes
Healing Foods: garlic, cabbage, rice, chickpeas, tomatoes, raisins
Ailments It Heals: depression, gallstones, infertility, obesity, psoriasis

1 Tbsp olive oil
1 large red onion, finely chopped
5 cloves garlic, thinly sliced
12 oz (375 g) green cabbage, cut into 1-in (2.5 cm) chunks (about 6 cups)
¾ cup brown rice
2 cups water
¾ tsp salt
19 oz (540 mL) canned chickpeas, drained and rinsed
1 cup canned tomatoes, chopped, with their juice
¾ cup raisins

1. In large saucepan, heat oil over medium heat. Add onion and garlic and cook, stirring frequently, for 7 minutes, or until onion is tender.

2. Stir in cabbage. Cover and cook for 5 minutes, or until cabbage begins to wilt.

3. Stir in brown rice, water, and salt and bring to a boil. Reduce to a simmer, cover, and cook for 25 minutes, or until rice is almost done.

4. Stir in chickpeas, tomatoes, and raisins and bring to a boil. Reduce to a simmer, cover, and cook for 10 minutes, or until rice is tender.

Per serving: 392 calories, 11 g protein, 75 g carbohydrates, 10 g fiber, 7 g total fat, 1 g saturated fat, 0 mg cholesterol, 710 mg sodium

FRIED RICE WITH TOFU AND VEGETABLES

Serves 4
Prep Time: 20 minutes plus marinating
Cook Time: 20 minutes
Healing Foods: ginger, tofu, rice
Ailments It Heals: cystic fibrosis, menopause, osteoporosis, stroke

1 cup dry white wine or chicken broth
¼ cup light soy sauce
2 Tbsp honey
1 Tbsp grated peeled fresh ginger
12 oz (375 g) extra-firm tofu, cut into 1-in (2.5 cm) cubes
1 cup long-grain white or brown rice
2 cloves garlic, minced
16 oz (480 g) frozen mixed Chinese vegetables, slightly thawed
¼ tsp ground black pepper
5 scallions, cut into 2-in (5 cm) pieces
1 large egg, lightly beaten

1. In large resealable plastic bag, combine wine, 1 Tbsp soy sauce, honey, and 1 tsp ginger. Add tofu, press out excess air, close bag, and shake gently to coat. Marinate in refrigerator for 1 hour, turning occasionally.

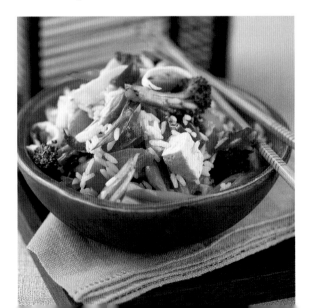

2. Cook rice according to package directions. Keep warm.

3. Meanwhile, lightly coat wok or large deep skillet with cooking spray and set over high heat until hot but not smoking. Stir-fry garlic and remaining ginger for 1 minute, or until fragrant. Add rice, mixed vegetables, pepper, half of scallions, and remaining soy sauce. Stir-fry for 4 minutes, or until mixed vegetables are heated through. Push ingredients to one side of wok, then pour in beaten egg. Cook egg until almost set, cutting into strips with heatproof spatula.

4. Pour marinade into small saucepan. Boil over high heat for 2 minutes. Add tofu and marinade to wok. Stir-fry for 4 minutes, or until tofu is heated. Sprinkle with remaining scallions.

Per serving: 442 calories, 21 g protein, 61 g carbohydrates, 3 g fiber, 9 g total fat, 2 g saturated fat, 53 mg cholesterol, 668 mg sodium

RICE SALAD WITH CHICKEN AND GRAPES

Serves 8
Prep Time: 15 minutes
Cook Time: 25 minutes
Healing Foods: onions, rice, vinegar, chicken, grapes
Ailments It Heals: celiac disease, insomnia, peptic ulcers

⅓ cup olive oil
2 onions, finely chopped
1 tsp sugar
2 cups jasmine rice (Thai fragrant rice) or basmati rice

1½ cups salt-reduced chicken stock
¾ tsp salt
1½ cups water
½ cup rice vinegar
4 cups shredded cooked chicken breasts, leftover or poached
2 cups seedless grapes
4 Tbsp chopped fresh cilantro
½ cup pine nuts, toasted

1. In large saucepan, heat 2 Tbsp oil over medium-low heat. Add onions and sugar and cook, stirring frequently, for 7 minutes, or until onions are tender. Stir in rice, stock, ½ tsp salt, and water. Bring to a boil, reduce to a simmer, cover, and cook for 17 minutes, or until rice is tender. Drain off any excess liquid.

2. In large bowl, whisk together vinegar and remaining oil and ¼ tsp salt. Add rice mixture to bowl and toss with a fork to combine.

3. Add chicken, grapes, coriander, and pine nuts and toss with a fork. Serve immediately, or chilled.

Per serving: 441 calories, 25 g protein, 45 g carbohydrates, 2 g fiber, 17 g total fat, 2 g saturated fat, 54 mg cholesterol, 276 mg sodium

RICE-STUFFED SQUASH

Serves 4
Prep Time: 25 minutes
Cook Time: 1 hour 5 minutes
Healing Foods: rice, acorn squash, cranberries, cheese
Ailments It Heals: blood pressure, eczema, gallstones

4. Spoon rice stuffing into squashes, pressing it down, and mounding it up neatly on top. Replace reserved hats on top. Bake for 45 minutes, or until flesh of squash is tender when pierced with a small sharp knife. Serve hot.

Per serving: 415 calories, 12 g protein, 89 g carbohydrates, 12 g fiber, 4 g total fat, 2 g saturated fat, 8 mg cholesterol, 85 mg sodium

- 1 cup mixed basmati and wild rice
- 3 cups water
- 4 small acorn squashes

Salt and ground black pepper

- ¾ cup cooked chestnuts (canned or vacuum packed), roughly chopped
- ¾ cup dried cranberries
- 1 small red onion, finely chopped
- 2 Tbsp chopped fresh thyme
- 2 Tbsp chopped parsley
- ¾ cup grated mozzarella cheese

1. Put rice and water in saucepan and bring to a boil. Cover and simmer very gently for 20 minutes, or until rice is just tender. Drain off any excess water.

2. Meanwhile, preheat oven to 350°F (180°C). Using a large, sharp knife, slice off top quarter (stalk end) of each squash. Set aside these little "hats," then scoop out seeds and fiber from center of squashes using a small spoon. Trim bases to make them level, if necessary. Season cavity of each squash lightly with salt and pepper, then place in large ovenproof dish or roasting pan.

3. In large bowl, mix together rice, chestnuts, cranberries, onion, thyme, parsley, and cheese. Season lightly with salt and pepper.

THAI COCONUT RICE

Serves 6
Prep Time: 5 minutes plus standing
Cook Time: 20 minutes
Healing Foods: coconuts, rice, cilantro
Ailments It Heals: celiac disease, insomnia

- 1¼ cups water
- ¾ cup canned light coconut milk
- ½ tsp salt

Pinch of allspice

- 1 cup jasmine rice, rinsed
- ¼ tsp coconut extract
- 1 Tbsp chopped fresh cilantro (optional)

1. In medium saucepan, bring water, coconut milk, salt, and allspice to a boil. Stir in rice and coconut extract, cover, and reduce heat to low. Simmer for 15 to 20 minutes, or until liquid is absorbed and rice is tender.

2. Remove pan from heat and let stand, covered, for 10 minutes. Fluff rice with a fork and scatter on the cilantro, if using.

Per serving: 75 calories, 2 g protein, 12 g carbohydrates, 1 g fiber, 2 g total fat, 2 g saturated fat, 0 mg cholesterol, 200 mg sodium

ARTICHOKES WITH LENTILS AND LIMA BEANS

Serves 4
Prep Time: 25 minutes
Cook Time: 45 minutes
Healing Foods: artichokes, lemons, garlic, lentils, lima beans
Ailments It Heals: constipation, irritable bowel syndrome, multiple sclerosis

- 4 large artichokes
- 3 Tbsp fresh lemon juice
- 1 Tbsp olive oil
- 1 small onion, finely chopped
- 3 cloves garlic, minced
- 1 large carrot, diced
- ¾ cup lentils, picked over and rinsed
- 1½ cups carrot juice
- ¾ tsp salt
- ½ tsp dried thyme
- 1 cup water
- 10 oz (300 g) frozen lima beans
- 3 oz (90 g) feta cheese

1. To trim artichokes: Remove tough outer leaves. Trim tough end of stem. Then, with a paring knife, peel tough skin off remaining stem. Cut off top of artichoke to just about 1 in (2.5 cm) above base. Halve artichokes lengthwise, then scoop out and discard chokes. Halve artichokes again. Place cleaned artichokes in a bowl with cold water to cover. Add 1 Tbsp lemon juice and set aside.

2. In Dutch oven, heat oil over medium heat. Add onion and garlic and cook, stirring frequently for 5 minutes, or until onion is golden brown. Stir in carrot and cook for 4 minutes.

3. Remove artichokes from water and place in Dutch oven. Stir in lentils, carrot juice, salt, thyme, water, and remaining 2 Tbsp lemon juice. Bring to a boil. Reduce to a simmer, cover, and cook for 25 minutes.

4. Stir in lima beans and cook for 10 minutes, or until artichokes, lima beans, and lentils are tender. Serve topped with crumbled feta cheese.

Per serving: 423 calories, 25 g protein, 68 g carbohydrates, 16 g fiber, 9 g total fat, 4 g saturated fat, 19 mg cholesterol, 907 mg sodium

BALSAMIC BEETS WITH TOASTED PECANS

Serves 4
Prep Time: 5 minutes
Cook Time: 10 minutes
Healing Foods: pecans, vinegar, beets
Ailments It Heals: cardiovascular disease, eye problems, menstrual problems

- 3 Tbsp chopped pecans
- 2 Tbsp balsamic vinegar
- 1 tsp sugar
- 2 tsp butter or margarine
- 3 medium beets, steamed, peeled, and sliced or 1 jar (15 oz or 450 g) sliced beets, drained

1. In medium nonstick skillet over medium heat, toast pecans, stirring often, for 4 minutes, or until browned. Transfer to plate.

2. In same skillet over medium-low heat, add vinegar, sugar, butter, and beets. Cook, stirring often, for 5 minutes, or until beets are heated through and liquid is absorbed. Top with pecans. Serve at once.

Per serving: 86 calories, 1 g protein, 8 g carbohydrates, 2 g fiber, 6 g total fat, 2 g saturated fat, 5 mg cholesterol, 140 mg sodium

ORANGE BEETS

Serves 6
Prep Time: 15 minutes
Cook Time: 50 minutes plus cooling
Healing Foods: beets, olive oil, vinegar
Ailments It Heals: cancer, circulatory disorders, psoriasis

4	medium beets with greens
1	Tbsp olive oil
1	clove garlic, minced
½	tsp salt
3	Tbsp orange marmalade
1	Tbsp white wine vinegar
¼	tsp ground black pepper

1. Preheat oven to 350°F (180°C). Trim greens from beets and set aside. Fold a 36-in (90 cm) piece of foil in half crosswise. Scrub beets and place in center of foil. Sprinkle with 1 tsp water and seal foil around beets. Roast for 45 minutes, or until tender. Let cool for 15 minutes, then remove skins and cut each beet into eight wedges.

2. Meanwhile, trim stems from beet greens, wash greens, and cut into 1-in (2.5 cm) strips. While beets are cooling, heat oil in skillet over medium-high heat. Add garlic and cook for 1 minute. Add greens and ¼ tsp salt and cook, stirring constantly, for 2 minutes, or until wilted. Transfer to a serving dish.

3. Add marmalade, vinegar, pepper, and remaining ¼ tsp salt to skillet over medium-high heat and cook for 5 minutes, or until hot and bubbling. Add beets and toss to coat well. Transfer to serving dish with greens and toss.

Per serving: 75 calories, 1 g protein, 13 g carbohydrates, 2 g fiber, 2 g total fat, 0 g saturated fat, 0 mg cholesterol, 253 mg sodium

SESAME GREENS AND BEAN SPROUTS

Serves 6
Prep Time: 10 minutes
Cook Time: 8 minutes
Healing Foods: seeds, cabbage, bean sprouts
Ailments It Heals: arthritis, bleeding problems, chronic fatigue syndrome, eczema, fibroids

1	Tbsp sesame seeds
2	tsp canola oil
1	onion, chopped
2	cloves garlic, chopped
1	small Savoy cabbage, finely shredded
1	small head bok choy, finely shredded
1	cup bean sprouts
4	Tbsp oyster sauce
2	Tbsp water

1. Salt and ground black pepper

2. Heat small saucepan over medium heat and dry-roast sesame seeds, shaking pan frequently, until they are just beginning to brown. Pour seeds into small bowl and set aside.

3. Heat oil in wok or large frying pan. Add onion and garlic and stir-fry for 2 to 3 minutes, or until softened slightly. Add cabbage and bok choy and stir-fry over high heat for 2 to 3 minutes, or until vegetables are just beginning to soften. Add bean sprouts and continue cooking for a few seconds.

4. Make a space in center of pan. Add oyster sauce and water and stir until hot, then toss vegetables into sauce. Taste and add salt if necessary (depending on the saltiness of the oyster sauce) and pepper. Serve immediately, sprinkled with toasted sesame seeds.

Per serving: 68 calories, 3 g protein, 10 g carbohydrates, 4 g fiber, 3 g total fat, 0 g saturated fat, 0 mg cholesterol, 336 mg sodium

ORANGE-WALNUT BROCCOLI

Serves 6
Prep Time: 5 minutes
Cook Time: 11 minutes
Healing Foods: nuts, broccoli, oranges
Ailments It Heals: gout, halitosis, infertility, varicose veins

- 6 large walnut halves
- 1 lb (500 g) broccoli florets
- 3 Tbsp orange juice
- 1½ Tbsp extra-virgin olive oil
- 1 Tbsp chopped fresh basil
- 1 tsp grated orange zest
- ¼ tsp salt
- ⅛ tsp ground black pepper

1. Heat large nonstick skillet over medium-high heat. When hot, add walnuts and toast for 2 to 3 minutes, or until fragrant. Remove to cutting board, cool, and chop.

2. Add broccoli and orange juice to same skillet, cover, and cook for 3 minutes. Uncover and cook until liquid evaporates.

3. Add oil and sauté for 5 to 6 minutes, or until broccoli is tender.

4. Add basil, orange zest, salt, and pepper and remove from heat. Sprinkle with walnuts.

Per serving: 70 calories, 3 g protein, 5 g carbohydrates, 2 g fiber, 5 total fat, 1 g saturated fat, 0 mg cholesterol, 117 mg sodium

BROCCOLI AND CAULIFLOWER WITH CREAM SAUCE

Serves 4
Prep Time: 10 minutes
Cook Time: 13 minutes
Healing Foods: carrots, broccoli, cauliflower
Ailments It Heals: dental problems, lupus, memory loss, prostate problems

- ½ cup carrot juice
- 3 Tbsp reduced-fat sour cream
- 2 cups broccoli florets
- 2 cups cauliflower florets

1. In small saucepan over high heat, boil carrot juice for 8 minutes, or until reduced to ¼ cup. Remove from heat. Whisk in sour cream.

2. In steamer set over a pan of boiling water, steam broccoli and cauliflower for 5 minutes, or until crisp-tender. Transfer to serving dish. Serve with sour cream sauce.

Per serving: 44 calories, 3 g protein, 6 g carbohydrates, 2 g fiber, 2 g total fat, 1 g saturated fat, 4 mg cholesterol, 45 mg sodium

3. Stir in basil, cover, and heat for a few more seconds. Serve immediately.

Per serving: 74 calories, 4 g protein, 11 g carbohydrates, 5 g fiber, 3 g total fat, 0 g saturated fat, 0 mg cholesterol, 43 mg sodium

BASIL-SCENTED SAUTÉED VEGETABLES

Serves 4
Prep Time: 10 minutes
Cook Time: 8 minutes
Healing Foods: broccoli, garlic, peppers, turnips
Ailments It Heals: acne, burns, gout, varicose veins

1   lb (500 g) broccoli
2   tsp olive oil
3   or 4 large cloves garlic, thinly sliced
1   large or 2 small red bell peppers, seeded and cut into 1-in (2.5 cm) squares
1   small turnip, cut into ½-in (1 cm) cubes
Pinch of sugar
Salt
6   Tbsp water
8   sprigs fresh basil, stems discarded, leaves finely shredded

1. Cut broccoli into small florets, then trim and thinly slice stalks. In large nonstick skillet or wok, heat oil over medium-high heat. Add garlic, bell pepper, turnip, and broccoli stalks. Sprinkle in sugar and salt to taste. Cook for 2 to 3 minutes, stirring frequently.

2. Add broccoli florets and stir. Add water to provide a thin covering on bottom of pan. Cover and cook over high heat for 3 to 4 minutes, or until just tender and bright green.

FRUITY BRUSSELS SPROUTS

Serves 4
Prep Time: 25 minutes
Healing Foods: brussels sprouts, apples, carrots, celery, dates
Ailments It Heals: colds and flu, fibroids, infertility, interstitial cystitis

3   tsp créme fraîche
1½ Tbsp low-fat mayonnaise
2   tsp olive oil
Grated zest and juice of 1 orange
2   tsp white wine vinegar
Salt and ground black pepper
8   oz (250 g) brussels sprouts
1   apple
1   carrot, grated
3   celery stalks, chopped
2   Tbsp chopped fresh cilantro
1   oz (30 g) fresh dates, stoned and chopped

1. In a small bowl, whisk together crème fraîche, mayonnaise, oil, orange zest and juice, and vinegar. Season to taste with salt and pepper. Set dressing aside.

2. Trim off and discard bases and outer leaves of sprouts, then shred finely and put into a large bowl. Cut unpeeled apple into quarters, remove core, and chop into small chunks. Add to bowl along with carrot and celery.

3. Stir in enough dressing to coat salad, saving any left over to serve on the side. Scatter cilantro and dates over salad and serve.

Per serving: 122 calories, 2 g protein, 18 g carbohydrates, 4 g fiber, 5 g total fat, 1 g saturated fat, 5 mg cholesterol, 104 mg sodium

½ cup reduced-sodium chicken broth or vegetable broth

3 Tbsp cider vinegar

¼ tsp salt, or to taste

1. Ground black pepper to taste

2. Quarter brussels sprouts with sharp knife or shred in food processor fitted with a slicing disk.

3. In large nonstick skillet, heat oil over medium-high heat. Add onion and bell pepper. Cook, stirring often, for 3 to 4 minutes, or until softened. Add caraway seeds and cook, stirring, for 30 seconds. Add brussels sprouts and cook, stirring, for 2 minutes.

4. Add broth, cover, and cook for 2 to 3 minutes, or until sprouts are crisp-tender. Stir in vinegar, salt, and pepper.

Per serving: 75 calories, 3 g protein, 11 g carbohydrates, 4 g fiber, 3 g total fat, 0 g saturated fat, 0 mg cholesterol, 233 mg sodium

BRUSSELS SPROUTS WITH CARAWAY SEEDS

Serves 4
Prep Time: 15 minutes
Cook Time: 10 minutes
Healing Foods: brussels sprouts, onions, peppers, seeds, vinegar
Ailments It Heals: Alzheimer's disease, bleeding disorders, fibroids

3 cups brussels sprouts, trimmed and cored
2 tsp canola oil
1 cup sliced onion (1 medium)
1 medium red bell pepper, cored, seeded, and cut into 2-in-long (5 cm) slivers
1½ tsp caraway seeds

NAPA CABBAGE SLAW WITH PEANUT DRESSING

Serves 6
Prep Time: 20 minutes
Healing Foods: peanut butter, tea, vinegar, chiles, cabbage
Ailments It Heals: blood pressure, cancer, osteoporosis

⅓ cup natural peanut butter
¼ cup hot brewed black or green tea
4 tsp reduced-sodium soy sauce
4 tsp rice vinegar
1½ tsp brown sugar
1 tsp hot sauce, such as sriracha, chile-garlic sauce, or Tabasco

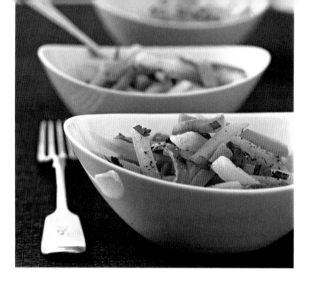

1 clove garlic, minced
4 cups thinly sliced napa cabbage
1 cup shredded carrots
½ cup chopped scallions
⅓ cup unsalted roasted peanuts

1. Place peanut butter in large bowl and gradually whisk in hot tea. Add soy sauce, vinegar, brown sugar, hot sauce, and garlic and whisk until smooth.

2. Add cabbage, carrots, and scallions and toss to coat well. Sprinkle with peanuts.

Per serving: 158 calories, 7 g protein, 11 g carbohydrates, 3 g fiber, 11 g total fat, 2 g saturated fat, 0 mg cholesterol, 226 mg sodium

BRAISED CARROT, CELERY, AND FENNEL

Serves 4
Prep Time: 10 minutes
Cook Time: 18 minutes
Healing Foods: carrots, celery, onions, fennel
Ailments It Heals: blood pressure, eye problems, obesity

4 carrots, peeled, halved lengthwise, and cut into 2½ x ¼-in (6 x 0.5 cm) pieces
3 celery ribs, peeled and cut into 2½ x ¼-in (6 x 0.5 cm) pieces
1 small red onion, thinly sliced
½ fennel bulb, cored and thinly sliced
14.5 oz (440 mL) reduced-sodium, fat-free chicken broth
Salt and ground black pepper
2 tsp butter

1. In large saucepan over medium-high heat, add carrots, celery, onion, fennel, and broth. Bring to

boil, then reduce heat and simmer, covered, for 15 minutes, or until vegetables are tender.

2. Uncover saucepan. Boil for 2 to 3 minutes, or until liquid reduces slightly. Season to taste with salt and pepper. Stir in butter and serve.

Per serving: 77 calories, 3 g protein, 13 g carbohydrates, 4 g fiber, 2 g total fat, 1 g saturated fat, 5 mg cholesterol, 616 mg sodium

CARROT AND PARSNIP PUREE

Serves 4
Prep Time: 10 minutes
Cook Time: 20 minutes
Healing Foods: carrots, parsnips
Ailments It Heals: dental problems, multiple sclerosis, Parkinson's disease, PCOS

3 large carrots, peeled and chopped
1 large parsnip, peeled and chopped
½ tsp salt
1 Tbsp butter or vegetable oil
1 tsp grated orange zest

1. In medium saucepan, combine carrots, parsnip, salt, and enough water to barely cover vegetables.

Simmer, uncovered, for 20 minutes, or until vegetables are very tender and most of liquid has evaporated.

2. Drain vegetables. Transfer to food processor or blender. Add butter and orange zest. Process until vegetables form a smooth puree.

Per serving: 82 calories, 1 g protein, 13 g carbohydrates, 3 g fiber, 3 g total fat, 2 g saturated fat, 8 mg cholesterol, 408 mg sodium

ROASTED ROOT VEGETABLES

Serves 4
Prep Time: 10 minutes
Cook Time: 40 minutes
Healing Foods: carrots, parsnips, ginger, cinnamon
Ailments It Heals: AIDS and HIV infections, migraines and other headaches, stroke, respiratory disorders

1 lb (500 g) carrots, peeled and sliced diagonally into ½-in (1 cm) pieces
1 lb (500 g) parsnips, peeled and sliced diagonally into ½-in (1 cm) pieces
2 Tbsp olive oil
1 Tbsp grated fresh ginger
1 tsp ground cinnamon
½ tsp salt

1. Preheat oven to 400°F (200°C). Place carrots, parsnips, oil, ginger, cinnamon, and salt in large roasting pan and toss to coat well. Roast, turning occasionally, for 40 minutes, or until tender and browned.

Per serving: 199 calories, 3 g protein, 33 g carbohydrates, 9 g fiber, 7 g total fat, 1 g saturated fat, 0 mg cholesterol, 361 mg sodium

CAULIFLOWER AND SPINACH CASSEROLE

Serves 6
Prep Time: 20 minutes
Cook Time: 50 minutes
Healing Foods: paprika, cauliflower, spinach, milk, cheese
Ailments It Heals: Alzheimer's disease, chronic fatigue syndrome, lupus, prostate problems

3 Tbsp plain dry bread crumbs
1 tsp olive oil
¼ tsp paprika
1 medium cauliflower (about 2½ lb or 1.25 kg), cored and cut into 1½-in (3.5 cm) florets (about 7 cups)
10 oz (300 g) fresh spinach or kale (12 cups), stems trimmed, washed
1¾ cups cold low-fat milk
3 Tbsp all-purpose flour
1⅓ cups grated extra-sharp cheddar cheese
1½ tsp dry mustard
½ tsp salt, or to taste
Ground black pepper to taste

1. Preheat oven to 425°F (220°C). Coat a 12 × 8-in (30 × 20 cm) shallow baking dish (2½-qt or 2½ L capacity) with cooking spray.

2. In small bowl, mix bread crumbs, oil, and paprika.

3. In large pot of lightly salted boiling water, cook cauliflower, uncovered, for 6 minutes, or until tender. Stir in spinach and cook for 1 minute, or until spinach has wilted. Drain and rinse vegetables with cold water to stop further cooking. Drain thoroughly and spread in baking dish.

4. In small bowl, whisk ¼ cup milk with flour until smooth. In heavy medium saucepan, heat remaining

1 Tbsp canola oil

1 tsp cumin seeds

2 medium onions, thinly sliced (2 cups)

2 jalapeño chile peppers, seeded and minced
(wear gloves when handling; they burn)

4 cloves garlic, minced

1 Tbsp grated fresh ginger

1 Tbsp ground coriander

1 tsp ground cumin

½ tsp turmeric

1 cup water

1 medium head cauliflower, cut into florets
(7 to 8 cups)

¾ tsp salt, or to taste

1 medium tomato, diced (1 cup)

1 cup frozen green peas, rinsed under cold
water to thaw

⅓ cup chopped fresh cilantro

Lime wedges

1½ cups milk over medium heat until steaming. Remove from heat and whisk in flour mixture. Return to medium heat and cook, whisking constantly, for 2 to 3 minutes, or until sauce bubbles and thickens. Remove from heat. Stir in cheese, mustard, salt, and pepper. Pour sauce over vegetables in baking dish, spreading evenly. Sprinkle with bread crumb mixture.

5. Bake, uncovered, for 30 to 35 minutes, or until golden and bubbly.

Per serving: 224 calories, 14 g protein, 21 g carbohydrates, 14 g fiber, 11 g total fat, 6 g saturated fat, 31 mg cholesterol, 530 mg sodium

1. In Dutch oven, heat oil over medium-high heat. Add cumin seeds and cook, stirring, for 10 to 20 seconds, or until they sizzle. Add onions, chile peppers, garlic, and ginger. Cook, stirring often, for 2 to 3 minutes, or until softened. Add coriander, ground cumin, and turmeric. Stir for 10 to 20 seconds, or until fragrant. Add water, cauliflower, and salt. Stir to coat well. Cover and cook for 8 minutes, or until cauliflower is almost tender.

2. Stir in tomato and peas. Cover and cook for 2 to 3 minutes, or until cauliflower is tender and peas are heated through. Sprinkle with cilantro and serve with lime wedges. Leftovers will keep, covered, in refrigerator for up to 2 days. Reheat in microwave.

Per serving: 85 calories, 4 g protein, 13 g carbohydrates, 4 g fiber, 3 g total fat, 0 g saturated fat, 0 mg cholesterol, 349 mg sodium

SPICED CAULIFLOWER WITH PEAS

Serves 6

Prep Time: 25 minutes

Cook Time: 15 minutes

Healing Foods: cumin, cauliflower, tomatoes, peas, cilantro

Ailments It Heals: diabetes, fibroids, neuralgia

GREEN BEANS WITH TOMATOES AND OLIVES

Serves 4

Prep Time: 5 minutes

Cook Time: 25 minutes

Healing Foods: onions, green beans, tomatoes, olives

Ailments It Heals: Alzheimer's disease, prostate problems, urinary tract infections

1 Tbsp olive oil

1 cup chopped onions

1 small clove garlic, minced

1 lb (500 g) green beans, trimmed

15 oz (425 mL) petite-cut diced tomatoes, with juice

½ tsp dried oregano

1 tsp red wine vinegar

1 Tbsp chopped pitted kalamata olives

⅛ tsp ground black pepper

1. In large nonstick skillet, heat oil over medium-high heat. Add onions and cook for 4 minutes, or until soft. Add garlic and green beans and cook for 1 minute.

2. Stir in tomatoes (with juice) and oregano. Reduce heat to medium-low, cover, and simmer gently for 15 to 20 minutes, or until green beans are tender.

3. Stir in vinegar, olives, and pepper.

Per serving: 107 calories, 3 g protein, 17 g carbohydrates, 4 g fiber, 4 g total fat, 1 g saturated fat, 0 mg cholesterol, 343 mg sodium

BRAISED MIXED GREENS WITH DRIED CURRANTS

Serves 4 to 6

Prep Time: 10 minutes

Cook Time: 16 minutes

Healing Foods: garlic, cooking greens

Ailments It Heals: hyperthyroidism, hypothyroidism, mood disorders, sex drive (diminished)

1 Tbsp extra-virgin olive oil

3 cloves garlic, thinly sliced

1 lb (500 g) mixed cooking greens (collards, kale, turnip greens, and mustard), rinsed and slightly drained

1 Tbsp dried currants

1. In small skillet, heat oil and garlic over low heat, stirring, until garlic begins to sizzle. Watch carefully and remove from heat when garlic begins to turn golden, after about 5 minutes. Set aside.

2. In large wide pan, cook greens and currants over medium heat, covered, turning once or twice with tongs, for 10 minutes, or until wilted and tender. Raise heat to high. Cook, uncovered, to evaporate any excess moisture.

3. Add garlic and reheat, stirring, for 1 minute.

Per serving: 81 calories, 3 g protein, 10 g carbohydrates, 4 g fiber, 4 g total fat, 1 g saturated fat, 0 mg cholesterol, 24 mg sodium

SWEET AND SOUR GREENS WITH BACON

Serves 4

Prep Time: 15 minutes

Cook Time: 15 minutes

Healing Foods: garlic, mustard greens, prunes, honey

Ailments It Heals: blood pressure, constipation, hyperthyroidism

1 Tbsp extra-virgin olive oil

3 slices turkey bacon, cut into thin strips

3 cloves garlic, thinly sliced

24 cups (loosely packed) cleaned mustard greens, shredded

¼ cup water

3 small pitted prunes, diced

¼ tsp salt

2 tsp red wine vinegar

1 tsp honey

¼ tsp hot sauce, or more to taste

1. In Dutch oven, heat oil over medium-low heat. Add turkey bacon and cook for 5 minutes, or until lightly crisped. Remove with slotted spoon. Add garlic to pan and cook for 3 minutes, or until golden brown.

2. Add mustard greens and toss to coat. Add water, prunes, and salt and cook, stirring occasionally, for 5 minutes, or until soft and tender.

3. Return bacon to pan along with vinegar, honey, and hot sauce and stir to combine. Serve hot.

Per serving: 163 calories, 10 g protein, 22 g carbohydrates, 10 g fiber, 6 g fat, 1 g saturated fat, 9 mg cholesterol, 464 mg sodium

NEW POTATOES WITH NORI

Serves 4

Prep Time: 5 minutes

Cook Time: 15 minutes

Healing Foods: potatoes, lemons, seaweed, chives

Ailments It Heals: celiac disease, mood disorders, neuralgia, stroke

1 lb (500 g) unpeeled small new potatoes

1 oz (30 g) butter

Grated zest and juice of ½ small lemon

1 sheet toasted sushi nori, about 8 x 7 in (20 x 18 cm)

Salt and ground black pepper

2 Tbsp snipped fresh chives

1. Cook potatoes in saucepan of boiling water for 12 minutes, or until just tender.

2. Reserve 3 Tbsp of cooking water, then drain potatoes and return them to saucepan with reserved water. Add butter and lemon zest and juice, and toss potatoes to coat with liquid.

3. Use scissors to snip sushi nori into fine strips. Sprinkle nori over potatoes and cover pan. Cook over low heat for 1 to 2 minutes, or until nori has softened. Add salt and pepper to taste, sprinkle with chives, and serve.

Per serving: 134 calories, 2 g protein, 19 g carbohydrates, 2 g fiber, 6 g total fat, 4 g saturated fat, 15 mg cholesterol, 22 mg sodium

SWEET POTATO AND CELERIAC PUREE

Serves 6
Prep Time: 15 minutes
Cook Time: 20 minutes
Healing Foods: sweet potatoes, celeriac, ginger, apples, coriander
Ailments It Heals: arthritis, cancer, cardiovascular disease

1 lb (500 g) sweet potato, peeled and cut into 1-in (2.5 cm) cubes
1 medium celeriac, peeled and cut into 1-in (2.5 cm) cubes
Juice of 1 lemon
1 Tbsp olive oil
2 cloves garlic, finely chopped
1 Tbsp coarsely grated fresh ginger
1 tsp ground cumin
1 Golden Delicious apple, peeled, cored, and finely chopped
1 Tbsp coriander seeds, roughly crushed

Per serving: 113 calories, 2 g protein, 22 g carbohydrates, 3 g fiber, 3 g total fat, 0 g saturated fat, 0 mg cholesterol, 46 mg sodium

1. Cut sweet potato and celeriac into similar-size chunks and place in large saucepan. Add half of lemon juice and enough water to cover vegetables and bring to a boil. Reduce heat and simmer gently for 15 to 20 minutes, or until vegetables are tender.

2. Meanwhile, heat oil in small saucepan. Add garlic, ginger, and cumin and cook for 30 seconds. Stir in apple and remaining lemon juice and cook for 5 minutes, or until apple begins to soften.

3. In small, dry pan, toast crushed coriander seeds, stirring occasionally, for a few minutes or until fragrant.

4. Drain vegetables well, place in large bowl, and mash them. Stir in apple mixture and sprinkle with toasted coriander seeds. Serve hot.

TWICE-BAKED STUFFED SWEET POTATOES

Serves 4
Prep Time: 10 minutes
Cook Time: 1 hour 10 minutes
Healing Foods: sweet potatoes, pineapples, pecans
Ailments It Heals: hypothyroidism, interstitial cystitis, memory loss

2 large sweet potatoes (1½ lb or 750 g)
8 oz (225 mL) crushed pineapple, drained
1 Tbsp vegetable oil
1 Tbsp butter
1 Tbsp light or dark brown sugar
1 tsp grated orange zest
½ tsp salt
2 Tbsp chopped pecans

1. Preheat oven to 350°F (180°C). Pierce each sweet potato twice with tip of knife.

2. Bake for 50 minutes, or until soft. Set aside until cool enough to handle but still very warm. Reduce oven heat to 325°F (160°C).

3. Cut potatoes in half lengthwise. Scoop out flesh and place in medium bowl, being careful not to tear skin. Reserve skins. Add pineapple, oil, butter, brown sugar, orange zest, and salt to potato flesh. Whip with electric mixer or whisk until slightly fluffy.

4. Place skin shells on baking sheet. Fill with potato mixture, mounding each. Bake for 15 minutes. Sprinkle with pecans and bake for 5 minutes.

Per serving: 236 calories, 2 g protein, 38 g carbohydrates, 4 g fiber, 9 g total fat, 2 g saturated fat, 8 mg cholesterol, 303 mg sodium

WHITE BEANS STEWED WITH SWISS CHARD

Serves 8
Prep Time: 10 minutes
Cook Time: 26 minutes
Healing Foods: cooking greens, carrots, beans, cheese
Ailments It Heals: diabetes, eye problems, fibroids, menstrual problems

1 small bunch Swiss chard (½ lb or 250 g)
2 Tbsp olive oil
1 small onion, finely chopped
1 carrot, peeled and finely chopped
1 tsp dried oregano, crumbled
1 bay leaf
2 cloves garlic, minced
1 cup reduced-sodium, fat-free chicken broth
38 oz (1,080 mL) cannellini beans, drained and rinsed
½ tsp salt
⅛ tsp ground black pepper
½ cup grated parmesan cheese

1. Remove tough stems from chard and finely chop. Coarsely chop leaves.

2. In large nonstick skillet, heat oil over medium heat. Add onion, carrot, oregano, and bay leaf. Sauté for 8 minutes, or until onion and carrot are very soft. Add garlic. Sauté 30 seconds.

3. Add chard and broth to skillet. Cook, stirring occasionally, for 2 minutes, or until chard just begins to wilt. Stir in beans. Simmer, covered, for 10 minutes. Uncover and cook for 5 minutes, or until chard is tender. Add salt and pepper. Remove bay leaf. Sprinkle with cheese and serve.

Per serving: 139 calories, 7 g protein, 16 g carbohydrates, 5 g fiber, 5 g total fat, 1 g saturated fat, 4 mg cholesterol, 482 mg sodium

ROASTED TOMATOES WITH GARLIC AND HERBS

Serves 4
Prep Time: 10 minutes
Cook Time: 3 hours
Healing Foods: tomatoes, garlic, basil, rosemary
Ailments It Heals: Alzheimer's disease, cancer, circulatory disorders, gallstones, prostate problems

3   lb (1.5 kg) plum tomatoes, halved lengthwise
2   Tbsp olive oil
5   cloves garlic, finely chopped
½   cup finely chopped fresh basil
2   Tbsp minced fresh rosemary
1   tsp sugar
¾   tsp salt

1. Preheat oven to 250°F (120°C). Line a jelly-roll pan with foil.

2. In large bowl, toss tomatoes with oil, garlic, basil, rosemary, sugar, and salt. Place tomatoes, cut side up, in prepared pan. Bake for 3 hours, or until tomatoes have collapsed and their skins have wrinkled.

3. Serve at room temperature, or refrigerate and serve chilled.

Per serving: 148 calories, 4 g protein, 19 g carbohydrates, 5 g fiber, 8 g total fat, 1 g saturated fat, 0 mg cholesterol, 468 mg sodium

HERB-BUTTERED TURNIPS

Serves 4
Prep Time: 5 minutes
Cook Time: 15 minutes
Healing Foods: turnips, chives, mint, parsley
Ailments It Heals: infertility, mood disorders, nail problems

10   tiny young turnips with leaves reserved and shredded (leaves optional)
3½   Tbsp butter
Rosemary sprig
Salt and ground black pepper
1   Tbsp snipped chives
1   Tbsp shredded mint
2   Tbsp chopped parsley

1. Wash turnips gently and cut off leaves, leaving ½ in (1 cm) green stalk attached. Put turnips in saucepan of salted water and bring to a boil. Cook for 10 minutes, or until just tender, then drain thoroughly.

2. In wide frying pan, heat butter and rosemary, then add turnips. Cook for 2 to 3 minutes, or until shiny and just beginning to show patches of color.

3. Remove rosemary, add salt and pepper to taste, and scatter on chives, mint, parsley, and turnip leaves, if using. Shake pan to coat turnips evenly. Serve warm.

Per serving: 124 calories, 1 g protein, 8 g carbohydrates, 2 g fiber, 10 g total fat, 6 g saturated fat, 27 mg cholesterol, 83 mg sodium

MASHED TURNIPS WITH CARROTS AND POTATOES

Serves 4

Prep Time: 15 minutes

Cook Time: 20 minutes

Healing Foods: turnips, potatoes, carrots, garlic, thyme

Ailments It Heals: cirrhosis, menstrual problems, sore throat

1¾ lb (875 g) turnips, peeled, quartered and thinly sliced

9 oz (275 g) potatoes (about 2 medium), peeled and thinly sliced

9 oz (275 g) carrots (about 4 medium), peeled and thinly sliced

5 cloves garlic, peeled

1 bay leaf

1 tsp fresh thyme leaves

4 cups water

Salt and ground black pepper

2 tsp olive oil

¼ cup grated parmesan cheese

1. In large saucepan, combine turnips, potatoes, carrots, garlic, bay leaf, thyme, water, and a pinch each of salt and pepper. Bring to a boil over medium heat, reduce to a simmer, cover, and cook for 15 minutes, or until tender. Drain, reserving ½ cup of cooking liquid. Discard bay leaf.

2. Mash vegetables and garlic with a potato masher, adding reserved cooking liquid and oil. Stir in cheese just before serving.

Per serving: 211 calories, 7 g protein, 36 g carbohydrates, 6 g fiber, 5 g total fat, 2 g saturated fat, 10 mg cholesterol, 292 mg sodium

CIDER-BAKED ACORN SQUASH WITH APPLE STUFFING

Serves 4

Prep Time: 15 minutes

Cook Time: 1 hour

Healing Foods: acorn squash, apples, cinnamon, nutmeg

Ailments It Heals: cardiovascular disease, indigestion and heartburn, interstitial cystitis

2 small acorn squash (about 1 lb or 500 g each), halved lengthwise and seeded

½ cup apple cider or apple juice

½ tsp salt

1 apple pared, cored, and chopped

1 Tbsp light brown sugar

¼ tsp ground cinnamon

⅛ tsp ground nutmeg

1. Preheat oven to 350°F (180°C).

2. Place squash halves, cut side down, in 13 × 9-in (33 x 23 cm) baking dish. Add cider to the dish.

3. Bake for 30 minutes. Remove from oven and leave oven on. Carefully turn squash cut side up and sprinkle with salt.

4. In small bowl, combine apple, brown sugar, cinnamon, and nutmeg. Spoon evenly into squash halves. Drizzle cider from baking dish over mixture, using a baster if you have one. Add a couple spoonfuls of water to dish.

5. Bake, stuffed side up, for 30 minutes or until tender.

Per serving: 123 calories, 2 g protein, 32 g carbohydrates, 7 g fiber, 0 g total fat, 0 g saturated fat, 0 mg cholesterol, 298 mg sodium

FRUITY BUTTER- NUT SQUASH CASSEROLE WITH PAPAYA

Serves 4
Prep Time: 15 minutes
Cook Time: 10 minutes
Healing Foods: butternut squash, papayas, sage, oranges, beans
Ailments It Heals: eczema, memory loss, multiple sclerosis

½ butternut squash (about 1¼ lb or 625 g)
1 papaya (about 10 oz or 300g)
1 red onion
1 Tbsp vegetable oil
4 to 6 large fresh sage leaves
1 tsp ground cinnamon
1 Juice of 1 large orange (about 7 Tbsp)
14 oz (398 mL) canned borlotti, kidney, or pinto beans, drained

1. Peel and seed butternut squash and dice flesh into 1-in (2.5 cm) chunks. Seed and peel papaya, then slice it and set aside. Thinly slice onion.

2. Heat oil in large pan with lid. Add onion and squash and cook over high heat, stirring occasionally, for 1 minute. Reduce heat to medium or medium-low, cover, and cook for 2 minutes.

3. Shred sage leaves. Stir leaves, cinnamon, and orange juice into pan. Bring to a boil, reduce heat to low, and cover again. Simmer for 5 minutes, stirring once, or until squash is tender but not soft.

4. Stir in beans, cover, and heat gently for 2 minutes. Top with papaya and serve immediately.

Per serving: 215 calories, 7 g protein, 42 g carbohydrates, 10 g fiber, 4 g total fat, 1 g saturated fat, 0 mg cholesterol, 295 mg sodium

BAKED YUCCA CHIPS

Serves 10
Prep Time: 10 minutes
Cook Time: 10 minutes
Healing Foods: yucca, cilantro, limes
Ailments It Heals: circulatory disorders, osteoporosis, varicose veins

1 large yucca root
2 Tbsp olive oil
½ cup chopped cilantro
2 tsp ground ginger
Pinch of salt
Pinch of ground black pepper
3 Tbsp fresh lime juice

1. Preheat oven to 375°F (190°C).

2. Peel yucca with vegetable peeler, removing all waxy brown skin and pinkish layer underneath. Then cut into ⅛ in (0.3 cm) slices.

3. Toss yucca and oil in bowl. Mix in cilantro, ginger, salt, pepper, and lime juice. Mix to coat.

4. Spread slices on nonstick baking sheet. Bake for 4 to 5 minutes on each side, or until golden brown.

Per serving: 93 calories, 1 g protein, 16 g carbohydrates, 1 g fiber, 3 g total fat, 0 g saturated fat, 0 mg cholesterol, 43 mg sodium

SAVORY CRANBERRY CHUTNEY

Serves 6
Prep Time: 10 minutes
Cook Time: 17 minutes
Healing Foods: onions, cranberries, cherries, oranges, allspice
Ailments It Heals: acne, urinary tract infections, varicose veins

2 tsp olive oil
1 large red onion, finely chopped
3 cloves garlic, minced
12 oz (375 g) fresh or frozen cranberries
½ cup firmly packed light brown sugar
½ cup dried cherries
2 tsp grated orange zest
½ cup orange juice
½ tsp ground black pepper
¼ tsp salt
⅛ tsp allspice

1. In large saucepan, heat oil over medium-low heat. Add onion and garlic and cook, stirring frequently, for 7 minutes, or until onion is tender.

2. Stir in cranberries, brown sugar, dried cherries, orange zest, orange juice, pepper, salt, and allspice. Cook, stirring occasionally, for 10 minutes, or until berries have popped. Cool to room temperature. Serve at room temperature or chilled.

Per serving: 174 calories, 1 g protein, 42 g carbohydrates, 3 g fiber, 2 g total fat, 0 g saturated fat, 0 mg cholesterol, 108 mg sodium

TOMATO BISCUITS

Makes 12
Prep Time: 12 minutes
Cook Time: 12 minutes
Healing Foods: tomatoes, yogurt, olive oil
Ailments It Heals: Alzheimer's disease, colds and flu, gallstones

1 medium tomato, seeded and finely chopped
1 cup all-purpose flour
1 cup whole wheat flour
1 Tbsp baking powder
½ tsp salt
1 cup low-fat plain yogurt
⅓ cup olive oil
2 Tbsp finely chopped scallions
1 Tbsp finely chopped sun-dried tomatoes

1. Preheat oven to 450°F (230°C). Lightly coat baking sheet with cooking spray. Drain chopped fresh tomato on paper towels.

2. In medium bowl, combine flour, baking powder, and salt. In small bowl, combine yogurt and oil. Stir into flour mixture until evenly moistened.

3. Stir fresh tomato, scallions, and sun-dried tomatoes into flour mixture. Drop dough, ¼ cup at a time, onto prepared baking sheet, for a total of 12 biscuits.

4. Bake for 12 minutes, or until tops are golden brown. Serve warm.

Per serving: 145 calories, 4 g protein, 18 g carbohydrates, 1 g fiber, 7 g total fat, 1 g saturated fat, 1 mg cholesterol, 255 mg sodium

WHOLE WHEAT PUMPKIN ROLLS

Per serving: 177 calories, 6 g protein, 27 g carbohydrates, 2 g fiber, 6 g total fat, 1 g saturated fat, 0 mg cholesterol, 197 mg sodium

Makes 24
Prep Time: 25 minutes plus rising
Cook Time: 12 minutes
Healing Foods: pumpkins, wheat, seeds
Ailments It Heals: arthritis, depression, diabetes

 1 envelope active dry yeast
 ½ cup warm water (105° to 115°F or 40° to 46°C)
 ¼ cup honey
 15 oz (450 g) solid-pack unsweetened pumpkin
 2 Tbsp olive oil
 4½ cups all-purpose flour
 1 cup whole wheat flour
 2 tsp salt
 1½ cups unsalted, shelled pumpkin seeds, lightly toasted

1. In large bowl, sprinkle yeast over warm water. Let stand for 5 minutes, or until foamy. Stir in honey until dissolved. Stir in pumpkin and oil. Stir in 4 cups all-purpose flour, whole wheat flour, and salt until dough forms.

2. Turn dough out onto floured surface. Knead for 10 minutes, or until smooth and elastic, adding more flour as needed to prevent sticking. Work in pumpkin seeds. Place dough in lightly oiled bowl. Turn to coat. Cover loosely with plastic wrap. Let rise in warm place until doubled in volume, about 1½ hours.

3. Line 2 baking sheets with foil. Punch dough down. Form dough into 24 equal-size rolls. Place on prepared baking sheets. Cover loosely with plastic wrap. Let rise in warm place for 1 hour, or until doubled in volume.

4. Preheat oven to 400°F (200°C). Uncover rolls.

5. Bake for 12 minutes, or until puffed and golden and sounds hollow when tapped on bottom. Serve warm or at room temperature.

MULTIGRAIN SEEDED LOAF

Serves 8
Prep Time: 25 minutes plus rising
Cook Time: 35 minutes
Healing Foods: wheat, buckwheat, seeds, flax
Ailments It Heals: chronic fatigue syndrome, circulatory disorders, menstrual problems, neuralgia, prostate problems

 2 cups white flour
 1⅓ cups whole wheat flour
 ¾ cup buckwheat flour
 ½ cup coarse polenta (cornmeal)
 2 tsp instant or rapid rise yeast
 1 tsp brown sugar
 3 Tbsp sunflower seeds
 2 Tbsp pumpkin seeds
 2 Tbsp flaxseed
 2 Tbsp sunflower oil
 2 cups tepid water
Low-fat milk to glaze

1. Sift flours into large bowl, tipping in any bran left in sieve. Stir in polenta, yeast, and brown sugar.

2. Mix seeds together, reserving 1 Tbsp for the topping. Stir remainder into flour mixture.

3. Make a well in dry ingredients and pour in oil and water. Mix with your hands to make a soft dough, adding more water if dough is too dry. Turn out onto lightly floured work surface and knead for 10 minutes, or until smooth and elastic. Place in large, lightly oiled bowl and cover with damp tea towel. Set aside in warm, draft-free place for 1½ hours, or until doubled in size.

4. Punch the dough and knead firmly for a few minutes. Shape into 8-in (20 cm) round and place on lightly greased baking sheet. Cover with oiled plastic wrap and leave for 20 to 30 minutes, or until well risen and springy to the touch.

5. Preheat oven to 450°F (230°C). Use a sharp knife to make slashes on top of loaf to mark eight wedges. Brush top with a little milk and sprinkle with reserved mixed seeds.

6. Bake for 15 minutes, then reduce oven temperature to 400°F (200°C). Bake for 15 to 20 minutes, or until golden brown and sounds hollow when tapped on bottom. Cool for 5 minutes on baking sheet, then transfer to wire rack to cool completely.

Per serving: 391 calories, 12 g protein, 62 g carbohydrates, 8 g fiber, 11 g total fat, 1 g saturated fat, 0 mg cholesterol, 10 mg sodium

WHOLE WHEAT FLAXSEED BREAD

Serves 8
Prep Time: 20 minutes plus rising
Cook Time: 30 minutes
Healing Foods: wheat, flax, olive oil
Ailments It Heals: chronic fatigue syndrome, hemorrhoids, menopause, osteoporosis, stress

1⅓   cups whole wheat flour
 ⅔   cup bread flour or all-purpose flour
 3   Tbsp whole flaxseed, ground, or ¼ cup flaxseed meal
 2   Tbsp nonfat dry milk
1½   tsp instant or rapid rise yeast
 ¾   tsp salt
 ¾   cup water, at room temperature
 1   Tbsp molasses or honey
 1   Tbsp olive oil
 1   egg white, lightly beaten with 1 Tbsp water
 1   Tbsp whole flaxseed

1. In food processor fitted with a metal chopping blade, combine flours, ground flaxseed (or flaxseed meal), dry milk, yeast, and salt. Pulse several times to blend. In a measuring cup, stir together water, molasses (or honey), and oil until molasses is fully dissolved. With motor running, slowly pour enough liquid through feeder tube to make a smooth dough that pulls away from the work bowl sides. Consistency should be smooth yet soft to the touch; adjust if necessary by adding flour 1 Tbsp at a time or water 1 tsp at a time. Process for 1 minute to knead. Transfer dough to a bowl coated with cooking spray and turn to coat. Cover with plastic wrap and let rise at room temperature until doubled in bulk, 1½ to 1¾ hours.

2. Coat a baking sheet with cooking spray. When dough has doubled, turn it out onto a lightly floured surface. Punch it down and shape into a round or oval loaf (or make 2 small loaves). Place loaf on baking sheet. Coat a sheet of plastic wrap with cooking spray and cover loaf with it. Let rise until almost doubled in bulk, about 1 hour.

3. Meanwhile, place a small metal baking pan on bottom oven rack. Preheat oven to 400°F (200°C).

4. When loaf has risen, brush it with egg white mixture and sprinkle with whole flaxseed. Pour 1 cup water into baking pan in oven to create steam. Use a serrated knife to score four ¼-in-deep (0.5 cm) slashes in loaf. Bake for 20 to 30 minutes, or until bread is golden and sounds hollow when tapped. Transfer to wire rack to cool.

Per serving: 155 calories, 5 g protein, 27 g carbohydrates, 3 g fiber, 4 g total fat, 1 g saturated fat, 0 mg cholesterol, 229 mg sodium

BANANA-PEANUT BREAD

Serves 10
Prep Time: 10 minutes
Cook Time: 50 minutes plus cooling
Healing Foods: bananas, peanut butter, wheat, oats, flax
Ailments It Heals: hypoglycemia, infertility, insomnia, muscle cramps, stress

3 very ripe medium bananas, mashed (about 1 cup)
½ cup natural peanut butter
2 eggs
1 Tbsp canola oil
1½ cups whole wheat pastry flour
½ cup whole oats, ground
¼ cup sugar
2 Tbsp ground flaxseed
2 tsp baking powder
½ tsp baking soda
½ tsp salt

1. Preheat oven to 350°F (180°C). Lightly coat a 9 x 5-in (23 x 12 cm) loaf pan with cooking spray.

2. In medium bowl, stir together bananas, peanut butter, eggs, and oil. In large bowl, mix together flour, oats, sugar, flaxseed, baking powder, baking soda, and salt.

3. Make a well in center of flour mixture, add banana mixture, and stir just until moistened. Place in pan.

4. Bake for 40 to 50 minutes, or until a wooden pick inserted in center comes out clean. Transfer to a rack and let cool for 5 minutes, then remove from pan and let cool completely.

Per serving: 234 calories, 7 g protein, 31 g carbohydrates, 4 g fiber, 9 g total fat, 1 g saturated fat, 42 mg cholesterol, 351 mg sodium

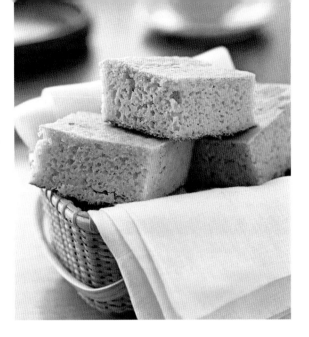

CARROT-FLECKED CORN BREAD

Serves 9
Prep Time: 10 minutes
Cook Time: 25 minutes plus cooling
Healing Foods: flour, eggs, carrots
Ailments It Heals: cirrhosis, indigestion and heartburn, migraines and other headaches, rosacea

2 Tbsp vegetable oil
2 cups white or yellow cornmeal
⅓ cup all-purpose flour
2 tsp baking powder
1 tsp baking soda
2 Tbsp sugar
1 tsp salt
1¾ cups low-fat buttermilk
1 large egg, lightly beaten
2 medium carrots, peeled and finely shredded

1. Preheat oven to 400°F (200°C). Swirl oil in 8 × 8 × 2-in (20 x 20 x 5 cm) baking pan. Place pan in oven for 5 minutes while preheating.

2. Meanwhile, in large bowl, combine cornmeal, flour, baking powder, baking soda, sugar, and salt. Stir in buttermilk, egg, and carrots. Carefully pour in oil from baking pan. Mix well. Pour batter into hot pan.

3. Bake for 25 minutes, or until wooden pick inserted in center comes out clean,. Let cool in pan 10 minutes. Turn out onto wire rack. Let cool slightly before cutting. Serve warm.

Per serving: 202 calories, 6 g protein, 34 g carbohydrates, 3 g fiber, 5 g total fat, 1 g saturated fat, 26 mg cholesterol, 550 mg sodium

TOASTED OAT-RAISIN BREAD

Serves 12

Prep Time: 15 minutes
Cook Time: 1 hour 29 minutes plus cooling
Healing Foods: oats, flax, bran, yogurt, raisins
Ailments It Heals: cholesterol (high), diverticulitis, stroke,

1½ cups old-fashioned rolled oats
½ cup flaxseed
½ cup wheat bran
1 cup all-purpose flour
½ cup firmly packed light brown sugar
2 tsp baking powder
¾ tsp salt
1½ cups low-fat plain yogurt
⅔ cup honey
1 large egg
1 cup raisins

1. Preheat oven to 350°F (180°C). Lightly grease a 9 x 5-in (23 x 12 cm) metal loaf pan.

2. Place oats, flaxseed, and wheat bran on a baking sheet. Bake for 7 to 9 minutes, or until oats are golden brown. Transfer to food processor and process until finely ground.

3. Transfer oat mixture to large bowl. Stir in flour, brown sugar, baking powder, and salt.

4. In separate bowl, whisk together yogurt, honey, and egg. Make a well in center of dry ingredients and fold in yogurt mixture until just combined. Fold in raisins.

5. Spoon batter into prepared pan, smoothing the top. Bake for 1 hour 20 minutes, or until a wooden pick inserted in center of loaf comes out clean. Cool for 5 minutes in pan, then invert loaf onto wire rack to cool completely.

Per serving: 276 calories, 7 g protein, 57 g carbohydrates, 5 g fiber, 4 g total fat, 1 g saturated fat, 20 mg cholesterol, 261 mg sodium

WALNUT SHORTBREAD

Serves 8

Prep Time: 15 minutes
Cook Time: 37 minutes
Healing Foods: nuts, wheat
Ailments It Heals: AIDS and HIV infection, cystic fibrosis, gallstones, hay fever, stroke

⅔ cup walnuts
¾ cup all-purpose flour
½ cup whole wheat flour
½ cup confectioners' sugar
¼ tsp salt
¼ cup walnut oil
¼ cup light olive oil
1½ tsp grated lemon zest
1 tsp vanilla extract

1. Preheat oven to 325°F (160°C). Place walnuts on baking sheet and toast for 7 minutes, or until crisp and fragrant. Leave oven on. Cool walnuts, then transfer to food processor with all-purpose flour, and process until nuts are finely ground.

2. Transfer flour-walnut mixture to large bowl. Stir in whole wheat flour, confectioners' sugar, and salt. Add walnut oil, olive oil, lemon zest, and vanilla and stir until well combined.

3. Press dough onto bottom of 9-in (23 cm) tart pan with removable bottom. With tines of a fork, prick dough. With a sharp knife, score dough into 16 wedges, cutting almost to bottom.

4. Bake for 30 minutes, or until crisp and light golden. Check shortbread after 20 minutes. If it is overbrowning, decrease oven temperature to 300°F (150°C). Remove from oven and, while shortbread is still warm, cut wedges through to bottom. Cool in pan on wire rack.

Per serving: 273 calories, 3 g protein, 24 g carbohydrates, 2 g fiber, 19 g total fat, 2 g saturated fat, 0 mg cholesterol, 73 mg sodium

SNACKS

BEEF, SCALLION, AND ASPARAGUS ROLL-UPS

Serves 4
Prep Time: 15 minutes
Cook Time: 6 minutes
Healing Foods: asparagus, beef, onions, seeds, cilantro
Ailments It Heals: mood disorders, PCOS, peptic ulcers

8 asparagus stalks, trimmed to 6-in (15 cm) lengths
8 thin slices sirloin steak (¼ lb or 125 g total)
4 scallions, trimmed to 6-in (15 cm) lengths
2 tsp vegetable oil
3 Tbsp bottled teriyaki sauce
1 Tbsp sesame seeds, toasted
1 Tbsp chopped cilantro

1. Heat saucepan of water to a boil. Cut each asparagus stalk in half. Blanch in boiling water for 1 minute, then drain. Meanwhile, pound sirloin slices to ⅛-in (0.3 cm) thickness. Cut each scallion into two 3-in (7.5 cm) pieces.

2. Place 2 pieces of asparagus and 1 piece of scallion near one end of each beef strip. Roll beef around middle of vegetables to form eight bundles.

3. In large nonstick skillet, heat oil over medium-high heat. Add rolls. Brown for 2 minutes, turning frequently. Add teriyaki sauce, lower heat to medium, and boil for 3 minutes.

4. Transfer rolls to serving platter. Sprinkle with sesame seeds and cilantro.

Per serving: 91 calories, 7 g protein, 4 g carbohydrates, 1 g fiber, 5 g total fat, 1 g saturated fat, 16 mg cholesterol, 533 mg sodium

BUFFALO CHICKEN FINGERS

Serves 4

Prep Time: 15 minutes

Cook Time: 4 minutes

Healing Foods: chicken, vinegar, cheese

Ailments It Heals: anorexia, cystic fibrosis, iron overload, PCOS

- 1 lb (500 g) boneless, skinless chicken breast halves
- ½ tsp celery salt
- ¼ tsp garlic powder
- 2 tsp margarine
- 2 Tbsp red wine vinegar
- ¼ tsp ground red pepper
- ¼ cup nonfat sour cream
- 1 Tbsp nonfat mayonnaise
- ¼ cup crumbled blue cheese
- 1 Tbsp Worcestershire sauce

1. Cut chicken into sixteen 4 x 1-in (10 x 2.5-cm) fingers. Mix celery salt and garlic powder. Sprinkle chicken with half of this mixture. Coat large nonstick skillet with cooking spray and set over medium-high heat. Pan-fry chicken for 2 minutes on each side, or until cooked through.

2. Remove skillet from heat and stir in margarine, vinegar, and red pepper. Toss with spatula to coat chicken evenly. Transfer to serving platter and keep warm.

3. In medium bowl, combine sour cream, mayonnaise, blue cheese, Worcestershire sauce, and remaining celery salt mixture to make dipping sauce.

Per serving: 188 calories, 29 g protein, 3 g carbohydrates, 0 g fiber, 6 g total fat, 2 g saturated fat, 72 mg cholesterol, 620 mg sodium

PESTO CHICKEN SPIRALS WITH ROASTED PEPPERS

Serves 4

Prep Time: 15 minutes

Cook Time: 15 minutes

Healing Foods: chicken, cheese, salad greens, peppers, basil

Ailments It Heals: bleeding problems, depression, hepatitis

- 4 boneless, skinless chicken breast halves (about 1½ lb or 750 g)
- ¼ tsp ground black pepper
- 4 oz (125 g) soft goat cheese
- 1 packed cup watercress leaves, thick stems removed
- ¾ cup jarred roasted red peppers
- 1 small scallion, finely chopped
- ¼ cup prepared reduced-fat basil pesto

1. Put chicken breasts one at a time, with smooth side down, between sheets of waxed paper or plastic wrap. Working from the center to the edges, pound lightly with flat side of a meat mallet or small skillet to make chicken an even ¼-in (0.5 cm) thickness. Remove waxed paper or plastic.

2. Sprinkle chicken with pepper, then spread on goat cheese, leaving a ¼-in (0.5 cm) border around edges. Top with watercress, roasted peppers, and scallion. Roll up jelly-roll style from short side, pushing in sides as you roll, to enclose filling. Secure with wooden picks.

3. Brush pesto over surface of chicken. If making ahead, bundles can be covered and refrigerated for up to 8 hours; bring to room temperature before cooking.

4. Heat large nonstick skillet or griddle over medium heat. When hot, coat with cooking spray and add chicken bundles. Cook for 10 to 15 minutes, or until chicken is no longer pink and filling is hot, turning now and then and covering pan for the last 5 to 7 minutes of cooking.

5. Cool slightly, then slice crosswise on a slight diagonal to reveal the filling.

Per serving: 338 calories, 47 g protein, 5 g carbohydrates, 1 g fiber, 13 g total fat, 6 g saturated fat, 115 mg cholesterol, 421 mg sodium

TURKEY BACON AND APRICOT BITES

Makes 24
Prep Time: 15 minutes
Cook Time: 2 minutes
Healing Foods: apricots, oranges, turkey
Ailments It Heals: blood pressure, hepatitis, yeast infections

Bites
24 dried apricots
Juice of 1 orange
  2 tsp no-sugar-added orange marmalade
  2 tsp dijon mustard
  6 slices lean turkey bacon
  1 tsp olive oil
Chopped fresh parsley (optional)

1. Place apricots in small bowl, pour orange juice over, and toss so that apricots are moistened all over (this will prevent them from burning when grilled).

2. Mix marmalade with mustard. Spread each slice of turkey bacon with a little mustard mixture. Using scissors, cut bacon in half lengthwise. Cut each piece in half again, this time across the middle, to make a total of 24 strips of bacon.

3. Preheat a ridged grill pan or oven broiler to medium. Drain apricots. Wrap a strip of turkey bacon around each apricot and secure it with a wooden pick.

4. Arrange turkey bites on grill pan, then brush each with a little oil. Grill on each side for 1 minute, or until bacon is just cooked.

5. Pile bites in small, shallow bowl and sprinkle with chopped parsley, if using. Serve hot.

Per serving: 29 calories, 1 g protein, 5 g carbohydrates, 1 g fiber, 1 g total fat, 0 g saturated fat, 3 mg cholesterol, 54 mg sodium

GRILLED OYSTERS WITH FENNEL AND SPINACH

Serves 4
Prep Time: 10 minutes
Cook Time: 17 minutes
Healing Foods: oysters, potatoes, fennel, spinach
Ailments It Heals: fibroids, flatulence, infertility, sex drive (diminished)

16 oysters in the shell, opened and top shell discarded
Salt and ground black pepper
1½ Tbsp butter
  1 shallot, finely chopped
  1 small potato, peeled and finely diced
½ cup fennel bulb, finely diced
  2 cups spinach, coarsely chopped
  1 Tbsp lemon juice
  2 Tbsp chopped fresh parsley
Lemon wedges

1. Check oysters to make sure there are no bits of shattered shell on them. Arrange them, on their half shells, in four individual flameproof dishes, or on one large dish. Season with salt and pepper to taste. (Propping shells with crumpled foil will prevent them from tipping.)

2. Preheat grill to medium. Heat butter in frying pan, add shallot, and cook over low heat for 2 minutes, or until shallot begins to soften. Add potato and fennel and cook gently, stirring occasionally, for 10 minutes, or until tender.

3. Stir in spinach and cook for 1 to 2 minutes, or until spinach has just wilted. Add lemon juice and parsley and season to taste with salt and pepper. Spoon 1 Tbsp of mixture over each oyster.

4. Grill oysters for 3 minutes, or until topping is tinged brown. Serve immediately, with lemon wedges.

Per serving: 98 calories, 4 g protein, 11 g carbohydrates, 2 g fiber, 5 g total fat, 3 g saturated fat, 29 mg cholesterol, 91 mg sodium

OYSTERS WITH TOMATO SALSA

Serves 4
Prep Time: 7 minutes
Healing Foods: tomatoes, onions, parsley, limes, oysters
Ailments It Heals: acne, chronic fatigue syndrome, respiratory disease

  1 large ripe tomato, seeded and diced
 ½ red onion, finely chopped
  2 Tbsp chopped fresh parsley
  2 Tbsp lime juice
Salt and ground black pepper
  2 dozen oysters, freshly opened

To make salsa: In medium bowl, combine tomato, onion, parsley, lime juice, a pinch of salt, and a good grinding of pepper. To serve, top each oyster with 1 tsp salsa.

Per serving: 80 calories, 7 g protein, 7 g carbohydrates, 1 g fiber, 3 g total fat, 1 g saturated fat, 53 mg cholesterol, 110 mg sodium

PITA PIZZAS

Serves 4
Prep Time: 10 minutes
Cook Time: 3 minutes
Healing Foods: peppers, seeds, cheese, wheat
Ailments It Heals: circulatory disorders, diabetes, jaundice, stroke

 ½ cup thinly sliced roasted red peppers
 ¼ tsp crushed fennel seeds or dried oregano, crumbled
 ¼ tsp salt
 ⅛ tsp ground black pepper
 ¼ cup shredded, reduced-fat mozzarella cheese
  2 Tbsp shredded, gruyère or jarlsberg cheese
  2 whole wheat pita breads (4 in or 10 cm)
  8 tsp bottled tomato sauce or pizza sauce
 ½ small red onion, thinly sliced

1. Preheat broiler.

2. In small bowl, combine red peppers, fennel or oregano, salt, and pepper. In another small bowl, combine cheeses.

3. Separate each pita bread into 2 flat rounds. Place rounds, rough side up, on baking sheet. Broil 4 in (10 cm) from heat for 1 minute, or until golden brown around edges. Remove from broiler.

4. Spread 2 tsp sauce over each pita, covering edges. Spoon 2 Tbsp red pepper mixture over each pita. Sprinkle with cheese, dividing equally, then add onion in rings.

5. Broil for 2 minutes, or until cheese is melted and pizzas are hot.

Per serving: 137 calories, 7 g protein, 23 g carbohydrates, 3 g fiber, 3 g total fat, 2 g saturated fat, 7 mg cholesterol, 475 mg sodium

VEGETABLE-STUFFED MUSHROOMS

Serves 4
Prep Time: 20 minutes
Cook Time: 25 minutes
Healing Foods: mushrooms, onions, carrots, peppers, cheese
Ailments It Heals: anorexia, diabetes, diverticulitis

24 large or 12 extra-large mushrooms, stems removed
2 tsp vegetable oil
1 onion, finely chopped
3 cloves garlic, minced
1 carrot, finely chopped
1 red bell pepper, finely chopped
½ cup chicken broth
½ tsp dried oregano
3 Tbsp grated parmesan cheese
2 Tbsp chopped parsley

1. Preheat oven to 400°F (200°C). In a medium pot of boiling water, cook mushroom caps for 2 minutes to blanch. Drain on paper towels.

2. In large skillet, heat oil over medium heat. Add onion and garlic and sauté for 5 minutes. Add carrot and pepper and cook for 4 minutes. Add broth and oregano and cook for 4 minutes, or until vegetables are very soft. Remove from heat and stir in cheese and parsley.

3. Spoon mixture into mushroom caps and place on baking sheet. Bake for 10 minutes, or until piping hot.

Per serving: 90 calories, 6 g protein, 9 g carbohydrates, 2 g fiber, 5 g total fat, 1 g saturated fat, 5 mg cholesterol, 120 mg sodium

ASIAN PEANUT DIP

Serves 8
Prep Time: 10 minutes
Healing Foods: peanut butter, tofu, limes
Ailments It Heals: anorexia, cardiovascular disease, hypoglycemia, infertility

½ cup natural-style peanut butter
⅓ cup low-fat firm silken tofu
3 Tbsp firmly packed light brown sugar
2 Tbsp reduced-sodium soy sauce
2 Tbsp lime juice
½ to ¾ tsp crushed red-pepper flakes
2 cloves garlic, crushed

1. In a food processor, combine peanut butter, tofu, brown sugar, soy sauce, lime juice, red pepper, and garlic. Process until smooth and creamy, stopping once or twice to scrape down sides of work bowl. The dip will keep, covered, in refrigerator for up to 2 days.

Per serving: 120 calories, 5 g protein, 10 g carbohydrates, 1 g fiber, 7 g total fat, 2 g saturated fat, 0 mg cholesterol, 216 mg sodium

Stir in cumin and coriander. Remove from heat and transfer to food processor.

2. Add chickpeas, yogurt, lime juice, salt, and black pepper to taste. Process until smooth. Transfer to medium bowl and stir in cilantro (or parsley).

Per serving: 65 calories, 2 g protein, 7 g carbohydrates, 2 g fiber, 3 g total fat, 0 g saturated fat, 0 mg cholesterol, 108 mg sodium

INDIAN CHICKPEA SPREAD

Serves 12
Prep Time: 10 minutes
Cook Time: 1 minute
Healing Foods: ginger, spices, chickpeas, yogurt, limes
Ailments It Heals: anemia, obesity, osteoporosis, psoriasis

2 Tbsp canola oil
2 jalapeño chile peppers, seeded and minced (wear gloves when handling; they burn)
1 Tbsp minced fresh ginger
2 cloves garlic, minced
2 tsp ground cumin
1 tsp ground coriander
19 oz (540 mL) canned chickpeas, drained and rinsed
⅓ cup nonfat plain yogurt
2 Tbsp lime juice
⅛ tsp salt
Ground black pepper
2 Tbsp chopped fresh cilantro or parsley

1. In small skillet, heat canola oil over medium-high heat. Add chile peppers, ginger, and garlic. Cook, stirring, until fragrant, about 30 seconds.

ITALIAN WHITE BEAN SPREAD

Serves 12
Prep Time: 10 minutes
Healing Foods: beans, lemons, rosemary
Ailments It Heals: arthritis, cancer, cirrhosis, shingles

19 oz (540 mL) cannellini beans, drained and rinsed
2 Tbsp extra-virgin olive oil
2 Tbsp lemon juice
1 clove garlic, minced
Pinch of cayenne pepper
Pinch of salt
Ground black pepper
1½ tsp chopped fresh rosemary

In a food processor, combine beans, oil, lemon juice, garlic, cayenne, and salt and black pepper to taste. Pulse into a chunky puree. Transfer to a medium bowl and stir in rosemary.

Per serving: 55 calories, 2 g protein, 6 g carbohydrates, 2 g fiber, 3 g total fat, 0 g saturated fat, 0 mg cholesterol, 66 mg sodium

WARM ARTICHOKE AND BEAN DIP

Serves 8
Prep Time: 10 minutes
Cook Time: 25 minutes
Healing Foods: beans, artichokes, garlic, cheese, parsley
Ailments It Heals: diverticulitis, irritable bowel syndrome, multiple sclerosis

19 oz (540 mL) cannellini beans, drained and rinsed
14 oz (398 mL) artichoke hearts, drained and rinsed
 3 cloves garlic, minced
 1 Tbsp reduced-fat mayonnaise
Pinch of cayenne pepper
Ground black pepper to taste
⅔ cup plus 2 Tbsp grated parmesan cheese
¼ cup chopped fresh parsley
 1 tsp freshly grated lemon zest

1. Preheat oven to 400°F (200°C). Coat 2- to 3-cup baking dish with cooking spray.

2. In food processor, place beans, artichoke hearts, garlic, mayonnaise, cayenne, and black pepper. Process until almost smooth, stopping to scrape down sides of work bowl once or twice. Transfer to medium bowl. Stir in ⅔ cup cheese, parsley, and lemon zest. Scrape into baking dish and smooth with spatula. Sprinkle with remaining 2 Tbsp cheese.

3. Bake, uncovered, for 20 to 25 minutes, or until heated through.

Per serving: 116 calories, 7 g protein, 16 g carbohydrates, 5 g fiber, 3 g total fat, 2 g saturated fat, 7 mg cholesterol, 517 mg sodium

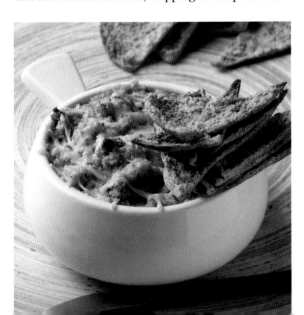

EDAMAME HUMMUS WITH PITA CRISPS

Serves 8
Prep Time: 20 minutes
Cook Time: 10 minutes
Healing Foods: edamame, lemons, garlic, olive oil
Ailments It Heals: constipation, dental problems, menopause

 4 whole wheat pita breads (8 in or 20 cm), halved crosswise
½ tsp ground cumin
 2 cups shelled edamame
⅓ cup water
¼ cup sesame tahini
 3 Tbsp lemon juice
 2 cloves garlic, mashed
½ tsp salt
 2 Tbsp extra-virgin olive oil

1. Preheat oven to 350°F (180°C). Place pita halves on cutting board and lightly coat with cooking spray. Sprinkle with cumin and cut each into eight wedges. Place on baking sheet and bake for 10 minutes, or until lightly browned. Transfer to a rack and let cool.

2. Meanwhile, place edamame in medium saucepan, add enough water to cover, and bring to a boil over medium-high heat. Cook for 10 minutes, or until very tender. Drain and rinse under cold water. Let cool slightly.

3. In food processor, combine edamame, ⅓ cup water, tahini, lemon juice, garlic, and salt. Process until smooth. With motor running, gradually add oil and blend until combined. Serve with pita wedges.

Per serving: 212 calories, 9 g protein, 24 g carbohydrates, 5 g fiber, 10 g total fat, 1 g saturated fat, 0 mg cholesterol, 333 mg sodium

SPICED ALMONDS

Serves 8
Prep Time: 5 minutes
Cook Time: 30 minutes
Healing Foods: almonds, olive oil, cumin
Ailments It Heals: cardiovascular disease, lupus, sex drive (diminished), stress

1 cup unpeeled whole almonds
1 tsp olive oil
¾ tsp ground cumin
¼ tsp salt
⅛ tsp cayenne pepper

1. Preheat oven to 350°F (180°C). In pie plate or shallow baking dish, toss almonds with olive oil, cumin, salt, and cayenne.

2. Bake, stirring occasionally, for 25 to 30 minutes, or until fragrant. Let cool. Almonds will keep, enclosed in an airtight container, for up to 1 week.

Per serving: 112 calories, 4 g protein, 4 g carbohydrates, 2 g fiber, 10 g total fat, 1 g saturated fat, 0 mg cholesterol, 73 mg sodium

SWEET AND SPICY SNACK MIX

Serves 16
Prep Time: 15 minutes
Cook Time: 15 minutes
Healing Foods: nuts and seeds, corn, spices
Ailments It Heals: atherosclerosis, memory loss, respiratory disease

1 cup walnut halves
10 cups air-popped popcorn
3 cups unsalted fat-free mini pretzel twists
1⅓ cups sugar
2 Tbsp lemon juice
⅓ cup hulled pumpkin seeds
1 Tbsp ground cumin
1 tsp salt
¾ tsp cayenne pepper

1. Preheat oven to 350°F (180°C). Bake walnuts for 7 minutes, or until lightly crisp and fragrant. Coarsely chop.

2. Coat large heatproof bowl with cooking spray. Add popcorn and pretzels and toss to combine.

3. In large heavy skillet, stir together sugar and lemon juice. Cook over medium heat, stirring, for 5 minutes, or until sugar has dissolved and just starts to color. Add walnuts, pumpkin seeds, cumin, salt, and cayenne. Stir quickly to thoroughly coat nuts in caramel. Cook, stirring constantly, until nuts are well coated.

4. Transfer to bowl with popcorn and pretzels. Stir quickly to combine. Let cool to room temperature. Store in an airtight container in the refrigerator.

Per serving: 178 calories, 4 g protein, 28 g carbohydrates, 2 g fiber, 7 g total fat, 1 g saturated fat, 0 mg cholesterol, 280 mg sodium

FRUITY GRANOLA MIX

Serves 12
Prep Time: 10 minutes
Cook Time: 55 minutes
Healing Foods: oats, nuts, cinnamon, cranberries, cherries
Ailments It Heals: anorexia, cholesterol (high), varicose veins

4 cups old-fashioned rolled oats
1 cup coarsely chopped walnuts
1 tsp ground cinnamon
⅛ tsp ground nutmeg
¼ tsp salt
½ cup maple syrup
¼ cup honey
¼ cup canola oil
2 tsp vanilla extract
1 cup dried cranberries
1 cup dried cherries

1. Preheat oven to 300°F (150°C). Coat large baking sheet with cooking spray.

2. In large bowl, combine oats, walnuts, cinnamon, nutmeg, and salt.

3. In small bowl, whisk together syrup, honey, oil, and vanilla. Pour over oats mixture and mix well to combine.

4. Spread mixture evenly onto baking sheet. Bake, stirring every 10 minutes, for 45 to 55 minutes, or until lightly golden and toasted.

5. Remove from oven and stir in cranberries and cherries. Cool completely on baking sheet. Store in an airtight container for up to 2 weeks.

Per serving: 353 calories, 6 g protein, 53 g carbohydrates, 5 g fiber, 13 g total fat, 1 g saturated fat, 0 mg cholesterol, 50 mg sodium

CHEWY DATE-WALNUT BARS

Makes 16
Prep Time: 15 minutes
Cook Time: 20 minutes
Healing Foods: oranges, dates, nuts and seeds, oats
Ailments It Heals: chronic fatigue syndrome, circulatory disorders, menstrual problems

2 Tbsp reduced-fat margarine spread
1 Tbsp canola oil
¼ cup light brown sugar
2 Tbsp honey
Zest of 1 orange
2 Tbsp orange juice
⅓ cup dried pitted dates, chopped
¼ cup walnuts, chopped
2 cups old-fashioned oats
2 Tbsp sunflower seeds

1. Preheat oven to 350°F (180°). Coat a 9-in (2.5 L) square baking pan with cooking spray and set aside.

2. In medium saucepan, place margarine, oil, brown sugar, honey, orange zest, and orange juice. Cook over low heat, stirring until butter has melted. Remove pan from heat and stir in dates and walnuts. Add oats, making sure they are evenly coated with butter mixture.

3. Spread mixture in prepared pan, pressing it down firmly and evenly. Sprinkle sunflower seeds over top and press down lightly to embed seeds.

4. Bake for 20 minutes, or until golden brown around edges. Remove from oven and allow to cool completely in pan. When cool, turn bars out onto cutting board and slice into 16 bars. They can be kept in an airtight container for up to 1 week.

1. Preheat oven to 350°F (180°C). Coat an 8-in (20 cm) square metal baking pan with cooking spray.

2. In large bowl, stir together cereal, peanuts, cranberries, and flaxseed.

3. In small saucepan over low heat, stir together peanut butter and agave syrup for 1 minute, or until mixture boils. Stir into cereal mixture until well-blended. Scrape into prepared pan and press down firmly with back of spatula to compact.

4. Bake for 15 minutes, or until edges are golden. Cool thoroughly before cutting into 24 squares.

Per serving: 112 calories, 3 g protein, 19 g carbohydrates, 2 g fiber, 4 g total fat, 1 g saturated fat, 0 mg cholesterol, 78 mg sodium

Per serving: 103 calories, 2 g protein, 12 g carbohydrates, 2 g fiber, 4 g total fat, 0 g saturated fat, 0 mg cholesterol, 12 mg sodium

CRANBERRY-PEANUT CEREAL BARS

Makes 24
Prep Time: 10 minutes
Cook Time: 16 minutes
Healing Foods: grains, peanuts and peanut butter, cranberries, flax
Ailments It Heals: cardiovascular disease, stroke, menopause

3 cups puffed whole grain cereal, like Kashi
½ cup chopped dry-roasted unsalted peanuts
¼ cup chopped unsweetened dried cranberries
2 Tbsp ground flaxseed
⅓ cup creamy peanut butter
½ cup agave syrup

SESAME-FIG BARS

Makes 32
Prep Time: 15 minutes
Cook Time: 47 minutes
Healing Foods: almonds, seeds, figs, carrots, cardamom
Ailments It Heals: Alzheimer's disease, atherosclerosis, menstrual problems

½ cup raw (unblanched) almonds
1 Tbsp sesame seeds
1 cup all-purpose flour
⅓ cup confectioners' sugar
½ tsp salt
⅓ cup dark sesame oil
1½ tsp grated orange zest
1 cup dried figs, coarsely chopped
2 carrots, very thinly sliced
¾ cup orange juice
2 Tbsp fresh lemon juice
¾ tsp ground cardamom
1 tsp vanilla extract

1. Preheat oven to 350°F (180°C). Place almonds and sesame seeds on baking sheet and toast for 5 to 7 minutes, or until almonds are fragrant and seeds are golden.

2. Transfer almonds and sesame seeds to food processor. Add flour, confectioners' sugar, and salt and process until powdery. Add sesame oil and orange zest and process until evenly moistened.

3. Press into 9-in (23 cm) square metal baking pan. Prick dough all over with fork and bake for 20 minutes. Remove crust from oven and cool on wire rack. Keep oven on.

4. While crust bakes, in a medium saucepan, combine figs, carrots, orange juice, lemon juice, and cardamom. Bring to a boil over medium heat. Reduce to a simmer, cover, and cook for 20 minutes, or until figs and carrots are soft and most liquid has been absorbed. Cool to room temperature.

5. Transfer fig-carrot mixture to food processor. Add vanilla and process to a coarse puree. Spread mixture over crust and bake for 20 minutes. Cool in pan on wire rack before slicing into 32 pieces.

Per serving: 75 calories, 1 g protein, 10 g carbohydrates, 1 g fiber, 4 g total fat, 0 g saturated fat, 0 mg cholesterol, 39 mg sodium

NO-BAKE FLAXSEED-NUT BARS

Makes 24
Prep Time: 25 minutes plus cooling
Cook Time: 8 minutes
Healing Foods: oats, flax, blueberries, nuts, peanut butter
Ailments It Heals: cardiovascular disease, depression, hypoglycemia

1 cup old-fashioned rolled oats
¼ cup whole flaxseed
1 cup whole grain puffed rice, puffed wheat, or toasted oat cereal
1 cup dried blueberries or cranberries
½ cup unsalted roasted peanuts
½ cup almonds, coarsely chopped
½ cup nonfat dry milk
¼ tsp salt
¾ cup natural peanut butter, almond butter, or cashew butter
⅔ cup honey
1 tsp vanilla extract

1. Line a 11 x 7-in (28 x 18-cm) or 9-in (23 cm) square baking dish with foil, leaving a 1-in (2.5 cm) overhang on opposite sides. Coat with cooking spray.

2. In medium skillet over medium-low heat, toast oats, stirring constantly, for 3 to 4 minutes, or until aromatic and golden. Transfer to large bowl. In small skillet over medium-low heat, toast flaxseed for 2 to 3 minutes, or until aromatic and starting to pop. Transfer to small bowl and let cool. In spice grinder (such as a clean coffee grinder) or blender, grind flaxseed into coarse meal. Add to oats. Add cereal, blueberries, peanuts, almonds, dry milk, and salt and stir to mix.

3. In small saucepan, combine peanut butter and honey. Cook, stirring, over low heat until blended and smooth about 1 minute. Stir in vanilla. Add to oat mixture, mix well, and transfer to baking dish. Use a piece of plastic wrap to press mixture firmly into an even layer. Cover with plastic wrap and refrigerate for 30 minutes, or until firm. Using foil overhang, lift bars and transfer to cutting board. Cut into 24 bars. Store, covered or individually wrapped, in refrigerator for up to 2 weeks.

Per serving: 171 calories, 5 g protein, 20 g carbohydrates, 3 g fiber, 8 g total fat, 1 g saturated fat, 1 mg cholesterol, 78 mg sodium

---

DESSERTS

CHEWY OATMEAL RAISIN COOKIES

Makes 3 dozen
Prep Time: 15 minutes
Cook Time: 12 minutes
Healing Foods: wheat, oats, raisins
Ailments It Heals: atherosclerosis, cholesterol (high), diverticulitis, inflammatory bowel disease

½ cup whole wheat pastry flour
½ cup all-purpose flour
1 tsp baking powder
½ tsp baking soda
½ tsp salt
¼ tsp ground cinnamon
2 Tbsp unsalted butter, softened
½ cup turbinado sugar
½ cup light brown sugar

1 large egg
¼ cup unsweetened applesauce
1 tsp vanilla extract
1⅓ cups old-fashioned rolled oats
½ cup raisins

1. Preheat oven to 375°F (190°C). Position oven racks in upper and lower thirds of oven. Line two cookie sheets with foil.

2. In medium bowl, stir together flours, baking powder, baking soda, salt, and cinnamon.

3. In large bowl, beat butter and turbinado sugar together with large rubber spatula. One at a time, beat in brown sugar, egg, applesauce, and vanilla, incorporating the ingredients thoroughly. Gently stir in flour mixture, oats, and raisins, one at a time.

4. Drop dough by teaspoonfuls about 2 in (5 cm) apart on prepared sheets. Use fork to gently flatten mounds of dough.

5. Bake both cookie sheets for 10 to 12 minutes, or until cookies look dull but are moist and soft.

6. Grab foil and slide each sheet of cookies from pans onto racks to cool.

Per cookie: 59 calories, 1 g protein, 12 g carbohydrates, 1 g fiber, 1 g total fat, 0 g saturated fat, 7 mg cholesterol, 86 mg sodium

NUTTY CHOCOLATE CHIP COOKIES

Makes 5 dozen
Prep Time: 15 minutes
Cook Time: 50 minutes
Healing Foods: wheat, oats, eggs, chocolate, raisins, nuts
Ailments It Heals: cystic fibrosis, hemorrhoids, stroke

Per cookie: 97 calories, 1 g protein, 12 g carbohydrates, 1 g fiber, 5 g total fat, 2 g saturated fat, 7 mg cholesterol, 77 mg sodium

1½	cups whole wheat pastry flour
1	cup rolled oats, ground
⅓	cup cocoa powder
1	tsp baking soda
½	tsp salt
1	cup nonhydrogenated stick margarine
½	cup granulated sugar
1	cup packed light brown sugar
2	eggs
1	Tbsp vanilla extract
1	cup bittersweet chocolate chips (60% or higher cocoa content)
1	cup raisins
1	cup walnuts, coarsely chopped

1. Preheat oven to 350°F (180°C). Line baking sheet with parchment paper. In medium bowl, whisk together flour, oats, cocoa, baking soda, and salt.

2. In large bowl with an electric mixer at medium speed, beat margarine and sugars for 2 minutes, or until light and fluffy. Add eggs and vanilla and beat until smooth. Beat in flour mixture until combined. Stir in chocolate chips, raisins, and walnuts. Drop by teaspoonful onto baking sheet.

3. Bake for 10 minutes, or until browned. Let cool on the baking sheet for 2 minutes, then transfer to a rack and let cool completely.

CHOCOLATE-ALMOND BISCOTTI

Makes 4 dozen
Prep Time: 20 minutes plus cooling
Cook Time: 1 hour
Healing Foods: wheat, almonds, chocolate, eggs
Ailments It Heals: atherosclerosis, depression

2½	cups whole wheat pastry flour
¾	cup sugar
2	tsp baking powder
1	tsp ground cinnamon
1	tsp salt
1½	cups whole almonds
6	oz (175 g) bittersweet chocolate (60% or higher cocoa content), chopped
4	large eggs

1. Preheat oven to 350°F (180°C). Line baking sheet with parchment paper. In large bowl, whisk together flour, sugar, baking powder, cinnamon, and salt. Stir in almonds and two-thirds of chocolate. In small bowl, beat eggs, then stir into flour mixture.

2. Place dough on lightly floured surface and knead until smooth. Cut in half and shape each piece into a log 12 in (30 cm) long and 3 in (7.5 cm) thick. Place on baking sheet and bake for 30 minutes, or until outside seems firm and puffed. Transfer to a rack and let cool for 2 hours.

3. With a serrated knife, cut logs crosswise into slices about ½ in (1 cm) thick. Place the slices on their sides on a parchment-lined baking sheet and bake, turning once, for 30 minutes, or until crisp and lightly browned. Transfer to a rack and let cool for 30 minutes.

4. Meanwhile, place remaining chocolate in small bowl and microwave on low for 1 minute, or until almost melted. Stir until melted completely. Drizzle over biscotti.

Per cookie: 80 calories, 2 g protein, 10 g carbohydrates, 1 g fiber, 4 g total fat, 1 g saturated fat, 18 mg cholesterol, 75 mg sodium

CHERRY CRISP

Serves 6

Prep Time: 15 minutes
Cook Time: 25 minutes
Healing Foods: cherries, oats, flour
Ailments It Heals: diabetes, peptic ulcers

¼ cup granulated sugar
2 Tbsp cornstarch
1 tsp ground cinnamon
½ tsp ground black pepper
½ tsp salt

⅛ tsp allspice
2 tsp grated lime zest
24 oz (750 g) frozen pitted sweet cherries, thawed
1 Tbsp fresh lime juice
¾ cup old-fashioned rolled oats
⅓ cup all-purpose flour
⅓ cup firmly packed light brown sugar
3 Tbsp cold unsalted butter, cut up

1. Preheat oven to 400°F (200°C). In large bowl, stir together granulated sugar, cornstarch, cinnamon, pepper, ¼ tsp salt, allspice, and lime zest. Add cherries and lime juice, tossing to coat. Pour into 9-in (23 cm) square glass baking dish and set aside.

2. In medium bowl, stir together oats, flour, brown sugar, and remaining ¼ tsp salt. With a pastry blender or two knives, cut in butter until mixture resembles coarse crumbs. Sprinkle mixture over fruit.

3. Bake for 25 minutes, or until fruit is bubbly and piping hot and topping is golden brown and crisp.

Per serving: 257 calories, 4 g protein, 48 g carbohydrates, 1 g fiber, 7 g total fat, 4 saturated fat, 16 mg cholesterol, 201 mg sodium

PEACH AND BLACKBERRY PHYLLO PIZZAS

Makes 6

Prep Time: 30 minutes

Cook Time: 15 minutes

Healing Foods: almonds, peaches, blackberries

Ailments It Heals: cancer, hemorrhoids, indigestion and heartburn

Butter-flavored cooking spray

- 5 sheets phyllo pastry (14 x 18 in or 36 x 46 cm)
- 2 Tbsp ground almonds
- 3 large ripe peaches
- 1 cup fresh blackberries
- 2 Tbsp sugar
- 1 cup reduced-fat sour cream (optional)
- 1 Tbsp light brown sugar (optional)

1. Preheat oven to 400°F (200°C) and coat baking sheet with cooking spray. Lay out phyllo sheets and immediately cover with plastic wrap, then a damp towel (phyllo dries out in a couple of minutes if left uncovered). Work fast!

2. Place a sheet of phyllo on work surface and spray with cooking spray. Layer four more phyllo sheets, spraying with cooking spray each time, and finally spray top sheet with cooking spray. Using a 5-in (13 cm) saucer as a guide, cut out 6 circles from the layered phyllo. Transfer each layered circle to baking sheet and sprinkle with ground almonds.

3. To decorate, cut peaches in half (do not peel), twist apart, and remove pits. Slice peaches very thin. Place slices on phyllo pastry circles in a pinwheel design. Divide blackberries among pizzas. Sprinkle 1 tsp sugar on top of each pizza.

4. Bake for 15 minutes, or until pastry is golden brown and peaches are very tender and light

brown. These pizzas are best served within 15 minutes, as pastry can lose its crispness quickly if fruit is juicy. If desired, serve with sour cream mixed with brown sugar. Each serving is 1 pizza.

Per serving: 107 calories, 2 g protein, 22 g carbohydrates, 3 g fiber, 2 g total fat, 0 g saturated fat, 0 mg cholesterol, 50 mg sodium

RHUBARB-BLACKBERRY CRUMBLE

Serves 8

Prep Time: 20 minutes

Cook Time: 50 minutes plus cooling

Healing Foods: rhubarb, blackberries, wheat, oats, almonds

Ailments It Heals: hemorrhoids, irritable bowel syndrome, lactose intolerance, stroke

- 5 cups diced (½-in or 1 cm pieces) rhubarb
- 1 cup blackberries
- ½ cup granulated sugar
- 1 Tbsp cornstarch
- ⅔ cup whole wheat flour
- ½ cup old-fashioned rolled oats
- ½ cup firmly packed light brown sugar
- 1 tsp ground cinnamon

Pinch of salt

- 1 Tbsp unsalted butter, cut into small pieces
- 1 Tbsp canola oil
- 3 Tbsp frozen orange juice concentrate
- 1 Tbsp chopped slivered almonds

1. Preheat oven to 375°F (190°C). Coat 8-in (20 cm) square baking dish with cooking spray.

2. Combine rhubarb, blackberries, granulated sugar, and cornstarch in baking dish. Toss to mix. Cover with foil and bake for 20 minutes.

3. Meanwhile, in medium bowl, mix flour, oats, brown sugar, cinnamon, and salt with fork. Add butter and crumble with pastry blender or your fingertips until well blended. Add oil and stir to coat. Add orange juice concentrate and stir until dry ingredients are moistened.

4. When crumble has baked for 20 minutes, sprinkle flour mixture evenly over fruit. Top with almonds. Bake, uncovered, for 20 to 30 minutes, or until fruit is bubbly and tender and topping is lightly browned. Let cool for at least 10 minutes before serving warm or at room temperature.

Per serving: 227 calories, 4 g protein, 45 g carbohydrates, 4 g fiber, 4 g total fat, 1 g saturated fat, 4 mg cholesterol, 28 mg sodium

LEMONY BLUE-BERRY CHEESE-CAKE BARS

Makes 24
Prep Time: 25 minutes
Cook Time: 1 hour
Healing Foods: wheat, eggs, cheese, blueberries
Ailments It Heals: chronic fatigue syndrome, hyperthyroidism, osteoporosis, varicose veins

CRUST
1½ cups whole wheat pastry flour
¼ tsp baking powder
¼ tsp baking soda
¼ tsp salt
2 Tbsp unsalted butter, softened
2 Tbsp canola oil
½ cup sugar
1 large egg, lightly beaten
1 tsp vanilla extract

FILLING
12 oz (375 g) reduced-fat cream cheese (Neufchâtel)
½ cup sugar
1 Tbsp cornstarch
2 large eggs, lightly beaten
4 tsp freshly grated lemon zest
1½ tsp vanilla extract
3 cups fresh or frozen and partially thawed blueberries

1. Preheat oven to 350°F (180°C). Coat a 13 x 9-in (33 x 23 cm) baking dish with cooking spray.

2. To make the crust: In medium bowl, whisk flour, baking powder, baking soda, and salt. In mixing bowl, beat butter, oil, and sugar with electric mixer until smooth. Add egg and vanilla and beat until smooth. Add dry ingredients and mix with rubber spatula just until dry ingredients are moistened. Transfer dough to prepared baking dish. Use a piece of plastic wrap to press it into an even layer.

3. Bake crust, uncovered, for 20 minutes, or until puffed and starting to brown around edges.

4. To make the filling: Blend cream cheese, sugar, and cornstarch in a bowl with an electric mixer or in a food processor, until smooth and creamy. Add eggs, lemon zest, and vanilla. Beat or process until smooth. Spread blueberries over crust. Pour cream cheese batter over blueberries, spreading evenly.

5. Bake for 35 to 40 minutes, or until filling has set. Let cool completely in pan on wire rack. Cut into 24 bars with a sharp knife coated with cooking spray. Bars will keep, covered, in refrigerator for up to 4 days or in freezer for up to 1 month.

Per serving: 140 calories, 3 g protein, 17 g carbohydrates, 1 g fiber, 6 g total fat, 3 g saturated fat, 40 mg cholesterol, 105 mg sodium

PUMPKIN MAPLE CHEESECAKE

Serves 16
Prep Time: 15 minutes
Cook Time: 1 hour 10 minutes plus cooling
Healing Foods: cheese, pumpkins, eggs
Ailments It Heals: arthritis, cystic fibrosis, Parkinson's disease

1   cup graham cracker crumbs
3   Tbsp vegetable oil
24 oz (750 g) ⅓-less-fat cream cheese, softened
½   cup firmly packed light brown sugar
15 oz (750 g) solid-pack pumpkin puree
½   cup maple syrup
3   large eggs
2   Tbsp cornstarch
2   tsp pumpkin pie spice
1   tsp vanilla extract
½   tsp salt

1. Preheat oven to 350°F (180°C). Lightly coat 9-in (23 cm) springform cake pan with cooking spray.

2. In small bowl, stir together cracker crumbs and oil. Press mixture over bottom and ½ in (1 cm) up side of pan. Bake for 10 minutes, or until crust just begins to color.

3. In large bowl, beat cream cheese and brown sugar until well blended. Beat in pumpkin, maple syrup, eggs, cornstarch, pie spice, vanilla, and salt until smooth. Pour filling into crust.

4. Bake for 55 to 60 minutes, or until center is just set. Transfer pan to wire rack. Let cool completely. Cover and refrigerate at least 4 hours before serving.

Per serving: 236 calories, 6 g protein, 22 g carbohydrates, 1 g fiber, 14 g total fat, 7 g saturated fat, 72 mg cholesterol, 291 mg sodium

ANGEL FOOD CAKE WITH STRAWBERRIES

Serves 12
Prep Time: 20 minutes
Cook Time: 50 minutes plus cooling
Healing Foods: strawberries, oranges, eggs, flour
Ailments It Heals: cholesterol (high), irritable bowel syndrome, obesity

20 oz (600 g) frozen strawberries, thawed
½   cup orange juice
12 large egg whites, at room temperature
1¼ tsp cream of tartar
½   tsp salt
1¼ cups sugar
3   Tbsp grated lemon zest
1   tsp vanilla extract
1   cup flour

1. In large bowl, combine strawberries and orange juice. Refrigerate.

2. Preheat oven to 325°F (160°C). In large bowl, beat egg whites, cream of tartar, and salt with electric mixer until foamy. Gradually beat in sugar,

2 Tbsp at a time, until thick, soft peaks form. Beat in lemon zest and vanilla.

3. Gently fold flour into mixture, ¼ cup at a time, until incorporated. Spoon into ungreased 10-in (25 cm) angel food or tube pan (3 L). Bake for 50 minutes, or until top springs back when lightly pressed.

4. Invert cake pan to cool. If pan does not have legs, hang pan over neck of bottle. Cool cake completely. Run metal spatula around edges and center of pan, then invert onto cake platter. Serve with strawberries and their juice.

Per serving: 159 calories, 5 g protein, 35 g carbohydrates, 1 g fiber, 0 g total fat, 0 g saturated fat, 0 mg cholesterol, 153 mg sodium

CARROT CAKE WITH CREAM CHEESE GLAZE

Serves 12

Prep Time: 10 minutes

Cook Time: 35 minutes plus cooling

Healing Foods: apples, eggs, wheat, carrots, nuts, milk

Ailments It Heals: iron overload, memory loss, stroke

½ cup applesauce
⅔ cup granulated sugar
2 large eggs
2 Tbsp canola oil
1 tsp vanilla extract
1¼ cups whole wheat pastry flour
1 tsp baking soda
1 tsp ground cinnamon
½ tsp salt
1½ cups shredded carrots (3 large)
½ cup chopped walnuts
1 oz (30 g) low-fat cream cheese
2 Tbsp low-fat milk
2 to 3 Tbsp confectioners' sugar

1. Preheat oven to 350°F (180°C). Coat 9-in (23 cm) round cake pan with cooking spray. In small bowl, whisk together applesauce, granulated sugar, eggs, oil, and vanilla.

2. In large bowl, whisk together flour, baking soda, cinnamon, and salt. Make a well in center, add applesauce mixture, and stir just until blended. Stir in carrots and walnuts. Pour batter into pan.

3. Bake for 35 minutes, or until a wooden pick inserted in center comes out clean. Transfer to a rack and let cool for 10 minutes, then remove from pan and let cool for 1 hour.

4. Meanwhile, in small bowl, whisk together cream cheese and milk until well combined. Add 2 Tbsp confectioners' sugar and whisk until smooth, adding more sugar if glaze is too thin. Place cake on serving plate and drizzle with glaze.

Per serving: 160 calories, 3 g protein, 23 g carbohydrates, 2 g fiber, 6 g total fat, 1 g saturated fat, 37 mg cholesterol, 236 mg sodium

CHOCOLATE BANANA SOUFFLÉS

Serves 8
Prep Time: 25 minutes
Cook Time: 20 minutes
Healing Foods: bananas, chocolate, eggs
Ailments It Heals: Alzheimer's disease, blood pressure, diverticulitis, muscle cramps

4 large, very ripe bananas, peeled and cut into
   2-in (5 cm) chunks
¼ cup water
¾ cup plus 2 Tbsp turbinado sugar
4 oz (125 g) bittersweet chocolate, cut into
   ¼-in (0.5 cm) pieces
⅛ tsp ground cinnamon
6 large egg whites
Pinch of salt

1. In a food processor or blender, add the bananas and puree. Measure 2 cups puree and set aside. Discard any extra puree.

2. In medium saucepan, combine water and ½ cup sugar. Bring to a boil over low heat, stirring occasionally. When mixture boils, stop stirring and continue cooking for 2 minutes, or until syrup thickens. Stir in banana puree. Remove from heat and stir in chocolate and cinnamon. Let stand a minute to melt chocolate, then whisk until smooth. Pour mixture into heatproof bowl and cool to room temperature, stirring occasionally.

3. Set rack in middle of oven and preheat to 400°F (200°C). Coat eight individual 4-oz (120 mL) ramekins with cooking spray, then coat the sprayed surface with 2 Tbsp sugar. Set aside on baking sheet.

4. In bowl of an electric mixer, combine egg whites and salt. Whip until egg whites just begin to hold a shape. Increase speed to medium high and whip in remaining ¼ cup sugar in a slow stream, until mixture holds a soft, glossy peak when whisk is lifted.

5. Gently fold banana puree into egg whites, working quickly to prevent egg whites from deflating. Divide soufflé batter evenly among ramekins, filling each to within ¼-in (0.5 cm) of the top. Bake for 12 to 15 minutes, or until well-risen.

6. Immediately remove baking sheet from oven. Use oven mitts to transfer ramekins to dessert plates and serve immediately.

Per serving: 229 calories, 4 g protein, 45 g carbohydrates, 3 g fiber, 6 g total fat, 3 g saturated fat, 0 mg cholesterol, 42 mg sodium

CREAMY CITRUS AND VANILLA RICE PUDDING

Serves 4
Prep Time: 10 minutes
Cook Time: 32 minutes plus cooling
Healing Foods: rice, cinnamon, eggs
Ailments It Heals: anemia, celiac disease, jaundice, lactose intolerance

4 cups rice milk
3 strips (3 x ½ in or 7.5 x 1 cm each) orange zest
3 strips (3 x ½ in or 7.5 x 1 cm each) lime zest
1 cinnamon stick, split lengthwise
½ tsp salt
½ cup basmati, jasmine, or texmati rice
¼ cup sugar
2 large egg yolks
½ tsp vanilla extract

1. In large saucepan, stir together rice milk, orange and lime zests, cinnamon, and salt. Add rice and bring to a simmer over medium-low heat. Cover and cook for 15 minutes, stirring occasionally.

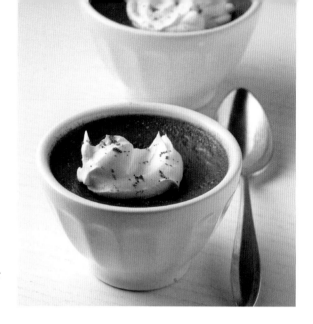

2. Meanwhile, in a medium bowl, whisk together sugar and egg yolks.

3. Uncover rice and cook, stirring frequently, for 15 minutes, or until rice is very tender. Whisk some of hot rice mixture into egg mixture to warm it, then whisk egg mixture into saucepan. Cook, stirring constantly, for 2 minutes, or until pudding is slightly thickened.

4. Transfer pudding to bowl and stir in vanilla. When cool, remove orange zest, lime zest, and cinnamon stick. Cool to room temperature, then cover and refrigerate until serving time.

Per serving: 279 calories, 5 g protein, 56 g carbohydrates, 0 g fiber, 5 g total fat, 1 g saturated fat, 106 mg cholesterol, 394 mg sodium

PUMPKIN CUSTARDS

Serves 6
Prep Time: 20 minutes
Cook Time: 55 minutes plus cooling
Healing Foods: eggs, pumpkins, cinnamon, soy
Ailments It Heals: hyperthyroidism, Parkinson's disease, sore throat

2	large eggs
2	large egg whites
⅔	cup sugar
¾	cup canned unseasoned pumpkin puree
1½	tsp ground cinnamon
½	tsp ground nutmeg
¼	tsp salt
½	tsp vanilla extract
1½	cups vanilla soymilk
3	Tbsp whipped cream or low-calorie whipped topping

1. Preheat oven to 325°F (160°C). Line roasting pan with folded kitchen towel (this prevents the custard cups from sliding around). Put a kettle of water on to boil for water bath.

2. In large bowl, whisk eggs, egg whites, and sugar until smooth. Add pumpkin, cinnamon, nutmeg, salt, and vanilla. Whisk until blended. Gently whisk in the soymilk.

3. Divide mixture among six ¾-cup (175 mL) custard cups. Skim foam from surface of custards. Set custard cups on towel in roasting pan. Pour enough boiling water into pan to come halfway up sides of custard cups. Place roasting pan in oven and bake, uncovered, for 50 to 55 minutes, or until custards are set. Transfer custard cups to a rack and let cool. Then cover and refrigerate for 1 hour, or until chilled.

4. Just before serving, top each custard with a dollop of whipped cream (or whipped topping).

Per serving: 166 calories, 5 g protein, 28 g carbohydrates, 1 g fiber, 4 g total fat, 1 g saturated fat, 75 mg cholesterol, 165 mg sodium

MELON BERRY COMPOTE WITH GREEN TEA AND LIME

Serves 6
Prep Time: 10 minutes plus steeping
Healing Foods: tea, limes, cantaloupe, blueberries
Ailments It Heals: bulimia, cancer, colds and flu, eye problems, varicose veins

- 2 green tea bags
- ⅔ cup boiling water
- 2 Tbsp sugar
- 1 tsp grated lime zest
- 2 Tbsp lime juice
- ½ cantaloupe, cut into 1½-in (3.5 cm) cubes (3 cups)
- 2 cups blueberries, rinsed and dried

1. Place tea bags in boiling water and let steep for 3 to 4 minutes. Remove tea bags. Add sugar to tea and stir until dissolved. Stir in lime zest and lime juice. Let cool to room temperature.

2. Combine cantaloupe and blueberries in large bowl. Pour green tea mixture over fruit and toss to coat well. The compote will keep, covered, in refrigerator for up to 2 days.

Per serving: 72 calories, 1 g protein, 18 g carbohydrates, 2 g fiber, 0 g total fat, 0 g saturated fat, 0 mg cholesterol, 13 mg sodium

ORANGE AND POMEGRANATE COMPOTE

Serves 4
Prep Time: 15 minutes
Healing Foods: oranges, pomegranates
Ailments It Heals: cholesterol (high), infertility, urinary tract infections

- 2 Tbsp orange liqueur, such as Grand Marnier or Cointreau, or orange juice
- 1 Tbsp sugar
- 3 medium-large navel oranges
- ½ pomegranate

1. In medium bowl, stir orange liqueur (or orange juice) and sugar together. Peel oranges, removing white pith with paring knife. Quarter oranges and slice. Add orange segments to bowl and toss to coat.

2. Scoop seeds from pomegranate half into small bowl, discarding membrane. Sprinkle pomegranate seeds over oranges. The compote will keep, covered, in refrigerator for up to 2 days.

Per serving: 94 calories, 2 g protein, 23 g carbohydrates, 3 g fiber, 0 g total fat, 0 g saturated fat, 0 mg cholesterol, 1 mg sodium

GUAVAS AND PLUMS WITH VANILLA SYRUP

Serves 4
Prep Time: 5 minutes
Cook Time: 5 minutes
Healing Foods: plums, guava, nuts
Ailments It Heals: cancer, constipation, obesity

14.5 oz (410 mL) can plums
14.5 oz (410 mL) can guava halves
 1 tsp vanilla extract
 ⅓ cup chopped pistachio nuts

1. Drain plums, pouring syrup into large saucepan. Drain syrup from guava halves into same pan. Boil syrup on high for 4 to 5 minutes, or until reduced by about half.

2. Meanwhile, pit the plums if necessary and divide them among four bowls. Add guava halves.

3. Stir vanilla into syrup and spoon evenly over fruit. Sprinkle with pistachio nuts and serve.

Per serving: 201 calories, 3 g protein, 39 g carbohydrates, 7 g fiber, 5 g fat, 1 g saturated fat, 0 mg cholesterol, 22 mg sodium

FRESH FIGS WITH RASPBERRIES AND ROSE CREAM

Serves 4
Prep Time: 15 minutes
Healing Foods: figs, raspberries
Ailments It Heals: constipation, diabetes, hemorrhoids

3½ oz (100 g) crème fraîche, or sour cream mixed with a little confectioners' sugar
 2 tsp raspberry jam
Finely grated zest of 1 lime
1 to 2 Tbsp rosewater, or to taste
 8 small ripe juicy figs
 4 large fresh fig leaves (optional)
 7 oz (210 g) fresh raspberries
Fresh mint leaves

1. Place crème fraîche in a bowl and beat in raspberry jam and lime zest until jam is well distributed. Add rosewater and stir to mix. Transfer rose cream to a serving bowl.

2. Cut each fig vertically into quarters without cutting all the way through, so they remain whole. Arrange fig leaves, if using, on four plates and place 2 figs on each plate.

3. Spoon a dollop of rose cream into center of each fig. Serve remaining cream separately. Scatter raspberries over plates, garnish with mint leaves, and serve.

Per serving: 162 calories, 2 g protein, 20 g carbohydrates, 5 g fiber, 10 g total fat, 6 g saturated fat, 34 mg cholesterol, 13 mg sodium

FRUIT PARFAIT WITH GINGER TEA CREAM

Serves 4

Prep Time: 10 minutes

Cook Time: 5 minutes plus cooling

Healing Foods: milk, tea, berries

Ailments It Heals: arthritis, motion sickness, respiratory disorders

    2   cups skim milk
    1   envelope unflavored gelatin
    2   ginger herbal tea bags
    3   Tbsp sugar
    ⅛   tsp salt
    4   cups mixed fruit such as cantaloupe cubes, sliced strawberries, and blueberries

1. Place 1 cup milk in small bowl. Sprinkle gelatin over cold milk. Set aside for 5 minutes, or until gelatin softens. Meanwhile, in large saucepan, bring the remaining 1 cup milk to a boil.

2. Add tea bags, sugar, salt, and softened gelatin mixture to boiling milk, stirring with each addition. Remove from heat and stir for 1 minute to dissolve gelatin and sugar. Set aside for 3 minutes to allow tea to steep.

3. Let mixture cool to room temperature, then refrigerate for 1 to 1½ hours, or until it begins to set. Spoon ¼ cup of tea cream into each of four large wine goblets or dessert cups. Top with fruit and remaining tea cream. Refrigerate at least 1 to 2 hours longer, until tea cream is set and chilled.

Per serving: 144 calories, 7 g protein, 30 g carbohydrates, 3 g fiber, 1 g total fat, 0 g saturated fat, 2 mg cholesterol, 146 mg sodium

GRILLED FRUIT EN BROCHETTE

Serves 8

Prep Time: 30 minutes

Cook Time: 8 minutes

Healing Foods: figs, pineapples, pears, peaches, bananas, raspberries

Ailments It Heals: blood pressure, cholesterol (high), hemorrhoids

Coulis

    2   cups fresh raspberries
    1½ tsp grated orange zest
    ½   cup orange juice
    1   Tbsp sugar

Brochettes

    4   fresh figs, or 4 dried figs, soaked and drained
    ½   large fresh pineapple (1 lb or 500 g)
    2   large pears, ripe but firm (1 lb or 500 g)
    2   large peaches, ripe but firm (1 lb or 500 g)
    2   large bananas, ripe but firm
    ⅓   cup fresh lemon juice
    1   Tbsp sugar
Fresh raspberries

1. Soak eight bamboo skewers, 10 to 12 in (25 to 30 cm) long, in cold water for 20 minutes.

2. To make coulis: In blender or food processor, puree raspberries, orange zest and juice, and sugar. Strain mixture to remove seeds, if you wish, but it's not necessary. Set aside.

3. Preheat grill or broiler.

4. To make brochettes: Cut figs lengthwise into 4 equal pieces (about 2 cups). Peel, core, and cut pineapple into bite-size chunks (3 cups). Core (do not peel) pears and cut into 1½-in (3.5 cm) cubes. Pit (do not peel) peaches and cut into 1½-in (3.5 cm) cubes. Peel bananas and cut crosswise into 1½-in (3.5 cm) pieces. Thread fruit onto soaked skewers, alternating them to make a colorful arrangement. Mix lemon juice and sugar in measuring cup. Baste brochettes with half of mixture.

5. Grill or broil brochettes for 4 minutes. Turn, baste with remaining lemon juice mixture, and grill or broil for 3 to 4 minutes, or until light golden brown.

6. For each serving, spread about ¼ cup coulis on a plate and arrange a fruit brochette on top. Garnish with raspberries, if you wish. Serve hot.

Per serving: 184 calories, 2 g protein, 47 g carbohydrates, 8 g fiber, 1 g total fat, 0 g saturated fat, 0 mg cholesterol, 6 mg sodium

THREE-BERRY FOOL

Serves 4
Prep Time: 20 minutes plus standing
Cook Time: 7 minutes
Healing Foods: yogurt, raspberries, strawberries, blueberries
Ailments It Heals: arthritis, blood pressure, flatulence, herpes

1 qt (1 L) low-fat plain yogurt
2 cups frozen unsweetened raspberries, thawed
2 cups frozen unsweetened strawberries, thawed
½ cup sugar
1½ tsp vanilla extract
3 tsp cornstarch blended with 2 Tbsp water
2 cups frozen unsweetened blueberries
2 Tbsp orange juice
¼ tsp ground black pepper
¼ tsp allspice
1 Tbsp fresh lemon juice

1. Spoon yogurt into fine-mesh strainer or coffee filter set over bowl to catch drips. Let yogurt stand for 4 hours at room temperature.

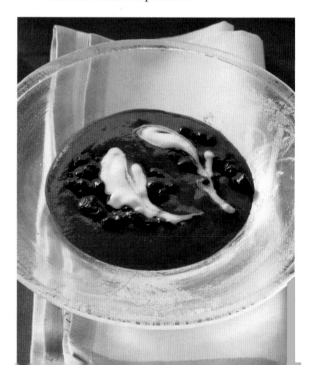

2. In food processor, combine raspberries, strawberries, ¼ cup sugar, and ½ tsp vanilla. Puree, then transfer to small saucepan and bring to a boil over medium heat. Stir in half of cornstarch mixture and bring to a boil. Cook, stirring constantly for 1 minute, until lightly thickened. Cool to room temperature, transfer to bowl, cover, and refrigerate.

3. In small saucepan, combine blueberries, orange juice, pepper, allspice, and 2 Tbsp sugar. Bring to a simmer over low heat. Cook, stirring frequently, for 5 minutes, or until blueberries are tender. Stir in remaining cornstarch mixture and bring to a boil. Cook, stirring constantly, for 1 minute, or until thickened. Transfer to bowl and stir in lemon juice. Cover and refrigerate.

4. In medium bowl, combine drained yogurt and remaining 2 Tbsp sugar and 1 tsp vanilla.

5. To serve, spoon raspberry-strawberry mixture into four bowls. Spoon blueberry mixture into the center and top with yogurt. Gently swirl mixture to lightly marble yogurt with fruit puree.

Per serving: 350 calories, 14 g protein, 68 g carbohydrates, 6 g fiber, 4 g total fat, 2 g saturated fat, 15 mg cholesterol, 172 mg sodium

TROPICAL FRUIT SALAD

Serves 6
Prep Time: 20 minutes
Healing Foods: yogurt, grapefuit, kiwis, banana, melons, ginger
Ailments It Heals: circulatory disorders, menstrual problems, prostate problems

1   cup low-fat vanilla yogurt
1   tsp grated lime zest
2   red grapefruits
2   kiwis, peeled and cut into thin slices
2   bananas, sliced
1   small cantaloupe or large papaya, seeded and cut into chunks
2   Tbsp crystallized ginger

1. In small bowl, combine yogurt and lime zest.

2. Over large bowl, cut grapefruits into sections, then place in bowl. Squeeze membranes over bowl to release juice. Add kiwis, bananas, cantaloupe, and ginger. Toss to blend.

3. To serve, divide fruit among six bowls. Top each with 1½ Tbsp yogurt mixture.

Per serving: 154 calories, 3 g protein, 36 g carbohydrates, 4 g fiber, 1 g total fat, 0 g saturated fat, 3 mg cholesterol, 34 mg sodium

KIWI-PASSION FRUIT SALAD

Serves 4
Prep Time: 15 minutes
Healing Foods: papayas, mangoes, kiwi, passion fruit
Ailments It Heals: acne, colds and flu, multiple sclerosis, stroke

1   large papaya
1   large mango
2   kiwi
½   cup (125 mL) orange juice
2   Tbsp lime juice
2   passion fruit

1. Peel and halve papaya and scoop out seeds. Slice fruit crosswise and arrange slices in two rows on serving platter, or cut into chunks and put into large serving bowl.

2. Peel mango, remove the pit, and cut lengthwise into wedges. Arrange wedges in a row between papaya slices. Or cut into chunks and add to serving bowl.

3. Peel kiwi and cut lengthwise into wedges or chunks. Scatter them over mango and papaya.

4. Mix orange juice with lime juice. Halve the passion fruit and scoop out seeds and pulp into juice mixture. Spoon over salad and serve immediately.

Per serving: 183 calories, 2 g protein, 45 g carbohydrates, 7 g fiber, 1 g total fat, 0 g saturated fat, 0 mg cholesterol, 20 mg sodium

2. Add strawberries, pear, and cucumber to bowl. Set aside 4 star-fruit slices for decoration. Dice remaining slices and add to bowl.

3. Drizzle Grand Marnier over fruit, sprinkle with mint, and toss gently to mix well. Cover with plastic wrap and refrigerate for 20 minutes.

4. Pile fruit mixture into shells and decorate with reserved star fruit.

Per serving: 107 calories, 1 g protein, 20 g carbohydrates, 3 g fiber, 1 g total fat, 0 g saturated fat, 0 mg cholesterol, 8 mg sodium

MINTY MELON CUPS

Serves 6
Prep Time: 25 minutes plus chilling
Healing Foods: cantaloupe, honeydew, strawberries, pears, mint
Ailments It Heals: celiac disease, diverticulitis, rosacea

1   small cantaloupe (about 1 lb or 500 g)
1   small honeydew melon (about 1 lb or 500 g)
1   pint ripe strawberries, hulled and sliced
    (1½ cups)
1   large pear, cut into ½-in (1 cm) pieces
½   small cucumber, diced (½ cup)
2   star fruits, sliced ¼ in (0.5 cm) thick
6   Tbsp Grand Marnier or brandy
2   Tbsp shredded fresh mint
Fresh mint sprigs

1. Cut both melons in half crosswise and scoop out seeds from center. Using melon baller or small spoon, scoop out balls of melon into large bowl. With a tablespoon, scoop out any remaining melon into the bowl, leaving smooth shells.

FRESH FRUIT SOUP

Serves 4
Prep Time: 30 minutes plus chilling
Healing Foods: peppers, chile, guava, kiwi
Ailments It Heals: acne, colds and flu, gout, jet lag

2   cups pineapple juice
2   cups orange juice
½   cucumber, diced
¼   red onion, finely chopped
1   small red bell pepper, seeded and chopped
½   red chile pepper, seeded and chopped
Juice of 1 lime
½   tsp sugar
1   guava, peeled and diced
1   kiwi, diced
1   Tbsp chopped fresh mint
2   Tbsp chopped fresh cilantro
Fresh mint sprigs (optional)

1. In large bowl, mix together pineapple and orange juices. Add cucumber, onion, bell pepper, chile pepper, lime juice, and sugar and stir well to mix. Cover and chill for 1 hour so flavors can develop.

2. Remove from refrigerator and stir in guava, kiwi, chopped mint, and cilantro.

3. Ladle soup into bowls and garnish with mint sprigs, if using, and serve at once.

Per serving: 171 calories, 2 g protein, 41 g carbohydrates, 3 g fiber, 1 g fat, 0 g saturated fat, 0 mg cholesterol, 8 mg sodium

orange juice concentrate and ice cubes to blender and blend until smooth. Scrape puree into bowl containing remaining fruit. Stir gently to combine.

2. To serve, ladle soup into dessert bowls and garnish each serving with a dollop of yogurt and mint sprig.

Per serving: 88 calories, 2 g protein, 21 g carbohydrates, 2 g fiber, 0 g total fat, 0 g saturated fat, 0 mg cholesterol, 10 mg sodium

MIXED BERRY AND STONE FRUIT SOUP

Serves 8
Prep Time: 20 minutes
Cook Time: 0 minutes
Healing Foods: nectarines, plums, blueberries, blackberries, yogurt
Ailments It Heals: flatulence, stroke, varicose veins

¼ cup orange juice
1 Tbsp lemon juice
3 Tbsp sugar
2 medium nectarines, pitted and cut into 1 x ½-in (2.5 × 1 cm) pieces (1½ cups)
3 medium plums, pitted and cut into 1 x ½-in (2.5 x 1 cm) pieces (1½ cups)
1 cup fresh blueberries, rinsed
1 cup fresh blackberries, rinsed
2 Tbsp frozen orange juice concentrate
2 ice cubes, crushed
½ cup nonfat vanilla yogurt
Mint sprigs for garnish

1. In large bowl, combine orange juice, lemon juice, and sugar. Stir to dissolve sugar. Gently stir in nectarines, plums, blueberries, and blackberries. Transfer ¾ cup of fruit and juices to blender. Add

DRINKS

CARROT-ORANGE JUICE

Serves 2
Prep Time: 5 minutes
Healing Foods: carrots, oranges, ginger
Ailments It Heals: colds and flu, fever, gout, varicose veins

1½ cups fresh or bottled carrot juice, chilled
⅔ cup fresh-squeezed orange juice (3 oranges)
½-in-thick (1 cm) slice peeled fresh ginger

1. In medium bowl, mix carrot juice and orange juice. Crush ginger in garlic press to fill ½ tsp. Stir crushed ginger into juice mixture and serve. (If making ahead, stir before serving.)

Per serving: 75 calories, 2 g protein, 17 g carbohydrates, 0 g fiber, 0 g total fat, 0 g saturated fat, 0 mg cholesterol, 93 mg sodium

WARM PINEAPPLE-GINGER PUNCH

Serves 4
Prep Time: 5 minutes
Cook Time: 10 minutes
Healing Foods: pineapples, ginger, cloves
Ailments It Heals: arthritis, flatulence, motion sickness, sore throat

4 cups pineapple juice
1 cup sliced fresh ginger, unpeeled
1 Tbsp honey
1 cinnamon stick, split lengthwise
8 whole cloves
¼ tsp ground black pepper

1. In medium saucepan, combine pineapple juice, ginger, honey, cinnamon, cloves, and pepper. Bring to a boil. Reduce to a simmer and cook for 10 minutes. Strain and serve warm.

Per serving: 152 calories, 1 g protein, 38 g carbohydrates, 0 g fiber, 0 g total fat, 0 g saturated fat, 0 mg cholesterol, 4 mg sodium

SPICY VEGETABLE COCKTAIL

Serves 4
Prep Time: 8 minutes
Healing Foods: tomatoes, onions, parsley
Ailments It Heals: colds and flu, muscle cramps, respiratory disorders

3 cups tomato juice
¼ cup coarsely chopped, seeded green bell pepper
1 scallion, trimmed to 4 in (10 cm), thinly sliced
1 Tbsp coarsely chopped parsley
1 Tbsp horseradish sauce
1 tsp Worcestershire sauce
½ tsp sugar
½ tsp Tabasco, or to taste
Celery stalks and lemon slices, for garnish (optional)

1. In blender, combine tomato juice, pepper, scallion, parsley, horseradish sauce, Worcestershire sauce, sugar, and Tabasco. Process for 2 to 3 minutes, or until smooth.

2. Serve over ice. Garnish with celery and lemon, if using.

Per serving: 55 calories, 2 g protein, 10 g carbohydrates, 1 g fiber, 1 g total fat, 0 g saturated fat, 1 mg cholesterol, 686 mg sodium

CHAI

Serves 2
Prep Time: 2 minutes
Cook Time: 5 minutes plus steeping
Healing Foods: ginger, tea, milk
Ailments It Heals: diabetes, fever, lupus, multiple sclerosis, osteoporosis

1½ cups water
¼ tsp ground cinnamon
¼ tsp ground cloves
¼ tsp ground ginger
⅔ cup low-fat milk or vanilla soymilk
3 black tea bags
2 tsp honey, or to taste

1. In small saucepan, combine water, cinnamon, cloves, and ginger. Bring to a simmer. Reduce heat to low, cover, and simmer for 5 minutes. Add milk (or soymilk) and heat until steaming but not boiling. Remove from heat.

2. Add tea bags, cover, and let steep for 3 to 4 minutes. Pour into 2 mugs and sweeten with honey to taste.

Per serving: 63 calories, 3 g protein, 11 g carbohydrates, 0 g fiber, 1 g total fat, 1 g saturated fat, 3 mg cholesterol, 49 mg sodium

ELECTROLYTE DRINK

Serves 1
Prep Time: 5 minutes
Healing Foods: apples, lemons
Ailments It Heals: diarrhea, fever, urinary tract infections

1 cup apple juice
2 cups water
½ to 1 tsp salt
Juice from 1 lemon or 1 lime

In a pitcher, combine apple juice, water, salt, and lemon or lime juice. Store in refrigerator.

Per serving: 127 calories, 0 g protein, 34 g carbohydrates, 0 g fiber, 0 g total fat, 0 g saturated fat, 0 mg cholesterol, 1,174 mg sodium

3

AILMENTS
Daily Meal Plans to Heal What Ails You

Now that you know food can be powerful medicine, it's time to take advantage of its healing powers. No food or diet is likely to cure an ailment, but eating the right foods and avoiding the wrong ones can go a long way toward improving your wellbeing. Healing foods provide nutrients your body needs to ease symptoms, fight disease, and repair itself.

To get started, check out an ailment that you or someone you know has been affected by. You can also be proactive by reviewing the diet advice for conditions you may be predisposed to develop because of a family history or other risk factors you may have. For instance, if you have a family history of diabetes, you may want to familiarize yourself with low glycemic and fiber-rich foods that help keep your blood sugar levels stable

Each entry begins with aquick lists, so you can see at a glance which foods may cause additional symptoms or worsen an ailment and which foods may improve or prevent it. These aren't compre-

hensive lists, but just highlight the best and worst foods to eat if you suffer from that condition. And because ailments often affect different people in different ways, we also highlight foods that you may consider limiting. If you suffer from migraines, for example, you may want to avoid aged cheeses, processed meats, red wine, or certain fruits and vegetables if they trigger your headaches.

At the heart of each entry is a sample one-day meal plan that shows you how to minimize harmful foods and maximize the healing ones. You'll also get a list of recipes to try (in the order they appear in Part 2) that feature one or more of the foods that heal. And to help you eat that way every day, we provide general diet advice for each condition.

Changing your diet is just one part of getting better, but its impact goes way beyond helping to heal a specific ailment. Some positive side effects include more energy, a stronger immune system, and a longer, healthier life.

ACNE

FOODS THAT HARM

Dairy products

High-glycemic foods, such as soft
  drinks, white flour, and refined
  sugars

FOODS THAT HEAL

Broccoli

Cabbage

Oranges

Berries

Kiwi

Melons

Peppers

Spinach and other dark leafy greens

Fish

Poultry

Whole grains

Lentils

Avocados

Potatoes

Bananas

Oysters

Flaxseed

FOODS TO LIMIT

Iodized salt

HOW TO EAT

Limiting dairy and increasing your intake
of vitamins and minerals will keep your
skin looking its best. Here's a meal plan
that does exactly that while providing
alternate sources of calcium. Eat this way
regularly to prevent outbreaks and heal
them quickly when they happen.

**Enjoy a wide variety of fruits and veg-
etables,** including a mix of colors to get all
the skin-clearing vitamins such as beta-
carotene and C.

Drink lots of water and eat high-water
content fruits and veggies such as watermelon, strawberries, tomatoes, and zucchini. Staying hydrated keeps your skin
glowing.

Get your vitamin B6 and zinc. Found
in meat, fish (especially oysters), poultry,
whole grains, beans, lentils, avocados,
nuts, potatoes, bananas, and leafy greens,
this vitamin and mineral may reduce acne
by helping to regulate hormones implicated in the development of acne lesions.

Load up on healthy fat. Omega-3 fatty
acids can help ward off the inflammation
of acne. Flaxseed and fish are rich in these
healthy fats.

SAMPLE MEAL PLAN

Breakfast: ¾ cup of whole grain cereal
with ½ cup of soymilk; ½ sliced banana

Lunch: *Chicken Salad with Citrus* (page
161); 1 whole wheat pita pocket, sliced in
quarters

Snack: ¼ cup of bean dip with 6 whole
grain crackers

Dinner: 3 oz of grilled fish; ½ cup of
cooked brown rice; at least ½ cup of
chopped, steamed kale; *Avocado, Jicama,
and Orange Salad* (page 174)

Dessert: 2 cups of cubed cantaloupe

OTHER RECIPES TO TRY

- Grilled Salmon Salad
- Spinach Salad with Chickpeas
- Orange Beef with Broccoli and Jicama
- Brown Rice with Cabbage and
  Chickpeas

ADHD (ATTENTION DEFICIT/HYPERACTIVITY DISORDER)

FOODS THAT HARM

Some children with ADHD may be sensitive to foods containing salicylates, including:

Processed foods

Foods containing dyes, particularly red or orange dyes

Dried fruits

FOODS THAT HEAL

Salicylate-free foods, such as:

Bananas

Pears

Lentils

Whole grain breads and cereals

Fish

Lean meat and poultry

Milk and cheese

Eggs

FOODS TO LIMIT

Sugary foods, such as cookies and soft drinks

HOW TO EAT

A diet filled with more complex carbs and protein instead of sugary carbs may promote better concentration and help you relax.

Nix simple carbs such as candy, honey, sugar, fruit drinks, soft drinks, and foods sweetened with corn syrup.

Eat complex carbs, especially later in the day.

Get more protein like beans, eggs, low-fat cheese, fish, and lean meat.

SAMPLE MEAL PLAN

Breakfast: 1 cup of oatmeal prepared with ½ cup of whole milk; 1 banana

Lunch: *Macaroni and Cheese with Spinach* (page 215); 1 cup of vegetable soup

Snack: 1 pear; 1 oz of low-fat cheese

Dinner: *Greek-Lamb Kebabs* (page 186); baked potato topped with 1 Tbsp reduced-fat sour cream, chopped chives, and ½ cup of steamed vegetables

Snack: ½ peanut butter sandwich made with 1 slice of whole grain bread

OTHER RECIPES TO TRY

- Summer Greens Scramble
- Beef-Fillet Salad with Mustard Vinaigrette
- Sloppy Joes
- Zucchini-Carrot Crustless Quiche Squares
- Savory Lamb Stew with Sweet Potatoes

AGE-RELATED MACULAR DEGENERATION

See Eye Problems, page 305

AIDS AND HIV INFECTION

See also Diarrhea, page 303

FOODS THAT HARM

Shellfish, hamburgers, sushi, homemade mayonnaise, and other undercooked food

FOODS THAT HEAL

Fish

Lean meats

Poultry without skin

Legumes

Cooked fruits and vegetables

Quinoa

Barley

Buckwheat

Olive oil

Walnuts

Flaxseed

FOODS TO LIMIT

Sugary foods, such as cookies and soft drinks

Raw fruits and vegetables

Red meat, butter, and other foods with saturated fats

HOW TO EAT

Good nutrition can prevent or delay weight loss and other complications associated with the disease.

Avoid empty calories—foods like cookies and soft drinks provide calories but little to no nutrition.

Aim for 5 to 6 servings of vegetables and fruits per day.

Choose whole grain carbohydrates at least 50 percent of the time.

Keep protein in check. To avoid overtaxing your kidneys, limit protein to 0.4 to 0.5 g per pound of body weight. That's 60 to 75 g if you weigh 150 lbs (68 kg).

Practice food safety. Wash hands before handling food, during its preparation, and after. Keep hot foods hot and cold foods cold. Avoid contact between raw and cooked foods. Eggs should be boiled for at least 7 minutes; meat and fish should be well cooked, with an internal temperature of 160° to 165°F (71° to 74°C).

Cook ahead. To make healthy eating easier on days when you're not feeling well, prepare dishes when you feel good and freeze them.

SAMPLE MEAL PLAN

Breakfast: *Hot Cereal with Apples and Dates* (page 121) topped with 1 tsp of ground flaxseeds

Lunch: 3 oz of baked skinless chicken breast; *Barley and Beet Salad* (page 168); 1 cup of chopped, steamed greens

Snack: small container of low-fat yogurt with ½ cup of fruit canned in its own juice

Dinner: *Flank Steak Roll with Carrots and Red Peppers* (page 181); small baked potato topped with 1 Tbsp of reduced-fat sour cream; 1 slice of whole grain bread

Dessert: 1 orange

OTHER RECIPES TO TRY

- Cod and Vegetable Stew
- Three-Bean Chili
- Asian Grilled Tuna Burgers
- Spinach-Stuffed Meat Loaf
- Tuscan Veal Chops
- Springtime Quinoa
- Roasted Root Vegetables

ALCOHOLISM

FOODS THAT HARM

Alcohol in any form

FOODS THAT HEAL

Legumes

Whole grain or fortified and
enriched grain products

Lean meat and poultry

Nuts

Mushrooms

Broccoli

Cabbage

Dairy products

Spinach

Kale

HOW TO EAT

Alcoholism can lead to malnutrition, not only because chronic drinkers tend to have poor diets, but also because alcohol alters the digestion and metabolism of most nutrients. To prevent problems, eat a wide variety of nutrient-packed foods and don't skip meals.

Add calcium. Dairy foods and dark leafy greens are good sources of this bone-strengthening mineral. Many alcoholics are at higher risk of bone fractures and osteoporosis.

Speak to a nutritionist. A nutritionist can help you customize your diet to address underlying problems such as obesity or liver damage.

SAMPLE MEAL PLAN

Breakfast: *Mushroom and Bell Pepper Frittata* (page 123); 1 slice of whole grain toast with 1 tsp of trans fat free soft spread; 1 cup of calcium-fortified orange juice

Lunch: *Pasta Primavera* (page 216), 2 cups of mixed green salad tossed with 2 Tbsp of low-fat dressing and 1 Tbsp of walnuts; 1 whole grain roll

Snack: 1 banana

Dinner: *Pork Chops and Cabbage* (page 188); ½ cup of cooked brown rice; ½ cup of steamed broccoli florets

Dessert: milkshake or protein smoothie, any flavor

OTHER RECIPES TO TRY

- One-Egg Omelet with Chopped Broccoli, Tomatoes, and Cheddar
- Grilled Salmon with Sautéed Greens
- Roasted Pork with Pomegranate Sauce
- Baked Pasta with Garlic and Greens
- Orange-Walnut Broccoli

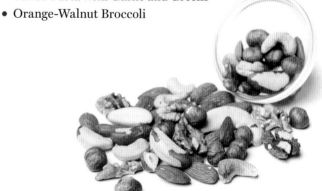

ALLERGIES, FOOD

FOODS THAT HARM

Almost any food can provoke an allergic reaction. Eight foods that account for 90% of allergic reactions are:

Milk and milk products

Eggs (especially egg whites)

Soy and soy products

Wheat and wheat products

Peanuts

Tree nuts

Fish

Shellfish

HOW TO EAT

Keep a food diary. Record the foods you eat each day and when you eat them. (Don't forget to include snacks and beverages!) Record any allergy symptoms you experience, as well as the time the symptoms begin. Share your food diary with your doctor to help determine which foods may be triggering your symptoms.

Read labels carefully. Once you identify what you're allergic to, learn to read labels to avoid exposure.

ALLERGIES, SEASONAL

See Hay Fever, page 312

ALZHEIMER'S DISEASE

FOODS THAT HARM

Alcohol

FOODS THAT HEAL

Olive oil

Tomatoes

Green beans

Zucchini

Cauliflower

Brussels sprouts

Eggplant

Peppers

Salmon

Mackerel

FOODS TO LIMIT

Red meat, butter, and other foods with saturated fats

Sugary foods, such as cookies and soft drinks

HOW TO EAT

There is evidence that some foods and nutrients are powerful allies in the battle against Alzheimer's. Here's how to protect against Alzheimer's and dementia or slow their effects if you have the disease.

Adopt a Mediterranean eating style that includes olive oil, tomatoes, fish, poultry, cruciferous vegetables, fruits, and leafy green vegetables, and less amounts of foods with saturated fat, such as butter and red meat.

Eat fatty fish at least three times a week. Good sources also include trout, sardines, herring, anchovies, halibut, bluefish, ocean perch, bass, and red snapper.

Toss aluminum cookware. Although a link between aluminum and Alzheimer's hasn't been proven, some scientists argue that increased concentration in the Alzheimer's brain worsens the condition. As a precaution, avoid using aluminum cookware because the metal can leach into food. Other sources: some antacids and drinking water in areas where aluminum compounds are used in city water treatment.

SAMPLE MEAL PLAN

Breakfast: 1 cup of oatmeal or cream of wheat prepared with skim milk; at least ½ cup of fresh fruit

Lunch: *Penne with Fresh Tomato Sauce and Grilled Eggplant* (page 218); at least ½ cup of steamed green string beans; 1 whole grain roll

Snack: 1 cup of cubed cantaloupe or honeydew with ¼ cup of low-fat cottage cheese

Dinner: *Salmon and Asparagus Farfalle with Walnut-Feta Sauce* (page 201); 1 cup of mixed green salad tossed with grated carrots, drizzled with 2 Tbsp low-fat dressing

Dessert: *Sesame-Fig Bars* (page 251)

OTHER RECIPES TO TRY

- Mediterranean Salad with Edamame
- Grilled Salmon with Sautéed Greens
- Roasted Mackerel with Cherry Tomatoes and Potatoes
- Roasted Tomatoes with Garlic and Herbs

- Trout with Lemon-Mushroom Stuffing
- Baked Pasta with Garlic and Greens
- Cauliflower and Spinach Casserole

ANEMIA

FOODS THAT HEAL

Organ meats
Beef
Poultry
Fish
Egg yolks
Soy products (except soy sauce)
Green leafy vegetables
Iron-enriched breads and cereals
Citrus fruits
Broccoli
Red peppers

FOODS TO LIMIT

Spinach
Rhubarb
Swiss chard
Chocolate
Bran
Nuts
Tea

HOW TO EAT

The most common type of anemia in North America is due to iron deficiency. Here are some general guidelines to boost iron levels to prevent or treat this type of anemia. Never take iron supplements without consulting your doctor.

Consume as much iron from foods as possible. The best sources are animal products—meat, fish, poultry, and egg yolks.

If you're a vegetarian, eat more vitamin C–rich foods. This vitamin enhances the body's absorption of iron from plant sources, such as green leafy vegetables, dried fruits, soy and other legumes, nuts, seeds, and iron-enriched breads and cereals.

Avoid drinking tea during meals. Tea contains natural compounds called tannins that inhibit iron absorption.

Watch for foods with oxalates, such as spinach, rhubarb, Swiss chard, and chocolate, and phytates, such as nuts and bran cereal. Both interfere with your body's ability to absorb and use iron.

QUICK TIP:
Cook with iron pots

Tomatoes and other acidic foods prepared in iron pots add large amounts of iron to food. Four ounces (120 mL) of tomato sauce heated in a regular pot provides 0.7 mg of iron; cooking it in an iron pot adds 5 mg. Ironware may discolor food, but the taste is unaffected.

SAMPLE MEAL PLAN

Breakfast: 2 scrambled eggs; 1 cup of Raisin Bran with ½ cup of skim milk; 1 orange

Lunch: *Chicken Salad with Citrus* (page 161) and 1 enriched soft breadstick; for vegetarians, a bowl of lentil soup, 1 enriched roll topped with 2 tsp of prepared red pepper pesto, and 1 cup of chopped steamed collards

Snack: ¼ cup of trail mix

Dinner: *Orange Beef with Broccoli and Jicama* (page 184), 1 cup of cooked brown rice, and a whole grain roll; for vegetarians, a bowl of chili, 1 cup of cooked brown rice, 1 cup of steamed kale, and 1 enriched roll

Dessert: *Chewy Date-Walnut Bars* (page 253)

OTHER RECIPES TO TRY

- Fish Tacos
- Zucchini-Carrot Crustless Quiche Squares
- Buckwheat Noodles with Tofu and Green Vegetables
- Pot Roast with Root Vegetables
- Calf's Liver with Rigatoni
- Orange Beets
- Creamy Citrus and Vanilla Rice Pudding

ANOREXIA NERVOSA

FOODS THAT HEAL

Eggs
Milk and other dairy foods
Meat, fish, and poultry
Whole grains

FOODS TO LIMIT

Low-calorie diet foods and soft drinks
Foods that have a diuretic or laxative effect (includes foods with sorbitol and some herbal teas like senna leaf tea)

HOW TO EAT

Here are steps to help achieve a stable weight. Consult with a dietitian to make sure all nutritional needs are met.

Start with small portions, then gradually increase food intake.

Choose nutritious and easily digestible foods, such as eggs, custards, soups, and milkshakes.

Suck on a lemon drop before meals.
Sour foods increase saliva flow, which can stimulate appetite.

Monitor food intake closely. Relapses are common, and close monitoring may be necessary to ensure that the person with anorexia is really eating. But avoid making food a constant source of attention and conflict.

SAMPLE MEAL PLAN

Mini Breakfast: 1 small container of 2% Greek yogurt, topped with 3 to 4 Tbsp of granola

A.M. Mini Meal: 1 sliced apple with 1 piece of string cheese

Mini Lunch: *Buffalo Chicken Fingers* (page 246) with your favorite steamed vegetables and rice

P.M. Mini Meal: 8 whole wheat pita chips with *Asian Peanut Dip* (page 249), or try a bean dip, guacamole, or cheese nachos

Mini Dinner: 1 cup of soup, any kind; ½ sandwich—try a turkey or tuna fish sandwich on whole grain bread—or have a grilled chicken or bean burger on a whole wheat bun; ½ cup of steamed vegetables or a small leafy green salad with your favorite dressing

Dessert: *Fruit Salad with Spiced Coconut* (page 176)

OTHER RECIPES TO TRY

- One-Egg Omelet with Chopped Broccoli, Tomatoes, and Cheddar
- Zucchini-Carrot Crustless Quiche Squares
- Asian Noodle Salad
- Rice Salad with Chicken and Grapes
- Turkey Bacon and Apricot Bites
- Vegetable-Stuffed Mushrooms

ANXIETY

See Mood Disorders, page 333

ARTHRITIS

FOODS THAT HARM

Red meat, butter, egg yolks, and other foods with saturated fat

Processed foods that contain trans fats

Refined carbohydrates, such as sugar and white flour

FOODS THAT HEAL

Salmon

Sardines

Trout

Anchovies

Citrus fruits

Kiwi

Pumpkin

Peppers

Sweet potatoes

Cabbage

Collard greens

Rhubarb

Spinach

Chia seeds

Walnuts

Pineapple

Beans

Soy products (except soy sauce)

HOW TO EAT

While medications are different for osteoarthritis and rheumatoid arthritis, the diet advice is similar. Both conditions benefit from reducing inflammation and pain with these tips.

Eat fish two to three times a week. The human body uses omega-3 fatty acids to manufacture prostaglandins, chemicals that play a role in inflammation and pain.

Pump up antioxidants. Vitamins C and E and beta-carotene help to make collagen, reduce inflammation, and slow the progression of this disease. In addition to the foods above, berries and melons are also packed with these vitamins.

Find more omega-3s. If you're not a fish fan or if you want more variety, try flaxseed, chia seed, and walnuts.

Enjoy more bromelain. This enzyme in pineapple may help reduce swelling.

Get more phytoestrogens. Food sources include beans and soy.

SAMPLE MEAL PLAN

Breakfast: ½ cup of low-fat cottage cheese mixed with fresh kiwi slices and 1 Tbsp of crushed walnuts; 1 slice of whole grain toast with 1 Tbsp of apple butter

Lunch: *Pineapple-Chipotle Chicken* (page 195); 1 small baked sweet potato; a side of coleslaw made with low-fat mayonnaise

Snack: 1 orange

Dinner: 3 oz of broiled salmon; *Pasta with Walnut Cream Sauce* (page 217); ½ cup of steamed broccoli

Dessert: *Pumpkin Maple Cheesecake* (page 261)

OTHER RECIPES TO TRY

- Carrot Ginger Yogurt Muffins
- Spinach, Sweet Potato, and Shiitake Salad Sesame Greens and Bean Sprouts
- Grilled Salmon with Sautéed Greens
- Bok Choy, Tofu, and Mushroom Stir-Fry
- Pasta with Cabbage, Apples, and Leeks

ASTHMA

FOODS THAT HARM

- Dried fruit
- Beer
- Wine
- White grape juice
- Instant soup mix
- Instant mashed potatoes
- Cheese
- Soy sauce
- Mushrooms

FOODS THAT HEAL

- Salmon
- Mackerel
- Sardines
- Berries
- Green leafy vegetables

HOW TO EAT

Food allergies can cause asthma attacks, so it's important to identify these types of triggers. See Allergies, Food (page 280) for more information. In addition, these general guidelines will help lessen your chances of attacks or complications.

Double up on fresh fruits and veggies. Aim to have at least 2 servings at every meal and one with every snack to protect lung function and boost immunity. However, beware of potential trigger foods.

Know your trigger foods and avoid them. Common trigger foods are those that contain sulfites (such as dried fruits, white grape juice, instant soup mix, and instant potatoes), salicylates (such as dried fruits and some fresh fruits), molds (such as cheese and mushrooms), and those that are fermented (such as soy sauce, beer, and wine).

Sip coffee or tea. It may help squelch a mild attack because it relaxes bronchial muscles. Skip this tip if you are sensitive to salicylates or take a theophylline drug.

SAMPLE MEAL PLAN

Breakfast: 1 cup of oatmeal with cinnamon, topped with ½ cup of skim milk; 1 cup of fresh fruit

Lunch: *Poached Salmon with Cucumber-Dill Sauce* (page 200); 1 cup of black bean soup; 1 small baked potato topped with 2 Tbsp of salsa and 1 cup of steamed vegetables

Snack: 1 banana

Dinner: 3 oz of baked chicken; 1 cup of a cooked whole grain such as brown rice, quinoa, or millet; at least ½ cup steamed green leafy vegetables and ½ cup steamed assorted other vegetables

Dessert: a bowl of fresh cherries

OTHER RECIPES TO TRY

- Raspberry-Beet Smoothie
- Buckwheat Noodles with Tofu and Green Vegetables
- Grilled Salmon with Sautéed Greens
- Roasted Mackerel with Cherry Tomatoes and Potatoes

ATHERO-SCLEROSIS

FOODS THAT HARM

Processed foods that contain trans fats

FOODS THAT HEAL

Olive oil
Almonds
Avocados
Oats
Lentils
Tofu
Salmon
Sardines
Apples
Pears
Citrus fruits

FOODS TO LIMIT

Red meat, butter, and other foods with saturated fats
High-cholesterol foods, such as eggs, shrimp, and organ meats

HOW TO EAT

Diet plays a critical role in both the development and treatment of atherosclerosis, or hardening of the arteries. Here are ways to delay or prevent the condition.

Limit total fat intake to 10% to 30% of calories.

Cut down on saturated fat. Some strategies include downsizing meat portions, substituting olive oil for butter or margarine, and eating low-fat dairy products.

Eliminate trans fats, which are found in packaged foods such as cookies and crackers and snack food such as chips.

Limit dietary cholesterol to 300 mg a day—about the amount in 1½ egg yolks.

Go fish at least twice a week. The omega-3 fatty acids in salmon, sardines, and other cold-water fish lower blood levels of triglycerides. They also reduce the tendency to form blood clots.

Eat 5 to 10 g of soluble fiber per day. Oat bran; oatmeal; lentils and legumes; pectin-containing fruits such as pears, apples, and citrus fruits; barley; guar gum; and psyllium all contain soluble fiber that lowers blood cholesterol—probably by interfering with the intestinal absorption of bile acids, which forces the liver to use circulating cholesterol to make more bile.

Eat more soy. Aim for 25 g of soy protein—about 1½ cups of edamame—per day.

SAMPLE MEAL PLAN

Breakfast: 1 apple-oat bran muffin; 1 slice of honeydew and 3 large strawberries mixed with ½ cup of yogurt and topped with 1 Tbsp of toasted, sliced almonds

Lunch: *Buckwheat Noodles with Tofu and Green Vegetables* (page 171); 1 whole grain roll; orange.

Snack: 1 pear; a soy protein snack bar

Dinner: 3 oz of grilled salmon; *Mediterranean Salad with Edamame* (page 177); 1 large ear of grilled corn on the cob with 1 tsp of trans fat free soft spread

Dessert: *Chocolate Almond Biscotti* (page 257)

OTHER RECIPES TO TRY

- Nutty Muesli
- Pear Rhubarb Muffins
- Lentil Soup with Canadian Bacon
- Grilled Salmon Salad
- Broiled Salmon with Avocado-Mango Salsa
- Chewy Oatmeal Raisin Cookies

WARNING! FOOD-DRUG INTERACTION

If you are taking anticoagulant medication such as Coumadin, you should limit foods high in vitamin K because they can counteract the desired effect of the drug.

BLEEDING PROBLEMS

FOODS THAT HARM

Alcohol

FOODS THAT HEAL

Green peas
Spinach
Broccoli
Liver
Lean meat
Legumes
Citrus fruits

HOW TO EAT

Bleeding disorders can be inherited such as hemophilia, related to certain cancers such as leukemia, or caused by vitamin K deficiencies. Here are some general guidelines that may help no matter what the cause.

Eat foods rich in vitamin K, which is necessary for the blood to clot normally. Sources include green peas, broccoli, spinach, brussels sprouts, and organ meats.

Eat more foods with vitamin C. Vitamin C deficiency can cause bleeding gums.

Up your iron intake. Chronic blood loss can lead to anemia, a blood disorder that is characterized by inadequate levels of red blood cells.

SAMPLE MEAL PLAN

Breakfast: 2 scrambled eggs; 2 slices of turkey bacon; 1 slice of whole grain toast with 1 tsp of jam; ½ cup of fresh grapefruit sections

Lunch: 3 oz of roasted turkey breast; *Brussels Sprouts with Caraway Seeds* (page 229); 1 small baked potato topped with 1 Tbsp reduced-fat sour cream

Snack: 1 tangerine; 1 oz of reduced-fat cheese; 4 low-sodium crackers

Dinner: 3 oz of baked chicken; *Springtime Quinoa* (page 220); ½ cup of lightly sautéed spinach and sliced carrots; 1 whole grain roll

Dessert: ½ cup of orange sherbet

OTHER RECIPES TO TRY

- Beef and Blue Cheese Burgers
- Spinach-Stuffed Meat Loaf
- Calf's Liver with Rigatoni
- Sesame Greens and Bean Sprouts
- Orange-Walnut Broccoli

BLOOD PRESSURE

FOODS THAT HARM

Salty and processed foods, such as pickles

FOODS THAT HEAL

Green leafy vegetables
Low-fat dairy products
Legumes
Bananas
Melons
Oranges
Dried fruit
Nuts and seeds
Whole wheat pasta
Carrots
Sweet potatoes

FOODS TO LIMIT

Red meat, butter, and other foods with saturated fats
Alcohol
Caffeinated drinks

HOW TO EAT

Following the DASH (Dietary Approaches to Stop Hypertension) diet, which is endorsed by numerous health organizations including the American Heart Association and the Mayo Clinic, will help lower blood pressure. Here is a synopsis of the DASH diet and accompanying strategies.

- Have 6 to 8 servings of grains daily.
- Eat 4 to 5 servings each of fruits and vegetables daily.
- Consume 2 to 3 servings of low-fat or nonfat dairy foods daily.
- Limit meats, poultry, and fish to 6 or fewer 1-oz servings daily.
- Eat 4 to 5 servings of nuts, seeds, or legumes per week.
- Limit fats to 2 to 3 servings daily.
- Limit sweets to 5 servings per week.

Limit your salt intake. A key component of what makes DASH effective is reducing sodium intake. The range of acceptable sodium intake per day is 1,500 to 2,300 mg. The best way to reduce sodium intake is to avoid adding salt and to avoid most processed foods, which are usually loaded with sodium. Check labels carefully—look for the term sodium to find hidden salt.

QUICK TIP:
Flavor without salt

To limit your sodium intake but still add flavor to your food, use herbs and spices instead. For example use tarragon in roasted poultry dishes or add a dried bay leaf or two to your soups and stocks instead of your usual amount of salt. For more suggestions, see Herbs and Spices on page 61.

SAMPLE MEAL PLAN

Breakfast: 1 cup of whole grain cereal with 1 cup of skim milk and 1 small sliced banana; 1 slice of whole grain cinnamon raisin bread with 1 tsp of trans fat-free soft spread

Lunch: 2 to 3 oz of baked chicken; *Rustic Grilled Vegetable and Rigatoni Salad* (page 172); 1 small baked sweet potato; 1 orange

Snack: 1 cup of fresh fruit salad—try grapes, cubed cantaloupe, and whole strawberries dipped in 1 cup of low-fat or fat-free yogurt

Dinner: 2 to 3 oz of lean meat, poultry, or fish; ½ cup of cooked brown rice; 1 cup of lightly sautéed carrots and collards; 1 whole grain roll

Dessert: *Grilled Fruit en Brochette* (page 267)

OTHER RECIPES TO TRY

- Zucchini Frittata
- Strawberry-Yogurt Smoothie
- Endive, Apple, and Watercress Salad
- Rice-Stuffed Squash

BRONCHITIS

See Respiratory Disorders, page 345

BULIMIA

FOODS THAT HARM

Trigger foods that are associated with binges

FOODS THAT HEAL

Bananas

Berries

Apples

Pears

Whole grain cereals and breads

Lean meat

HOW TO EAT

Like all eating disorders, bulimia can be difficult to treat and usually requires a team approach under the guidance of a dietitian or a physician. Here are some general guidelines.

Eat more high-potassium foods like bananas, cantaloupe, potatoes, and spinach.

Emphasize foods high in protein such as lean meats, salmon, chicken, fish, beans, low-fat dairy.

Add fiber-filled foods such as whole grain cereals and breads and fresh fruits and vegetables.

Drink fluids regularly. This will help to restore normal bowel function, which may have been affected by laxative use.

SAMPLE MEAL PLAN

Breakfast: 1 cup of whole grain cereal with ½ cup of skim milk and ¼ cup of fresh berries

Lunch: chicken salad sandwich on 2 slices of whole grain bread with lettuce, tomato, and sprouts; small bunch of grapes

Snack: 1 pear; 1 oz of low-fat cheese

Dinner: 3 oz of grilled salmon; *Watermelon and Feta Salad* (page 180); 1 whole wheat pita bread

Dessert: 1 banana

OTHER RECIPES TO TRY

- Multigrain Pancakes or Waffles
- Beef, Onion, and Pepper Fajitas
- Beef and Blue Cheese Burgers
- Cauliflower Salad with Cashews
- Pot Roast with Root Vegetables

BURNS

FOODS THAT HARM
Caffeinated drinks
Alcohol

FOODS THAT HEAL
Lean meat
Poultry
Fish
Shellfish
Eggs
Legumes
Whole grains
Citrus fruit
Melons
Water

HOW TO EAT

A well-balanced diet that provides extra calories will promote healing and tissue repair. Here are some additional suggestions.

Up your zinc intake. Good sources of this wound healer include seafood, meat, and poultry. You'll also get some from eggs, milk, beans, nuts, and whole grains.

Choose vitamin C–rich fruits and vegetables. Top sources include citrus fruits, melons, broccoli, and bell peppers, especially red ones.

Stay hydrated. Drink 4 to 6 cups of water a day, along with other noncaffeinated and nonalcoholic beverages.

SAMPLE MEAL PLAN

Breakfast: 2 eggs poached, scrambled or sunny-side up; 2 slices of whole grain toast with 2 tsp of trans fat free soft spread; ½ cup fresh grapefruit sections

Lunch: *Curried Chicken Salad Sandwiches* (page 148); 12 baked crinkle-cut sweet potato fries; 1 orange; 1 protein shake

Snack: 1 thick slice of watermelon; a small handful of mixed nuts

Dinner: *Shrimp Seviche with Avocado and Pumpkin Seeds* (page 210); ½ cup of cooked brown rice; 1 cup of steamed broccoli; 1 whole grain roll with 1 tsp trans fat free soft spread

Dessert: 2 cups of cubed cantaloupe dipped in ½ cup of 2% Greek yogurt

OTHER RECIPES TO TRY

- Cod and Vegetable Stew
- Three-Bean Chili
- Cantaloupe and Orange Soup
- Beef and Blue Cheese Burgers
- Crab Cakes with a Melon Relish
- Roasted Pork with Pomegranate Sauce
- Broiled Salmon with an Avocado-Mango Salsa
- Thai Roasted Shrimp

CANCER

FOODS THAT HARM

Foods that may contain pesticide residues and environmental pollutants

FOODS THAT HEAL

Lean meat

Fish

Shellfish

Apples

Berries

Citrus fruit

Tomatoes

Onions and garlic

Green tea

Wheat bran and wheat germ

Brown rice

Brazil nuts

FOODS TO LIMIT

Red meat, butter, and other foods with saturated fats

Alcohol

Foods that have been salt-cured, smoked, fermented, or charbroiled

HOW TO EAT

The following guidelines will help protect you against cancer. If you're being treated for cancer, you can still follow the suggestions below, but you should consult a doctor or dietitian for a more personalized plan.

Go overboard with fruits and vegetables. Five servings a day is the minimum.

Reduce fat intake. Choose lean cuts of meat and trim away all visible fat. Eat vegetarian dishes several times a week. Adopt low-fat cooking methods such as baking and steaming, and limit use of added fats such as butter, margarine, mayonnaise, shortening, and oils.

Fill up with fiber. To hit the recommended 25 g a day for women and 38 g a day for men, eat plenty of beans, legumes, whole grain cereals and pasta, fruits, and vegetables.

Limit processed meats such as bacon, hot dogs, and luncheon meats.

SAMPLE MEAL PLAN

Breakfast: 1 cup of whole grain cereal with ½ cup of skim milk, 2 tsp of wheat germ, and ½ cup of fresh berries; a cup of green tea

Lunch: *Salmon Cake Sandwiches* (page 152; 1 cup of tomato soup; 1 orange

Snack: 1 apple; 8 brazil nuts

Dinner: *Three-Bean Chili* (page 141); 1 cup of mixed green salad with grated carrots, sliced cucumbers, and 2 Tbsp low-fat dressing; 1 whole grain roll

Dessert: *Melon Berry Compote with Green Tea and Lime* (page 265)

OTHER RECIPES TO TRY

- Beef, Onion, and Pepper Fajitas
- Couscous-Stuffed Peppers
- Beef Filet Salad with Mustard
- Warm Kasha and Seafood Salad
- Endive, Apple, and Watercress Salad

QUICK TIP:
Have oranges with bacon

Can't pass up the bacon when you go out for brunch? You can mitigate some of negative effects of eating processed meat by including good sources of vitamins C and E with your meal.

- Spinach Stuffed Meat Loaf
- Creamy Citrus and Vanilla Rice Pudding

CANKER SORES

See Dental Problems, page 300

CARDIO-VASCULAR DISEASE

FOODS THAT HARM

Salty foods, such as pickles

FOODS THAT HEAL

Citrus fruits
Green leafy vegetables
Salmon
Trout
Tofu
Oats
Apples
Pears
Olive oil
Whole grain breads and cereals
Flaxseed
Nuts

FOODS TO LIMIT

Red meat, butter, and other foods with saturated fats
Processed foods with trans fats
High-cholesterol foods, such as eggs, shrimp, and organ meats

HOW TO EAT

Diet plays a significant role in preventing cardiovascular disease, and it can minimize problems if you already have heart disease. Here are the guidelines for a heart-healthy diet.

Consume 2 or 3 servings of fish high in omega-3 fats a week. Salmon, sardines, herring, trout, and other fatty cold-water fish are good sources. Plant sources of omega-3s include canola, soybean, and flaxseed oil, ground flaxseed, and nuts.

Include 5 to 10 g of soluble fiber a day. Oat bran, oats, psyllium, flax, lentils, legumes, apples, pears, grapes, and other fruits are high in soluble fiber.

Swap out white bread and low-fiber cereals for whole wheat bread and whole grain cereals. Look for products that list whole grain or whole wheat as one of their first ingredients and contain 3 g or more of fiber per serving.

Use healthy oils, such as olive and canola.

Eat more soy. It contains plant compounds called isoflavones that appear to benefit the heart by lowering cholesterol levels.

Eat a small handful of nuts daily. They're rich sources of fiber, vitamin E, essential fatty acids, and minerals—all linked to heart health.

Try going meatless one day a week. A combination of legumes and whole grains is a prudent, low-fat meat alternative.

Limit alcohol intake. A glass of red wine or beer may be "heart-healthy," but excessive amounts of alcohol over time may lead to increased blood pressure, obesity, or other health problems.

SAMPLE MEAL PLAN

Breakfast: 1 cup of whole grain, high fiber cereal with ½ cup of soymilk and 2 tsp of ground flaxseeds; a couple sections of orange

Lunch: *Open-Faced Grilled Vegetable Sandwich* (page 154); cup of lentil soup; 1 apple

Snack: small handful of nuts; 1 large pear

Dinner: *Broiled Salmon with Avocado-Mango Salsa* (page 199); ½ cup of cooked brown basmati rice; 2 cups of mixed salad greens with 2 tbsp of olive oil and vinegar dressing; 1 slice of whole wheat bread

Dessert: 1 cup of grapes or 5-oz glass of red wine

OTHER RECIPES TO TRY

- Pear Rhubarb Muffins
- Berry-Flaxseed Smoothie
- Cantaloupe and Orange Soup
- Whole Wheat Noodles with Peanut Sauce and Chicken No-Bake Flaxseed-Nut Bars
- Grilled Salmon with Sautéed Greens
- Cider-Baked Acorn Squash with Apple Stuffing
- Spiced Almonds

CARPAL TUNNEL SYNDROME

See Arthritis, page 283

CATARACTS

See Eye Problems, page 305

CELIAC DISEASE

FOODS THAT HARM

Foods made with wheat, rye, barley, oats, bulgur, spelt, or triticale

Foods using wheat products as a thickening agent or coating, such as meat loaf and certain soups and sauces

Beverages containing gluten, such as beer

Many commercial salad dressings, except pure mayonnaise

FOODS THAT HEAL

Skim milk

Eggs

Fish

Meat and poultry

Fresh fruits and vegetables

Legumes

Potatoes

Rice

Quinoa

HOW TO EAT

These recommendations can help make living with celiac disease a little easier.

Be a gluten sleuth. Read all labels. Gluten is used in some surprising places—candy, ice creams, supplements, medications, sausages bound with bread crumbs, and foods coated with batter.

Don't deprive yourself. Try gluten-free items such as rice pasta and baked goods made with corn, rice, potato, or soy flours.

Prepare most foods at home to ensure a healthy diet without risking exposure to gluten.

SAMPLE MEAL PLAN

Breakfast: *Spinach and Goat Cheese Omelet* (page 122); 1 slice of gluten-free bread, toasted, with 1 tsp of trans fat free soft spread; 1 cup of your favorite fresh fruit

Lunch: 3 oz of grilled chicken breast; *Quinoa with Chiles and Cilantro* (page 200); at least ½ cup steamed sliced carrots with 1 tsp trans fat free soft spread

Snack: 1 apple; 1 oz of low-fat cheddar cheese

Dinner: 3 oz of grilled tilapia; 1 medium baked potato with 1 Tbsp of reduced-fat sour cream; ½ cup of succotash; 1 gluten-free roll

Dessert: 1 frozen fruit sorbet bar

OTHER RECIPES TO TRY

- Summer Greens Scramble
- Three-Bean Chili
- Tuscan Bean Soup
- Pork Chops and Cabbage
- Springtime Quinoa
- Rice Salad with Chicken and Grapes
- Minty Melon Cups

CHOLES-TEROL, HIGH

FOODS THAT HARM

Heavily marbled red meat

Pizza

Hard margarines

Store-bought baked goods

Fast foods and junk foods

Full-fat dairy products

Fried foods

FOODS THAT HEAL

Sterol-fortified orange juice

Oats and oat bran

Kidney beans

Apples

Pears

Fish

Extra-virgin olive oil

FOODS TO LIMIT

Salt and salty foods

HOW TO EAT

Diet plays a key role in keeping cholesterol levels in the healthy range or lowering them if they are high. Here's how.

Choose lean meats. Trim all visible fat before cooking. Remove poultry skin before (or at least after) cooking.

Get 2 g of sterols a day. Find them in labeled buttery spreads, orange juice, and yogurt drinks.

Eat 5 to 10 g of soluble fiber a day. Good sources include kidney beans, apples, pears, and prunes.

Moderate alcohol to one (for women) or two (for men) drinks a day.

Add omega-3s from fish, soybeans, and nuts.

SAMPLE MEAL PLAN

Breakfast: *Pear Rhubarb Muffins* (page 128); 1 small container of low-fat yogurt; 8 oz of sterol-fortified orange juice

Lunch: *Tuna and Cannellini Salad with Lemon* (page 165); 2 whole wheat bread sticks; 1 sliced apple

Snack: 3 pitted prunes; small handful of nuts

Dinner: grilled chicken sandwich on a whole grain roll; 1 cup of vegetable-pasta salad; 1 ear of corn on the cob with 1 Tbsp of a sterol-containing spread

Dessert: 8-oz of sterol-fortified orange juice

OTHER RECIPES TO TRY

- Fish Tacos
- Grilled Salmon Salad
- Poached Salmon with Cucumber-Dill Sauce
- Cod with Gremolata Crust
- Scallops Florentine
- Toasted Oat-Raisin Bread
- Chewy Oatmeal Raisin Cookies
- Grilled Fruit en Brochette

CHRONIC FATIGUE SYNDROME

FOODS THAT HARM

Alcohol

FOODS THAT HEAL

Complex carbohydrates, such as whole grain cereals and breads
Green leafy vegetables
Fish
Nuts
Oysters
Eggs
Melons
Kiwi
Sunflower seeds
Salty foods (only for those with low blood pressure)

FOODS TO LIMIT

Caffeinated drinks

HOW TO EAT

Although there is no known cure, certain nutrients may help prevent or manage chronic fatigue syndrome.

Eliminate food allergies. Work with a registered dietitian to examine your diet and discover potential food allergies.

Eat more immune-boosting zinc and vitamin C. Foods rich in zinc include seafood (especially oysters), meat, poultry, eggs, milk, beans, nuts, and whole grains. Good sources of vitamin C include citrus fruits, berries, melons, kiwi, broccoli, and cauliflower.

Consume more essential fatty acids from fish, nuts, seeds, flaxseed and flaxseed oil, canola oil, wheat germ, and leafy green vegetables.

QUICK TIP: Add a shake of salt

If low blood pressure is part of your diagnosis, you may benefit from an increase in your sodium intake. Pickles, capers, anchovies, potato chips, and other salty foods can help.

Get more magnesium. Good sources include legumes, nuts, sunflower seeds, green vegetables, avocados, and amaranth.

SAMPLE MEAL PLAN

Breakfast: 1 cup of whole grain amaranth flakes (dry cereal) with 1 cup of skim milk, ¼ cup of fresh berries, and 2 tsp of ground flaxseed

Lunch: *Crab and Avocado Salad* (page 167); 1 oz of sweet potato chips

Snack: 1 hard-cooked egg; a small handful of roasted sunflower seeds

Dinner: *Thai Roasted Shrimp* (page 211) served over ½ cup of cooked brown rice and 1 cup of lightly steamed watercress

Dessert: a couple slices of kiwi and cubed cantaloupe stirred into ½ cup of 2% Greek yogurt

OTHER RECIPES TO TRY

- Fish Tacos
- Watermelon and Feta Salad
- Grilled Salmon with Sautéed Greens
- Cod with Gremolata Crust
- Shrimp Seviche with Avocado and Pumpkin Seeds
- Sesame Greens and Bean Sprouts
- Whole Wheat Flaxseed Bread
- Oysters with Tomato Salsa

CIRCULATORY DISORDERS

(Including aneurysms, intermittent claudication, phlebitis, and Raynaud's disease)

See also Atherosclerosis, page 285; Blood Pressure, page 287

FOODS THAT HEAL
Citrus fruits
Onions
Garlic
Salmon
Sardines

FOODS TO LIMIT
Fried foods
Salty foods, such as pickles

HOW TO EAT

There are no specific dietary treatments for circulatory disorders. However, these suggestions may help prevent or manage some conditions.

Adopt a low-fat, low-salt diet. Aim for less than 30% of calories from fat and under 2,000 mg of sodium.

Add more fish. Eat at least 2 servings a week of fatty fish or other sources of omega-3 fatty acids.

Get your vitamin E. Good sources include sunflower seeds, almonds, wheat germ, and sunflower and safflower oils.

SAMPLE MEAL PLAN

Breakfast: *Tropical Fruit Salad* (page 269); 1 multigrain bagel, toasted, with 2 Tbsp of trans fat free soft spread

Lunch: 6 oz-serving of vegetable lasagna; 1 cup of mixed green salad with grated carrots, sliced cucumbers, and 2 Tbsp of low-fat dressing

Snack: 1 oz of almonds or roasted sun-flower seeds, unsalted

Dinner: 3 oz of baked salmon; *Roasted Tomatoes with Garlic and Herbs* (page 000); 3 baked red-skinned potatoes; ½ cup of steamed broccoli florets

Dessert: 2 tangerines

OTHER RECIPES TO TRY

- Turkey, Spinach and Rice in Roasted Garlic Broth
- Grilled Salmon Salad
- Broiled Salmon with Avocado-Mango Salsa
- Grilled Salmon with Sautéed Greens
- Orange Beets

CIRRHOSIS

FOODS THAT HARM

Salty foods, such as pickles

Alcohol

FOODS THAT HEAL

Berries

Papayas

Bell peppers

Fortified and enriched cereals and breads

Soy products (except soy sauce)

Peas

Legumes

Fish

Water

FOODS TO LIMIT

Fatty foods

HOW TO EAT

A healthy, low-sodium diet can help to slow the progression of the disease. Here are more diet suggestions that can help.

Eat small, frequent meals or snacks to combat appetite loss.

Up your protein. People with cirrhosis need more protein—a recommended 0.54 g per pound (1.2 g per kg) of body weight. Include vegetable proteins like soy, peas, and legumes.

Have healthy fats. Moderate amounts of mono- and polyunsaturated fats (oily fish, olive oil, safflower oil) provide needed calories without overburdening the liver.

SAMPLE MEAL PLAN

Mini Breakfast: 2 slices of french toast made with enriched low-sodium bread and drizzled with 2 Tbsp of syrup

A.M. Mini Meal: ½ cup of cottage cheese mixed with ¼ cup of berries or sliced papaya

Mini Lunch: *Couscous-Stuffed Peppers* (page 158); 1 slice of enriched low-sodium bread

P.M. Mini Meal: 1 cup of low-sodium bean soup; 4 low-sodium crackers

Mini Dinner: 2 oz of baked skinless chicken breast; 2 small roasted red potatoes; at least ½ cup of cooked peas and carrots

Dessert: 1 cup of fresh strawberries dipped in ½ cup of soy yogurt

OTHER RECIPES TO TRY

- Multigrain Pancakes or Waffles
- Jamaican Jerked Chicken Salad
- Papaya and Avocado Salad

- Whole Wheat Noodles with Peanut Sauce and Chicken
- Carrot-Flecked Corn Bread

COLD SORES

See Herpes, page 315

COLDS AND FLU

FOODS THAT HEAL

Citrus fruits

Berries

Brussels sprouts

Chicken soup and other broths

Yogurt

Wheat germ and wheat bran

HOW TO EAT

You won't cure a cold or flu by eating certain foods, but there are some nutrients to focus on that may protect you from getting sick—or if you do, they may ease symptoms and speed your recovery.

Get your vitamin C. Besides citrus, other good sources are peppers, kiwi, broccoli, brussels sprouts, cantaloupe, and tomato juice.

Drink lots of fluids. A minimum of eight to 10 glasses of fluids, such as water, tea, and broth, are recommended daily.

Abstain from alcohol to keep your immune system on its toes.

Spice up your meals with capsaicin, hot peppers, chiles, garlic, and turmeric.

Eat foods rich in zinc. You'll find this immune booster in seafood (especially oysters), red meat and poultry, yogurt and other dairy products, wheat germ, wheat bran, and whole grains.

SAMPLE MEAL PLAN

Breakfast: 1 poached egg; 1 slice of whole wheat toast; *Carrot-Orange Juice* (page 000); if you're still hungry, add ½ cup of yogurt with berries and 1 tsp of wheat germ

Lunch: *Quick Chicken Noodle Soup* (page 136); 6 whole wheat crackers; if you feel hungry, try ½ roasted turkey sandwich on whole wheat bread and a little cranberry relish

Snack: fruit juice, vegetable juice, a banana, applesauce, tea, toast, peanut butter crackers, an orange, or pudding (optional if you are hungry)

Dinner: As you start to feel better and your appetite picks up, add more variety to your meal plan such as 2 oz of baked fish or chicken, ½ cup of soft cooked whole grains, and ½ cup of cooked vegetables

Dessert: a cup of herbal tea

OTHER RECIPES TO TRY

- Blueberry and Cranberry Granola
- Berry Salad with Passion Fruit
- Wheat Germ Smoothie
- Chicken-Kale Soup with Roasted Pepper Puree
- Cantaloupe and Orange Soup
- Chicken Salad with Citrus
- Fruity Brussels Sprouts

AILMENTS

CONSTIPATION

FOODS THAT HEAL

Bran cereals

Beans

Legumes

Berries

Water

HOW TO EAT

Your diet can contribute to constipation, or it can relieve it. Here are suggestions for what to eat to get and keep things moving.

Get 25 to 38 g of fiber daily. To do that, eat more whole grain products, legumes, fruits, and vegetables. See the Sample Meal Plan below, which reflects a fiber intake that's within this goal. Gradually increase fiber intake until you reach this goal.

Down the H$_2$O. Aim for 8 glasses of nonalcoholic fluids every day.

Avoid alcohol. It can cause dehydration and prevents the body from properly absorbing nutrients.

Drink hot liquids. Try herbal tea, a glass of hot water with lemon, or coffee in the morning.

SAMPLE MEAL PLAN

Breakfast: ½ cup of hot oat bran cereal prepared with skim milk; 1 tangerine

Lunch: *Black Bean and Sweet Potato Burritos* (page 211)

Snack: 1 container low-fat vanilla yogurt with ¼ cup of berries

Dinner: 3 oz of grilled halibut; *Tuscan Bean Soup* (page 141); ½ cup of cooked brown rice; at least ½ cup of steamed vegetables (or if you prefer, have 1 cup of mixed green salad and 2 Tbsp of low-fat dressing)

Dessert: 1 frozen fruit sorbet bar

OTHER RECIPES TO TRY

- Hot Cereal with Apples and Dates
- Blueberry-Oatmeal Muffins
- Lentil Soup with Canadian Bacon
- Three-Bean Chili
- Lentil and Rice Paella with Clams
- Artichokes with Lentils and Lima Beans
- Edamame Hummus with Pita Crisps

CROHN'S DISEASE

See Inflammatory Bowel Disease, page 320

CYSTIC FIBROSIS

FOODS THAT HEAL

Meat

Poultry

Eggs

Milk and yogurt

Pasta

Cookies

Cakes

Salty foods

Juices

HOW TO EAT

While there isn't a special diet to treat cystic fibrosis, eating certain foods can have an effect on managing the disease. Here are some general guidelines, but it's also important to consult with a dietitian.

Eat larger portions and lots of snacks.

Eat more protein. Along with sources listed at left, enrich whole milk by adding 1 cup of dried milk per quart or liter.

Combine sugary foods with protein, such as peanut butter and jelly, milkshakes, or trail mix.

Consume more sodium, especially during hot weather or exercise.

Stay hydrated. In addition to high-calorie juices and nectars, sip water to help prevent constipation.

SAMPLE MEAL PLAN

Breakfast: *Huevos Rancheros* (page 124); a glass of whole milk, or coffee or tea with half-and half

Snack: cheese and crackers or peanut butter crackers; 1 cup of fruit juice

Lunch: *Shrimp and Vegetable Stir-Fry* (page 209); a bowl of cream soup such as cream of broccoli, cream of potato soup, or New England clam chowder; 1 roll with 2 tsp of butter

Snack: a milkshake: blend ½ cup of whole milk, ½ cup of half and half, 2 cups of vanilla ice cream, 2 Tbsp of malt powder, and an envelope of instant breakfast powder (any flavor)

QUICK TIP:
Bump up the calories

Add shredded cheese or butter to soups, sauces, casseroles, vegetables, mashed potatoes, rice, noodles or meat loaf. For heartier entrées, bread meat, poultry, and fish before frying or broiling it.

Dinner: 3 to 4 oz of baked salmon or 2 pieces of fried chicken; *Baked Rice with Wild Mushrooms and Cheese* (page 221); steamed broccoli with ¼ cup of cheese sauce

Dessert: strawberry shortcake topped with fresh strawberries and lots of whipped cream

Snack: *Walnut Shortbread* (page 254); ½ cup of pudding

OTHER RECIPES TO TRY

- Hot Cereal with Apples and Dates
- Zucchini-Carrot Crustless Quiche Squares
- Shrimp Seviche with Avocado and Pumpkin Seeds
- Thai Roasted Shrimp
- Macaroni and Cheese with Spinach
- Pasta with Walnut Cream Sauce
- Fried Rice with Tofu and Vegetables
- Buffalo Chicken Fingers

D

DENTAL PROBLEMS

FOODS THAT HARM

Starchy snacks and sugary foods, such as sweetened cereals and cookies

Acidic drinks sipped over prolonged periods of time, such as wine or unsweetened fruit juice

FOODS THAT HEAL

Low-fat dairy products

Aged cheeses

Fortified soy beverages

Eggs

Legumes

Carrots

Sweet potatoes

Broccoli

Oranges

Dark leafy green vegetables, especially spinach

Apples

Celery

Yogurt

Rice

FOODS TO LIMIT

Dried fruit and other sticky foods

HOW TO EAT

Calcium is important for your teeth and gums, so a diet high in calcium is essential. Here are more eating tips for your teeth.

Finish a meal with aged cheese. It helps prevent cavities. Other postmeal teeth protectors are fresh fruit such as apples, carrots, and celery.

Chew gum with xylitol. It helps counter harmful bacteria if you chew it for at least 5 minutes right after a meal.

SAMPLE MEAL PLAN

Breakfast: 1 sunny-side up egg; 1 slice of whole grain toast; ½ cup of fresh fruit

Lunch: cheese sandwich made with 2 slices of whole grain bread, 2 oz of low-fat colby cheese, sliced tomato, lettuce, mustard, and 1 Tbsp of your favorite spread; a cup of bean soup; 1 orange

Snack: ½ cup of raw vegetables dipped in ¼ cup of low-fat dressing—try a mix of baby carrots, celery sticks, and broccoli florets.

Dinner: *Savory Lamb Stew with Sweet Potatoes* (page 133); at least ½ cup of cooked spinach; 1 whole grain roll

Dessert: ½ cup vanilla yogurt with ¼ cup chopped apples

OTHER RECIPES TO TRY

- Carrot Soup with Dill
- Broccoli Salad with Almonds and Dried Cranberries
- Spinach, Sweet Potato, and Shiitake Salad
- Calf's Liver with Rigatoni
- Carrot and Parsnip Puree

DEPRESSION

FOODS THAT HARM

Aged cheeses and other foods and drinks that contain tyramine, if you are taking MAO inhibitors

FOODS THAT HEAL

Turkey
Almonds and other nuts
Pumpkin seeds and other seeds
Watercress and other green leafy vegetables
Lentils and other beans
Whole grains
Corn
Asparagus
Peas

FOODS TO LIMIT

Sugary foods, such as cookies and soft drinks

HOW TO EAT

The right foods can help to stabilize your mood. For example, carbohydrates can have a calming, relaxing effect. Here's how to eat to beat depression.

Combine tryptophan with carbs. This serotonin booster is found in turkey, almonds, and pumpkin seeds. Eating them with carbs like beans and whole grains helps to convert the tryptophan into serotonin.

Get your B vitamins. In addition to the healing foods listed above, good sources are meat, fish, poultry, potatoes, orange juice, and fortified soy and rice beverages.

Add omega-3 fats. Seek sources such as salmon, trout, mackerel, and flaxseed.

Eat a small piece of dark chocolate occasionally. The naturally occurring substance in chocolate called phenylethylamine (PEA) has been found to elevate endorphin levels and act as a natural anti-depressant. Just don't go overboard.

SAMPLE MEAL PLAN

Breakfast: ½ cup of fruit and nut whole grain cereal with 1 cup of skim milk; 2 Tbsp of roasted pumpkin seeds

Lunch: 3 oz of baked salmon; *Endive, Apple, and Watercress Salad* (page 177); ½ cup cooked basmati or wild rice blend

Snack: bowl of lentil, split pea, or low-fat cream of asparagus soup; 1 crusty whole grain roll; 1 orange

Dinner: 3 oz of roasted turkey breast; baked sweet potato; ½ cup of corn; 1 cup of steamed collards or kale

Dessert: small piece of dark chocolate

OTHER RECIPES TO TRY

- Three-Bean Chili
- Pork, Pear, and Potato Salad
- Bulgur with Spring Vegetables
- Brown Rice with Cabbage and Chickpeas
- Spiced Cauliflower with Peas
- Edamame Hummus with Pita Crisps

QUICK TIP: Eat more beans

They're a rich source of carbohydrates, which have been associated with relaxation. Beans also help convert tryptophan into serotonin, a feel-good hormone.

WARNING! FOOD-DRUG INTERACTION

If you are taking an antidepressant in the class called monoamine oxidase (MAO) inhibitors, such as phenelzine (Nardil) and tranylcypromine (Parnate), your blood pressure could rise dangerously when you eat foods rich in the amino acid tyramine. Tyramines are found in protein-rich foods that have been aged, dried, fermented, pickled, or bacterially treated—such as aged cheeses, tofu or soy, and alcohol.

DIABETES

FOODS THAT HARM

- Red meat, butter, and other foods with saturated fats
- Processed foods that contain trans fats

FOODS THAT HEAL

- Whole grain breads, cereals, and pasta
- Oats
- Barley
- Peas
- Low-fat dairy products
- Avocados
- Apples
- Pears
- Oranges
- Chicken breast
- Mushrooms

FOODS TO LIMIT

- High glycemic foods such as potatoes, soft drinks, white flour, and refined sugars

HOW TO EAT

Diet is the cornerstone of diabetes management, and it can help you avoid developing diabetes in the first place. Here are some guidelines.

Balance, balance, balance. Meals and snacks should provide a mixture of carbohydrates, fats, and proteins.

Seek fiber-rich carbohydrates like barley, oat cereals, oatmeal, beans, peas, and lentils.

Follow a low-fat diet. Limit saturated fats from animal foods and avoid hydrogenated fats in packaged foods.

Monounsaturated and polyunsaturated fats—vegetable oils, nuts, fish, and avocados—are good in moderation.

Eat foods low on the glycemic index (GI). This index (see page 354) is a measure of how quickly foods are broken down into glucose. The faster a food is digested and absorbed into the bloodstream, the higher its GI. High-GI foods cause a rapid rise in blood sugar, which can be dangerous, especially for people with diabetes. People who have diets with lot of high-GI foods have higher rates of obesity, diabetes, heart disease, and cancer.

Get enough chromium, found in foods such as wheat bran, whole grains, chicken breast, mushrooms, and blackstrap molasses. Aim for 50 to 200 mg a day.

Drink coffee. Studies suggest that the caffeinated variety may reduce your risk of developing type 2 diabetes.

Keep carbs steady throughout the day. In order to avoid swings in blood sugar levels, don't go more than 3 or 4 hours without eating something.

SAMPLE MEAL PLAN

Breakfast: *Individual Breakfast Tortilla* (page 125); ½ cup of low-fat cottage cheese with ¼ cup of fresh red or black raspberries

Snack: 1 plum; a small handful of nuts

Lunch: *Whole Wheat Noodles with Peanut Sauce and Chicken* (page 196); ½ cup of cooked carrots and peas

Snack: ½ whole wheat pita with 2 Tbsp hummus or guacamole dip

Dinner: *Spinach-Stuffed Meat Loaf* (page 183); a cup of barley-mushroom soup; 3 roasted new potatoes; 1 cup of mixed green salad with 2 Tbsp low-fat dressing

Evening snack: 1 apple, sliced with 2 tsp of peanut butter

OTHER RECIPES TO TRY

- Blueberry Oatmeal Muffins
- Barley and Beet Salad
- Wheat Berry Salad with Dried Apricots
- Buckwheat Noodles with Tofu and Green Vegetables
- White Beans Stewed with Swiss Chard
- Vegetable-Stuffed Mushrooms

DIARRHEA

FOODS THAT HEAL

Water

Herbal teas

Ginger ale

Broth

Bananas

Rice

Applesauce

Toast

Salted crackers

Chicken soup

FOODS TO LIMIT

Dairy products

Apple juice

Prunes

Sugarless chewing gum

HOW TO EAT

When diarrhea starts up, stop eating solid food and focus on rehydrating. Sip warm or tepid drinks. Drink half a cup of fluid—water, mineral water, herbal teas, clear broths, or ginger ale—every 15 minutes. As you start to feel better, you can reintroduce solid foods by following the tips below.

Repeat a meal plan like the one below for 1 or 2 days. Once symptoms start to taper off more completely, try additional foods such as gelatin, cooked oatmeal, cream of wheat, cooked eggs, plain cooked pasta, or skinless baked potatoes. If symptoms last longer than 1 or 2 days, consult your doctor. Note that this diet is designed for adults and children over age 3. Please consult your doctor for recommendations for infants.

Slowly introduce low-fiber foods. When you feel like eating (but preferably not within the first 24 hours), try crackers, toast, rice, bananas, cooked carrots, boiled potatoes, applesauce, or chicken. See the meal plan below for suggestions.

Keep food as bland as possible. It's easier on the GI system.

Choose flat soda, if you're drinking clear carbonated beverages such as ginger ale or 7Up. If you have diabetes, opt for diet soda.

SAMPLE MEAL PLAN

Breakfast: banana; cream of rice cereal; applesauce; toast; broth or tea

Lunch: a bowl of chicken soup; soft cooked grains; soft noodles; cooked carrots; lightly buttered toast or saltines

Dinner: a bowl of chicken noodle or rice soup; boiled potatoes; soft cooked grains; soft cooked vegetables; stewed chicken; applesauce; banana; tea or ginger ale

OTHER RECIPES TO TRY

- Basic Chicken Stock
- Electrolyte Drink

DIVERTICU-LITIS

FOODS THAT HEAL

- Berries
- Bananas
- Figs
- Bran
- Brown rice
- Black beans
- Split peas
- Artichokes
- Water
- Broth

HOW TO EAT

Diets lacking in dietary fiber can lead to the formation of diverticula, small pouches in the intestinal wall. This condition is called diverticulosis. When the diverticula become inflamed or infected, you have diverticulitis. A bout of acute diverticulitis can be extremely painful. In severe and acute cases, your doctor may need to hospitalize you and your diet may be temporarily modified to a liquid diet until the inflammation has subsided. When you resume eating after an acute bout of diverticulitis, your doctor may temporarily prescribe lower fiber before advancing you to a higher fiber diet. To prevent or delay diverticulosis or diverticulitis, eat a high-fiber diet such as the one below.

Eat more vegetables and whole grains. Raw fruits and vegetables, especially with the skin on, are particularly good.

Drink fluids. At least eight glasses a day of water, tea, or other clear liquids will help prevent constipation while you add fiber.

SAMPLE MEAL PLAN

Breakfast: 1 cup of cooked oat bran cereal prepared with skim milk; ½ cup of blueberries or sliced strawberries

Lunch: chicken salad wrap made with a whole wheat tortilla, lettuce, grated carrots, and tomato; 1 cup of black bean soup

Snack: ½ cup of low-fat yogurt; 1 banana

Dinner: 3 oz of baked fish, *Baked Rice with Wild Mushrooms and Cheese* (page 221); 1 cup vegetable medley with steamed broccoli, cauliflower, and carrots

Dessert: 3 dried figs

OTHER RECIPES TO TRY

- Hot Cereal with Apples and Dates
- Blueberry-Oatmeal Muffins
- Three-Bean Chili
- Black Bean and Sweet Potato Burritos
- Brown Rice with Cabbage and Chickpeas
- Rice Salad with Chicken and Grapes
- Chewy Oatmeal Raisin Cookies

ECZEMA

FOODS THAT HARM

Milk, eggs, nuts, or any other foods that trigger or worsen eczema

FOODS THAT HEAL

- Apricots
- Carrots
- Mangoes
- Bananas
- Squash
- Green leafy vegetables
- Legumes

Salmon

Flaxseed

Canola oil

Brown rice

Wheat germ

HOW TO EAT

The trick is to avoid foods that may trigger eczema and to fill up on those that may help alleviate it. Here are some guidelines.

Test for allergies. Common culprits include eggs, dairy products, seafood, walnuts, and pecans.

Consume more antioxidants. Brightly colored fruits and vegetables like apricots, squash, mangoes, carrots, pumpkin, and sweet potatoes may prevent breakouts by countering the formation of free radicals.

Eat foods rich in essential fatty acids (EFAs), such as vegetable oils, fatty fish, and flaxseed to decrease swelling.

Get lots of vitamin B6 to protect against sensitivity rashes. Good sources include lean meat, fish, poultry, legumes, brown rice, wheat germ, avocado, banana, potato, and leafy green vegetables.

Drink 3 cups of oolong tea. Polyphenols in the tea suppress allergic responses.

SAMPLE MEAL PLAN

Breakfast: 1 cup of whole grain cereal with 1 cup of soy or almond milk and 2 Tbsp of toasted wheat germ; 1 banana; a cup of oolong tea

Lunch: *Fruit Salad with Spiced Coconut* (page 176); 1 whole wheat soft bread stick; a cup of oolong tea

Snack: 1 oz of carrot chips; 3 pieces of dried mango

Dinner: *Grilled Salmon with Sautéed Greens* (page 200); ½ cup of cooked brown rice; ½ of a baked acorn squash

Dessert: a cup of oolong tea

OTHER RECIPES TO TRY

- Ginger Butternut Squash Soup
- Grilled Salmon Salad
- Lentil and Rice Paella with Clams
- Rice-Stuffed Squash
- Sesame Greens and Bean Sprouts

EMPHYSEMA

See Respiratory Disorders, page 345

EYE PROBLEMS

FOODS THAT HARM

Red meat, butter, and other foods with saturated fats

FOODS THAT HEAL

Carrots

Corn

Red bell peppers

Dark leafy greens like kale or collard greens

Fish

HOW TO EAT

You can protect yourself against age-related eye problems such as cataracts and macular degeneration, which can both lead to blindness, by following these tips.

Start your day with fruit. Add a vision-saving burst of antioxidants to your morning meal with a glass of orange or tomato juice, grapefruit, kiwi, strawberries, or cantaloupe.

Eat a variety of veggies. While carrots are good for your eyes and you should eat them, dark leafy greens, corn, and red peppers actually have more peeper-protecting antioxidants.

Maintain a healthy weight. Excess pounds may increase your risk for cataracts.

Eat fish at least twice a week. Studies show that it can protect against macular degeneration.

Cut back on saturated fats. These artery-clogging fats may contribute to problems by blocking arteries in the retina.

SAMPLE MEAL PLAN

Breakfast: 1 cup of whole grain cereal with ½ cup of skim milk and ½ cup of sliced strawberries; 1 cup of orange juice

Lunch: *Grilled Eggplant Sandwiches with Red-Pepper-Walnut Sauce* (page 156)

Snack: ½ cup of roasted red bell pepper, carrots, and 4 olives dipped in ¼ cup of hummus

Dinner: 3 oz of baked salmon with 2 Tbsp of fruit chutney; *Spinach Salad with Chickpeas* (page 173); 1 piece of corn bread

Dessert: 2 cups of cubed cantaloupe

OTHER RECIPES TO TRY

- Chicken-Kale Soup with Roasted Pepper Puree
- Tuna and Carrot Sandwiches on Rye
- Grilled Salmon with Sautéed Greens
- Mackerel Tandoori Style
- Snapper and Snaps in a Packet
- White Beans Stewed with Swiss Chard

FEVER

FOODS THAT HEAL

Water
Fruit juice
Chicken broth or soup
Herbal teas
Bananas
Rice
Applesauce
Toast
Eggs
Rice cereals

HOW TO EAT

A fever is one of the body's natural ways of fighting disease and should not be suppressed unless very high or accompanied by other symptoms. The following tips will help you feel better while you have a fever.

Don't starve. The old adage "Feed a cold, starve a fever" has no medical basis. If anything, you need more calories than normal because your metabolic rate rises when you have a fever.

Load up on liquids. Sip often on water, fruit juice, herbal teas, broth, soup, or even frozen fruit juice bars.

Try the BRAT diet. Eat bananas, rice, applesauce, and toast for fever-related diarrhea. Also good: chicken or beef broth, chicken-rice soup, rice cereals, and boiled or poached eggs. See Diarrhea, page 303.

SAMPLE MEAL PLAN

Breakfast: 1 slice of toast with 1 tsp trans fat free soft spread; 1 scrambled egg; 1 piece of fruit; a cup of fruit juice or tea

Lunch: 1 cup of soup or broth; 1 cup of spaghetti with plain marinara sauce; 1 slice of bread; a cup of fruit juice or tea

Snack: ½ cup of cottage cheese with ¼ cup of sliced fruit

Dinner: 2 oz cooked lean beef or poultry; 1 cup of chicken rice soup; ½ cup of mashed potatoes; ½ cup of cooked carrots and greens

Dessert: frozen fruit sorbet bar or ½ cup of sherbet

OTHER RECIPES TO TRY

- One-Egg Omelets with Chopped Broccoli, Tomatoes, and Cheddar
- Basic Chicken Stock
- Quick Chicken Noodle Soup
- Vegetable Stock
- Miso Soup with Tofu
- Cantaloupe and Orange Soup
- Carrot-Orange Juice
- Chai

FIBROIDS

FOODS THAT HARM

Beer

FOODS THAT HEAL

Dairy products
Broccoli
Spinach
Swiss chard
Brussels sprouts
Oranges

FOODS TO LIMIT

Breads, pasta, and other foods made with white flour

HOW TO EAT

Hormones are likely to play a role in the development of fibroids, and your diet can affect hormone levels. Here's how to eat to reduce your risk and minimize the impact of fibroids if you have them.

Cut carbs, especially refined white flour ones. The blood sugar spikes they cause over time may affect hormone levels that can fuel the development of fibroids.

Get milk and other dairy products to lower your risk of fibroids.

Gobble oranges. In one study, they protected women. However, OJ didn't have the same effect.

Graze on green veggies. Eating more than a serving a day may slash your risk by up to 50%.

Watch calories. Being overweight increases your risk of fibroids.

SAMPLE MEAL PLAN

Breakfast: 1 whole grain English muffin, toasted, with 2 tsp of fruit spread; ½ cup of low-fat cottage cheese mixed with a couple of mandarin oranges

Lunch: a cup of low-fat cream of broccoli soup; 3 oz of roasted chicken or turkey; 1 baked potato topped with 1 Tbsp reduced-fat sour cream; 1 cup of cooked spinach

Snack: apple slices; 1 piece of string cheese

Dinner: 3 oz of roasted pork loin; *Fruity Brussels Sprouts* (page 228); ½ cup of baked squash (acorn, butternut, or buttercup); 1 whole grain roll

Dessert: ½ cup 2% Greek yogurt

OTHER RECIPES TO TRY

- Endive, Apple, and Watercress Salad
- Sesame Greens and Bean Sprouts
- Orange-Walnut Broccoli
- Brussels Sprouts with Caraway Seeds
- Cauliflower and Spinach Casserole
- White Beans Stewed with Swiss Chard
- Carrot-Orange Juice

FLATULENCE

FOODS THAT HARM

Carbonated drinks

Chewing gum

Bran

Milk, for those who are lactose
   intolerant

FOODS THAT HEAL

Peppermint, chamomile, fennel,
   or ginger tea

Yogurt

Anise

Rosemary

Bay leaf

Kombu seaweed

FOODS TO LIMIT

Kidney beans and other dried beans

Brussels sprouts

Onions

Corn

Asparagus

Sorbitol

HOW TO EAT

Unfortunately, flatulence can be an unpleasant side effect of eating a healthier, high-fiber diet. Passing gas also seems to worsen with age. Here are some dietary changes that may help:

Gulp less air when eating. Eating smaller portions, chewing food thoroughly, and not gulping liquids can help minimize episodes.

Drink herbal tea after meals. It helps improve digestion.

Try yogurt with live cultures. It may help cut gas production.

Soak dried beans first. Aim for at least 4 hours (preferably 8 or more) to reduce the amount of gas they may produce.

Spice up gas producers. You may be able to reduce gas by adding anise, ginger, rosemary, bay leaves, and fennel seeds to cruciferous veggies like broccoli and cauliflower and other veggies that tend to cause gas. Add kombu seaweed to cooking water (find it in Asian markets and natural food stores) for the same purpose.

Stay away from artificial sweeteners, such as sorbitol.

SAMPLE MEAL PLAN

Breakfast: 2 pancakes with 2 tsp of maple syrup; ¼ cup of sliced fresh fruit; 1 slice of turkey bacon; a cup of peppermint tea

Snack: low-fat yogurt (choose a brand with live cultures, probiotics); ¼ cup of sliced fruit

Lunch: *Tuna and Cannellini Salad with Lemon* (page 165); 1 slice whole wheat crusty bread; an orange.

Snack: ½ cup of kefir

Dinner: beef stew (made with lean meat, potatoes, carrots, broth, and simple seasonings such as rosemary, thyme, and bay leaf); 1 whole grain roll; applesauce

Dessert: cup of chamomile, ginger, or fennel tea

OTHER RECIPES TO TRY

- Strawberry-Yogurt Smoothie
- Three-Berry Fool
- Mixed Berry and Stone Fruit Soup

FOOD POISONING

See Diarrhea, page 303

GALLSTONES

FOODS THAT HEAL

Tomatoes
Salmon
Brown rice
Whole wheat bread
Barley
Avocado
Olive oil
Walnuts
Flaxseeds

FOODS TO LIMIT

Red meat, butter, and foods with saturated fat
Processed foods that contain trans fats
Sugary foods, such as cookies and soft drinks

HOW TO EAT

Consistently following a low-fat diet can help prevent gallstones or minimize symptoms if you already have them. Here are more tips that can help.

Always eat breakfast. A substantial breakfast causes the gallbladder to empty itself and flush out any small stones and stagnant bile.

Consume small, frequent meals. They help to spur the gallbladder to empty stones and bile.

Avoid extreme dieting. Bile is more likely to form stones after fasting.

SAMPLE MEAL PLAN

Mini Breakfast: 1 cup of bran flakes with ½ cup of skim milk, 2 tsp of flaxseeds, and ¼ cup of sliced peaches

A.M. Mini Meal: ½ whole wheat bagel with 1 tsp of trans fat free soft spread

Mini Lunch: veggie burger on whole wheat bun with lettuce, tomato, avocado, and sprouts; *Brown Rice with Cabbage and Chickpeas* (page 222)

P.M. Mini Meal: 1 cup of barley-mushroom soup; 2 whole grain crackers

Mini Dinner: 3 oz of baked or grilled salmon; ½ cup of cooked brown rice or barley; a small mixed green salad with sliced cucumbers, tomatoes, grated carrots, and 2 Tbsp of low-fat dressing

Dessert: ½ cup of fresh fruit salad topped with 6 walnuts

OTHER RECIPES TO TRY

- Barley and Beet Salad
- Papaya and Avocado Salad
- Broiled Salmon with Avocado-Mango Salsa Whole Wheat Flaxseed Bread
- Grilled Salmon with Sautéed Greens
- Salmon and Asparagus Farfalle with Walnut-Feta Sauce
- Rice-Stuffed Squash
- Roasted Tomatoes with Garlic and Herbs

GASTRITIS

See Indigestion and Heartburn, page 318

GASTROEN-TERITIS

See Diarrhea, page 303

GASTRO-ESOPHAGEAL REFLUX (GERD)

See Indigestion and Heartburn, page 318

GOUT

FOODS THAT HARM

Organ meats
Game meats
Anchovies
Sardines
Herring

FOODS THAT HEAL

Water
Fruit juice
Herbal teas
Vegetable broth
Soy products

FOODS TO LIMIT

Cauliflower
Asparagus
Dried beans and peas
Oats
Whole grain cereals
Wheat germ and wheat bran
Mushrooms
Poultry
Alcohol

HOW TO EAT

Gout is a type of arthritis that is caused by an inherited defect in the kidney's ability to excrete uric acid. You can reduce your production of uric acid and enhance the beneficial effect of drug treatment with these dietary guidelines.

Limit meat, fish, and poultry to 4 to 6 oz (125 to 175 g) a day. Animal proteins are high in purines that promote the overproduction of uric acid.

Get your protein from plants, such as soy.

Chug at least 2 qt (2 L) of liquids daily. It helps to dilute urine.

Pass on alcohol. It interferes with the elimination of uric acid.

Avoid low-carb diets. They encourage the formation of ketones, metabolic byproducts that hamper the body's ability to excrete uric acid.

Don't skip meals or fast. Both, along with rapid weight loss, can raise blood levels of uric acid.

SAMPLE MEAL PLAN

Breakfast: 1 cup of cornflakes with ½ cup of soymilk and ¼ cup sliced strawberries; a cup of fruit juice such as apple, cranberry, orange, or black cherry

Lunch: *Miso Soup with Tofu* (page 140); 1 slice of sourdough bread; 8 oz of water

Snack: 4 whole grain crackers with 2 tsp of soy nut butter; ½ cup of fruit juice

Dinner: 3 oz of cheese lasagna; 2 cups of mixed green salad and chopped fresh vegetables drizzled with 2 Tbsp of low-fat dressing; 1 small dinner roll; 8 oz of water

Dessert: ½ cup of fruited gelatin or ½ cup of Italian ice

OTHER RECIPES TO TRY

- Vegetable Stock
- Cantaloupe and Orange Soup
- Romaine Lettuce with Chunky Tomato Vinaigrette
- Carrot-Orange Juice

HALITOSIS

FOODS THAT HARM

Garlic

Onions

FOODS THAT HEAL

Water

Red bell pepper

Broccoli

Fennel seeds

Chewing gum with xylitol

HOW TO EAT

Your food choices have a big impact on your breath. Here's how to keep it fresh.

Drink plenty of water. Have a glass at the end of every meal or snack.

Make gum your aperitif. Sugar-free gum sweetened with xylitol helps cleanse the breath and curbs bacteria growth. Chew for at least 5 minutes for best results.

Reach for raw veggies. They help remove food particles stuck between teeth. And those rich in vitamin C, like broccoli and red bell peppers, create an unfriendly environment for bacteria.

Chew a few fennel seeds after mealtime to freshen your breath.

SAMPLE MEAL PLAN

Breakfast: 1 cup of low-fat yogurt mixed with ¼ cup of granola; ½ cup of sliced fresh fruit

Lunch: 3 oz of lean roasted pork; a baked sweet potato with 1 tsp of brown sugar; 2 cups of mixed green salad with chopped fresh vegetables and 2 Tbsp low-fat dressing

Snack: raw veggies such as carrots and red pepper strips dipped in low-fat dressing

Dinner: 3 oz of roasted lean meat, fish, or poultry; *Broccoli Salad with Almonds and Dried Cranberries* (page 175); ½ cup of brown rice pilaf; 1 whole grain roll

Dessert: 1 cup of fresh fruit cocktail, canned in its own juice

OTHER RECIPES TO TRY

- Mushroom and Bell Pepper Frittata
- Asian Grilled Tuna Burgers
- Asian Noodle Salad
- Orange-Walnut Broccoli
- Broccoli and Cauliflower with Cream Sauce
- Braised Carrot, Celery, and Fennel

HAY FEVER

FOODS THAT HARM

Artichokes

Chamomile tea

Endives

Escarole

Tarragon

Beer and wine

Sourdough bread

Blue cheese

Dried fruit

Mushrooms

Sausages

Sauerkraut

Soy sauce

Vinegar

Honey

FOODS THAT HEAL

Salmon

Herring

Flaxseeds

HOW TO EAT

The best strategy is to avoid foods that may trigger a flare-up.

Get to know the family. If ragweed triggers symptoms, so can foods in the sunflower plant family, such as artichokes, chamomile tea, chicory, dandelions, endives, escarole, Jerusalem artichokes, salsify, safflower (found in vegetable oils and margarines), sunflower seeds and oil, and tarragon.

If you're allergic to mold, avoid fermented foods. These include alcoholic beverages, beer, wine, and other drinks made by fermentation; breads made with lots of yeast or sourdough varieties; cheeses, especially blue cheese; dried fruits; mushrooms; processed meats or fish, including hot dogs, sausages, and smoked fish; sauerkraut and other fermented or pickled foods, including soy sauce; and vinegar and vinegary products, such as salad dressings, mayonnaise, ketchup, and pickles.

Watch out for honey. It may harbor bits of pollen.

Make friends with fatty fish and other foods high in omega-3s like flaxseed, soybean oil, and walnuts.

SAMPLE MEAL PLAN

Breakfast: *Berry-Flaxseed Smoothie* (page 131); 2 toaster waffles drizzled with 2 Tbsp of reduced-calorie syrup (stay away from honey), or topped with ½ cup fresh fruit slices

Lunch: a cup of bean soup; a low-fat cheese sandwich

Snack: 1 small banana; 6 walnuts; ½ cup of plain vanilla yogurt

Dinner: 3 oz grilled salmon steak topped with fresh fruit relish; baked potato with

2 Tbsp reduced-fat sour cream; ½ cup of cooked vegetables

Dessert: ½ cup of vanilla pudding

OTHER RECIPES TO TRY

- Salmon and Fennel Lettuce Wraps
- Broiled Salmon with Avocado-Mango Salsa
- Salmon and Asparagus Farfalle with Walnut-Feta Sauce
- Walnut Shortbread

HEARTBURN

See Indigestion and Heartburn, page 318

HEMORRHOIDS

FOODS THAT HEAL

Water
Black beans
Lima beans
Barley
Bran flakes
Raspberries
Apples
Pears
Oats
Flaxseeds

HOW TO EAT

These guidelines can help prevent the formation of hemorrhoids or ease some of the pain and bleeding if you have them.

Drink lots of water or other caffeine-free beverages. It helps to soften stools.

Fill up on fiber. Try to include two high-fiber servings (3 or more grams) at every meal. Good options include whole grains, popcorn, baked potato with skin, nuts, beans, fruits, and vegetables. Women need 21 to 25 g daily; men, 30 to 38 g.

Top with flax. Sprinkle ground flaxseeds on top of cereal, smoothies, or yogurt for more fiber.

SAMPLE MEAL PLAN

Breakfast: 1 cup of bran flakes with ½ cup of skim milk and 1 tsp of ground flaxseeds; *Pear Rhubarb Muffins* (page 128); ½ cup of fruit juice with pulp

Lunch: *Three-Bean Salad with Manchego Cheese* (page 174); a cup of barley soup topped with chopped scallions

Snack: 1 apple

Dinner: 3 oz of baked fish or chicken; ½ cup of mashed potatoes; at least ½ cup of succotash; 1 cup of mixed green salad with grated carrots, croutons, and 2 Tbsp of low-fat dressing

Dessert: ½ cup of vanilla yogurt with ½ cup of fresh raspberries

OTHER RECIPES TO TRY

- Hot Cereal with Apples and Dates
- Tuscan Bean Soup
- Broccoli and Pearl Barley Salad
- Black Bean and Sweet Potato Burritos
- Whole Wheat Flaxseed Bread

HEPATITIS

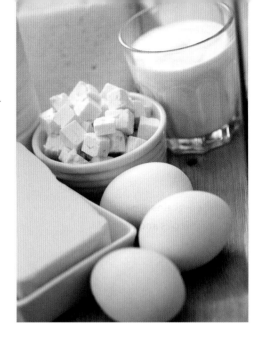

FOODS THAT HARM

Alcohol

Raw shellfish

Sweets

FOODS THAT HEAL

Lean meat

Poultry

Fish

Eggs

Dairy

Legumes

Whole grains

FOODS TO LIMIT

Fried and fatty foods

HOW TO EAT

The following strategies can help ease symptoms of all forms of hepatitis such as appetite loss and nausea.

Try to have breakfast. Often, appetite decreases and nausea increases as the day progresses. Breakfast may be the best-tolerated meal.

Graze throughout the day. It can help encourage eating when you don't have much of an appetite.

Get some protein at every meal. Choose from animal and vegetable sources.

Have a little fat. It provides calories and adds flavor. Good sources are dairy products and eggs because they're easy to digest.

SAMPLE MEAL PLAN

Mini Breakfast: 1 sunny-side up or scrambled egg; 1 slice of whole wheat toast with 1 tsp of jam; 1 banana

A.M. Mini Meal: ½ whole grain bagel with 2 tsp of peanut butter

Mini Lunch: *Pesto Chicken Spirals with Roasted Peppers* (page 246); a cup of low-sodium bean soup

P.M. Mini Meal: 4 oz enriched high-protein shake

Mini Dinner: *Cod with Gremolata Crust* (page 203); ½ cup of mashed potatoes; ½ cup of steamed broccoli, peas, or carrots; 1 small dinner roll

Dessert: ½ cup of frozen vanilla yogurt with 2 Tbsp of crushed peanuts and a maraschino cherry

OTHER RECIPES TO TRY

- One-Egg Omelet with Chopped Broccoli, Tomatoes, and Cheddar
- Zucchini Frittata
- Strawberry-Yogurt Smoothie
- Cod and Vegetable Stew
- Beef, Onion, and Pepper Fajitas
- Asian Chicken Salad
- Braised Chicken with Winter Vegetables
- Turkey Bacon and Apricot Bites

HERPES

FOODS THAT HEAL

Lean meat

Fish

Yogurt

Milk

Whole grains

Fresh fruits and vegetables

FOODS TO LIMIT

Alcohol

Caffeinated drinks

HOW TO EAT

To help prevent recurrences, eat a well-balanced diet.

Load up on lysine. This amino acid, found in meat, fish, milk, and dairy products, may reduce the frequency of breakouts.

Choose yogurt with live or "active" cultures. *Lactobacillus acidophilus*, a healthy bacteria found in yogurts, may help prevent recurrences of cold sores.

SAMPLE MEAL PLAN

Breakfast: 2 slices of whole grain toast with 2 tsp of trans fat free soft spread; ½ cup of low-fat cottage cheese with ½ cup sliced mangoes, peaches, or pineapple chunks

Lunch: *Beef in Lettuce Wraps* (page 143); an Asian-inspired noodle salad; ½ cup of vegetables, steamed, grilled, or baked

Snack: 1 cup of low-fat yogurt with ½ cup sliced fresh fruit

Dinner: *Roasted Pork with Pomegranate Sauce* (page 189); a medium baked sweet potato; ½ cup of steamed string bean

Dessert: 1 cup of kefir

OTHER RECIPES TO TRY

- Fish Tacos
- Broccoli and Pearl Barley Salad
- Pot Roast with Root Vegetables
- Spinach-Stuffed Meat Loaf
- Orange Beef with Broccoli and Jicama
- Pork Chops and Cabbage

HIATAL HERNIA

See Indigestion and Heartburn, page 318

HIVES

FOODS THAT HARM

Yellow food color no. 5 (tartrazine)

Shellfish

Nuts

Berries

Apricots

Grapes

Dried fruits

Tea

FOODS THAT HEAL

Poultry

Seafood

Seeds

Fortified and enriched cereals and breads

HOW TO EAT

Follow these tips to avoid an outbreak.

Steer clear of trigger foods. Some common ones are shellfish, nuts, and berries. Keep a food diary to identify ones that are problematic for you.

- Maple-Glazed Chicken with Root Vegetables
- Carrot-Flecked Corn Bread

HYPER-THYROIDISM

FOODS THAT HARM
Caffeinated drinks

FOODS THAT HEAL
Dairy products
Soy products
Collard greens
Mustard greens

Seek out foods that are high in niacin, such as chicken, tuna, beef, whole grains, and enriched cereals.

Read food labels to avoid tartrazine. This food additive (yellow food color no. 5) causes hives in some people.

HOW TO EAT

Dietary changes won't prevent or reverse this condition, but you can protect yourself with this advice.

Get enough calcium and vitamin D to keep your bones strong. An overactive thyroid may contribute to bone loss. Find D in salmon, tuna, mackerel, and fortified milk, soy beverages, and orange juice. Good calcium sources include milk, yogurt, cheese, broccoli, and kale.

SAMPLE MEAL PLAN

Breakfast: 1 cup of fortified and enriched whole grain cereal with 1 cup of skim milk; 1 small banana

Lunch: *Turkey Cobb Salad Sandwiches* (page 150); 8 baked potato chips.

Snack: handful of roasted sunflower seeds; 1 pear

Dinner: *Scallops Florentine* (page 209); 1 medium baked potato with 2 Tbsp of reduced-fat sour cream; 1 cup mixed green salad with 2 Tbsp low-fat dressing.

Dessert: *Carrot Ginger Yogurt Muffins* (page 129)

OTHER RECIPES TO TRY

- Papaya and Avocado Salad
- Watermelon and Feta Salad
- Braised Chicken Thighs with Winter Vegetables

SAMPLE MEAL PLANS

Breakfast: 2 slices of whole grain toast with 2 Tbsp of jam; a glass of calcium-fortified orange juice

Lunch: grilled chicken sandwich made with 3 oz of boneless, skinless chicken breast, 2 Tbsp low-fat mayonnaise, lettuce, and tomato; 1 cup of steamed collards

Snack: 1 cup soy yogurt

**WARNING!
FOOD-DRUG
INTERACTION**

If you're taking a synthetic thyroid hormone, limit dietary fiber. Certain foods (walnuts, soybean flour), supplements (iron, calcium), and medications (some antacids, ulcer medications, and cholesterol drugs) can also affect the effectiveness of the treatment. To avoid potential interactions, eat these foods or use these products several hours before or after you take your thyroid medication.

Dinner: *Pasta Primavera* (page 216); ½ cup of lightly steamed mustard greens

Dessert: 1 cup of frozen strawberry yogurt

OTHER RECIPES TO TRY

- Spinach and Goat Cheese Omelet
- Zucchini-Carrot Crustless Quiche Squares
- Mediterranean Salad with Edamame
- Braised Mixed Greens with Dried Currants
- Lemony Blueberry Cheesecake Bars
- Pumpkin Custards

HYPO-GLYCEMIA

FOODS THAT HEAL

Apples
Lentils
Barley
Oats

FOODS TO LIMIT

Alcohol
Sugary foods, such as candy

HOW TO EAT

You may need to consult a dietitian or your physician to adjust your meals and snacks further, but here are some strategies to prevent drops in your blood sugar that can trigger a hypoglycemic episode.

Think small, frequent meals. Eating at regular intervals—about every 2 to 3 hours—helps to keep blood sugar levels more stable.

Balance your meals. Get an even mix of carbohydrates, fats, and proteins in every meal. This will help your body metabo-lize the foods slowly to allow for a steady release of energy. The meals below all have between 30 to 45 g of carbohydrates.

Fill up on fiber. Make sure you have a high-fiber food at every meal. In addition to those listed at left, other good sources include fruits, vegetables, and whole grains.

Choose low glycemic load (GL) foods. GL is a measurement of how readily foods are converted to blood glucose. See page 357 for foods.

Choose sugar-free or no-added sugar beverages, unless you are having a low-blood sugar episode.

SAMPLE MEAL PLAN

Mini Breakfast: 1 soft cooked egg; 1 slice of whole grain toast with 1 tsp of trans fat free soft spread; ½ cup of citrus fruit

A.M. Mini Meal: *Blueberry-Oatmeal Muffins* (page 127)

Mini -Lunch: *Lentil Soup with Canadian Bacon* (page 134); ½ whole wheat pita; ½ cup steamed collards

P.M. Mini Meal: 4 whole grain crackers with 1 oz low fat cheese; ½ cup skim milk

Mini Dinner: 3 oz of baked boneless, skinless, chicken breast; ⅔ cup of cooked brown rice or risotto; ½ cup of diced carrots and peas

Dessert: 1 apple, sliced, with 2 tsp of peanut butter

OTHER RECIPES TO TRY

- Broccoli and Pearl Barley Salad
- Herbed Chicken and Apple Burgers
- Lentil and Rice Paella with Clams
- No-Bake Flaxseed-Nut Bars

HYPO-THYROIDISM

FOODS THAT HARM
- Walnuts
- Soybean flour

FOODS THAT HEAL
- Carrots
- Sweet potato
- Papaya
- Cantaloupe
- Spinach
- Turnip greens

HOW TO EAT

These dietary strategies, along with medication, can help control hypothyroidism, a condition in which the thyroid gland isn't producing enough hormones.

Eat more foods rich in beta-carotene. You may need a higher intake because the hormone thyroxine, which is used to treat hypothyroidism, accelerates the conversion of beta-carotene to vitamin A in the body.

Cook your broccoli. Cabbage, broccoli, and other cruciferous vegetables contain substances called goitrogens, which block the effects of thyroid hormones. Cooking these foods inactivates the goitrogens.

SAMPLE MEAL PLAN

Breakfast: ½ multigrain bagel with 1 oz of smoked salmon, red onions, and 1 Tbsp low-fat cream cheese; 1 cup of fruit salad made with fresh cantaloupe, mango, and strawberry slices

Lunch: *Carrot Soup with Dill* (page 138); 3 oz of grilled chicken; 1 cup of cooked cauliflower or broccoli florets

Snack: 1 oz of sweet potato chips; 1 apple

Dinner: 3 oz of broiled lean beef or roasted pork tenderloin; *Twice-Baked Stuffed Sweet Potatoes* (page 235); ½ cup of cooked spinach

Dessert: 1 cup sliced fruit—try papaya, mango, and kiwi drizzled with 1 tsp of honey.

OTHER RECIPES TO TRY

- Cantaloupe and Orange Soup
- Papaya and Avocado Salad
- Braised Mixed Greens with Dried Currants

IMPOTENCE

See Sex Drive, Diminished, page 347

INDIGES-TION AND HEARTBURN

FOODS THAT HARM
- Fatty foods

FOODS THAT HEAL
- Small meals at regular intervals

FOODS TO LIMIT
- Alcohol
- Caffeinated drinks
- Chocolate
- Spicy foods
- Peppermint
- Tomatoes

Pickles
Vinegar
Citrus fruits

HOW TO EAT

Follow this dietary advice to prevent or ease symptoms of occasional or chronic indigestion.

Eat small, frequent meals. They're easier to digest.

Adopt a low-fat, balanced diet. Fatty foods take longer to digest, staying in the stomach for more time and increasing the chance of heartburn or indigestion.

Keep your distance from prime offenders, such as acidic and spicy foods and drinks.

Watch out for chocolate or peppermint. They relax the diaphragmatic muscle, making it easier for stomach acid to flow up into the esophagus.

Chew nonmint gum for dessert. It stimulates saliva, which neutralizes acid in the esophagus.

Close the kitchen 2 hours before bedtime. You shouldn't eat anything within 2 hours of going to sleep.

SAMPLE MEAL PLAN

Mini Breakfast: Spinach and mushroom omelet using ½ cup of fat-free liquid egg substitute; 1 slice of whole grain toast with 1 tsp of jam

A.M. Mini Meal: ½ cup low-fat yogurt; 1 small cookie

Mini Lunch: 2 oz of sliced turkey; *Rice-Stuffed Squash* (page 223); ½ cup of steamed green string beans, carrots, or broccoli

P.M. Mini Meal: Banana-Peanut Bread (page 243)

Mini Dinner: 2 oz of grilled or baked boneless, skinless chicken breast; 2 cups mixed green salad with 2 Tbsp low-fat dressing; *Carrot-Flecked Corn Bread* (page 243)

Dessert: ½ cup of fruited gelatin

OTHER RECIPES TO TRY

- Yogurt Parfait
- Cauliflower Salad with Cashews
- Asparagus and Chicken Stir-Fry
- Braised Chicken with Winter Vegetables
- Snapper and Snaps in a Packet
- Cider-Baked Acorn Squash with Apple Stuffing

INFERTILITY

FOODS THAT HEAL

Enriched or fortified cereals
Brussels sprouts
Broccoli
Turnip greens
Yogurt
Legumes
Lean meat
Fish
Orange juice

FOODS TO LIMIT

Caffeinated drinks (for women)
Alcohol

HOW TO EAT

While nutrition is not a leading cause of infertility, it's important for both men and women to consume a healthful diet to enhance the chances of conceiving and delivering a healthy baby. The best way to do that is to eat a variety of foods from all food groups and follow these tips.

Get more folate. Women with a high intake are less likely to have children with neural tube defects such as spina bifida. Good sources include fortified breakfast cereals, leafy greens, legumes, and orange juice.

Seek out zinc. Inadequate intakes may lower male fertility. Good sources include oysters, lean roast beef, and peanuts.

Go for B12. Even in men who aren't deficient, vitamin B12—found in fortified breads and cereals, lean meat, poultry, and seafood—may improve sperm count and motility.

Cut back on coffee. Research has found that women who drink more than 3 cups of coffee a day reduce their chances of conceiving in any given month by 25%.

SAMPLE MEAL PLAN

Breakfast: 1 cup of fortified whole grain cereal with ½ cup of skim milk; ½ cup low-fat fruit yogurt; ½ cup of orange juice

Lunch: *Grilled Oysters with Fennel and Spinach* (page 247); 6 whole grain crackers; at least 1 cup of steamed broccoli florets

Snack: ½ cup of yogurt with sliced fruit or berries

Dinner: 3 oz of cooked lean roast beef or pork; *Brussels Sprouts with Caraway Seeds* (page 229); ½ cup of mashed sweet potatoes; at least ½ cup of steamed turnip greens or kale

Dessert: ½ cup frozen vanilla yogurt with 2 Tbsp of chopped peanuts and a cherry on top

OTHER RECIPES TO TRY

- Strawberry-Yogurt Smoothie
- Beef Fillet Salad with Mustard Vinaigrette
- Pork, Pear, and Potato Salad
- Calf's Liver with Rigatoni
- Whole Wheat Noodles with Peanut Sauce and Chicken
- Brown Rice with Cabbage and Chickpeas
- Orange-Walnut Broccoli
- Fruity Brussels Sprouts

INFLAMMA-TORY BOWEL DISEASE

FOODS THAT HARM

Fried foods, artificial sweeteners, or any other trigger foods
Alcohol
Caffeinated beverages

FOODS THAT HEAL

Water
Bananas
Rice
Applesauce
Toast
White meat poultry

FOODS TO LIMIT

Bran
Whole grains
Nuts
Dried fruits

HOW TO EAT

While diet doesn't cause IBD and can't cure it, some foods may ease symptoms while others may trigger a flare-up. These are different for each person, so identify your trigger foods. Then stick to your safe foods and follow these tips.

Eat five to six smaller meals. This puts less strain on the intestinal tract.

Drink up between meals. It's important to stay hydrated, and drinking lots of fluids helps prevent kidney problems and gallstones. However, taking in liquids at the same time as food may sometimes cause diarrhea, so do your sipping in between meals.

Focus on soluble fiber found in oats, poached and peeled fruits, and cooked leafy green vegetables. Insoluble fiber (found in the Foods to Limit offerings at left) tends to be more irritating to the colon.

Choose soft foods like those in the meal plan below. They are easier to digest.

SAMPLE MEAL PLAN

Mini Breakfast: 1 slice of toast with 1 Tbsp of apple butter; 1 banana

A.M. Mini Meal: ½ cup of cottage-cheese with ¼ cup of sliced peaches, fresh or canned

Mini Lunch: 2 oz of baked salmon; 1 cup of vegetable soup; ½ cup of cooked white rice (or brown rice if you tolerate it); ½ cup of sautéed greens such as spinach, bok choy, or cabbage

P.M. Mini Meal: 4 saltines with 2 tsp of nut butter

Dinner: 2 oz of poached chicken; ½ cup of cooked white rice (or brown rice if you tolerate it); ½ cup of cooked carrots

Dessert: 1 poached pear

OTHER RECIPES TO TRY

- Zucchini Frittata
- Quick Chicken Noodle Soup
- Carrot Soup with Dill
- Braised Chicken with Winter Vegetables
- Grilled Salmon with Sautéed Greens
- Chewy Oatmeal Raisin Cookies

INSOMNIA

FOODS THAT HARM
Alcohol
Caffeinated drinks

FOODS THAT HEAL
Milk and honey
Turkey sandwich
Banana

HOW TO EAT

Your eating habits can certainly affect your sleeping habits. Here's some diet advice that can help you get a better night's sleep.

Skip caffeine. If you can't cut it out completely, at least avoid having any about 8 hours before bed.

Combine foods for better sleep. Milk and turkey contain sleep-inducing tryptophan, which works by increasing the amount of serotonin, a natural sedative, in the brain. But you need carbs—like honey or bread—to get tryptophan into your brain.

Don't go to bed full. Too much food can cause digestive discomfort that can keep you awake.

Try rice for dinner. In one study, eating a high-carb meal, in this case featuring jasmine rice, 4 hours before bed can halve the time it takes to fall asleep.

Stop drinking fluids a couple of hours before bed. It will reduce your chances of having to get up during the night.

SAMPLE MEAL PLAN

Breakfast: 1 cup of whole grain cereal with ½ cup of skim milk; 1 sliced banana

Lunch: *Turkey Cobb Salad Sandwiches* (page 150); 1 oz of carrot chips

Snack: 4 honey mustard pretzels, or a serving of nugget-size pretzels

Dinner: *Rice Salad with Chicken and Grapes* (page 223) made with jasmine rice; a bowl of lentil soup; 1 piece of French bread

Dessert: a cup of warm skim milk with 1 tsp of honey

OTHER RECIPES TO TRY

- Turkey, Spinach, and Rice in Roasted Garlic Broth
- Turkey Braciola Stuffed with Provolone and Spinach
- Thai Coconut Rice

INTERSTITIAL CYSTITIS

FOODS THAT HARM

Hot peppers
Coffee
Cranberry juice
Artificial sweeteners

FOODS THAT HEAL

Water
Fresh fruits and vegetables
Dairy products

FOODS TO LIMIT

Processed foods containing preservatives and other chemicals

HOW TO EAT

Many foods are reported to worsen symptoms, but people react differently to different foods. Once you've identified your trigger foods, be especially careful not to eat them when you're starting a new drug therapy.

Eliminate one at a time. Rather than cutting suspected food triggers from your diet all at once, eliminate one at a time for several days and note if your symptoms improve. Foods that are common troublemakers are listed above.

Consider going organic. Buy fresh food as much as possible and organic food whenever you can.

Sip water. Keeping urine diluted may help. Speak with your doctor about how much you should drink.

SAMPLE MEAL PLAN

Breakfast: *Carrot Ginger Yogurt Muffins* (page 129); ½ cup of low-fat cottage cheese with ¼ cup of fresh sliced fruit

Lunch: *Zucchini-Carrot Crustless Quiche Squares* (page 157); at least 1 cup of your favorite steamed vegetables

Snack: 1 pear

Dinner: *Pasta Primavera* (page 216); 2 cups of mixed salad greens with 2 Tbsp low-fat dressing; 1 slice of whole grain bread with 1 tsp trans fat free spread

Dessert: organic fresh fruit

OTHER RECIPES TO TRY

- Cauliflower Salad with Cashews
- Papaya and Avocado Salad
- Baked Pasta with Garlic and Greens
- Macaroni and Cheese with Spinach
- Twice-Baked Stuffed Sweet Potatoes
- Cider-Baked Acorn Squash with Apple Stuffing

IRON OVERLOAD

FOODS THAT HARM

Alcohol (if there is liver damage)
Raw shellfish

FOODS TO LIMIT

Iron-rich foods, such as lean red meats and organ meats
Dark green leafy vegetables

HOW TO EAT

Hemachromatosis is the most common form of iron overload disease and can be inherited or caused by anemia or alcoholism. Left untreated, it can cause irreversible damage and lead to serious conditions such as cancer, heart disease, and liver disease. That's why it's important to see your doctor and work with a registered dietitian to develop a personal nutrition plan to meet your specific needs. Here are some general guidelines.

Eat more low-iron foods. Choose fresh fruit over dried; unfortified grain, cereal, or bread; chicken and fish instead of red meat; and veggies except for leafy greens.

Avoid foods that increase iron absorption. Vitamin C boosts absorption of iron, so it's best to eat foods high in vitamin C between meals or with foods that contain little iron.

IRRITABLE BOWEL SYNDROME

FOODS THAT HARM

Fatty and fried foods
Sugar alcohols, such as sorbitol, lactitol, mannitol, and maltitol

FOODS THAT HEAL

Water
Whole grain breads and cereals
Berries
Lentils
Artichokes
Bananas

HOW TO EAT

What you eat definitely affects your symptoms, although the effects of certain foods can vary from person to person. A food diary can help you to identify those foods that exacerbate or calm IBS for you. Here is some general advice.

Eat several small meals to reduce symptoms.

Chew food thoroughly. Poorly chewed food is harder to digest. Eating too fast also causes you to swallow more air that can result in irritating intestinal gas.

Drink lots of water to promote better digestion.

Know which fiber you need. Insoluble fiber, found in whole grain cereals and vegetables like peas and broccoli, helps to bulk up stools and ease elimination, relieving constipation. Foods high in soluble fiber, such as oats, barley, apples, and kidney beans, absorb water and are helpful for bouts of diarrhea.

SAMPLE MEAL PLAN

Mini Breakfast: 1 cup of whole grain cereal with ½ cup of skim milk; *Blueberry-Oatmeal Muffins* (page 127)

A.M. Mini Meal: ½ cup of yogurt; 1 banana

Mini Lunch: 2 oz of baked chicken; ½ cup of mashed potatoes topped with chives or parsley; ½ cup of cooked wax beans

P.M. Mini Meal: *Warm Artichoke and Bean Dip* (page 251) with ½ whole wheat pita

Mini Dinner: 2 oz of broiled lean meat; 1 cup of lentil soup; ½ cup of cooked broccoli, or 2 cups of mixed green salad with 2 Tbsp of low-fat dressing; 1 slice of whole grain bread

Dessert: *Angel Food Cake with Strawberries* (page 261)

OTHER RECIPES TO TRY

- Berry Salad with Passion Fruit
- Berry-Flaxseed Smoothie
- Lentil Soup with Canadian Bacon
- Cauliflower Salad with Cashews
- Artichokes with Lentils and Lima Beans
- Rhubarb-Blackberry Crumble

JAUNDICE

FOODS THAT HARM
Alcohol

FOODS THAT HEAL
Lean meat
Poultry
Fish
Eggs
Dairy products
Quinoa
Lentils

FOODS TO LIMIT
Fatty and fried foods
Sugary foods

HOW TO EAT

Eating a nutritious, well-balanced diet can help to resolve some types of jaundice. Here are some guidelines.

Be a grazer. Several small meals throughout the day may be the best way to get a balanced diet since appetite tends to decrease and nausea is common.

For hepatitis suffers, eat a diet high in protein. Consume a healthy diet with sufficient protein daily, from both animal and vegetable sources. (See Hepatitis, page 314.)

Opt for fats in dairy and eggs. They're easier to digest than other fatty foods.

Stay away from sweets. They may squelch your appetite for more nutritious foods.

SAMPLE MEAL PLAN

Mini Breakfast: an omelet made with broccoli and cheese; 1 slice of whole wheat toast; 1 small banana

A.M. Mini Meal: ½ cup of low-fat cottage cheese with ¼ cup sliced peaches (peeled or from a can, with no added sugar)

Mini Lunch: 3 oz of chicken salad stuffed into a small pita pocket; *Lentil Soup with Canadian Bacon* (page 134)

P.M. Mini Meal: 1 apple; 1 oz low-fat string cheese; 4 whole grain crackers

Mini Dinner: 3 oz of cooked lean roast beef, baked fish, or roasted chicken or turkey; *Springtime Quinoa* (page 220); ½ cup of lightly sautéed vegetables, or a small mixed green salad with 2 Tbsp of low-fat dressing

Dessert: ½ cup of *Creamy Citrus and Vanilla Rice Pudding* (page 263)

OTHER RECIPES TO TRY

- Zucchini Frittata
- Quick Chicken Noodle Soup
- Sloppy Joes
- Fish Tacos
- Pineapple-Chipotle Chicken
- Cod with Gremolata Crust
- Pasta Primavera

JET LAG

FOODS THAT HEAL
Water
Cucumber
Celery
Watermelon
Grapes
Papaya

FOODS TO LIMIT
Alcohol
Caffeinated beverages

HOW TO EAT

To minimize jet lag, you'll need to change your eating habits 2 days before your flight if you're traveling within a country. If you're traveling farther, you'll need to follow this diet plan for about 4 days before takeoff.

Feast and fast. The scientifically tested anti–jet lag diet alternates feast days (high-protein breakfasts and lunches, high-carb dinners) with fast days (low-cal, low-carb meals) to trick your body to be right on time.

Lose the booze. Don't drink any alcohol the day before your flight, during the flight, and the day after the flight. The same goes for caffeine.

Eat your water. In addition to drinking lots of water, bring watery fruits and vegetables, such as those listed above, as snacks.

SAMPLE MEAL PLAN
DAY 1—FEAST
(2 to 4 days before you leave)

Breakfast: *One-Egg Omelet with Chopped Broccoli, Tomatoes, and Cheddar* (page 123); 2 oz of turkey bacon, smoked salmon, or lean meat; decaffeinated coffee or tea

Lunch: 3 to 4 oz of baked, grilled, broiled, or roasted lean meat, chicken, turkey, or fish; 1 cup of bean soup, or 2 oz of low-fat cheese; decaffeinated coffee or tea

Dinner: *Baked Pasta with Garlic and Greens* (page 213); 1 whole grain roll; 1 slice of pie a la mode; decaffeinated coffee or tea

DAY 2—FAST
(the day before you leave)

Eat lightly; choose small salads, broth or thin soups, fruit or fruit juice. Break your fast with a high-protein breakfast when you arrive at your destination the next day.

OTHER RECIPES TO TRY
- Individual Breakfast Tortilla
- Curried Chicken Salad Sandwich
- Turkey Cobb Salad Sandwiches
- Japanese Sushi Rolls
- Potato Salad with Sun-Dried Tomatoes, Scallions, and Basil
- Watermelon and Feta Salad
- Macaroni and Cheese with Spinach
- Cherry Crisp

KIDNEY DISEASE
(including kidney stones, nephritis, kidney failure)

FOODS THAT HARM
Salty foods, such as pickles

FOODS THAT HEAL
Water
Cranberry juice
Lemon juice

FOODS TO LIMIT
Berries
Soybeans
Beet greens
Quinoa
Chocolate
Tea

HOW TO EAT

Diet modifications will vary depending on the type and severity of the kidney disorder. It is best to seek the advice of a physician or registered dietitian who can help you with your diet as it relates to your disorder. Here are some general guidelines, including a meal plan that can help prevent and ease problems with kidney stones, one of the most common types of kidney problems.

For kidney stones, drink plenty of fluids throughout the day, include vegetarian sources of protein, and reduce oxalate-rich foods such as rhubarb, spinach, nuts, sweet potatoes, tea, soy, and chocolate (see meal plan below).

For nephritis, including cranberry juice daily in your diet may be helpful.

For stages of kidney failure, most people will need to limit sodium, protein, phosphorus-containing foods such as dairy products, and potassium-containing foods such as potatoes, citrus, and bananas. Fluids may or may not be restricted. If you are on dialysis, your diet may need to be modified further.

SAMPLE MEAL PLAN

Breakfast: *Zucchini Frittata* (page 124); 2 slices of white toast with 2 Tbsp of apple-butter spread; 8 oz of juice or water

Lunch: chicken sandwich made with 3 oz of grilled chicken on a kaiser roll, stuffed with iceberg lettuce and drizzled with

2 Tbsp of low-fat dressing; ½ cup steamed broccoli or peas; 1 cup of cantaloupe chunks; 8 oz of juice or water

Snack: 6 low-fat vanilla wafers; 8 oz of juice or water

Dinner: *Vegetable Pot Pie* (page 000); 1 whole grain roll; 8 oz of juice or water

Dessert: *Angel Food Cake with Strawberries* (page 213)

OTHER RECIPES TO TRY

- Open-Faced Grilled Vegetable Sandwich
- Cod with a Gremolata Crust
- Savory Cranberry Chutney

LACTOSE INTOLERANCE

FOODS THAT HARM

Milk
Soft cheeses

FOODS THAT HEAL

Lactose-free dairy products
Broccoli
Fortified and enriched breads
Fortified and enriched juices
Fortified soy beverages
Canned salmon (with bones)
Pinto beans
Rhubarb

FOODS TO LIMIT

Yogurt
Hard cheeses

HOW TO EAT

You can control symptoms of lactose intolerance by limiting dairy products in your diet. Here are some helpful strategies.

Read labels carefully. Look for ingredients like milk, milk solids, cream, whey, cheese flavors, curds, and nonfat milk powder. Such dairy products can be an ingredient or component of various food products such as cookies, breads, processed meats, hot dogs, some artificial sweeteners, and even some medications.

Eat lactose-reduced or lactose-free products. Most lactose-intolerant people can eat cultured dairy products, like yogurt. Others options are hard cheeses, like cheddar, edam, and gouda.

Try adding milk to your diet slowly. Start with a quarter-cup of milk and gradually increase the amount. Avoid drinking milk on an empty stomach.

Get calcium from other sources, if you are very intolerant. Good sources include sardines (with bones), black beans, kale, and almonds.

Eat foods rich in vitamin D. Since vitamin D is also needed for strong bones, eat eggs, salmon, and yogurt.

SAMPLE MEAL PLAN

Breakfast: 2 pieces of French toast (made with almond or fortified rice milk) with 2 Tbsp reduced-calorie syrup; 2 slices of lean bacon or low-fat sausage links

Lunch: *Salmon and Fennel Lettuce Wraps* (page 152); 8 whole grain crackers; ½ cup of steamed carrots, cauliflower, and snow peas

Snack: 1 medium orange

Dinner: 3 oz of roasted turkey; *Broccoli and Pearl Barley Salad* (page 169); 1 cup of cooked spinach

Dessert: *Rhubarb-Blackberry Crumble* (page 259) made with soymilk

OTHER RECIPES TO TRY

- Turkey, Spinach, and Rice in Roasted Garlic Broth
- Calf's Liver with Rigatoni
- Creamy Citrus and Vanilla Rice Pudding

LUPUS

FOODS THAT HARM

Alfalfa

Celery

Parsnips

Parsley

Lemons

Limes

Mushrooms

Smoked food

Grapefruit

FOODS THAT HEAL

Broccoli

Cabbage

Cauliflower

Spinach

Milk

Fortified soy and rice beverages

Salmon

Mackerel

Herring

Nuts

Flaxseeds

Wheat germ

FOODS TO LIMIT

Fatty, high-protein foods, especially animal products

WARNING! FOOD-DRUG INTERACTION

Do not consume grapefruit or grapefruit juice if you are taking cyclosporine, a powerful immune system suppressor. They can dramatically increase the body's ability to absorb cyclosporine, leading to severe toxicity. If you are taking corticosteroids, cut back on salt. It will increase water retention and contribute to high blood pressure.

HOW TO EAT

Lupus is an inflammatory disease so eating more foods that fight and reduce inflammation (fruits and veggies) and avoiding those that promote inflammation (animal products) is prudent. Here are more diet guidelines that may help.

Go for variety. Eating a colorful array of fruits, vegetables, and whole grains can also protect you from heart disease in addition to providing essential nutrients.

Chomp on cruciferous veggies regularly. Foods such as broccoli, cabbage, and cauliflower contain indoles that alter the metabolism of estrogen in a way that has a positive impact on lupus.

Fish for omega-3s. Their anti-inflammatory effects may relieve the joint pain, soreness, and stiffness associated with lupus.

Eat foods rich in vitamin D. Because most lupus patients must avoid exposure to the sun, they need to get this bone-strengthening vitamin from milk and fortified soy and rice beverages. Extra calcium is also beneficial.

Avoid alfalfa in any form. Even herbal supplements containing alfalfa worsen lupus symptoms. Other legumes may have a similar effect.

SAMPLE MEAL PLAN

Breakfast: 1 cup of whole grain cereal with ½ cup skim milk or fortified soy or rice beverage, and 1 tsp of ground flaxseeds on top; ½ cup of fresh fruit

Lunch: 1 can of mackerel or sardines in olive oil (well-drained) on 8 whole grain low-sodium crackers; 1 cup of mixed green salad with chopped tomatoes, cucumbers, low-fat grated cheese, and 2 Tbsp of low-fat dressing

Snack: small handful of nuts

Dinner: 3 oz of baked salmon; *Cauliflower and Spinach Casserole* (page 231); 1 cup of cooked orzo with chopped fresh herbs

Dessert: *Wheat Germ Smoothie* (page 132)

OTHER RECIPES TO TRY

- Berry-Flaxseed Smoothie
- Grilled Salmon with Sautéed Greens
- Pasta with Cabbage, Apple, and Leeks
- Spiced Almonds

MEMORY LOSS

FOODS THAT HEAL

Lean meat

Whole grains

Beans

Oranges

Cantaloupes

Eggs

Nuts and seeds

Spinach

Soybeans

HOW TO EAT

A healthy diet can help to keep your brain sharp. Here are a few dietary changes that can make a difference.

Make time for a good breakfast. A Toronto study found that breakfast helped men and women ages 61 to 79 score better on memory tests. And when kids eat a morning meal, their exam scores improve.

Get plenty of beta-carotene and vitamin C found in sweet potatoes, butternut squash, carrots, red peppers, and broccoli.

Add vitamin E. Rich sources of this antioxidant include wheat germ, vegetable oils, and nuts.

Get enough iron. Lean meat, soybeans, and dark leafy greens like spinach are good sources.

Drink some coffee. A University of Arizona study showed that seniors who drank 12 oz (355 mL) of caffeinated coffee in the morning and afternoon maintained their memory better than the group of seniors who drank decaffeinated coffee.

Limit alcohol. In one study, adults who drank one to six alcoholic beverages a week were 54% less likely than abstainers to develop dementia over 6 years. However, 14 or more drinks weekly increased the risk of dementia by 22%.

SAMPLE MEAL PLAN

Breakfast: 1 sunny-side up egg; 1 slice of whole grain toast; ½ cup low-fat fruit-flavored yogurt sprinkled with 2 tsp of wheat germ; ½ cup of orange juice

Lunch: grilled salmon burger on a whole wheat bun; *Lentil Soup with Canadian Bacon* (page 134); ½ cup of cooked spinach

Snack: *Sweet and Spicy Snack Mix* (page 252)

Dinner: *Flank Steak Roll with Carrots and Red Pepper* (page 181); 1 cup of cooked angel hair pasta sautéed in 2 tsp of olive oil and crushed garlic, and tossed with parmesan cheese to taste; 1 whole grain roll

Dessert: 2 cups of cubed cantaloupe

OTHER RECIPES TO TRY

- Cantaloupe and Orange Soup
- Beef, Onion, and Pepper Fajitas
- Pork, Pear, and Potato Salad
- Buckwheat Noodles with Tofu and Green Vegetables
- Spinach Salad with Chickpeas
- Spinach-Stuffed Meatloaf

MENOPAUSE

FOODS THAT HEAL

Fortified and enriched cereals

Spinach

Tofu and other soy products

Nuts and seeds, especially flaxseeds

Vegetable oil

FOODS TO LIMIT

Alcohol

Caffeinated drinks

Chocolate

Spicy foods

HOW TO EAT

Enjoy a diet rich in whole grains, fruits, vegetables, and low-fat dairy products to help ease the symptoms of menopause and reduce your risk for chronic disease. Follow these additional strategies for even greater benefits.

Watch out for trigger foods. Some foods can worsen symptoms like hot flashes, insomnia, and mood swings. Common culprits include coffee, tea, chocolate, colas, alcohol, and spicy foods.

Include soy foods. Studies have shown that they can help ease hot flashes.

Try vitamin E. For some women, vitamin E, found in many of the healing foods at left, helps tame hot flashes.

Eat 1 to 2 Tbsp of ground flaxseed a day. Grind the seeds and add to cereal, yogurt, or oatmeal.

SAMPLE MEAL PLAN

Breakfast: spinach omelet; *Whole Wheat Flaxseed Bread* (page 242), toasted, with 2 tsp of jam; 1 cup of fresh orange or grapefruit sections

Lunch: 3 oz of baked or grilled salmon; *Mediterranean Salad with Edamame* (page 177); 1 medium baked potato with 1 tsp of trans fat free soft spread

Snack: *Cranberry-Peanut Cereal Bars* (page 254)

Dinner: *Fried Rice with Tofu and Vegetables* (page 222); a bowl of soup

Dessert: ½ cup of low-fat yogurt with sliced bananas and 1 Tbsp of ground flaxseeds

OTHER RECIPES TO TRY

- Spinach and Goat Cheese Omelet
- Buckwheat Noodles with Tofu and Green Vegetables
- Spinach Salad with Chickpeas
- Bok Choy, Tofu, and Mushroom Stir-Fry
- Edamame Hummus with Pita Crisps

MENSTRUAL PROBLEMS

FOODS THAT HARM
Fatty and highly refined foods

FOODS THAT HEAL
Apples

Pears

Whole grain and fortified and
  enriched cereals

Lean meat

Green leafy vegetables

Sunflower seeds

Nuts

Lentils

Dairy products

Soy products

Figs

Salmon

Avocados

Potatoes

Raspberry leaf tea

Chamomile tea

FOODS TO LIMIT
Alcohol

Salty foods

HOW TO EAT

Follow these suggestions to prevent or ease some of the symptoms of premenstrual syndrome, the most common menstrual problem.

Eat low glycemic foods. Fiber-rich choices such as apples and pears keep blood sugar more stable to tame cravings. See the glycemic index chart on page 357.

Get more calcium. Low levels may contribute to mood swings, cramping, and bloating. Best sources include dairy products, fortified soy beverages, canned salmon or sardines, and leafy greens.

Add more magnesium. Munch on a handful of sunflower seeds, nuts, figs, and green vegetables to reduce your chances of PMS-induced headaches and depression.

Boost vitamin B6. Beef, pork, chicken, fish, whole grain cereals, bananas, avocados, and potatoes are good sources of this vitamin, which may reduce anxiety and depression.

Indulge cravings carefully. Too many sugary, empty calories may stimulate more cravings.

Sip herbal teas for painful cramps. Try raspberry leaf or chamomile tea.

Load up on iron-rich foods, if you bleed a lot. When eating red meat, legumes, fortified cereals, leafy green vegetables, and dried fruits include some vitamin C-rich foods like cantaloupe or kiwis to improve iron absorption.

SAMPLE MEAL PLAN

Breakfast: 1 cup of whole grain cereal or a fruit and nut muesli, with 1 cup of skim or soy milk; 1 slice of cantaloupe

Lunch: *Crab and Avocado Salad* (page 167); 1 medium ear of corn on the cob with 1 tsp of trans fat free soft spread; 1 medium apple

Snack: 1 oz low-fat cheese; 1 medium pear; a small handful of unsalted nuts

Dinner: veggie burger on a whole wheat bun with lettuce, tomato, sprouts, 1 Tbsp of your favorite spread; a cup of lentil soup; 8 baked potato fries; ½ cup of steamed collard greens

Dessert: *Sesame-Fig Bars* (page 254); a cup of chamomile or raspberry leaf tea

OTHER RECIPES TO TRY

- Hot Cereal with Apples and Dates
- Raspberry-Beet Smoothie
- Pork, Pear, and Potato Salad
- Buckwheat Noodles with Tofu and Green Vegetables
- Mediterranean Salad with Edamame
- Papaya and Avocado Salad
- Potato Salad with Sun-Dried Tomatoes, Scallions, and Basil
- White Beans Stewed with Swiss Chard

METABOLIC SYNDROME

See Diabetes, page 302

MIGRAINES AND OTHER HEADACHES

FOODS THAT HARM

Individual trigger foods, such as aged cheeses, processed meats, fermented foods, and more

FOODS TO LIMIT

Caffeinated drinks

HOW TO EAT

When it comes to migraines, the key dietary advice is to avoid foods that bring on the pain. Here's what you need to know, along with a meal plan featuring bland foods that are less likely to trigger a headache.

Know and avoid common dietary triggers. Keep a diary to learn what foods prompt symptoms, and then eliminate those foods. Common culprits in addition to those listed at left include pickles; legumes, especially dried beans, lentils, and soy products; nuts, seeds, and peanut butter; chocolate; organ meats and meats that are salted, dried, cured, smoked, or contain nitrites; sardines and anchovies; fruits, including avocados, bananas, citrus, figs, grapes, pineapples, raspberries, red plums, and raisins; red wine; artificial sweeteners; sulfites; and monosodium glutamate (MSG).

Don't skip meals. Eating regular meals will prevent hunger or low blood sugar, which can trigger a headache.

Cut caffeine. Drinking too much can contribute to the frequency of headaches. However, if you are completely off caffeine, you may be able to use it to fend off an attack because it constricts dilated blood vessels. At the first sign of an aura or pain, drink a cup of strong coffee or a cola, take two aspirin, and lie down in a dark, quiet room. The episode may pass within an hour or so.

SAMPLE MEAL PLAN

Breakfast: 2 scrambled eggs with chopped vegetables; 1 slice of toast with 1 tsp trans fat free soft spread; ½ cup of sliced peaches

Lunch: Roast turkey sandwich on 2 slices of whole wheat bread with 2 oz of turkey breast, warmed, 2 strips of nitrite-free bacon, cooked, 1 Tbsp cranberry sauce, 1 slice tomato, 1 leaf lettuce, 1 Tbsp low-fat mayonnaise; *Ginger Butternut Squash Soup* (page 139)

Snack: 1 medium apple

Dinner: *Braised Chicken with Winter Vegetables* (page 191); 1 soft whole grain dinner roll

Dessert: 1 piece of angel food cake topped with sliced strawberries

OTHER RECIPES TO TRY

- Cod and Vegetable Stew
- Bok Choy, Tofu, and Mushroom Stir-Fry
- Springtime Quinoa
- Roasted Root Vegetables
- Carrot-Flecked Corn Bread

MOOD DISORDERS

FOODS THAT HARM

Foods with additives, if allergic

FOODS THAT HEAL

Turkey

Milk

Eggs

Pasta

Breads

Kale

Orange juice

Corn

Asparagus

Tuna

Salmon

FOODS TO LIMIT

Caffeinated drinks

Alcohol

Sugary foods

HOW TO EAT

Food can have an effect on the brain chemicals that control your mood. Here's how to ensure the effect is positive.

Don't skip meals. Eating small amounts of food frequently throughout the day can keep your energy level and mood more constant.

Combine tryptophan and carbs. This feel-good amino acid found in turkey, milk, and eggs works best when consumed with carbohydrates like bread.

Fill your plate with veggies. Leafy greens and other veggies listed at left are high in folate. Many depressed people are deficient in this mineral. Other good sources include lentils, peas, nuts, and seeds.

Feast on fish. Aim to eat fish three times a week or more.

SAMPLE MEAL PLAN

Breakfast: *Asparagus, Egg, and Ham Sandwiches* (page 121); 1 cup of sliced fresh fruit, or ½ cup of orange juice

Lunch: *Tossed Tuna Salad Niçoise* (page 165); 1 whole grain roll

Snack: small handful of nuts or seeds; 1 banana

Dinner: *Indian-Style Turkey Burgers* (page 150); ½ cup cooked basmati rice; 1 medium ear of corn on the cob; ½ cup of steamed greens such as collards or kale

Dessert: 1 cup of milk with 1 tsp of honey

OTHER RECIPES TO TRY

- Summer Greens Scramble
- Chicken-Kale Soup with Roasted Pepper Puree
- Cantaloupe and Orange Soup

- Turkey Cobb Salad Sandwiches
- Herbed Turkey Meatballs and Fusilli
- Braised Mixed Greens with Dried Currants
- Jerk Turkey Breast with Ginger Barbecue Sauce
- Carrot-Flecked Corn Bread

MOTION SICKNESS

FOODS THAT HEAL

Ginger
Saltines or other dry crackers
Ginger ale
Water

FOODS TO LIMIT

Alcohol
Fatty and fried foods
Salty foods, such as pickles
Dairy products
Caffeinated drinks

HOW TO EAT

Try these suggestions to avoid feeling queasy. If you get sick and aren't up to making the recipes at right, or if they sound unappetizing, opt for simple, bland foods until you're feeling better.

Nix feasting. Keep meals light during the 24 hours before your trip. And avoid salty foods and dairy products. (See meal plan at right for suggestions.)

Season pretravel meals with ginger. Add 1 Tbsp of chopped ginger to fish, eggs, chicken, or turkey dishes.

Hydrate ahead of time. Down at least 8 glasses of water, ginger ale, or iced tea 24 hours before you travel.

Sip while en route. Ginger ale and ginger tea are good choices.

Munch on dry crackers if your stomach gets queasy.

SAMPLE MEAL PLAN

Breakfast: toasted English muffin with 2 tsp apple butter or jam; a cup of peppermint or ginger tea

Lunch: *Chicken Breasts with Peaches and Ginger* (page 193); ½ cup of cooked rice

Snack: a cup of vegetable soup garnished with a smidge of grated gingerroot; a couple of unsalted crackers or saltines

Dinner: 1 lean turkey or chicken burger on a soft kaiser roll with 1 Tbsp of low-fat mayonnaise, lettuce, and a sliced tomato; a plain baked sweet potato

Dessert: *Warm Pineapple-Ginger Punch* (page 272)

OTHER RECIPES TO TRY

- Indian-Style Turkey Burgers
- Asparagus and Chicken Stir-Fry
- Pineapple-Chipotle Chicken
- Jerk Turkey Breast with Ginger Barbecue Sauce
- Fruit Parfait with Ginger Tea Cream

QUICK TIP: Snack on Protein

Before you hop in the car or board a plane, train, or boat, have a protein bar or drink. According to research from Penn State University, travellers who ate protein pre-travel fared better than those who filled up on carbohydrates.

MULTIPLE SCLEROSIS

FOODS THAT HEAL

- Prune juice
- Berries
- Whole grain breads and cereals
- Split peas
- Artichoke
- Nuts
- Papaya
- Milk
- Fish
- Cranberry juice
- Water

FOODS TO LIMIT

- Alcohol
- Spicy foods

HOW TO EAT

Diet can help minimize MS symptoms such as fatigue, constipation, urinary tract infections, and problems with chewing and swallowing.

Think low fat, high fiber. Eating this way will provide energy and nutrients to maintain and repair tissues, fight infections, and reduce your risk of constipation. (See the meal plan below.)

Eat foods rich in antioxidants to counter free radical damage that may promote the progression of MS. Good sources of beta-carotene, vitamins C and E, and selenium include oranges, carrots, vegetable oils, nuts, seeds, and seafood, along with the healing foods above.

Get plenty of vitamin D from milk or fortified soy and rice beverages. It may help slow progression of the disease and will keep your bones strong.

Increase fluid intake, but avoid caffeine. Prune juice and cranberry juice are good choices, and help prevent constipation and urinary tract infections, respectively.

Eat small, frequent meals and don't skip breakfast.

Choose soft textures if you have difficulties with chewing or swallowing. For example, substitute shakes, yogurt, fruit and vegetable purees, puddings, and thick soups for firm or dry dishes.

SAMPLE MEAL PLAN

Mini Breakfast: 1 serving of a high-fiber, whole grain cold cereal with 1 cup of skim milk and ¼ cup of fresh berries

A.M. Mini Snack: a tangerine; a small handful of nuts

Mini Lunch: 1 cup of split pea soup; ½ a grilled cheese sandwich

P.M. Mini Meal: a small high fiber-muffin; ½ cup of cranberry or prune juice

Mini Dinner: 3 oz of grilled fish; *Fruity Butternut Squash Casserole with Papaya* (page 239); ½ cup of steamed collards or kale

Dessert: 1 cup of strawberries dipped in ¼ cup of yogurt.

AILMENTS

M

OTHER RECIPES TO TRY

- Berry-Flaxseed Smoothie
- Papaya and Avocado Salad
- Whole Wheat Noodles with Peanut Sauce and Chicken
- Artichokes with Lentils and Lima Beans
- Carrot and Parsnip Puree
- Carrot-Flecked Cornbread
- Warm Artichoke and Bean Dip

MUSCLE CRAMPS

FOODS THAT HEAL

Bananas

Tomato juice

Milk

Water

Oranges

Melons

FOODS TO LIMIT

Caffeinated drinks

HOW TO EAT

You can ward off cramps or lessen their severity by following these guidelines.

Guzzle H2O throughout the day. Drink an extra 16 oz for every hour of exercise to help flush cramp-causing waste products from muscles.

Eat lots of high-potassium foods. A daily serving of one of the foods listed above can help banish cramps and prevent recurrences.

Avoid caffeine. It decreases circulation, which may contribute to cramps.

SAMPLE MEAL PLAN

Breakfast: *Multi-Grain Pancakes or Waffles* (page 130) with 2 Tbsp of reduced-calorie syrup; 1 medium piece of fresh fruit such as an orange or a banana; 1 cup of milk

Lunch: roasted turkey sandwich (without the skin) on whole wheat bread with 1 Tbsp low-fat mayonnaise, lettuce, tomato, honey mustard, and a slice swiss cheese; 1 cup of tomato juice or V-8

Snack: 2 cups of cubed cantaloupe, honeydew, or watermelon

Dinner: 3 oz of grilled or baked chicken; 2 small ears of corn on the cob; 1 cup of steamed broccoli drizzled with 2 tsp melted trans fat free soft spread

Dessert: *Banana-Peanut Bread* (page 243); 1 cup of milk

OTHER RECIPES TO TRY

- Cantaloupe and Orange Soup
- Avocado, Jicama, and Orange Salad
- Cauliflower Salad with Cashews
- Chocolate Banana Soufflés

NAIL PROBLEMS

FOODS THAT HEAL

Lean meat

Poultry

Fish, especially salmon and
  mackerel

Citrus fruits

Dried apricots

Dark green leafy vegetables

Fortified and enriched cereals and
  breads

Legumes

Peas

Flaxseed oil

HOW TO EAT

While most nail problems aren't related to your diet, nutritional deficiencies can impact your nails. Here are a few guidelines to keep your nails healthy.

Get enough protein. It's essential so your body can make keratin, a strong protein that's a major component of nails, hair, and skin.

Add iron-rich foods. Iron-deficiency anemia can prevent adequate nutrients from getting to your nails. For maximum absorption, consume iron-rich foods along with foods high in vitamin C.

Consume more folate. Some types of anemia that affect the nails are caused by a deficiency of folate, an essential B vitamin found in foods listed above.

Bump up essential fatty acids. Try 1 Tbsp of flaxseed oil a day (use it for salad dressing), or sprinkle ground flaxseeds on your cereal or smoothie.

SAMPLE MEAL PLAN

Breakfast: 2 scrambled eggs; 1 slice of enriched bread, toasted, with 1 tsp of trans fat free soft spread; ½ grapefruit

Lunch: grilled salmon burger on an enriched or whole wheat bun; ½ cup of steamed green peas; 1 tangerine

Snack: 3 to 5 dried apricots; a small handful of nuts

Dinner: *Whole Wheat Pasta with Sausage and Greens* (page 190); ½ cup of steamed cauliflower; 1 whole grain roll

Dessert: fruit smoothie with 1 Tbsp of flaxseed oil

OTHER RECIPES TO TRY

- Chicken-Kale Soup with Roasted Pepper Puree
- Celeriac and Spinach Soup
- Three-Bean Chili
- Beef, Onion, and Pepper Fajitas
- Wheat Berry Salad with Dried Apricots
- Asparagus and Chicken Stir-Fry
- Broiled Salmon with Avocado-Mango Salsa
- Snapper and Snaps in a Packet

QUICK TIP: Try biotin

Some research suggests that this B vitamin can help make nails firmer and harder. Good sources include Swiss chard, carrots, eggs, milk, strawberries, raspberries, halibut, onions, cucumbers, cauliflower, walnuts, and almonds.

NEURALGIA

FOODS THAT HARM

Alcohol

FOODS THAT HEAL

Lean meat

Poultry

Fish

Spinach

Potatoes

Nuts and seeds

Wheat germ

Vegetable oils

HOW TO EAT

Deficiencies in certain vitamins can contribute to neuralgia. Here's how to eat to protect yourself.

Maintain vitamin B12 levels. Lean meat and poultry are some options.

Keep up vitamin B6. If you take hydralazine (a powerful antihypertensive medication) or isoniazid (used to treat tuberculosis), you need extra vitamin B6. In addition to the foods above, good sources are bananas, avocado, and bran.

Pump up vitamin E. Try fortified and enriched cereals and eggs along with foods listed above.

SAMPLE MEAL PLAN

Breakfast: 1 cup of whole grain cereal with 1 cup of skim milk, ½ sliced banana, 1 Tbsp of wheat germ, 1 Tbsp of almonds, and 1 Tbsp of sunflower seeds

Lunch: 1 slice of spinach quiche; a small baked potato topped with 1 Tbsp of reduced-fat sour cream; a small bunch of grapes

Snack: fruit and nut bar

Dinner: *Pork, Pear, and Potato Salad* (page 159); 1 soft whole grain bread stick

Snack: 2 cups of popcorn tossed with 1 Tbsp of vegetable oil and salt, to taste

OTHER RECIPES TO TRY

- Wheat Germ Smoothie
- Savory Lamb Stew with Sweet Potatoes
- Beef and Blue Cheese Burgers
- Jerk Turkey Breast with Ginger Barbeque Sauce
- Cauliflower and Spinach Casserole
- Multigrain Seeded Loaf

OBESITY

FOODS THAT HEAL

Chickpeas

Carrots

Zucchini

Broccoli

Fish

Chicken

Beans

Skim milk and other dairy products

Whole wheat pasta

FOODS TO LIMIT

Alcohol

Sugary desserts

Salty processed snack foods

HOW TO EAT

Here are some guidelines to help you drop pounds.

Limit calories. A reasonable approach is 1,500 a day for women and 2,000 for men.

Watch empty calories. No foods should be totally forbidden, but limit the ones that don't provide any nutrition, such as those noted at left.

Eat in the AM. Research shows that breakfast eaters weigh less than those who skip this meal.

Fill up on fiber. High-fiber foods—such as fruits and vegetables—have few calories, little fat, and lots of bulk to keep you satisfied longer.

Add protein to every meal and snack. Fish, chicken, or beans are good sources.

Get enough low-fat dairy. Being deficient can make you hungrier.

Grab a handful of healthy nuts. They'll fill you up.

SAMPLE MEAL PLAN

Breakfast: 1 cup of high-fiber cereal with ½ cup of skim milk topped with ½ cup of your favorite fresh fruit; 1 slice of whole grain toast with 1 tsp of trans fat free soft spread

Lunch: *Tuscan Bean Soup* (page 141); 2 cups of mixed green salad with chopped fresh vegetables, 3 oz chicken or turkey (without the skin), and 2 Tbsp of reduced-fat dressing; 1 whole grain roll

Snack: 1 cup 2% Greek yogurt

Dinner: 1 cup of bean soup; *Grilled Salmon Salad* (page 164); ½ cup of cooked brown rice

Dessert: 1 slice of angel food cake with sliced fresh strawberries

OTHER RECIPES TO TRY

- Cod and Vegetable Stew
- Fish Tacos
- Asian Chicken Salad
- Broccoli and Pearl Barley Salad
- Spinach Salad with Chickpeas
- Brown Rice with Cabbage and Chickpeas
- Flank Steak Roll with Carrots and Red Pepper

OSTEO-ARTHRITIS

See Arthritis, page 283

OSTEOPOROSIS

FOODS THAT HARM
- Salty foods
- High levels of protein

FOODS THAT HEAL
- Skim milk and other dairy foods
- Tofu
- Romaine lettuce
- Cabbage
- Kale
- Fortified soy or rice beverages
- Flaxseed
- Eggs
- Citrus fruit
- Melons
- Berries

FOODS TO LIMIT
- Caffeinated drinks
- Spinach

HOW TO EAT

While calcium is needed for strong bones, it can't get the job done all by itself. Here are other essential nutrients to help you ward off osteoporosis.

Go overboard with calcium. In addition to the above foods, other good sources are canned fish eaten with the bones, nuts, dried beans, peas, and dark green leafy vegetables. The darker the greens, the more calcium they contain. An exception is spinach, which inhibits calcium absorption.

QUICK TIP: Add milk to your coffee

Caffeine can cause calcium to be excreted, so your best bet is to avoid caffeinated drinks as much as possible. If you really can't do without your morning joe, though, moderate your consumption to under 400 mg per day (or less, if you already have osteoporosis), make sure you meet your daily calcium requirement, and add at least 3 Tbsp skim milk, fortified soy milk, or almond milk to your coffee or tea.

Don't forget calcium's BFF. The body needs vitamin D to absorb calcium. You can get it from milk, fortified soy or rice beverages, egg yolks, and fatty fish like mackerel.

Slip in some tofu. Isoflavones found in soy products may help conserve bone mass.

Add flaxseed. Compounds called lignans may help keep your bones strong.

Don't forget C. This vitamin helps to form the connective tissue that holds bones together, and studies have linked higher intakes of C to higher bone density.

SAMPLE MEAL PLAN

Breakfast: 1 cup of fortified whole grain cereal with 1 cup of skim milk; ¼ cup of sliced fresh strawberries; 1 tsp of flaxseeds

Lunch: *Romaine Lettuce with Chunky Tomato Vinaigrette* (page 179); a slice of vegetable quiche

Snack: 2 cups of honeydew or cantaloupe; 1 cup calcium-fortified soy or rice beverage

Dinner: *Pasta with Cabbage, Apples, and Leeks* (page 217); 1 whole grain roll

Dessert: *Lemony Blueberry Cheesecake Bars* (page 260); 1 cup of skim milk

OTHER RECIPES TO TRY

- Summer Greens Scramble
- Yogurt Parfait
- Berry-Flaxseed Smoothie
- Cantaloupe and Orange Soup
- Buckwheat Noodles with Tofu and Green Vegetables
- Pork Chops and Cabbage
- Fried Rice with Tofu and Vegetables
- Whole Wheat Flaxseed Bread

PARKINSON'S DISEASE

FOODS THAT HEAL

Broccoli

Spinach

Whole grain cereals and breads

Soft or pureed foods

FOODS TO LIMIT

High-protein foods, if taking medications such as levodopa

HOW TO EAT

Diet can help ease some of the symptoms of Parkinson's disease.

Put easy-to-chew foods on the menu. If you have trouble chewing or swallowing, eat more cooked cereals or well-moistened dry cereals, poached or scrambled eggs, soups, mashed vegetables, rice, soft-cooked pasta, tender chicken or turkey, well-cooked boneless fish, pureed fruits, custard, yogurt, and juices.

Don't forget vitamin K. Get it from green vegetables such as broccoli and spinach to keep up your energy level.

Make dining easier. Take small bites, chew thoroughly, and swallow everything before taking another bite. Sip a liquid between bites to help wash food down.

Try smaller but more frequent meals, if eating is tiring.

SAMPLE MEAL PLAN

Mini Breakfast: ½ cup of cooked oatmeal or cream of rice made with ½ cup of skim milk; 1 bran muffin with 1 tsp of trans fat free soft spread

A.M. Mini Snack: 1 cup of vegetable soup; 4 crackers

Mini Lunch: 1 cup of spinach lasagna; ½ cup of steamed broccoli; 1 soft roll

P.M. Mini Snack: ½ cup of sliced soft fruit, applesauce, or stewed fruit

Mini Dinner: *Spinach-Stuffed Meat Loaf* (page 183); *Carrot and Parsnip Puree* (page 230); 1 slice of soft bread

Dessert: ½ cup of gelatin with whipped cream

OTHER RECIPES TO TRY

- Quick Chicken Noodle Soup
- Broccoli Potato Soup
- Sloppy Joes
- Herbed Chicken and Apple Burgers
- Herbed Turkey Meatballs and Fusilli
- Farfalle with Winter Squash Sauce
- Macaroni and Cheese with Spinach
- Cauliflower and Spinach Casserole

PEPTIC ULCERS

FOODS THAT HARM

Coffee, including decaffeinated, and other sources of caffeine

Alcohol

Peppermint

Tomatoes

Black pepper

Chile peppers

Garlic

Cloves

FOODS THAT HEAL

Lean meat

Poultry

Fortified and enriched breads and cereals

Dried fruits

Legumes

Yogurt

FOODS TO LIMIT

Fatty foods

Milk

Citrus juice

HOW TO EAT

You can reduce the pain of peptic ulcers and possibly avoid them in the future with these eating strategies.

Avoid trigger foods. Common culprits are listed on page 341.

Close the kitchen after dinner. Late-evening eating can stimulate acid secretion during sleep.

WARNING!
FOOD-DRUG INTERACTION

If you're taking levodopa, some physicians advise having it 20 to 30 minutes before meals to be most effective. If this provokes nausea, it can be taken with a carbohydrate snack, such as crackers or bread. Protein delays the absorption of levodopa, so avoid high-protein diets while on this medication. Some doctors suggest eating the day's protein in the evening, when it's less likely to create problems.

Reduce fat and dairy. See the meal plan below for how to achieve this without missing out on key nutrients like calcium.

Turn down the spice. Some, like those listed on page 341, stimulate stomach acid. Citrus juices may also cause discomfort.

Spoon some yogurt. The kind with live lactobacilli and bifidobacteria may help reduce symptoms.

Up your iron, if you have iron-deficiency anemia due to bleeding ulcers.

Sip aloe vera juice. This home remedy recommends ½ cup three times a day.

SAMPLE MEAL PLAN

Breakfast: omelet with fresh chopped vegetables; 2 slices of turkey bacon; a glass of calcium-fortified soy or rice beverage

Lunch: *Ham and Celeriac Pitas* (page 147); a bowl of bean or vegetable soup; 6 whole grain crackers; a small box of raisins

Snack: 1 cup of yogurt with ¼ cup of sliced papaya or mango stirred in.

Dinner: *Asparagus and Chicken Stir-Fry* (page 190); 1 dinner roll

---

QUICK TIP: Check out licorice

One home remedy for peptic ulcers that seems to work well is a form of licorice called deglycyrrhizinated licorice (DGL). DGL is sold in wafer form at health food stores. Follow the dosage instructions on the package. Don't use regular licorice, though, especially if you have high blood pressure, as it can raise blood pressure if eaten in large enough amounts.

OTHER RECIPES TO TRY

- Yogurt Parfait
- Lamb Burgers with Fruit Relish
- Rice Salad with Chicken and Grapes
- Beef, Scallion, and Asparagus Roll-Ups

PMS

See Menstrual Problems, page 331

PNEUMONIA

See Respiratory Disorders, page 345

PCOS (POLY-CYSTIC OVARY DISEASE)

FOODS THAT HARM

High-glycemic foods such as white bread and refined cereals

FOODS THAT HEAL

Apples

Pears

Berries

Beans

Peas

Whole grains

FOODS TO LIMIT

Alcohol

HOW TO EAT

Dietary advice is similar to what doctors recommend for people with type 2 diabetes, but women with PCOS may have a more difficult time losing weight because of hormone imbalances.

Be vigilant about portions. Downsize all of your plates to make portion control and weight loss easier. Losing just 5% of your weight can improve symptoms.

Increase fiber intake. Aim for at least 5 g of fiber per meal or snack to satisfy an increased appetite, which can be a symptom of PCOS.

Choose low-glycemic foods, which can help improve insulin resistance, a problem for PCOS sufferers. See page 357.

SAMPLE MEAL PLAN

Breakfast: *Hot Cereal with Apples and Dates* (page 121); 1 cup of fresh fruit

Lunch: pita sandwich made with 1 whole wheat pita bread, 3 oz of cooked chicken breast or roasted turkey (without the skin), ½ cup veggies (shredded lettuce, grated carrots, sliced cucumbers, and sprouts), and 2 Tbsp of low-fat dressing; 1 medium pear

Snack: ¼ cup of hummus with 6 whole grain high-fiber crackers

Dinner: veggie burger on a whole grain roll; 1 cup of bean soup; 1 cup of steamed vegetables

Dessert: 2 cups of berries

OTHER RECIPES TO TRY

- Berry Salad with Passion Fruit
- Pear Rhubarb Muffins
- Raspberry-Beet Smoothie
- Tuscan Bean Soup
- Herbed Chicken and Apple Burgers
- Springtime Quinoa
- Beef, Scallion, and Asparagus Roll-Ups

PROSTATE PROBLEMS

FOODS THAT HEAL

Tomatoes and tomato products
Red grapefruit
Watermelon
Brazil nuts
Salmon
Trout
Arctic char
Wheat bran and wheat germ
Oats
Brown rice
Soy products (except soy sauce)
Broccoli
Cauliflower
Cabbage
Whole grains
Water

FOODS TO LIMIT

Fatty foods, especially animal products
Caffeinated drinks

HOW TO EAT

A low-fat diet that limits animal proteins is healthy for many reasons, including better prostate health. Here are more ways a man can prevent problems.

Mix in foods with lycopene. Red fruits and veggies like tomatoes and watermelon tend to be the best sources. Lycopene is fat soluble and absorbed best when eaten with a little fat, such as turkey meatballs, grated cheese, or olive oil.

Go nuts. They tend to be a good source of both selenium and vitamin E, nutrients that may protect against cancer. Other good sources are listed on page 343.

Seek out soy. It may help prevent prostate enlargement and protect against cancer.

Eat more fish and use vegetable oils high in omega-3 fats. They seem to reduce cancer risk.

Dish out plenty of veggies, especially the cruciferous kind like broccoli.

SAMPLE MEAL PLAN

Breakfast: 1 cup of whole grain cereal with ½ cup of soymilk; 1 slice of whole wheat toast with trans fat free soft spread; 1 cup of red grapefruit juice

Lunch: *Penne with Fresh Tomato Sauce and Grilled Eggplant* (page 218); 1 cup of mixed green salad with 2 Tbsp of reduced-fat dressing; 1 whole wheat roll

Snack: a protein shake made with soy protein; brazil nuts

Dinner: *Roasted Mackerel with Cherry Tomatoes and Potatoes* (page 204); 1 cup of chopped greens such as collards, kale, or broccoli rabe (steam or sauté with a little vegetable oil); 1 whole grain roll

Dessert: watermelon slices or red grapefruit

OTHER RECIPES TO TRY

- Wheat Germ Smoothie
- Potato Salad with Sun-Dried Tomatoes, Scallions, and Basil
- Watermelon and Feta Salad
- Monkfish and Mussel Kebabs
- Trout with Lemon-Mushroom Stuffing
- Spiced Cauliflower with Peas
- Green Beans with Tomatoes and Olives
- Multigrain Seeded Loaf

PSORIASIS

FOODS THAT HARM

Products with gluten, for those who are allergic

FOODS THAT HEAL

Asparagus

Spinach

Avocados

Chickpeas

Lentils

Flaxseeds

Oranges

Salmon

Mackerel

Herring

HOW TO EAT

Boosting your immune system with a healthy diet can keep your skin looking better.

Lace your diet with folate. Good sources are listed at left.

Befriend flax. Seeds and oil are rich in anti-inflammatory essential fatty acids that may calm skin conditions.

Opt for omega-3s. In one study, eating 5.5 oz (156 g) of fatty fish a day improved symptoms.

SAMPLE MEAL PLAN

Breakfast: 2 whole grain waffles with 2 tsp of reduced-calorie syrup; 1 cup low-fat yogurt sprinkled with 1 tsp of ground flaxseeds

Lunch: 1 can of wild salmon, drained and flaked, with 2 Tbsp low-fat mayonnaise on a pumpernickel bagel; 8 steamed asparagus spears

Snack: ¼ cup of hummus spread on 2 rice cakes

Dinner: 2 mini crab cakes made with fresh lump crabmeat; *Papaya and Avocado Salad* (page 178); ½ cup of cooked orzo

Dessert: 1 orange

OTHER RECIPES TO TRY

- Grilled Salmon Salad
- Spinach Salad with Chickpeas
- Avocado, Jicama, and Orange Salad
- Salmon and Asparagus Farfalle with Walnut-Feta Sauce
- Brown Rice with Cabbage and Chickpeas
- Artichokes with Lentils and Lima Beans
- Orange Beets
- Whole Wheat Flaxseed Bread

RESPIRATORY DISORDERS

(Including bronchitis, emphysema, pneumonia, and sinusitis)

See also Colds and Flu, page 297; Asthma, page 284

FOODS THAT HARM

- Alcohol
- Fatty and fried food

FOODS THAT HEAL

- Tomatoes
- Cantaloupe
- Leafy green vegetables
- Lean meat
- Oysters
- Yogurt
- Whole grains
- Garlic
- Chiles
- Horseradish

FOODS TO LIMIT

- Milk
- Beans
- Legumes
- Cabbage
- Brussels sprouts
- Broccoli
- Onions

HOW TO EAT

A nutritious and well-balanced diet can help prevent or reduce the severity of bronchitis, pneumonia, and other lung infections.

Drink plenty of fluids, especially warm liquids like chicken broth and hot tea, to help thin mucus and make breathing easier.

Fill your plate with antioxidant foods. Vitamins A, C, and beta-carotene, found in many fruits and vegetablese.

Balance zinc content. Up to 40 mg a day of this mineral (found in lean meat, oysters, yogurt, whole grain products, and seeds) boost immunity, but consuming more depresses your immune system.

Get hot. Spicy foods are natural decongestants.

Pass on the gas. Bloating and flatulence make breathing difficult. Avoid gas-producing foods like beans, eat slowly, and have small servings.

SAMPLE MEAL PLAN

Breakfast: 1 poached egg; 1 whole wheat English muffin; 1 cup of cubed cantaloupe with ½ cup of low-fat yogurt

Lunch: *Chicken-Kale Soup with Roasted Pepper Puree* (page 135); 2 whole grain soft bread sticks

Snack: *Sweet and Spicy Snack Mix* (page 252)

Dinner: *Oysters with Tomato Salsa* (page 248); 8 baked whole grain tortilla chips with a ¼ cup of spicy guacamole

Dessert: 1 piece of fresh fruit

OTHER RECIPES TO TRY

- Basic Chicken Stock
- Chunky Gazpacho with Garlicky Croutons
- Shrimp Ceviche with Avocado and Pumpkin Seeds
- Thai Roasted Shrimp
- Roasted Root Vegetables
- Carrot-Orange Juice

ROSACEA

FOODS THAT HEAL
Cucumbers
Ice water

FOODS TO LIMIT
Specific trigger foods, such as alcohol and spicy foods

HOW TO EAT

Follow these tips to avoid flare-ups.

Chill out. Eat cool foods from both a spice and temperature standpoint.

Stay hydrated. Choose water or non-caffeinated beverages, chilled or at room temperature. Drink more when it's hot out or when you're exercising.

Keep a food diary to figure out trigger foods.

SAMPLE MEAL PLAN

Breakfast: ½ cup of chilled peach slices with ½ cup low-fat cottage cheese; 1 granola bar

Lunch: cheese sandwich with 1 Tbsp of low-fat mayonnaise, sliced cucumbers, grated carrots, and sprouts; 2 cups of mixed greens salad with 2 Tbsp low-fat dressing

Snack: a fruit smoothie

Dinner: *Poached Salmon with Cucumber-Dill Sauce* (page 200); 1 cup of chilled pasta salad; 1 whole grain roll

Dessert: 17 frozen grapes or a popsicle

OTHER RECIPES TO TRY

- Berry Salad with Passion Fruit
- Cantaloupe and Orange Soup

- Japanese Sushi Rolls (cold)
- Tropical Fruit Salad
- Yogurt Parfait
- Tuna and Carrot Sandwich on Rye

SEX DRIVE, DIMINISHED

FOODS THAT HARM

Alcohol

FOODS THAT HEAL

Citrus fruits
Skim milk and other dairy products
Green leafy vegetables
Wheat germ
Lean beef
Poultry
Liver
Fortified and enriched cereals
Oysters
Pine nuts
Beans
Garlic

FOODS TO LIMIT

Red meat, butter, and other foods
with saturated fat

HOW TO EAT

A healthy sex life depends on a balanced diet, good nerve function, healthy hormone levels, and an unobstructed blood flow to the pelvic area.

Eat a diet high in complex carbs and low in saturated fats. This is important for maintaining good blood circulation to your sex organs.

Consume more zinc, found in many of the foods listed at left, as well as eggs, nuts, and whole grains.

Pump up iron. Iron-deficiency anemia can dampen desire.

Mix in some garlic. It's high in allicin, which stimulates circulation and blood flow to sexual organs in both men and women.

Get a daily dose of pine nuts. They're a great source of arginine, the precursor for nitric oxide, a main ingredient in drugs like Viagra.

SAMPLE MEAL PLAN

Breakfast: 1 serving of whole grain cereal (look for 16 g of whole grains per serving) with 1 cup of skim milk, a handful of berries, and 2 Tbsp of wheat germ

Lunch: quick chicken pasta salad: mix ¼ cup reduced-fat pesto (jarred variety is fine) with 1 cup cooked pasta, 1 cup of your favorite roasted, steamed or grilled vegetables, and 3 oz of sliced roasted chicken (without the skin)

Snack: 1 orange

Dinner: *Grilled Oysters with Fennel and Spinach* (page 247); 2 small ears of grilled corn on the cob; ½ cup of coleslaw made with low-fat mayonnaise

Dessert: 1 cup of low-fat ice cream with 2 Tbsp of crushed nuts

OTHER RECIPES TO TRY

- Individual Breakfast Tortilla
- Wheat Germ Smoothie
- Beef Fillet Salad with Mustard Vinaigrette
- Endive, Apple, and Watercress Salad
- Braised Mixed Greens with Dried Currants
- Beef, Scallion, and Asparagus Roll-Ups
- Oysters with Tomato Salsa

SHINGLES

FOODS THAT HEAL

Nuts and seeds
Wheat germ
Vegetable oils
Seafood
Lean meat
Poultry
Milk
Yogurt
Beans
Whole grains

HOW TO EAT

Good nutrition may help prevent postherpetic neuralgia, a long-term complication of shingles.

Get plenty of E and C. These antioxidants help prevent inflammation and boost immunity. Vitamin E is found in some of the foods above. Good sources for C include citrus, melons, and peppers.

Eat a little extra zinc. It strengthens your immune system.

SAMPLE MEAL PLAN

Breakfast: 2 buttermilk pancakes with 2 Tbsp reduced-calorie syrup; 1 slice of lean turkey bacon; ½ cup of fresh fruit

Lunch: *Green Pork Chili* (page 127); 2 cups mixed greens salad with 2 Tbsp reduced-fat dressing; 1 whole grain roll

Snack: 1 oz of nuts or seeds

Dinner: Stir-fry made with vegetables, brown rice, and shrimp, chicken, pork, or lean beef; garnish with fresh orange sections

Dessert: *Yogurt Parfait* (page 000)

OTHER RECIPES TO TRY

- Broccoli and Pearl Barley Salad
- Orange Beef with Broccoli and Jicama
- Pork Chops and Cabbage
- Scallops Florentine
- Springtime Quinoa
- Rice Salad with Chicken and Grapes
- Rice-Stuffed Squash

SINUSITIS

See Respiratory Disorders, page 345

SLEEP DISORDERS

See Insomnia, page 321

SORE THROAT

FOODS THAT HARM
Alcohol
Caffeine

FOODS THAT HEAL
Lemon
Honey
Yogurt
Eggs
Seafood
Lean meat
Whole grains
Fruit juice
Water
Tea

HOW TO EAT

Prevent that initial sore throat from becoming a more serious condition with these tips.

Switch to a liquid diet. See the meal plan below to maintain nutrition without exacerbating throat pain.

Aim for 5 to 10 servings of fruits and vegetables a day. Initially, get them in smoothies and shakes. You can also stew fruits until they're very soft and mash cooked vegetables.

Sip some lemon tea. Squeeze the juice of a lemon—high in immune-boosting vitamin C—into a cup of boiling water and add a teaspoon of honey.

Gargle with honey. Stir 1 to 3 tsp (5 to 15 mL) of honey into 1 cup (250 mL) of warm water, and gargle two or three times a day.

SAMPLE MEAL PLAN

Breakfast: 1 cup of oatmeal prepared with skim milk; ½ cup of stewed fruit; cup of hot water with lemon and honey

Snack: *Strawberry-Yogurt Smoothie* (page 131)

Lunch: *Vegetable Stock* (page 137) with your favorite vegetables, cooked grains, or soft noodles

Snack: 1 cup of fruit-flavored Jell-O

Dinner: *Carrot Soup with Dill* (page 138) with 2 Tbsp of grated cheese; 1 soft whole grain roll

Dessert: 8 oz protein shake

OTHER RECIPES TO TRY

- Quick Chicken Noodle Soup
- Cod and Vegetable Stew
- Miso Soup with Tofu
- Cantaloupe and Orange Soup
- Zucchini-Carrot Crustless Quiche Squares
- Warm Kasha and Seafood Salad
- Mashed Turnips with Carrots and Potatoes

STRESS

FOODS THAT HEAL
Whole grains
Seafood
Lean meat
Poultry
Milk
Eggs
Nuts
Herbal tea

FOODS TO LIMIT
Alcohol
Caffeinated drinks
Fatty foods
Hot or spicy foods

HOW TO EAT

The right foods provide energy, while vitamins and minerals help your body maintain resistance to infection when under stress.

Zap stress with zinc. It helps keep your immune system strong. See foods on page 349.

Eat four to six small meals. Stress interferes with digestion, so small meals throughout the day are best.

Enjoy carbs. Studies have shown that a diet higher in carbohydrates and lower in protein can reduce your chance of stress-induced depression. See the meal plan below.

Eat breakfast. You'll handle stress much better if you're fueled.

Munch slowly. Eating quickly can promote more stress-related GI troubles.

Sip chamomile or peppermint tea. They have a calming effect.

SAMPLE MEAL PLAN

Mini Breakfast: *Mushroom and Bell Pepper Frittata* (page 123)

A.M. Mini Meal: *Whole Wheat Flaxseed Bread* (page 242), toasted, with 1 tsp of jam; 1 cup peppermint tea

Mini Lunch: large baked potato topped with 1 Tbsp grated low-fat cheese and ¼ cup of salsa; small salad with 2 Tbsp low-fat dressing

P.M. Mini Meal: 1 piece of fresh fruit; 1 cup chamomile tea

Mini Dinner: *Pasta with Walnut Cream Sauce* (page 217).

Dessert: 8 oz milkshake

OTHER RECIPES TO TRY

- Lamb Burgers with Fruit Relish
- Couscous-Stuffed Peppers
- Spinach-Stuffed Meat Loaf
- Twice Baked Stuffed Sweet Potatoes
- Spiced Almonds

STROKE

FOODS THAT HARM

Red meat, butter, and other foods with saturated fats

Palm and coconut oil

Salty foods, such as pickles

FOODS THAT HEAL

Oats

Lentils

Flaxseeds

Whole grains

Grapes

Nuts

Red wine

Apples

Berries

Trout

Mackerel

Walnuts

Canola oil

Soybeans

Green leafy vegetables

Low-fat dairy products

Garlic

Onions

HOW TO EAT

Diet plays an important role in reducing or eliminating stroke risk factors.

Adopt a low-fat, low-sodium, high-fiber diet. This will help to lower your chances of developing risk factors for a stroke such as high blood pressure, diabetes, or high cholesterol.

Add important phytochemicals. Resveratrol, found in grapes, nuts, and red wine, may inhibit blood clots and relax blood vessels. Quercetin, found in apples and berries, may reduce fat deposits in arteries.

Eat fatty fish two or three times a week. No fan of fish? Try walnuts, walnut oil, canola (rapeseed) oil, flaxseed oil, soybeans, and leafy greens.

Cook with garlic and onions. They boost the body's natural clot-dissolving mechanism.

Get milk. Nutrients such as calcium, potassium, magnesium, and vitamin D in low-fat dairy products help lower blood pressure.

SAMPLE MEAL PLAN

Breakfast: *Buckwheat Pancakes with Fruit Sauce* (page 129); a cup of skim milk

Lunch: grilled chicken sandwich (without the skin) made on 2 slices of low-sodium whole grain bread with lettuce, tomato, and red onion; at least 1 cup steamed broccoli

Snack: 1 medium apple

Dinner: 3 oz of baked salmon; *Braised Mixed Greens with Dried Currants* (page 233); a small, baked sweet potato

Dessert: a glass of red wine

OTHER RECIPES TO TRY

- Hot Cereal with Apples and Dates
- Salmon and Fennel Lettuce Wraps
- Grilled Salmon Salad
- Spinach Salad with Chickpeas
- Mediterranean Salad with Edamame
- Poached Salmon with Cucumber-Dill Sauce
- Fried Rice with Tofu and Vegetables
- Toasted Oat-Raisin Bread

ULCERATIVE COLITIS

See Inflammatory Bowel Disease, page 320

URINARY TRACT INFECTIONS

FOODS THAT HARM
Caffeinated drinks
Alcohol
Spicy food

FOODS THAT HEAL
Cranberries and cranberry juice
Water
Oranges
Tomatoes
Broccoli
Yogurt

HOW TO EAT

You can speed healing and help prevent recurrences with these tips.

Drink plenty of water, at least 8 to 10 glasses a day to increase urine flow and flush out infectious material.

Drink cranberry juice. Research shows that cranberries and blueberries contain substances that speed the elimination of bacteria.

Pump up vitamin C to boost immunity and fight infection.

Go for yogurt. It can inhibit the growth of microorganisms that cause UTIs, and it can maintain healthy bacteria when you're taking antibiotics.

SAMPLE MEAL PLAN

Breakfast: *Blueberry and Cranberry Granola* (page 120) with ½ cup of low-fat yogurt; 1 cup of cranberry juice

Lunch: cheese sandwich made with 2 slices of whole grain bread, 2 oz of low-fat colby cheese, a slice of tomato, and 1 Tbsp of low-fat mayonnaise or spread; *Green Beans with Tomatoes and Olives* (page 233)

Snack: 1 orange

Dinner: 3 oz of sliced turkey breast; half of a baked acorn squash; 1 cup of steamed broccoli

Dessert: 1 cup of low-fat yogurt with sliced fruit

OTHER RECIPES TO TRY

- Yogurt Parfait
- Strawberry-Yogurt Smoothie
- Broccoli Potato Soup
- Avocado, Jicama, and Orange Salad
- Romaine Lettuce with Chunky Tomato Vinaigrette
- Pan-Seared Scallops with Oranges and Sun-Dried Tomatoes
- Penne with Fresh Tomato Sauce and Grilled Eggplant
- Savory Cranberry Chutney

VARICOSE VEINS

FOODS THAT HEAL

Oranges and other citrus fruits
Berries
Broccoli
Red peppers
Whole grain cereals
Whole wheat pasta
Popcorn
Grapes

HOW TO EAT

A well-balanced diet that helps you maintain a healthy weight or lose weight is key since obesity is a risk factor for varicose veins. Some foods may even have an effect on blood vessels to minimize the problem. Here's how.

Hit high C. Getting lots of vitamin C strengthens blood vessels. Foods high in C also provide other healthy compounds. In fact, one small study showed that the flavonoid hesperidin in oranges improved varicose veins.

Feast on fiber. It can prevent constipation, which can make varicose veins worse by increasing pressure.

Pick some berries. Blueberries, raspberries, blackberries, and grapes contain antioxidants that help reduce blood vessel leakage.

SAMPLE MEAL PLAN

Breakfast: *Blueberry-Oatmeal Muffins* (page 120); ½ cup of low-fat yogurt with strawberries

Lunch: veggie burger on a whole wheat roll with lettuce, tomato, and 2 Tbsp of low-fat dressing; 1 cup of minestrone soup; ½ cup of steamed broccoli

Snack: a small bunch of grapes

Dinner: *Pan-Seared Scallops with Oranges and Sun-Dried Tomatoes* (page 208); 1 cup of whole wheat pasta salad with added vegetables; 1 medium ear of grilled corn on the cob

Snack: 2 cups of air-popped popcorn

OTHER RECIPES TO TRY

- Chicken Salad with Citrus
- Whole Wheat Noodles with Peanut Sauce and Chicken
- Mixed Berry and Stone Fruit Soup
- Fruity Granola Mix
- Orange-Walnut Broccoli
- Carrot-Orange Juice

YEAST INFECTIONS

FOODS THAT HARM
Sugary foods

FOODS THAT HEAL
Yogurt with live cultures

Sauerkraut

Tempeh

Kefir

Miso

Cherries

Grapes

Apricots

HOW TO EAT

Follow these tips to reduce your chance of getting a yeast infection or ease symptoms if you have one.

Avoid sweetened yogurts. Sugar can worsen symptoms.

Get some garlic. It's a powerful bacterial fighter. Aim for 2 raw cloves per day.

Try fermented foods, such as sauerkraut, tempeh (a fermented soy product), kefir (a yogurtlike drink), and miso. They contain probiotics that in theory could work against infections in the same way live cultures in yogurt do.

Ditch the sweet stuff—fruit juices, sweetened breakfast cereals, ice cream, and desserts as well as anything made with high-fructose corn syrup. Satisfy your sweet tooth with cherries, grapes, fresh apricots, or carrots. Yeast thrives on sugar.

Steer clear of yeast. Choose yeast-free sprouted bread instead of regular.

SAMPLE MEAL PLAN

Breakfast: 1 slice of toasted yeast-free bread with 1 tsp of trans fat free soft spread; *Strawberry-Yogurt Smoothie* (page 131)

Lunch: bowl of vegetable soup seasoned with miso; 1 cup of brown rice; 1 cup steamed vegetables; 2 Tbsp of sauerkraut

Snack: 2 rice cakes with 2 tsp of almond butter

Dinner: *Caraway-Coated Pepper Steak with Cherry Sauce* (page 181); ½ cup of mashed potatoes; ½ cup of cooked carrots

Dessert: 1 cup of grapes dipped in ½ cup low-fat yogurt made with live cultures

OTHER RECIPES TO TRY

- Yogurt Parfait
- Strawberry-Yogurt Smoothie
- Miso Soup with Tofu
- Fruit Salad with Spiced Coconut
- Baked Pasta with Garlic and Greens
- Braised Mixed Greens with Dried Currants
- Turkey Bacon and Apricot Bites
- Cherry Crisp

GLYCEMIC INDEX AND GLYCEMIC LOAD

To gauge how efficiently food works its way through your digestive system to affect your blood sugar, researchers at the University of Toronto developed the glycemic index (GI). The faster a food is digested and absorbed into your bloodstream, the higher its GI. High-GI foods cause a rapid increase in blood sugar, which is dangerous, especially for people with diabetes.

But GI was based on a standard measurement (50 g of carbohydrates) for all foods. In real life, people don't tend to eat the same amounts of sugar as they do pasta or carrots.

GLYCEMIC INDEX VS. GLYCEMIC LOAD

Below are a few common foods and their GI and GL values. Note the differences and how the GL becomes a better way to look at the effect that foods have on blood sugar.

FOOD	GI	SIZE	GL
Grains and Cereals			
Bagel, white	72	2 ½ oz (70 g)	25
Barley, pearled	25	5 oz (150 g)	11
Bread, white	71	1 oz (30 g)	10
Bread, whole grain, pumpernickel	46	1 oz (30 g)	5
Bread, whole wheat	67	1 oz (30 g)	8
Cereal, All-Bran	50	1 oz (30 g)	9
Cereal, cornflakes	80	1 oz (30 g)	21
Cereal, muesli	66	1 oz (30 g)	16
Fruits			
Apple	39	4 oz (125 g)	6
Apple juice, unsweetened	41	8 ½ oz (250 mL)	12
Banana	46	4 oz (125 g)	12
Grapefruit	25	4 oz (125 g)	3
Grapes	43	4 oz (125 g)	7
Orange	40	4 oz (125 g)	4
Peach	42	4 oz (125 g)	5
Watermelon	72	4 oz (125 g)	4
Vegetables			
Baked potato	60	5 oz (150 g)	18
Baked potato, mashed	74	5 oz (150 g)	15
Carrots	92	3 oz (90 g)	5
Kidney beans	29	5.2 oz (150 g)	7
Lentils	29	5.2 oz (150 g)	5
Peas	51	3 oz (90 g)	4
Soybeans	15	5.2 oz (150 g)	1
Sweet potato	48	5 oz (150 g)	16

So scientists used a little math wizardry to translate the glycemic index into more practical terms. What emerged is the glycemic load (GL). This tool considers the type of carbohydrate in the food and the amount of carbohydrate in a standard serving. By this new criterion, sugar and starchy foods and some fruits have high GL values whereas most vegetables and fruits have low GL values, meaning they are less likely to make your blood sugar spike.

Both are useful—GI helps you choose better carbs while GL helps with portion sizes. Today, there are more than 750 published GI and GL values of various foods. However, you should take all GL lists as a general guide only. As it turns out, one person's glycemic response can differ from another's. It may vary even in the same person from day to day. Also, the state of food can change its GL.

For example, small differences in a banana's ripeness can double its GL. Plus, fat and protein slow down digestion, making the GL of a baked potato topped with sour cream and served with a steak different than the GL of the potato itself.

People who eat diets with a high GL have a higher rate of obesity, diabetes, heart disease, and cancer. One study found that swapping just one baked potato per week for a serving of brown rice could reduce a person's odds of developing type 2 diabetes by up to 30%.

RECIPE INDEX

INDEX